PEARSON   ALWAYS LEARNING

Elayn Martin-Gay

Prealgebra & Introductory Algebra
MATH 009

Custom Edition for University of Maryland University College

Taken from:
Prealgebra & Introductory Algebra, Fourth Edition
by Elayn Martin-Gay

Cover Art: Courtesy of Pearson Learning Solutions.

Taken from:

Prealgebra & Introductory Algebra, Fourth Edition
by Elayn Martin-Gay
Copyright © 2015, 2011, 2008, 2005 by Pearson Education, Inc.
Boston, Massachusetts 02116

This special edition published in cooperation with Pearson Learning Solutions.

Pearson Learning Solutions, 501 Boylston Street, Suite 900, Boston, MA 02116
A Pearson Education Company
www.pearsoned.com

Printed in the United States of America

1 2 3 4 5 6 7 8 9 10 V3N4 18 17 16 15 14

000200010271906110
000200010271648002

SH

Print ISBN: 1-269-93627-1; 978-1-269-93627-9
Ebook ISBN: 1-256-67069-3; 978-1-256-67069-8

Dear Students,

The text that you have purchased for this course is a customized version of the full text. We felt this custom version would better serve your needs in that least two very important ways, reducing the cost to you and focusing the content of the text most relevant to the course.

The cost savings comes in to play via a special arrangement between the mathematics and statistics department and the publisher. We were able to take out material that would not be needed for this course and reduce the cost accordingly. This will also enable you to spend your time preparing for only what is needed for this course.

Good luck with the course.

Sincerely,

Academic Director for Mathematics and Statistics

UMUC

In loving memory of my uncle,
Leonel Leal

Although he had to quit school far too early to support his family,
he was a self-educated businessman who understood the
precious value of education.

Contents

Appendices

Preface

Prealgebra & Introductory Algebra **Fourth Edition** was written in response to the needs of those teaching combined courses. My goals were to help students make the transition from arithmetic to algebra and to provide a solid foundation in algebra. To achieve these goals, I introduce algebraic concepts early and repeat them often, as traditional arithmetic topics are discussed, thus laying the groundwork for algebra. Specific care was taken to ensure that all core topics of an introductory algebra course are covered and that students have the most up-to-date, relevant text preparation for future courses that require an understanding of algebraic fundamentals.

The many factors that contributed to the success of the previous editions have been retained. In preparing the Fourth Edition, I considered comments and suggestions of colleagues, students, and many users of the prior edition throughout the country.

What's New in the Fourth Edition?

- **The Martin-Gay Program** has been revised and enhanced with a new design in the text and MyMathLab® to actively encourage students to use the text, video program, Video Organizer, and Student Organizer as an integrated learning system.

- **The new Video Organizer** is designed to help students take notes and work practice exercises while watching the Interactive Lecture Series videos (available in MyMathLab and on DVD). All content in the Video Organizer is presented in the same order as it is presented in the videos, making it easy for students to create a course notebook and build good study habits.
  - Covers all of the video examples in order.
  - Provides ample space for students to write down key definitions and properties.
  - Includes "Play" and "Pause" button icons to prompt students to follow along with the author for some exercises while they try others on their own.

  The Video Organizer is available in a loose-leaf, notebook-ready format. It is also available for download in MyMathLab.

- **Vocabulary, Readiness & Video Check** questions have been added prior to every section exercise set. These exercises quickly check a student's understanding of new vocabulary words. The **readiness** exercises center on a student's understanding of a concept that is necessary in order to continue to the exercise set. **New Video check questions for the Martin-Gay Interactive Lecture videos** are now included in every section for each learning objective. **These exercises are all available for assignment in MyMathLab** and are a great way to assess whether students have viewed and understood the key concepts presented in the videos.

- **New Student Success Tips Videos** are 3- to -5-minute video segments designed to be daily reminders to students to continue practicing and maintaining good organizational and study habits. They are organized in three categories and are available in MyMathLab and the Interactive Lecture Series. The categories are:
  1. Success Tips that apply to any course in college in general, such as Time Management.
  2. Success Tips that apply to any mathematics course. One example is based on understanding that mathematics is a course that requires homework to be completed in a timely fashion.

3. Section- or Content-specific Success Tips to help students avoid common mistakes or to better understand concepts that often prove challenging. One example of this type of tip is how to apply the order of operations to simplify an expression such as $5 - 3(x + 2)$.

● **Interactive DVD Lecture Series**, featuring your text author (Elayn Martin-Gay), provides students with active learning at their own pace. The videos offer the following resources and more:

A complete lecture for each section of the text highlights key examples and exercises from the text. "Pop-ups" reinforce key terms, definitions, and concepts.

An interface with menu navigation features allows students to quickly find and focus on the examples and exercises they need to review.

Interactive Concept Check exercises measure students' understanding of key concepts and common trouble spots.

New Student Success Tips Videos.

● **The Interactive DVD Lecture Series** also includes the following resources for test prep:

The Chapter Test Prep Videos help students during their most teachable moment—when they are preparing for a test. This innovation provides step-by-step solutions for the exercises found in each Chapter Test. For the Fourth Edition, the chapter test prep videos are also available on YouTube™. The videos are captioned in English and Spanish.

The Practice Final Exam Videos help students prepare for an end-of-course final. Students can watch full video solutions to each exercise in the Practice Final Exam at the end of this text.

● **The Martin-Gay MyMathLab** course has been updated and revised to provide more exercise coverage, including assignable video check questions and an expanded video program. There are section lecture videos for every section, which students can also access at the specific objective level; Student Success Tips Videos; and an increased number of watch clips at the exercise level to help students while doing homework in MathXL. Suggested homework assignments have been premade for assignment at the instructor's discretion.

● **New MyMathLab Ready to Go courses** (access code required) provide students with all the same great MyMathLab features that you're used to, but make it easier for instructors to get started. Each course includes preassigned homework and quizzes to make creating your course even simpler. Ask your Pearson representative about the details for this particular course or to see a copy of this course.

Key Pedagogical Features

The following key features have been retained and/or updated for the Fourth Edition of the text:

Problem-Solving Process This is formally introduced in Chapter 3 with a four-step process that is integrated throughout the text. The four steps are **Understand, Translate, Solve,** and **Interpret**. The repeated use of these steps in a variety of examples shows their wide applicability. Reinforcing the steps can increase students' comfort level and confidence in tackling problems.

Exercise Sets Revised and Updated The exercise sets have been carefully examined and extensively revised. Special focus was placed on making sure that even- and odd-numbered exercises are paired and that real-life applications are updated.

Examples   Detailed, step-by-step examples were added, deleted, replaced, or updated as needed. Many examples reflect real life. Additional instructional support is provided in the annotated examples.

Practice Exercises   Throughout the text, each worked-out example has a parallel Practice exercise. These invite students to be actively involved in the learning process. Students should try each Practice exercise after finishing the corresponding example. Learning by doing will help students grasp ideas before moving on to other concepts. Answers to the Practice exercises are provided at the bottom of each page.

Helpful Hints   Helpful Hints contain practical advice on applying mathematical concepts. Strategically placed where students are most likely to need immediate reinforcement, Helpful Hints help students avoid common trouble areas and mistakes.

Concept Checks   This feature allows students to gauge their grasp of an idea as it is being presented in the text. Concept Checks stress conceptual understanding at the point-of-use and help suppress misconceived notions before they start. Answers appear at the bottom of the page. Exercises related to Concept Checks are included in the exercise sets.

Mixed Practice Exercises   In the section exercise sets, these exercises require students to determine the problem type and strategy needed to solve it just as they would need to do on a test.

Integrated Reviews   This unique, mid-chapter exercise set helps students assimilate new skills and concepts that they have learned separately over several sections. These reviews provide yet another opportunity for students to work with "mixed" exercises as they master the topics.

Vocabulary Check   This feature provides an opportunity for students to become more familiar with the use of mathematical terms as they strengthen their verbal skills. These appear at the end of each chapter before the Chapter Highlights. Vocabulary, Readiness & Video exercises provide practice at the section level.

Chapter Highlights   Found at the end of every chapter, these contain key definitions and concepts with examples to help students understand and retain what they have learned and help them organize their notes and study for tests.

Chapter Review   The end of every chapter contains a comprehensive review of topics introduced in the chapter. The Chapter Review offers exercises keyed to every section in the chapter, as well as Mixed Review exercises that are not keyed to sections.

Chapter Test and Chapter Test Prep Videos   The Chapter Test is structured to include those problems that involve common student errors. The **Chapter Test Prep Videos** give students instant access to a step-by-step video solution of each exercise in the Chapter Test.

Cumulative Review   This review follows every chapter in the text (except Chapter 1). Each odd-numbered exercise contained in the Cumulative Review is an earlier worked example in the text that is referenced in the back of the book along with the answer.

Writing Exercises These exercises occur in almost every exercise set and require students to provide a written response to explain concepts or justify their thinking.

Applications Real-world and real-data applications have been thoroughly updated, and many new applications are included. These exercises occur in almost every exercise set and show the relevance of mathematics and help students gradually and continuously develop their problem-solving skills.

Review Exercises These exercises occur in each exercise set (except in Chapter 1) and are keyed to earlier sections. They review concepts learned earlier in the text that will be needed in the next section or chapter.

Exercise Set Resource Icons Located at the opening of each exercise set, these icons remind students of the resources available for extra practice and support:

MyMathLab®

See Student Resources descriptions on page xiv for details on the individual resources available.

Exercise Icons These icons facilitate the assignment of specialized exercises and let students know what resources can support them.

- DVD Video icon: exercise worked on the Interactive DVD Lecture Series and available in MyMathLab.
- Triangle icon: identifies exercises involving geometric concepts.
- Pencil icon: indicates a written response is needed.
- Calculator icon: optional exercises intended to be solved using a scientific or graphing calculator.

Group Activities Found at the end of each chapter, these activities are for individual or group completion, and are usually hands-on or data-based activities that extend the concepts found in the chapter, allowing students to make decisions and interpretations and to think and write about algebra.

Optional: Calculator Exploration Boxes and Calculator Exercises The optional Calculator Explorations provide keystrokes and exercises at appropriate points to give students an opportunity to become familiar with these tools. Section exercises that are best completed by using a calculator are identified by for ease of assignment.

Student and Instructor Resources

Student Organizer	**Student Solutions Manual**
Guides students through the 3 main components of studying effectively—notetaking, practice, and homework.	Provides completely worked-out solutions to the odd-numbered section exercises; all exercises in the Integrated Reviews, Chapter Reviews, Chapter Tests, and Cumulative Reviews
The Organizer includes before-class preparation exercises, notetaking pages in a 2-column format for use in class, and examples paired with exercises for practice for each section. Includes an outline and questions for use with the Student Success Tips Videos. It is 3-hole-punched.	
Available in loose-leaf, notebook-ready format and in MyMathLab.	
Interactive DVD Lecture Series Videos	**Video Organizer**
Provides students with active learning at their pace. The videos offer:	Designed to help students take notes and work practice exercises while watching the Interactive Lecture Series Videos.
<ul><li>A complete lecture for each text section. The interface allows easy navigation to examples and exercises students need to review.</li><li>Interactive Concept Check exercises</li><li>Student Success Tips Videos</li><li>Practice Final Exam</li><li>Chapter Test Prep Videos</li></ul>	<ul><li>Covers all of the video examples in order.</li><li>Provides ample space for students to write down key definitions and rules.</li><li>Includes "Play" and "Pause" button icons to prompt students to follow along with the author for some exercises while they try others on their own.</li><li>Includes Student Success Tips Outline and Questions</li></ul> Available in loose-leaf, notebook-ready format and in MyMathLab.

Annotated Instructor's Edition	**Instructor's Resource Manual with Tests and Mini-Lectures**
Contains all the content found in the student edition, plus the following: <ul><li>Answers to exercises on the same text page</li><li>Teaching Tips throughout the text placed at key points</li><li>Video Answer Section</li></ul>	<ul><li>Mini-lectures for each text section</li><li>Additional practice worksheets for each section</li><li>Several forms of test per chapter—free response and multiple choice</li><li>Answers to all items</li></ul> **Instructor's Solutions Manual** **TestGen**® (Available for download from the IRC)
Instructor-to-Instructor Videos—available in the Instructor Resources section of the MyMathLab course.	**Online Resources** **MyMathLab**® (access code required) **MathXL**® (access code required)

Acknowledgments

There are many people who helped me develop this text, and I will attempt to thank some of them here. Courtney Slade and Cindy Trimble were *invaluable* for contributing to the overall accuracy of the text. Dawn Nuttall was *invaluable* for her many suggestions and contributions during the development and writing of this Fourth Edition. Debbie Meyer and Patty Bergin provided guidance throughout the production process.

A very special thank you goes to my editor, Mary Beckwith, for being there 24/7/365, as my students say. And my thanks to the staff at Pearson for all their support: Heather Scott, Lauren Morse, Matt Summers, Michelle Renda, Michael Hirsch, Chris Hoag, and Greg Tobin.

I would like to thank the following reviewers for their input and suggestions:

Lisa Angelo, *Bucks Community College*
Victoria Baker, *Nicholls State College*
Teri Barnes, *McLennan Community College*
Laurel Berry, *Bryant & Stratton*
Thomas Blackburn, *Northeastern Illinois University*
Gail Burkett, *Palm Beach Community College*
Anita Collins, *Mesa Community College*
Lois Colpo, *Harrisburg Area Community College*
Fay Dang, *Joliet Junior. College*
Robert Diaz, *Fullerton College*
Tamie Dickson, *Reading Area Community College*
Latonya Ellis, *Gulf Coast Community College*
Sonia Ford, *Midland College*
Cheryl Gibby, *Cypress College*
Kathryn Gunderson, *Three Rivers Community College*
Elizabeth Hamman, *Cypress College*
Craig Hardesty, *Hillsborough Community College*
Lloyd Harris, *Gulf Coast Community College*

Teresa Hasenauer, *Indian River College*
Julia Hassett, *Oakton Community College*
Jeff Koleno, *Lorain County Community College*
Judy Langer, *Westchester Community College*
Sandy Lofstock, *St. Petersburg College*
Stan Mattoon, *Merced College*
Dr. Kris Mudunuri, *Long Beach City College*
Carol Murphy, *San Diego Miramar College*
Greg Nguyen, *Fullerton College*
Jean Olsen, *Pikes Peak Community College*
Darlene Ornelas, *Fullerton College*
Warren Powell, *Tyler Junior College*
Jeanette Shea, *Central Texas College*
Katerina Vishnyakova, *Collin County Community College*
Corey Wadlington, *West Kentucky Community and Technical College*
Edward Wagner, *Central Texas College*
Jenny Wilson, *Tyler Junior College*

I would also like to thank the following dedicated group of instructors who participated in our focus groups, Martin-Gay Summits, and our design review for the series. Their feedback and insights have helped to strengthen this edition of the text. These instructors include:

Billie Anderson, *Tyler Junior College*
Cedric Atkins, *Mott Community College*
Lois Beardon, *Schoolcraft College*
Laurel Berry, *Bryant & Stratton*
John Beyers, *University of Maryland*
Bob Brown, *Community College of Baltimore County–Essex*
Lisa Brown, *Community College of Baltimore County–Essex*
NeKeith Brown, *Richland College*
Gail Burkett, *Palm Beach Community College*

Cheryl Cantwell, *Seminole Community College*
Jackie Cohen, *Augusta State College*
Julie Dewan, *Mohawk Valley Community College*
Janice Ervin, *Central Piedmont Community College*
Richard Fielding, *Southwestern College*
Cindy Gaddis, *Tyler Junior College*
Nita Graham, *St. Louis Community College*
Pauline Hall, *Iowa State College*
Pat Hussey, *Triton College*

Dorothy Johnson, *Lorain County Community College*
Sonya Johnson, *Central Piedmont Community College*
Irene Jones, *Fullerton College*
Paul Jones, *University of Cincinnati*
Kathy Kopelousous, *Lewis and Clark Community College*
Nancy Lange, *Inver Hills Community College*
Judy Langer, *Westchester Community College*
Lisa Lindloff, *McLinnan Community College*
Sandy Lofstock, *St. Petersburg College*
Kathy Lovelle, *Westchester Community College*
Jean McArthur, *Joliet Junior College*
Kevin McCandless, *Evergreen Valley College*
Daniel Miller, *Niagra County Community College*
Marica Molle, *Metropolitan Community College*
Carol Murphy, *San Diego Miramar College*
Greg Nguyen, *Fullerton College*

Eric Oilila, *Jackson Community College*
Linda Padilla, *Joliet Junior College*
Davidson Pierre, *State College of Florida*
Marilyn Platt, *Gaston College*
Ena Salter, *Manatee Community College*
Carole Shapero, *Oakton Community College*
Janet Sibol, *Hillsborough Community College*
Anne Smallen, *Mohawk Valley Community College*
Barbara Stoner, *Reading Area Community College*
Jennifer Strehler, *Oakton Community College*
Ellen Stutes, *Louisiana State University Elinice*
Tanomo Taguchi, *Fullerton College*
MaryAnn Tuerk, *Elsin Community College*
Walter Wang, *Baruch College*
Leigh Ann Wheeler, *Greenville Technical Community College*
Valerie Wright, *Central Piedmont Community College*

A special thank you to those students who participated in our design review: Katherine Browne, Mike Bulfin, Nancy Canipe, Ashley Carpenter, Jeff Chojnachi, Roxanne Davis, Mike Dieter, Amy Dombrowski, Kay Herring, Todd Jaycox, Kaleena Levan, Matt Montgomery, Tony Plese, Abigail Polkinghorn, Harley Price, Eli Robinson, Avery Rosen, Robyn Schott, Cynthia Thomas, and Sherry Ward.

Elayn Martin-Gay

About the Author

Elayn Martin-Gay has taught mathematics at the University of New Orleans for more than 25 years. Her numerous teaching awards include the local University Alumni Association's Award for Excellence in Teaching, and Outstanding Developmental Educator at University of New Orleans, presented by the Louisiana Association of Developmental Educators.

Prior to writing textbooks, Elayn Martin-Gay developed an acclaimed series of lecture videos to support developmental mathematics students in their quest for success. These highly successful videos originally served as the foundation material for her texts. Today, the videos are specific to each book in the Martin-Gay series. The author has also created Chapter Test Prep Videos to help students during their most "teachable moment"—as they prepare for a test—along with Instructor-to-Instructor videos that provide teaching tips, hints, and suggestions for each developmental mathematics course, including basic mathematics, prealgebra, beginning algebra, and intermediate algebra.

Elayn is the author of 12 published textbooks as well as multimedia, interactive mathematics, all specializing in developmental mathematics courses. She has also published series in Algebra 1, Algebra 2, and Geometry. She has participated as an author across the broadest range of educational materials: textbooks, videos, tutorial software, and courseware. This provides an opportunity of various combinations for an integrated teaching and learning package offering great consistency for the student.

Applications Index

The Whole Numbers

A Selection of Resources for Success in this Mathematics Course

Text book

Instructor

MyMathLab and MathXL

Video Organizer

Student Organizer

Interactive Lecture Series

F or more information about the resources illustrated above, read Section 1.1.

Whole numbers are the basic building blocks of mathematics. The whole numbers answer the question "How many?"

This chapter covers basic operations on whole numbers. Knowledge of these operations provides a good foundation on which to build further mathematical skills.

1.1 Study Skill Tips for Success in Mathematics

Objectives

A Get Ready for This Course.

B Understand Some General Tips for Success.

C Know How to Use This Text.

D Know How to Use Text Resources.

E Get Help as Soon as You Need It.

F Learn How to Prepare for and Take an Exam.

G Develop Good Time Management.

Before reading Section 1.1, you might want to ask yourself a few questions.

1. When you took your last math course, were you organized? Were your notes and materials from that course easy to find, or were they disorganized and hard to find—if you saved them at all?

2. Were you satisfied—really satisfied—with your performance in that course? In other words, do you feel that your outcome represented your best effort?

If the answer is "no" to these questions, then it is time to make a change. Changing to or resuming good study skill habits is not a process you can start and stop as you please. It is something that you must remember and practice each and every day. To begin, continue reading this section.

Objective A Getting Ready for This Course

Now that you have decided to take this course, remember that a *positive attitude* will make all the difference in the world. Your belief that you can succeed is just as important as your commitment to this course. Make sure you are ready for this course by having the time and positive attitude that it takes to succeed.

Make sure that you are familiar with the way that this course is being taught. Is it a traditional course, in which you have a printed textbook and meet with an instructor? Is it taught totally online, and your textbook is electronic and you e-mail your instructor? Or is your course structured somewhere in between these two methods? (Not all of the tips that follow will apply to all forms of instruction.)

Also make sure that you have scheduled your math course for a time that will give you the best chance for success. For example, if you are also working, you may want to check with your employer to make sure that your work hours will not conflict with your course schedule.

On the day of your first class period, double-check your schedule and allow yourself extra time to arrive on time in case of traffic problems or difficulty locating your classroom. Make sure that you are aware of and bring all necessary class materials.

Objective B General Tips for Success

Below are some general tips that will increase your chance for success in a mathematics class. Many of these tips will also help you in other courses you may be taking.

Most important! Organize your class materials. In the next couple pages, many ideas will be presented to help you organize your class materials—notes, any handouts, completed homework, previous tests, etc. In general, you MUST have these materials organized. All of them will be valuable references throughout your course and when studying for upcoming tests and the final exam. One way to make sure you can locate these materials when you need them is to use a three-ring binder. This binder should be used solely for your mathematics class and should be brought to each and every class or lab. This way, any material can be immediately inserted in a section of this binder and will be there when you need it.

Form study groups and/or exchange names and e-mail addresses. Depending on how your course is taught, you may want to keep in contact with your fellow students. Some ways of doing this are to form a study group—whether in person or through the Internet. Also, you may want to ask if anyone is interested in exchanging e-mail addresses or any other form of contact.

Helpful Hint

MyMathLab® and MathXL® When assignments are turned in online, keep a hard copy of your complete written work. You will need to refer to your written work to be able to ask questions and to study for tests later.

Choose to attend all class periods. If possible, sit near the front of the classroom. This way, you will see and hear the presentation better. It may also be easier for you to participate in classroom activities.

Do your homework. You've probably heard the phrase "practice makes perfect" in relation to music and sports. It also applies to mathematics. You will find that the more time you spend solving mathematics exercises, the easier the process becomes. Be sure to schedule enough time to complete your assignments before the due date assigned by your instructor.

Check your work. Review the steps you took while working a problem. Learn to check your answers in the original exercises. You may also compare your answers with the "Answers to Selected Exercises" section in the back of the book. If you have made a mistake, try to figure out what went wrong. Then correct your mistake. If you can't find what went wrong, **don't** erase your work or throw it away. Show your work to your instructor, a tutor in a math lab, or a classmate. It is easier for someone to find where you had trouble if he or she looks at your original work.

Learn from your mistakes and be patient with yourself. Everyone, even your instructor, makes mistakes. (That definitely includes me—Elayn Martin-Gay.) Use your errors to learn and to become a better math student. The key is finding and understanding your errors.

Was your mistake a careless one, or did you make it because you can't read your own math writing? If so, try to work more slowly or write more neatly and make a conscious effort to carefully check your work.

Did you make a mistake because you don't understand a concept? Take the time to review the concept or ask questions to better understand it.

Did you skip too many steps? Skipping steps or trying to do too many steps mentally may lead to preventable mistakes.

Know how to get help if you need it. It's all right to ask for help. In fact, it's a good idea to ask for help whenever there is something that you don't understand. Make sure you know when your instructor has office hours and how to find his or her office. Find out whether math tutoring services are available on your campus. Check on the hours, location, and requirements of the tutoring service.

Don't be afraid to ask questions. You are not the only person in class with questions. Other students are normally grateful that someone has spoken up.

Turn in assignments on time. This way, you can be sure that you will not lose points for being late. Show every step of a problem and be neat and organized. Also be sure that you understand which problems are assigned for homework. If allowed, you can always double-check the assignment with another student in your class.

Objective C Knowing and Using Your Text

Flip through the pages of this text or view the e-text pages on a computer screen. Start noticing examples, exercise sets, end-of-chapter material, and so on. Every text is organized in some manner. Learn the way this text is organized by reading about and then finding an example in your text of each type of resource listed below. Finding and using these resources throughout your course will increase your chance of success.

- *Practice Exercises.* Each example in every section has a parallel Practice exercise. As you read a section, try each Practice exercise after you've finished the corresponding example. Answers are at the bottom of the page. This "learn-by-doing" approach will help you grasp ideas before you move on to other concepts.

- *Symbols at the Beginning of an Exercise Set.* If you need help with a particular section, the symbols listed at the beginning of each exercise set will remind you of the resources available.

Helpful Hint

MyMathLab® and MathXL®
If you are doing your homework online, you can work and re-work those exercises that you struggle with until you master them. Try working through all the assigned exercises twice before the due date.

Helpful Hint

MyMathLab® and MathXL®
If you are completing your homework online, it's important to work each exercise on paper before submitting the answer. That way, you can check your work and follow your steps to find and correct any mistakes.

Helpful Hint

MyMathLab® and MathXL®
Be aware of assignments and due dates set by your instructor. Don't wait until the last minute to submit work online.

- *Objectives.* The main section of exercises in each exercise set is referenced by an objective, such as **A** or **B**, and also an example(s). There is also often a section of exercises entitled "Mixed Practice," which is referenced by two or more objectives or sections. These are mixed exercises written to prepare you for your next exam. Use all of this referencing if you have trouble completing an assignment from the exercise set.

- *Icons (Symbols).* Make sure that you understand the meaning of the icons that are beside many exercises. ▶ tells you that the corresponding exercise may be viewed on the video Lecture Series that corresponds to that section. ✎ tells you that this exercise is a writing exercise in which you should answer in complete sentences. △ tells you that the exercise involves geometry.

- *Integrated Reviews.* Found in the middle of each chapter, these reviews offer you a chance to practice—in one place—the many concepts that you have learned separately over several sections.

- *End-of-Chapter Opportunities.* There are many opportunities at the end of each chapter to help you understand the concepts of the chapter.

  Vocabulary Checks contain key vocabulary terms introduced in the chapter.

  Chapter Highlights contain chapter summaries and examples.

  Chapter Reviews contain review problems. The first part is organized section by section and the second part contains a set of mixed exercises.

  Chapter Tests are sample tests to help you prepare for an exam. The Chapter Test Prep Videos found in the Interactive Lecture Series, MyMathLab, and YouTube provide the video solution to each question on each Chapter Test.

  Cumulative Reviews start at Chapter 2 and are reviews consisting of material from the beginning of the book to the end of that particular chapter.

- *Student Resources in Your Textbook.* You will find a **Student Resources** section at the back of this textbook. It contains the following to help you study and prepare for tests:

  Study Skill Builders contain study skills advice. To increase your chance for success in the course, read these study tips, and answer the questions.

  Bigger Picture—Study Guide Outline provides you with a study guide outline of the course, with examples.

  Practice Final provides you with a Practice Final Exam to help you prepare for a final.

- *Resources to Check Your Work.* The **Answers to Selected Exercises** section provides answers to all odd-numbered section exercises and to all integrated review, chapter test, and cumulative review exercises. Use the **Solutions to Selected Exercises** to see the worked-out solution to every other odd-numbered exercise.

> **Helpful Hint**
>
> **MyMathLab®**
> In MyMathLab, you have access to the following video resources:
> - Lecture Videos for each section
> - Chapter Test Prep Videos
>
> Use these videos provided by the author to prepare for class, review, and study for tests.

Objective **D** Knowing and Using Video and Notebook Organizer Resources ▶

Video Resources

Below is a list of video resources that are all made by me—the author of your text, Elayn Martin-Gay. By making these videos, I can be sure that the methods presented are consistent with those in the text.

- *Interactive DVD Lecture Series.* Exercises marked with a ▶ are fully worked out by the author on the DVDs and within MyMathLab. The lecture series provides approximately 20 minutes of instruction per section and is organized by Objective.

- *Chapter Test Prep Videos.* These videos provide solutions to all of the Chapter Test exercises worked out by the author. They can be found in MyMathLab, the Interactive Lecture series, and You Tube. This supplement is very helpful before a test or exam.
- *Student Success Tips.* These video segments are about 3 minutes long and are daily reminders to help you continue practicing and maintaining good organizational and study habits.
- *Final Exam Videos.* These video segments provide solutions to each question. These videos can be found within MyMathLab and the Interactive Lecture Series.

Notebook Organizer Resources

The resources below are in three-ring notebook ready form. They are to be inserted in a three-ring binder and completed. Both resources are numbered according to the sections in your text to which they refer.

- *Video Organizer.* This organizer is closely tied to the Interactive Lecture (Video) Series. Each section should be completed while watching the lecture video on the same section. Once completed, you will have a set of notes to accompany the Lecture (Video) Series section by section.
- *Student Organizer.* This organizer helps you study effectively through note-taking hints, practice, and homework while referencing examples in the text and examples in the Lecture Series.

Objective E Getting Help

If you have trouble completing assignments or understanding the mathematics, get help as soon as you need it! This tip is presented as an objective on its own because it is so important. In mathematics, usually the material presented in one section builds on your understanding of the previous section. This means that if you don't understand the concepts covered during a class period, there is a good chance that you will not understand the concepts covered during the next class period. If this happens to you, get help as soon as you can.

Where can you get help? Many suggestions have been made in this section on where to get help, and now it is up to you to get it. Try your instructor, a tutoring center, or a math lab, or you may want to form a study group with fellow classmates. If you do decide to see your instructor or go to a tutoring center, make sure that you have a neat notebook and are ready with your questions.

Objective F Preparing for and Taking an Exam

Make sure that you allow yourself plenty of time to prepare for a test. If you think that you are a little "math anxious," it may be that you are not preparing for a test in a way that will ensure success. The way that you prepare for a test in mathematics is important. To prepare for a test:

1. Review your previous homework assignments.
2. Review any notes from class and section-level quizzes you have taken. (If this is a final exam, also review chapter tests you have taken.)
3. Review concepts and definitions by reading the Chapter Highlights at the end of each chapter.
4. Practice working out exercises by completing the Chapter Review found at the end of each chapter. (If this is a final exam, go through a Cumulative Review. There is one found at the end of each chapter except Chapter 1. Choose the review found at the end of the latest chapter that you have covered in your course.) *Don't stop here!*

Helpful Hint

MyMathLab® and MathXL®

- Use the **Help Me Solve This** button to get step-by-step help for the exercise you are working. You will need to work an additional exercise of the same type before you can get credit for having worked it correctly.
- Use the **Video** button to view a video clip of the author working a similar exercise.

Helpful Hint

MyMathLab® and MathXL® Review your written work for previous assignments. Then, go back and re-work previous assignments. Open a previous assignment, and click **Similar Exercise** to generate new exercises. Re-work the exercises until you fully understand them and can work them without help features.

5. It is important that you place yourself in conditions similar to test conditions to find out how you will perform. In other words, as soon as you feel that you know the material, get a few blank sheets of paper and take a sample test. There is a Chapter Test available at the end of each chapter, or you can work selected problems from the Chapter Review. Your instructor may also provide you with a review sheet. During this sample test, do not use your notes or your textbook. Then check your sample test. If your sample test is the Chapter Test in the text, don't forget that the video solutions are in MyMathLab, the Interactive Lecture Series, and YouTube. If you are not satisfied with the results, study the areas that you are weak in and try again.

6. On the day of the test, allow yourself plenty of time to arrive at where you will be taking your exam.

When taking your test:

1. Read the directions on the test carefully.

2. Read each problem carefully as you take the test. Make sure that you answer the question asked.

3. Watch your time and pace yourself so that you can attempt each problem on your test.

4. If you have time, check your work and answers.

5. Do not turn your test in early. If you have extra time, spend it double-checking your work.

Objective G Managing Your Time

As a college student, you know the demands that classes, homework, work, and family place on your time. Some days you probably wonder how you'll ever get everything done. One key to managing your time is developing a schedule. Here are some hints for making a schedule:

1. Make a list of all of your weekly commitments for the term. Include classes, work, regular meetings, extracurricular activities, etc. You may also find it helpful to list such things as laundry, regular workouts, grocery shopping, etc.

2. Next, estimate the time needed for each item on the list. Also make a note of how often you will need to do each item. Don't forget to include time estimates for the reading, studying, and homework you do outside of your classes. You may want to ask your instructor for help estimating the time needed.

3. In the exercise set that follows, you are asked to block out a typical week on the schedule grid given. Start with items with fixed time slots like classes and work.

4. Next, include the items on your list with flexible time slots. Think carefully about how best to schedule items such as study time.

5. Don't fill up every time slot on the schedule. Remember that you need to allow time for eating, sleeping, and relaxing! You should also allow a little extra time in case some items take longer than planned.

6. If you find that your weekly schedule is too full for you to handle, you may need to make some changes in your workload, classload, or other areas of your life. You may want to talk to your advisor, manager or supervisor at work, or someone in your college's academic counseling center for help with such decisions.

1.1 Exercise Set MyMathLab®

1. What is your instructor's name?

2. What are your instructor's office location and office hours?

3. What is the best way to contact your instructor?

4. Do you have the name and contact information of at least one other student in class?

5. Will your instructor allow you to use a calculator in this class?

6. Why is it important that you write step-by-step solutions to homework exercises and keep a hard copy of all work submitted?

7. Is there a tutoring service available on campus? If so, what are its hours? What services are available?

8. Have you attempted this course before? If so, write down ways that you might improve your chances of success during this next attempt.

9. List some steps that you can take if you begin having trouble understanding the material or completing an assignment. If you are completing your homework in MyMathLab ® and MathXL ®, list the resources you can use for help.

10. How many hours of studying does your instructor advise for each hour of instruction?

11. What does the ＼ icon in this text mean?

12. What does the △ icon in this text mean?

13. What does the ◐ icon in this text mean?

14. Search the minor columns in your text. What are Practice exercises?

15. When might be the best time to work a Practice exercise?

16. Where are the answers to Practice exercises?

17. What answers are contained in this text and where are they?

18. What are Study Skill Tips of the Day and where are they?

19. What and where are Integrated Reviews?

20. How many times is it suggested that you work through the homework exercises in MathXL ® before the submission deadline?

21. How far in advance of the assigned due date is it suggested that homework be submitted online? Why?

22. Chapter Highlights are found at the end of each chapter. Find the Chapter 1 Highlights and explain how you might use it and how it might be helpful.

23. Chapter Reviews are found at the end of each chapter. Find the Chapter 1 Review and explain how you might use it and how it might be helpful.

24. Chapter Tests are found at the end of each chapter. Find the Chapter 1 Test and explain how you might use it and how it might be helpful when preparing for an exam on Chapter 1. Include how the Chapter Test Prep Videos may help. If you are working in MyMathLab ® and MathXL ®, how can you use previous homework assignments to study?

25. What is the Video Organizer? Explain the contents and how it might be used.

26. What is the Student Organizer? Explain the contents and how it might be used.

27. Read or reread objective **G** and fill out the schedule grid on the next page.

	Monday	Tuesday	Wednesday	Thursday	Friday	Saturday	Sunday
4:00 a.m.							
5:00 a.m.							
6:00 a.m.							
7:00 a.m.							
8:00 a.m.							
9:00 a.m.							
10:00 a.m.							
11:00 a.m.							
12:00 p.m.							
1:00 p.m.							
2:00 p.m.							
3:00 p.m.							
4:00 p.m.							
5:00 p.m.							
6:00 p.m.							
7:00 p.m.							
8:00 p.m.							
9:00 p.m.							
10:00 p.m.							
11:00 p.m.							
Midnight							
1:00 a.m.							
2:00 a.m.							
3:00 a.m.							

1.2 Place Value, Names for Numbers, and Reading Tables

Objectives

A Find the Place Value of a Digit in a Whole Number.

B Write a Whole Number in Words and in Standard Form.

C Write a Whole Number in Expanded Form.

D Read Tables.

The **digits** 0, 1, 2, 3, 4, 5, 6, 7, 8, and 9 can be used to write numbers. For example, the **whole numbers** are

0, 1, 2, 3, 4, 5, 6, 7, 8, 9, 10, 11, . . .

and the **natural numbers** are 1, 2, 3, 4, 5, 6, 7, 8, 9, 10, 11, . . .

The three dots (. . .) after the 11 mean that this list continues indefinitely. That is, there is no largest whole number. The smallest whole number is 0.

Objective A Finding the Place Value of a Digit in a Whole Number

The position of each digit in a number determines its **place value.** For example, the average distance (in miles) between the planet Mercury and the planet Earth can be represented by the whole number 48,337,000. On the next page, is a place-value chart for this whole number.

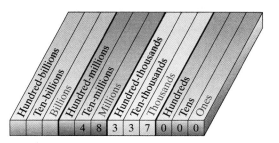

The two 3s in 48,337,000 represent different amounts because of their different place-ments. The place value of the 3 on the left is hundred-thousands. The place value of the 3 on the right is ten-thousands.

Examples Find the place value of the digit 3 in each whole number.

1. 396,418
↑
hundred-thousands

2. 93,192
↑
thousands

3. 534,275,866
↑
ten-millions

■ Work Practice 1–3

Practice 1–3

Find the place value of the digit 8 in each whole number.
1. 38,760,005
2. 67,890
3. 481,922

Objective B Writing a Whole Number in Words and in Standard Form

A whole number such as 1,083,664,500 is written in **standard form.** Notice that com-mas separate the digits into groups of three, starting from the right. Each group of three digits is called a **period.** The names of the first four periods are shown in red.

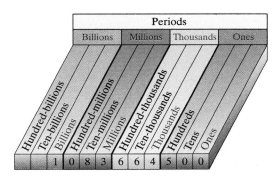

Writing a Whole Number in Words

To write a whole number in words, write the number in each period followed by the name of the period. (The ones period name is usually not written.) This same procedure can be used to read a whole number.

Fox example, we write 1,083,664,500 as

one **billion,**
eighty-three **million,**
six hundred sixty-four **thousand,**
five **hundred**

Helpful Hint Notice the commas after the name of each period.

Answers
1. millions   **2.** hundreds
3. ten-thousands

Helpful Hint

The name of the ones period is not used when reading and writing whole numbers. For example,

9,265

is read as

"nine **thousand**, two hundred sixty-five."

Practice 4-6

Write each whole number in words.

4. 54

5. 678

6. 93,205

Examples Write each whole number in words.

4. 72   seventy-two

5. 546   five hundred forty-six

6. 27,034   twenty-seven thousand, thirty-four

■ Work Practice 4–6

Helpful Hint The word "and" is *not* used when reading and writing whole numbers. It is used only when reading and writing mixed numbers and some decimal values, as shown later in this text.

Practice 7

Write 679,430,105 in words.

Example 7 Write 308,063,557 in words.

Solution: 308,063,557 is written as

three hundred eight **million**, sixty-three **thousand**, five hundred fifty-seven

■ Work Practice 7

✓**Concept Check** True or false? When writing a check for $2600, the word name we write for the dollar amount of the check is "two thousand sixty." Explain your answer.

Practice 8-11

Write each whole number in standard form.

8. thirty-seven

9. two hundred twelve

10. eight thousand, two hundred seventy-four

11. five million, fifty-seven thousand, twenty-six

Writing a Whole Number in Standard Form

To write a whole number in standard form, write the number in each period, followed by a comma.

Examples Write each whole number in standard form.

8. forty-one   41   **9.** seven hundred eight   708

10. six thousand, four hundred ninety-three

6,493   or   6493

11. three million, seven hundred forty-six thousand, five hundred twenty-two

3,746,522

■ Work Practice 8–11

Answers

4. fifty-four

5. six hundred seventy-eight

6. ninety-three thousand, two hundred five

7. six hundred seventy-nine million, four hundred thirty thousand, one hundred five

8. 37   **9.** 212

10. 8,274 or 8274   **11.** 5,057,026

✓**Concept Check Answer**

false

Helpful Hint

A comma may or may not be inserted in a four-digit number. For example, both

6,493 and 6493

are acceptable ways of writing six thousand, four hundred ninety-three.

Objective C Writing a Whole Number in Expanded Form

The place value of a digit can be used to write a number in expanded form. The **expanded form** of a number shows each digit of the number with its place value. For example, 5672 is written in expanded form as

$$5672 = 5000 + 600 + 70 + 2$$

Example 12 Write 5,207,034 in expanded form.

Solution: $5,000,000 + 200,000 + 7000 + 30 + 4$

Work Practice 12

We can visualize whole numbers by points on a line. The line below is called a **number line.** This number line has equally spaced marks for each whole number. The arrow to the right simply means that the whole numbers continue indefinitely. In other words, there is no largest whole number.

Number Line

We will study number lines further in Section 1.4.

Objective D Reading Tables

Now that we know about place value and names for whole numbers, we introduce one way that whole number data may be presented. **Tables** are often used to organize and display facts that contain numbers. The following table shows the countries that won the most medals during the Summer Olympic Games in London in 2012. (Although the medals are truly won by athletes from the various countries, for simplicity we will state that countries have won the medals.)

Practice 12

Write 4,026,301 in expanded form.

Answer
12. $4,000,000 + 20,000 + 6000 + 300 + 1$

| 2012 London Summer Olympics Medal Count |||||| | |||||
Country	Gold	Silver	Bronze	Total		Country	Gold	Silver	Bronze	Total
United States	46	29	29	104		Australia	7	16	12	35
China	38	27	23	88		France	11	11	12	34
Russian Federation	24	26	32	82		South Korea	13	8	7	28
Great Britain	29	17	19	65		Italy	8	9	11	28
Germany	11	19	14	44		Netherlands	6	6	8	20
Japan	7	14	17	38		Ukraine	6	5	9	20

(*Source:* International Olympic Committee)

For example, by reading from left to right along the row marked "Japan," we find that Japan won 7 gold, 14 silver, and 17 bronze medals during the 2012 Summer Olympic Games.

Practice 13

Use the 2012 Summer Games table to answer each question.

a. How many bronze medals did Great Britain win during the 2012 Summer Olympic Games?

b. Which countries won more than 80 medals?

Answers

13. **a.** 19   **b.** United States, China, Russia

Example 13   Use the 2012 Summer Games table to answer each question.

a. How many silver medals did the Russian Federation win during the 2012 Summer Olympic Games?

b. Which countries shown won fewer gold medals than Italy?

Solution:

a. Find "Russian Federation" in the left-hand column. Then read from left to right until the "silver" column is reached. We find that the Russian Federation won 26 silver medals.

b. Italy won 8 gold medals. Of the countries shown, Australia, the Netherlands, Ukraine, and Japan each won fewer than 8 gold medals.

▪ Work Practice 13

Vocabulary, Readiness & Video Check

Use the choices below to fill in each blank.

standard form	period	whole
expanded form	place value	words

1. The numbers 0, 1, 2, 3, 4, 5, 6, 7, 8, 9, 10, 11, 12, … are called _____ numbers.

2. The number 1286 is written in _____.

3. The number "twenty-one" is written in _____.

4. The number 900 + 60 + 5 is written in _____.

5. In a whole number, each group of three digits is called a(n) _____.

6. The _____ of the digit 4 in the whole number 264 is ones.

Martin-Gay Interactive Videos   Watch the section lecture video and answer the following questions.

Objective A   **7.** In ⊟ Example 1, what is the place value of the digit 6? ▶

Objective B   **8.** Complete this statement based on ⊟ Example 3. To read (or write) a number, read from _____ to _____. ▶

Objective C   **9.** In ⊟ Example 5, what is the expanded form value of the digit 8? ▶

Objective D   **10.** Use the table given in ⊟ Example 6 to determine which breed shown has the fewest American Kennel Club registrations. ▶

See Video 1.2 ●

1.2 Exercise Set MyMathLab® ▶

Objective A *Determine the place value of the digit 5 in each whole number. See Examples 1 through 3.*

▶ **1.** 657   **2.** 905   ▶ **3.** 5423   **4.** 6527

5. 43,526,000   **6.** 79,050,000   **7.** 5,408,092   **8.** 51,682,700

Objective B *Write each whole number in words. See Examples 4 through 7.*

9. 354   **10.** 316   **11.** 8279   **12.** 5445

▶ **13.** 26,990   **14.** 42,009   **15.** 2,388,000   **16.** 3,204,000

17. 24,350,185   **18.** 47,033,107

Write each number in the sentence in words. (Do not write the years in words.) See Examples 4 through 7.

19. In 2013, the population of Iceland was 321,800. (*Source: Statistics: Iceland*)

20. Between 1990 and 2010, Brazil lost 553,170 square kilometers of forest area.

21. The Burj Khalifa, in Dubai, United Arab Emirates, a hotel and office building, is currently the tallest in the world at a height of 2720 feet. (*Source:* Council on Tall Buildings and Urban Habitat)

22. In 2012, there were 124,681 patients in the United States waiting for an organ transplant. (*Source:* United Network for Organ Sharing)

23. Each day, UPS delivers an average of 16,300,000 packages and documents worldwide. (*Source:* UPS)

24. Each day, FedEx delivers an average of 3,300,000 packages and documents worldwide. (*Source:* FedEx)

25. The highest point in Colorado is Mount Elbert, at an elevation of 14,433 feet. (*Source:* U.S. Geological Survey)

26. The highest point in Oregon is Mount Hood, at an elevation of 11,239 feet. (*Source:* U.S. Geological Survey)

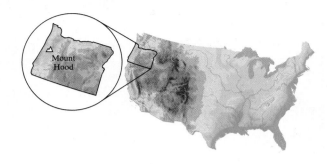

27. The average low price for a 2013 Honda Civic was $18,027. (*Source: U.S. News*)

28. The Goodyear blimp *Eagle* holds 202,700 cubic feet of helium. (*Source:* The Goodyear Tire & Rubber Company)

Write each whole number in standard form. See Examples 8 through 11.

29. Six thousand, five hundred eighty-seven

30. Four thousand, four hundred sixty-eight

31. Fifty-nine thousand, eight hundred

32. Seventy-three thousand, two

33. Thirteen million, six hundred one thousand, eleven

34. Sixteen million, four hundred five thousand, sixteen

35. Seven million, seventeen

36. Two million, twelve

37. Two hundred sixty thousand, nine hundred ninety-seven

38. Six hundred forty thousand, eight hundred eighty-one

Write the whole number in each sentence in standard form. See Examples 8 through 11.

39. The Mir Space Station orbits above Earth at an average altitude of three hundred ninety-five kilometers. (*Source:* Heavens Above)

40. The average distance between the surfaces of the Earth and the Moon is about two hundred thirty-four thousand miles.

41. The world's tallest free-standing tower is the Tokyo Sky Tree in Tokyo, Japan. Its height is two thousand eighty feet. (*Source:* Council on Tall Buildings and Urban Habitat)

42. The world's second-tallest free-standing tower is the Canton Tower in Guanzhou, China. Its height is one thousand nine hundred sixty-nine feet. (*Source:* Council on Tall Buildings and Urban Habitat)

43. The film *The Avengers* grabbed hold of the world record for opening weekend income when it took in two hundred million, three hundred thousand dollars in 2012. (*Source: Guinness World Records*)

44. The film *Harry Potter and the Deathly Hallows—Part II* holds the record for second-highest opening weekend income; it took in one hundred sixty-nine million, two hundred thousand dollars in 2011. (*Source: Guinness World Records*)

45. Morten Anderson, who played in the National Football League in 1982–2007, holds the record for most career field goals at five hundred sixty-five. (*Source:* NFL)

46. Morten Anderson also holds the record for the most field goals attempted in a career at seven hundred nine. (*Source:* NFL)

Objective C *Write each whole number in expanded form. See Example 12.*

47. 209

48. 789

49. 3470

50. 6040

51. 80,774

52. 20,215

53. 66,049

54. 99,032

55. 39,680,000

56. 47,703,029

Objective D *The table shows the beginning year of recent eruptions of major volcanoes in the Cascade Mountains. Use this table to answer Exercises 57 through 62. See Example 13.*

Recent Eruptions of Major Cascade Mountain Volcanoes (1750–present) *							
		Year of Eruption (beginning year)					
Volcano	State Location	1750–1799	1800–1849	1850–1899	1900–1949	1950–1999	2000–present
Mt. Baker	Washington	1792	1843	1870, 1880			
Glacier Peak	Washington	1750(?)					
Mt. Rainier	Washington		1841, 1843	1854			
Mt. St. Helens	Washington		1800			1980	
Mt. Hood	Oregon			1854, 1859, 1865			
Three Sisters	Oregon			1853(?)			
Medicine Lake	California				1910		
Mt. Shasta	California	1786		1855			
Cinder Cone*	California			1850			
Lassen Peak	California				1914		
Chaos Crags*	California			1854			

Other major volcanoes in the Cascades have had no eruptions from 1750 to present; *Source:* Harris
*Cinder Cone and Chaos Crags are located by Lassen Peak.

57. Mount Shasta erupted in the 1700s. Locate, then write this eruption year in standard form.

58. Mount Baker erupted in the 1700s. Locate, then write this eruption year in standard form.

59. Which volcano in the table has had the most eruptions?

60. Which volcano(es) in the table has had two eruptions?

61. Which volcano in the table had the earliest eruption?

62. Which volcano in the table had the most recent eruption?

The table shows the top ten popular breeds of dogs in 2012 according to the American Kennel Club. The breeds are listed in the order of number of registrations. Use this table to answer Exercises 63 through 68. See Example 13.

Top Ten American Kennel Club Registrations in 2012		
Breed	**Average Dog Maximum Height (in inches)**	**Average Dog Maximum Weight (in pounds)**
Labrador retriever	25	75
German shepherd	26	95
Golden retriever	24	80
Beagle	15	30
Bulldog	26	90
Yorkshire terrier	9	7
Boxer	25	70
Poodle (standard, miniature, and toy)	standard: 26	standard: 70
Rottweiler	26	none given
Dachshund	9	25

(*Source:* American Kennel Club)

63. Which breed has a greater average weight, the Bulldog or the German shepherd?

64. Which breed has more dogs registered, Golden retriever or German shepherd?

65. Which breed is the most popular dog? Write the maximum weight for this breed in words.

66. Which of the listed breeds has the fewest registrations? Write the average weight for this breed in words.

67. What is the maximum weight of an average-size Boxer?

68. What is the maximum height of an average-size standard poodle?

Concept Extensions

69. Write the largest four-digit number that can be made from the digits 1, 9, 8, and 6 if each digit must be used once. _____ _____ _____ _____

70. Write the largest five-digit number that can be made using the digits 5, 3, and 7 if each digit must be used at least once. _____ _____ _____ _____ _____

Check to see whether each number written in standard form matches the number written in words. If not, correct the number in words. See the Concept Check in this section.

71.

72.

73. If a number is given in words, describe the process used to write this number in standard form.

74. If a number is written in standard form, describe the process used to write this number in expanded form.

75. How large is a trillion? To get an idea, one trillion seconds is over 31 thousand years. Look up "trillion" in a dictionary and use the definition to write this number in standard form.

76. How large is a quadrillion? To get an idea, if one quadrillion dollars were divided among the population of the United States, we would each receive over 9 million dollars. Look up "quadrillion" (in the American system) and write this number in standard form.

1.3 Adding and Subtracting Whole Numbers, and Perimeter

Objective A Adding Whole Numbers

An iPod is a hard drive–based portable audio player. In 2013, it was still the most popular digital music player in the United States.

Suppose that an electronics store received a shipment of two boxes of iPods one day and an additional four boxes of iPods the next day. The **total** shipment in the two days can be found by adding 2 and 4.

2 boxes of iPods + 4 boxes of iPods = 6 boxes of iPods

The **sum** (or total) is 6 boxes of iPods. Each of the numbers 2 and 4 is called an **addend,** and the process of finding the sum is called **addition.**

$$\underset{\text{addend}}{2} \quad + \quad \underset{\text{addend}}{4} \quad = \quad \underset{\text{sum}}{6}$$

To add whole numbers, we add the digits in the ones place, then the tens place, then the hundreds place, and so on. For example, let's add 2236 + 160.

```
  2236
+  160
  2396
```
Line up numbers vertically so that the place values correspond. Then add digits in corresponding place values, starting with the ones place.

- sum of ones
- sum of tens
- sum of hundreds
- sum of thousands

Example 1 Add: 46 + 713

Solution:
```
   46
+ 713
  759
```

■ Work Practice 1

Adding by Carrying

When the sum of digits in corresponding place values is more than 9, **carrying** is necessary. For example, to add 365 + 89, add the ones-place digits first.

Carrying
```
   ¹
  365
+  89
    4
```
5 ones + 9 ones = **14 ones** or **1 ten + 4 ones**
Write the 4 ones in the ones place and carry the 1 ten to the tens place.

Next, add the tens-place digits.

```
  ¹¹
  365
+  89
   54
```
1 ten + 6 tens + 8 tens = **15 tens** or **1 hundred + 5 tens**
Write the 5 tens in the tens place and carry the 1 hundred to the hundreds place.

Objectives

A Add Whole Numbers.

B Subtract Whole Numbers.

C Find the Perimeter of a Polygon.

D Solve Problems by Adding or Subtracting Whole Numbers.

Practice 1
Add: 4135 + 252

Answer
1. 4387

17

Next, add the hundreds-place digits.

$$\overset{1\ 1}{365}$$
$$\underline{+\ \ 89}\quad \text{1 hundred + 3 hundreds = 4 hundreds}$$
$$454\quad \text{Write the 4 hundreds in the hundreds place.}$$

Practice 2

Add: 47,364 + 135,898

Example 2 Add: 46,278 + 124,931

Solution:
$$\overset{1\ 1\ 1}{46,278}$$
$$\underline{+\ 124,931}$$
$$171,209$$

■ Work Practice 2

✓**Concept Check** What is wrong with the following computation?

$$394$$
$$\underline{+\ 283}$$
$$577$$

Before we continue adding whole numbers, let's review some properties of addition that you may have already discovered. The first property that we will review is the **addition property of 0.** This property reminds us that the sum of 0 and any number is that same number.

Addition Property of 0

The sum of 0 and any number is that number. For example,

$$7 + 0 = 7$$
$$0 + 7 = 7$$

Next, notice that we can add any two whole numbers in any order and the sum is the same. For example,

$$4 + 5 = 9 \quad \text{and} \quad 5 + 4 = 9$$

We call this special property of addition the **commutative property of addition.**

Commutative Property of Addition

Changing the **order** of two addends does not change their sum. For example,

$$2 + 3 = 5 \quad \text{and} \quad 3 + 2 = 5$$

Another property that can help us when adding numbers is the **associative property of addition.** This property states that when adding numbers, the grouping of the numbers can be changed without changing the sum. We use parentheses to group numbers. They indicate which numbers to add first. For example, let's use two different groupings to find the sum of 2 + 1 + 5.

$$(2 + 1) + 5 = 3 + 5 = 8$$

Also,

$$2 + (1 + 5) = 2 + 6 = 8$$

Both groupings give a sum of 8.

Answer

2. 183,262

✓**Concept Check Answer**

forgot to carry 1 hundred to the hundreds place

Associative Property of Addition

Changing the **grouping** of addends does not change their sum. For example,

$$3 + (5 + 7) = 3 + 12 = 15 \quad \text{and} \quad (3 + 5) + 7 = 8 + 7 = 15$$

The commutative and associative properties tell us that we can add whole numbers using any order and grouping that we want.

When adding several numbers, it is often helpful to look for two or three numbers whose sum is 10, 20, and so on. Why? Adding multiples of 10 such as 10 and 20 is easier.

Example 3 Add: $13 + 2 + 7 + 8 + 9$

Solution:

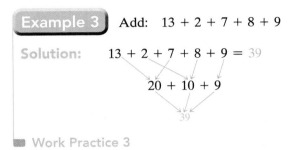

Practice 3

Add: $12 + 4 + 8 + 6 + 5$

■ Work Practice 3

Feel free to use the process of Example 3 anytime when adding.

Example 4 Add: $1647 + 246 + 32 + 85$

Solution:

$$
\begin{array}{r}
\scriptstyle 1\,2\,2 \\
1647 \\
246 \\
32 \\
+\quad 85 \\
\hline
2010
\end{array}
$$

Practice 4

Add: $6432 + 789 + 54 + 28$

■ Work Practice 4

Objective B Subtracting Whole Numbers

If you have \$5 and someone gives you \$3, you have a total of \$8, since $5 + 3 = 8$. Similarly, if you have \$8 and then someone borrows \$3, you have \$5 left. **Subtraction** is finding the **difference** of two numbers.

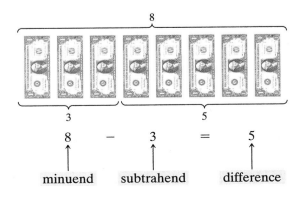

Answers

3. 35   **4.** 7303

In this example, 8 is the **minuend,** and 3 is the **subtrahend.** The **difference** between these two numbers, 8 and 3, is 5.

Notice that addition and subtraction are very closely related. In fact, subtraction is defined in terms of addition.

$$8 - 3 = 5 \text{ because } 5 + 3 = 8$$

This means that subtraction can be *checked* by addition, and we say that addition and subtraction are reverse operations.

Practice 5

Subtract. Check each answer by adding.

a. $14 - 6$

b. $20 - 8$

c. $93 - 93$

d. $42 - 0$

Example 5 Subtract. Check each answer by adding.

a. $12 - 9$ **b.** $22 - 7$ **c.** $35 - 35$ **d.** $70 - 0$

Solution:

a. $12 - 9 = 3$ because $3 + 9 = 12$

b. $22 - 7 = 15$ because $15 + 7 = 22$

c. $35 - 35 = 0$ because $0 + 35 = 35$

d. $70 - 0 = 70$ because $70 + 0 = 70$

Work Practice 5

Look again at Examples 5(c) and 5(d).

5(c) $35 - 35 = 0$ 5(d) $70 - 0 = 70$

| same number | difference is 0 | | a number minus 0 | difference is the same number |

These two examples illustrate the subtraction properties of 0.

Subtraction Properties of 0

The difference of any number and that same number is 0. For example,

$$11 - 11 = 0$$

The difference of any number and 0 is that same number. For example,

$$45 - 0 = 45$$

To subtract whole numbers we subtract the digits in the ones place, then the tens place, then the hundreds place, and so on. When subtraction involves numbers of two or more digits, it is more convenient to subtract vertically. For example, to subtract $893 - 52$,

```
  893   ⟵ minuend       Line up the numbers vertically so that the minuend is on top
 - 52   ⟵ subtrahend     and the place values correspond. Subtract in corresponding
  841   ⟵ difference      place values, starting with the ones place.
```

$3 - 2$
$9 - 5$
$8 - 0$

To check, add.

```
  difference    or      841
+ subtrahend          + 52
   minuend              893   ⟵ Since this is the original minuend,
                                  the problem checks.
```

Answers

5. a. 8   **b.** 12   **c.** 0   **d.** 42

Example 6 Subtract: 7826 − 505. Check by adding.

Solution:
```
  7826  ←                    Check:    7321
−  505                                +  505
  7321                                  7826
```

■ Work Practice 6

Subtracting by Borrowing

When subtracting vertically, if a digit in the second number (subtrahend) is larger than the corresponding digit in the first number (minuend), **borrowing** is necessary. For example, consider

```
  8 |1|
− 6 |3|
```

Since the 3 in the ones place of 63 is larger than the 1 in the ones place of 81, borrowing is necessary. We borrow 1 ten from the tens place and add it to the ones place.

Borrowing

```
 8  −  1  =  7   →     7 11  ← 1 ten + 1 one = 11 ones
tens  ten   tens       8 1̸
                     − 6 3
```

Now we subtract the ones-place digits and then the tens-place digits.

```
  7 11
  8 1̸  ←                              18
 −6 3                      Check:    +63
  1 8 ← 11 − 3 = 8                     81    The original minuend.
      └── 7 − 6 = 1
```

Example 7 Subtract: 543 − 29. Check by adding.

Solution:
```
     3 13
  5 4̸ 3̸  ←                  Check:    514
  −  29                             +  29
   5 1 4                              543
```

■ Work Practice 7

Sometimes we may have to borrow from more than one place. For example, to subtract 7631 − 152, we first borrow from the tens place.

```
      2 11
  76 3̸ 1̸
 −  1 5 2
        9 ← 11 − 2 = 9
```

In the tens place, 5 is greater than 2, so we borrow again. This time we borrow from the hundreds place.

```
                    ┌── 6 hundreds − 1 hundred = 5 hundreds
     5 12 11
  76 3̸ 1̸  ←── 1 hundred + 2 tens        Check:    7479
 − 1 5 2          or                             + 152
  7 4 7 9    10 tens + 2 tens = 12 tens            7631   The original minuend.
```

Practice 6

Subtract. Check by adding.
a. 9143 − 122
b. 978 − 851

Practice 7

Subtract. Check by adding.
a.
```
  697
−  49
```
b.
```
  326
− 245
```
c.
```
  1234
−  822
```

Answers
6. a. 9021 **b.** 127
7. a. 648 **b.** 81 **c.** 412

Practice 8

Subtract. Check by adding.

a.   400
     − 164

b.   1000
     − 762

Example 8   Subtract: 900 − 174. Check by adding.

Solution: In the ones place, 4 is larger than 0, so we borrow from the tens place. But the tens place of 900 is 0, so to borrow from the tens place, we must first borrow from the hundreds place.

$$\begin{array}{r} \overset{8}{\cancel{9}}\ \overset{10}{\cancel{0}}\ 0 \\ -1\ 7\ 4 \end{array}$$

Now borrow from the tens place.

$$\begin{array}{r} \overset{8}{\cancel{9}}\ \overset{\overset{9}{\cancel{10}}}{\cancel{0}}\ \overset{10}{\cancel{0}} \\ -1\ 7\ 4 \\ \hline 7\ 2\ 6 \end{array}$$

Check: 726
          +174
           900

■ Work Practice 8

Objective C Finding the Perimeter of a Polygon

In geometry, addition is used to find the perimeter of a polygon. A **polygon** can be described as a flat figure formed by line segments connected at their ends. (For more review, see Appendix A.1.) Geometric figures such as triangles, squares, and rectangles are called polygons.

Triangle   Square   Rectangle

The **perimeter** of a polygon is the *distance around* the polygon, shown in red above. This means that the perimeter of a polygon is the sum of the lengths of its sides.

Practice 9

Find the perimeter of the polygon shown. (A centimeter is a unit of length in the metric system.)

2 centimeters
5 centimeters   8 centimeters
15 centimeters

Example 9   Find the perimeter of the polygon shown.

3 inches
2 inches   1 inch
4 inches   3 inches

Solution: To find the perimeter (distance around), we add the lengths of the sides.

2 in. + 3 in. + 1 in. + 3 in. + 4 in. = 13 in.

The perimeter is 13 inches.

■ Work Practice 9

To make the addition appear simpler, we will often not include units with the addends. If you do this, make sure units are included in the final answer.

Answers

8. a. 236   **b.** 238
9. 30 cm

Example 10 Calculating the Perimeter of a Building

The largest commercial building in the world under one roof is the flower auction building of the cooperative VBA in Aalsmeer, Netherlands. The floor plan is a rectangle that measures 776 meters by 639 meters. Find the perimeter of this building. (A meter is a unit of length in the metric system.) (*Source: The Handy Science Answer Book*, Visible Ink Press)

Solution: Recall that opposite sides of a rectangle have the same length. To find the perimeter of this building, we add the lengths of the sides. The sum of the lengths of its sides is

776 meters

639 meters   639 meters

776 meters

$$
\begin{array}{r}
639 \\
639 \\
776 \\
+ \ 776 \\
\hline
2830
\end{array}
$$

The perimeter of the building is 2830 meters.

◼ Work Practice 10

Practice 10

A park is in the shape of a triangle. Each of the park's three sides is 647 feet. Find the perimeter of the park.

Objective D Solving Problems by Adding or Subtracting

Often, real-life problems occur that can be solved by adding or subtracting. The first step in solving any word problem is to *understand* the problem by reading it carefully.

Descriptions in problems solved through addition or subtraction *may* include any of these key words or phrases:

Helpful Hint Be careful when solving applications that suggest subtraction. Although order *does not* matter when adding, order *does* matter when subtracting. For example, $20 - 15$ and $15 - 20$ do not simplify to the same number.

Addition		
Key Words or Phrases	**Examples**	**Symbols**
added to	5 added to 7	$7 + 5$
plus	0 plus 78	$0 + 78$
increased by	12 increased by 6	$12 + 6$
more than	11 more than 25	$25 + 11$
total	the total of 8 and 1	$8 + 1$
sum	the sum of 4 and 133	$4 + 133$

Subtraction		
Key Words or Phrases	**Examples**	**Symbols**
subtract	subtract 5 from 8	$8 - 5$
difference	the difference of 10 and 2	$10 - 2$
less	17 less 3	$17 - 3$
less than	2 less than 20	$20 - 2$
take away	14 take away 9	$14 - 9$
decreased by	7 decreased by 5	$7 - 5$
subtracted from	9 subtracted from 12	$12 - 9$

✓**Concept Check** In each of the following problems, identify which number is the minuend and which number is the subtrahend.

a. What is the result when 6 is subtracted from 40?
b. What is the difference of 15 and 8?
c. Find a number that is 15 fewer than 23.

To solve a word problem that involves addition or subtraction, we first use the facts given to write an addition or subtraction statement. Then we write the corresponding solution of the real-life problem. It is sometimes helpful to write the statement in words (brief phrases) and then translate to numbers.

Answer
10. 1941 ft

✓**Concept Check Answers**
a. minuend: 40; subtrahend: 6
b. minuend: 15; subtrahend: 8
c. minuend: 23; subtrahend: 15

Practice 11

The radius of Uranus is 15,759 miles. The radius of Neptune is 458 miles less than the radius of Uranus. What is the radius of Neptune? (*Source:* National Space Science Data Center)

Since subtraction and addition are reverse operations, don't forget that a subtraction problem can be checked by adding.

Example 11   Finding the Radius of a Planet

The radius of Jupiter is 43,441 miles. The radius of Saturn is 7257 miles less than the radius of Jupiter. Find the radius of Saturn. (*Source:* National Space Science Data Center)

Solution:

In Words		Translate to Numbers
radius of Jupiter	$\longrightarrow$	43,441
$-$ 7257	$\longrightarrow$	$-$ 7257
radius of Saturn	$\longrightarrow$	36,184

The radius of Saturn is 36,184 miles.

■ **Work Practice 11**

Graphs can be used to visualize data. The graph shown next is called a **bar graph.** For this bar graph, the height of each bar is labeled above the bar. To check this height, follow the top of each bar to the vertical line to the left. For example, the first bar is labeled 214. Follow the top of that bar to the left until the vertical line is reached, a bit more than halfway between 200 and 225, or 214.

Practice 12

Use the graph in Example 12 to answer the following:

a. Which country shown has the fewest threatened amphibians?

b. Find the total number of threatened amphibians for Brazil, Peru, and Mexico.

Example 12   Reading a Bar Graph

As years pass, the number of endangered species per country increases. In the following graph, each bar represents a country and the height of each bar represents the number of endangered species identified in that country.

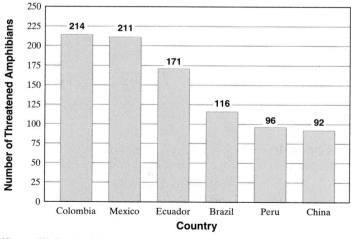

Number of Threatened Amphibians (frogs, toads, salamanders, etc.)

(*Source: The Top 10 of Everything,* 2013)

a. Which country shown has the greatest number of threatened amphibians?

b. Find the total number of threatened amphibians for Ecuador, China, and Colombia.

Answers

11. 15,301 miles

12. a. China   b. 423

Solution:

a. The country with the greatest number of threatened amphibians corresponds to the tallest bar, which is Colombia.

b. The key word here is "total." To find the total number of threatened amphibians for Ecuador, China, and Colombia, we add.

In Words		Translate to Numbers
Ecuador	$\longrightarrow$	171
China	$\longrightarrow$	92
Colombia	$\longrightarrow$	+ 214
		Total 477

The total number of threatened amphibians for Ecuador, China, and Colombia is 477.

■ Work Practice 12

Calculator Explorations Adding and Subtracting Numbers

Adding Numbers

To add numbers on a calculator, find the keys marked $\boxed{+}$ and $\boxed{=}$ or $\boxed{\text{ENTER}}$.

For example, to add 5 and 7 on a calculator, press the keys $\boxed{5}\ \boxed{+}\ \boxed{7}$ then $\boxed{=}$ or $\boxed{\text{ENTER}}$.

The display will read $\boxed{12}$.

Thus, $5 + 7 = 12$.

To add 687, 981, and 49 on a calculator, press the keys $\boxed{687}$ $\boxed{+}\ \boxed{981}\ \boxed{+}\ \boxed{49}$ then $\boxed{=}$ or $\boxed{\text{ENTER}}$.

The display will read $\boxed{1717}$.

Thus, $687 + 981 + 49 = 1717$. (Although entering 687, for example, requires pressing more than one key, here numbers are grouped together for easier reading.)

Use a calculator to add.

1. $89 + 45$ **2.** $76 + 97$

3. $285 + 55$ **4.** $8773 + 652$

5.   985   **6.**   465
            1210   9888
            562   620
      +   77   + 1550

Subtracting Numbers

To subtract numbers on a calculator, find the keys marked $\boxed{-}$ and $\boxed{=}$ or $\boxed{\text{ENTER}}$.

For example, to find $83 - 49$ on a calculator, press the keys $\boxed{83}\ \boxed{-}\ \boxed{49}$ then $\boxed{=}$ or $\boxed{\text{ENTER}}$.

The display will read $\boxed{34}$. Thus, $83 - 49 = 34$.

Use a calculator to subtract.

7. $865 - 95$

8. $76 - 27$

9. $147 - 38$

10. $366 - 87$

11. $9625 - 647$

12. $10{,}711 - 8925$

Vocabulary, Readiness & Video Check

Use the choices below to fill in each blank. Some choices may be used more than once and some may not be used at all.

0	order	addend	associative
sum	number	grouping	commutative
perimeter	minuend	subtrahend	difference

1. The sum of 0 and any number is the same _____ .
2. In $35 + 20 = 55$, the number 55 is called the _____ and 35 and 20 are each called a(n) _____ .
3. The difference of any number and that same number is _____ .
4. The difference of any number and 0 is the same _____ .
5. In $37 - 19 = 18$, the number 37 is the _____ , the 19 is the _____ , and the 18 is the _____ .
6. The distance around a polygon is called its _____ .
7. Since $7 + 10 = 10 + 7$, we say that changing the _____ in addition does not change the sum. This property is called the _____ property of addition.
8. Since $(3 + 1) + 20 = 3 + (1 + 20)$, we say that changing the _____ in addition does not change the sum. This property is called the _____ property of addition.

Martin-Gay Interactive Videos   Watch the section lecture video and answer the following questions.

See Video 1.3

Objective A 9. Complete this statement based on the lecture before ⊞ Example 1. To add whole numbers, we line up _____ values and add from _____ to _____ .

Objective B 10. In ⊞ Example 5, explain how we end up subtracting 7 from 12 in the ones place.

Objective C 11. In ⊞ Example 7, the perimeter of what type of polygon is found? How many addends are in the resulting addition problem?

Objective D 12. Complete this statement based on ⊞ Example 8. To find the sale price, subtract the _____ from the _____ price.

1.3 Exercise Set MyMathLab®

Objective A *Add. See Examples 1 through 4.*

1. $14 + 22$

2. $27 + 31$

3. $\begin{array}{r} 62 \\ + 230 \\ \hline \end{array}$

4. $\begin{array}{r} 37 \\ + 542 \\ \hline \end{array}$

5. $\begin{array}{r} 12 \\ 13 \\ + 24 \\ \hline \end{array}$

6. $\begin{array}{r} 23 \\ 45 \\ + 30 \\ \hline \end{array}$

▶ 7. $\begin{array}{r} 5267 \\ + 132 \\ \hline \end{array}$

8. $\begin{array}{r} 236 \\ + 6243 \\ \hline \end{array}$

9. $22{,}781 + 186{,}297$ 10. $17{,}427 + 821{,}059$

11.
$$\begin{array}{r} 8 \\ 9 \\ 2 \\ 5 \\ +1 \\ \hline \end{array}$$

12.
$$\begin{array}{r} 3 \\ 5 \\ 8 \\ 5 \\ +7 \\ \hline \end{array}$$

13.
$$\begin{array}{r} 81 \\ 17 \\ 23 \\ 79 \\ +12 \\ \hline \end{array}$$

14.
$$\begin{array}{r} 64 \\ 28 \\ 56 \\ 25 \\ +32 \\ \hline \end{array}$$

15. $24 + 9006 + 489 + 2407$

16. $16 + 1056 + 748 + 7770$

17.
$$\begin{array}{r} 6820 \\ 4271 \\ +5626 \\ \hline \end{array}$$

18.
$$\begin{array}{r} 6789 \\ 4321 \\ +5555 \\ \hline \end{array}$$

19.
$$\begin{array}{r} 49 \\ 628 \\ 5\,762 \\ +29,462 \\ \hline \end{array}$$

20.
$$\begin{array}{r} 26 \\ 582 \\ 4\,763 \\ +62,511 \\ \hline \end{array}$$

21.
$$\begin{array}{r} 121,742 \\ 57,279 \\ 26,586 \\ +426,782 \\ \hline \end{array}$$

22.
$$\begin{array}{r} 504,218 \\ 321,920 \\ 38,507 \\ +594,687 \\ \hline \end{array}$$

Objective B   *Subtract. Check by adding. See Examples 5 through 8.*

23.
$$\begin{array}{r} 749 \\ -149 \\ \hline \end{array}$$

24.
$$\begin{array}{r} 957 \\ -257 \\ \hline \end{array}$$

25.
$$\begin{array}{r} 62 \\ -37 \\ \hline \end{array}$$

26.
$$\begin{array}{r} 55 \\ -29 \\ \hline \end{array}$$

27.
$$\begin{array}{r} 922 \\ -634 \\ \hline \end{array}$$

28.
$$\begin{array}{r} 674 \\ -299 \\ \hline \end{array}$$

29.
$$\begin{array}{r} 600 \\ -432 \\ \hline \end{array}$$

30.
$$\begin{array}{r} 300 \\ -149 \\ \hline \end{array}$$

31.
$$\begin{array}{r} 6283 \\ -560 \\ \hline \end{array}$$

32.
$$\begin{array}{r} 5349 \\ -720 \\ \hline \end{array}$$

33.
$$\begin{array}{r} 533 \\ -29 \\ \hline \end{array}$$

34.
$$\begin{array}{r} 724 \\ -16 \\ \hline \end{array}$$

35. $1983 - 1904$

36. $1983 - 1914$

37. $50,000 - 17,289$

38. $40,000 - 23,582$ **39.** $7020 - 1979$ **40.** $6050 - 1878$ **41.** $51,111 - 19,898$ **42.** $62,222 - 39,898$

Objectives A B   Mixed Practice   *Add or subtract as indicated. See Examples 1 through 8.*

43.
$$\begin{array}{r} 986 \\ +48 \\ \hline \end{array}$$

44.
$$\begin{array}{r} 986 \\ -48 \\ \hline \end{array}$$

45. $76 - 67$

46. $80 + 93 + 17 + 9 + 2$

47.
$$\begin{array}{r} 9000 \\ -482 \\ \hline \end{array}$$

48.
$$\begin{array}{r} 10,000 \\ -1786 \\ \hline \end{array}$$

49.
$$\begin{array}{r} 10,962 \\ 4851 \\ +7063 \\ \hline \end{array}$$

50.
$$\begin{array}{r} 12,468 \\ 3211 \\ +1988 \\ \hline \end{array}$$

Objective C *Find the perimeter of each figure. See Examples 9 and 10.*

51.

52.

53.

54.

55.

56.

57.

58.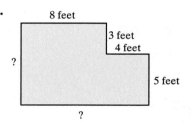

Objectives A B D Mixed Practice–Translating *Solve. See Examples 9 through 12.*

59. Find the sum of 297 and 1796.

60. Find the sum of 802 and 6487.

61. Find the total of 76, 39, 8, 17, and 126.

62. Find the total of 89, 45, 2, 19, and 341.

63. Find the difference of 41 and 21.

64. Find the difference of 16 and 5.

65. What is 452 increased by 92?

66. What is 712 increased by 38?

67. Find 108 less 36.

68. Find 25 less 12.

69. Find 12 subtracted from 100.

70. Find 86 subtracted from 90.

Solve.

71. The population of Florida is projected to grow from 19,308 thousand in 2010 to 22,478 thousand in 2020. What is Florida's projected population increase over this time period?

72. The population of California is projected to grow from 39,136 thousand in 2010 to 44,126 thousand in 2020. What is California's projected population increase over this time period?

73. A new DVD player with remote control costs $295. A college student has $914 in her savings account. How much will she have left in her savings account after she buys the DVD player?

74. A stereo that regularly sells for $547 is discounted by $99 in a sale. What is the sale price?

A river basin is the geographic area drained by a river and its tributaries. The Mississippi River Basin is the third largest in the world and is divided into six sub-basins, whose areas are shown in the following bar graph. Use this graph for Exercises 75 through 78.

75. Find the total U.S. land area drained by the Upper Mississippi and Lower Mississippi sub-basins.

76. Find the total U.S. land area drained by the Ohio and Tennessee sub-basins.

77. How many more square miles of land are drained by the Missouri sub-basin than the Arkansas Red-White sub-basin?

78. How many more square miles of land are drained by the Upper Mississippi sub-basin than the Lower Mississippi sub-basin?

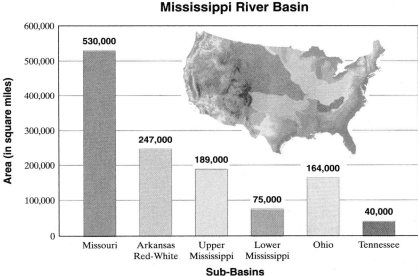

Mississippi River Basin

79. A homeowner is installing a fence in his backyard. How many feet of fencing are needed to enclose the yard below?

70 feet · 78 feet · 90 feet · 102 feet

80. A homeowner is considering installing gutters around her home. Find the perimeter of her rectangular home.

60 feet · 45 feet

81. Professor Graham is reading a 503-page book. If she has just finished reading page 239, how many more pages must she read to finish the book?

82. When a couple began a trip, the odometer read 55,492. When the trip was over, the odometer read 59,320. How many miles did they drive on their trip?

83. In 2013, the country of New Zealand had 26,820,424 more sheep than people. If the human population of New Zealand in 2013 was 4,479,576, what was the sheep population? (*Source: Statistics: New Zealand*)

84. During one month in 2013, the two top-selling vehicles in the United States were the Ford F-Series and the Chevrolet Silverado, both trucks. There were 60,449 F-Series trucks and 42,080 Silverados sold that month. What was the total number of these trucks sold in that month? (*Source:* cars.com)

The decibel (dB) is a unit of measurement for sound. Every increase of 10 dB is a tenfold increase in sound intensity. The bar graph shows the decibel levels for some common sounds. Use this graph for Exercises 85 through 88.

85. What is the dB level for live rock music?

86. Which is the quietest of all the sounds shown in the graph?

87. How much louder is the sound of snoring than normal conversation?

88. What is the difference in sound intensity between live rock music and loud television?

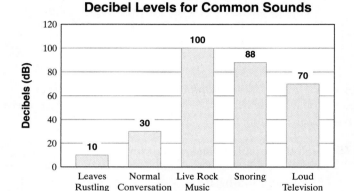

89. In 2013, there were 2410 Gap Inc. (Gap, Banana Republic, Old Navy) stores located in the United States and 1034 located outside the United States. How many Gap Inc. stores were located worldwide? (*Source:* Gap, Inc.)

90. Automobile classes are defined by the amount of interior room. A subcompact car is defined as a car with a maximum interior space of 99 cubic feet. A midsize car is defined as a car with a maximum interior space of 119 cubic feet. What is the difference in volume between a midsize and a subcompact car?

91. The largest permanent Monopoly board is made of granite and is located in San Jose, California. It is in the shape of a square with side lengths of 31 ft. Find the perimeter of the square playing board.

92. The smallest commercially available jigsaw puzzle is a 1000-piece puzzle manufactured in Spain. It is in the shape of a rectangle with length of 18 inches and width of 12 inches. Find the perimeter of this rectangular-shaped puzzle.

The table shows the number of Target stores in ten states. Use this table to answer Exercises 93 through 98.

The Top States for Target Stores in 2012	
State	**Number of Stores**
Pennsylvania	63
California	257
Florida	123
Virginia	57
Illinois	89
New York	67
Michigan	59
Minnesota	75
Ohio	64
Texas	149
(*Source:* Target Corporation)	

93. Which state has the most Target stores?

94. Which of the states listed in the table has the fewest Target stores?

95. What is the total number of Target stores located in the three states with the most Target stores?

96. How many Target stores are located in the ten states listed in the table?

97. Which pair of neighboring states have more Target stores combined, Pennsylvania and New York or Michigan and Ohio?

98. There are 775 Target stores located in the states not listed in the table. How many Target stores are in the United States?

99. The state of Delaware has 2029 miles of urban highways and 3865 miles of rural highways. Find the total highway mileage in Delaware. (*Source:* U.S. Federal Highway Administration)

100. The state of Rhode Island has 5193 miles of urban highways and 1222 miles of rural highways. Find the total highway mileage in Rhode Island. (*Source:* U.S. Federal Highway Administration)

Concept Extensions

For Exercises 101–104, identify which number is the minuend and which number is the subtrahend. See the second Concept Check in this section.

101.
$$\begin{array}{r} 48 \\ -\ 1 \\ \hline \end{array}$$

102.
$$\begin{array}{r} 2863 \\ -1904 \\ \hline \end{array}$$

103. Subtract 7 from 70.

104. Find 86 decreased by 25.

105. In your own words, explain the commutative property of addition.

106. In your own words, explain the associative property of addition.

Check each addition below. If it is incorrect, find the correct answer. See the first Concept Check in this section.

107.
$$\begin{array}{r} 566 \\ 932 \\ +\ 871 \\ \hline 2369 \end{array}$$

108.
$$\begin{array}{r} 773 \\ 659 \\ +\ 481 \\ \hline 1913 \end{array}$$

109.
$$\begin{array}{r} 14 \\ 173 \\ 86 \\ +\ 257 \\ \hline 520 \end{array}$$

110.
$$\begin{array}{r} 19 \\ 214 \\ 49 \\ +\ 651 \\ \hline 923 \end{array}$$

Identify each answer as correct or incorrect. Use addition to check. If the answer is incorrect, write the correct answer.

111.
$$\begin{array}{r} 741 \\ -\ 56 \\ \hline 675 \end{array}$$

112.
$$\begin{array}{r} 478 \\ -\ 89 \\ \hline 389 \end{array}$$

113.
$$\begin{array}{r} 1029 \\ -\ 888 \\ \hline 141 \end{array}$$

114.
$$\begin{array}{r} 7615 \\ -\ 547 \\ \hline 7168 \end{array}$$

Fill in the missing digits in each problem.

115.
$$\begin{array}{r} 526\_ \\ -2\_85 \\ \hline 28\_4 \end{array}$$

116.
$$\begin{array}{r} 10,\_4\_ \\ -\ 8\ 5\_4 \\ \hline \_710 \end{array}$$

117. Is there a commutative property of subtraction? In other words, does order matter when subtracting? Why or why not?

118. Explain why the phrase "Subtract 7 from 10" translates to "10 − 7."

119. The local college library is having a Million Pages of Reading promotion. The freshmen have read a total of 289,462 pages; the sophomores have read a total of 369,477 pages; the juniors have read a total of 218,287 pages; and the seniors have read a total of 121,685 pages. Have they reached a goal of one million pages? If not, how many more pages need to be read?

Objectives

A Round Whole Numbers.

B Use Rounding to Estimate Sums and Differences.

C Solve Problems by Estimating.

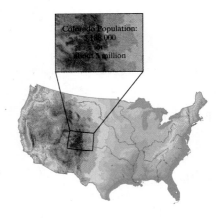

Objective A Rounding Whole Numbers

Rounding a whole number means approximating it. A rounded whole number is often easier to use, understand, and remember than the precise whole number. For example, instead of trying to remember the Colorado state population as 5,188,000, it is much easier to remember it rounded to the nearest million: 5,000,000, or 5 million people. (*Source:* U.S. census)

Recall from Section 1.2 that the line below is called a number line. To **graph** a whole number on this number line, we darken the point representing the location of the whole number. For example, the number 4 is graphed below.

On the number line, the whole number 36 is closer to 40 than 30, so 36 rounded to the nearest ten is 40.

The whole number 52 is closer to 50 than 60, so 52 rounded to the nearest ten is 50.

In trying to round 25 to the nearest ten, we see that 25 is halfway between 20 and 30. It is not closer to either number. In such a case, we round to the larger ten, that is, to 30.

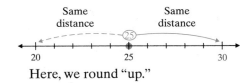

Here, we round "up."

To round a whole number without using a number line, follow these steps:

Rounding a Whole Number to a Given Place Value

Step 1: Locate the digit to the right of the given place value.

Step 2: If this digit is 5 or greater, add 1 to the digit in the given place value and replace each digit to its right by 0.

Step 3: If this digit is less than 5, replace it and each digit to its right by 0.

Example 1 Round 568 to the nearest ten.

Solution: 5 6 ⑧   The digit to the right of the tens place is the ones
          ↑   place, which is circled.
       tens place

        5 6 ⑧   Since the circled digit is 5 or greater, add 1 to the 6 in
        ↑ ↖   the tens place and replace the digit to the right by 0.
      Add 1. Replace
           with 0.

We find that 568 rounded to the nearest ten is 570.

■ Work Practice 1

Example 2 Round 278,362 to the nearest thousand.

Solution: Thousands place
                        ↓   ┌─3 is less than 5.
                     278,③62
                      ↑   ↑
              Do not add 1.   Replace with zeros.

The number 278,362 rounded to the nearest thousand is 278,000.

■ Work Practice 2

Example 3 Round 248,982 to the nearest hundred.

Solution: Hundreds place
                        ↓   ┌─8 is greater than or equal to 5.
                     248,9⑧2
                        ↑

                     Add 1.   9 + 1 = 10, so replace the digit 9 by 0 and carry 1 to the
                              place value to the left.

                        8+1 0
                  2 4 8, 9̷ 8 2
                        ↑   ↑
                     Add 1.   Replace with zeros.

The number 248,982 rounded to the nearest hundred is 249,000.

■ Work Practice 3

✔**Concept Check** Round each of the following numbers to the nearest *hundred*.
Explain your reasoning.

a. 59   **b.** 29

Objective B Estimating Sums and Differences

By rounding addends, minuends, and subtrahends, we can **estimate** sums and differences. An estimated sum or difference is appropriate when the exact number is not
necessary. Also, an estimated sum or difference can help us determine if we made

---

Practice 1

Round to the nearest ten.
a. 57
b. 641
c. 325

Practice 2

Round to the nearest thousand.
a. 72,304
b. 9222
c. 671,800

Practice 3

Round to the nearest hundred.
a. 3474
b. 76,243
c. 978,965

Answers
1. a. 60 **b.** 640 **c.** 330
2. a. 72,000 **b.** 9000 **c.** 672,000
3. a. 3500 **b.** 76,200 **c.** 979,000

✔**Concept Check Answers**
a. 100 **b.** 0

a mistake in calculating an exact amount. To estimate the sum below, round each number to the nearest hundred and then add.

768	rounds to	800
1952	rounds to	2000
225	rounds to	200
+ 149	rounds to	+ 100
		3100

The estimated sum is 3100, which is close to the **exact** sum of 3094.

Practice 4

Round each number to the nearest ten to find an estimated sum.

49
25
32
51
+ 98

Example 4 Round each number to the nearest hundred to find an estimated sum.

294
625
1071
+ 349

Solution:

Exact:		**Estimate:**
294	rounds to	300
625	rounds to	600
1071	rounds to	1100
+ 349	rounds to	+ 300
		2300

The estimated sum is 2300. (The exact sum is 2339.)

Work Practice 4

Practice 5

Round each number to the nearest thousand to find an estimated difference.

3785
− 2479

Example 5 Round each number to the nearest hundred to find an estimated difference.

4725
− 2879

Solution:

Exact:		**Estimate:**
4725	rounds to	4700
− 2879	rounds to	− 2900
		1800

The estimated difference is 1800. (The exact difference is 1846.)

Work Practice 5

Objective C Solving Problems by Estimating

Making estimates is often the quickest way to solve real-life problems when solutions do not need to be exact.

Answers
4. 260
5. 2000

Example 6 Estimating Distances

A driver is trying to quickly estimate the distance from Temple, Texas, to Brenham, Texas. Round each distance given on the map to the nearest ten to estimate the total distance.

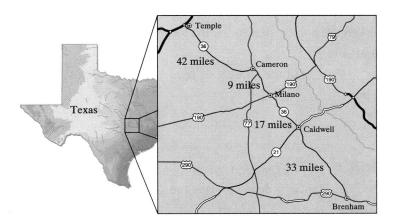

Practice 6

Tasha Kilbey is trying to estimate how far it is from Gove, Kansas, to Hays, Kansas. Round each given distance on the map to the nearest ten to estimate the total distance.

Solution:

Exact Distance:		Estimate:
42	rounds to	40
9	rounds to	10
17	rounds to	20
+33	rounds to	+30
		100

It is approximately 100 miles from Temple to Brenham. (The exact distance is 101 miles.)

■ Work Practice 6

Example 7 Estimating Data

In three recent years the numbers of tons of air cargo and mail that went through Hartsfield-Jackson Atlanta International Airport were 629,700, 685,550, and 737,655. Round each number to the nearest thousand to estimate the tons of mail that passed through this airport.

Solution:

Exact Tons of Cargo Mail:		Estimate:
629,700	rounds to	630,000
685,550	rounds to	686,000
+737,655	rounds to	+738,000
		2,054,000

The approximate tonnage of mail that moved through Atlanta's airport over this 3-year period was 2,054,000 tons. (The exact tonnage was 2,052,905 tons.)

■ Work Practice 7

Practice 7

In 2010, there were 15,427 reported cases of chicken pox, 2612 reported cases of mumps, and 27,550 reported cases of pertussis (whooping cough). Round each number to the nearest thousand to estimate the total number of cases reported for these preventable diseases. (*Source:* Centers for Disease Control and Prevention)

Answers

6. 80 mi

7. 46,000 total cases

Vocabulary, Readiness & Video Check

Use the choices below to fill in each blank.

60	rounding	exact
70	estimate	graph

1. To _____ a number on a number line, darken the point representing the location of the number.
2. Another word for approximating a whole number is _____.
3. The number 65 rounded to the nearest ten is _____, but the number 61 rounded to the nearest ten is _____.
4. A(n) _____ number of products is 1265, but a(n) _____ is 1000.

Martin-Gay Interactive Videos   *Watch the section lecture video and answer the following questions.*

Objective A 5. In ▤ Example 1, when rounding the number to the nearest ten, why do we replace the digit 3 with a 4?

Objective B 6. As discussed in ▤ Example 3, explain how a number line can help us understand how to round 22 to the nearest ten. ▶

Objective C 7. What is the significance of the circled digit in each height value in ▤ Example 5? ▶

See Video 1.4

1.4 Exercise Set MyMathLab® ▶

Objective A *Round each whole number to the given place. See Examples 1 through 3.*

1. 423 to the nearest ten

2. 273 to the nearest ten

▶ **3.** 635 to the nearest ten

4. 846 to the nearest ten

5. 2791 to the nearest hundred

6. 8494 to the nearest hundred

7. 495 to the nearest ten

8. 898 to the nearest ten

9. 21,094 to the nearest thousand

10. 82,198 to the nearest thousand

11. 33,762 to the nearest thousand

12. 42,682 to the nearest ten-thousand

13. 328,495 to the nearest hundred

14. 179,406 to the nearest hundred

▶ **15.** 36,499 to the nearest thousand

16. 96,501 to the nearest thousand

17. 39,994 to the nearest ten

18. 99,995 to the nearest ten

19. 29,834,235 to the nearest ten-million

20. 39,523,698 to the nearest million

Complete the table by estimating the given number to the given place value.

		Tens	Hundreds	Thousands
21.	5281			
22.	7619			
23.	9444			
24.	7777			
25.	14,876			
26.	85,049			

Round each number to the indicated place.

27. The state of Texas contains 310,850 miles of urban and rural highways. Round this number to the nearest thousand. (*Source:* U.S. Federal Highway Administration)

28. The state of California contains 171,874 miles of urban and rural highways. Round this number to the nearest thousand. (*Source:* U.S. Federal Highway Administration)

29. It takes 60,149 days for Neptune to make a complete orbit around the Sun. Round this number to the nearest hundred. (*Source:* National Space Science Data Center)

30. Kareem Abdul-Jabbar holds the NBA record for points scored, a total of 38,387 over his NBA career. Round this number to the nearest thousand. (*Source:* National Basketball Association)

31. In 2013, the most valuable brand in the world was Apple, Inc. The estimated brand value at this time of Apple was $185,000,000,000. Round this to the nearest ten billion. (*Source:* Millward Brown)

32. According to the U.S. Population Clock, the population of the United States was 316,539,415 in August 2013. Round this population figure to the nearest million. (*Source:* U.S. Census population clock)

33. The average salary for a baseball player in 2012 was $3,213,479. Round this average salary to the nearest hundred-thousand. (*Source:* Major League Baseball Players Association)

34. The average salary for a football player in 2012 was $1,900,000. Round this average salary to the nearest million. (*Source:* Businessweek.com)

35. The United States currently has 331,600,000 cellular phone users, while India has 893,862,500 users. Round each of the user numbers to the nearest million. (*Source: World Almanac*, 2013)

36. U.S. farms produced 3,112,500,000 bushels of soybeans in 2011. Round the soybean production figure to the nearest ten-million. (*Source:* U.S. Department of Agriculture)

Objective **B** *Estimate the sum or difference by rounding each number to the nearest ten. See Examples 4 and 5.*

37.
$$\begin{array}{r} 39 \\ 45 \\ 22 \\ +\,17 \\ \hline \end{array}$$

38.
$$\begin{array}{r} 52 \\ 33 \\ 15 \\ +\,29 \\ \hline \end{array}$$

39.
$$\begin{array}{r} 449 \\ -\,373 \\ \hline \end{array}$$

40.
$$\begin{array}{r} 555 \\ -\,235 \\ \hline \end{array}$$

Estimate the sum or difference by rounding each number to the nearest hundred. See Examples 4 and 5.

41.
$$\begin{array}{r} 1913 \\ 1886 \\ +\,1925 \\ \hline \end{array}$$

42.
$$\begin{array}{r} 4050 \\ 3133 \\ +\,1220 \\ \hline \end{array}$$

43.
$$\begin{array}{r} 1774 \\ -\,1492 \\ \hline \end{array}$$

44.
$$\begin{array}{r} 1989 \\ -\,1870 \\ \hline \end{array}$$

45.
$$\begin{array}{r} 3995 \\ 2549 \\ +\,4944 \\ \hline \end{array}$$

46.
$$\begin{array}{r} 799 \\ 1655 \\ +\,271 \\ \hline \end{array}$$

Three of the given calculator answers below are incorrect. Find them by estimating each sum.

47. 463 + 219   600

48. 522 + 785   1307

49. 229 + 443 + 606   1278

50. 542 + 789 + 198   2139

51. 7806 + 5150   12,956

52. 5233 + 4988   9011

> **Helpful Hint**   Estimation is useful to check for incorrect answers when using a calculator. For example, pressing a key too hard may result in a double digit, while pressing a key too softly may result in the digit not appearing in the display.

Objective **C** *Solve each problem by estimating. See Examples 6 and 7.*

53. An appliance store advertises three refrigerators on sale at $899, $1499, and $999. Round each cost to the nearest hundred to estimate the total cost.

54. Suppose you scored 89, 97, 100, 79, 75, and 82 on your biology tests. Round each score to the nearest ten to estimate your total score.

55. The distance from Kansas City to Boston is 1429 miles and from Kansas City to Chicago is 530 miles. Round each distance to the nearest hundred to estimate how much farther Boston is from Kansas City than Chicago is.

56. The Gonzales family took a trip and traveled 588, 689, 277, 143, 59, and 802 miles on six consecutive days. Round each distance to the nearest hundred to estimate the distance they traveled.

57. The peak of Mt. McKinley, in Alaska, is 20,320 feet above sea level. The top of Mt. Rainier, in Washington, is 14,410 feet above sea level. Round each height to the nearest thousand to estimate the difference in elevation of these two peaks. (*Source:* U.S. Geological Survey)

58. A student is pricing new car stereo systems. One system sells for $1895 and another system sells for $1524. Round each price to the nearest hundred dollars to estimate the difference in price of these systems.

59. In 2012, the population of Springfield, Illinois, was 117,126, and the population of Champaign, Illinois, was 82,517. Round each population to the nearest ten-thousand to estimate how much larger Springfield was than Champaign. (*Source:* U.S. Census Bureau)

60. Round each distance given on the map to the nearest ten to estimate the total distance from North Platte, Nebraska, to Lincoln, Nebraska.

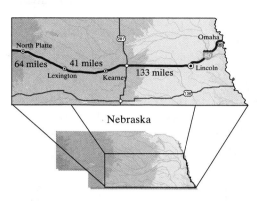

61. Head Start is a national program that provides developmental and social services for America's low-income preschool children ages three to five. Enrollment figures in Head Start programs showed an increase from 1,073,440 in 2010 to 1,128,030 in 2012. Round each number of children to the nearest thousand to estimate this increase. (*Source:* U.S. Department of Health and Human Services)

62. Enrollment figures at a local community college showed an increase from 49,713 credit hours in 2005 to 51,746 credit hours in 2006. Round each number to the nearest thousand to estimate the increase.

Mixed Practice (Sections 1.2 and 1.4) *The following table shows a few of the airports in the United States with the largest volumes of passengers. Complete this table. The first line is completed for you. (Source: 2011 World Annual Trafic Report)*

	City Location of Airport	Total Passengers in 2011 (in hundred-thousands of passengers)	Amount Written in Standard Form	Standard Form Rounded to the Nearest Million	Standard Form Rounded to the Nearest Ten-Million
	Atlanta, GA	924	92,400,000	92,000,000	90,000,000
63.	Chicago, IL	667			
64.	Los Angeles, CA	619			
65.	Dallas/Fort Worth, TX	578			
66.	Denver, CO	528			

Concept Extensions

67. Find one number that when rounded to the nearest hundred is 5700.

68. Find one number that when rounded to the nearest ten is 5700.

69. A number rounded to the nearest hundred is 8600.

    a. Determine the smallest possible number.

    b. Determine the largest possible number.

70. On August 23, 1989, it was estimated that 1,500,000 people joined hands in a human chain stretching 370 miles to protest the fiftieth anniversary of the pact that allowed what was then the Soviet Union to annex the Baltic nations in 1939. If the estimate of the number of people is to the nearest hundred-thousand, determine the largest possible number of people in the chain.

71. In your own words, explain how to round a number to the nearest thousand.

72. In your own words, explain how to round 9660 to the nearest thousand.

73. Estimate the perimeter of the rectangle by first rounding the length of each side to the nearest ten.

54 meters

Rectangle   17 meters

74. Estimate the perimeter of the triangle by first rounding the length of each side to the nearest hundred.

5950 miles   7693 miles

8203 miles

1.5   **Multiplying Whole Numbers and Area**

Objectives

A Use the Properties of Multiplication. ▶

B Multiply Whole Numbers. ▶

C Find the Area of a Rectangle. ▶

D Solve Problems by Multiplying Whole Numbers. ▶

Multiplication Shown as Repeated Addition Suppose that we wish to count the number of laptops provided in a computer class. The laptops are arranged in 5 rows, and each row has 6 laptops.

6 laptops in each row

Adding 5 sixes gives the total number of laptops. We can write this as $6 + 6 + 6 + 6 + 6 = 30$ laptops. When each addend is the same, we refer to this as **repeated addition.**

    Multiplication is repeated addition but with different notation.

$$6 + 6 + 6 + 6 + 6 \quad = \quad 5 \quad \times \quad 6 \quad = \quad 30$$

| 5 addends; each addend is 6 | (number of addends) factor | (each addend) factor | product |

The $\times$ is called a **multiplication sign.** The numbers 5 and 6 are called **factors.** The number 30 is called the **product.** The notation 5×6 is read as "five times six." The symbols $\cdot$ and ( ) can also be used to indicate multiplication.

$$5 \times 6 = 30, \quad 5 \cdot 6 = 30, \quad (5)(6) = 30, \quad \text{and} \quad 5(6) = 30$$

✔Concept Check

a. Rewrite $5 + 5 + 5 + 5 + 5 + 5 + 5$ using multiplication.

b. Rewrite 3×16 as repeated addition. Is there more than one way to do this? If so, show all ways.

Objective A Using the Properties of Multiplication ▶

As with addition, we memorize products of one-digit whole numbers and then use certain properties of multiplication to multiply larger numbers. (If necessary, review the multiplication of one-digit numbers.)

Notice that when any number is multiplied by 0, the result is always 0. This is called the **multiplication property of 0.**

Multiplication Property of 0

The product of 0 and any number is 0. For example,

$$5 \cdot 0 = 0 \quad \text{and} \quad 0 \cdot 8 = 0$$

Also notice that when any number is multiplied by 1, the result is always the original number. We call this result the **multiplication property of 1.**

Multiplication Property of 1

The product of 1 and any number is that same number. For example,

$$1 \cdot 9 = 9 \quad \text{and} \quad 6 \cdot 1 = 6$$

Example 1 Multiply.

a. 4×1 **b.** $0(3)$ **c.** $1 \cdot 64$ **d.** $(48)(0)$

Solution:

a. $4 \times 1 = 4$ **b.** $0(3) = 0$
c. $1 \cdot 64 = 64$ **d.** $(48)(0) = 0$

🔲 Work Practice 1

Practice 1

Multiply.

a. 6×0

b. $(1)8$

c. $(50)(0)$

d. $75 \cdot 1$

✔**Concept Check Answers**

a. 7×5

b. $16 + 16 + 16$; yes,
$3 + 3 + 3 + 3 + 3 + 3 + 3 + 3 + 3 + 3 + 3 + 3 + 3 + 3 + 3 + 3$

Answers

1. a. 0 **b.** 8 **c.** 0 **d.** 75

Like addition, multiplication is commutative and associative. Notice that when multiplying two numbers, the order of these numbers can be changed without changing the product. For example,

$$3 \cdot 5 = 15 \quad \text{and} \quad 5 \cdot 3 = 15$$

This property is called the **commutative property of multiplication.**

Commutative Property of Multiplication

Changing the **order** of two factors does not change their product. For example,

$$9 \cdot 2 = 18 \quad \text{and} \quad 2 \cdot 9 = 18$$

Another property that can help us when multiplying is the **associative property of multiplication.** This property states that when multiplying numbers, the grouping of the numbers can be changed without changing the product. For example,

$$(2 \cdot 3) \cdot 4 = 6 \cdot 4 = 24$$

Also,

$$2 \cdot (3 \cdot 4) = 2 \cdot 12 = 24$$

Both groupings give a product of 24.

Associative Property of Multiplication

Changing the **grouping** of factors does not change their product. From the previous work, we know that, for example,

$$(2 \cdot 3) \cdot 4 = 2 \cdot (3 \cdot 4)$$

With these properties, along with the **distributive property,** we can find the product of any whole numbers. The distributive property says that multiplication **distributes** over addition. For example, notice that $3(2 + 5)$ simplifies to the same number as $3 \cdot 2 + 3 \cdot 5$.

$$3(2 + 5) = 3(7) = 21$$

$$3 \cdot 2 + 3 \cdot 5 = 6 + 15 = 21$$

Since $3(2 + 5)$ and $3 \cdot 2 + 3 \cdot 5$ both simplify to 21, then

$$3(2 + 5) = 3 \cdot 2 + 3 \cdot 5$$

Notice in $3(2 + 5) = 3 \cdot 2 + 3 \cdot 5$ that each number inside the parentheses is multiplied by 3.

Distributive Property

Multiplication distributes over addition. For example,

$$2(3 + 4) = 2 \cdot 3 + 2 \cdot 4$$

Example 2 Rewrite each using the distributive property.

a. $5(6 + 5)$ **b.** $20(4 + 7)$ **c.** $2(7 + 9)$

Solution: Using the distributive property, we have

a. $5(6 + 5) = 5 \cdot 6 + 5 \cdot 5$
b. $20(4 + 7) = 20 \cdot 4 + 20 \cdot 7$
c. $2(7 + 9) = 2 \cdot 7 + 2 \cdot 9$

■ Work Practice 2

Practice 2

Rewrite each using the distributive property.
a. $6(4 + 5)$
b. $30(2 + 3)$
c. $7(2 + 8)$

Objective B Multiplying Whole Numbers

Let's use the distributive property to multiply 7(48). To do so, we begin by writing the expanded form of 48 (see Section 1.2) and then applying the distributive property.

$$7(48) = 7(40 + 8) \quad \text{Write 48 in expanded form.}$$
$$= 7 \cdot 40 + 7 \cdot 8 \quad \text{Apply the distributive property.}$$
$$= 280 + 56 \quad \text{Multiply.}$$
$$= 336 \quad \text{Add.}$$

This is how we multiply whole numbers. When multiplying whole numbers, we will use the following notation.

First:

$$\overset{5}{48}$$
$$\times\ 7$$
$$\overline{336} \longleftarrow 7 \cdot 8 = 56$$

Write 6 in the ones place and carry 5 to the tens place.

Next:

$$\overset{5}{48}$$
$$\times\ 7$$
$$\overline{336} \qquad 7 \cdot 4 + 5 = 28 + 5 = 33$$

The product of 48 and 7 is 336.

Example 3 Multiply:

a. $\quad 25$
    $\times\ 8$

b. $\quad 246$
    $\times\ 5$

Solution:

a. $\quad \overset{4}{25}$
    $\times\ 8$
    $\overline{200}$

b. $\quad \overset{2\,3}{246}$
    $\times\ 5$
    $\overline{1230}$

■ Work Practice 3

Practice 3

Multiply.
a. $\quad 29$
    $\times\ 6$
b. $\quad 648$
    $\times\ 5$

Answers

2. a. $6(4 + 5) = 6 \cdot 4 + 6 \cdot 5$
  b. $30(2 + 3) = 30 \cdot 2 + 30 \cdot 3$
  c. $7(2 + 8) = 7 \cdot 2 + 7 \cdot 8$
3. a. 174 **b.** 3240

To multiply larger whole numbers, use the following similar notation. Multiply 89×52.

Step 1	**Step 2**	**Step 3**
$\overset{1}{8}9$	$\overset{4}{8}9$	89
$\times\ 52$	$\times\ 52$	$\times\ 52$
$\overline{178}$ ← Multiply 89×2.	178	$\overline{178}$
	$\times 4450$ ← Multiply 89×50.	4450
		$\overline{4628}$ Add.

The numbers 178 and 4450 are called **partial products.** The sum of the partial products, 4628, is the product of 89 and 52.

Practice 4

Multiply.

$$\begin{array}{r} 306 \\ \times\ 81 \\ \hline \end{array}$$

Example 4   Multiply: 236×86

Solution:
$$\begin{array}{r} 236 \\ \times\ 86 \\ \hline 1416 \\ 18880 \\ \hline 20{,}296 \end{array}$$

← $6(236)$
← $80(236)$
Add.

▇ Work Practice 4

Practice 5

Multiply.

$$\begin{array}{r} 726 \\ \times 142 \\ \hline \end{array}$$

Example 5   Multiply: 631×125

Solution:
$$\begin{array}{r} 631 \\ \times\ 125 \\ \hline 3155 \\ 12620 \\ 63100 \\ \hline 78{,}875 \end{array}$$

← $5(631)$
← $20(631)$
← $100(631)$
Add.

▇ Work Practice 5

✔**Concept Check** Find and explain the error in the following multiplication problem.

$$\begin{array}{r} 102 \\ \times\ 33 \\ \hline 306 \\ 306 \\ \hline 612 \end{array}$$

Answers

4. 24,786   **5.** 103,092

✔**Concept Check Answer**

$$\begin{array}{r} 102 \\ \times\ 33 \\ \hline 306 \\ 3060 \\ \hline 3366 \end{array}$$

Objective C   Finding the Area of a Rectangle ▶

A special application of multiplication is finding the **area** of a region. Area measures the amount of surface of a region. For example, we measure a plot of land or the living space of a home by its area. The figures on the next page show two examples of units of area measure. (A centimeter is a unit of length in the metric system.)

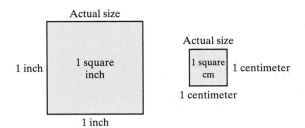

For example, to measure the area of a geometric figure such as the rectangle below, count the number of square units that cover the region.

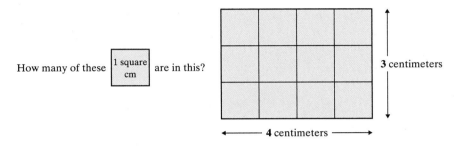

This rectangular region contains 12 square units, each 1 square centimeter. Thus, the area is 12 square centimeters. This total number of squares can be found by counting or by multiplying **4 · 3** (length · width).

Area of a rectangle = length · width
= (4 centimeters)(3 centimeters)
= 12 square centimeters

In this section, we find the areas of rectangles only. In later sections, we will find the areas of other geometric regions.

Helpful Hint

Notice that area is measured in **square** units while perimeter is measured in units.

Example 6 Finding the Area of a State

The state of Colorado is in the shape of a rectangle whose length is 380 miles and whose width is 280 miles. Find its area.

Solution: The area of a rectangle is the product of its length and its width.

Area = length · width
= (380 miles)(280 miles)
= 106,400 square miles

The area of Colorado is 106,400 square miles.

Practice 6

The state of Wyoming is in the shape of a rectangle whose length is 360 miles and whose width is 280 miles. Find its area.

Answer
6. 100,800 sq mi

■ Work Practice 6

Objective D Solving Problems by Multiplying ▶

There are several words or phrases that indicate the operation of multiplication. Some of these are as follows:

Multiplication		
Key Words or Phrases	**Examples**	**Symbols**
multiply	multiply 5 by 7	$5 \cdot 7$
product	the product of 3 and 2	$3 \cdot 2$
times	10 times 13	$10 \cdot 13$

Many key words or phrases describing real-life problems that suggest addition might be better solved by multiplication instead. For example, to find the **total** cost of 8 shirts, each selling for $27, we can either add

$$27 + 27 + 27 + 27 + 27 + 27 + 27 + 27$$

or we can multiply 8(27).

Practice 7

A particular computer printer can print 16 pages per minute in color. How many pages can it print in 45 minutes?

Example 7 Finding DVD Space

A digital video disc (DVD) can hold about 4800 megabytes (MB) of information. How many megabytes can 12 DVDs hold?

Solution: Twelve DVDs will hold 12×4800 megabytes.

In Words		Translate to Numbers
megabytes per disc	→	4800
$\times$ DVDs	→	$\times$ 12
		9600
		48000
total megabytes		57,600

Twelve DVDs will hold 57,600 megabytes.

■ Work Practice 7

Practice 8

A professor of history purchased DVDs and CDs through a club. Each DVD was priced at $11 and each CD cost $9. He bought eight DVDs and five CDs. Find the total cost of the order.

Example 8 Budgeting Money

A woman and her friend plan to take their children to the Georgia Aquarium in Atlanta, the world's largest aquarium. The ticket price for each child is $22 and for each adult, $26. If five children and two adults plan to go, how much money is needed for admission? (*Source:* GeorgiaAquarium.org)

Solution: If the price of one child's ticket is $22, the price for 5 children is $5 \times 22 = \$110$. The price of one adult ticket is $26, so the price for two adults is $2 \times 26 = \$52$. The total cost is:

In Words		Translate to Numbers
cost for 5 children	→	110
+ cost for 2 adults	→	+ 52
total cost		162

The total cost is $162.

■ Work Practice 8

Answers
7. 720 pages **8.** $133

Example 9 Estimating Word Count

The average page of a book contains 259 words. Estimate, rounding each number to the nearest hundred, the total number of words contained on 212 pages.

Solution: The exact number of words is 259×212. Estimate this product by rounding each factor to the nearest hundred.

$$
\begin{array}{rl}
259 & \text{rounds to} \quad 300 \\
\times\,212 & \text{rounds to} \quad \times\,200,
\end{array}
$$

$$300 \times 200 = 60{,}000$$

$$3 \cdot 2 = 6$$

There are approximately 60,000 words contained on 212 pages.

◾ Work Practice 9

Practice 9

If an average page in a book contains 163 words, estimate, rounding each number to the nearest hundred, the total number of words contained on 391 pages.

Answer
9. 80,000 words

🖩 **Calculator Explorations   Multiplying Numbers**

To multiply numbers on a calculator, find the keys marked ⨉ and = or ENTER . For example, to find $31 \cdot 66$ on a calculator, press the keys 31 ⨉ 66 then = or ENTER . The display will read ⎣ 2046 . Thus, $31 \cdot 66 = 2046$.

Use a calculator to multiply.

1. 72×48 **2.** 81×92

3. $163 \cdot 94$ **4.** $285 \cdot 144$

5. $983(277)$ **6.** $1562(843)$

Vocabulary, Readiness & Video Check

Use the choices below to fill in each blank.

area	grouping	commutative	1	product	length
factor	order	associative	0	distributive	number

1. The product of 0 and any number is _____.

2. The product of 1 and any number is the _____.

3. In $8 \cdot 12 = 96$, the 96 is called the _____ and 8 and 12 are each called a(n) _____.

4. Since $9 \cdot 10 = 10 \cdot 9$, we say that changing the _____ in multiplication does not change the product. This property is called the _____ property of multiplication.

5. Since $(3 \cdot 4) \cdot 6 = 3 \cdot (4 \cdot 6)$, we say that changing the _____ in multiplication does not change the product. This property is called the _____ property of multiplication.

6. _____ measures the amount of surface of a region.

7. Area of a rectangle $= $ _____ $\cdot$ width.

8. We know $9(10 + 8) = 9 \cdot 10 + 9 \cdot 8$ by the _____ property.

Martin-Gay Interactive Videos   Watch the section lecture video and answer the following questions.

Objective A 9. The expression in ▤ Example 3 is rewritten using what property? ▶

Objective B 10. During the multiplication process for ▤ Example 5, why is a single zero placed at the end of the second partial product? ▶

Objective C 11. Why are the units to the answer to ▤ Example 6 not just meters? What are the correct units? ▶

Objective D 12. In ▤ Example 7, why can "total" imply multiplication as well as addition? ▶

See Video 1.5

1.5 Exercise Set MyMathLab® ▶

Objective A *Multiply. See Example 1.*

▶ **1.** $1 \cdot 24$ **2.** $55 \cdot 1$ ▶ **3.** $0 \cdot 19$ **4.** $27 \cdot 0$

5. $8 \cdot 0 \cdot 9$ **6.** $7 \cdot 6 \cdot 0$ **7.** $87 \cdot 1$ **8.** $1 \cdot 41$

Use the distributive property to rewrite each expression. See Example 2.

9. $6(3 + 8)$ **10.** $5(8 + 2)$ **11.** $4(3 + 9)$

12. $6(1 + 4)$ ▶ **13.** $20(14 + 6)$ **14.** $12(12 + 3)$

Objective B *Multiply. See Example 3.*

15. $\begin{array}{r} 64 \\ \times\ 8 \\ \hline \end{array}$ **16.** $\begin{array}{r} 79 \\ \times\ 3 \\ \hline \end{array}$ **17.** $\begin{array}{r} 613 \\ \times\ \ 6 \\ \hline \end{array}$ **18.** $\begin{array}{r} 638 \\ \times\ \ 5 \\ \hline \end{array}$

▶ **19.** 277×6 **20.** 882×2 **21.** 1074×6 **22.** 9021×3

Objectives A B Mixed Practice *Multiply. See Examples 1 through 5.*

23. $\begin{array}{r} 89 \\ \times 13 \\ \hline \end{array}$ **24.** $\begin{array}{r} 91 \\ \times 72 \\ \hline \end{array}$ **25.** $\begin{array}{r} 421 \\ \times\ 58 \\ \hline \end{array}$ **26.** $\begin{array}{r} 526 \\ \times\ 23 \\ \hline \end{array}$ **27.** $\begin{array}{r} 306 \\ \times\ 81 \\ \hline \end{array}$ **28.** $\begin{array}{r} 708 \\ \times\ 21 \\ \hline \end{array}$

29. $(780)(20)$ **30.** $(720)(80)$ **31.** $(495)(13)(0)$ **32.** $(593)(47)(0)$ **33.** $(640)(1)(10)$

34. (240)(1)(20)   **35.** 1234 × 39   **36.** 1357 × 79   **37.** 609 × 234   **38.** 807 × 127

39. 8649   **40.**   1234   **41.**   589   **42.**   426   **43.**   1941   **44.**   1876
      × 274   × 567   ×110   ×110   ×2035   ×1407

Objective C Mixed Practice (Section 1.3) *Find the area and the perimeter of each rectangle. See Example 6.*

45.

9 meters / 7 meters

46. 3 inches

13 inches

47. 17 feet

40 feet

48. 25 centimeters

20 centimeters

Objective D *Estimate the products by rounding each factor to the nearest hundred. See Example 9.*

49. 576 × 354   **50.** 982 × 650   **51.** 604 × 451   **52.** 111 × 999

Without actually calculating, mentally round, multiply, and choose the best estimate.

53. 38 × 42 =
  a. 16
  b. 160
  c. 1600
  d. 16,000

54. 2872 × 12 =
  a. 2872
  b. 28,720
  c. 287,200
  d. 2,872,000

55. 612 × 29 =
  a. 180
  b. 1800
  c. 18,000
  d. 180,000

56. 706 × 409 =
  a. 280
  b. 2800
  c. 28,000
  d. 280,000

Objectives C D Mixed Practice–Translating *Solve. See Examples 6 through 9.*

57. Multiply 80 by 11.   **58.** Multiply 70 by 12.   **59.** Find the product of 6 and 700.

60. Find the product of 9 and 900.   **61.** Find 2 times 2240.   **62.** Find 3 times 3310.

63. One tablespoon of olive oil contains 125 calories. How many calories are in 3 tablespoons of olive oil? (*Source: Home and Garden Bulletin No. 72,* U.S. Department of Agriculture).

64. One ounce of hulled sunflower seeds contains 14 grams of fat. How many grams of fat are in 8 ounces of hulled sunflower seeds? (*Source: Home and Garden Bulletin No. 72,* U.S. Department of Agriculture).

65. The textbook for a course in biology costs $94. There are 35 students in the class. Find the total cost of the biology books for the class.

66. The seats in a large lecture hall are arranged in 14 rows with 34 seats in each row. Find how many seats are in this room.

67. Cabot Creamery is packing a pallet of 20-lb boxes of cheddar cheese to send to a local restaurant. There are five layers of boxes on the pallet, and each layer is four boxes wide by five boxes deep.
  a. How many boxes are in one layer?
  b. How many boxes are on the pallet?
  c. What is the weight of the cheese on the pallet?

68. An apartment building has *three floors*. Each floor has five rows of apartments with four apartments in each row.
  a. How many apartments are on 1 floor?
  b. How many apartments are in the building?

△ **69.** A plot of land measures 80 feet by 110 feet. Find its area.

△ **70.** A house measures 45 feet by 60 feet. Find the floor area of the house.

△ **71.** The largest hotel lobby can be found at the Hyatt Regency in San Francisco, CA. It is in the shape of a rectangle that measures 350 feet by 160 feet. Find its area.

△ **72.** Recall from an earlier section that the largest commercial building in the world under one roof is the flower auction building of the cooperative VBA in Aalsmeer, Netherlands. The floor plan is a rectangle that measures 776 meters by 639 meters. Find the area of this building. (A meter is a unit of length in the metric system.) (*Source: The Handy Science Answer Book,* Visible Ink Press)

73. A pixel is a rectangular dot on a graphing calculator screen. If a graphing calculator screen contains 62 pixels in a row and 94 pixels in a column, find the total number of pixels on a screen.

74. A certain compact disc (CD) can hold 700 megabytes (MB) of information. How many MBs can 17 discs hold?

75. A line of print on a computer contains 60 characters (letters, spaces, punctuation marks). Find how many characters there are in 35 lines.

76. An average cow eats 3 pounds of grain per day. Find how much grain a cow eats in a year. (Assume 365 days in 1 year.)

77. One ounce of Planters® Dry Roasted Peanuts has 160 calories. How many calories are in 8 ounces? (*Source:* RJR Nabisco, Inc.)

78. One ounce of Planters® Dry Roasted Peanuts has 13 grams of fat. How many grams of fat are in 16 ounces? (*Source:* RJR Nabisco, Inc.)

79. The Thespian club at a local community college is ordering T-shirts. T-shirts size S, M, or L cost $10 each and T-shirts size XL or XXL cost $12 each. Complete the table below and use it to find the total cost. (The first row is filled in for you.)

T-Shirt Size	Number of Shirts Ordered	Cost per Shirt	Cost per Size Ordered
S	4	$10	$40
M	6		
L	20		
XL	3		
XXL	3		

80. The student activities group at North Shore Community College is planning a trip to see the local minor league baseball team. Tickets cost $5 for students, $7 for non-students, and $2 for children under 12. Complete the following table and use it to find the total cost.

Person	Number of Persons	Cost per Person	Cost per Category
Student	24	$5	$120
Nonstudent	4		
Children under 12	5		

81. Celestial Seasonings of Boulder, Colorado, is a tea company that specializes in herbal teas. Their plant in Boulder has bagging machines capable of bagging over 1000 bags of tea per minute. If the plant runs 24 hours day, how many tea bags are produced in one day? (*Source:* Celestial Seasonings)

82. There were about 3 million "older" Americans (ages 65 and older) in 1900. By 2020, this number is projected to increase eighteen times. Find this projected number of "older" Americans in 2020. (*Source:* Administration on Aging, U.S. Census Bureau)

Mixed Practice (*Sections 1.3, 1.5*) *Perform each indicated operation.*

83. $\begin{array}{r} 128 \\ + \ \ 7 \\ \hline \end{array}$

84. $\begin{array}{r} 126 \\ - \ \ 8 \\ \hline \end{array}$

85. $\begin{array}{r} 134 \\ \times \ 16 \\ \hline \end{array}$

86. $47 + 26 + 10 + 231 + 50$

87. Find the sum of 19 and 4.

88. Find the product of 19 and 4.

89. Find the difference of 19 and 4.

90. Find the total of 14 and 9.

Concept Extensions

Solve. See the first Concept Check in this section.

91. Rewrite $6 + 6 + 6 + 6 + 6$ using multiplication.

92. Rewrite $11 + 11 + 11 + 11 + 11 + 11$ using multiplication.

93. a. Rewrite $3 \cdot 5$ as repeated addition.
    b. Explain why there is more than one way to do this.

94. a. Rewrite $4 \cdot 5$ as repeated addition.
    b. Explain why there is more than one way to do this.

Find and explain the error in each multiplication problem. See the second Concept Check in this section.

95.
```
   203
 ×  14
 ─────
   812
   203
 ─────
  1015
```

96.
```
   31
 × 50
 ────
  155
```

Fill in the missing digits in each problem.

97.
```
      4_
 ×   _3
 ──────
    126
   3780
 ──────
   3906
```

98.
```
     _7
 ×  6_
 ─────
    171
   3420
 ─────
   3591
```

 99. Explain how to multiply two 2-digit numbers using partial products.

100. In your own words, explain the meaning of the area of a rectangle and how this area is measured.

101. A window washer in New York City is bidding for a contract to wash the windows of a 23-story building. To write a bid, the number of windows in the building is needed. If there are 7 windows in each row of windows on 2 sides of the building and 4 windows per row on the other 2 sides of the building, find the total number of windows.

102. During the NBA's 2012–2013 regular season, Carmelo Anthony of the New York Knicks scored 157 three-point field goals, 512 two-point field goals, and 425 free throws (worth one point each). How many points did Carmelo Anthony score during the 2012–2013 regular season? (*Source:* NBA)

1.6 Dividing Whole Numbers

Objectives

A Divide Whole Numbers.

B Perform Long Division.

C Solve Problems That Require Dividing by Whole Numbers.

D Find the Average of a List of Numbers.

Suppose three people pooled their money and bought a raffle ticket at a local fundraiser. Their ticket was the winner and they won a $75 cash prize. They then divided the prize into three equal parts so that each person received $25.

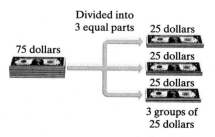

Objective A Dividing Whole Numbers

The process of separating a quantity into equal parts is called **division**. The division above can be symbolized by several notations.

quotient
→ 25
3)75 ← dividend
↑
divisor

dividend
↓
$\frac{75}{3} = 25$ ← quotient
↑
divisor

quotient
↓
75 ÷ 3 = 25
↑   ↑
dividend divisor

dividend quotient
↓   ↓
75/3 = 25
↑
divisor

(In the notation $\frac{75}{3}$, the bar separating 75 and 3 is called a **fraction bar**.) Just as subtraction is the reverse of addition, division is the reverse of multiplication. This means that division can be checked by multiplication.

$\overset{25}{3\overline{)75}}$ because 25 · 3 = 75

Quotient · Divisor = Dividend

Since multiplication and division are related in this way, you can use your knowledge of multiplication facts to review quotients of one-digit divisors if necessary.

Example 1 Find each quotient. Check by multiplying.

a. 42 ÷ 7   **b.** $\frac{64}{8}$ **c.** 3)21

Solution:

a. 42 ÷ 7 = 6 because 6 · 7 = 42

b. $\frac{64}{8}$ = 8 because 8 · 8 = 64

c. $\overset{7}{3\overline{)21}}$ because 7 · 3 = 21

▪ Work Practice 1

Example 2 Find each quotient. Check by multiplying.

a. 1)7   **b.** 12 ÷ 1   **c.** $\frac{6}{6}$ **d.** 9 ÷ 9   **e.** $\frac{20}{1}$ **f.** 18)18

Solution:

a. $\overset{7}{1\overline{)7}}$ because 7 · 1 = 7   **b.** 12 ÷ 1 = 12 because 12 · 1 = 12

c. $\frac{6}{6}$ = 1 because 1 · 6 = 6   **d.** 9 ÷ 9 = 1 because 1 · 9 = 9

e. $\frac{20}{1}$ = 20 because 20 · 1 = 20   **f.** $\overset{1}{18\overline{)18}}$ because 1 · 18 = 18

▪ Work Practice 2

Practice 1

Find each quotient. Check by multiplying.

a. 9)72

b. 40 ÷ 5

c. $\frac{24}{6}$

Practice 2

Find each quotient. Check by multiplying.

a. $\frac{7}{7}$ **b.** 5 ÷ 1

c. 1)11   **d.** 4 ÷ 1

e. $\frac{10}{1}$ **f.** 21 ÷ 21

Answers
1. a. 8 **b.** 8 **c.** 4 **2. a.** 1 **b.** 5
c. 11 **d.** 4 **e.** 10 **f.** 1

Example 2 illustrates the important properties of division described next:

Division Properties of 1

The quotient of any number (except 0) and that same number is 1. For example,

$$8 \div 8 = 1 \qquad \frac{5}{5} = 1 \qquad 4\overline{)4}^{\,1}$$

The quotient of any number and 1 is that same number. For example,

$$9 \div 1 = 9 \qquad \frac{6}{1} = 6 \qquad 1\overline{)3}^{\,3} \qquad \frac{0}{1} = 0$$

Practice 3

Find each quotient. Check by multiplying.

a. $\dfrac{0}{7}$ **b.** $8\overline{)0}$

c. $7 \div 0$ **d.** $0 \div 14$

Example 3   Find each quotient. Check by multiplying.

a. $9\overline{)0}$ **b.** $0 \div 12$ **c.** $\dfrac{0}{5}$ **d.** $\dfrac{3}{0}$

Solution:

a. $9\overline{)0}^{\,0}$ because $0 \cdot 9 = 0$

b. $0 \div 12 = 0$ because $0 \cdot 12 = 0$

c. $\dfrac{0}{5} = 0$ because $0 \cdot 5 = 0$

d. If $\dfrac{3}{0} = a$ *number*, then the *number* times $0 = 3$. Recall from Section 1.5 that any number multiplied by 0 is 0 and not 3. We say, then, that $\dfrac{3}{0}$ is **undefined.**

■ Work Practice 3

Example 3 illustrates important division properties of 0.

Division Properties of 0

The quotient of 0 and any number (except 0) is 0. For example,

$$0 \div 9 = 0 \qquad \frac{0}{5} = 0 \qquad 14\overline{)0}^{\,0}$$

The quotient of any number and 0 is not a number. We say that

$$\frac{3}{0}, \quad 0\overline{)3}, \quad \text{and} \quad 3 \div 0$$

are **undefined.**

Objective B Performing Long Division ▶

When dividends are larger, the quotient can be found by a process called **long division.** For example, let's divide 2541 by 3.

$$\text{divisor} \longrightarrow 3\overline{)2541}$$
$$\uparrow$$
$$\text{dividend}$$

We can't divide 3 into 2, so we try dividing 3 into the first two digits.

$$\dfrac{8}{3\overline{)2541}}$$ $25 \div 3 = 8$ with 1 left, so our best estimate is 8. We place 8 over the 5 in 25.

Next, multiply 8 and 3 and subtract this product from 25. Make sure that this difference is less than the divisor.

$$
\begin{array}{r}
8 \\
3\overline{)2541} \\
-24 \\
\hline
1
\end{array}
\qquad
\begin{array}{l}
8(3) = 24 \\
25 - 24 = 1, \text{ and } 1 \text{ is less than the divisor } 3.
\end{array}
$$

Bring down the next digit and go through the process again.

$$
\begin{array}{r}
84 \\
3\overline{)2541} \\
-24\downarrow \\
\hline
14 \\
-12 \\
\hline
2
\end{array}
\qquad
\begin{array}{l}
14 \div 3 = 4 \text{ with } 2 \text{ left} \\
\\
\\
4(3) = 12 \\
14 - 12 = 2
\end{array}
$$

Once more, bring down the next digit and go through the process.

$$
\begin{array}{r}
847 \\
3\overline{)2541} \\
-24 \\
\hline
14 \\
-12 \\
\hline
21 \\
-21 \\
\hline
0
\end{array}
\qquad
\begin{array}{l}
21 \div 3 = 7 \\
\\
\\
\\
\\
7(3) = 21 \\
21 - 21 = 0
\end{array}
$$

The quotient is 847. To check, see that $847 \times 3 = 2541$.

Example 4   Divide: $3705 \div 5$. Check by multiplying.

Solution:

$$
\begin{array}{r}
7 \\
5\overline{)3705} \\
-35\downarrow \\
\hline
20
\end{array}
\qquad
\begin{array}{l}
37 \div 5 = 7 \text{ with } 2 \text{ left. Place this estimate, } 7, \text{ over the } 7 \text{ in } 37. \\
7(5) = 35 \\
37 - 35 = 2, \text{ and } 2 \text{ is less than the divisor } 5. \\
\text{Bring down the } 0.
\end{array}
$$

$$
\begin{array}{r}
74 \\
5\overline{)3705} \\
-35 \\
\hline
20 \\
-20\downarrow \\
\hline
05
\end{array}
\qquad
\begin{array}{l}
20 \div 5 = 4 \\
\\
\\
4(5) = 20 \\
20 - 20 = 0. \text{ and } 0 \text{ is less than the divisor } 5. \\
\text{Bring down the } 5.
\end{array}
$$

$$
\begin{array}{r}
741 \\
5\overline{)3705} \\
-35 \\
\hline
20 \\
-20\downarrow \\
\hline
5 \\
-5 \\
\hline
0
\end{array}
\qquad
\begin{array}{l}
5 \div 5 = 1 \\
\\
\\
\\
\\
1(5) = 5 \\
5 - 5 = 0
\end{array}
$$

Practice 4

Divide. Check by multiplying.

a. $4908 \div 6$

b. $2212 \div 4$

c. $753 \div 3$

Answers

4. a. 818 **b.** 553 **c.** 251

(Continued on next page)

Helpful Hint   Since division and multiplication are reverse operations, don't forget that a division problem can be checked by multiplying.

Practice 5

Divide and check by multiplying.

a. $7\overline{)2128}$

b. $9\overline{)45,900}$

Check:

$$
\begin{array}{r}
741 \\
\times\ \ \ 5 \\
\hline
3705
\end{array}
$$

■ Work Practice 4

Example 5   Divide and check: $1872 \div 9$

Solution:

$$
\begin{array}{r}
208 \\
9\overline{)1872} \\
-18\downarrow \\
\hline
07 \\
-0\downarrow \\
\hline
72 \\
-72 \\
\hline
0
\end{array}
$$

$2(9) = 18$

$18 - 18 = 0$; bring down the 7.

$0(9) = 0$

$7 - 0 = 7$; bring down the 2.

$8(9) = 72$

$72 - 72 = 0$

Check: $208 \cdot 9 = 1872$

■ Work Practice 5

Naturally, quotients don't always "come out even." Making 4 rows out of 26 chairs, for example, isn't possible if each row is supposed to have exactly the same number of chairs. Each of 4 rows can have 6 chairs, but 2 chairs are still left over.

4 rows   6 chairs in each row

2 chairs left over

We signify "leftovers" or **remainders** in this way:

$$
4\overline{)26}\ \ ^{6\ R\ 2}
$$

The **whole number part of the quotient** is 6; the **remainder part of the quotient** is 2. Checking by multiplying,

whole number part	·	divisor	+	remainder part	=	dividend
↓		↓		↓		↓
6	·	4	+	2		
		24	+	2	=	26

Answers

5. a. 304   **b.** 5100

Example 6 Divide and check: 2557 ÷ 7

Solution:

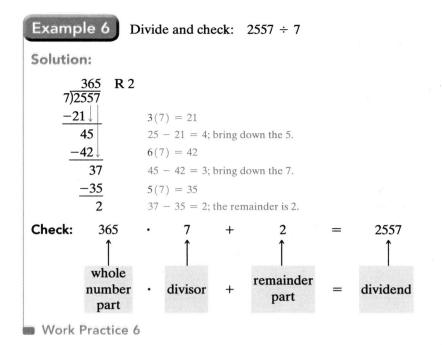

```
      365  R 2
   7)2557
    −21↓│
      45│         3(7) = 21
    −42↓         25 − 21 = 4; bring down the 5.
      37          6(7) = 42
    −35           45 − 42 = 3; bring down the 7.
       2          5(7) = 35
                  37 − 35 = 2; the remainder is 2.
```

Check: 365 ·   7   +   2   =   2557

          ↑   ↑   ↑   ↑
      whole
      number   · divisor + remainder = dividend
       part   part

■ Work Practice 6

Practice 6

Divide and check.
a. 4)939
b. 5)3287

Example 7 Divide and check: 56,717 ÷ 8

Solution:

```
     7089  R 5
  8)56717
   −56↓││
     07││        7(8) = 56
    −0↓│         Subtract and bring down the 7.
     71│          0(8) = 0
   −64↓          Subtract and bring down the 1.
     77           8(8) = 64
   −72            Subtract and bring down the 7.
     5            9(8) = 72
                  Subtract. The remainder is 5.
```

Check: 7089 ·   8   +   5   =   56,717

          ↑   ↑   ↑   ↑
      whole
      number   · divisor + remainder = dividend
       part   part

■ Work Practice 7

Practice 7

Divide and check.
a. 9)81,605
b. 4)23,310

When the divisor has more than one digit, the same pattern applies. For example, let's find 1358 ÷ 23.

```
        5      135 ÷ 23 = 5 with 20 left over. Our estimate is 5.
  23)1358
   −115↓     5(23) = 115
     208      135 − 115 = 20. Bring down the 8.
```

Answers
6. a. 234 R 3 **b.** 657 R 2
7. a. 9067 R 2 **b.** 5827 R 2

(Continued on next page)

Now we continue estimating.

$$\begin{array}{r} 59 \text{ R } 1 \\ 23\overline{)1358} \\ -115 \\ \hline 208 \\ -207 \\ \hline 1 \end{array}$$

208 ÷ 23 = 9 with 1 left over.

9(23) = 207

208 − 207 = 1. The remainder is 1.

To check, see that $59 \cdot 23 + 1 = 1358$.

Practice 8
Divide: 8920 ÷ 17

Example 8 Divide: 6819 ÷ 17

Solution:

$$\begin{array}{r} 401 \text{ R } 2 \\ 17\overline{)6819} \\ -68 \\ \hline 01 \\ -0 \\ \hline 19 \\ -17 \\ \hline 2 \end{array}$$

4(17) = 68

Subtract and bring down the 1.

0(17) = 0

Subtract and bring down the 9.

1(17) = 17

Subtract. The remainder is 2.

To check, see that $401 \cdot 17 + 2 = 6819$.

■ Work Practice 8

Practice 9
Divide: 33,282 ÷ 678

Example 9 Divide: 51,600 ÷ 403

Solution:

$$\begin{array}{r} 128 \text{ R } 16 \\ 403\overline{)51600} \\ -403 \\ \hline 1130 \\ -806 \\ \hline 3240 \\ -3224 \\ \hline 16 \end{array}$$

1(403) = 403

Subtract and bring down the 0.

2(403) = 806

Subtract and bring down the 0.

8(403) = 3224

Subtract. The remainder is 16.

To check, see that $128 \cdot 403 + 16 = 51{,}600$.

■ Work Practice 9

Division Shown as Repeated Subtraction To further understand division, recall from Section 1.5 that addition and multiplication are related in the following manner:

$$\underbrace{3 + 3 + 3 + 3}_{\text{4 addends; each addend is 3}} = 4 \times 3 = 12$$

In other words, multiplication is repeated addition. Likewise, division is repeated subtraction.

For example, let's find

35 ÷ 8

Answers
8. 524 R 12   **9.** 49 R 60

by repeated subtraction. Keep track of the number of times 8 is subtracted from 35. We are through when we can subtract no more because the difference is less than 8.

35 ÷ 8:   Repeated subtraction

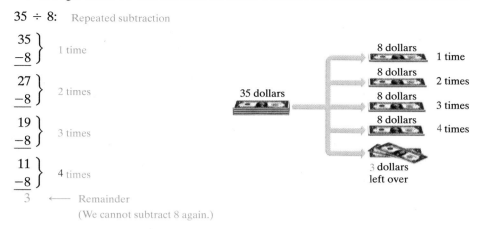

$$35 \begin{cases} 35 \\ -8 \end{cases} 1 \text{ time}$$

$$\begin{cases} 27 \\ -8 \end{cases} 2 \text{ times}$$

$$\begin{cases} 19 \\ -8 \end{cases} 3 \text{ times}$$

$$\begin{cases} 11 \\ -8 \end{cases} 4 \text{ times}$$

$$3 \longleftarrow \text{Remainder}$$

(We cannot subtract 8 again.)

Thus, $35 \div 8 = 4 \, \mathbf{R} \, 3$.

To check, perform the same multiplication as usual, but finish by adding in the remainder.

whole number part of quotient	·	divisor	+	remainder	=	dividend
↓		↓		↓		↓
4	·	8	+	3	=	35

Objective C Solving Problems by Dividing ▶

Below are some key words and phrases that may indicate the operation of division:

Division		
Key Words or Phrases	**Examples**	**Symbols**
divide	divide 10 by 5	$10 \div 5$ or $\dfrac{10}{5}$
quotient	the quotient of 64 and 4	$64 \div 4$ or $\dfrac{64}{4}$
divided by	9 divided by 3	$9 \div 3$ or $\dfrac{9}{3}$
divided or shared equally among	$100 divided equally among five people	$100 \div 5$ or $\dfrac{100}{5}$
per	100 miles per 2 hours	$\dfrac{100 \text{ miles}}{2 \text{ hours}}$

✔**Concept Check** Which of the following is the correct way to represent "the quotient of 60 and 12"? Or are both correct? Explain your answer.

a. $12 \div 60$

b. $60 \div 12$

✔**Concept Check Answers**
a. incorrect   **b.** correct

Practice 10

Three students bought 171 blank CDs to share equally. How many CDs did each person get?

Example 10   Finding Shared Earnings

Three college freshmen share a paper route to earn money for expenses. The total in their fund after expenses is $2895. How much is each person's equal share?

Solution:

In words: Each person's share = total money ÷ number of persons

Translate: Each person's share = 2895 ÷ 3

Then

$$\begin{array}{r} 965 \\ 3\overline{)2895} \\ -27 \\ \hline 19 \\ -18 \\ \hline 15 \\ -15 \\ \hline 0 \end{array}$$

Each person's share is $965.

■ Work Practice 10

Practice 11

Printers can be packed 12 to a box. If 532 printers are to be packed but only full boxes are shipped, how many full boxes will be shipped? How many printers are left over and not shipped?

Example 11   Dividing Number of Downloads

As part of a promotion, an executive receives 238 cards, each good for one free song download. If she wants to share them evenly with 19 friends, how many download cards will each friend receive? How many will be left over?

Solution:

In words: Number of cards for each person = number of cards ÷ number of friends

Translate: Number of cards for each person = 238 ÷ 19

$$\begin{array}{r} 12 \quad \text{R } 10 \\ 19\overline{)238} \\ -19 \\ \hline 48 \\ -38 \\ \hline 10 \end{array}$$

Each friend will receive 12 download cards. The cards cannot be divided equally among her friends since there is a nonzero remainder. There will be 10 download cards left over.

■ Work Practice 11

Answers
10. 57 CDs
11. 44 full boxes; 4 printers left over

Objective D Finding Averages

A special application of division (and addition) is finding the average of a list of numbers. The **average** of a list of numbers is the sum of the numbers divided by the *number* of numbers.

$$\text{average} = \frac{\text{sum of numbers}}{\textit{number} \text{ of numbers}}$$

Example 12	Averaging Scores

A mathematics instructor is checking a simple program she wrote for averaging the scores of her students. To do so, she averages a student's scores of 75, 96, 81, and 88 by hand. Find this average score.

Solution: To find the average score, we find the sum of the student's scores and divide by 4, the number of scores.

$$
\begin{array}{r}
75 \\
96 \\
81 \\
+88 \\
\hline
340 \quad \text{sum}
\end{array}
\qquad
\text{average} = \frac{340}{4} = 85
\qquad
\begin{array}{r}
85 \\
4\overline{)340} \\
-32 \\
\hline
20 \\
-20 \\
\hline
0
\end{array}
$$

The average score is 85.

■ Work Practice 12

Practice 12

To compute a safe time to wait for reactions to occur after allergy shots are administered, a lab technician is given a list of elapsed times between administered shots and reactions. Find the average of the times 4 minutes, 7 minutes, 35 minutes, 16 minutes, 9 minutes, 3 minutes, and 52 minutes.

Answer

12. 18 min

🖩 Calculator Explorations Dividing Numbers

To divide numbers on a calculator, find the keys marked $\div$ and $=$ or ENTER. For example, to find $435 \div 5$ on a calculator, press the keys 435 $\div$ 5 then $=$ or ENTER. The display will read 87. Thus, $435 \div 5 = 87$.

Use a calculator to divide.

1. $848 \div 16$ **2.** $564 \div 12$

3. $95\overline{)5890}$ **4.** $27\overline{)1053}$

5. $\dfrac{32{,}886}{126}$ **6.** $\dfrac{143{,}088}{264}$

7. $0 \div 315$ **8.** $315 \div 0$

Vocabulary, Readiness & Video Check

Use the choices below to fill in each blank. Some choices may be used more than once.

| 1 | number | divisor | dividend |
| 0 | undefined | average | quotient |

1. In $90 \div 2 = 45$, the answer 45 is called the _____ , 90 is called the _____ , and 2 is called the _____ .

2. The quotient of any number and 1 is the same _____ .

3. The quotient of any number (except 0) and the same number is _____ .

4. The quotient of 0 and any number (except 0) is _____ .

5. The quotient of any number and 0 is _____ .

6. The _____ of a list of numbers is the sum of the numbers divided by the _____ of numbers.

Martin-Gay Interactive Videos

See Video 1.6

Watch the section lecture video and answer the following questions.

Objective A 7. Look at 🎞 Examples 6–8. What number can never be the divisor in division?

Objective B 8. In 🎞 Example 10, how many 102s are in 21? How does this result affect the quotient? ▶

9. What calculation would you use to check the answer in 🎞 Example 10?

Objective C 10. In 🎞 Example 11, what is the importance of knowing that the distance to each hole is the same? ▶

Objective D 11. As shown in 🎞 Example 12, what two operations are used when finding an average? ▶

1.6 Exercise Set MyMathLab® ▶

Objective A *Find each quotient. See Examples 1 through 3.*

1. $54 \div 9$ **2.** $72 \div 9$ ▶ **3.** $36 \div 3$ **4.** $24 \div 3$ **5.** $0 \div 8$

6. $0 \div 4$ ▶ **7.** $31 \div 1$ **8.** $38 \div 1$ ▶ **9.** $\dfrac{18}{18}$ **10.** $\dfrac{49}{49}$

11. $\dfrac{24}{3}$ **12.** $\dfrac{45}{9}$ ▶ **13.** $26 \div 0$ **14.** $\dfrac{12}{0}$ **15.** $26 \div 26$

16. $6 \div 6$ ▶ **17.** $0 \div 14$ **18.** $7 \div 0$ **19.** $18 \div 2$ **20.** $18 \div 3$

Objectives A B **Mixed Practice** *Divide and then check by multiplying. See Examples 1 through 5.*

21. $3\overline{)87}$ **22.** $5\overline{)85}$ **23.** $3\overline{)222}$ **24.** $8\overline{)640}$ **25.** $3\overline{)1014}$ **26.** $4\overline{)2104}$

27. $\dfrac{30}{0}$ **28.** $\dfrac{0}{30}$ **29.** $63 \div 7$ **30.** $56 \div 8$ **31.** $150 \div 6$ **32.** $121 \div 11$

Divide and then check by multiplying. See Examples 6 and 7.

33. $7\overline{)479}$ **34.** $7\overline{)426}$ **35.** $6\overline{)1421}$ **36.** $3\overline{)1240}$

37. $305 \div 8$ **38.** $167 \div 3$ **39.** $2286 \div 7$ **40.** $3333 \div 4$

Divide and then check by multiplying. See Examples 8 and 9.

▶ **41.** $55\overline{)715}$ **42.** $23\overline{)736}$ **43.** $23\overline{)1127}$ **44.** $42\overline{)2016}$ **45.** $97\overline{)9417}$

46. $44\overline{)1938}$ **47.** $3146 \div 15$ **48.** $7354 \div 12$ **49.** $6578 \div 13$ **50.** $5670 \div 14$

51. $9299 \div 46$ **52.** $2505 \div 64$ **53.** $\dfrac{12{,}744}{236}$ **54.** $\dfrac{5781}{123}$ **55.** $\dfrac{10{,}297}{103}$

56. $\dfrac{23{,}092}{240}$ ▶ **57.** $20{,}619 \div 102$ **58.** $40{,}853 \div 203$ **59.** $244{,}989 \div 423$ **60.** $164{,}592 \div 543$

Divide. See Examples 1 through 9.

61. $7\overline{)119}$ **62.** $8\overline{)104}$ **63.** $7\overline{)3580}$ **64.** $5\overline{)3017}$

65. $40\overline{)85{,}312}$ **66.** $50\overline{)85{,}747}$ **67.** $142\overline{)863{,}360}$ **68.** $214\overline{)650{,}560}$

Objective C Translating *Solve. See Examples 10 and 11.*

69. Find the quotient of 117 and 5.

70. Find the quotient of 94 and 7.

71. Find 200 divided by 35.

72. Find 116 divided by 32.

73. Find the quotient of 62 and 3.

74. Find the quotient of 78 and 5.

Solve.

75. Martin Thieme teaches American Sign Language classes for $65 per student for a 7-week session. He collects $2145 from the group of students. Find how many students are in the group.

76. Kathy Gomez teaches Spanish lessons for $85 per student for a 5-week session. From one group of students, she collects $4930. Find how many students are in the group.

77. The gravity of Jupiter is 318 times as strong as the gravity of Earth, so objects on Jupiter weigh 318 times as much as they weigh on Earth. If a person would weigh 52,470 pounds on Jupiter, find how much the person weighs on Earth.

78. Twenty-one people pooled their money and bought lottery tickets. One ticket won a prize of $5,292,000. Find how many dollars each person received.

▶ **79.** An 18-hole golf course is 5580 yards long. If the distance to each hole is the same, find the distance between holes.

80. A truck hauls wheat to a storage granary. It carries a total of 5768 bushels of wheat in 14 trips. How much does the truck haul each trip if each trip it hauls the same amount?

81. There is a bridge over highway I-35 every three miles. The first bridge is at the beginning of a 265-mile stretch of highway. Find how many bridges there are over 265 miles of I-35.

82. The white stripes dividing the lanes on a highway are 25 feet long, and the spaces between them are 25 feet long. Let's call a "lane divider" a stripe followed by a space. Find how many whole "lane dividers" there are in 1 mile of highway. (A mile is 5280 feet.)

83. Ari Trainor is in the requisitions department of Central Electric Lighting Company. Light poles along a highway are placed 492 feet apart. The first light pole is at the beginning of a 1-mile strip. Find how many poles he should order for the 1-mile strip of highway. (A mile is 5280 feet.)

84. Professor Lopez has a piece of rope 185 feet long that she wants to cut into pieces for an experiment in her physics class. Each piece of rope is to be 8 feet long. Determine whether she has enough rope for her 22-student class. Determine the amount extra or the amount short.

85. Broad Peak in Pakistan is the twelfth-tallest mountain in the world. Its elevation is 26,400 feet. A mile is 5280 feet. How many miles tall is Broad Peak? (*Source:* National Geographic Society)

86. Randy Moss of the New England Patriots led the NFL in touchdowns during the 2007 regular football season, scoring a total of 138 points from touchdowns. If a touchdown is worth 6 points, how many touchdowns did Moss make during the 2007 season? (*Source:* NFL)

87. Find how many yards are in 1 mile. (A mile is 5280 feet; a yard is 3 feet.)

88. Find how many whole feet are in 1 rod. (A mile is 5280 feet; 1 mile is 320 rods.)

Objective D *Find the average of each list of numbers. See Example 12.*

89. 10, 24, 35, 22, 17, 12

90. 37, 26, 15, 29, 51, 22

91. 205, 972, 210, 161

92. 121, 200, 185, 176, 163

▷ 93. 86, 79, 81, 69, 80

94. 92, 96, 90, 85, 92, 79

The normal monthly temperatures in degrees Fahrenheit for Salt Lake City, Utah, are given in the graph. Use this graph to answer Exercises 95 and 96. (Source: National Climatic Data Center)

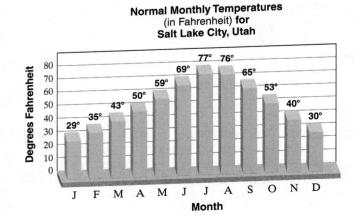

95. Find the average temperature for June, July, and August.

96. Find the average temperature for October, November, and December.

Mixed Practice (Sections 1.3, 1.5, 1.6) *Perform each indicated operation. Watch the operation symbol.*

97. $82 + 463 + 29 + 8704$

98. $23 + 407 + 92 + 7011$

99. $\begin{array}{r} 546 \\ \times\ 28 \\ \hline \end{array}$

100. $\begin{array}{r} 712 \\ \times\ 54 \\ \hline \end{array}$

101. $\begin{array}{r} 722 \\ -\ 43 \\ \hline \end{array}$

102. $\begin{array}{r} 712 \\ -\ 54 \\ \hline \end{array}$

103. $\dfrac{45}{0}$

104. $\dfrac{0}{23}$

105. $228 \div 24$

106. $304 \div 31$

Concept Extensions

Match each word phrase to the correct translation. (Not all letter choices will be used.) See the Concept Check in this section.

107. The quotient of 40 and 8

108. The quotient of 200 and 20

a. $20 \div 200$ **b.** $200 \div 20$
c. $40 \div 8$ **d.** $8 \div 40$

109. 200 divided by 20

110. 40 divided by 8

The following table shows the top five leading U.S. television advertisers during the first half of 2013 and the amount of money spent that half-year on advertising. Use this table to answer Exercises 111 and 112. (Source: Local Media Marketing Solutions*)*

Advertiser	Amount Spent on Television Advertising in 1st half of 2013
Ford Motor Company, dealers and corporate	$191,055,900
AT&T Inc.	$170,634,500
Comcast Corp	$157,780,500
Toyota, Dealers and corporate	$153,946,200
Chrysler-Cerberus	$122,784,200

111. Find the average amount of money spent on television ads for the half-year by the top two advertisers.

112. Find the average amount of money spent on television advertising by the top four advertisers.

In Example 12 in this section, we found that the average of 75, 96, 81, and 88 is 85. Use this information to answer Exercises 113 and 114.

113. If the number 75 is removed from the list of numbers, does the average increase or decrease? Explain why.

114. If the number 96 is removed from the list of numbers, does the average increase or decrease? Explain why.

115. Without computing it, tell whether the average of 126, 135, 198, and 113 is 86. Explain why it is possible or why it is not.

116. Without computing it, tell whether the average of 38, 27, 58, and 43 is 17. Explain why it is possible or why it is not.

117. If the area of a rectangle is 60 square feet and its width is 5 feet, what is its length?

118. If the area of a rectangle is 84 square inches and its length is 21 inches, what is its width?

119. Write down any two numbers whose quotient is 25.

120. Write down any two numbers whose quotient is 1.

121. Find $26 \div 5$ using the process of repeated subtraction.

122. Find $86 \div 10$ using the process of repeated subtraction.

Operations on Whole Numbers

Answers

Perform each indicated operation.

1. _____

2. _____

3. _____

4. _____

5. _____

6. _____

7. _____

8. _____

9. _____

10. _____

11. _____

12. _____

13. _____

14. _____

15. _____

16. _____

17. _____

18. _____

19. _____

20. _____

21. _____

22. _____

23. _____

24. _____

25. _____

26. _____

27. _____

28. _____

29. _____

30. _____

1. 42
        63
      $+ \, 89$

2. 7006
      $- \, 451$

3.   87
      $\times \, 52$

4. $8\overline{)4496}$

5. $1 \cdot 67$

6. $\dfrac{36}{0}$

7. $16 \div 16$

8. $5 \div 1$

9. $0 \cdot 21$

10. $7 \cdot 0 \cdot 8$

11. $0 \div 7$

12. $12 \div 4$

13. $9 \cdot 7$

14. $45 \div 5$

15. 207
       $- \, 69$

16. 207
       $+ \, 69$

17. $3718 - 2549$

18. $1861 + 7965$

19. $7\overline{)1278}$

20. 1259
       $\times \, 63$

21. $7\overline{)7695}$

22. $9\overline{)1000}$

23. $32\overline{)21{,}240}$

24. $65\overline{)70{,}000}$

25. $4000 - 2963$

26. $10{,}000 - 101$

27.   303
       $\times \, 101$

28. $(475)(100)$

29. Find the total of 62 and 9.

30. Find the product of 62 and 9.

31. Find the quotient of 62 and 9.

32. Find the difference of 62 and 9.

33. Subtract 17 from 200.

34. Find the difference of 432 and 201.

Complete the table by rounding the given number to the given place value.

		Tens	Hundrds	Thousands
35.	9735			
36.	1429			
37.	20,801			
38.	432,198			

Find the perimeter and area of each figure.

△ **39.**

Square   6 feet

△ **40.**

14 inches
Rectangle   7 inches

Find the perimeter of each figure.

△ **41.**

13 miles   9 miles
6 miles

△ **42.**

3 meters
4 meters
3 meters
3 meters

Find the average of each list of numbers.

43. 19, 15, 25, 37, 24

44. 108, 131, 98, 159

45. The Mackinac Bridge is a suspension bridge that connects the lower and upper peninsulas of Michigan across the Straits of Mackinac. Its total length is 26,372 feet. The Lake Pontchartrain Bridge is a twin concrete trestle bridge in Slidell, Louisiana. Its total length is 28,547 feet. Which bridge is longer and by how much? (*Sources:* Mackinac Bridge Authority and Federal Highway Administration, Bridge Division)

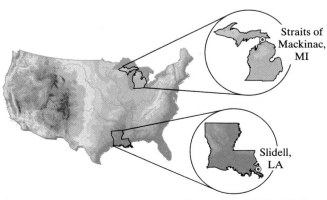
Straits of Mackinac, MI
Slidell, LA

46. In the United States, the average toy expenditure per child is $309 per year. On average, how much is spent on toys for a child by the time he or she reaches age 18? (*Source:* statista)

31. _____

32. _____

33. _____

34. _____

35. _____

36. _____

37. _____

38. _____

39. _____

40. _____

41. _____

42. _____

43. _____

44. _____

45. _____

46. _____

Objectives

A Write Repeated Factors Using Exponential Notation. ▶

B Evaluate Expressions Containing Exponents. ▶

C Use the Order of Operations. ▶

D Find the Area of a Square. ▶

Objective A Using Exponential Notation ▶

In the product $3 \cdot 3 \cdot 3 \cdot 3 \cdot 3$, notice that 3 is a factor several times. When this happens, we can use a shorthand notation, called an **exponent,** to write the repeated multiplication.

$\underbrace{3 \cdot 3 \cdot 3 \cdot 3 \cdot 3}_{3 \text{ is a factor 5 times}}$ can be written as

3^5 Read as "three to the fifth power."

(exponent, base labeled)

This is called **exponential notation.** The **exponent,** 5, indicates how many times the **base,** 3, is a factor.

The table below shows examples of reading exponential notation in words.

Expression	In Words
5^2	"five to the second power" or "five squared"
5^3	"five to the third power" or "five cubed"
5^4	"five to the fourth power"

Usually, an exponent of 1 is not written, so when no exponent appears, we assume that the exponent is 1. For example, $2 = 2^1$ and $7 = 7^1$.

Practice 1–4

Write using exponential notation.
1. $8 \cdot 8 \cdot 8 \cdot 8$
2. $3 \cdot 3 \cdot 3$
3. $10 \cdot 10 \cdot 10 \cdot 10 \cdot 10$
4. $5 \cdot 5 \cdot 4 \cdot 4 \cdot 4 \cdot 4 \cdot 4 \cdot 4$

Examples Write using exponential notation.

1. $7 \cdot 7 \cdot 7 = 7^3$
2. $3 \cdot 3 = 3^2$
3. $6 \cdot 6 \cdot 6 \cdot 6 \cdot 6 = 6^5$
4. $3 \cdot 3 \cdot 3 \cdot 3 \cdot 9 \cdot 9 \cdot 9 = 3^4 \cdot 9^3$

■ Work Practice 1–4

Objective B Evaluating Exponential Expressions

To **evaluate** an exponential expression, we write the expression as a product and then find the value of the product.

Practice 5–8

Evaluate.
5. 4^2 6. 7^3
7. 11^1 8. $2 \cdot 3^2$

Answers
1. 8^4 2. 3^3 3. 10^5 4. $5^2 \cdot 4^6$
5. 16 6. 343 7. 11 8. 18

Examples Evaluate.

5. $9^2 = 9 \cdot 9 = 81$
6. $6^1 = 6$
7. $3^4 = 3 \cdot 3 \cdot 3 \cdot 3 = 81$
8. $5 \cdot 6^2 = 5 \cdot 6 \cdot 6 = 180$

■ Work Practice 5–8

Example 8 illustrates an important property: An exponent applies only to its base. The exponent 2, in $5 \cdot 6^2$, applies only to its base, 6.

> **Helpful Hint**
>
> An exponent applies only to its base. For example, $4 \cdot 2^3$ means $4 \cdot 2 \cdot 2 \cdot 2$.

> **Helpful Hint**
>
> Don't forget that 2^4, for example, is *not* $2 \cdot 4$. The expression 2^4 means repeated multiplication of the same factor.
>
> $2^4 = 2 \cdot 2 \cdot 2 \cdot 2 = 16$,   whereas $2 \cdot 4 = 8$

✓**Concept Check** Which of the following statements is correct?

a. 3^5 is the same as $5 \cdot 5 \cdot 5$.
b. "Ten cubed" is the same as 10^2.
c. "Six to the fourth power" is the same as 6^4.
d. 12^2 is the same as $12 \cdot 2$.

Objective C Using the Order of Operations

Suppose that you are in charge of taking inventory at a local cell phone store. An employee has given you the number of a certain cell phone in stock as the expression

$6 + 2 \cdot 30$

To calculate the value of this expression, do you add first or multiply first? If you add first, the answer is 240. If you multiply first, the answer is 66.

Mathematical symbols wouldn't be very useful if two values were possible for one expression. Thus, mathematicians have agreed that, given a choice, we multiply first.

$6 + 2 \cdot 30 = 6 + 60$ Multiply.
$\qquad\qquad = 66$ Add.

This agreement is one of several **order of operations** agreements.

> ## Order of Operations
>
> **1.** Perform all operations within parentheses ( ), brackets [ ], or other grouping symbols such as fraction bars, starting with the innermost set.
> **2.** Evaluate any expressions with exponents.
> **3.** Multiply or divide in order from left to right.
> **4.** Add or subtract in order from left to right.

✓**Concept Check Answer**
c

Below we practice using order of operations to simplify expressions.

Practice 9
Simplify: $9 \cdot 3 - 8 \div 4$

Example 9   Simplify: $2 \cdot 4 - 3 \div 3$

Solution: There are no parentheses and no exponents, so we start by multiplying and dividing, from left to right.

$$
\begin{aligned}
2 \cdot 4 - 3 \div 3 &= 8 - 3 \div 3 \quad \text{Multiply.} \\
&= 8 - 1 \quad \text{Divide.} \\
&= 7 \quad \text{Subtract.}
\end{aligned}
$$

■ Work Practice 9

Practice 10
Simplify: $48 \div 3 \cdot 2^2$

Example 10   Simplify: $4^2 \div 2 \cdot 4$

Solution: We start by evaluating 4^2.

$$4^2 \div 2 \cdot 4 = 16 \div 2 \cdot 4 \quad \text{Write } 4^2 \text{ as 16.}$$

Next we multiply or divide *in order* from left to right. Since division appears before multiplication from left to right, we divide first, then multiply.

$$
\begin{aligned}
16 \div 2 \cdot 4 &= 8 \cdot 4 \quad \text{Divide.} \\
&= 32 \quad \text{Multiply.}
\end{aligned}
$$

■ Work Practice 10

Practice 11
Simplify: $(10 - 7)^4 + 2 \cdot 3^2$

Example 11   Simplify: $(8 - 6)^2 + 2^3 \cdot 3$

Solution:
$$
\begin{aligned}
(8 - 6)^2 + 2^3 \cdot 3 &= 2^2 + 2^3 \cdot 3 \quad \text{Simplify inside parentheses.} \\
&= 4 + 8 \cdot 3 \quad \text{Write } 2^2 \text{ as 4 and } 2^3 \text{ as 8.} \\
&= 4 + 24 \quad \text{Multiply.} \\
&= 28 \quad \text{Add.}
\end{aligned}
$$

■ Work Practice 11

Practice 12
Simplify:
$36 \div [20 - (4 \cdot 2)] + 4^3 - 6$

Example 12   Simplify: $4^3 + [3^2 - (10 \div 2)] - 7 \cdot 3$

Solution: Here we begin with the innermost set of parentheses.

$$
\begin{aligned}
4^3 + [3^2 - (10 \div 2)] - 7 \cdot 3 &= 4^3 + [3^2 - 5] - 7 \cdot 3 \quad \text{Simplify inside parentheses.} \\
&= 4^3 + [9 - 5] - 7 \cdot 3 \quad \text{Write } 3^2 \text{ as 9.} \\
&= 4^3 + 4 - 7 \cdot 3 \quad \text{Simplify inside brackets.} \\
&= 64 + 4 - 7 \cdot 3 \quad \text{Write } 4^3 \text{ as 64.} \\
&= 64 + 4 - 21 \quad \text{Multiply.} \\
&= 47 \quad \text{Add and subtract from left to right.}
\end{aligned}
$$

■ Work Practice 12

Example 13 Simplify: $\dfrac{7 - 2 \cdot 3 + 3^2}{5(2 - 1)}$

Solution: Here, the fraction bar is a grouping symbol. We simplify above and below the fraction bar separately.

$$\frac{7 - 2 \cdot 3 + 3^2}{5(2 - 1)} = \frac{7 - 2 \cdot 3 + 9}{5(1)}$$ Evaluate 3^2 and $(2 - 1)$.

$$= \frac{7 - 6 + 9}{5}$$ Multiply $2 \cdot 3$ in the numerator and multiply 5 and 1 in the denominator.

$$= \frac{10}{5}$$ Add and subtract from left to right.

$$= 2$$ Divide.

■ Work Practice 13

Practice 13

Simplify: $\dfrac{25 + 8 \cdot 2 - 3^3}{2(3 - 2)}$

Example 14 Simplify: $64 \div 8 \cdot 2 + 4$

Solution: $64 \div 8 \cdot 2 + 4 = \underbrace{8 \cdot 2}_{} + 4$ Divide.

$$= 16 + 4$$ Multiply.

$$= 20$$ Add.

■ Work Practice 14

Practice 14

Simplify: $36 \div 6 \cdot 3 + 5$

Objective D Finding the Area of a Square

Since a square is a special rectangle, we can find its area by finding the product of its length and its width.

Area of a rectangle = length · width

By recalling that each side of a square has the same measurement, we can use the following procedure to find its area:

Area of a square = length · width
= side · side
= (side)^2

Square   Side
Side

Helpful Hint

Recall from Section 1.5 that area is measured in **square** units while perimeter is measured in units.

Example 15 Find the area of a square whose side measures 4 inches.

Solution: Area of a square = (side)^2
= (4 inches)^2
= 16 square inches

4 inches

The area of the square is 16 square inches.

■ Work Practice 15

Practice 15

Find the area of a square whose side measures 12 centimeters.

Answers
13. 7   **14.** 23   **15.** 144 sq cm

Calculator Explorations **Exponents**

To evaluate an exponential expression such as 4^7 on a calculator, find the keys marked $\boxed{y^x}$ or $\boxed{\wedge}$ and $\boxed{=}$ or $\boxed{\text{ENTER}}$. To evaluate 4^7, press the keys $\boxed{4}$ $\boxed{y^x}$ (or $\boxed{\wedge}$) $\boxed{7}$ then $\boxed{=}$ or $\boxed{\text{ENTER}}$. The display will read $\boxed{\qquad 16384}$. Thus, $4^7 = 16{,}384$.

Use a calculator to evaluate.

1. 4^6 **2.** 5^6 **3.** 5^5

4. 7^6 **5.** 2^{11} **6.** 6^8

Order of Operations

To see whether your calculator has the order of operations built in, evaluate $5 + 2 \cdot 3$ by pressing the keys $\boxed{5}$ $\boxed{+}$ $\boxed{2}$ $\boxed{\times}$ $\boxed{3}$ then $\boxed{=}$ or $\boxed{\text{ENTER}}$. If the display reads $\boxed{11}$, your calculator does have the order of operations built in. This means that most of the time,

you can key in a problem exactly as it is written, and the calculator will perform operations in the proper order. When evaluating an expression containing parentheses, key in the parentheses. (If an expression contains brackets, key in parentheses.) For example, to evaluate $2[25 - (8 + 4)] - 11$, press the keys $\boxed{2}$ $\boxed{\times}$ $\boxed{(}$ $\boxed{25}$ $\boxed{-}$ $\boxed{(}$ $\boxed{8}$ $\boxed{+}$ $\boxed{4}$ $\boxed{)}$ $\boxed{)}$ $\boxed{-}$ $\boxed{11}$ then $\boxed{=}$ or $\boxed{\text{ENTER}}$.

The display will read $\boxed{\qquad 15}$.

Use a calculator to evaluate.

7. $7^4 + 5^3$

8. $12^4 - 8^4$

9. $63 \cdot 75 - 43 \cdot 10$

10. $8 \cdot 22 + 7 \cdot 16$

11. $4(15 \div 3 + 2) - 10 \cdot 2$

12. $155 - 2(17 + 3) + 185$

Vocabulary, Readiness & Video Check

Use the choices below to fill in each blank.

addition   multiplication   exponent
subtraction   division   base

1. In $2^5 = 32$, the 2 is called the _____ and the 5 is called the _____ .

2. To simplify $8 + 2 \cdot 6$, which operation should be performed first? _____

3. To simplify $(8 + 2) \cdot 6$, which operation should be performed first? _____

4. To simplify $9(3 - 2) \div 3 + 6$, which operation should be performed first? _____

5. To simplify $8 \div 2 \cdot 6$, which operation should be performed first? _____

Martin-Gay Interactive Videos

See Video 1.7

Watch the section lecture video and answer the following questions.

Objective A **6.** In the ▣ Example 1 expression, what is the 3 called and what is the 12 called? ▶

Objective B **7.** As mentioned in ▣ Example 4, what "understood exponent" does any number we've worked with before have? ▶

Objective C **8.** List the three operations needed to evaluate ▣ Example 7 in the order they should be performed. ▶

Objective D **9.** As explained in the lecture before ▣ Example 10, why does the area of a square involve an exponent whereas the area of a rectangle usually does not? ▶

1.7 Exercise Set MyMathLab®

Objective A *Write using exponential notation. See Examples 1 through 4.*

1. $4 \cdot 4 \cdot 4$ **2.** $5 \cdot 5 \cdot 5 \cdot 5$ **3.** $7 \cdot 7 \cdot 7 \cdot 7 \cdot 7 \cdot 7$ **4.** $6 \cdot 6 \cdot 6 \cdot 6 \cdot 6 \cdot 6 \cdot 6$

5. $12 \cdot 12 \cdot 12$ **6.** $10 \cdot 10 \cdot 10$ **7.** $6 \cdot 6 \cdot 5 \cdot 5 \cdot 5$ **8.** $4 \cdot 4 \cdot 3 \cdot 3 \cdot 3$

9. $9 \cdot 8 \cdot 8$ **10.** $7 \cdot 4 \cdot 4 \cdot 4$ **11.** $3 \cdot 2 \cdot 2 \cdot 2 \cdot 2$ **12.** $4 \cdot 6 \cdot 6 \cdot 6 \cdot 6$

13. $3 \cdot 2 \cdot 2 \cdot 2 \cdot 2 \cdot 5 \cdot 5 \cdot 5 \cdot 5 \cdot 5$ **14.** $6 \cdot 6 \cdot 2 \cdot 9 \cdot 9 \cdot 9 \cdot 9$

Objective B *Evaluate. See Examples 5 through 8.*

15. 8^2 **16.** 6^2 **17.** 5^3 **18.** 6^3 **19.** 2^5 **20.** 3^5

21. 1^{10} **22.** 1^{12} **23.** 7^1 **24.** 8^1 **25.** 2^7 **26.** 5^4

27. 2^8 **28.** 3^3 **29.** 4^4 **30.** 4^3 **31.** 9^3 **32.** 8^3

33. 12^2 **34.** 11^2 **35.** 10^2 **36.** 10^3 **37.** 20^1 **38.** 14^1

39. 3^6 **40.** 4^5 **41.** $3 \cdot 2^6$ **42.** $5 \cdot 3^2$ **43.** $2 \cdot 3^4$ **44.** $2 \cdot 7^2$

Objective C *Simplify. See Examples 9 through 14.*

45. $15 + 3 \cdot 2$ **46.** $24 + 6 \cdot 3$ **47.** $14 \div 7 \cdot 2 + 3$ **48.** $100 \div 10 \cdot 5 + 4$

49. $32 \div 4 - 3$ **50.** $42 \div 7 - 6$ **51.** $13 + \dfrac{24}{8}$ **52.** $32 + \dfrac{8}{2}$

53. $6 \cdot 5 + 8 \cdot 2$ **54.** $3 \cdot 4 + 9 \cdot 1$ **55.** $\dfrac{5 + 12 \div 4}{1^7}$ **56.** $\dfrac{6 + 9 \div 3}{3^2}$

57. $(7 + 5^2) \div 4 \cdot 2^3$ **58.** $6^2 \cdot (10 - 8)$ **59.** $5^2 \cdot (10 - 8) + 2^3 + 5^2$

60. $5^3 \div (10 + 15) + 9^2 + 3^3$ **61.** $\dfrac{18 + 6}{2^4 - 2^2}$ **62.** $\dfrac{40 + 8}{5^2 - 3^2}$

63. $(3 + 5) \cdot (9 - 3)$ **64.** $(9 - 7) \cdot (12 + 18)$ **65.** $\dfrac{7(9 - 6) + 3}{3^2 - 3}$

66. $\dfrac{5(12-7)-4}{5^2-18}$

67. $8 \div 0 + 37$

68. $18 - 7 \div 0$

69. $2^4 \cdot 4 - (25 \div 5)$

70. $2^3 \cdot 3 - (100 \div 10)$

71. $3^4 - [35 - (12 - 6)]$

72. $[40 - (8 - 2)] - 2^5$

▶ **73.** $(7 \cdot 5) + [9 \div (3 \div 3)]$

74. $(18 \div 6) + [(3 + 5) \cdot 2]$

75. $8 \cdot [2^2 + (6 - 1) \cdot 2] - 50 \cdot 2$

76. $35 \div [3^2 + (9 - 7) - 2^2] + 10 \cdot 3$

77. $\dfrac{9^2 + 2^2 - 1^2}{8 \div 2 \cdot 3 \cdot 1 \div 3}$

78. $\dfrac{5^2 - 2^3 + 1^4}{10 \div 5 \cdot 4 \cdot 1 \div 4}$

79. $\dfrac{2 + 4^2}{5(20 - 16) - 3^2 - 5}$

80. $\dfrac{3 + 9^2}{3(10 - 6) - 2^2 - 1}$

81. $9 \div 3 + 5^2 \cdot 2 - 10$

82. $10 \div 2 + 3^3 \cdot 2 - 20$

83. $[13 \div (20 - 7) + 2^5] - (2 + 3)^2$

84. $[15 \div (11 - 6) + 2^2] + (5 - 1)^2$

85. $7^2 - \{18 - [40 \div (5 \cdot 1) + 2] + 5^2\}$

86. $29 - \{5 + 3[8 \cdot (10 - 8)] - 50\}$

△ **Objective D Mixed Practice (Section 1.3)** *Find the area and perimeter of each square. See Example 15.*

▶ **87.**

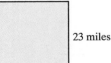

7 meters

△ **88.**

9 centimeters

△ **89.**

23 miles

△ **90.**

41 feet

Concept Extensions

Answer the following true or false. See the Concept Check in this section.

91. "Six to the fifth power" is the same as 6^5.

92. "Seven squared" is the same as 7^2.

93. 2^5 is the same as $5 \cdot 5$.

94. 4^9 is the same as $4 \cdot 9$.

Insert grouping symbols (parentheses) so that each given expression evaluates to the given number.

95. $2 + 3 \cdot 6 - 2$; evaluates to 28

96. $2 + 3 \cdot 6 - 2$; evaluates to 20

97. $24 \div 3 \cdot 2 + 2 \cdot 5$; evaluates to 14

98. $24 \div 3 \cdot 2 + 2 \cdot 5$; evaluates to 15

△**99.** A building contractor is bidding on a contract to install gutters on seven homes in a retirement community, all in the shape shown. To estimate the cost of materials, she needs to know the total perimeter of all seven homes. Find the total perimeter.

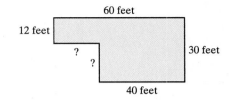

100. The building contractor from Exercise 99 plans to charge \$4 per foot for installing vinyl gutters. Find the total charge for the seven homes given the total perimeter answer to Exercise 99.

Simplify.

101. $(7 + 2^4)^5 - (3^5 - 2^4)^2$

102. $25^3 \cdot (45 - 7 \cdot 5) \cdot 5$

103. Write an expression that simplifies to 5. Use multiplication, division, addition, subtraction, and at least one set of parentheses. Explain the process you would use to simplify the expression.

104. Explain why $2 \cdot 3^2$ is not the same as $(2 \cdot 3)^2$.

1.8 Introduction to Variables, Algebraic Expressions, and Equations

Objective A Evaluating Algebraic Expressions

Perhaps the most important quality of mathematics is that it is a science of patterns. Communicating about patterns is often made easier by using a letter to represent all the numbers fitting a pattern. We call such a letter a **variable.** For example, in Section 1.3 we presented the addition property of 0, which states that the sum of 0 and any number is that number. We might write

$0 + 1 = 1$
$0 + 2 = 2$
$0 + 3 = 3$
$0 + 4 = 4$
$0 + 5 = 5$
$0 + 6 = 6$
⋮

Objectives

A Evaluate Algebraic Expressions Given Replacement Values.

B Identify Solutions of Equations.

C Translate Phrases into Variable Expressions.

continuing indefinitely. This is a pattern, and all whole numbers fit the pattern. We can communicate this pattern for all whole numbers by letting a letter, such as a, represent all whole numbers. We can then write

$$0 + a = a$$

Using variable notation is a primary goal of learning **algebra.** We now take some important first steps in beginning to use variable notation.

A combination of operations on letters (variables) and numbers is called an **algebraic expression** or simply an **expression.**

Algebraic Expressions

$$3 + x \qquad 5 \cdot y \qquad 2 \cdot z - 1 + x$$

If two variables or a number and a variable are next to each other, with no operation sign between them, the operation is multiplication. For example,

$$2x \quad \text{means} \quad 2 \cdot x$$

and

$$xy \text{ or } x(y) \quad \text{means} \quad x \cdot y$$

Also, the meaning of an exponent remains the same when the base is a variable. For example,

$$x^2 = \underbrace{x \cdot x}_{\text{2 factors of } x} \qquad \text{and} \qquad y^5 = \underbrace{y \cdot y \cdot y \cdot y \cdot y}_{\text{5 factors of } y}$$

Algebraic expressions such as $3x$ have different values depending on replacement values for x. For example, if x is 2, then $3x$ becomes

$$3x = 3 \cdot 2$$
$$= 6$$

If x is 7, then $3x$ becomes

$$3x = 3 \cdot 7$$
$$= 21$$

Replacing a variable in an expression by a number and then finding the value of the expression is called **evaluating the expression** for the variable. When finding the value of an expression, remember to follow the order of operations given in Section 1.7.

Practice 1

Evaluate $x - 2$ if x is 7.

Example 1 Evaluate $x + 6$ if x is 8.

Solution: Replace x with 8 in the expression $x + 6$.

$$x + 6 = 8 + 6 \qquad \text{Replace } x \text{ with 8.}$$
$$= 14 \qquad \text{Add.}$$

Work Practice 1

When we write a statement such as "x is 5," we can use an equal sign ($=$) to represent "is" so that

$$x \text{ is 5} \quad \text{can be written as} \quad x = 5.$$

Answer

1. 5

Example 2 Evaluate $2(x - y)$ for $x = 6$ and $y = 3$.

Solution: $2(x - y) = 2(6 - 3)$ Replace x with 6 and y with 3.

$ = 2(3)$ Subtract.

$ = 6$ Multiply.

🔲 Work Practice 2

Practice 2

Evaluate $y(x - 3)$ for $x = 8$ and $y = 4$.

Example 3 Evaluate $\dfrac{x - 5y}{y}$ for $x = 35$ and $y = 5$.

Solution: $\dfrac{x - 5y}{y} = \dfrac{35 - 5(5)}{5}$ Replace x with 35 and y with 5.

$\phantom{\dfrac{x - 5y}{y}} = \dfrac{35 - 25}{5}$ Multiply.

$\phantom{\dfrac{x - 5y}{y}} = \dfrac{10}{5}$ Subtract.

$\phantom{\dfrac{x - 5y}{y}} = 2$ Divide.

🔲 Work Practice 3

Practice 3

Evaluate $\dfrac{y + 6}{x}$ for $x = 6$ and $y = 18$.

Example 4 Evaluate $x^2 + z - 3$ for $x = 5$ and $z = 4$.

Solution: $x^2 + z - 3 = 5^2 + 4 - 3$ Replace x with 5 and z with 4.

$ = 25 + 4 - 3$ Evaluate 5^2.

$ = 26$ Add and subtract from left to right.

🔲 Work Practice 4

Practice 4

Evaluate $25 - z^3 + x$ for $z = 2$ and $x = 1$.

Helpful Hint

If you are having difficulty replacing variables with numbers, first replace each variable with a set of parentheses, then insert the replacement number within the parentheses.

Example:

$x^2 + z - 3 = (\ \ )^2 + (\ \ ) - 3$

$ = (5)^2 + (4) - 3$

$ = 25 + 4 - 3$

$ = 26$

✓**Concept Check** What's wrong with the solution to the following problem?

Evaluate $3x + 2y$ for $x = 2$ and $y = 3$.

Solution: $3x + 2y = 3(3) + 2(2)$

$ = 9 + 4$

$ = 13$

Answers

2. 20   **3.** 4   **4.** 18

✓**Concept Check Answer**

$3x + 2y = 3(2) + 2(3)$

$ = 6 + 6$

$ = 12$

Practice 5

Evaluate $\dfrac{5(F-32)}{9}$ for $F = 41$.

Example 5 The expression $\dfrac{5(F-32)}{9}$ can be used to write degrees Fahrenheit F as degrees Celsius C. Find the value of this expression for $F = 86$.

Solution:
$$\frac{5(F-32)}{9} = \frac{5(86-32)}{9}$$
$$= \frac{5(54)}{9}$$
$$= \frac{270}{9}$$
$$= 30$$

Thus 86°F is the same temperature as 30°C.

■ Work Practice 5

Objective B Identifying Solutions of Equations

In Objective **A**, we learned that a combination of operations on variables and numbers is called an algebraic expression or simply an expression. Frequently in this book, we have written statements like $7 + 4 = 11$ or area = length · width. Each of these statements is called an **equation.** An equation is of the form

Helpful Hint An equation contains "=," while an expression does not.

expression = expression

An equation can be labeled as

equal sign
$$\underset{\text{left side}}{\underline{x + 7}} \;\; \underset{}{=} \;\; \underset{\text{right side}}{10}$$

When an equation contains a variable, deciding which values of the variable make an equation a true statement is called **solving** an equation for the variable. A **solution** of an equation is a value for the variable that makes an equation a true statement. For example, 2 is a solution of the equation $x + 5 = 7$, since replacing x with 2 results in the *true* statement $2 + 5 = 7$. Similarly, 3 is not a solution of $x + 5 = 7$, since replacing x with 3 results in the *false* statement $3 + 5 = 7$.

Practice 6

Determine whether 8 is a solution of the equation $3(y - 6) = 6$.

Example 6 Determine whether 6 is a solution of the equation $4(x - 3) = 12$.

Solution: We replace x with 6 in the equation.

$$4(x - 3) = 12$$
$$4(6 - 3) \overset{?}{=} 12 \quad \text{Replace } x \text{ with 6.}$$
$$4(3) \overset{?}{=} 12$$
$$12 = 12 \quad \text{True}$$

Since $12 = 12$ is a true statement, 6 *is* a solution of the equation.

Answers
5. 5 **6.** yes

■ Work Practice 6

A collection of numbers enclosed by braces is called a set. For example,

$$\{0, 1, 2, 3, \ldots\}$$

is the set of whole numbers that we are studying about in this chapter. The three dots after the number 3 in the set mean that this list of numbers continues in the same manner indefinitely.

The next example contains set notation.

Example 7   Determine which numbers in the set $\{26, 40, 20\}$ are solutions of the equation $2n - 30 = 10$.

Solution: Replace n with each number from the set to see if a true statement results.

Let n be 26.	**Let n be 40.**	**Let n be 20.**
$2n - 30 = 10$	$2n - 30 = 10$	$2n - 30 = 10$
$2 \cdot 26 - 30 \overset{?}{=} 10$	$2 \cdot 40 - 30 \overset{?}{=} 10$	$2 \cdot 20 - 30 \overset{?}{=} 10$
$52 - 30 \overset{?}{=} 10$	$80 - 30 \overset{?}{=} 10$	$40 - 30 \overset{?}{=} 10$
$22 = 10$ False	$50 = 10$ False	$10 = 10$ True ✓

Thus, 20 is a solution while 26 and 40 are not solutions.

Work Practice 7

Practice 7

Determine which numbers in the set $\{10, 6, 8\}$ are solutions of the equation $5n + 4 = 34$.

Objective C Translating Phrases into Variable Expressions ▶

To aid us in solving problems later, we practice translating verbal phrases into algebraic expressions. Certain key words and phrases suggesting addition, subtraction, multiplication, or division are reviewed next.

Addition (+)	Subtraction (−)	Multiplication (·)	Division (÷)
sum	difference	product	quotient
plus	minus	times	divide
added to	subtract	multiply	shared equally among
more than	less than	multiply by	per
increased by	decreased by	of	divided by
total	less	double/triple	divided into

Example 8   Write as an algebraic expression. Use x to represent "a number."

a. 7 increased by a number
b. 15 decreased by a number
c. The product of 2 and a number
d. The quotient of a number and 5
e. 2 subtracted from a number

Solution:

a. In words: 7   increased by   a number
       Translate: 7   + x

(Continued on next page)

Practice 8

Write as an algebraic expression. Use x to represent "a number."

a. Twice a number
b. 8 increased by a number
c. 10 minus a number
d. 10 subtracted from a number
e. The quotient of 6 and a number

Answers

7. 6 is a solution.
8. a. $2x$ **b.** $8 + x$ **c.** $10 - x$
d. $x - 10$ **e.** $6 \div x$ or $\frac{6}{x}$

b. In words: 15   decreased by   a number
Translate: 15   − x

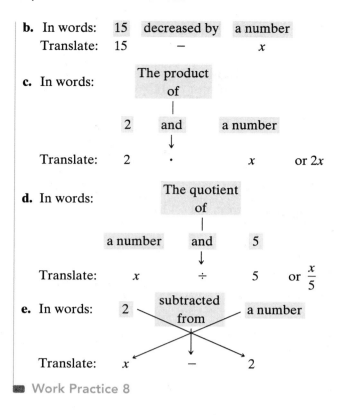

c. In words: The product of

                2   and   a number

Translate: 2   · x or $2x$

d. In words: The quotient of

        a number   and   5

Translate: x ÷   5   or $\dfrac{x}{5}$

e. In words: 2   subtracted from   a number

Translate: x −   2

■ Work Practice 8

Helpful Hint

Remember that order is important when subtracting. Study the order of numbers and variables below.

Phrase	Translation
a number *decreased by* 5	$x - 5$
a number *subtracted from* 5	$5 - x$

Vocabulary, Readiness & Video Check

Use the choices below to fill in each blank. You may use each choice more than once.

   evaluating the expression   variable(s)   expression   equation   solution

1. A combination of operations on letters (variables) and numbers is a(n) _____.

2. A letter that represents a number is a(n) _____.

3. $3x - 2y$ is called a(n) _____ and the letters x and y are _____.

4. Replacing a variable in an expression by a number and then finding the value of the expression is called _____.

5. A statement of the form "expression = expression" is called a(n) _____.

6. A value for the variable that makes an equation a true statement is called a(n) _____.

Martin-Gay Interactive Videos   Watch the section lecture video and answer the following questions.

See Video 1.8

Objective A 7. Complete this statement based on the lecture before ⊞ Example 1: When a letter and a variable are next to each other, the operation is an understood _____. ▶

Objective B 8. In ⊞ Example 5, why is a question mark written over the equal sign? ▶

Objective C 9. In ⊞ Example 6, what phrase translates to subtraction? ▶

1.8 Exercise Set MyMathLab®

Objective A *Complete the table. The first row has been done for you. See Examples 1 through 5.*

	a	b	$a + b$	$a - b$	$a \cdot b$	$a \div b$
	45	9	54	36	405	5
1.	21	7				
2.	24	6				
3.	152	0				
4.	298	0				
5.	56	1				
6.	82	1				

Evaluate each following expression for $x = 2$, $y = 5$, and $z = 3$. See Examples 1 through 5.

▶ **7.** $3 + 2z$

8. $7 + 3z$

9. $3xz - 5x$

10. $4yz + 2x$

11. $z - x + y$

12. $x + 5y - z$

13. $4x - z$

14. $2y + 5z$

▶ **15.** $y^3 - 4x$

16. $y^3 - z$

17. $2xy^2 - 6$

18. $3yz^2 + 1$

19. $8 - (y - x)$

20. $3 + (2y - 4)$

21. $x^5 + (y - z)$

22. $x^4 - (y - z)$

23. $\dfrac{6xy}{z}$

24. $\dfrac{8yz}{15}$

25. $\dfrac{2y - 2}{x}$

26. $\dfrac{6 + 3x}{z}$

27. $\dfrac{x + 2y}{z}$

28. $\dfrac{2z + 6}{3}$

29. $\dfrac{5x}{y} - \dfrac{10}{y}$

30. $\dfrac{70}{2y} - \dfrac{15}{z}$

31. $2y^2 - 4y + 3$

32. $3x^2 + 2x - 5$

33. $(4y - 5z)^3$

34. $(4y + 3z)^2$

35. $(xy + 1)^2$

36. $(xz - 5)^4$

▶ **37.** $2y(4z - x)$

38. $3x(y + z)$

39. $xy(5 + z - x)$ **40.** $xz(2y + x - z)$ **41.** $\dfrac{7x + 2y}{3x}$ **42.** $\dfrac{6z + 2y}{4}$

43. The expression $16t^2$ gives the distance in feet that an object falls after t seconds. Complete the table by evaluating $16t^2$ for each given value of t.

t	1	2	3	4
$16t^2$				

44. The expression $\dfrac{5(F - 32)}{9}$ gives the equivalent degrees Celsius for F degrees Fahrenheit. Complete the table by evaluating this expression for each given value of F.

F	50	59	68	77
$\dfrac{5(F - 32)}{9}$				

Objective B *Decide whether the given number is a solution of the given equation. See Example 6.*

45. Is 10 a solution of $n - 8 = 2$?

46. Is 9 a solution of $n - 2 = 7$?

47. Is 3 a solution of $24 = 80n$?

48. Is 50 a solution of $250 = 5n$?

49. Is 7 a solution of $3n - 5 = 10$?

50. Is 8 a solution of $11n + 3 = 91$?

51. Is 20 a solution of $2(n - 17) = 6$?

52. Is 0 a solution of $5(n + 9) = 40$?

53. Is 0 a solution of $5x + 3 = 4x + 13$?

54. Is 2 a solution of $3x - 6 = 5x - 10$?

55. Is 8 a solution of $7f = 64 - f$?

56. Is 5 a solution of $8x - 30 = 2x$?

Determine which numbers in each set are solutions to the corresponding equations. See Example 7.

57. $n - 2 = 10;\ \{10, 12, 14\}$

58. $n + 3 = 16;\ \{9, 11, 13\}$

59. $5n = 30;\ \{6, 25, 30\}$

60. $3n = 45;\ \{15, 30, 45\}$

61. $6n + 2 = 26;\ \{0, 2, 4\}$

62. $4n - 14 = 6;\ \{0, 5, 10\}$

63. $3(n - 4) = 10;\ \{5, 7, 10\}$

64. $6(n + 2) = 23;\ \{1, 3, 5\}$

65. $7x - 9 = 5x + 13;\ \{3, 7, 11\}$

66. $9x - 15 = 5x + 1;\ \{2, 4, 11\}$

Objective C Translating *Write each phrase as a variable expression. Use x to represent "a number." See Example 8.*

67. Eight more than a number

68. The sum of three and a number

69. The total of a number and eight

70. The difference of a number and five hundred

71. Twenty decreased by a number

72. A number less thirty

73. The product of 512 and a number

74. A number times twenty

75. The quotient of eight and a number

76. A number divided by 11

77. The sum of seventeen and a number added to the product of five and the number

78. The quotient of twenty and a number, decreased by three

79. The product of five and a number

80. The difference of twice a number, and four

81. A number subtracted from 11

82. Twelve subtracted from a number

83. A number less 5

84. The sum of a number and 7

85. 6 divided by a number

86. The product of a number and 7

87. Fifty decreased by eight times a number

88. Twenty decreased by twice a number

Concept Extensions

For Exercises 89 through 92, use a calculator to evaluate each expression for $x = 23$ and $y = 72$.

89. $x^4 - y^2$

90. $2(x + y)^2$

91. $x^2 + 5y - 112$

92. $16y - 20x + x^3$

93. If x is a whole number, which expression is the largest: $2x, 5x,$ or $\frac{x}{3}$?
Explain your answer.

94. If x is a whole number, which expression is the smallest: $2x, 5x,$ or $\frac{x}{3}$?
Explain your answer.

95. In Exercise 43, what do you notice about the value of $16t^2$ as t gets larger?

96. In Exercise 44, what do you notice about the value of $\frac{5(F - 32)}{9}$ as F gets larger?

Chapter 1 Group Activity

Investigating Endangered and Threatened Species

An **endangered** species is one that is thought to be in danger of becoming extinct throughout all or a major part of its habitat. A **threatened** species is one that may become endangered. The Division of Endangered Species at the U.S. Fish and Wildlife Service keeps close tabs on the state of threatened and endangered wildlife in the United States and around the world. The table below was compiled from 2013 data in the Division of Endangered Species' box score. The "Total Species" column gives the total number of endangered and threatened species for each group.

1. Round each number of *endangered animal species* to the nearest ten to estimate the Animal Total.

2. Round each number of *endangered plant species* to the nearest ten to estimate the Plant Total.

3. Add the exact numbers of endangered animal species to find the exact Animal Total and record it in the table in the Endangered Species column. Add the exact numbers of endangered plant species to find the Plant Total and record it in the table in the Endangered Species column. Then find the total number of endangered species (animals and plants combined) and record this number in the table as the Grand Total in the Endangered Species column.

4. Find the Animal Total, Plant Total, and Grand Total for the Total Species column. Record these values in the table.

5. Use the data in the table to complete the Threatened Species column.

6. Write a paragraph discussing the conclusions that can be drawn from the table.

Endangered and Threatened Species Worldwide			
Group	**Endangered Species**	**Threatened Species**	**Total Species**
Mammals	325		361
Birds	286		317
Reptiles	84		126
Amphibians	25		37
Fishes	95		166
Snails	34		47
Clams	74		86
Crustaceans	20		23
Insects	61		71
Arachnids	12		12
Corals	0		2
Animal Total			
Flowering Plants	571		820
Conifers	2		5
Ferns and others	26		30
Lichens	2		2
Plant Total			
Grand Total			

Chapter 1 Vocabulary Check

Fill in each blank with one of the words or phrases listed below.

difference	factor	perimeter	dividend	minuend
place value	whole numbers	equation	divisor	variable
sum	set	addend	exponent	expression
solution	quotient	subtrahend	product	digits area

1. The _____ are 0, 1, 2, 3, . . .

2. The _____ of a polygon is its distance around or the sum of the lengths of its sides.

3. The position of each digit in a number determines its _____.

4. A(n) _____ is a shorthand notation for repeated multiplication of the same factor.

5. To find the _____ of a rectangle, multiply length times width.

6. The _____ used to write numbers are 0, 1, 2, 3, 4, 5, 6, 7, 8, and 9.

7. A letter used to represent a number is called a(n) _____.

8. A(n) _____ can be written in the form "expression = expression."

9. A combination of operations on variables and numbers is called a(n) _____.

10. A(n) _____ of an equation is a value of the variable that makes the equation a true statement.

11. A collection of numbers (or objects) enclosed by braces is called a(n) _____.

Use the facts below for Exercises 12 through 21.

$$2 \cdot 3 = 6 \quad 4 + 17 = 21 \quad 20 - 9 = 11 \quad 5\overline{)35}^{\,7}$$

12. The 21 above is called the _____.

13. The 5 above is called the _____.

14. The 35 above is called the _____.

15. The 7 above is called the _____.

16. The 3 above is called a(n) _____.

17. The 6 above is called the _____.

18. The 20 above is called the _____.

19. The 9 above is called the _____.

20. The 11 above is called the _____.

21. The 4 above is called a(n) _____.

Helpful Hint ▶ Are you preparing for your test? Don't forget to take the Chapter 1 Test on page 95. Then check your answers at the back of the text and use the Chapter Test Prep Videos to see the fully worked-out solutions to any of the exercises you want to review.

1 Chapter Highlights

Definitions and Concepts	Examples
Section 1.2 Place Value, Names for Numbers, and Reading Tables	
The **whole numbers** are 0, 1, 2, 3, 4, 5, ... The position of each digit in a number determines its **place value.** A place-value chart is shown next with the names of the periods given.	Examples of whole numbers: 0, 14, 968, 5,268,619

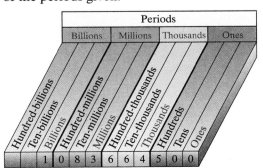

(continued)

Definitions and Concepts	Examples
Section 1.2 Place Value, Names for Numbers, and Reading Tables (*continued*)	
To write a whole number in words, write the number in each period followed by the name of the period. (The name of the ones period is not included.)	9,078,651,002 is written as nine billion, seventy-eight million, six hundred fifty-one thousand, two.
To write a whole number in standard form, write the number in each period, followed by a comma.	Four million, seven hundred six thousand, twenty-eight is written as 4,706,028.
Section 1.3 Adding and Subtracting Whole Numbers, and Perimeter	
To add whole numbers, add the digits in the ones place, then the tens place, then the hundreds place, and so on, carrying when necessary.	Find the sum: $\overset{2\ 1\ 1}{2689} \leftarrow$ addend $1735 \leftarrow$ addend $+\ \ 662 \leftarrow$ addend $5086 \leftarrow$ sum
To subtract whole numbers, subtract the digits in the ones place, then the tens place, then the hundreds place, and so on, borrowing when necessary.	Subtract: $\overset{8\ 15}{79\cancel{5}4} \leftarrow$ minuend $-5673 \leftarrow$ subtrahend $2281 \leftarrow$ difference
The **perimeter** of a polygon is its distance around or the sum of the lengths of its sides.	△ Find the perimeter of the polygon shown. The perimeter is 5 feet + 3 feet + 9 feet + 2 feet = 19 feet.
Section 1.4 Rounding and Estimating	

Rounding Whole Numbers to a Given Place Value
 	
Step 1:   Locate the digit to the right of the given place value.
 	
Step 2:   If this digit is 5 or greater, add 1 to the digit in the given place value and replace each digit to its right with 0.
 	
Step 3:   If this digit is less than 5, replace it and each digit to its right with 0.
	Round 15,721 to the nearest thousand.
	
	15, ⑦ 21
	Add 1 ⌐ Replace Since the circled digit is 5 or greater, add 1 to
	    with the given place value and replace digits to its
	    zeros. right with zeros.
	
	15,721 rounded to the nearest thousand is 16,000.

Definitions and Concepts	Examples

Section 1.5   Multiplying Whole Numbers and Area

To multiply 73 and 58, for example, multiply 73 and 8, then 73 and 50. The sum of these partial products is the product of 73 and 58. Use the notation to the right.

$$
\begin{array}{r}
73 \quad \leftarrow \text{ factor} \\
\times\ 58 \quad \leftarrow \text{ factor} \\
\hline
584 \quad \leftarrow \ 73 \times 8 \\
3650 \quad \leftarrow \ 73 \times 50 \\
\hline
4234 \quad \leftarrow \text{ product}
\end{array}
$$

To find the **area** of a rectangle, multiply length times width.

△ Find the area of the rectangle shown.

11 meters

7 meters

$$
\begin{aligned}
\text{area of rectangle} &= \text{length} \cdot \text{width} \\
&= (11 \text{ meters})(7 \text{ meters}) \\
&= 77 \text{ square meters}
\end{aligned}
$$

Section 1.6   Dividing Whole Numbers

Division Properties of 0

The quotient of 0 and any number (except 0) is 0.

The quotient of any number and 0 is not a number. We say that this quotient is undefined.

To divide larger whole numbers, use the process called **long division** as shown to the right.

$\dfrac{0}{5} = 0$

$\dfrac{7}{0}$ is undefined

$$
\begin{array}{r}
507 \ \ \text{R } 2 \quad \leftarrow \text{ quotient} \\
\text{divisor} \rightarrow 14\overline{)7100} \quad \longleftarrow \text{ dividend} \\
-70 \qquad 5(14) = 70 \\
\hline
10 \qquad \text{Subtract and bring down the 0.} \\
-0 \qquad 0(14) = 0 \\
\hline
100 \qquad \text{Subtract and bring down the 0.} \\
-98 \qquad 7(14) = 98 \\
\hline
2 \qquad \text{Subtract. The remainder is 2.}
\end{array}
$$

To check, see that $507 \cdot 14 + 2 = 7100$.

The **average** of a list of numbers is

$$
\text{average} = \frac{\text{sum of numbers}}{\textit{number of numbers}}
$$

Find the average of 23, 35, and 38.

$$
\text{average} = \frac{23 + 35 + 38}{3} = \frac{96}{3} = 32
$$

Definitions and Concepts	Examples

Section 1.7 Exponents and Order of Operations

An **exponent** is a shorthand notation for repeated multiplication of the same factor.

Order of Operations

1. Perform all operations within parentheses ( ), brackets [ ], or other grouping symbols such as fraction bars, starting with the innermost set.

2. Evaluate any expressions with exponents.

3. Multiply or divide in order from left to right.

4. Add or subtract in order from left to right.

The **area of a square** is $(\text{side})^2$.

$$3^4 = \underbrace{3 \cdot 3 \cdot 3 \cdot 3}_{4 \text{ factors of } 3} = 81$$

base, exponent

Simplify: $\dfrac{5 + 3^2}{2(7 - 6)}$

Simplify above and below the fraction bar separately.

$$\frac{5 + 3^2}{2(7 - 6)} = \frac{5 + 9}{2(1)}$$ Evaluate 3^2 above the fraction bar.
Subtract $7 - 6$ below the fraction bar.

$$= \frac{14}{2}$$ Add.
Multiply.

$$= 7$$ Divide.

Find the area of a square with side length 9 inches.

$$\text{Area of the square} = (\text{side})^2$$
$$= (9 \text{ inches})^2$$
$$= 81 \text{ square inches}$$

Section 1.8 Introduction to Variables, Algebraic Expressions, and Equations

A letter used to represent a number is called a **variable.**

A combination of operations on variables and numbers is called an **algebraic expression.**

Replacing a variable in an expression by a number, and then finding the value of the expression, is called **evaluating the expression** for the variable.

A statement written in the form "expression = expression" is an **equation.**

A **solution** of an equation is a value for the variable that makes the equation a true statement.

Variables:

$$x, \quad y, \quad z, \quad a, \quad b$$

Algebraic expressions:

$$3 + x, \quad 7y, \quad x^3 + y - 10$$

Evaluate $2x + y$ for $x = 22$ and $y = 4$.

$$2x + y = 2 \cdot 22 + 4$$ Replace x with 22 and y with 4.
$$= 44 + 4$$ Multiply.
$$= 48$$ Add.

Equations:

$$n - 8 = 12$$
$$2(20 - 7n) = 32$$
$$\text{Area} = \text{length} \cdot \text{width}$$

Determine whether 2 is a solution of the equation $4(x - 1) = 7$.

$$4(2 - 1) \stackrel{?}{=} 7$$ Replace x with 2.
$$4(1) \stackrel{?}{=} 7$$ Subtract.
$$4 = 7$$ False

No, 2 is not a solution.

(1.2) *Determine the place value of the digit 4 in each whole number.*

1. 7640

2. 46,200,120

Write each whole number in words.

3. 7640

4. 46,200,120

Write each whole number in expanded form.

5. 3158

6. 403,225,000

Write each whole number in standard form.

7. Eighty-one thousand, nine hundred

8. Six billion, three hundred four million

The following table shows the Internet use by world regions. Use this table to answer Exercises 9 through 12 and other exercises throughout this review. (Source: International Telecommunications Union and Internet World Stats)

Internet Use by World Regions (in millions)			
World Region	**2004**	**2008**	**2013**
Africa	21	51	140
Asia	296	579	1268
Europe	241	385	467
Middle East	29	42	141
North America	218	248	302
Latin America/ Caribbean	51	139	280
Oceania/ Australia	12	20	145

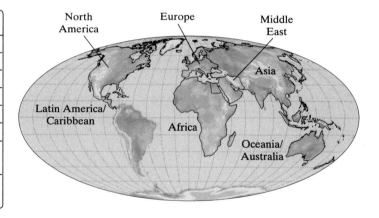

9. Find the number of Internet users in 2013 in Europe. Write your answer in standard form.

10. Find the number of Internet users in Oceania/ Australia in 2013. Write your answer in standard form.

11. Which world region had the smallest number of Internet users in 2008?

12. Which world region had the greatest number of Internet users in 2008?

(1.3) *Add or subtract as indicated.*

13. $18 + 49$ **14.** $28 + 39$ **15.** $462 - 397$ **16.** $583 - 279$ **17.** $428 + 21$

18. $819 + 21$ **19.** $4000 - 86$ **20.** $8000 - 92$ **21.** $91 + 3623 + 497$ **22.** $82 + 1647 + 238$

Translating *Solve.*

23. Find the sum of 74, 342, and 918.

24. Find the sum of 49, 529, and 308.

25. Subtract 7965 from 25,862.

26. Subtract 4349 from 39,007.

27. The distance from Washington, DC, to New York City is 205 miles. The distance from New York City to New Delhi, India, is 7318 miles. Find the total distance from Washington, DC, to New Delhi if traveling by air through New York City.

28. Susan Summerline earned salaries of $62,589, $65,340, and $69,770 during the years 2004, 2005, and 2006, respectively. Find her total earnings during those three years.

Find the perimeter of each figure.

△ **29.**

52 feet
40 feet
52 feet
72 feet

△ **30.**

11 kilometers   20 kilometers
35 kilometers

Use the Internet Use by World Regions table for Exercises 31 and 32.

31. Find the increase in Internet users in Europe from 2008 to 2013.

32. Find the difference in the number of Internet users in 2013 between Oceania/Australia and the Middle East.

The following bar graph shows the monthly savings account balances for a freshman attending a local community college. Use this graph to answer Exercises 33 through 36.

33. During what month was the balance the least?

34. During what month was the balance the greatest?

35. By how much did the balance decrease from February to April?

36. By how much did the balance increase from June to August?

(1.4) *Round to the given place.*

37. 43 to the nearest ten

38. 45 to the nearest ten

39. 876 to the nearest ten

40. 493 to the nearest hundred

41. 3829 to the nearest hundred

42. 57,534 to the nearest thousand

43. 39,583,819 to the nearest million

44. 768,542 to the nearest hundred-thousand

Estimate the sum or difference by rounding each number to the nearest hundred.

45. $3785 + 648 + 2866$

46. $5925 - 1787$

47. A group of students took a week-long driving trip and traveled 630, 192, 271, 56, 703, 454, and 329 miles on seven consecutive days. Round each distance to the nearest hundred to estimate the distance they traveled.

48. In 2012, the population of Europe was 820,918,446 while the population of Latin America/Caribbean was 593,688,638. Round each number to the nearest million, and estimate their difference in population in 2012. (Source: Internet World Stats)

(1.5) *Multiply.*

49. $\begin{array}{r} 276 \\ \times\ 8 \\ \hline \end{array}$

50. $\begin{array}{r} 349 \\ \times\ 4 \\ \hline \end{array}$

51. $\begin{array}{r} 57 \\ \times 40 \\ \hline \end{array}$

52. $\begin{array}{r} 69 \\ \times 42 \\ \hline \end{array}$

53. $20(7)(4)$

54. $25(9)(4)$

55. $26 \cdot 34 \cdot 0$

56. $62 \cdot 88 \cdot 0$

57. $\begin{array}{r} 586 \\ \times\ 29 \\ \hline \end{array}$

58. $\begin{array}{r} 242 \\ \times\ 37 \\ \hline \end{array}$

59. $\begin{array}{r} 642 \\ \times 177 \\ \hline \end{array}$

60. $\begin{array}{r} 347 \\ \times 129 \\ \hline \end{array}$

61. $\begin{array}{r} 1026 \\ \times 401 \\ \hline \end{array}$

62. $\begin{array}{r} 2107 \\ \times\ 302 \\ \hline \end{array}$

Translating *Solve.*

63. Find the product of 6 and 250.

64. Find the product of 6 and 820.

65. A golf pro orders shirts for the company sponsoring a local charity golfing event. Shirts size large cost $32 while shirts size extra large cost $38. If 15 large shirts and 11 extra-large shirts are ordered, find the cost.

66. The cost for a South Dakota resident to attend Black Hills State University full-time is $6112 per semester. Determine the cost for 20 students to attend full-time. (*Source:* Black Hills State University)

Find the area of each rectangle.

△ **67.**

13 miles

7 miles

△ **68.**   20 centimeters

25 centimeters

(1.6) *Divide and then check.*

69. $\dfrac{49}{7}$

70. $\dfrac{36}{9}$

71. $27 \div 5$

72. $18 \div 4$

73. $918 \div 0$

74. $0 \div 668$

75. $5\overline{)167}$

76. $8\overline{)159}$

77. $26\overline{)626}$

78. $19\overline{)680}$

79. $47\overline{)23,792}$

80. $53\overline{)48,111}$

81. $207\overline{)578,291}$

82. $306\overline{)615,732}$

Translating   *Solve.*

83. Find the quotient of 92 and 5.

84. Find the quotient of 86 and 4.

85. A box can hold 24 cans of corn. How many boxes can be filled with 648 cans of corn?

86. One mile is 1760 yards. Find how many miles there are in 22,880 yards.

87. Find the average of the numbers 76, 49, 32, and 47.

88. Find the average of the numbers 23, 85, 62, and 66.

(1.7) *Simplify.*

89. 8^2

90. 5^3

91. $5 \cdot 9^2$

92. $4 \cdot 10^2$

93. $18 \div 2 + 7$

94. $12 - 8 \div 4$

95. $\dfrac{5(6^2 - 3)}{3^2 + 2}$

96. $\dfrac{7(16 - 8)}{2^3}$

97. $48 \div 8 \cdot 2$

98. $27 \div 9 \cdot 3$

99. $2 + 3[1^5 + (20 - 17) \cdot 3] + 5 \cdot 2$

100. $21 - [2^4 - (7 - 5) - 10] + 8 \cdot 2$

101. $19 - 2(3^2 - 2^2)$

102. $16 - 2(4^2 - 3^2)$

103. $4 \cdot 5 - 2 \cdot 7$

104. $8 \cdot 7 - 3 \cdot 9$

105. $(6 - 4)^3 \cdot [10^2 \div (3 + 17)]$

106. $(7 - 5)^3 \cdot [9^2 \div (2 + 7)]$

107. $\dfrac{5 \cdot 7 - 3 \cdot 5}{2(11 - 3^2)}$

108. $\dfrac{4 \cdot 8 - 1 \cdot 11}{3(9 - 2^3)}$

Find the area of each square.

△ **109.** A square with side length of 7 meters.

△ **110.**

3 inches

(1.8) *Evaluate each expression for $x = 5$, $y = 0$, and $z = 2$.*

111. $\dfrac{2x}{z}$

112. $4x - 3$

113. $\dfrac{x + 7}{y}$

114. $\dfrac{y}{5x}$

115. $x^3 - 2z$

116. $\dfrac{7 + x}{3z}$

117. $(y + z)^2$

118. $\dfrac{100}{x} + \dfrac{y}{3}$

Translating *Translate each phrase into a variable expression. Use x to represent a number.*

119. Five subtracted from a number

120. Seven more than a number

121. Ten divided by a number

122. The product of 5 and a number

Decide whether the given number is a solution of the given equation.

123. Is 5 a solution of $n + 12 = 20 - 3$?

124. Is 23 a solution of $n - 8 = 10 + 6$?

125. Is 14 a solution of $30 = 3(n - 3)$?

126. Is 20 a solution of $5(n - 7) = 65$?

Determine which numbers in each set are solutions to the corresponding equations.

127. $7n = 77$; $\{6, 11, 20\}$

128. $n - 25 = 150$; $\{125, 145, 175\}$

129. $5(n + 4) = 90$; $\{14, 16, 26\}$

130. $3n - 8 = 28$; $\{3, 7, 15\}$

Mixed Review

Perform the indicated operations.

131. $485 - 68$

132. $729 - 47$

133. 732×3

134. 629×4

135. $374 + 29 + 698$

136. $593 + 52 + 766$

137. $13\overline{)5962}$

138. $18\overline{)4267}$

139. 1968×36

140. 5324×18

141. $2000 - 356$

142. $9000 - 519$

Round to the given place.

143. 842 to the nearest ten

144. 258,371 to the nearest hundred-thousand

Simplify.

145. $24 \div 4 \cdot 2$

146. $\dfrac{(15 + 3) \cdot (8 - 5)}{2^3 + 1}$

Solve.

147. Is 9 a solution of $5n - 6 = 40$?

148. Is 3 a solution of $2n - 6 = 5n - 15$?

149. A manufacturer of drinking glasses ships his delicate stock in special boxes that can hold 32 glasses. If 1714 glasses are manufactured, how many full boxes are filled? Are there any glasses left over?

150. A teacher orders 2 small whiteboards for $27 each and 8 boxes of dry erase pens for $4 each. What is her total bill before taxes?

Simplify.

Answers

1. Write 82,426 in words.

2. Write "four hundred two thousand, five hundred fifty" in standard form.

3. $59 + 82$

4. $600 - 487$

5. $\begin{array}{r} 496 \\ \times\ \ 30 \\ \hline \end{array}$

6. $52,896 \div 69$

7. $2^3 \cdot 5^2$

8. $98 \div 1$

9. $0 \div 49$

10. $62 \div 0$

11. $(2^4 - 5) \cdot 3$

12. $16 + 9 \div 3 \cdot 4 - 7$

13. $6^1 \cdot 2^3$

14. $2[(6 - 4)^2 + (22 - 19)^2] + 10$

15. $5698 \cdot 1000$

16. Find the average of 62, 79, 84, 90, and 95.

17. Round 52,369 to the nearest thousand.

Estimate each sum or difference by rounding each number to the nearest hundred.

18. $6289 + 5403 + 1957$

19. $4267 - 2738$

Solve.

20. Subtract 15 from 107.

21. Find the sum of 15 and 107.

22. Find the product of 15 and 107.

23. Find the quotient of 107 and 15.

1. _____
2. _____
3. _____
4. _____
5. _____
6. _____
7. _____
8. _____
9. _____
10. _____
11. _____
12. _____
13. _____
14. _____
15. _____
16. _____
17. _____
18. _____
19. _____
20. _____
21. _____
22. _____
23. _____

24. _____

25. _____

26. _____

27. _____

28. _____

29. _____

30. _____

31. _____

32. a. _____

    b. _____

33. _____

34. _____

24. Twenty-nine cans of Sherwin-Williams paint cost $493. How much was each can?

25. Jo McElory is looking at two new refrigerators for her apartment. One costs $599 and the other costs $725. How much more expensive is the higher-priced one?

26. One tablespoon of white granulated sugar contains 45 calories. How many calories are in 8 tablespoons of white granulated sugar? (*Source: Home and Garden Bulletin No. 72, U.S. Department of Agriculture*)

27. A small business owner recently ordered 16 digital cameras that cost $430 each and 5 printers that cost $205 each. Find the total cost for these items.

Find the perimeter and the area of each figure.

△**28.**

Square   5 centimeters

△**29.**

20 yards

Rectangle   10 yards

30. Evaluate $5(x^3 - 2)$ for $x = 2$.

31. Evaluate $\dfrac{3x - 5}{2y}$ for $x = 7$ and $y = 8$.

32. Translate the following phrases into mathematical expressions. Use x to represent "a number."

   a. The quotient of a number and 17

   b. Twice a number, decreased by 20

33. Is 6 a solution of the equation $5n - 11 = 19$?

34. Determine which number in the set is a solution to the given equation.
$n + 20 = 4n - 10; \{0, 10, 20\}$

Integers and Introduction to Solving Equations

Director James Cameron made the deepest solo descent so far into the Mariana Trench in the Pacific Ocean. He reached a depth of 35,756 feet in the Deepsea Challenger, shown above. Next, may be Richard Branson?

The Krubera Cave now holds the title of deepest. In this cave, many new depth records have been set—each one deeper than the last. The latest record is 7188 feet but who knows how deeply this cave will be explored next?

Where do we explore next? Throughout this chapter, we present many applications having to do with water depths below sea level and land depths below the surface of Earth by way of mines and caves. Recently, there has been a surge of interest in exploring these depths. Although we have already reached the deepest-known part of our oceans—the Mariana Trench in the Pacific Ocean—cave exploration is a little more tricky. For example, with so many "branches" of a cave, we are never certain that it has been totally explored. New caves are being discovered and explored even as this is written. The deepest-known cave in the world, the Krubera, was not discovered until 2001 by Ukrainian cave explorers. See exercises throughout this chapter.

Thus far, we have studied whole numbers, but these numbers are not sufficient for representing many situations in real life. For example, to express 5 degrees below zero or $100 in debt, numbers less than 0 are needed. This chapter is devoted to integers, which include numbers less than 0, and operations on these numbers.

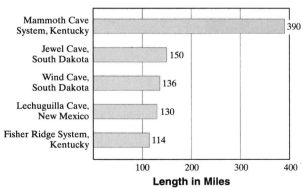

Top 5 Longest Caves in U.S.

Mammoth Cave System, Kentucky — 390
Jewel Cave, South Dakota — 150
Wind Cave, South Dakota — 136
Lechuguilla Cave, New Mexico — 130
Fisher Ridge System, Kentucky — 114

Length in Miles

Source: Top 10 of Everything, 2013

Objectives

A Represent Real-Life Situations with Integers.

B Graph Integers on a Number Line.

C Compare Integers.

D Find the Absolute Value of a Number.

E Find the Opposite of a Number.

F Read Bar Graphs Containing Integers.

Objective A Representing Real-Life Situations

Thus far in this text, all numbers have been 0 or greater than 0. Numbers greater than 0 are called **positive numbers.** However, sometimes situations exist that cannot be represented by a number greater than 0. For example,

To represent these situations, we need numbers less than 0.

Extending the number line to the left of 0 allows us to picture **negative numbers,** which are numbers that are less than 0.

When a single + sign or no sign is in front of a number, the number is a positive number. When a single − sign is in front of a number, the number is a negative number. Together, we call positive numbers, negative numbers, and zero the **signed numbers.**

−5 indicates "negative five."

5 and +5 both indicate "positive five."

The number 0 is neither positive nor negative.

Some signed numbers are integers. The **integers** consist of the numbers labeled on the number line above. The integers are

. . . , −3, −2, −1, 0, 1, 2, 3, . . .

Now we have numbers to represent the situations previously mentioned.

5 degrees below 0   −5°

20 feet below sea level   −20 feet

> **Helpful Hint** Notice that 0 is neither positive nor negative.

> **Helpful Hint**
>
> A − sign, such as the one in −1, tells us that the number is to the left of 0 on the number line. −1 is read "negative one."
>
> A + sign or no sign tells us that a number lies to the right of 0 on the number line. For example, 3 and +3 both mean "positive three."

Example 1   Representing Depth with an Integer

The world's deepest cave is Krubera (or Voronja), in the country of Georgia, located by the Black Sea in Asia. It has been explored to a depth of 7188 feet below the surface of Earth. Represent this position using an integer. (*Source:* MessagetoEagle.com and Wikipedia)

Solution: If 0 represents the surface of Earth, then 7188 feet below the surface can be represented by -7188.

■ Work Practice 1

Objective B Graphing Integers

Example 2   Graph $0, -3, 5,$ and -5 on the number line.

Solution:

■ Work Practice 2

Objective C Comparing Integers

We can compare integers by using a number line. For any two numbers graphed on a number line, the number to the **right** is the **greater number** and the number to the **left** is the **smaller number.** Also, the symbols $<$ and $>$ are called **inequality symbols.**

The inequality symbol $>$ means "is greater than" and
the inequality symbol $<$ means "is less than."

For example, both -5 and -7 are graphed on the number line below.

On the graph, -7 is **to the left of** -5, so -7 **is less than** -5, written as

$$-7 < -5$$

We can also write

$$-5 > -7$$

since -5 is **to the right of** -7, so -5 **is greater than** -7.

✓**Concept Check** Is there a largest positive number? Is there a smallest negative number? Explain.

Practice 1

a. The world's deepest bat colony spends each winter in a New York zinc mine at a depth of 3805 feet. Represent this position with an integer. (*Source: Guinness Book of World Records*)

b. The tamarack tree, a type of conifer, commonly grows at the edge of the arctic tundra and survives winter temperatures of 85 degrees below zero, Fahrenheit. Represent this temperature with an integer in degrees Fahrenheit.

Practice 2

Graph $-4, -1, 2,$ and -2 on the number line.

Answers
1. a. -3805 **b.** $-85°F$
2.

✓**Concept Check Answer**
no

Practice 3

Insert < or > between each pair of numbers to make a true statement.

a. 0   −5   **b.** −3   3

c. −7   −12

Example 3   Insert < or > between each pair of numbers to make a true statement.

a. −7   7   **b.** 0   −4   **c.** −9   −11

Solution:

a. −7 is to the left of 7 on a number line, so −7 < 7.

b. 0 is to the right of −4 on a number line, so 0 > −4.

c. −9 is to the right of −11 on a number line, so −9 > −11.

■ Work Practice 3

Helpful Hint

If you think of < and > as arrowheads, notice that in a true statement the arrow always points to the smaller number.

$$5 > -4 \qquad -3 < -1$$

smaller   smaller
number   number

Objective D Finding the Absolute Value of a Number

The **absolute value** of a number is the number's distance from 0 on the number line. The symbol for absolute value is | |. For example, |3| is read as "the absolute value of 3."

$|3| = 3$ because 3 is 3 units from 0.

$|-3| = 3$ because −3 is 3 units from 0.

Practice 4

Simplify.

a. $|-6|$

b. $|4|$

c. $|-12|$

Example 4   Simplify.

a. $|-9|$ **b.** $|8|$ **c.** $|0|$

Solution:

a. $|-9| = 9$ because −9 is 9 units from 0.

b. $|8| = 8$ because 8 is 8 units from 0.

c. $|0| = 0$ because 0 is 0 units from 0.

■ Work Practice 4

Helpful Hint

Since the absolute value of a number is that number's *distance* from 0, the absolute value of a number is always 0 or positive. It is never negative.

$$|0| = 0 \qquad |-6| = 6$$

zero   a positive number

Answers

3. a. >   **b.** <   **c.** >

4. a. 6   **b.** 4   **c.** 12

Objective E Finding Opposites

Two numbers that are the same distance from 0 on the number line but are on opposite sides of 0 are called **opposites.**

4 and −4 are opposites.

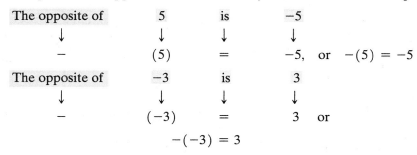

When two numbers are opposites, we say that each is the opposite of the other. Thus **4 is the opposite of −4** and **−4 is the opposite of 4.**

The phrase "the opposite of" is written in symbols as "−". For example,

The opposite of	5	is	−5
↓	↓	↓	↓
−	(5)	=	−5, or −(5) = −5

The opposite of	−3	is	3
↓	↓	↓	↓
−	(−3)	=	3 or

$$-(-3) = 3$$

In general, we have the following:

Opposites

If a is a number, then $-(-a) = a$.

Notice that because "the opposite of" is written as "−", to find the opposite of a number we place a "−" sign in front of the number.

Example 5 Find the opposite of each number.

a. 13 **b.** −2 **c.** 0

Solution:

a. The opposite of 13 is −13.
b. The opposite of −2 is −(−2) or 2.
c. The opposite of 0 is 0.

> **Helpful Hint**
> Remember that 0 is neither positive nor negative.

Work Practice 5

Practice 5

Find the opposite of each number.

a. 14 **b.** −9

✓**Concept Check** True or false? The number 0 is the only number that is its own opposite.

Example 6 Simplify.

a. −(−4) **b.** −|−5| **c.** −|6|

Solution:

a. −(−4) = 4 The opposite of negative 4 is 4.

b. −|−5| = −5 The opposite of the absolute value of −5 is the opposite of 5, or −5.

c. −|6| = −6 The opposite of the absolute value of 6 is the opposite of 6, or −6.

Work Practice 6

Practice 6

Simplify.
a. −|−7|
b. −|4|
c. −(−12)

Answers
5. **a.** −14 **b.** 9
6. **a.** −7 **b.** −4 **c.** 12

✓**Concept Check Answer**
true

Practice 7

Evaluate $-|x|$ if $x = -6$.

> **Example 7** Evaluate $-|-x|$ if $x = -2$.
>
> **Solution:** Carefully replace x with -2; then simplify.
>
> $-|-x| = -|-(-2)|$ Replace x with -2.
>
> Then $-|-(-2)| = -|2| = -2$.
>
> ■ Work Practice 7

Objective F Reading Bar Graphs Containing Integers

The bar graph below shows the average daytime surface temperatures (in degrees Fahrenheit) of the eight planets, excluding the newly classified "dwarf planet," Pluto. Notice that a negative temperature is illustrated by a bar below the horizontal line representing 0°F, and a positive temperature is illustrated by a bar above the horizontal line representing 0°F.

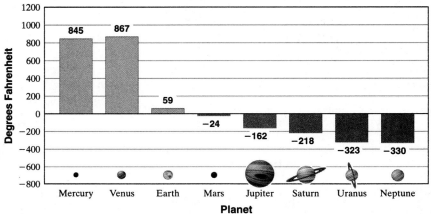

Average Daytime Surface Temperatures of Planets*

Source: *The World Almanac*, 2013
* For some planets, the temperature given is the temperature where the atmospheric pressure equals 1 Earth atmosphere.

Practice 8

Which planet has the highest average daytime surface temperature?

> **Example 8** Which planet has the lowest average daytime surface temperature?
>
> **Solution:** The planet with the lowest average daytime surface temperature is the one that corresponds to the bar that extends the farthest in the negative direction (downward). Neptune has the lowest average daytime surface temperature, -330°F.
>
> ■ Work Practice 8

Answers

7. -6 **8.** Venus

Vocabulary, Readiness & Video Check

Use the choices below to fill in each blank. Not all choices will be used.

opposites	absolute value	right	is less than
inequality symbols	negative	positive	left
signed	integers	is greater than	

1. The numbers ... $-3, -2, -1, 0, 1, 2, 3, ...$ are called _____.

2. Positive numbers, negative numbers, and zero together are called _____ numbers.

3. The symbols "$<$" and "$>$" are called _____.

4. Numbers greater than 0 are called _____ numbers while numbers less than 0 are called _____ numbers.

5. The sign "<" means _____ and ">" means _____.

6. On a number line, the greater number is to the _____ of the lesser number.

7. A number's distance from 0 on a number line is the number's _____.

8. The numbers −5 and 5 are called _____.

Martin-Gay Interactive Videos

See Video 2.1

Watch the section lecture video and answer the following questions.

Objective A **9.** In ▥ Example 1, what application is used to represent a negative number?

Objective B **10.** In ▥ Example 2, the tick marks are labelled with what numbers on the number line?

Objective C **11.** From ▥ Example 3 and your knowledge of a number line, complete this statement: 0 will always be greater than any of the _____ integers.

Objective D **12.** What is the answer to ▥ Example 5? The absolute value of what other integer has this same answer?

Objective E **13.** Complete this statement based on ▥ Example 10: A negative sign can be translated to the phrase "_____."

Objective F **14.** In ▥ Examples 13 and 14, what other lake has a negative integer elevation?

2.1 Exercise Set MyMathLab®

Objective A *Represent each quantity by an integer. See Example 1.*

1. A worker in a silver mine in Nevada works 1235 feet underground.

2. A scuba diver is swimming 25 feet below the surface of the water in the Gulf of Mexico.

3. The peak of Mount Elbert in Colorado is 14,433 feet above sea level. (*Source:* U.S. Geological Survey)

4. The lowest elevation in the United States is found at Death Valley, California, at an elevation of 282 feet below sea level. (*Source:* U.S. Geological Survey)

5. The record high temperature in Arkansas is 120 degrees above zero Fahrenheit. (*Source:* National Climatic Data Center)

6. The record high temperature in California is 134 degrees above zero Fahrenheit. (*Source:* National Climatic Data Center.)

7. The average depth of the Atlantic Ocean is 11,810 feet below its surface. (*Source: The World Almanac,* 2013)

8. The average depth of the Pacific Ocean is 14,040 feet below its surface. (*Source: The World Almanac,* 2013)

9. Sears had a loss of $3140 million for the fiscal year 2011. (*Source:* CNN Money)

10. Rite Aid had a loss of $555 million for the fiscal year 2011. (*Source:* CNN Money)

11. Two divers are exploring the wreck of the *Andrea Doria,* south of Nantucket Island, Massachusetts. Guillermo is 160 feet below the surface of the ocean and Luigi is 147 feet below the surface. Represent each quantity by an integer and determine who is deeper.

12. The temperature on one January day in Minneapolis was 10° below 0° Celsius. Represent this quantity by an integer and tell whether this temperature is cooler or warmer than 5° below 0° Celsius.

13. For the first half of 2013, digital track sales declined 2 percent when compared to the first half of 2012. (*Source:* Nielsen Sound Scan)

14. In a recent year, the number of CDs shipped to music retailers reflected a 23 percent decrease from the previous year. Write an integer to represent the percent decrease in CDs shipped. (*Source:* Recording Industry Association of America)

Objective **B** *Graph each integer in the list on the same number line. See Example 2.*

15. 0, 3, 4, 6

16. 7, 5, 2, 0

17. 1, −1, 2, −2, −4

18. 3, −3, 5, −5, 6

19. 0, 1, 9, 14

20. 0, 3, 10, 11

21. 0, −2, −7, −5

22. 0, −7, 3, −6

Objective **C** *Insert < or > between each pair of integers to make a true statement. See Example 3.*

23. 0 ___ −7

24. −8 ___ 0

25. −7 ___ −5

26. −12 ___ −10

27. −30 ___ −35

28. −27 ___ −29

29. −26 ___ 26

30. 13 ___ −13

Objective **D** *Simplify. See Example 4.*

31. $|5|$

32. $|7|$

33. $|-8|$

34. $|-19|$

35. $|0|$

36. $|100|$

37. $|-55|$

38. $|-10|$

Objective **E** *Find the opposite of each integer. See Example 5.*

39. 5   **40.** 8   **41.** -4 **42.** -6

43. 23   **44.** 123   **45.** -85 **46.** -13

Objectives **D** **E** Mixed Practice *Simplify. See Example 6.*

47. $|-7|$ **48.** $|-11|$ **49.** $-|20|$ **50.** $-|43|$

51. $-|-3|$ **52.** $-|-18|$ **53.** $-(-43)$ **54.** $-(-27)$

55. $|-15|$ **56.** $-(-14)$ **57.** $-(-33)$ **58.** $-|-29|$

Evaluate. See Example 7.

59. $|-x|$ if $x = -6$ **60.** $-|x|$ if $x = -8$ **61.** $-|-x|$ if $x = 2$ **62.** $-|-x|$ if $x = 10$

63. $|x|$ if $x = -32$ **64.** $|x|$ if $x = 32$ **65.** $-|x|$ if $x = 7$ **66.** $|-x|$ if $x = 1$

Insert $<$, $>$, or $=$ between each pair of numbers to make a true statement. See Examples 3 through 6.

67. $-12 \quad -6$ **68.** $-4 \quad -17$ **69.** $|-8| \quad |-11|$ **70.** $|-8| \quad |-4|$

71. $|-47| \quad -(-47)$ **72.** $-|17| \quad -(-17)$ **73.** $-|-12| \quad -(-12)$ **74.** $|-24| \quad -(-24)$

75. $0 \quad -9$ **76.** $-45 \quad 0$ **77.** $|0| \quad |-9|$ **78.** $|-45| \quad |0|$

79. $-|-2| \quad -|-10|$ **80.** $-|-8| \quad -|-4|$ **81.** $-(-12) \quad -(-18)$ **82.** $-22 \quad -(-38)$

Objectives **D** **E** Mixed Practice *Fill in the chart. See Examples 4 through 7.*

	Number	Absolute Value of Number	Opposite of Number
83.	31		
85.			-28

	Number	Absolute Value of Number	Opposite of Number
84.	-13		
86.			90

Objective **F** *The bar graph shows the elevations of selected lakes. Use this graph For Exercises 87 through 90.* (*Source:* U.S. Geological Survey) *See Example 8.*

Elevations of Selected Lakes

Feet Above or Below Sea Level

600 — Superior, North America
245 — Ontario, North America
−92 — Caspian Sea, Asia-Europe
0 — Maracaibo, South America
512 — Great Bear, North America
−52 — Eyre, Australia
144 — Vanern, Europe

87. Which lake shown has the lowest elevation?

88. Which lake has an elevation at sea level?

89. Which lake shown has the highest elevation?

90. Which lake shown has the second-lowest elevation?

The following bar graph represents the boiling temperature, the temperature at which a substance changes from liquid to gas at standard atmospheric pressure. Use this graph to answer Exercises 91 through 94.

"Boiling" Temperature of Various Elements

91. Which element has a positive boiling temperature closest to that of water?

92. Which element has the lowest boiling temperature?

93. Which element has a boiling temperature closest to −200°C?

94. Which element has an average boiling temperature closest to +300°C?

Review

Add. See Section 1.3.

95. 0 + 13

96. 9 + 0

97. 15 + 20

98. 20 + 15

99. 47 + 236 + 77

100. 362 + 37 + 90

Concept Extensions

Write the given numbers in order from least to greatest.

101. $2^2, -|3|, -(-5), -|-8|$

102. $|10|, 2^3, -|-5|, -(-4)$

103. $|-1|, -|-6|, -(-6), -|1|$

104. $1^4, -(-3), -|7|, |-20|$

105. $-(-2), 5^2, -10, -|-9|, |-12|$

106. $3^3, -|-11|, -(-10), -4, -|2|$

Choose all numbers for x from each given list that make each statement true.

107. $|x| > 8$
    a. −9   **b.** −5   **c.** 8   **d.** −12

108. $|x| > 4$
    a. 0   **b.** −4   **c.** 5   **d.** −100

109. Evaluate: $-(-|-8|)$

110. Evaluate: $(-|-(-7)|)$

Answer true or false for Exercises 111 through 115.

111. If $a > b$, then a must be a positive number.

112. The absolute value of a number is *always* a positive number.

113. A positive number is always greater than a negative number.

114. Zero is always less than a positive number.

115. The number $-a$ is always a negative number. (*Hint:* Read "$-$" as "the opposite of.")

116. Given the number line is it true that $b < a$?

117. Write in your own words how to find the absolute value of a signed number.

118. Explain how to determine which of two signed numbers is larger.

For Exercises 119 and 120, see the first Concept Check in this section.

119. Is there a largest negative number? If so, what is it?

120. Is there a smallest positive number? If so, what is it?

2.2 Adding Integers

Objective A Adding Integers

Adding integers can be visualized using a number line. A positive number can be represented on the number line by an arrow of appropriate length pointing to the right, and a negative number by an arrow of appropriate length pointing to the left.

Objectives

A Add Integers.

B Evaluate an Algebraic Expression by Adding.

C Solve Problems by Adding Integers.

Both arrows represent 2 or +2. They both point to the right and they are both 2 units long.

Both arrows represent -3. They both point to the left and they are both 3 units long.

Example 1 Add using a number line: $5 + (-2)$

Solution: To add integers on a number line, such as $5 + (-2)$, we start at 0 on the number line and draw an arrow representing 5. From the tip of this arrow, we draw another arrow representing -2. The tip of the second arrow ends at their sum, 3.

$5 + (-2) = 3$

Work Practice 1

Practice 1

Add using a number line:
$5 + (-1)$

Answer

1.
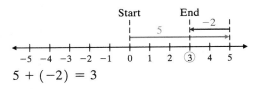
$5 + (-1) = 4$

Practice 2

Add using a number line:
$-6 + (-2)$

Practice 3

Add using a number line:
$-8 + 3$

Practice 4

Add: $(-3) + (-19)$

Practice 5–6

Add.

5. $-12 + (-30)$ **6.** $9 + 4$

Answers

2.

$-6 + (-2) = -8$

3.

$-8 + 3 = -5$

4. -22 **5.** -42 **6.** 13

Example 2   Add using a number line: $-1 + (-4)$

Start at 0 and draw an arrow representing -1. From the tip of this arrow, we draw another arrow representing -4. The tip of the second arrow ends at their sum, -5.

Solution:

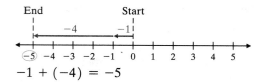

$-1 + (-4) = -5$

■ Work Practice 2

Example 3   Add using a number line: $-7 + 3$

Solution:

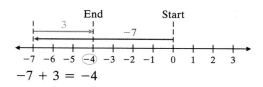

$-7 + 3 = -4$

■ Work Practice 3

Using a number line each time we add two numbers can be time consuming. Instead, we can notice patterns in the previous examples and write rules for adding signed numbers.

Rules for adding signed numbers depend on whether we are adding numbers with the same sign or different signs. When adding two numbers with the same sign, as in Example 2, notice that the sign of the sum is the same as the sign of the addends.

Adding Two Numbers with the Same Sign

Step 1: Add their absolute values.
Step 2: Use their common sign as the sign of the sum.

Example 4   Add: $-2 + (-21)$

Solution:

Step 1: $|-2| = 2, |-21| = 21,$ and $2 + 21 = 23.$
Step 2: Their common sign is negative, so the sum is negative:
$$-2 + (-21) = -23$$

■ Work Practice 4

Examples   Add.

5. $-15 + (-10) = -25$
6. $2 + 6 = 8$

■ Work Practice 5–6

When adding two numbers with different signs, as in Examples 1 and 3, the sign of the result may be positive or negative, or the result may be 0.

Adding Two Numbers with Different Signs

Step 1: Find the larger absolute value minus the smaller absolute value.

Step 2: Use the sign of the number with the larger absolute value as the sign of the sum.

Example 7   Add: $-2 + 25$

Solution:

Step 1: $|-2| = 2, |25| = 25,$ and $25 - 2 = 23.$

Step 2: 25 has the larger absolute value and its sign is an understood $+$:
$$-2 + 25 = +23 \text{ or } 23$$

■ Work Practice 7

Practice 7

Add: $-1 + 26$

Example 8   Add: $3 + (-17)$

Solution:

Step 1: $|3| = 3, |-17| = 17,$ and $17 - 3 = 14.$

Step 2: -17 has the larger absolute value and its sign is $-$:
$$3 + (-17) = -14$$

■ Work Practice 8

Practice 8

Add: $2 + (-18)$

Examples   Add.

9. $-18 + 10 = -8$

10. $12 + (-8) = 4$

11. $0 + (-5) = -5$ The sum of 0 and any number is the number.

■ Work Practice 9–11

Practice 9–11

Add.

9. $-54 + 20$

10. $7 + (-2)$

11. $-3 + 0$

Recall that numbers such as 7 and -7 are called opposites. In general, the sum of a number and its opposite is always 0.

$$\underset{\text{opposites}}{7 + (-7) = 0} \qquad \underset{\text{opposites}}{-26 + 26 = 0} \qquad \underset{\text{opposites}}{1008 + (-1008) = 0}$$

If a is a number, then

$-a$ is its opposite. Also,

$$\left.\begin{array}{l} a + (-a) = 0 \\ -a + a = 0 \end{array}\right\} \quad \text{The sum of a number and its opposite is 0.}$$

Examples   Add.

12. $-21 + 21 = 0$

13. $36 + (-36) = 0$

■ Work Practice 12–13

Practice 12–13

Add.

12. $18 + (-18)$

23. $-64 + 64$

Answers

7. 25   **8.** -16 **9.** -34 **10.** 5

11. -3 **12.** 0   **13.** 0

✔ **Concept Check Answer**

$5 + (-22) = -17$

✔**Concept Check** What is wrong with the following calculation?

$$\cancel{5 + (-22) = 17}$$

In the following examples, we add three or more integers. Remember that by the associative and commutative properties for addition, we may add numbers in any order that we wish. In Examples 14 and 15, let's add the numbers from left to right.

Practice 14

Add: $6 + (-2) + (-15)$

Example 14 Add: $(-3) + 4 + (-11)$

Solution: $(-3) + 4 + (-11) = 1 + (-11)$
$$= -10$$

■ Work Practice 14

Practice 15

Add: $5 + (-3) + 12 + (-14)$

Example 15 Add: $1 + (-10) + (-8) + 9$

Solution: $1 + (-10) + (-8) + 9 = -9 + (-8) + 9$
$$= -17 + 9$$
$$= -8$$

■ Work Practice 15

Helpful Hint Don't forget that addition is commutative and associative. In other words, numbers may be added in any order.

A sum is the same if we add the numbers in any order. To see this, let's add the numbers in Example 15 by first adding the positive numbers together and the negative numbers together.

$$1 + (-10) + (-8) + 9 = 10 + (-18)$$
$$= -8$$

Add the positive numbers: $1 + 9 = 10$.
Add the negative numbers: $(-10) + (-8) = -18$.
Add these results.

The sum is -8.

Objective B Evaluating Algebraic Expressions

We can continue our work with algebraic expressions by evaluating expressions given integer replacement values.

Practice 16

Evaluate $x + 3y$ for $x = -6$ and $y = 2$.

Example 16 Evaluate $2x + y$ for $x = 3$ and $y = -5$.

Solution: Replace x with 3 and y with -5 in $2x + y$.

$$2x + y = 2 \cdot 3 + (-5)$$
$$= 6 + (-5)$$
$$= 1$$

■ Work Practice 16

Practice 17

Evaluate $x + y$ for $x = -13$ and $y = -9$.

Example 17 Evaluate $x + y$ for $x = -2$ and $y = -10$.

Solution: $x + y = (-2) + (-10)$ Replace x with -2 and y with -10.
$$= -12$$

■ Work Practice 17

Practice 18

If the temperature was $-7°$ Fahrenheit at 6 a.m., and it rose 4 degrees by 7 a.m. and then rose another 7 degrees in the hour from 7 a.m. to 8 a.m., what was the temperature at 8 a.m.?

Objective C Solving Problems by Adding Integers

Next, we practice solving problems that require adding integers.

Example 18 Calculating Temperature

In Philadelphia, Pennsylvania, the record extreme high temperature is 104°F. Decrease this temperature by 111 degrees, and the result is the record extreme low temperature. Find this temperature. (*Source:* National Climatic Data Center)

Answers
14. -11 **15.** 0 **16.** 0 **17.** -22
18. $4°$F

Solution:

In words: | extreme low temperature | = | extreme high temperature | + | decrease of of 111° |
|---|---|---|---|---|

↓   ↓   ↓

Translate: extreme low temperature = 104 + (−111)

= −7

The record extreme low temperature in Philadelphia, Pennsylvania, is −7°F.

■ Work Practice 18

🖩 Calculator Explorations   Entering Negative Numbers

To enter a negative number on a calculator, find the key marked ⎡+/−⎤. (Some calculators have a key marked ⎡CHS⎤ and some calculators have a special key ⎡(−)⎤ for entering a negative sign.) To enter the number −2, for example, press the keys ⎡2⎤⎡+/−⎤. The display will read ⎡   −2⎤.

To find −32 + (−131), press the keys
⎡32⎤⎡+/−⎤⎡+⎤⎡131⎤⎡+/−⎤⎡=⎤ or
⎡(−)⎤⎡32⎤⎡+⎤⎡(−)⎤⎡131⎤⎡ENTER⎤
The display will read ⎡   −163⎤.
Thus −32 + (−131) = −163.

Use a calculator to perform each indicated operation.

1. −256 + 97

2. 811 + (−1058)

3. 6(15) + (−46)

4. −129 + 10(48)

5. −108,650 + (−786,205)

6. −196,662 + (−129,856)

Vocabulary, Readiness & Video Check

Use the choices below to fill in each blank. Not all choices will be used.

−a   a   0   commutative   associative

1. If *n* is a number, then −*n* + *n* = _____.

2. Since *x* + *n* = *n* + *x*, we say that addition is _____.

3. If *a* is a number, then −(−*a*) = _____.

4. Since *n* + (*x* + *a*) = (*n* + *x*) + *a*, we say that addition is _____.

Martin-Gay Interactive Videos   *Watch the section lecture video and answer the following questions.*

Objective A **5.** What is the sign of the sum in ▯ Example 6 and why? ▶

Objective B **6.** What is the sign of the sum in ▯ Example 8 and why? ▶

Objective C **7.** What does the answer to ▯ Example 10, −231, mean in the context of the application? ▶

See Video 2.2 ●

2.2 Exercise Set MyMathLab®

Objective A *Add using a number line. See Examples 1 through 3.*

1. −1 + (−6)

2. −6 + (−5)

3. −4 + 7

4. 10 + (−3)

5. −13 + 7

6. 9 + (−4)

Add. See Examples 4 through 13.

7. 46 + 21

8. 15 + 42

9. −8 + (−2)

10. −5 + (−4)

11. −43 + 43

12. −62 + 62

13. 6 + (−2)

14. 8 + (−3)

15. −6 + 0

16. −8 + 0

17. 3 + (−5)

18. 5 + (−9)

19. −2 + (−7)

20. −6 + (−1)

21. −12 + (−12)

22. −23 + (−23)

23. −640 + (−200)

24. −400 + (−256)

25. 12 + (−5)

26. 24 + (−10)

27. −6 + 3

28. −8 + 4

29. −56 + 26

30. −89 + 37

31. −45 + 85

32. −32 + 62

33. 124 + (−144)

34. 325 + (−375)

35. −82 + (−43)

36. −56 + (−33)

Add. See Examples 14 and 15.

37. −4 + 2 + (−5)

38. −1 + 5 + (−8)

39. −52 + (−77) + (−117)

40. −103 + (−32) + (−27)

41. 12 + (−4) + (−4) + 12

42. 18 + (−9) + 5 + (−2)

43. (−10) + 14 + 25 + (−16)

44. 34 + (−12) + (−11) + 213

Objective A Mixed Practice *Add. See Examples 1 through 15.*

45. $-6 + (-15) + (-7)$

46. $-12 + (-3) + (-5)$

47. $-26 + 15$

48. $-35 + (-12)$

49. $5 + (-2) + 17$

50. $3 + (-23) + 6$

51. $-13 + (-21)$

52. $-100 + 70$

53. $3 + 14 + (-18)$

54. $(-45) + 22 + 20$

55. $-92 + 92$

56. $-87 + 0$

57. $-13 + 8 + (-10) + (-27)$

58. $-16 + 6 + (-14) + (-20)$

Objective B *Evaluate $x + y$ for the given replacement values. See Examples 16 and 17.*

▶ 59. $x = -20$ and $y = -50$

60. $x = -1$ and $y = -29$

Evaluate $3x + y$ for the given replacement values. See Examples 16 and 17.

▶ 61. $x = 2$ and $y = -3$

62. $x = 7$ and $y = -11$

63. $x = 3$ and $y = -30$

64. $x = 13$ and $y = -17$

Objective C Translating *Translate each phrase; then simplify. See Example 18.*

65. Find the sum of -6 and 25.

66. Find the sum of -30 and 15.

67. Find the sum of -31, -9, and 30.

68. Find the sum of -49, -2, and 40.

Solve. See Example 18.

▶ 69. Suppose a deep-sea diver dives from the surface to 215 feet below the surface. He then dives down 16 more feet. Use positive and negative numbers to represent this situation. Then find the diver's present depth.

70. Suppose a diver dives from the surface to 248 meters below the surface and then swims up 8 meters, down 16 meters, down another 28 meters, and then up 32 meters. Use positive and negative numbers to represent this situation. Then find the diver's depth after these movements.

In golf, it is possible to have positive and negative scores. The following table shows the results of the eighteen-hole Round 2 for Jim Furyk and Jason Dufner at the 2013 PGA Championship in Rochester, New York. Use the table to answer Exercises 71 and 72.

Player/Hole	1	2	3	4	5	6	7	8	9	10	11	12	13	14	15	16	17	18
Furyk	−1	0	0	0	0	0	0	0	0	−1	0	0	0	0	0	−1	1	0
Dufner	0	−2	0	−1	−1	0	0	0	0	0	−1	0	−1	0	0	−1	0	0

(*Source*: Professional Golfers' Association)

71. Find the total score for each of the athletes in the round.

72. In golf, the lower score is the winner. Use the result of Exercise 71 to determine who won Round 2.

The following bar graph shows the yearly net income for Apple, Inc. Net income is one indication of a company's health. It measures revenue (money taken in) minus cost (money spent). Use this graph to answer Exercises 73 through 76. (Source: Apple, Inc.)

73. What was the net income (in dollars) for Apple, Inc. in 2012?

74. What was the net income (in dollars) for Apple, Inc. in 2001?

75. Find the total net income for the years 2011 and 2012.

76. Find the total net income for the years 2007, 2009, and 2011.

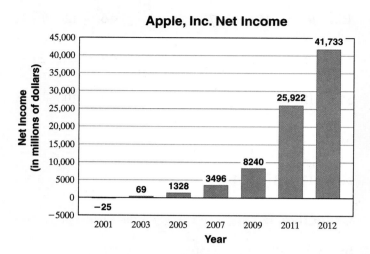

77. The temperature at 4 p.m. on February 2 was −10° Celsius. By 11 p.m. the temperature had risen 12 degrees. Find the temperature at 11 p.m.

78. In some card games, it is possible to have both positive and negative scores. After four rounds of play, Michelle had scores of 14, −5, −8, and 7. What was her total score for the game?

A small business reports the following net incomes. Use this table to answer Exercises 79 and 80.

Year	Net Income (in dollars)
2009	−$10,412
2010	−$1786
2011	$15,395
2012	$31,418

79. Find the sum of the net incomes for 2010 and 2011.

80. Find the sum of the net incomes for all four years shown.

81. The all-time record low temperature for Texas is −23°F. Florida's all-time record low temperature is 21°F higher than Texas' record low. What is Florida's record low temperature? (*Source:* National Climatic Data Center)

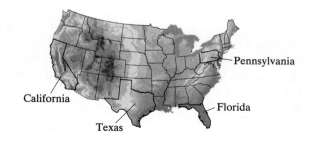

82. The all-time record low temperature for California is −45°F. In Pennsylvania, the lowest temperature ever recorded is 3°F higher than California's all-time low temperature. What is the all-time record low temperature for Pennsylvania? (*Source:* National Climatic Data Center)

83. The deepest spot in the Atlantic Ocean is the Puerto Rico Trench, which has an elevation of 8605 meters below sea level. The bottom of the Atlantic's Cayman Trench has an elevation 1070 meters above the level of the Puerto Rico Trench. Use a negative number to represent the depth of the Cayman Trench. (*Source:* Defense Mapping Agency)

84. The deepest spot in the Pacific Ocean is the Mariana Trench, which has an elevation of 10,924 meters below sea level. The bottom of the Pacific's Aleutian Trench has an elevation 3245 meters higher than that of the Mariana Trench. Use a negative number to represent the depth of the Aleutian Trench. (*Source:* Defense Mapping Agency)

Review

Subtract. See Section 1.3.

85. $44 - 0$ **86.** $91 - 0$ **87.** $200 - 59$ **88.** $400 - 18$

Concept Extensions

89. Name 2 numbers whose sum is -17.

90. Name 2 numbers whose sum is -30.

Each calculation below is incorrect. Find the error and correct it. See the Concept Check in this section.

91. $7 + (-10) \overset{?}{=} 17$

92. $-4 + 14 \overset{?}{=} -18$

93. $-10 + (-12) \overset{?}{=} -120$

94. $-15 + (-17) \overset{?}{=} 32$

For Exercises 95 through 98, determine whether each statement is true or false.

95. The sum of two negative numbers is always a negative number.

96. The sum of two positive numbers is always a positive number.

97. The sum of a positive number and a negative number is always a negative number.

98. The sum of zero and a negative number is always a negative number.

99. In your own words, explain how to add two negative numbers.

100. In your own words, explain how to add a positive number and a negative number.

2.3 Subtracting Integers

In Section 2.1, we discussed the opposite of an integer.

> The opposite of 3 is -3.
> The opposite of -6 is 6.

In this section, we use opposites to subtract integers.

Objective A Subtracting Integers

To subtract integers, we will write the subtraction problem as an addition problem. To see how to do this, study the examples below.

$$10 - 4 = 6$$
$$10 + (-4) = 6$$

Since both expressions simplify to 6, this means that

$$10 - 4 = 10 + (-4) = 6$$

Also,

$$3 - 2 = 3 + (-2) = 1$$
$$15 - 1 = 15 + (-1) = 14$$

Objectives

A Subtract Integers.

B Add and Subtract Integers.

C Evaluate an Algebraic Expression by Subtracting.

D Solve Problems by Subtracting Integers.

Thus, to subtract two numbers, we add the first number to the opposite of the second number. (The opposite of a number is also known as its **additive inverse.**)

> ## Subtracting Two Numbers
>
> If a and b are numbers, then $a - b = a + (-b)$.

Practice 1–4

Subtract.

1. $13 - 4$
2. $-8 - 2$
3. $11 - (-15)$
4. $-9 - (-1)$

Examples Subtract.

	subtraction	=	first number	+	opposite of the second number		
1.	$8 - 5$	=	8	+	(-5)	=	3
2.	$-4 - 10$	=	-4	+	(-10)	=	-14
3.	$6 - (-5)$	=	6	+	5	=	11
4.	$-11 - (-7)$	=	-11	+	7	=	-4

■ Work Practice 1–4

Practice 5–7

Subtract.

5. $6 - 9$
6. $-14 - 5$
7. $-3 - (-4)$

Examples Subtract.

5. $-10 - 5 = -10 + (-5) = -15$

6. $8 - 15 = 8 + (-15) = -7$

7. $-4 - (-5) = -4 + 5 = 1$

■ Work Practice 5–7

> ### Helpful Hint
>
> To visualize subtraction, try the following:
>   The difference between $5°$F and $-2°$F can be found by subtracting. That is,
>
> $$5 - (-2) = 5 + 2 = 7$$
>
> Can you visually see from the thermometer on the right that there are actually 7 degrees between $5°$F and $-2°$F?

5° F

0° F

−2° F

7 degrees

✓**Concept Check** What is wrong with the following calculation?

$$-9 - (-5) = -14$$

Practice 8

Subtract 6 from -15.

Example 8 Subtract 7 from -3.

Solution: To subtract 7 *from* -3, we find

$$-3 - 7 = -3 + (-7) = -10$$

■ Work Practice 8

Answers

1. 9   **2.** -10 **3.** 26   **4.** -8
5. -3 **6.** -19 **7.** 1   **8.** -21

✓**Concept Check Answer**

$-9 - (-5) = -9 + 5 = -4$

Objective B Adding and Subtracting Integers

If a problem involves adding or subtracting more than two integers, we rewrite differences as sums and add. Recall that by associative and commutative properties, we may add numbers in any order. In Examples 9 and 10, we will add from left to right.

Example 9 Simplify: $7 - 8 - (-5) - 1$

Solution:
$$7 - 8 - (-5) - 1 = \underbrace{7 + (-8)} + 5 + (-1)$$
$$= \underbrace{-1 + 5} + (-1)$$
$$= \underbrace{4 + (-1)}$$
$$= 3$$

■ Work Practice 9

Practice 9
Simplify: $-6 - 5 - 2 - (-3)$

Example 10 Simplify: $7 + (-12) - 3 - (-8)$

Solution:
$$7 + (-12) - 3 - (-8) = \underbrace{7 + (-12)} + (-3) + 8$$
$$= \underbrace{-5 + (-3)} + 8$$
$$= \underbrace{-8 + 8}$$
$$= 0$$

■ Work Practice 10

Practice 10
Simplify: $8 + (-2) - 9 - (-7)$

Objective C Evaluating Expressions

Now let's practice evaluating expressions when the replacement values are integers.

Example 11 Evaluate $x - y$ for $x = -3$ and $y = 9$.

Solution: Replace x with -3 and y with 9 in $x - y$.

$$\begin{array}{ccc} x & - & y \\ \downarrow & \downarrow & \downarrow \end{array}$$
$$= (-3) - 9$$
$$= (-3) + (-9)$$
$$= -12$$

■ Work Practice 11

Practice 11
Evaluate $x - y$ for $x = -5$ and $y = 13$.

Example 12 Evaluate $2a - b$ for $a = 8$ and $b = -6$.

Solution: Watch your signs carefully!

$$\begin{array}{ccc} 2a & - & b \\ \downarrow & \downarrow & \downarrow \end{array}$$
$$= 2 \cdot 8 - (-6) \qquad \text{Replace } a \text{ with 8 and } b \text{ with } -6.$$
$$= 16 + 6 \qquad \text{Multiply.}$$
$$= 22 \qquad \text{Add.}$$

■ Work Practice 12

Helpful Hint Watch carefully when replacing variables in the expression $2a - b$. Make sure that all symbols are inserted and accounted for.

Practice 12
Evaluate $3y - z$ for $y = 9$ and $z = -4$.

Answers
9. -10 $\quad$ **10.** 4 $\quad$ **11.** -18 $\quad$ **12.** 31

Objective D Solving Problems by Subtracting Integers

Solving problems often requires subtraction of integers.

Practice 13

The highest point in Asia is the top of Mount Everest, at a height of 29,028 feet above sea level. The lowest point is the Dead Sea, which is 1312 feet below sea level. How much higher is Mount Everest than the Dead Sea? (*Source: National Geographic Society*)

Example 13 Finding a Change in Elevation

The highest point in the United States is the top of Mount McKinley, at a height of 20,320 feet above sea level. The lowest point is Death Valley, California, which is 282 feet below sea level. How much higher is Mount McKinley than Death Valley? (*Source:* U.S. Geological Survey)

Solution:

1. UNDERSTAND. Read and reread the problem. To find "how much higher," we subtract. Don't forget that since Death Valley is 282 feet *below* sea level, we represent its height by -282. Draw a diagram to help visualize the problem.

2. TRANSLATE.

In words:	how much higher is Mt. McKinley	=	height of Mt. McKinley	minus	height of Death Valley
	↓	↓	↓	↓	↓
Translate:	how much higher is Mt. McKinley	=	20,320	−	(-282)

3. SOLVE:

$$20,320 - (-282) = 20,320 + 282 = 20,602$$

4. INTERPRET. Check and state your conclusion: Mount McKinley is 20,602 feet higher than Death Valley.

Answer

13. 30,340 ft

▪ Work Practice 13

Vocabulary, Readiness & Video Check

Multiple choice: Select the correct lettered response following each exercise.

1. It is true that $a - b =$ _____.
   a. $b - a$ **b.** $a + (-b)$ **c.** $a + b$

2. The opposite of n is _____.
   a. $-n$ **b.** $-(-n)$ **c.** n

3. To evaluate $x - y$ for $x = -10$ and $y = -14$, we replace x with -10 and y with -14 and evaluate _____.
   a. $10 - 14$ **b.** $-10 - 14$ **c.** $-14 - 10$ **d.** $-10 - (-14)$

4. The expression $-5 - 10$ equals _____.
   a. $5 - 10$ **b.** $5 + 10$ **c.** $-5 + (-10)$ **d.** $10 - 5$

Martin-Gay Interactive Videos   Watch the section lecture video and answer the following questions.

Objective A **5.** In the lecture before ▥ Example 1, what can the "opposite" of a number also be called?

Objective B **6.** In ▥ Example 7, how is the example rewritten in the first step of simplifying and why? ◯

Objective C **7.** In ▥ Example 8, why do we multiply first? ◯

Objective D **8.** What does the answer to ▥ Example 9, 265, mean in the context of the application? ◯

See Video 2.3 ●

2.3 Exercise Set MyMathLab® ◯

Objective A *Subtract. See Examples 1 through 7.*

1. $-8 - (-8)$

2. $-6 - (-6)$

3. $19 - 16$

4. $15 - 12$

◯ **5.** $3 - 8$

6. $2 - 5$

7. $11 - (-11)$

8. $12 - (-12)$

9. $-4 - (-7)$

10. $-25 - (-25)$

11. $-16 - 4$

12. $-2 - 42$

13. $3 - 15$

14. $8 - 9$

15. $42 - 55$

16. $17 - 63$

17. $478 - (-30)$

18. $844 - (-20)$

◯ **19.** $-4 - 10$

20. $-5 - 8$

◯ **21.** $-7 - (-3)$

22. $-12 - (-5)$

23. $17 - 29$

24. $16 - 45$

Translating *Translate each phrase; then simplify. See Example 8.*

◯ **25.** Subtract 17 from -25.

26. Subtract 10 from -22.

27. Find the difference of -22 and -3.

28. Find the difference of -8 and -13.

29. Subtract -12 from 2.

30. Subtract -50 from -50.

Mixed Practice (Sections 2.2, 2.3) *Add or subtract as indicated.*

31. $-37 + (-19)$

32. $-35 + (-11)$

33. $8 - 13$

34. $4 - 21$

35. $-56 - 89$

36. $-105 - 68$

37. $30 - 67$

38. $86 - 98$

Objective B *Simplify. See Examples 9 and 10.*

39. $8 - 3 - 2$

40. $8 - 4 - 1$

41. $13 - 5 - 7$

42. $30 - 18 - 12$

43. $-5 - 8 - (-12)$

44. $-10 - 6 - (-9)$

45. $-11 + (-6) - 14$

46. $-15 + (-8) - 4$

47. $18 - (-32) + (-6)$

48. $23 - (-17) + (-9)$

49. $-(-5) - 21 + (-16)$

50. $-(-9) - 14 + (-23)$

51. $-10 - (-12) + (-7) - 4$

52. $-6 - (-8) + (-12) - 7$

▶ **53.** $-3 + 4 - (-23) - 10$

54. $5 + (-18) - (-21) - 2$

Objective C *Evaluate* $x - y$ *for the given replacement values. See Examples 11 and 12.*

55. $x = -4$ and $y = 7$

56. $x = -7$ and $y = 1$

57. $x = 8$ and $y = -23$

58. $x = 9$ and $y = -2$

Evaluate $2x - y$ *for the given replacement values. See Examples 11 and 12.*

▶ **59.** $x = 4$ and $y = -4$

60. $x = 8$ and $y = -10$

61. $x = 1$ and $y = -18$

62. $x = 14$ and $y = -12$

Objective **D** *Solve. See Example 13.*

The bar graph shows the monthly average temperatures in Fairbanks, Alaska. Notice that a negative temperatures is illustrated by a bar below the horizontal line representing 0°F. Use this graph to answer Exercises 63 through 66.

63. Find the difference in temperature between the months of March and February.

64. Find the difference in temperature between the months of November and December.

65. Find the difference in temperature between the two months with the lowest temperatures.

66. Find the difference in temperature between the month with the warmest temperature and the month with the coldest temperature.

Monthly Average Temperatures in Fairbanks, AK

Source: National Climatic Data Center

Solve.

▶ **67.** The coldest temperature ever recorded on Earth was −129°F in Antarctica. The warmest temperature ever recorded was 134°F in Death Valley, California. How many degrees warmer is 134°F than −129°F? (*Source: The World Almanac,* 2013)

68. The coldest temperature ever recorded in the United States was −80°F in Alaska. The warmest temperature ever recorded was 134°F in California. How many degrees warmer is 134°F than −80°F? (*Source: The World Almanac,* 2013)

69. Adam Scott from Australia finished first in the 2013 PGA Master's Tournament at Augusta National Golf Club with a score of −9, or nine strokes under par. Tied for 46th place was Thomas Bjorn from Denmark, with a score of +5, or 5 strokes over par. What was the difference in scores between Scott and Bjorn?

70. A woman received a statement of her charge account at Old Navy. She spent $93 on purchases last month. She returned an $18 blouse because she didn't like the color. She also returned a $26 pajama set because it was damaged. What does she actually owe on her account?

71. The temperature on a February morning was −4° Celsius at 6 a.m. If the temperature drops 3 degrees by 7 a.m., rises 4 degrees between 7 a.m. and 8 a.m., and then drops 7 degrees between 8 a.m. and 9 a.m., find the temperature at 9 a.m.

72. Mauna Kea in Hawaii has an elevation of 13,796 feet above sea level. The Mid-America Trench in the Pacific Ocean has an elevation of 21,857 feet below sea level. Find the difference in elevation between those two points. (*Source:* National Geographic Society and Defense Mapping Agency)

Some places on Earth lie below sea level, which is the average level of the surface of the oceans. Use this diagram to answer Exercises 73 through 76. (Source: Fantastic Book of Comparisons, Russell Ash)

73. Find the difference in elevation between Death Valley and Qattâra Depression.

74. Find the difference in elevation between the Danakil and Turfan Depressions.

75. Find the difference in elevation between the two lowest elevations shown.

76. Find the difference in elevation between the highest elevation shown and the lowest elevation shown.

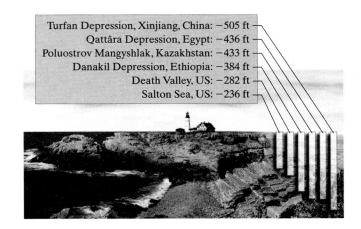

Turfan Depression, Xinjiang, China: −505 ft
Qattâra Depression, Egypt: −436 ft
Poluostrov Mangyshlak, Kazakhstan: −433 ft
Danakil Depression, Ethiopia: −384 ft
Death Valley, US: −282 ft
Salton Sea, US: −236 ft

The bar graph from Section 2.1 shows heights of selected lakes. For Exercises 77 through 80, find the difference in elevation for the lakes listed. (Source: U.S. Geological Survey)

77. Lake Superior and Lake Eyre

78. Great Bear Lake and Caspian Sea

79. Lake Maracaibo and Lake Vanern

80. Lake Eyre and Caspian Sea

Elevations of Selected Lakes

Feet Above or Below Sea Level

600 — Superior, North America
245 — Ontario, North America
−92 — Caspian Sea, Asia-Europe
0 — Maracaibo, South America
512 — Great Bear, North America
−52 — Eyre, Australia
144 — Vanern, Europe

Solve.

81. The average daytime surface temperature of the hottest planet, Venus, is 867°F, while the average daytime surface temperature of the coldest planet, Neptune, is −330°F. Find the difference in temperatures.

82. The average daytime surface temperature of Mercury is 845°F, while the average daytime surface temperature of Jupiter is −162°F. Find the difference in temperatures.

83. The difference between a country's exports and imports is called the country's *trade balance*. In June 2013, the United States had $191 billion in exports and $225 billion in imports. What was the U.S. trade balance in June 2013? (*Source:* U.S. Department of Commerce)

84. In 2012, the United States exported 1165 million barrels of petroleum products and imported 3878 million barrels of petroleum products. What was the U.S. trade balance for petroleum products in 2012? (*Source:* U.S. Energy Information Administration)

Mixed Practice–Translating (*Sections 2.2, 2.3*) *Translate each phrase to an algebraic expression. Use "x" to represent "a number."*

85. The sum of −5 and a number.

86. The difference of −3 and a number.

87. Subtract a number from −20.

88. Add a number and −36.

Review

Multiply or divide as indicated. See Sections 1.5 and 1.6.

89. $\dfrac{100}{20}$

90. $\dfrac{96}{3}$

91. $\begin{array}{r} 23 \\ \times\,46 \\ \hline \end{array}$

92. $\begin{array}{r} 51 \\ \times\,89 \\ \hline \end{array}$

Concept Extensions

93. Name two numbers whose difference is −3.

94. Name two numbers whose difference is −10.

*Each calculation below is **incorrect**. Find the error and correct it. See the Concept Check in this section.*

95. $9 - (-7) \overset{?}{=} 2$

96. $-4 - 8 \overset{?}{=} 4$

97. $10 - 30 \overset{?}{=} 20$

98. $-3 - (-10) \overset{?}{=} -13$

Simplify. (Hint: Find the absolute values first.)

▶ **99.** $|-3| - |-7|$

100. $|-12| - |-5|$

101. $|-5| - |5|$

102. $|-8| - |8|$

103. $|-15| - |-29|$

104. $|-23| - |-42|$

For Exercises 105 and 106, determine whether each statement is true or false.

105. $|-8 - 3| = 8 - 3$

106. $|-2 - (-6)| = |-2| - |-6|$

107. In your own words, explain how to subtract one signed number from another.

108. A student explains to you that the first step to simplify $8 + 12 \cdot 5 - 100$ is to add 8 and 12. Is the student correct? Explain why or why not.

2.4 Multiplying and Dividing Integers

Multiplying and dividing integers is similar to multiplying and dividing whole numbers. One difference is that we need to determine whether the result is a positive number or a negative number.

Objective A Multiplying Integers

Consider the following pattern of products.

First factor decreases by 1 each time.
$$3 \cdot 2 = 6$$
$$2 \cdot 2 = 4$$ Product decreases by 2 each time.
$$1 \cdot 2 = 2$$
$$0 \cdot 2 = 0$$

This pattern can be continued, as follows.

$$-1 \cdot 2 = -2$$
$$-2 \cdot 2 = -4$$
$$-3 \cdot 2 = -6$$

This suggests that the product of a negative number and a positive number is a negative number.

What is the sign of the product of two negative numbers? To find out, we form another pattern of products. Again, we decrease the first factor by 1 each time, but this time the second factor is negative.

$$2 \cdot (-3) = -6$$
$$1 \cdot (-3) = -3$$ Product increases by 3 each time.
$$0 \cdot (-3) = 0$$

This pattern continues as:

$$-1 \cdot (-3) = 3$$
$$-2 \cdot (-3) = 6$$
$$-3 \cdot (-3) = 9$$

This suggests that the product of two negative numbers is a positive number. Thus we can determine the sign of a product when we know the signs of the factors.

Objectives

A Multiply Integers.

B Divide Integers.

C Evaluate an Algebraic Expression by Multiplying or Dividing.

D Solve Problems by Multiplying or Dividing Integers.

Multiplying Numbers

The product of two numbers having the same sign is a positive number.

The product of two numbers having different signs is a negative number.

Product of Like Signs

$(+)(+) = +$

$(-)(-) = +$

Product of Different Signs

$(-)(+) = -$

$(+)(-) = -$

Examples Multiply.

1. $-7 \cdot 3 = -21$

2. $-3(-5) = 15$

3. $0 \cdot (-4) = 0$

4. $10(-8) = -80$

Work Practice 1–4

Practice 1–4

Multiply.

1. $-3 \cdot 8$ **2.** $-5(-2)$

3. $0 \cdot (-20)$ **4.** $10(-5)$

Answers

1. -24 **2.** 10 **3.** 0 **4.** -50

Recall that by the associative and commutative properties for multiplication, we may multiply numbers in any order that we wish. In Example 5, we multiply from left to right.

Practice 5–7

Multiply.

5. $8(-6)(-2)$
6. $(-9)(-2)(-1)$
7. $(-3)(-4)(-5)(-1)$

Examples Multiply.

5. $7(-6)(-2) = -42(-2)$
$\qquad\qquad\qquad = 84$

6. $(-2)(-3)(-4) = 6(-4)$
$\qquad\qquad\qquad\ = -24$

7. $(-1)(-2)(-3)(-4) = -1(-24)$ We have -24 from Example 6.
$\qquad\qquad\qquad\qquad\quad = 24$

■ Work Practice 5–7

✔**Concept Check** What is the sign of the product of five negative numbers? Explain.

Recall from our study of exponents that $2^3 = 2 \cdot 2 \cdot 2 = 8$. We can now work with bases that are negative numbers. For example,

$$(-2)^3 = (-2)(-2)(-2) = -8$$

Practice 8

Evaluate $(-2)^4$.

Example 8 Evaluate: $(-5)^2$

Solution: Remember that $(-5)^2$ means 2 factors of -5.

$$(-5)^2 = (-5)(-5) = 25$$

■ Work Practice 8

Helpful Hint

Have you noticed a pattern when multiplying signed numbers?
    If we let $(-)$ represent a negative number and $(+)$ represent a positive number, then

The product of an even number of negative numbers is a positive result.

$(-)(-) = (+)$
$(-)(-)(-) = (-)$
$(-)(-)(-)(-) = (+)$
$(-)(-)(-)(-)(-) = (-)$

The product of an odd number of negative numbers is a **negative** result.

Notice in Example 8 the parentheses around -5 in $(-5)^2$. With these parentheses, -5 is the base that is squared. Without parentheses, such as -5^2, only the 5 is squared. In other words, $-5^2 = -(5 \cdot 5) = -25$.

Practice 9

Evaluate: -8^2

Answers
5. 96   **6.** -18 **7.** 60   **8.** 16   **9.** -64

✔**Concept Check Answer**
negative; answers may vary

Example 9 Evaluate: -7^2

Solution: Remember that without parentheses, only the 7 is squared.

$$-7^2 = -(7 \cdot 7) = -49$$

■ Work Practice 9

Helpful Hint

Make sure you understand the difference between Examples 8 and 9.

↱ parentheses, so −5 is squared

$$(-5)^2 = (-5)(-5) = 25$$

↱ no parentheses, so only the 7 is squared

$$-7^2 = -(7 \cdot 7) = -49$$

Objective B Dividing Integers

Division of integers is related to multiplication of integers. The sign rules for division can be discovered by writing a related multiplication problem. For example,

$$\frac{6}{2} = 3 \quad \text{because } 3 \cdot 2 = 6$$

$$\frac{-6}{2} = -3 \quad \text{because } -3 \cdot 2 = -6$$

$$\frac{6}{-2} = -3 \quad \text{because } -3 \cdot (-2) = 6$$

$$\frac{-6}{-2} = 3 \quad \text{because } 3 \cdot (-2) = -6$$

Helpful Hint Just as for whole numbers, division can be checked by multiplication.

Dividing Numbers

The quotient of two numbers having the same sign is a positive number.

The quotient of two numbers having different signs is a negative number.

Quotient of Like Signs

$$\frac{(+)}{(+)} = + \qquad \frac{(-)}{(-)} = +$$

Quotient of Different Signs

$$\frac{(+)}{(-)} = - \qquad \frac{(-)}{(+)} = -$$

Examples Divide.

10. $\dfrac{-12}{6} = -2$

11. $-20 \div (-4) = 5$

12. $\dfrac{48}{-3} = -16$

■ Work Practice 10–12

Practice 10–12

Divide.

10. $\dfrac{42}{-7}$

11. $-16 \div (-2)$

12. $\dfrac{-80}{10}$

✓**Concept Check** What is wrong with the following calculation?

$$\frac{-36}{-9} = -4$$

Answers

10. −6 **11.** 8 **12.** −8

✓**Concept Check Answer**

$$\frac{-36}{-9} = 4$$

Practice 13–14

Divide, if possible.

13. $\dfrac{-6}{0}$ **14.** $\dfrac{0}{-7}$

Examples Divide, if possible.

13. $\dfrac{0}{-5} = 0$ because $0 \cdot -5 = 0$

14. $\dfrac{-7}{0}$ is undefined because there is no number that gives a product of -7 when multiplied by 0.

▪ Work Practice 13–14

Objective C Evaluating Expressions

Next, we practice evaluating expressions given integer replacement values.

Practice 15

Evaluate xy for $x = 5$ and $y = -8$.

Example 15 Evaluate xy for $x = -2$ and $y = 7$.

Solution: Recall that xy means $x \cdot y$.

Replace x with -2 and y with 7.

$xy = -2 \cdot 7$
$ = -14$

▪ Work Practice 15

Practice 16

Evaluate $\dfrac{x}{y}$ for $x = -12$ and $y = -3$.

Example 16 Evaluate $\dfrac{x}{y}$ for $x = -24$ and $y = 6$.

Solution: $\dfrac{x}{y} = \dfrac{-24}{6}$ Replace x with -24 and y with 6.

$\phantom{\dfrac{x}{y}} = -4$

▪ Work Practice 16

Objective D Solving Problems by Multiplying and Dividing Integers

Many real-life problems involve multiplication and division of signed numbers.

Practice 17

A card player had a score of -13 for each of four games. Find the total score.

Example 17 Calculating a Total Golf Score

A professional golfer finished seven strokes under par (-7) for each of three days of a tournament. What was his total score for the tournament?

Solution:

1. UNDERSTAND. Read and reread the problem. Although the key word is "total," since this is repeated addition of the same number, we multiply.
2. TRANSLATE.

In words:	golfer's total score	=	number of days	·	score each day
	↓	↓	↓	↓	↓
Translate:	golfer's total	=	3	·	(-7)

3. SOLVE: $3 \cdot (-7) = -21$
4. INTERPRET. Check and state your conclusion: The golfer's total score was -21, or 21 strokes under par.

▪ Work Practice 17

Answers

13. undefined **14.** 0 **15.** -40
16. 4 **17.** -52

Vocabulary, Readiness & Video Check

Use the choices below to fill in each blank. Each choice may be used more than once.

negative   0
positive   undefined

1. The product of a negative number and a positive number is a(n) _____ number.
2. The product of two negative numbers is a(n) _____ number.
3. The quotient of two negative numbers is a(n) _____ number.
4. The quotient of a negative number and a positive number is a(n) _____ number.
5. The product of a negative number and zero is _____.
6. The quotient of 0 and a negative number is _____.
7. The quotient of a negative number and 0 is _____.

Martin-Gay Interactive Videos

See Video 2.4

Watch the section lecture video and answer the following questions.

Objective A 8. Explain the role of parentheses when comparing ▯ Examples 3 and 4. ▶

Objective B 9. Complete this statement based on the lecture before ▯ Example 6: We can find out about sign rules for division because we know sign rules for _____. ▶

Objective C 10. In ▯ Example 10, what are you asked to remember about the algebraic expression *ab*? ▶

Objective D 11. In ▯ Example 12, how do we know the example will involve a negative number? ▶

2.4 Exercise Set MyMathLab®

Objective A *Multiply. See Examples 1 through 4.*

1. $-6(-2)$ 2. $5(-3)$ ▶ 3. $-4(9)$ 4. $-7(-2)$

5. $9(-9)$ 6. $-9(7)$ 7. $0(-11)$ 8. $-6(0)$

Multiply. See Examples 5 through 7.

9. $6(-2)(-4)$ 10. $-2(3)(-7)$ 11. $-1(-3)(-4)$ 12. $-8(-3)(-3)$

13. $-4(4)(-5)$ 14. $2(-5)(-4)$ 15. $10(-5)(0)(-7)$ 16. $3(0)(-4)(-8)$

17. $-5(3)(-1)(-1)$ 18. $-2(-1)(3)(-2)$

Evaluate. See Examples 8 and 9.

▶ **19.** -3^2 **20.** -2^4 ▶ **21.** $(-3)^3$ **22.** $(-1)^4$

23. -6^2 **24.** -4^3 **25.** $(-4)^3$ **26.** $(-3)^2$

Objective **B** *Find each quotient. See Examples 10 through 14.*

27. $-24 \div 3$ **28.** $90 \div (-9)$ ▶ **29.** $\dfrac{-30}{6}$ **30.** $\dfrac{56}{-8}$

31. $\dfrac{-77}{-11}$ **32.** $\dfrac{-32}{4}$ **33.** $\dfrac{0}{-21}$ **34.** $\dfrac{-13}{0}$

▶ **35.** $\dfrac{-10}{0}$ ▶ **36.** $\dfrac{0}{-15}$ **37.** $\dfrac{56}{-4}$ **38.** $\dfrac{-24}{-12}$

Objectives **A** **B** **Mixed Practice** *Multiply or divide as indicated. See Examples 1 through 14.*

39. $-14(0)$ **40.** $0(-100)$ **41.** $-5(3)$ **42.** $-6 \cdot 2$

43. $-9 \cdot 7$ **44.** $-12(13)$ ▶ **45.** $-7(-6)$ **46.** $-9(-5)$

▶ **47.** $-3(-4)(-2)$ **48.** $-7(-5)(-3)$ **49.** $(-7)^2$ **50.** $(-5)^2$

51. $-\dfrac{25}{5}$ **52.** $-\dfrac{30}{5}$ **53.** $-\dfrac{72}{8}$ **54.** $-\dfrac{49}{7}$

55. $-18 \div 3$ **56.** $-15 \div 3$ **57.** $4(-10)(-3)$ **58.** $6(-5)(-2)$

59. $-30(6)(-2)(-3)$ **60.** $-20 \cdot 5 \cdot (-5) \cdot (-3)$ **61.** $\dfrac{-25}{0}$ **62.** $\dfrac{0}{-14}$

63. $\dfrac{120}{-20}$ **64.** $\dfrac{63}{-9}$ **65.** $280 \div (-40)$ **66.** $480 \div (-8)$

▶ **67.** $\dfrac{-12}{-4}$ **68.** $\dfrac{-36}{-3}$ **69.** -1^4 **70.** -2^3

71. $(-2)^5$ **72.** $(-11)^2$ **73.** $-2(3)(5)(-6)$ **74.** $-1(2)(7)(-3)$

75. $(-1)^{32}$ **76.** $(-1)^{33}$ **77.** $-2(-3)(-5)$ **78.** $-2(-2)(-3)(-2)$

79. $-48 \cdot 23$ **80.** $-56 \cdot 43$ **81.** $35 \cdot (-82)$ **82.** $70 \cdot (-23)$

Objective C *Evaluate ab for the given replacement values. See Example 15.*

83. $a = -8$ and $b = 7$

84. $a = 5$ and $b = -1$

85. $a = 9$ and $b = -2$

86. $a = -8$ and $b = 8$

87. $a = -7$ and $b = -5$

88. $a = -9$ and $b = -6$

Evaluate $\dfrac{x}{y}$ for the given replacement values. See Example 16.

89. $x = 5$ and $y = -5$

90. $x = 9$ and $y = -3$

91. $x = -15$ and $y = 0$

92. $x = 0$ and $y = -5$

93. $x = -36$ and $y = -6$

94. $x = -10$ and $y = -10$

Evaluate xy and also $\dfrac{x}{y}$ for the given replacement values. See Examples 15 and 16.

95. $x = -8$ and $y = -2$

96. $x = 20$ and $y = -5$

97. $x = 0$ and $y = -8$

98. $x = -3$ and $y = 0$

Objective D Translating *Translate each phrase; then simplify. See Example 17.*

99. Find the quotient of -54 and 9.

100. Find the quotient of -63 and -3.

101. Find the product of -42 and -6.

102. Find the product of -49 and 5.

Translating *Translate each phrase to an expression. Use x to represent "a number." See Example 17.*

103. The product of -71 and a number

104. The quotient of -8 and a number

105. Subtract a number from -16.

106. The sum of a number and -12

107. -29 increased by a number

108. The difference of a number and -10

109. Divide a number by -33.

110. Multiply a number by -17.

Solve. See Example 17.

111. A football team lost four yards on each of three consecutive plays. Represent the total loss as a product of signed numbers and find the total loss.

112. An investor lost $400 on each of seven consecutive days in the stock market. Represent his total loss as a product of signed numbers and find his total loss.

113. A deep-sea diver must move up or down in the water in short steps in order to keep from getting a physical condition called the "bends." Suppose a diver moves down from the surface in five steps of 20 feet each. Represent his total movement as a product of signed numbers and find the product.

114. A weather forecaster predicts that the temperature will drop five degrees each hour for the next six hours. Represent this drop as a product of signed numbers and find the total drop in temperature.

The graph shows melting points in degrees Celsius of selected elements. Use this graph to answer Exercises 115 through 118.

115. The melting point of nitrogen is 3 times the melting point of radon. Find the melting point of nitrogen.

116. The melting point of rubidium is −1 times the melting point of mercury. Find the melting point of rubidium.

117. The melting point of argon is −3 times the melting point of potassium. Find the melting point of argon.

118. The melting point of strontium is −11 times the melting point of radon. Find the melting point of strontium.

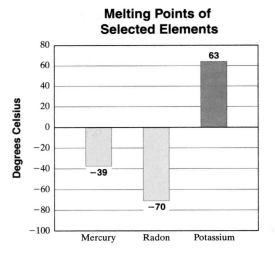

Melting Points of Selected Elements

Solve. See Example 17.

119. For the first quarter of 2013, Wal-Mart, Inc. posted a loss of $33 million in membership and other income. If this trend was consistent for each month of the quarter, how much would you expect this loss to have been for each month? (*Source:* Wal-Mart Stores, Inc.)

120. For the first quarter of 2013, Chrysler Group LLC, maker of Jeep vehicles, posted a loss of about 30,000 Jeep Liberty shipments because they had stopped producing the vehicle in 2012. If this trend was consistent for each month of the quarter, how much would you expect this loss to have been for each month? (*Source:* Chrysler Group, LLC)

121. In 2008, there were 33,319 analog (nondigital) U.S. movie screens. In 2012, this number of screens dropped to 6387. (*Source:* Motion Picture Association: Worldwide Market Research)

   a. Find the change in the number of U.S. analog movie screens from 2008 to 2012.

   b. Find the average change per year in the number of analog movie screens over this period.

122. In 1987, the California Condor was all but extinct in the wild, with about 30 condors in the world. The condors in the wild were captured by the U.S. Fish and Wildlife Service in an aggressive move to rebuild the population by breeding them in captivity and releasing the chicks in to the wild. The condor population increased to approximately 405 birds in 2012. (*Source:* Arizona Game and Fish Department)

   a. Find the change in the number of California Condors from 1987 to 2012.

   b. Find the average change per year in the California Condor population over the period in part **a.**

California Condor: Average life span, 60 years

Review

Perform each indicated operation. See Section 1.7.

123. $90 + 12^2 - 5^3$ **124.** $3 \cdot (7 - 4) + 2 \cdot 5^2$ **125.** $12 \div 4 - 2 + 7$ **126.** $12 \div (4 - 2) + 7$

Concept Extensions

Mixed Practice (Sections 2.2, 2.3, 2.4) *Perform the indicated operations.*

127. $-57 \div 3$ **128.** $-9(-11)$ **129.** $-8 - 20$

130. $-4 + (-3) + 21$ **131.** $-4 - 15 - (-11)$ **132.** $-16 - (-2)$

Solve. For Exercises 133 and 134, see the first Concept Check in this section.

133. What is the sign of the product of seven negative numbers?

134. What is the sign of the product of ten negative numbers?

Without actually finding the product, write the list of numbers in Exercises 135 and 136 in order from least to greatest. For help, see a helpful hint box in this section.

135. $(-2)^{12}, (-2)^{17}, (-5)^{12}, (-5)^{17}$

136. $(-1)^{50}, (-1)^{55}, 0^{15}, (-7)^{20}, (-7)^{23}$

137. In your own words, explain how to divide two integers.

138. In your own words, explain how to multiply two integers.

Answers

1. _____

2. _____

3. _____

4. _____

5. _____

6. _____

7. _____

8. _____

9. _____

10. _____

11. _____

12. _____

13. _____

14. _____

15. _____

16. _____

17. _____

18. _____

19. _____

20. _____

21. _____

22. _____

Integers

1. The record low temperature in New Mexico is 50 degrees Fahrenheit below zero. The highest temperature in that state is 122 degrees above zero. Represent each quantity by an integer.

2. Graph the signed numbers on the given number line. $-4, 0, -1, 3$

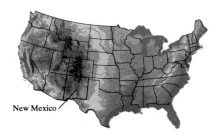

New Mexico

Insert $<$ *or* $>$ *between each pair of numbers to make a true statement.*

3. $0 \quad -10$

4. $-4 \quad 4$

5. $-15 \quad -5$

6. $-2 \quad -7$

Simplify.

7. $|-3|$

8. $|-9|$

9. $-|-4|$

10. $-(-5)$

Find the opposite of each number.

11. 11

12. -3

13. 64

14. 0

Perform the indicated operation.

15. $-3 + 15$

16. $-9 + (-11)$

17. $-8(-6)(-1)$

18. $-18 \div 2$

19. $65 + (-55)$

20. $1000 - 1002$

21. $53 - (-53)$

22. $-2 - 1$

23. $\dfrac{0}{-47}$

24. $\dfrac{-36}{-9}$

25. $-17 - (-59)$

26. $-8 + (-6) + 20$

27. $\dfrac{-95}{-5}$

28. $-9(100)$

29. $-12 - 6 - (-6)$

30. $-4 + (-8) - 16 - (-9)$

31. $\dfrac{-105}{0}$

32. $7(-16)(0)(-3)$

Translating *Translate each phrase; then simplify.*

33. Subtract -8 from -12.

34. Find the sum of -17 and -27.

35. Find the product of -5 and -25.

36. Find the quotient of -100 and -5.

Translating *Translate each phrase to an expression. Use x to represent "a number."*

37. Divide a number by -17

38. The sum of -3 and a number

39. A number decreased by -18

40. The product of -7 and a number

Evaluate the expressions below for $x = -3$ and $y = 12$.

41. $x + y$

42. $x - y$

43. $2y - x$

44. $3y + x$

45. $5x$

46. $\dfrac{y}{x}$

23. _____

24. _____

25. _____

26. _____

27. _____

28. _____

29. _____

30. _____

31. _____

32. _____

33. _____

34. _____

35. _____

36. _____

37. _____

38. _____

39. _____

40. _____

41. _____

42. _____

43. _____

44. _____

45. _____

46. _____

2.5 Order of Operations

Objectives

A Simplify Expressions by Using the Order of Operations.

B Evaluate an Algebraic Expression.

C Find the Average of a List of Numbers.

Objective A Simplifying Expressions

We first discussed the order of operations in Chapter 1. In this section, you are given an opportunity to practice using the order of operations when expressions contain signed numbers. The rules for the order of operations from Section 1.7 are repeated here.

> ### Order of Operations
>
> 1. Perform all operations within parentheses ( ), brackets [ ], or other grouping symbols such as fraction bars, starting with the innermost set.
> 2. Evaluate any expressions with exponents.
> 3. Multiply or divide in order from left to right.
> 4. Add or subtract in order from left to right.

Before simplifying other expressions, make sure you are confident simplifying Examples 1 through 3.

Practice 1-3

Find the value of each expression.

1. $(-2)^4$

2. -2^4

3. $3 \cdot 6^2$

Examples Find the value of each expression.

1. $(-3)^2 = (-3)(-3) = 9$ The base of the exponent is -3.

2. $-3^2 = -(3)(3) = -9$ The base of the exponent is 3.

3. $2 \cdot 5^2 = 2 \cdot (5 \cdot 5) = 2 \cdot 25 = 50$ The base of the exponent is 5.

■ Work Practice 1–3

Helpful Hint

When simplifying expressions with exponents, remember that parentheses make an important difference.

$(-3)^2$ and -3^2 **do not** mean the same thing.

$(-3)^2$ means $(-3)(-3) = 9$.

-3^2 means the opposite of $3 \cdot 3$, or -9.

Only with parentheses around it is the -3 squared.

Practice 4

Simplify: $\dfrac{-25}{5(-1)}$

Example 4 Simplify: $\dfrac{-6(2)}{-3}$

Solution: First we multiply -6 and 2. Then we divide.

$$\frac{-6(2)}{-3} = \frac{-12}{-3}$$
$$= 4$$

■ Work Practice 4

Answers

1. 16   **2.** -16 **3.** 108   **4.** 5

134

Example 5 Simplify: $\dfrac{12 - 16}{-1 + 3}$

Solution: We simplify above and below the fraction bar separately. Then we divide.

$$\dfrac{12 - 16}{-1 + 3} = \dfrac{-4}{2}$$
$$= -2$$

■ Work Practice 5

Practice 5

Simplify: $\dfrac{-18 + 6}{-3 - 1}$

Example 6 Simplify: $60 + 30 + (-2)^3$

Solution: $60 + 30 + (-2)^3 = 60 + 30 + (-8)$ Write $(-2)^3$ as -8.
$$= 90 + (-8)$$ Add from left to right.
$$= 82$$

■ Work Practice 6

Practice 6

Simplify: $30 + 50 + (-4)^3$

Example 7 Simplify: $-4^2 + (-3)^2 - 1^3$

Solution:

$-4^2 + (-3)^2 - 1^3 = -16 + 9 - 1$ Simplify expressions with exponents.
$$= -7 - 1$$ Add or subtract from left to right.
$$= -8$$

■ Work Practice 7

Practice 7

Simplify: $-2^3 + (-4)^2 + 1^5$

Example 8 Simplify: $3(4 - 7) + (-2) - 5$

Solution:

$3(4 - 7) + (-2) - 5 = 3(-3) + (-2) - 5$ Simplify inside parentheses.
$$= -9 + (-2) - 5$$ Multiply.
$$= -11 - 5$$ Add or subtract from left to right.
$$= -16$$

■ Work Practice 8

Practice 8

Simplify:
$2(2 - 9) + (-12) - 3$

Example 9 Simplify: $(-3) \cdot |-5| - (-2) + 4^2$

Solution:

$(-3) \cdot |-5| - (-2) + 4^2 = (-3) \cdot 5 - (-2) + 4^2$ Write $|-5|$ as 5.
$$= (-3) \cdot 5 - (-2) + 16$$ Write 4^2 as 16.
$$= -15 - (-2) + 16$$ Multiply.
$$= -13 + 16$$ Add or subtract from left to right.
$$= 3$$

■ Work Practice 9

Practice 9

Simplify:
$(-5) \cdot |-8| + (-3) + 2^3$

Answers
5. 3   **6.** 16   **7.** 9   **8.** −29   **9.** −35

Practice 10

Simplify:
$-4[-6 + 5(-3 + 5)] - 7$

Example 10 Simplify: $-2[-3 + 2(-1 + 6)] - 5$

Solution: Here we begin with the innermost set of parentheses.

$$-2[-3 + 2(-1 + 6)] - 5 = -2[-3 + 2(5)] - 5 \quad \text{Write } -1 + 6 \text{ as } 5.$$
$$= -2[-3 + 10] - 5 \quad \text{Multiply.}$$
$$= -2(7) - 5 \quad \text{Add.}$$
$$= -14 - 5 \quad \text{Multiply.}$$
$$= -19 \quad \text{Subtract.}$$

■ Work Practice 10

✓**Concept Check** True or false? Explain your answer. The result of

$$-4(3 - 7) - 8(9 - 6)$$

is positive because there are four negative signs.

Objective B Evaluating Expressions

Now we practice evaluating expressions.

Practice 11

Evaluate x^2 and $-x^2$ for
$x = -15$.

Example 11 Evaluate x^2 and $-x^2$ for $x = -11$.

Solution: $x^2 = (-11)^2 = (-11)(-11) = 121$

$-x^2 = -(-11)^2 = -(-11)(-11) = -121$

■ Work Practice 11

Practice 12

Evaluate $5y^2$ for $y = 4$ and
$y = -4$.

Example 12 Evaluate $6z^2$ for $z = 2$ and $z = -2$.

Solution: $6z^2 = 6(2)^2 = 6(4) = 24$

$6z^2 = 6(-2)^2 = 6(4) = 24$

■ Work Practice 12

Practice 13

Evaluate $x^2 + y$ for $x = -6$
and $y = -3$.

Example 13 Evaluate $x + 2y - z$ for $x = 3$, $y = -5$, and $z = -4$.

Solution: Replace x with 3, y with -5, z with -4, and simplify.

Helpful Hint

Remember to rewrite the subtraction sign.

$$x + 2y - z = 3 + 2(-5) - (-4) \quad \text{Let } x = 3, y = -5, \text{ and } z = -4.$$
$$= 3 + (-10) + 4 \quad \text{Replace } 2(-5) \text{ with its product, } -10.$$
$$= -3 \quad \text{Add.}$$

■ Work Practice 13

Answers

10. -23 **11.** $225; -225$ **12.** $80; 80$
13. 33

✓**Concept Check Answer**

false; $-4(3 - 7) - 8(9 - 6) = -8$

Example 14 Evaluate $7 - x^2$ for $x = -4$.

Solution: Replace x with -4 and simplify carefully!

$$7 - x^2 = 7 - (-4)^2$$
$$= 7 - 16 \qquad (-4)^2 = (-4)(-4) = 16$$
$$= -9 \qquad \text{Subtract.}$$

■ Work Practice 14

Practice 14
Evaluate $4 - x^2$ for $x = -8$.

Objective C Finding Averages

Recall from Chapter 1 that the average of a list of numbers is

$$\text{average} = \frac{\text{sum of numbers}}{\text{number of numbers}}$$

Example 15 The graph shows the monthly normal temperatures for Barrow, Alaska. Use this graph to find the average of the temperatures for the months January through April.

Practice 15
Find the average of the temperatures for the months October through April.

Monthly Normal Temperatures for Barrow, Alaska

Solution: By reading the graph, we have

$$\text{average} = \frac{-13 + (-16) + (-13) + 2}{4} \qquad \text{There are 4 months from January through April.}$$
$$= \frac{-40}{4}$$
$$= -10$$

The average of the temperatures is $-10°F$.

■ Work Practice 15

Answers
14. -60 **15.** $-5°F$

⌨ **Calculator Explorations Simplifying an Expression Containing a Fraction Bar**

Recall that even though most calculators follow the order of operations, parentheses must sometimes be inserted. For example, to simplify $\dfrac{-8 + 6}{-2}$ on a calculator, enter parentheses around the expression above the fraction bar so that it is simplified separately.

To simplify $\dfrac{-8 + 6}{-2}$, press the keys

[(] [8] [+/−] [+] [6] [)] [÷] [2] [+/−] [=] or

[(] [(−)] [8] [+] [6] [)] [÷] [(−)] [2] [ENTER]

The display will read [1].

Thus, $\dfrac{-8 + 6}{-2} = 1$.

Use a calculator to simplify.

1. $\dfrac{-120 - 360}{-10}$

2. $\dfrac{4750}{-2 + (-17)}$

3. $\dfrac{-316 + (-458)}{28 + (-25)}$

4. $\dfrac{-234 + 86}{-18 + 16}$

Vocabulary, Readiness & Video Check

Use the choices below to fill in each blank. Not all choices will be used.

average	subtraction	division	$-7 - 3(1)$
addition	multiplication	$-7 - 3(-1)$	

1. To simplify $-2 \div 2 \cdot (3)$, which operation should be performed first? _____
2. To simplify $-9 - 3 \cdot 4$, which operation should be performed first? _____
3. The _____ of a list of numbers is $\dfrac{\text{sum of numbers}}{\text{number of numbers}}$.
4. To simplify $5[-9 + (-3)] \div 4$, which operation should be performed first? _____
5. To simplify $-2 + 3(10 - 12) \cdot (-8)$, which operation should be performed first? _____
6. To evaluate $x - 3y$ for $x = -7$ and $y = -1$, replace x with -7 and y with -1 and evaluate _____.

Martin-Gay Interactive Videos Watch the section lecture video and answer the following questions.

See Video 2.5

Objective A 7. In Example 1, what two things about the fraction bar are we reminded of?

Objective B 8. In Example 5, why is it important to place the replacement value for x within parentheses?

Objective C 9. From the lecture before Example 6, explain why finding the average is a good example of an application for this section.

2.5 Exercise Set MyMathLab®

Objective A *Simplify. See Examples 1 through 10.*

1. $(-5)^3$
2. -2^4
3. -4^3
4. $(-2)^4$

5. $8 \cdot 2^2$
6. $5 \cdot 2^3$
7. $8 - 12 - 4$
8. $10 - 23 - 12$

9. $7 + 3(-6)$
10. $-8 + 4(3)$
11. $5(-9) + 2$
12. $7(-6) + 3$

13. $-10 + 4 \div 2$
14. $-12 + 6 \div 3$
15. $6 + 7 \cdot 3 - 10$
16. $5 + 9 \cdot 4 - 20$

17. $\dfrac{16 - 13}{-3}$
18. $\dfrac{20 - 15}{-1}$
19. $\dfrac{24}{10 + (-4)}$
20. $\dfrac{88}{-8 - 3}$

21. $5(-3) - (-12)$
22. $7(-4) - (-6)$
23. $[8 + (-4)]^2$
24. $[9 + (-2)]^3$

25. $8 \cdot 6 - 3 \cdot 5 + (-20)$ **26.** $7 \cdot 6 - 6 \cdot 5 + (-10)$ ▶ **27.** $4 - (-3)^4$ **28.** $7 - (-5)^2$

29. $|7 + 3| \cdot 2^3$ **30.** $|-3 + 7| \cdot 7^2$ **31.** $7 \cdot 6^2 + 4$ **32.** $10 \cdot 5^3 + 7$

33. $7^2 - (4 - 2^3)$ **34.** $8^2 - (5 - 2)^4$ **35.** $|3 - 15| \div 3$ **36.** $|12 - 19| \div 7$

37. $-(-2)^6$ **38.** $-(-2)^3$ **39.** $(5 - 9)^2 \div (4 - 2)^2$ **40.** $(2 - 7)^2 \div (4 - 3)^4$

▶ **41.** $|8 - 24| \cdot (-2) \div (-2)$ **42.** $|3 - 15| \cdot (-4) \div (-16)$ **43.** $(-12 - 20) \div 16 - 25$

44. $(-20 - 5) \div 5 - 15$ **45.** $5(5 - 2) + (-5)^2 - 6$ **46.** $3 \cdot (8 - 3) + (-4) - 10$

47. $(2 - 7) \cdot (6 - 19)$ **48.** $(4 - 12) \cdot (8 - 17)$ **49.** $(-36 \div 6) - (4 \div 4)$

50. $(-4 \div 4) - (8 \div 8)$ **51.** $(10 - 4^2)^2$ **52.** $(11 - 3^2)^3$

53. $2(8 - 10)^2 - 5(1 - 6)^2$ **54.** $-3(4 - 8)^2 + 5(14 - 16)^3$ **55.** $3(-10) \div [5(-3) - 7(-2)]$

56. $12 - [7 - (3 - 6)] + (2 - 3)^3$ **57.** $\dfrac{(-7)(-3) - (4)(3)}{3[7 \div (3 - 10)]}$ **58.** $\dfrac{10(-1) - (-2)(-3)}{2[-8 \div (-2 - 2)]}$

▶ **59.** $-3[5 + 2(-4 + 9)] + 15$ **60.** $-2[6 + 4(2 - 8)] - 25$

Objective B *Evaluate each expression for* $x = -2, y = 4,$ *and* $z = -1$. *See Examples 11 through 14.*

61. $x + y + z$ **62.** $x - y - z$ **63.** $2x - 3y - 4z$ **64.** $5x - y + 4z$

▶ **65.** $x^2 - y$ **66.** $x^2 + z$ **67.** $\dfrac{5y}{z}$ **68.** $\dfrac{4x}{y}$

Evaluate each expression for $x = -3$ *and* $z = -4$. *See Examples 11 through 14.*

69. x^2 **70.** z^2 **71.** $-z^2$ **72.** $-x^2$

73. $2z^3$ **74.** $3x^2$ **75.** $10 - x^2$ **76.** $3 - z^2$

77. $2x^3 - z$ **78.** $3z^2 - x$

Objective C *Find the average of each list of numbers. See Example 15.*

79. $-10, 8, -4, 2, 7, -5, -12$

80. $-18, -8, -1, -1, 0, 4$

81. $-17, -26, -20, -13$

82. $-40, -20, -10, -15, -5$

Scores in golf can be 0 (also called par), a positive integer (also called above par), or a negative integer (also called below par). The bar graph shows final scores of selected golfers from a 2013 tournament. Use this graph for Exercises 83 through 88. (Source: LPGA)

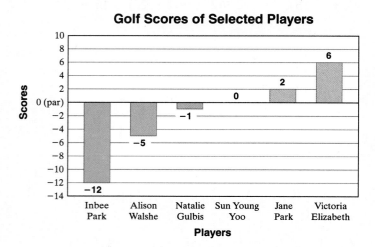

Golf Scores of Selected Players

83. Find the difference between the lowest score shown and the highest score shown.

84. Find the difference between the two lowest scores.

85. Find the average of the scores for Walshe, Gulbis, Yoo, and Jane Park. (*Hint:* Here, the average is the sum of the scores divided by the number of players.)

86. Find the average of the scores for Inbee Park, Walshe, Gulbis, and Elizabeth.

87. Can the average for the scores in Exercise **86** be greater than the highest score, 6? Explain why or why not.

88. Can the average of the scores in Exercise **86** be less than the lowest score, -12? Explain why or why not.

Review

Perform each indicated operation. See Sections 1.3, 1.5, and 1.6.

89. $45 \cdot 90$

90. $90 \div 45$

91. $90 - 45$

92. $45 + 90$

Find the perimeter of each figure. See Section 1.3.

△ **93.** Square

8 in.

△ **94.** Parallelogram

5 cm

3 cm

△ **95.** Rectangle

6 ft

9 ft

△ **96.** Triangle

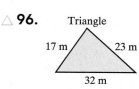

17 m   23 m

32 m

Concept Extensions

Insert parentheses where needed so that each expression evaluates to the given number.

97. $2 \cdot 7 - 5 \cdot 3$; evaluates to 12

98. $7 \cdot 3 - 4 \cdot 2$; evaluates to 34

99. $-6 \cdot 10 - 4$; evaluates to -36

100. $2 \cdot 8 \div 4 - 20$; evaluates to -36

101. Are parentheses necessary in the expression $3 + (4 \cdot 5)$? Explain your answer.

102. Are parentheses necessary in the expression $(3 + 4) \cdot 5$? Explain your answer.

103. Discuss the effect parentheses have in an exponential expression. For example, what is the difference between $(-6)^2$ and -6^2?

104. Discuss the effect parentheses have in an exponential expression. For example, what is the difference between $(2 \cdot 4)^2$ and $2 \cdot 4^2$?

Evaluate.

105. $(-12)^4$

106. $(-17)^6$

107. $x^3 - y^2$ for $x = 21$ and $y = -19$

108. $3x^2 + 2x - y$ for $x = -18$ and $y = 2868$

109. $(xy + z)^x$ for $x = 2, y = -5$, and $z = 7$

110. $5(ab + 3)^b$ for $a = -2, b = 3$

2.6 Solving Equations: The Addition and Multiplication Properties

In this section, we introduce properties of equations and we use these properties to begin solving equations. Now that we know how to perform operations on integers, this is an excellent way to practice these operations.

First, let's recall the difference between an equation and an expression. From Section 1.8, a combination of operations on variables and numbers is an expression, and an equation is of the form "expression = expression."

Equations	Expressions
$3x - 1 = -17$	$3x - 1$
area $=$ length $\cdot$ width	$5(20 - 3) + 10$
$8 + 16 = 16 + 8$	y^3
$-9a + 11b = 14b + 3$	$-x^2 + y - 2$

Objectives

A Identify Solutions of Equations.

B Use the Addition Property of Equality to Solve Equations.

C Use the Multiplication Property of Equality to Solve Equations.

> **Helpful Hint**
>
> Simply stated, an equation contains "=" while an expression does not. Also, we *simplify* expressions and *solve* equations.

Objective A Identifying Solutions of Equations

Let's practice identifying solutions of equations. Recall from Section 1.8 that a solution of an equation is a number that when substituted for a variable makes the equation a true statement.

For example,

-8 is a solution of

$\dfrac{x}{2} = -4$, because

$\dfrac{-8}{2} = -4$, or

$-4 = -4$ is true.

Also,

-8 is not a solution of

$x + 6 = 2$, because

$-8 + 6 = 2$ is false.

Let's practice determining whether a number is a solution of an equation. In this section, we will be performing operations on integers.

Practice 1

Determine whether -2 is a solution of the equation $-4x - 3 = 5$.

Example 1 Determine whether -1 is a solution of the equation $3y + 1 = 3$.

Solution:

$$3y + 1 = 3$$
$$3(-1) + 1 \overset{?}{=} 3$$
$$-3 + 1 \overset{?}{=} 3$$
$$-2 = 3 \quad \text{False}$$

Since $-2 = 3$ is false, -1 is *not* a solution of the equation.

■ Work Practice 1

Now we know how to check whether a number is a solution. But, given an equation, how do we find its **solution**? In other words, how do we find a number that makes the equation true? How do we solve an equation?

Objective B Using the Addition Property to Solve Equations

To solve an equation, we use properties of equality to write simpler equations, all equivalent to the original equation, until the final equation has the form

$x =$ **number** or **number** $= x$

Equivalent equations have the same solution, so the word "number" above represents the solution of the original equation. The first property of equality to help us write simpler, equivalent equations is the **addition property of equality.**

Answer

1. yes

Addition Property of Equality

Let a, b, and c represent numbers. Then

$a = b$	Also, $a = b$
and $a + c = b + c$	and $a - c = b - c$
are equivalent equations.	are equivalent equations.

In other words, the same number may be added to or subtracted from both sides of an equation without changing the solution of the equation. (Recall from Section 2.3 that we defined subtraction as addition of the first number and the opposite of the second number. Because of this, the addition property of equality also allows us to subtract the same number from both sides.)

A good way to visualize a true equation is to picture a balanced scale. Since it is balanced, each side of the scale weighs the same amount. Similarly, in a true equation the expressions on each side have the same value. Picturing our balanced scale, if we add the same weight to each side, the scale remains balanced.

Example 2   Solve: $x - 2 = -1$ for x.

Solution: To solve the equation for x, we need to rewrite the equation in the form $x = $ number. In other words, our goal is to get x alone on one side of the equation. To do so, we add 2 to both sides of the equation.

$$x - 2 = -1$$
$$x - 2 + 2 = -1 + 2 \qquad \text{Add 2 to both sides of the equation.}$$
$$x + 0 = 1 \qquad \text{Replace } -2 + 2 \text{ with } 0.$$
$$x = 1 \qquad \text{Simplify by replacing } x + 0 \text{ with } x.$$

Check: To check, we replace x with 1 in the *original* equation.

$$x - 2 = -1 \qquad \text{Original equation}$$
$$1 - 2 \overset{?}{=} -1 \qquad \text{Replace } x \text{ with 1.}$$
$$-1 = -1 \qquad \text{True}$$

Since $-1 = -1$ is a true statement, 1 is the solution of the equation.

■ Work Practice 2

Practice 2

Solve the equation for y: $y - 6 = -2$

Helpful Hint

Note that it is always a good idea to check the solution in the *original* equation to see that it makes the equation a true statement.

Let's visualize how we used the addition property of equality to solve an equation. Picture the equation $x - 2 = 1$ as a balanced scale. The left side of the equation has the same value as the right side.

Answer
2. 4

If the same weight is added to each side of a scale, the scale remains balanced. Likewise, if the same number is added to each side of an equation, the left side continues to have the same value as the right side.

Practice 3

Solve: $-2 = z + 8$

Example 3 Solve: $-8 = n + 1$

Solution: To get n alone on one side of the equation, we subtract 1 from both sides of the equation.

$$-8 = n + 1$$
$$-8 - 1 = n + 1 - 1 \quad \text{Subtract 1 from both sides.}$$
$$-9 = n + 0 \qquad\quad \text{Replace } 1 - 1 \text{ with } 0.$$
$$-9 = n \qquad\qquad \text{Simplify.}$$

Check:

$$-8 = n + 1$$
$$-8 \stackrel{?}{=} -9 + 1 \quad \text{Replace } n \text{ with } -9.$$
$$-8 = -8 \qquad\quad \text{True}$$

The solution is -9.

■ Work Practice 3

Helpful Hint   R e m e m b e r
that we can get the variable alone on either side of the equation. For example, the equations $-9 = n$ and $n = -9$ both have the solution of -9.

✓**Concept Check** What number should be added to or subtracted from both sides of the equation in order to solve the equation $-3 = y + 2$?

Practice 4

Solve: $x = -2 + 90 + (-100)$

Example 4 Solve: $x = -60 + 4 + 10$

Solution: Study this equation for a moment. Notice that our variable x is alone on the left side. Thus, we only need to add on the right side to find the value of x.

$$x = -60 + 4 + 10$$
$$x = -56 + 10 \qquad \text{Add } -60 \text{ and } 4.$$
$$x = -46 \qquad\quad \text{Add } -56 \text{ and } 10.$$

Check to see that -46 is the solution.

■ Work Practice 4

Answers
3. -10 **4.** -12

✓**Concept Check Answer**
Subtract 2 from both sides.

Objective C Using the Multiplication Property to Solve Equations ▶

Although the addition property of equality is a powerful tool for helping us solve equations, it cannot help us solve all types of equations. For example, it cannot help us solve an equation such as $2x = 6$. To solve this equation, we use a second property of equality called the **multiplication property of equality.**

Multiplication Property of Equality

Let a, b, and c represent numbers and let $c \neq 0$. Then

$a = b$ and $a \cdot c = b \cdot c$ are equivalent equations.	Also, $a = b$ and $\dfrac{a}{c} = \dfrac{b}{c}$ are equivalent equations.

In other words, both sides of an equation may be multiplied or divided by the same nonzero number without changing the solution of the equation. (We will see in Chapter 4 how the multiplication property allows us to divide both sides of an equation by the same nonzero number.)

To solve an equation like $2x = 6$ for x, notice that 2 is *multiplied* by x. To get x alone, we use the multiplication property of equality to *divide* both sides of the equation by 2, and simplify as follows:

$$2x = 6$$

$$\frac{2 \cdot x}{2} = \frac{6}{2} \quad \text{Divide both sides by 2.}$$

Then it can be shown that an expression such as $\dfrac{2 \cdot x}{2}$ is equivalent to $\dfrac{2}{2} \cdot x$, so

$$\frac{2 \cdot x}{2} = \frac{6}{2} \quad \text{can be written as} \quad \frac{2}{2} \cdot x = \frac{6}{2}$$

$$1 \cdot x = 3 \quad \text{or} \quad x = 3$$

Picturing again our balanced scale, if we multiply or divide the weight on each side by the same nonzero number, the scale (or equation) remains balanced.

Example 5 Solve: $-5x = 15$

Solution: To get x alone, divide both sides by -5.

$$-5x = 15 \qquad \text{Original equation}$$

$$\frac{-5x}{-5} = \frac{15}{-5} \qquad \text{Divide both sides by } -5.$$

$$\frac{-5}{-5} \cdot x = \frac{15}{-5}$$

$$1x = -3 \quad \text{or} \quad x = -3 \quad \text{Simplify.}$$

(Continued on next page)

Practice 5

Solve: $3y = -18$

Answer
5. -6

Check: To check, replace x with -3 in the original equation.

$$-5x = 15 \quad \text{Original equation}$$
$$-5(-3) \stackrel{?}{=} 15 \quad \text{Let } x = -3.$$
$$15 = 15 \quad \text{True}$$

The solution is -3.

■ Work Practice 5

Practice 6

Solve: $-32 = 8x$

Example 6 Solve: $-27 = 3y$

Solution: To get y alone, divide both sides of the equation by 3.

$$-27 = 3y$$
$$\frac{-27}{3} = \frac{3y}{3} \quad \text{Divide both sides by 3.}$$
$$\frac{-27}{3} = \frac{3}{3} \cdot y$$
$$-9 = 1y \quad \text{or} \quad y = -9$$

Check to see that -9 is the solution.

■ Work Practice 6

Practice 7

Solve: $-3y = -27$

Example 7 Solve: $-12x = -36$

Solution: To get x alone, divide both sides of the equation by -12.

$$-12x = -36$$
$$\frac{-12x}{-12} = \frac{-36}{-12}$$
$$\frac{-12}{-12} \cdot x = \frac{-36}{-12}$$
$$x = 3$$

Check: To check, replace x with 3 in the original equation.

$$-12x = -36$$
$$-12(3) \stackrel{?}{=} -36 \quad \text{Let } x = 3.$$
$$-36 = -36 \quad \text{True}$$

Since $-36 = -36$ is a true statement, the solution is 3.

■ Work Practice 7

✓**Concept Check** Which operation is appropriate for solving each of the following equations, addition or division?

a. $12 = x - 3$

b. $12 = 3x$

The multiplication property also allows us to solve equations like

$$\frac{x}{5} = 2$$

Answers

6. -4 **7.** 9

✓**Concept Check Answers**

a. addition

b. division

Here, x is *divided* by 5. To get x alone, we use the multiplication property to *multiply* both sides by 5.

$$5 \cdot \frac{x}{5} = 5 \cdot 2 \quad \text{Multiply both sides by 5.}$$

Then it can be shown that

$$5 \cdot \frac{x}{5} = 5 \cdot 2 \text{ can be written as } \frac{5}{5} \cdot x = 5 \cdot 2$$

$$1 \cdot x = 10 \quad \text{or} \quad x = 10$$

Example 8 Solve: $\dfrac{x}{3} = -2$

Solution: To get x alone, multiply both sides by 3.

$$\frac{x}{3} = -2$$

$$3 \cdot \frac{x}{3} = 3 \cdot (-2) \qquad \text{Multiply both sides by 3.}$$

$$\frac{3}{3} \cdot x = 3 \cdot (-2)$$

$$1x = -6 \quad \text{or} \quad x = -6 \quad \text{Simplify.}$$

Check: Replace x with -6 in the original equation.

$$\frac{x}{3} = -2 \quad \text{Original equation}$$

$$\frac{-6}{3} \stackrel{?}{=} -2 \quad \text{Let } x = -6.$$

$$-2 = -2 \quad \text{True}$$

The solution is -6.

■ Work Practice 8

Practice 8

Solve: $\dfrac{x}{-4} = 7$

Answer
8. -28

Vocabulary, Readiness & Video Check

Use the choices below to fill in each blank. Some choices may be used more than once.

equation	multiplication	addition
expression	solution	equivalent

1. A combination of operations on variables and numbers is called a(n) _____.

2. A statement of the form "expression = expression" is called a(n) _____.

3. A(n) _____ contains an equals sign ($=$) while a(n) _____ does not.

4. A(n) _____ may be simplified and evaluated while a(n) _____ may be solved.

5. A(n) _____ of an equation is a number that when substituted for a variable makes the equation a true statement.

6. _____ equations have the same solution.

7. By the _____ property of equality, the same number may be added to or subtracted from both sides of an equation without changing the solution of the equation.

8. By the _____ property of equality, both sides of an equation may be multiplied or divided by the same non-zero number without changing the solution of the equation.

Martin-Gay Interactive Videos   *Watch the section lecture video and answer the following questions.*

Objective A 9. From the lecture before ⊞ Example 1, what does an equation have that an expression does not? ▶

Objective B 10. In the lecture before ⊞ Example 2, what does the addition property of equality mean in words? ▶

Objective C 11. Complete this statement based on ⊞ Example 7: To check a solution, we go back to the _____ equation, replace the variable with the proposed solution, and see if we get a _____ statement. ▶

See Video 2.6 ●

2.6 Exercise Set MyMathLab® ▶

Objective A *Determine whether the given number is a solution of the given equation. See Example 1.*

1. Is 6 a solution of $x - 8 = -2$?

2. Is 9 a solution of $y - 16 = -7$?

▶ **3.** Is -5 a solution of $x + 12 = 17$?

4. Is -7 a solution of $a + 23 = -16$?

5. Is -8 a solution of $-9f = 64 - f$?

6. Is -6 a solution of $-3k = 12 - k$?

7. Is 3 a solution of $5(c - 5) = -10$?

8. Is 1 a solution of $2(b - 3) = 10$?

Objective B *Solve. Check each solution. See Examples 2 through 4.*

▶ **9.** $a + 5 = 23$

10. $f + 4 = -6$

11. $d - 9 = -21$

12. $s - 7 = -15$

▶ **13.** $7 = y - 2$

14. $1 = y + 7$

▶ **15.** $-7 + 10 - 20 = x$

16. $-50 + 40 - 5 = z$

Objective C *Solve. Check each solution. See Examples 5 through 8.*

▶ **17.** $5x = 20$

18. $6y = 48$

▶ **19.** $-3z = 12$

20. $-2x = 26$

21. $\dfrac{n}{7} = -2$ **22.** $\dfrac{n}{11} = -5$ **23.** $2z = -34$ **24.** $7y = -21$

25. $-4y = 0$ **26.** $-9x = 0$ **27.** $-10x = -10$ **28.** $-31x = -31$

Objectives **B** **C** **Mixed Practice** *Solve. See Examples 2 through 8.*

29. $5x = -35$ **30.** $3y = -27$ **31.** $n - 5 = -55$ **32.** $n - 4 = -48$

33. $-15 = y + 10$ **34.** $-36 = y + 12$ **35.** $\dfrac{x}{-6} = -6$ **36.** $\dfrac{x}{-9} = -9$

37. $n = -10 + 31$ **38.** $z = -28 + 36$ **39.** $-12y = -144$ **40.** $-11x = -121$

▶ **41.** $\dfrac{n}{4} = -20$ **42.** $\dfrac{n}{5} = -20$ **43.** $-64 = 32y$ **44.** $-81 = 27x$

Review

Translate each phrase to an algebraic expression. Use x to represent "a number." See Section 1.8.

45. A number decreased by -2 **46.** A number increased by -5 **47.** The product of -6 and a number

48. The quotient of a number and -20 **49.** The sum of -15 and a number   **50.** -32 multiplied by a number

51. -8 divided by a number   **52.** Subtract a number from -18.

Concept Extensions

Solve.

53. $n - 42{,}860 = -1286$ **54.** $n + 961 = 120$

55. $-38x = 15{,}542$ **56.** $\dfrac{y}{-18} = 1098$

57. Explain the differences between an equation and an expression.

58. Explain the differences between the addition property of equality and the multiplication property of equality.

59. Write an equation that can be solved using the addition property of equality.

60. Write an equation that can be solved using the multiplication property of equality.

Chapter 2 Group Activity

Magic Squares

Sections 2.1–2.3

A magic square is a set of numbers arranged in a square table so that the sum of the numbers in each column, row, and diagonal is the same. For instance, in the magic square below, the sum of each column, row, and diagonal is 15. Notice that no number is used more than once in the magic square.

2	9	4
7	5	3
6	1	8

The properties of magic squares have been known for a very long time and once were thought to be good luck charms. The ancient Egyptians and Greeks understood their patterns. A magic square even made it into a famous work of art. The engraving titled *Melencolia I,* created by German artist Albrecht Dürer in 1514, features the following four-by-four magic square on the building behind the central figure.

16	3	2	13
5	10	11	8
9	6	7	12
4	15	14	1

Exercises

1. Verify that what is shown in the Dürer engraving is, in fact, a magic square. What is the common sum of the columns, rows, and diagonals?

2. Negative numbers can also be used in magic squares. Complete the following magic square:

	−1	
0		−4

3. Use the numbers $-16, -12, -8, -4, 0, 4, 8, 12,$ and 16 to form a magic square:

Chapter 2 Vocabulary Check

Fill in each blank with one of the words or phrases listed below.

inequality symbols	addition	solution	is less than	integers
expression	average	negative	absolute value	equation
positive	opposites	is greater than	multiplication	

1. Two numbers that are the same distance from 0 on the number line but are on opposite sides of 0 are called _____.

2. The _____ of a number is that number's distance from 0 on a number line.

3. The _____ are … , $-3, -2, -1, 0, 1, 2, 3, \ldots$.

4. The _____ numbers are numbers less than zero.

5. The _____ numbers are numbers greater than zero.

6. The symbols "<" and ">" are called _____.

7. A(n) _____ of an equation is a number that when substituted for a variable makes the equation a true statement.

8. The _____ of a list of numbers is $\dfrac{\text{sum of numbers}}{\text{number of numbers}}$.

9. A combination of operations on variables and numbers is called a(n) _____.

10. A statement of the form "expression = expression" is called a(n) _____.

11. The sign "<" means _____ and ">" means _____.

12. By the _____ property of equality, the same number may be added to or subtracted from both sides of an equation without changing the solution of the equation.

13. By the _____ property of equality, both sides of an equation may be multiplied or divided by the same nonzero number without changing the solution of the equation.

Helpful Hint
▶ Are you preparing for your test? Don't forget to take the Chapter 2 Test on page 158. Then check your answers at the back of the text and use the Chapter Test Prep Videos to see the fully worked-out solutions to any of the exercises you want to review.

2 Chapter Highlights

Definitions and Concepts	Examples
Section 2.1 Introduction to Integers	
Together, positive numbers, negative numbers, and 0 are called **signed numbers**.	$-432, -10, 0, 15$
The **integers** are … , $-3, -2, -1, 0, 1, 2, 3, \ldots$.	
The **absolute value** of a number is that number's distance from 0 on a number line. The symbol for absolute value is $\lvert \ \rvert$.	$\lvert -2 \rvert = 2$ 2 units $\begin{array}{cccccccc} -3 & -2 & -1 & 0 & 1 & 2 & 3 \end{array}$
	$\lvert 2 \rvert = 2$ 2 units $\begin{array}{cccccccc} -3 & -2 & -1 & 0 & 1 & 2 & 3 \end{array}$

(continued)

Definitions and Concepts	Examples
Section 2.1 Introduction to Integers (*continued*)	
Two numbers that are the same distance from 0 on the number line but are on opposite sides of 0 are called **opposites**.	5 and −5 are opposites. 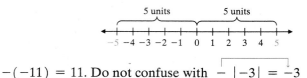
If a is a number, then $-(-a) = a$.	$-(-11) = 11$. Do not confuse with $-\lvert -3\rvert = -3$
Section 2.2 Adding Integers	
Adding Two Numbers with the Same Sign **Step 1:** Add their absolute values. **Step 2:** Use their common sign as the sign of the sum.	Add: $$-3 + (-2) = -5$$ $$-7 + (-15) = -22$$
Adding Two Numbers with Different Signs **Step 1:** Find the larger absolute value minus the smaller absolute value. **Step 2:** Use the sign of the number with the larger absolute value as the sign of the sum.	$$-6 + 4 = -2$$ $$17 + (-12) = 5$$ $$-32 + (-2) + 14 = -34 + 14$$ $$= -20$$
Section 2.3 Subtracting Integers	
Subtracting Two Numbers If a and b are numbers, then $a - b = a + (-b)$.	Subtract: $$-35 - 4 = -35 + (-4) = -39$$ $$3 - 8 = 3 + (-8) = -5$$ $$-10 - (-12) = -10 + 12 = 2$$ $$7 - 20 - 18 - (-3) = 7 + (-20) + (-18) + (+3)$$ $$= -13 + (-18) + 3$$ $$= -31 + 3$$ $$= -28$$
Section 2.4 Multiplying and Dividing Integers	
Multiplying Numbers The product of two numbers having the same sign is a positive number. The product of two numbers having different signs is a negative number.	Multiply: $$(-7)(-6) = 42$$ $$9(-4) = -36$$ Evaluate: $$(-3)^2 = (-3)(-3) = 9$$
Dividing Numbers The quotient of two numbers having the same sign is a positive number. The quotient of two numbers having different signs is a negative number.	Divide: $$-100 \div (-10) = 10$$ $$\frac{14}{-2} = -7, \quad \frac{0}{-3} = 0, \quad \frac{22}{0} \text{ is undefined.}$$

Definitions and Concepts	Examples

Section 2.5 Order of Operations

Order of Operations

1. Perform all operations within parentheses ( ), brackets [ ], or other grouping symbols such as fraction bars, starting with the innermost set.
2. Evaluate any expressions with exponents.
3. Multiply or divide in order from left to right.
4. Add or subtract in order from left to right.

Simplify:

$$3 + 2 \cdot (-5) = 3 + (-10)$$
$$= -7$$

$$\frac{-2(5-7)}{-7 + |-3|} = \frac{-2(-2)}{-7 + 3}$$
$$= \frac{4}{-4}$$
$$= -1$$

Section 2.6 Solving Equations: The Addition and Multiplication Properties

Addition Property of Equality

Let a, b, and c represent numbers.

If $a = b$, then

$$a + c = b + c \quad \text{and} \quad a - c = b - c$$

In other words, the same number may be added to or subtracted from both sides of an equation without changing the solution of the equation.

Multiplication Property of Equality

Let a, b, and c represent numbers and let $c \neq 0$.

If $a = b$, then

$$a \cdot c = b \cdot c \quad \text{and} \quad \frac{a}{c} = \frac{b}{c}$$

In other words, both sides of an equation may be multiplied or divided by the same nonzero number without changing the solution of the equation.

Solve:

$$x + 8 = 1$$
$$x + 8 - 8 = 1 - 8 \quad \text{Subtract 8 from both sides.}$$
$$x = -7 \quad \text{Simplify.}$$

The solution is -7.

Solve:

$$-6y = 30$$
$$\frac{-6y}{-6} = \frac{30}{-6} \quad \text{Divide both sides by } -6.$$
$$\frac{-6}{-6} \cdot y = \frac{30}{-6}$$
$$y = -5 \quad \text{Simplify.}$$

The solution is -5.

Chapter 2 Review

(2.1) *Represent each quantity by an integer.*

1. A gold miner is working 1572 feet down in a mine.

2. Mount Hood, in Oregon, has an elevation of 11,239 feet.

Graph each integer in the list on the same number line.

3. $-3, -5, 0, 7$

4. $-6, -1, 0, 5$

Simplify.

5. $|-11|$

6. $|0|$

7. $-|8|$

8. $-(-9)$

9. $-|-16|$

10. $-(-2)$

Insert $<$ or $>$ between each pair of integers to make a true statement.

11. $-18 \quad -20$

12. $-5 \quad 5$

13. $|-123| \quad -|-198|$

14. $|-12| \quad -|-16|$

Find the opposite of each integer.

15. -18

16. 42

Answer true or false for each statement.

17. If $a < b$, then a must be a negative number.

18. The absolute value of an integer is always 0 or a positive number.

19. A negative number is always less than a positive number.

20. If a is a negative number, then $-a$ is a positive number.

Evaluate.

21. $|y|$ if $y = -2$

22. $|-x|$ if $x = -3$

23. $-|-z|$ if $z = -5$

24. $-|-n|$ if $n = -10$

Elevator shafts in some buildings extend not only above ground, but in many cases below ground to accommodate basements, underground parking, etc. The bar graph shows four such elevators and their shaft distance above and below ground. Use the bar graph to answer Exercises 25 and 26.

25. Which elevator shaft extends the farthest below ground?

26. Which elevator shaft extends the highest above ground?

(2.2) *Add.*

27. $5 + (-3)$ **28.** $18 + (-4)$ **29.** $-12 + 16$

31. $-8 + (-15)$ **32.** $-5 + (-17)$ **33.** $-24 + 3$ **34.** $-89 + 19$

35. $15 + (-15)$ **36.** $-24 + 24$ **37.** $-43 + (-108)$ **38.** $-100 + (-506)$

Solve.

39. The temperature at 5 a.m. on a day in January was $-15°$ Celsius. By 6 a.m. the temperature had fallen 5 degrees. Use a signed number to represent the temperature at 6 a.m.

40. A diver starts out at 127 feet below the surface and then swims downward another 23 feet. Use a signed number to represent the diver's current depth.

41. During the PGA 2008 Wyndham Championship tournament, the winner, Carl Pettersson, had scores of -6, -9, -4, and -2. What was his total score for the tournament? (*Source:* Professional Golfers' Association)

42. The Solheim Cup, a biannual pro women golfers' tournament between an American team and a European team, scores holes won. During the 2007 Solheim Cup, the winners, the American team, had a score of 16. The losing team, the Europeans, had a score 4 less than the Americans' score. What was the European team's score? (*Source:* Professional Golfers' Association)

(2.3) *Subtract.*

43. $12 - 4$ **44.** $-12 - 4$ **45.** $-7 - 17$ **46.** $7 - 17$

47. $7 - (-13)$ **48.** $-6 - (-14)$ **49.** $16 - 16$ **50.** $-16 - 16$

51. $-12 - (-12)$ **52.** $-5 - (-12)$

53. $-(-5) - 12 + (-3)$ **54.** $-8 + (-12) - 10 - (-3)$

Solve.

55. If the elevation of Lake Superior is 600 feet above sea level and the elevation of the Caspian Sea is 92 feet below sea level, find the difference of the elevations.

56. Josh Weidner has $142 in his checking account. He writes a check for $125, makes a deposit of $43, and then writes another check for $85. Represent the balance in his account by an integer.

57. Some roller coasters travel above and below ground. One such roller coaster is Tremors, located in Silverwood Theme Park, Athol, Idaho. If this coaster rises to a height of 85 feet above ground, then drops 99 feet, how many feet below ground are you at the end of the drop? (*Source:* ultimateroller-coaster.com)

58. Go to the bar graph for Review Exercises **25** and **26** and find the total length of the elevator shaft for Elevator C.

60. $|-5 - (-6)| = 5 + 6$

$-23 + 40$

$\cdot 6(3)$

63. $-4(16)$

64. $-5(-12)$

√6. $(-1)^5$

67. $12(-3)(0)$

68. $-1(6)(2)(-2)$

155

Divide.

69. $-15 \div$

70. $\dfrac{-24}{-8}$

71. $\dfrac{0}{-3}$

72. $\dfrac{-46}{0}$

73. $\dfrac{100}{-5}$

74. $\dfrac{-72}{8}$

75. $\dfrac{-38}{-1}$

76. $\dfrac{45}{-9}$

Solve.

77. A football team lost 5 yards on each of two consecutive plays. Represent the total loss by a product of integers, and find the product.

78. A horse race bettor lost $50 on each of four consecutive races. Represent the total loss by a product of integers, and find the product.

79. A person has a debt of $1024 and is ordered to pay it back in four equal payments. Represent the amount of each payment by a quotient of integers, and find the quotient.

80. Overnight, the temperature dropped 45 degrees Fahrenheit. If this took place over a time period of nine hours, represent the average temperature drop each hour by a quotient of integers. Then find the quotient.

(2.5) *Simplify.*

81. $(-7)^2$

82. -7^2

83. $5 - 8 + 3$

84. $-3 + 12 + (-7) - 10$

85. $-10 + 3 \cdot (-2)$

86. $5 - 10 \cdot (-3)$

87. $16 \div (-2) \cdot 4$

88. $-20 \div 5 \cdot 2$

89. $16 + (-3) \cdot 12 \div 4$

90. $-12 + 10 \div (-5)$

91. $4^3 - (8 - 3)^2$

92. $(-3)^3 - 90$

93. $\dfrac{(-4)(-3) - (-2)(-1)}{-10 + 5}$

94. $\dfrac{4(12 - 18)}{-10 \div (-2 - 3)}$

Find the average of each list of numbers.

95. $-18, 25, -30, 7, 0, -2$

96. $-45, -40, -30, -25$

Evaluate each expression for $x = -2$ *and* $y = 1$.

97. $2x - y$

98. $y^2 + x^2$

99. $\dfrac{3x}{6}$

100. $\dfrac{5y - x}{-y}$

(2.6) *For Exercises 101 and 102, answer "yes" or "no."*

101. Is -5 a solution of $2n - 6 = 16$?

102. Is -2 a solution of $2(c - 8) = -20$?

Solve.

103. $n - 7 = -20$

104. $-5 = n + 15$

105. $10x = -30$

106. $-8x = 72$

107. $-20 + 7 = y$

108. $x - 31 = -62$

109. $\dfrac{n}{-4} = -11$

110. $\dfrac{x}{-2} = 13$

111. $n + 12 = -7$

112. $n - 40 = -2$

113. $-36 = -6x$

114. $-40 = 8y$

Mixed Review

Perform the indicated operations.

115. $-6 + (-9)$

116. $-16 - 3$

117. $-4(-12)$

118. $\dfrac{84}{-4}$

119. $-76 - (-97)$

120. $-9 + 4$

Solve.

121. Wednesday's lowest temperature was $-18°$C. The cold weather continued and by Friday, it had dropped another $9°$C. What was the temperature on Friday?

122. The temperature at noon on a Monday in December was $-11°$C. By noon on Tuesday, it had warmed by $17°$C. What was the temperature at noon on Tuesday?

123. The top of a mountain has an altitude of 12,923 feet. The bottom of a valley is 195 feet below sea level. Find the difference between these two elevations.

124. Joe owed his mother \$32. He gave her \$23. Write his financial situation as a signed number.

Simplify.

125. $(3 - 7)^2 \div (6 - 4)^3$

126. $3(4 + 2) + (-6) - 3^2$

127. $2 - 4 \cdot 3 + 5$

128. $4 - 6 \cdot 5 + 1$

129. $\dfrac{-|-14| - 6}{7 + 2(-3)}$

130. $5(7 - 6)^3 - 4(2 - 3)^2 + 2^4$

Solve.

131. $n - 9 = -30$

132. $n + 18 = 1$

133. $-4x = -48$

134. $9x = -81$

135. $\dfrac{n}{-2} = 100$

136. $\dfrac{y}{-1} = -3$

Chapter 2 Test

Step-by-step test solutions are found on the Chapter Test Prep Videos. Where available: **MyMathLab®** or **You Tube**

Answers

Simplify each expression.

1. $-5 + 8$

2. $18 - 24$

3. $5 \cdot (-20)$

4. $-16 \div (-4)$

5. $-18 + (-12)$

6. $-7 - (-19)$

7. $-5 \cdot (-13)$

8. $\dfrac{-25}{-5}$

9. $|-25| + (-13)$

10. $14 - |-20|$

11. $|5| \cdot |-10|$

12. $\dfrac{|-10|}{-|-5|}$

13. $-8 + 9 \div (-3)$

14. $-7 + (-32) - 12 + 5$

15. $(-5)^3 - 24 \div (-3)$

16. $(5 - 9)^2 \cdot (8 - 2)^3$

17. $-(-7)^2 \div 7 \cdot (-4)$

18. $3 - (8 - 2)^3$

1. _____

2. _____

3. _____

4. _____

5. _____

6. _____

7. _____

8. _____

9. _____

10. _____

11. _____

12. _____

13. _____

14. _____

15. _____

16. _____

17. _____

18. _____

19. $\dfrac{4}{2} - \dfrac{8^2}{16}$

20. $\dfrac{-3(-2) + 12}{-1(-4 - 5)}$

21. $\dfrac{|25 - 30|^2}{2(-6) + 7}$

22. $5(-8) - [6 - (2 - 4)] + (12 - 16)^2$

Evaluate each expression for $x = 0, y = -3,$ *and* $z = 2.$

23. $7x + 3y - 4z$

24. $10 - y^2$

25. $\dfrac{3z}{2y}$

26. Mary Dunstan, a diver, starts at sea level and then makes 4 successive descents of 22 feet. After the descents, what is her elevation?

27. Aaron Hawn has $129 in his checking account. He writes a check for $79, withdraws $40 from an ATM, and then deposits $35. Represent the new balance in his account by an integer.

28. Mt. Washington in New Hampshire has an elevation of 6288 feet above sea level. The Romanche Gap in the Atlantic Ocean has an elevation of 25,354 feet below sea level. Represent the difference in elevation between these two points by an integer.
(*Source:* National Geographic Society and Defense Mapping Agency)

29. Lake Baykal in Siberian Russia is the deepest lake in the world, with a maximum depth of 5315 feet. The elevation of the lake's surface is 1495 feet above sea level. What is the elevation (with respect to sea level) of the deepest point in the lake?
(*Source:* U.S. Geological Survey)

1495 feet above sea level

Sea level — 1495 feet

5315 feet

? elevation

30. Find the average of $-12, -13, 0, 9.$

31. Translate the following phrases into mathematical expressions. Use x to represent "a number."

   a. The product of a number and 17

   b. A number subtracted from 20

Solve.

32. $-9n = -45$

33. $\dfrac{n}{-7} = 4$

34. $x - 16 = -36$

35. $-20 + 8 + 8 = x$

19. _____

20. _____

21. _____

22. _____

23. _____

24. _____

25. _____

26. _____

27. _____

28. _____

29. _____

30. _____

31. a. _____

    b. _____

32. _____

33. _____

34. _____

35. _____

Answers

1. _____
2. _____
3. _____
4. _____
5. _____
6. _____
7. a. _____
   b. _____
   c. _____
8. a. _____
   b. _____
   c. _____
9. _____
10. _____
11. _____
12. _____
13. _____
14. _____
15. _____
16. _____
17. _____
18. _____
19. a. _____
    b. _____
    c. _____
20. a. _____
    b. _____
    c. _____
21. _____
22. _____
23. a. _____
    b. _____
    c. _____
24. a. _____
    b. _____
    c. _____

Find the place value of the digit 3 in each whole number.

1. 396,418

2. 4308

3. 93,192

4. 693,298

5. 534,275,866

6. 267,301,818

7. Insert $<$ or $>$ to make a true statement.
   a. $-7 \quad 7$
   b. $0 \quad -4$
   c. $-9 \quad -11$

8. Insert $<$ or $>$ to make a true statement
   a. $12 \quad -4$
   b. $-13 \quad -31$
   c. $-82 \quad 79$

9. Add:
   $13 + 2 + 7 + 8 + 9$

10. Add:
   $11 + 3 + 9 + 16$

11. Subtract: $7826 - 505$
   Check by adding.

12. Subtract: $3285 - 272$
   Check by adding.

13. The radius of Jupiter is 43,441 miles. The radius of Saturn is 7257 miles less than the radius of Jupiter. Find the radius of Saturn. (*Source:* National Space Science Data Center)

14. C. J. Dufour wants to buy a digital camera. She has $762 in her savings account. If the camera costs $237, how much money will she have in her account after buying the camera?

15. Round 568 to the nearest ten.

16. Round 568 to the nearest hundred.

17. Round each number to the nearest hundred to find an estimated difference.
   $$\begin{array}{r} 4725 \\ -2879 \\ \hline \end{array}$$

18. Round each number to the nearest thousand to find an estimated difference.
   $$\begin{array}{r} 8394 \\ -2913 \\ \hline \end{array}$$

19. Rewrite each using the distributive property.
   a. $5(6 + 5)$
   b. $20(4 + 7)$
   c. $2(7 + 9)$

20. Rewrite each using the distributive property.
   a. $5(2 + 12)$
   b. $9(3 + 6)$
   c. $4(8 + 1)$

21. Multiply: 631×125

22. Multiply: 299×104

23. Find each quotient. Check by multiplying.
   a. $42 \div 7$
   b. $\dfrac{64}{8}$
   c. $3\overline{)21}$

24. Find each quotient. Check by multiplying.
   a. $\dfrac{35}{5}$
   b. $64 \div 8$
   c. $4\overline{)48}$

25. Divide: $3705 \div 5$. Check by multiplying.

26. Divide: $3648 \div 8$. Check by multiplying.

27. As part of a promotion, an executive receives 238 cards, each good for one free song download. If she wants to share them evenly with 19 friends, how many download cards will each friend receive? How many will be left over?

28. Mrs. Mallory's first-grade class is going to the zoo. She pays a total of $324 for 36 admission tickets. How much does each ticket cost?

Evaluate.

29. 9^2

30. 5^3

31. 6^1

32. 4^1

33. $5 \cdot 6^2$

34. $2^3 \cdot 7$

35. Simplify: $\dfrac{7 - 2 \cdot 3 + 3^2}{5(2 - 1)}$

36. Simplify: $\dfrac{6^2 + 4 \cdot 4 + 2^3}{37 - 5^2}$

37. Evaluate $x + 6$ if x is 8.

38. Evaluate $5 + x$ if x is 9.

39. Simplify:
   a. $|-9|$
   b. $|8|$
   c. $|0|$

40. Simplify:
   a. $|4|$
   b. $|-7|$

41. Add: $-2 + 25$

42. Add: $8 + (-3)$

43. Evaluate $2a - b$ for $a = 8$ and $b = -6$.

44. Evaluate $x - y$ for $x = -2$ and $y = -7$.

45. Multiply: $-7 \cdot 3$

46. Multiply: $5(-2)$

47. Multiply: $0 \cdot (-4)$

48. Multiply: $-6 \cdot 9$

49. Simplify: $3(4 - 7) + (-2) - 5$

50. Simplify: $4 - 8(7 - 3) - (-1)$

25. _____
26. _____
27. _____
28. _____
29. _____
30. _____
31. _____
32. _____
33. _____
34. _____
35. _____
36. _____
37. _____
38. _____
39. a. _____
    b. _____
    c. _____
40. a. _____
    b. _____
41. _____
42. _____
43. _____
44. _____
45. _____
46. _____
47. _____
48. _____
49. _____
50. _____

3

Solving Equations and Problem Solving

In this chapter, we continue making the transition from arithmetic to algebra. Recall that in algebra, letters (called variables) represent unknown quantities. Using variables is a very powerful method for solving problems that cannot be solved with arithmetic alone. This chapter introduces operations on algebraic expressions, and we continue solving variable equations.

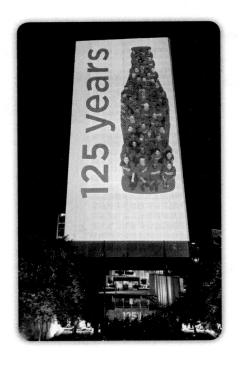

Coca-Cola recently celebrated the 125th anniversary of its namesake brand. The illumination in the photo was on display for a month in Atlanta, Georgia. At this writing, the illumination holds the world record for largest single-building illumination. Also, Coca-Cola was recently named the Most Valuable Global Brand, as shown in the graph below. What is a global brand? There are many definitions, but a brand is the identity of a product or a service. The identity can be projected through its name, a symbol, a slogan, or something similar. A global brand, then, is a product whose brand is easily recognized throughout the world. Read the list of company names in the graph below and see how many of these brand names you know.

In Section 3.4, Exercises 31 and 32, we will solve applications that give us the unknown bar heights in the bar graph.

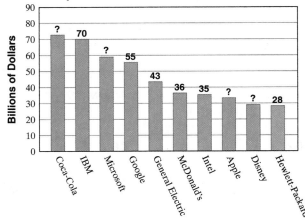

Top Ten Most Valuable Global Brands

Source: Interbrand, *Top 10 of Everything*, 2013

Recall from Section 1.8 that a combination of numbers, letters (variables), and operation symbols is called an **algebraic expression** or simply an **expression.** Examples of expressions are below.

Algebraic Expressions

$4 \cdot x$, $n + 7$, and $3y - 5 - x$

Recall that if two variables or a number and a variable are next to each other, with no operation sign between them, the indicated operation is multiplication. For example,

$3y$ means $3 \cdot y$

and

xy or $x(y)$ means $x \cdot y$

Also, the meaning of an exponent remains the same when the base is a variable. For example,

$$y^2 = \underbrace{y \cdot y}_{\text{2 factors of } y} \quad \text{and} \quad x^4 = \underbrace{x \cdot x \cdot x \cdot x}_{\text{4 factors of } x}$$

Just as we can add, subtract, multiply, and divide numbers, we can add, subtract, multiply, and divide algebraic expressions. In previous sections we evaluated algebraic expressions like $x + 3$, $4x$, and $x + 2y$ for particular values of the variables. In this section, we explore working with variable expressions without evaluating them. We begin with a definition of a term.

Objective A Combining Like Terms

The addends of an algebraic expression are called the **terms** of the expression.

$x + 3$
2 terms

$3y^2 + (-6y) + 4$
3 terms

A term that is only a number has a special name. It is called a **constant term,** or simply a **constant.** A term that contains a variable is called a **variable term.**

x	$+$	3	and	$3y^2 + (-6y)$	$+$	4
↑		↑		↑		↑
variable term		constant term		variable terms		constant term

The number factor of a variable term is called the **numerical coefficient.** A numerical coefficient of 1 is usually not written.

$5x$	x or $1x$	$3y^2$	$-6y$
↑	↑	↑	↑
Numerical coefficient is 5.	Understood numerical coefficient is 1.	Numerical coefficient is 3.	Numerical coefficient is −6.

Objectives

A Use Properties of Numbers to Combine Like Terms.

B Use Properties of Numbers to Multiply Expressions.

C Simplify Expressions by Multiplying and Then Combining Like Terms.

D Find the Perimeter and Area of Figures.

> **Helpful Hint** Recall that $1 \cdot$ any number = that number. This means that
>
> $1 \cdot x = x$ or that $1x = x$
>
> Thus x can always be replaced by $1x$ or $1 \cdot x$.

Terms with the same variable factors, except that they may have different numerical coefficients, are called **like terms.**

Like Terms	Unlike Terms
$3x, -4x$	$5x, x^2$
$-6y, 2y, y$	$7x, 7y$

✓**Concept Check** True or false? The terms $-7xz^2$ and $3z^2x$ are like terms. Explain.

A sum or difference of like terms can be simplified using the **distributive property.** Recall from Section 1.5 that the distributive property says that multiplication distributes over addition (and subtraction). Using variables, we can write the distributive property as follows:

$$(\overset{\frown}{a + b})c = ac + bc.$$

If we write the right side of the equation first, then the left side, we have the following:

> **Distributive Property**
>
> If a, b, and c are numbers, then
>
> $$ac + bc = (a + b)c$$
>
> Also,
>
> $$ac - bc = (a - b)c$$

The distributive property guarantees that, no matter what number x is, $7x + 2x$ (for example) has the same value as $(7 + 2)x$, or $9x$. We then have that

$$7x + 2x = (7 + 2)x = 9x$$

This is an example of **combining like terms.** An algebraic expression is **simplified** when all like terms have been combined.

Practice 1

Simplify each expression by combining like terms.

a. $8m - 14m$

b. $6a + a$

c. $-y^2 + 3y^2 + 7$

Answers

1. a. $-6m$ **b.** $7a$ **c.** $2y^2 + 7$

✓**Concept Check Answer**

true

Example 1 Simplify each expression by combining like terms.

a. $4x + 6x$ **b.** $y - 5y$ **c.** $3x^2 + 5x^2 - 2$

Solution: Add or subtract like terms.

a. $4x + 6x = (4 + 6)x$
$\qquad\qquad = 10x$

b. $\overset{\text{Understood 1}}{}$
$y - 5y = 1y - 5y$
$\qquad\quad = (1 - 5)y$
$\qquad\quad = -4y$

c. $3x^2 + 5x^2 - 2 = (3 + 5)x^2 - 2$
$\qquad\qquad\qquad\quad = 8x^2 - 2$

▪ Work Practice 1

Helpful Hint

In this section, we are simplifying expressions. Try not to confuse the two processes below.

Expression: $5y - 8y$	Equation: $8n = -40$

Simplify the expression:

Solve the equation:

$$5y - 8y = (5 - 8)y$$
$$= -3y$$

$$8n = -40$$
$$\frac{8n}{8} = \frac{-40}{8} \qquad \text{Divide both sides by 8.}$$
$$n = -5 \qquad \text{The solution is } -5.$$

The commutative and associative properties of addition and multiplication can also help us simplify expressions. We presented these properties in Sections 1.3 and 1.5 and state them again using variables.

Properties of Addition and Multiplication

If a, b, and c are numbers, then

$$a + b = b + a \qquad \text{Commutative property of addition}$$
$$a \cdot b = b \cdot a \qquad \text{Commutative property of multiplication}$$

That is, the **order** of adding or multiplying two numbers can be changed without changing their sum or product.

$$(a + b) + c = a + (b + c) \qquad \text{Associative property of addition}$$
$$(a \cdot b) \cdot c = a \cdot (b \cdot c) \qquad \text{Associative property of multiplication}$$

That is, the **grouping** of numbers in addition or multiplication can be changed without changing their sum or product.

Helpful Hint

- Examples of these properties are

$$2 + 3 = 3 + 2 \qquad \text{Commutative property of addition}$$
$$7 \cdot 9 = 9 \cdot 7 \qquad \text{Commutative property of multiplication}$$
$$(1 + 8) + 10 = 1 + (8 + 10) \qquad \text{Associative property of addition}$$
$$(4 \cdot 2) \cdot 3 = 4 \cdot (2 \cdot 3) \qquad \text{Associative property of multiplication}$$

- These properties are not true for subtraction or division.

Example 2 Simplify: $2y - 6 + 4y + 8$

Solution: We begin by writing subtraction as the opposite of addition.

$$\begin{aligned}
2y - 6 + 4y + 8 &= 2y + (-6) + 4y + 8 & \text{Apply the commutative property} \\
&= 2y + 4y + (-6) + 8 & \text{of addition.} \\
&= (2 + 4)y + (-6) + 8 & \text{Apply the distributive property.} \\
&= 6y + 2 & \text{Simplify.}
\end{aligned}$$

Work Practice 2

Practice 2

Simplify: $6z + 5 + z - 4$

Answer
2. $7z + 1$

Practice 3–5

Simplify each expression by combining like terms.

3. $6y + 12y - 6$

4. $7y - 5 + y + 8$

5. $-7y + 2 - 2y - 9x + 12 - x$

Examples   Simplify each expression by combining like terms.

3. $6x + 2x - 5 = 8x - 5$

4. $4x + 2 - 5x + 3 = 4x + 2 + (-5x) + 3$
$$= 4x + (-5x) + 2 + 3$$
$$= -1x + 5 \quad \text{or} \quad -x + 5$$

5. $2x - 5 + 3y + 4x - 10y + 11$
$$= 2x + (-5) + 3y + 4x + (-10y) + 11$$
$$= 2x + 4x + 3y + (-10y) + (-5) + 11$$
$$= 6x - 7y + 6$$

■ Work Practice 3–5

As we practice combining like terms, keep in mind that some of the steps may be performed mentally.

Objective B Multiplying Expressions ▶

We can also use properties of numbers to multiply expressions such as $3(2x)$. By the associative property of multiplication, we can write the product $3(2x)$ as $(3 \cdot 2)x$, which simplifies to $6x$.

Practice 6–7

Multiply.

6. $6(4a)$

7. $-8(9x)$

Examples   Multiply.

6. $5(3y) = (5 \cdot 3)y$ Apply the associative property of multiplication.
$$= 15y$$ Multiply.

7. $-2(4x) = (-2 \cdot 4)x$ Apply the associative property of multiplication.
$$= -8x$$ Multiply.

■ Work Practice 6–7

We can use the distributive property to combine like terms, which we have done, and also to multiply expressions such as $2(3 + x)$. By the distributive property, we have

$$2(3 + x) = 2 \cdot 3 + 2 \cdot x \quad \text{Apply the distributive property.}$$
$$= 6 + 2x \quad \text{Multiply.}$$

Practice 8

Use the distributive property to multiply: $8(y + 2)$

Example 8   Use the distributive property to multiply: $5(x + 4)$

Solution: By the distributive property,

$$5(x + 4) = 5 \cdot x + 5 \cdot 4 \quad \text{Apply the distributive property.}$$
$$= 5x + 20 \quad \text{Multiply.}$$

■ Work Practice 8

Answers

3. $18y - 6$ **4.** $8y + 3$
5. $-9y - 10x + 14$ **6.** $24a$
7. $-72x$ **8.** $8y + 16$

✓ Concept Check Answer

did not distribute the 8;
$8(a - b) = 8a - 8b$

✓**Concept Check** What's wrong with the following?

$$8(a - b) = 8a - b$$

Example 9   Multiply: $-3(5a + 2)$

Solution: By the distributive property,

$$-3(5a + 2) = -3(5a) + (-3)(2) \quad \text{Apply the distributive property.}$$
$$= (-3 \cdot 5)a + (-6) \quad \text{Use the associative property and multiply.}$$
$$= -15a - 6 \quad \text{Multiply.}$$

■ Work Practice 9

Practice 9

Multiply: $3(7a - 5)$

Example 10   Multiply: $8(x - 4)$

Solution:

$$8(x - 4) = 8 \cdot x - 8 \cdot 4$$
$$= 8x - 32$$

■ Work Practice 10

Practice 10

Multiply: $6(5 - y)$

Objective C   Simplifying Expressions ▶

Next we will **simplify** expressions by first using the distributive property to multiply and then **combining** any like terms.

Example 11   Simplify: $2(3 + 7x) - 15$

Solution: First we use the distributive property to remove parentheses.

$$2(3 + 7x) - 15 = 2(3) + 2(7x) - 15 \quad \text{Apply the distributive property.}$$
$$= 6 + 14x - 15 \quad \text{Multiply.}$$
$$= 14x + (-9) \quad \text{or} \quad 14x - 9 \quad \text{Combine like terms.}$$

■ Work Practice 11

Practice 11

Simplify: $5(2y - 3) - 8$

Helpful Hint   2 is *not* distributed to the -15 since it is not within the parentheses.

Example 12   Simplify: $-2(x - 5) + 4(2x + 2)$

Solution: First we use the distributive property to remove parentheses.

$$-2(x - 5) + 4(2x + 2) = -2(x) - (-2)(5) + 4(2x) + 4(2) \quad \text{Apply the distributive property.}$$
$$= -2x + 10 + 8x + 8 \quad \text{Multiply.}$$
$$= 6x + 18 \quad \text{Combine like terms.}$$

■ Work Practice 12

Practice 12

Simplify:
$-7(x - 1) + 5(2x + 3)$

Example 13   Simplify: $-(x + 4) + 5x + 16$

Solution: The expression $-(x + 4)$ means $-1(x + 4)$.

$$-(x + 4) + 5x + 16 = -1(x + 4) + 5x + 16$$
$$= -1 \cdot x + (-1)(4) + 5x + 16 \quad \text{Apply the distributive property.}$$
$$= -x + (-4) + 5x + 16 \quad \text{Multiply.}$$
$$= 4x + 12 \quad \text{Combine like terms.}$$

■ Work Practice 13

Practice 13

Simplify: $-(y + 1) + 3y - 12$

Answers

9. $21a - 15$ **10.** $30 - 6y$
11. $10y - 23$ **12.** $3x + 22$
13. $2y - 13$

Objective D Finding Perimeter and Area

Practice 14

Find the perimeter of the square.

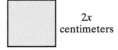

2x centimeters

Example 14   Find the perimeter of the triangle.

2z feet   3z feet   5z feet

Solution: Recall that the perimeter of a figure is the distance around the figure. To find the perimeter, then, we find the sum of the lengths of the sides. We use the letter P to represent perimeter.

$$P = 2z + 3z + 5z$$
$$= 10z$$

Helpful Hint   Don't forget to insert proper units.

The perimeter is $10z$ feet.

■ Work Practice 14

Practice 15

Find the area of the rectangular garden.

(12y + 9) yards   3 yards

Example 15   Finding the Area of a Basketball Court

Find the area of this YMCA basketball court.

(2x − 6) ft

45 ft

Solution: Recall how to find the area of a rectangle. **Area = Length · Width**, or if A represents area, l represents length, and w represents width, we have $A = l \cdot w$.

$$A = l \cdot w$$
$$= 45(2x - 6) \quad \text{Let length} = 45 \text{ and width} = (2x - 6).$$
$$= 90x - 270 \quad \text{Multiply.}$$

The area is $(90x - 270)$ *square* feet.

■ Work Practice 15

Helpful Hint

Don't forget…

Area:	Perimeter:
• surface enclosed	• distance around
• measured in square units	• measured in units

Answers

14. $8x$ cm   **15.** $(36y + 27)$ sq yd

Vocabulary, Readiness & Video Check

Use the choices below to fill in each blank. Some choices may be used more than once.

numerical coefficient	combine like terms	like	term	variable	associative
constant	expression	unlike	distributive	commutative	

1. $14y^2 + 2x - 23$ is called a(n) _____ while $14y^2$, $2x$, and -23 are each called a(n) _____.

2. To multiply $3(-7x + 1)$, we use the _____ property.

3. To simplify an expression like $y + 7y$, we _____.

4. By the _____ properties, the *order* of adding or multiplying two numbers can be changed without changing their sum or product.

5. The term $5x$ is called a(n) _____ term while the term 7 is called a(n) _____ term.

6. The term z has an understood _____ of 1.

7. By the _____ properties, the *grouping* of adding or multiplying numbers can be changed without changing their sum or product.

8. The terms $-x$ and $5x$ are _____ terms and the terms $5x$ and $5y$ are _____ terms.

9. For the term $-3x^2 y$, -3 is called the _____.

Martin-Gay Interactive Videos   *Watch the section lecture video and answer the following questions.*

Objective A **10.** In Example 2, why can't the expression be simplified after the first step?

Objective B **11.** In Example 5, what property is used to multiply?

Objective C **12.** In Example 6, why is the 20 not multiplied by the 2?

Objective D **13.** In Example 8, what operation is used to find P? What operation is used to find A? What do P and A stand for?

See Video 3.1

3.1 Exercise Set MyMathLab®

Objective A *Simplify each expression by combining like terms. See Examples 1 through 5.*

1. $3x + 5x$ **2.** $8y + 3y$ **3.** $2n - 3n$ **4.** $7z - 10z$

5. $4c + c - 7c$ **6.** $5b - 8b - b$ **7.** $4x - 6x + x - 5x$ **8.** $8y + y - 2y - 8y$

9. $3a + 2a + 7a - 5$ **10.** $5b - 4b + b - 15$

Objective B *Multiply. See Examples 6 and 7.*

11. $6(7x)$ **12.** $4(4x)$ **13.** $-3(11y)$ **14.** $-3(21z)$

15. $12(6a)$ **16.** $13(5b)$

Multiply. See Examples 8 through 10.

17. $2(y + 3)$ **18.** $3(x + 1)$ **19.** $3(a - 6)$ **20.** $4(y - 6)$

21. $-4(3x + 7)$ **22.** $-8(8y + 10)$

Objective C *Simplify each expression. First use the distributive property to multiply and remove parentheses. See Examples 11 through 13.*

23. $2(x + 4) - 7$ **24.** $5(6 - y) - 2$ **25.** $8 + 5(3c - 1)$ **26.** $10 + 4(6d - 2)$

27. $-4(6n - 5) + 3n$ **28.** $-3(5 - 2b) - 4b$ **29.** $3 + 6(w + 2) + w$ **30.** $8z + 5(6 + z) + 20$

31. $2(3x + 1) + 5(x - 2)$ **32.** $3(5x - 2) + 2(3x + 1)$ **33.** $-(2y - 6) + 10$ **34.** $-(5x - 1) - 10$

Objectives A B C Mixed Practice *Simplify each expression. See Examples 1 through 13.*

35. $18y - 20y$ **36.** $x + 12x$ **37.** $z - 8z$ **38.** $-12x + 8x$

39. $9d - 3c - d$ **40.** $8r + s - 7s$ **41.** $2y - 6 + 4y - 8$ **42.** $a + 4 - 7a - 5$

43. $5q + p - 6q - p$ **44.** $m - 8n + m + 8n$ **45.** $2(x + 1) + 20$ **46.** $5(x - 1) + 18$

47. $5(x - 7) - 8x$ **48.** $3(x + 2) - 11x$ **49.** $-5(z + 3) + 2z$

50. $-8(1 + v) + 6v$ **51.** $8 - x + 4x - 2 - 9x$ **52.** $5y - 4 + 9y - y + 15$

53. $-7(x + 5) + 5(2x + 1)$ **54.** $-2(x + 4) + 8(3x - 1)$ **55.** $3r - 5r + 8 + r$

56. $6x - 4 + 2x - x + 3$ **57.** $-3(n - 1) - 4n$ **58.** $5(c + 2) + 7c$

59. $4(z - 3) + 5z - 2$ **60.** $8(m + 3) - 20 + m$ **61.** $6(2x - 1) - 12x$

62. $5(2a + 3) - 10a$ **63.** $-(4x - 5) + 5$ **64.** $-(7y - 2) + 6$

65. $-(4x - 10) + 2(3x + 5)$ **66.** $-(12b - 10) + 5(3b - 2)$ **67.** $3a + 4(a + 3)$

68. $b + 2(b - 5)$ **69.** $5y - 2(y - 1) + 3$ **70.** $3x - 4(x + 2) + 1$

Objective D *Find the perimeter of each figure. See Example 14.*

△ **71.**   △ **72.**   △ **73.**

△ **74.**   △ **75.**   △ **76.**

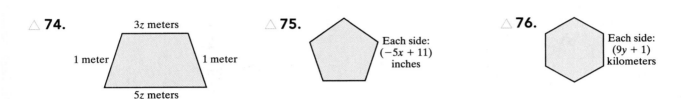

△ 74. 3z meters / 1 meter / 1 meter / 5z meters

△ 75. Each side: $(-5x + 11)$ inches

△ 76. Each side: $(9y + 1)$ kilometers

Find the area of each rectangle. See Example 15.

△ **77.**   △ **78.**   △ **79.**

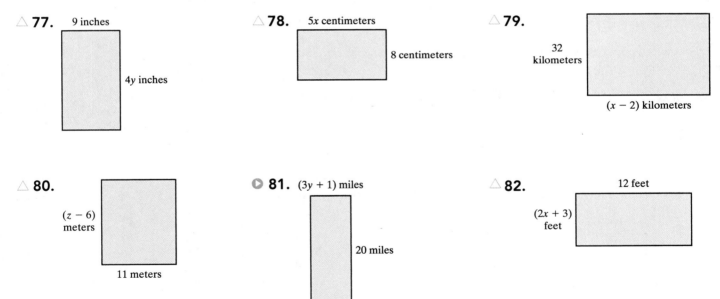

△ 77. 9 inches / 4y inches

△ 78. 5x centimeters / 8 centimeters

△ 79. 32 kilometers / $(x - 2)$ kilometers

△ **80.**   ▶ **81.** $(3y + 1)$ miles   △ **82.** 12 feet

△ 80. $(z - 6)$ meters / 11 meters

▶ 81. $(3y + 1)$ miles / 20 miles

△ 82. $(2x + 3)$ feet / 12 feet

Objectives A B C D Mixed Practice *Solve. See Examples 1 through 15.*

83. Find the area of a regulation NCAA basketball court that is 94 feet long and 50 feet wide.

84. Find the area of a rectangular movie screen that is 50 feet long and 40 feet high.

85. A decorator wishes to put a wallpaper border around a rectangular room that measures 14 feet by 18 feet. Find the room's perimeter.

86. How much fencing will a rancher need for a rectangular cattle lot that measures 80 feet by 120 feet?

87. Find the perimeter of a triangular garden that measures 5 feet by x feet by $(2x + 1)$ feet.

88. Find the perimeter of a triangular picture frame that measures x inches by x inches by $(x - 14)$ inches.

Review

Perform each indicated operation. See Sections 2.2 and 2.3.

89. $-13 + 10$

90. $-15 + 23$

91. $-4 - (-12)$

92. $-7 - (-4)$

93. $-4 + 4$

94. $8 + (-8)$

Concept Extensions

If the expression on the left side of the equal sign is equivalent to the right side, write "correct." If not, write "incorrect" and then write an expression that is equivalent to the left side. See the second Concept Check in this section.

95. $5(3x - 2) \overset{?}{=} 15x - 2$

96. $-2(4x - 1) \overset{?}{=} -8x - 2$

97. $2(xy) \overset{?}{=} 2x \cdot 2y$

98. $-8(ab) \overset{?}{=} -8a \cdot (-8b)$

99. $7x - (x + 2) \overset{?}{=} 7x - x - 2$

100. $12y - (3y - 1) \overset{?}{=} 12y - 3y + 1$

101. $4(y - 3) + 11 \overset{?}{=} 4y - 7 + 11$

102. $6(x + 5) + 2 \overset{?}{=} 6x + 30 + 12$

Review commutative, associative, and distributive properties. Then identify which property allows us to write the equivalent expression on the right side of the equal sign.

103. $6(2x - 3) + 5 = 12x - 18 + 5$

104. $9 + 7x + (-2) = 7x + 9 + (-2)$

105. $-7 + (4 + y) = (-7 + 4) + y$

106. $(x + y) + 11 = 11 + (x + y)$

Write the expression that represents the area of each composite figure. Then simplify to find the total area.

△ **107.**

$(2x + 1)$ miles

7 miles | Rectangle | $(2x + 3)$ miles

Rectangle | 3 miles

△ **108.**

12 kilometers

$(3x - 5)$ kilometers | Rectangle

$(5x - 1)$ kilometers | Rectangle

4 kilometers

Simplify.

109. $9684q - 686 - 4860q + 12{,}960$

110. $76(268x + 592) - 2960$

111. If x is a whole number, which expression is greater: $2x$ or $5x$? Explain your answer.

112. If x is a whole number, which expression is greater: $-2x$ or $-5x$? Explain your answer.

113. Explain what makes two terms "like terms."

114. Explain how to combine like terms.

3.2 **Solving Equations: Review of the Addition and Multiplication Properties** ▶

Objective A Using the Addition Property or the Multiplication Property ▶

In this section, we continue solving equations using the properties first introduced in Section 2.6.

First, let's recall the difference between an **expression** and an **equation.** Remember—an equation contains an equal sign and an expression does not.

	Equations	Expressions	
equal signs	$7x = 6x + 4$	$7x - 6x + 4$	no equal signs
	$3(3y - 5) = 10y$	$y - 1 + 11y - 21$	

Thus far in this text, we have

Solved some equations (Section 2.6)

and

Simplified some expressions (Section 3.1)

As we will see in this section, the ability to simplify expressions will help us as we solve more equations.

The addition and multiplication properties are reviewed below.

Addition Property of Equality

Let a, b, and c represent numbers. Then

$$a = b$$
$$\text{and } a + c = b + c$$

are equivalent equations.

Also, $a = b$
and $a - c = b - c$

are equivalent equations.

Multiplication Property of Equality

Let a, b, and c represent numbers and let $c \neq 0$. Then

$$a = b$$
$$\text{and } a \cdot c = b \cdot c$$

are equivalent equations.

Also, $a = b$
and $\dfrac{a}{c} = \dfrac{b}{c}$

are equivalent equations.

In other words, the same number may be added to or subtracted from *both* sides of an equation without changing the solution of the equation. Also, *both* sides of an equation may be multiplied or divided by the same nonzero number without changing the solution of the equation.

Many equations in this section will contain expressions that can be simplified. If one or both sides of an equation can be simplified, do that first.

Example 1 Solve: $y - 5 = -2 - 6$

Solution: First we simplify the right side of the equation.

$y - 5 = -2 - 6$
$y - 5 = -8$ Combine like terms.

(Continued on next page)

Objectives

A Use the Addition Property or the Multiplication Property to Solve Equations. ▶

B Use Both Properties to Solve Equations. ▶

C Translate Word Phrases to Mathematical Expressions. ▶

Practice 1

Solve: $x + 6 = 1 - 3$

Answer
1. -8

Next we get y alone by using the addition property of equality. We add 5 to both sides of the equation.

$$y - 5 + 5 = -8 + 5 \quad \text{Add 5 to both sides.}$$
$$y = -3 \quad \text{Simplify.}$$

Check: To see that -3 is the solution, replace y with -3 in the original equation.

$$y - 5 = -2 - 6$$
$$-3 - 5 \stackrel{?}{=} -2 - 6 \quad \text{Replace } y \text{ with } -3.$$
$$-8 = -8 \quad \text{True}$$

Since $-8 = -8$ is true, the solution is -3.

▰ Work Practice 1

Practice 2

Solve: $10 = 2m - 4m$

Example 2 Solve: $3y - 7y = 12$

Solution: First, simplify the left side of the equation by combining like terms.

$$3y - 7y = 12$$
$$-4y = 12 \quad \text{Combine like terms.}$$

Next, we get y alone by using the multiplication property of equality and dividing both sides by -4.

$$\frac{-4y}{-4} = \frac{12}{-4} \quad \text{Divide both sides by } -4.$$
$$y = -3 \quad \text{Simplify.}$$

Check: Replace y with -3 in the original equation.

$$3y - 7y = 12$$
$$3(-3) - 7(-3) \stackrel{?}{=} 12$$
$$-9 + 21 \stackrel{?}{=} 12$$
$$12 = 12 \quad \text{True}$$

The solution is -3.

▰ Work Practice 2

✓**Concept Check** What's wrong with the following solution?

$$4x - 6x = 10$$
$$2x = 10$$
$$\frac{2x}{2} = \frac{10}{2}$$
$$x = 5$$

Practice 3

Solve: $-8 + 6 = \dfrac{a}{3}$

Answers

2. -5 **3.** -6

✓**Concept Check answer**

On the left side of the equation, $4x - 6x$ simplifies to $-2x$ *not* $2x$.

Example 3 Solve: $\dfrac{z}{-4} = 11 - 5$

Solution: Simplify the right side of the equation first.

$$\frac{z}{-4} = 11 - 5$$
$$\frac{z}{-4} = 6$$

Next, to get z alone, multiply both sides by -4.

$$-4 \cdot \frac{z}{-4} = -4 \cdot 6 \qquad \text{Multiply both sides by } -4.$$

$$\frac{-4}{-4} \cdot z = -4 \cdot 6$$

$$1z = -24 \quad \text{or} \quad z = -24$$

Check to see that -24 is the solution.

■ Work Practice 3

Example 4 Solve: $5x + 2 - 4x = 7 - 19$

Solution: First we simplify each side of the equation separately.

$$5x + 2 - 4x = 7 - 19$$

$$\underline{5x - 4x} + 2 = \underline{7 - 19}$$

$$1x + 2 = -12 \qquad \text{Combine like terms.}$$

To get x alone on the left side, we subtract 2 from both sides.

$$1x + 2 - 2 = -12 - 2 \qquad \text{Subtract 2 from both sides.}$$

$$1x = -14 \quad \text{or} \quad x = -14 \quad \text{Simplify.}$$

Check to see that -14 is the solution.

■ Work Practice 4

Practice 4

Solve:
$-6y - 1 + 7y = 17 + 2$

Example 5 Solve: $8x - 9x = 12 - 17$

Solution: First combine like terms on each side of the equation.

$$8x - 9x = 12 - 17$$

$$-x = -5$$

Recall that $-x$ means $-1x$ and divide both sides by -1.

$$\frac{-1x}{-1} = \frac{-5}{-1} \qquad \text{Divide both sides by } -1.$$

$$x = 5 \qquad \text{Simplify.}$$

Check to see that the solution is 5.

■ Work Practice 5

Practice 5

Solve: $-4 - 10 = 4y - 5y$

Example 6 Solve: $3(3x - 5) = 10x$

Solution: First we multiply on the left side to remove the parentheses.

$$3(3x - 5) = 10x$$

$$3 \cdot 3x - 3 \cdot 5 = 10x \qquad \text{Use the distributive property.}$$

$$9x - 15 = 10x$$

Now we subtract $9x$ from both sides.

$$9x - 15 - 9x = 10x - 9x \qquad \text{Subtract } 9x \text{ from both sides.}$$

$$-15 = 1x \quad \text{or} \quad x = -15 \quad \text{Simplify.}$$

■ Work Practice 6

Practice 6

Solve: $13x = 4(3x - 1)$

Answers

4. 20   **5.** 14   **6.** -4

Objective B Using Both Properties to Solve Equations

We now solve equations in one variable using more than one property of equality. To solve an equation such as $2x - 6 = 18$, we first get the variable term $2x$ alone on one side of the equation.

Practice 7

Solve: $5y + 2 = 17$

Example 7 Solve: $2x - 6 = 18$

Solution: We start by adding 6 to both sides to get the variable term $2x$ alone.

$$2x - 6 = 18$$
$$2x - 6 + 6 = 18 + 6 \qquad \text{Add 6 to both sides.}$$
$$2x = 24 \qquad \text{Simplify.}$$

To finish solving, we divide both sides by 2.

$$\frac{2x}{2} = \frac{24}{2} \qquad \text{Divide both sides by 2.}$$
$$x = 12 \qquad \text{Simplify.}$$

Check:

$$2x - 6 = 18$$
$$2(12) - 6 \stackrel{?}{=} 18 \qquad \text{Replace } x \text{ with 12 and simplify.}$$
$$24 - 6 \stackrel{?}{=} 18$$
$$18 = 18 \qquad \text{True}$$

Helpful Hint Don't forget to check the proposed solution in the *original* equation.

The solution is 12.

■ Work Practice 7

Don't forget, if one or both sides of an equation can be simplified, do that first.

Practice 8

Solve:
$-4(x + 2) - 60 = 2 - 10$

Example 8 Solve: $2 - 6 = -5(x + 4) - 39$

Solution: First, simplify each side of the equation.

$$2 - 6 = -5(x + 4) - 39$$
$$2 - 6 = -5x - 20 - 39 \qquad \text{Use the distributive property.}$$
$$-4 = -5x - 59 \qquad \text{Combine like terms on each side.}$$
$$-4 + 59 = -5x - 59 + 59 \qquad \text{Add 59 to both sides to get the variable term alone.}$$
$$55 = -5x \qquad \text{Simplify.}$$
$$\frac{55}{-5} = \frac{-5x}{-5} \qquad \text{Divide both sides by } -5.$$
$$-11 = x \quad \text{or} \quad x = -11 \qquad \text{Simplify.}$$

Check to see that -11 is the solution.

■ Work Practice 8

Answers

7. 3   **8.** −15

Objective C Translating Word Phrases into Expressions ▶

Section 3.4 in this chapter contains a formal introduction to problem solving. To prepare for this section, let's once again review writing phrases as algebraic expressions using the following key words and phrases as a guide:

Addition	Subtraction	Multiplication	Division
sum	difference	product	quotient
plus	minus	times	divided
added to	subtracted from	multiply	shared equally among
more than	less than	twice	per
increased by	decreased by	of	divided by
total	less	twice/double/triple	divided into

Example 9 Write each phrase as an algebraic expression. Use x to represent "a number."

a. a number increased by -5
b. the product of -7 and a number
c. a number less 20
d. the quotient of -18 and a number
e. a number subtracted from -2

Solution:

a. In words: a number increased by -5

Translate: x $+$ (-5) or $x - 5$

b. In words: the product of -7 and a number

Translate: -7 · x or $-7x$

c. In words: a number less 20

Translate: x $-$ 20

d. In words: the quotient of -18 and a number

Translate: -18 ÷ x or $\dfrac{-18}{x}$ or $-\dfrac{18}{x}$

e. In words: a number subtracted from -2

Translate: -2 $-$ x

■ Work Practice 9

Practice 9

Write each phrase as an algebraic expression. Use x to represent "a number."
a. the sum of -3 and a number
b. -5 decreased by a number
c. three times a number
d. a number subtracted from 83
e. the quotient of a number and -4

Answers
9. a. $-3 + x$ **b.** $-5 - x$ **c.** $3x$
d. $83 - x$ **e.** $\dfrac{x}{-4}$ or $-\dfrac{x}{4}$

> **Helpful Hint**
>
> As we reviewed in Chapter 1, don't forget that order is important when subtracting. Notice the translation order of numbers and variables below.
>
> | Phrase | Translation |
> |---|---|
> | a number less 9 | $x - 9$ |
> | a number subtracted from 9 | $9 - x$ |

Practice 10

Translate each phrase into an algebraic expression. Let x be the unknown number.

a. The product of 5 and a number, decreased by 25

b. Twice the sum of a number and 3

c. The quotient of 39 and twice a number

Answers

10. a. $5x - 25$ **b.** $2(x + 3)$

c. $39 \div (2x)$ or $\dfrac{39}{2x}$

Example 10 Write each phrase as an algebraic expression. Let x be the unknown number.

a. Twice a number, increased by -9

b. Three times the difference of a number and 11

c. The quotient of 5 times a number and 17

Solution:

a. In words:

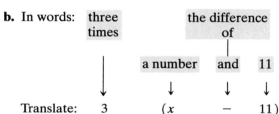

Translate: $2x + (-9)$ or $2x - 9$

b. In words:

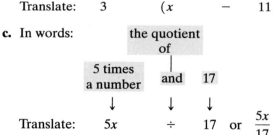

Translate: $3 \quad (x - 11)$

c. In words:

the quotient of

5 times a number · and · 17

Translate: $5x \div 17$ or $\dfrac{5x}{17}$

■ **Work Practice 10**

Vocabulary, Readiness & Video Check

Use the choices below to fill in each blank.

equation	multiplication	equivalent	expression
solving	addition	simplifying	

1. The equations $-3x = 51$ and $\dfrac{-3x}{-3} = \dfrac{51}{-3}$ are called _____ equations.

2. The difference between an equation and an expression is that a(n) _____ contains an equal sign, while a(n) _____ does not.

3. The process of writing $-3x + 10x$ as $7x$ is called _____ the expression.

4. For the equation $-5x - 1 = -21$, the process of finding that 4 is the solution is called _____ the equation.

5. By the _____ property of equality, $x = -2$ and $x + 7 = -2 + 7$ are equivalent equations.

6. By the _____ property of equality, $y = 8$ and $3 \cdot y = 3 \cdot 8$ are equivalent equations.

Martin-Gay Interactive Videos   Watch the section lecture video and answer the following questions.

See Video 3.2

Objective A **7.** When solving ⊞ Example 1, what must be done before applying the multiplication property of equality? ⊳

8. When solving ⊞ Example 4, what must be done before applying the addition property of equality? ⊳

Objective B **9.** In ⊞ Examples 5 and 6, both the addition and the multiplication properties of equality are used. Which property is used first both times? ⊳

Objective C **10.** In ⊞ Example 7, why are we told to be careful when translating a subtraction phrase? ⊳

3.2 Exercise Set MyMathLab® ⊳

Objective A *Solve each equation. First combine any like terms on each side of the equation. See Examples 1 through 5.*

1. $x - 3 = -1 + 4$

2. $x + 7 = 2 + 3$

⊳ **3.** $-7 + 10 = m - 5$

4. $1 - 8 = n + 2$

5. $2w - 12w = 40$

6. $10y - y = 45$

7. $24 = t + 3t$

8. $100 = 15y + 5y$

⊳ **9.** $2z = 12 - 14$

10. $-3x = 11 - 2$

11. $4 - 10 = \dfrac{z}{-3}$

12. $20 - 22 = \dfrac{z}{-4}$

13. $-3x - 3x = 50 - 2$

14. $5y - 9y = -14 + (-14)$

15. $\dfrac{x}{5} = -26 + 16$

16. $\dfrac{y}{3} = 32 - 52$

17. $7x + 7 - 6x = 10$

18. $-3 + 5x - 4x = 13$

19. $-8 - 9 = 3x + 5 - 2x$

20. $-7 + 10 = 4x - 6 - 3x$

Solve. First multiply to remove parentheses. See Example 6.

⊳ **21.** $2(5x - 3) = 11x$

22. $6(3x + 1) = 19x$

23. $3y = 2(y + 12)$

24. $17x = 4(4x - 6)$

25. $21y = 5(4y - 6)$

26. $28z = 9(3z - 2)$

27. $-3(-4 - 2z) = 7z$

28. $-2(-1 - 3y) = 7y$

Objective B *Solve each equation. See Examples 7 and 8.*

29. $2x - 8 = 0$

30. $3y - 12 = 0$

⊳ **31.** $7y + 3 = 24$

32. $5m + 1 = 46$

33. $-7 = 2x - 1$

34. $-11 = 3t - 2$

35. $6(6 - 4y) = 12y$

36. $4(3y - 5) = 14y$

37. $11(x - 6) = -4 - 7$

38. $5(x - 6) = -2 - 8$

39. $-3(x + 1) - 10 = 12 + 8$

40. $-2(x + 5) - 2 = -8 - 4$

41. $y - 20 = 6y$

42. $x - 63 = 10x$

43. $22 - 42 = 4(x - 1) - 4$

44. $35 - (-3) = 3(x - 2) + 17$

Objectives A B Mixed Practice *Solve each equation. See Examples 1 through 8.*

45. $-2 - 3 = -4 + x$

46. $7 - (-10) = x - 5$

47. $y + 1 = -3 + 4$

48. $y - 8 = -5 - 1$

49. $3w - 12w = -27$

50. $y - 6y = 20$

51. $-4x = 20 - (-4)$

52. $6x = 5 - 35$

53. $18 - 11 = \dfrac{x}{-5}$

54. $9 - 14 = \dfrac{x}{-12}$

55. $9x - 12 = 78$

56. $8x - 8 = 32$

57. $10 = 7t - 12t$

58. $-30 = t + 9t$

59. $5 - 5 = 3x + 2x$

60. $-42 + 20 = -2x + 13x$

61. $50y = 7(7y + 4)$

62. $65y = 8(8y - 9)$

63. $8x = 2(6x + 10)$

64. $10x = 6(2x - 3)$

65. $7x + 14 - 6x = -4 - 10$

66. $-10x + 11x + 5 = 9 - 5$

67. $\dfrac{x}{-4} = -1 - (-8)$

68. $\dfrac{y}{-6} = 6 - (-1)$

69. $23x + 8 - 25x = 7 - 9$

70. $8x - 4 - 6x = 12 - 22$

71. $-3(x + 9) - 41 = 4 - 60$

72. $-4(x + 7) - 30 = 3 - 37$

Objective C Translating *Write each phrase as a variable expression. Use x to represent "a number." See Examples 9 and 10.*

73. The sum of -7 and a number

74. Negative eight plus a number

75. Eleven subtracted from a number

76. A number subtracted from twelve

77. The product of -13 and a number

78. Twice a number

79. A number divided by -12

80. The quotient of negative six and a number

81. The product of -11 and a number, increased by 5

82. Negative four times a number, increased by 18

83. Negative ten decreased by 7 times a number

84. Twice a number, decreased by thirty

85. Seven added to the product of 4 and a number

86. The product of 7 and a number, added to 100

87. Twice a number, decreased by 17

88. The difference of -9 times a number, and 1

89. The product of -6 and the sum of a number and 15

90. Twice the sum of a number and -5

91. The quotient of 45 and the product of a number and -5

92. The quotient of ten times a number, and -4

93. The quotient of seventeen and a number, increased by -15

94. The quotient of -20 and a number, decreased by three

Review

This horizontal bar graph shows the top ten states for traveler spending in a recent year. Use this graph to answer Exercises 95 through 98. See Sections 1.2 and 1.3.

95. For what state do travelers spend the most money?

96. For the states shown, which states have traveler amounts less than $20 billion?

97. What is the combined spending for the neighboring states of Florida and Georgia?

98. What is the combined spending for the two largest states, Texas and California?

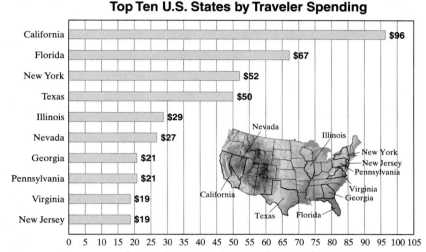

Top Ten U.S. States by Traveler Spending

California $96
Florida $67
New York $52
Texas $50
Illinois $29
Nevada $27
Georgia $21
Pennsylvania $21
Virginia $19
New Jersey $19

0 5 10 15 20 25 30 35 40 45 50 55 60 65 70 75 80 85 90 95 100 105

Domestic and International Traveler Spending Within State (in billions of dollars)

Source: U.S. Travel Association, 2010

Concept Extensions

99. In your own words, explain the addition property of equality.

100. Write an equation that can be solved using the addition property of equality.

101. Are the equations below equivalent? Why or why not?

$$x + 7 = 4 + (-9)$$
$$x + 7 \stackrel{?}{=} 5$$

102. Are the equations below equivalent? Why or why not?

$$3x - 6x = 12$$
$$3x \stackrel{?}{=} 12$$

103. Why does the multiplication property of equality not allow us to divide both sides of an equation by zero?

104. Is the equation $-x = 6$ solved for the variable? Explain why or why not.

Solve.

105. $\dfrac{y}{72} = -86 - (-1029)$

106. $\dfrac{x}{-13} = 4^6 - 5^7$

107. $\dfrac{x}{-2} = 5^2 - |-10| - (-9)$

108. $\dfrac{y}{10} = (-8)^2 - |20| + (-2)^2$

109. $|-13| + 3^2 = 100y - |-20| - 99y$

110. $4(x - 11) + |90| - |-86| + 2^5 = 5x$

Expressions and Equations

Answers

For the table below, identify each as an expression or an equation.

Expression or Equation	
1. $7x - 5y + 14$	
2. $7x = 35 + 14$	
3. $3(x - 2) = 5(x + 1) - 17$	
4. $-9(2x + 1) - 4(x - 2) + 14$	

1. _____

2. _____

3. _____

4. _____

Fill in each blank with "simplify" or "solve."

5. To _____ an expression, we combine any like terms.

5. _____

6. To _____ an equation, we use the properties of equality to find any value of the variable that makes the equation a true statement.

6. _____

7. _____

Simplify each expression by combining like terms.

7. $7x + x$ **8.** $6y - 10y$

8. _____

9. _____

9. $2a + 5a - 9a - 2$ **10.** $6a - 12 - a - 14$

10. _____

11. _____

Multiply and simplify if possible.

11. $-2(4x + 7)$ **12.** $-3(2x - 10)$

12. _____

13. _____

13. $5(y + 2) - 20$ **14.** $12x + 3(x - 6) - 13$

14. _____

15. _____

△ **15.** Find the area of the rectangle.

| Rectangle | 3 meters |

$(4x - 2)$ meters

16. _____

△ **16.** Find the perimeter of the triangle.

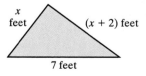

17. _____

Solve and check.

17. $12 = 11x - 14x$ **18.** $8y + 7y = -45$

18. _____

19. _____

19. $x - 12 = -45 + 23$ **20.** $6 - (-5) = x + 5$

20. _____

Solve and check.

21. $\frac{x}{3} = -14 + 9$

22. $\frac{z}{4} = -23 - 7$

23. $-6 + 2 = 4x + 1 - 3x$

24. $5 - 8 = 5x + 10 - 4x$

25. $6(3x - 4) = 19x$

26. $25x = 6(4x - 9)$

27. $-36x - 10 + 37x = -12 - (-14)$

28. $-8 + (-14) = -80y + 20 + 81y$

29. $3x - 16 = -10$

30. $4x - 21 = -13$

31. $-8z - 2z = 26 - (-4)$

32. $-12 + (-13) = 5x - 10x$

33. $-4(x + 8) - 11 = 3 - 26$

34. $-6(x - 2) + 10 = -4 - 10$

Translating *Write each phrase as an algebraic expression. Use x to represent "a number."*

35. The difference of a number and 10

36. The sum of -20 and a number

37. The product of 10 and a number

38. The quotient of 10 and a number

39. Five added to the product of -2 and a number

40. The product of -4 and the difference of a number and 1

21. _____

22. _____

23. _____

24. _____

25. _____

26. _____

27. _____

28. _____

29. _____

30. _____

31. _____

32. _____

33. _____

34. _____

35. _____

36. _____

37. _____

38. _____

39. _____

40. _____

Solving Linear Equations in One Variable ▶

Objectives

A Solve Linear Equations Using the Addition and Multiplication Properties. ▶

B Solve Linear Equations Containing Parentheses. ▶

C Write Numerical Sentences as Equations. ▶

In this chapter, the equations we are solving are called **linear equations in one variable** or **first-degree equations in one variable**. For example, an equation such as $5x - 2 = 6x$ is a linear equation in one variable. It is called linear or first degree because the exponent on each x is 1 and there is no variable below a fraction bar. It is an equation in one variable because it contains one variable, x.

Let's continue solving linear equations in one variable.

Objective **A** Solving Equations Using the Addition and Multiplication Properties ▶

If an equation contains variable terms on both sides, we use the addition property of equality to get all the variable terms on one side and all the constants or numbers on the other side.

Practice 1

Solve: $7x + 12 = 3x - 4$

Example 1 Solve: $3a - 6 = a + 4$

Solution: Although it makes no difference which side we choose, let's move variable terms to the left side and constants to the right side.

$$3a - 6 = a + 4$$
$$3a - 6 + 6 = a + 4 + 6 \qquad \text{Add 6 to both sides.}$$
$$3a = a + 10 \qquad \text{Simplify.}$$
$$3a - a = a + 10 - a \qquad \text{Subtract } a \text{ from both sides.}$$
$$2a = 10 \qquad \text{Simplify.}$$
$$\frac{2a}{2} = \frac{10}{2} \qquad \text{Divide both sides by 2.}$$
$$a = 5 \qquad \text{Simplify.}$$

Check:
$$3a - 6 = a + 4 \qquad \text{Original equation}$$
$$3 \cdot 5 - 6 \overset{?}{=} 5 + 4 \qquad \text{Replace } a \text{ with 5.}$$
$$15 - 6 \overset{?}{=} 9 \qquad \text{Simplify.}$$
$$9 = 9 \qquad \text{True}$$

The solution is 5.

▶ Work Practice 1

Helpful Hint

Make sure you understand which property to use to solve an equation.

Addition
$$x + 2 = 10$$

To undo addition of 2, we subtract 2 from both sides.
$$x + 2 - 2 = 10 - 2 \qquad \text{Use addition property of equality.}$$
$$x = 8$$

Check:
$$x + 2 = 10$$
$$8 + 2 \overset{?}{=} 10$$
$$10 = 10 \qquad \text{True}$$

Understood multiplication
$$2x = 10$$

To undo multiplication of 2, we divide both sides by 2.
$$\frac{2x}{2} = \frac{10}{2} \qquad \text{Use multiplication property of equality.}$$
$$x = 5$$

Check:
$$2x = 10$$
$$2 \cdot 5 \overset{?}{=} 10$$
$$10 = 10 \qquad \text{True}$$

Answer

1. -4

184

Example 2 Solve: $17 - 7x + 3 = -3x + 21 - 3x$

Solution: First, simplify both sides of the equation.

$$17 - 7x + 3 = -3x + 21 - 3x$$
$$20 - 7x = -6x + 21 \qquad \text{Simplify.}$$

Next, move variable terms to one side of the equation and constants, or numbers, to the other side. To begin, let's add $6x$ to both sides.

$$20 - 7x + 6x = -6x + 21 + 6x \qquad \text{Add } 6x \text{ to each side.}$$
$$20 - x = 21 \qquad \text{Simplify.}$$
$$20 - x - 20 = 21 - 20 \qquad \text{Subtract 20 from both sides.}$$
$$-1x = 1 \qquad \text{Simplify. Recall that } -x \text{ means } -1x.$$
$$\frac{-1x}{-1} = \frac{1}{-1} \qquad \text{Divide both sides by } -1.$$
$$x = -1 \qquad \text{Simplify.}$$

Check:
$$17 - 7x + 3 = -3x + 21 - 3x$$
$$17 - 7(-1) + 3 \stackrel{?}{=} -3(-1) + 21 - 3(-1)$$
$$17 + 7 + 3 \stackrel{?}{=} 3 + 21 + 3$$
$$27 = 27 \qquad \text{True}$$

The solution is -1.

■ Work Practice 2

Practice 2

Solve:
$$40 - 5y + 5 = -2y - 10 - 4y$$

Objective B Solving Equations Containing Parentheses

Recall from the previous section that if an equation contains parentheses, we will first use the distributive property to remove them.

Example 3 Solve: $7(x - 2) = 9x - 6$

Solution: First we apply the distributive property.

$$7(x - 2) = 9x - 6$$
$$7x - 14 = 9x - 6 \qquad \text{Apply the distributive property.}$$

Next we move variable terms to one side of the equation and constants to the other side.

$$7x - 14 - 9x = 9x - 6 - 9x \qquad \text{Subtract } 9x \text{ from both sides.}$$
$$-2x - 14 = -6 \qquad \text{Simplify.}$$
$$-2x - 14 + 14 = -6 + 14 \qquad \text{Add 14 to both sides.}$$
$$-2x = 8 \qquad \text{Simplify.}$$
$$\frac{-2x}{-2} = \frac{8}{-2} \qquad \text{Divide both sides by } -2.$$
$$x = -4 \qquad \text{Simplify.}$$

Check to see that -4 is the solution.

■ Work Practice 3

Practice 3

Solve: $6(a - 5) = 4a + 4$

Answers
2. -55 **3.** 17

✓**Concept Check** In Example 3, the solution is -4. To check this solution, what equation should we use?

✓**Concept Check Answer**
$7(x - 2) = 9x - 6$

You may want to use the following steps to solve equations.

Steps for Solving an Equation

Step 1: If parentheses are present, use the distributive property.

Step 2: Combine any like terms on each side of the equation.

Step 3: Use the addition property of equality to rewrite the equation so that variable terms are on one side of the equation and constant terms are on the other side.

Step 4: Use the multiplication property of equality to divide both sides by the numerical coefficient of the variable to solve.

Step 5: Check the solution in the *original equation*.

Practice 4

Solve: $4(x + 3) + 1 = 13$

Example 4 Solve: $3(2x - 6) + 6 = 0$

Solution: $3(2x - 6) + 6 = 0$

Step 1: $6x - 18 + 6 = 0$ Apply the distributive property.

Step 2: $6x - 12 = 0$ Combine like terms on the left side of the equation.

Step 3: $6x - 12 + 12 = 0 + 12$ Add 12 to both sides.

$6x = 12$ Simplify.

Step 4: $\dfrac{6x}{6} = \dfrac{12}{6}$ Divide both sides by 6.

$x = 2$ Simplify.

Check:

Step 5: $3(2x - 6) + 6 = 0$

$3(2 \cdot 2 - 6) + 6 \overset{?}{=} 0$

$3(4 - 6) + 6 \overset{?}{=} 0$

$3(-2) + 6 \overset{?}{=} 0$

$-6 + 6 \overset{?}{=} 0$

$0 = 0$ True

The solution is 2.

■ Work Practice 4

Objective C Writing Numerical Sentences as Equations

Next, we practice translating sentences into equations. Below are key words and phrases that translate to an equal sign. (*Note:* For a review of key words and phrases that translate to addition, subtraction, multiplication, and division, see Sections 1.8 and 3.2.)

Key Words or Phrases	Examples	Symbols
equals	3 equals 2 plus 1	$3 = 2 + 1$
gives	the quotient of 10 and −5 gives −2	$\dfrac{10}{-5} = -2$
is/was	17 minus 12 is 5	$17 - 12 = 5$
yields	11 plus 2 yields 13	$11 + 2 = 13$
amounts to	twice −15 amounts to −30	$2(-15) = -30$
is equal to	−24 is equal to 2 times −12	$-24 = 2(-12)$

Answer

4. 0

Example 5 Translate each sentence into an equation.

a. The product of 7 and 6 is 42.

b. Twice the sum of 3 and 5 is equal to 16.

c. The quotient of −45 and 5 yields −9.

Solution:

a. In words:

the product of 7 and 6	is	42
↓	↓	↓

Translate: $7 \cdot 6 = 42$

b. In words:

twice	the sum of 3 and 5	is equal to	16
↓	↓	↓	↓

Translate: $2 \quad (3 + 5) = 16$

c. In words:

the quotient of −45 and 5	yields	−9
↓	↓	↓

Translate: $\dfrac{-45}{5} = -9$

■ Work Practice 5

 Calculator Explorations **Checking Equations**

A calculator can be used to check possible solutions of equations. To do this, replace the variable by the possible solution and evaluate each side of the equation separately. For example, to see whether 7 is a solution of the equation $52x = 15x + 259$, replace x with 7 and use your calculator to evaluate each side separately.

Equation: $52x = 15x + 259$

$52 \cdot 7 \overset{?}{=} 15 \cdot 7 + 259$ Replace x with 7.

Evaluate left side: $\boxed{52}$ $\boxed{\times}$ $\boxed{7}$ then $\boxed{=}$ or $\boxed{\text{ENTER}}$.
Display: $\boxed{364}$.

Evaluate right side: $\boxed{15}$ $\boxed{\times}$ $\boxed{7}$ $\boxed{+}$ $\boxed{259}$ then $\boxed{=}$ or $\boxed{\text{ENTER}}$.
Display: $\boxed{364}$.

Since the left side equals the right side, 7 is a solution of the equation $52x = 15x + 259$.

Use a calculator to determine whether the numbers given are solutions of each equation.

1. $76(x - 25) = -988$;   12

2. $-47x + 862 = -783$;   35

3. $x + 562 = 3x + 900$;   −170

4. $55(x + 10) = 75x + 910$;   −18

5. $29x - 1034 = 61x - 362$;   −21

6. $-38x + 205 = 25x + 120$;   25

Vocabulary, Readiness & Video Check

Use the choices below to fill in each blank. Some choices may be used more than once.

addition	multiplication	combine like terms
$5(2x + 6) - 1 = 39$	$3x - 9 + x - 16$	distributive

1. An example of an expression is _____ while an example of an equation is _____ .

2. To solve $\dfrac{x}{-7} = -10$, we use the _____ property of equality.

3. To solve $x - 7 = -10$, we use the _____ property of equality.

Use the order of the Steps for Solving an Equation in this section to answer Exercises 4 through 6.

4. To solve $9x - 6x = 10 + 6$, first _____.

5. To solve $5(x - 1) = 25$, first use the _____ property.

6. To solve $4x + 3 = 19$, first use the _____ property of equality.

Martin-Gay Interactive Videos   *Watch the section lecture video and answer the following questions.*

See Video 3.3

Objective A **7.** In ▤ Example 1, the number 1 is subtracted from the left side of the equation. What property tells us we must also subtract 1 from the right side? Why is it important to do the same thing to both sides?

Objective B **8.** From ▤ Example 3, what is the first step when solving an equation that contains parentheses? What property do we use to perform this step? ▶

Objective C **9.** What word or phrase translates to "equals" in ▤ Example 5? In ▤ Example 6? ▶

3.3 Exercise Set MyMathLab® ▶

Objective A *Solve each equation. See Examples 1 and 2.*

1. $3x - 7 = 4x + 5$

2. $7x - 1 = 8x + 4$

▶ **3.** $10x + 15 = 6x + 3$

4. $5x - 3 = 2x - 18$

5. $19 - 3x = 14 + 2x$

6. $4 - 7m = -3m + 4$

7. $-14x - 20 = -12x + 70$

8. $57y + 140 = 54y - 100$

9. $x + 20 + 2x = -10 - 2x - 15$

10. $2x + 10 + 3x = -12 - x - 20$

11. $40 + 4y - 16 = 13y - 12 - 3y$

12. $19x - 2 - 7x = 31 + 6x - 15$

Objective B *Solve each equation. See Examples 3 and 4.*

13. $35 - 17 = 3(x - 2)$

14. $22 - 42 = 4(x - 1)$

▶ **15.** $3(x - 1) - 12 = 0$

16. $2(x + 5) + 8 = 0$

17. $2(y - 3) = y - 6$

18. $3(z + 2) = 5z + 6$

19. $-2(y + 4) = 2$

20. $-1(y + 3) = 10$

21. $2t - 1 = 3(t + 7)$

22. $-4 + 3c = 4(c + 2)$

23. $3(5c + 1) - 12 = 13c + 3$

24. $4(3t + 4) - 20 = 3 + 5t$

Mixed Practice (Sections 2.6, 3.2, 3.3) *Solve each equation.*

25. $-4x = 44$

26. $-3x = 51$

27. $x + 9 = 2$

28. $y - 6 = -11$

29. $8 - b = 13$

30. $7 - z = 15$

31. $-20 - (-50) = \dfrac{x}{9}$

32. $-2 - 10 = \dfrac{z}{10}$

33. $3r + 4 = 19$

34. $7y + 3 = 38$

35. $-7c + 1 = -20$

36. $-2b + 5 = -7$

37. $8y - 13y = -20 - 25$

38. $4x - 11x = -14 - 14$

39. $6(7x - 1) = 43x$

40. $5(3y - 2) = 16y$

41. $-4 + 12 = 16x - 3 - 15x$

42. $-9 + 20 = 19x - 4 - 18x$

43. $-10(x + 3) + 28 = -16 - 16$

44. $-9(x + 2) + 25 = -19 - 19$

45. $4x + 3 = 2x + 11$

46. $6y - 8 = 3y + 7$

47. $-2y - 10 = 5y + 18$

48. $7n + 5 = 12n - 10$

49. $-8n + 1 = -6n - 5$

50. $10w + 8 = w - 10$

51. $9 - 3x = 14 + 2x$

52. $4 - 7m = -3m$

53. $9a + 29 + 7 = 0$

54. $10 + 4v + 6 = 0$

55. $7(y - 2) = 4y - 29$

56. $2(z - 2) = 5z + 17$

57. $12 + 5t = 6(t + 2)$

58. $4 + 3c = 2(c + 2)$

59. $3(5c - 1) - 2 = 13c + 3$

60. $4(2t + 5) - 21 = 7t - 6$

61. $10 + 5(z - 2) = 4z + 1$

62. $14 + 4(w - 5) = 6 - 2w$

63. $7(6 + w) = 6(2 + w)$

64. $6(5 + c) = 5(c - 4)$

Objective C Translating *Write each sentence as an equation. See Example 5.*

65. The sum of -42 and 16 is -26.

66. The difference of -30 and 10 equals -40.

67. The product of -5 and -29 gives 145.

68. The quotient of -16 and 2 yields -8.

69. Three times the difference of -14 and 2 amounts to -48.

70. Negative 2 times the sum of 3 and 12 is -30.

71. The quotient of 100 and twice 50 is equal to 1.

72. Seventeen subtracted from -12 equals -29.

Review

The following bar graph shows the number of U.S. federal individual income tax returns that are filed electronically during the years shown. Electronically filed returns include Telefile and online returns. Use this graph to answer Exercises 73 through 76. Write number answers in standard form. See Sections 1.2 and 1.3.

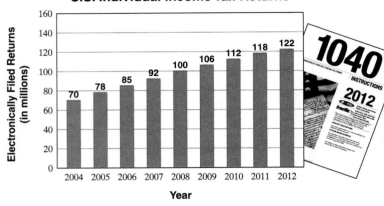

Total Electronically Filed U.S. Individual Income Tax Returns

Source: IRS Compliance Research Division

73. Determine the number of electronically filed returns for 2012.

74. Determine the number of electronically filed returns for 2010.

75. By how much did the number of electronically filed returns increase from 2006 to 2012?

76. Describe any trends shown in this graph.

Evaluate each expression for $x = 3$, $y = -1$, and $z = 0$. See Section 2.5.

77. $x^3 - 2xy$ **78.** $y^3 + 3xyz$ **79.** $y^5 - 4x^2$ **80.** $(-y)^3 + 3xyz$

Concept Extensions

Using the Steps for Solving an Equation, choose the next operation for solving the given equation.

81. $2x - 5 = -7$
- **a.** Add 7 to both sides.
- **b.** Add 5 to both sides.
- **c.** Divide both sides by 2.

82. $3x + 2x = -x - 4$
- **a.** Add 4 to both sides.
- **b.** Subtract $2x$ from both sides.
- **c.** Add $3x$ and $2x$.

83. $-3x = -12$
- **a.** Divide both sides by -3.
- **b.** Add 12 to both sides.
- **c.** Add $3x$ to both sides.

84. $9 - 5x = 15$
- **a.** Divide both sides by -5.
- **b.** Subtract 15 from both sides.
- **c.** Subtract 9 from both sides.

A classmate shows you steps for solving an equation. The solution does not check, but the classmate is unable to find the error. For each set of steps, check the solution, find the error, and correct it.

85.
$$2(3x - 5) = 5x - 7$$
$$6x - 5 = 5x - 7$$
$$6x - 5 + 5 = 5x - 7 + 5$$
$$6x = 5x - 2$$
$$6x - 5x = 5x - 2 - 5x$$
$$x = -2$$

86.
$$37x + 1 = 9(4x - 7)$$
$$37x + 1 = 36x - 7$$
$$37x + 1 - 1 = 36x - 7 - 1$$
$$37x = 36x - 8$$
$$37x - 36x = 36x - 8 - 36x$$
$$x = -8$$

Solve.

87. $(-8)^2 + 3x = 5x + 4^3$ **88.** $3^2 \cdot x = (-9)^3$ **89.** $2^3(x + 4) = 3^2(x + 4)$ **90.** $x + 45^2 = 54^2$

91. A classmate tries to solve $3x = 39$ by subtracting 3 from both sides of the equation. Will this step solve the equation for x? Why or why not?

92. A classmate tries to solve $2 + x = 20$ by dividing both sides by 2. Will this step solve the equation for x? Why or why not?

Linear Equations in One Variable and Problem Solving

Objective A Writing Sentences as Equations

Now that we have practiced solving equations for a variable, we can extend considerably our problem-solving skills. We begin by writing sentences as equations using the following key words and phrases as a guide:

Addition	Subtraction	Multiplication	Division	Equal Sign
sum	difference	product	quotient	equals
plus	minus	times	divide	gives
added to	subtracted from	multiply	shared equally among	is/was
more than	less than	twice	per	yields
increased by	decreased by	of	divided by	amounts to
total	less	double	divided into	is equal to

Objectives

A Write Sentences as Equations.

B Use Problem-Solving Steps to Solve Problems.

Example 1 Write each sentence as an equation. Use x to represent "a number."

a. Twenty increased by a number is 5.
b. Twice a number equals -10.
c. A number minus 11 amounts to 168.
d. Three times the sum of a number and 5 is -30.
e. The quotient of twice a number and 8 is equal to 2.

Solution:

a. In words:

twenty	increased by	a number	is	5
↓	↓	↓	↓	↓

Translate: $20 \quad + \quad x \quad = \quad 5$

b. In words:

twice a number	equals	-10
↓	↓	↓

Translate: $2x \quad = \quad -10$

c. In words:

a number	minus	11	amounts to	168
↓	↓	↓	↓	↓

Translate: $x \quad - \quad 11 \quad = \quad 168$

d. In words:

three times	the sum of a number and 5	is	-30
↓	↓	↓	↓

Translate: $3 \quad (x + 5) \quad = \quad -30$

(Continued on next page)

(Continued on next page)

Practice 1

Write each sentence as an equation. Use x to represent "a number."

a. Four times a number is 20.
b. The sum of a number and -5 yields 32.
c. Fifteen subtracted from a number amounts to -23.
d. Five times the difference of a number and 7 is equal to -8.
e. The quotient of triple a number and 5 gives 1.

Answers

1. a. $4x = 20$ **b.** $x + (-5) = 32$
c. $x - 15 = -23$
d. $5(x - 7) = -8$
e. $\dfrac{3x}{5} = 1$

e. In words:

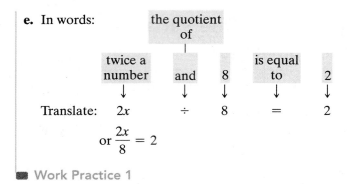

Translate: $2x$ $\div$ 8 $=$ 2

or $\dfrac{2x}{8} = 2$

■ Work Practice 1

Objective B   Using Problem-Solving Steps to Solve Problems ▶

Our main purpose for studying arithmetic and algebra is to solve problems. In previous sections, we have prepared for problem solving by writing phrases as algebraic expressions and sentences as equations. We now draw upon this experience as we solve problems. The following problem-solving steps will be used throughout this text.

> **Problem-Solving Steps**
>
> 1. UNDERSTAND the problem. During this step, become comfortable with the problem. Some ways of doing this are as follows:
>   - Read and reread the problem.
>   - Construct a drawing.
>   - Propose a solution and check. Pay careful attention to how you check your proposed solution. This will help when writing an equation to model the problem.
>   - Choose a variable to represent the unknown. Use this variable to represent any other unknowns.
> 2. TRANSLATE the problem into an equation.
> 3. SOLVE the equation.
> 4. INTERPRET the results: *Check* the proposed solution in the stated problem and *state* your conclusion.

The first problem that we solve consists of finding an unknown number.

Practice 2

Translate "the sum of a number and 2 equals 6 added to three times the number" into an equation and solve.

Example 2   Finding an Unknown Number

Twice a number plus 3 is the same as the number minus 6. Find the unknown number.

Solution:

1. UNDERSTAND the problem. To do so, we read and reread the problem.

   Let's propose a solution to help us understand. Suppose the unknown number is 5. Twice this number plus 3 is $2 \cdot 5 + 3$ or 13. Is this the same as the number minus 6, or $5 - 6$, or -1? Since 13 is not the same as -1, we know that 5 is not the solution. However, remember that the purpose of proposing a solution is not to guess correctly, but to better understand the problem.

   Now let's choose a variable to represent the unknown. Let's let

   $x =$ unknown number

Answer

2. -2

2. TRANSLATE the problem into an equation.

In words:	twice a number	plus 3	is the same as	the number minus 6
	↓	↓	↓	↓
Translate:	$2x$	$+ 3$	$=$	$x - 6$

3. SOLVE the equation. To solve the equation, we first subtract x from both sides.

$$2x + 3 = x - 6$$
$$2x + 3 - x = x - 6 - x$$
$$x + 3 = -6 \qquad \text{Simplify.}$$
$$x + 3 - 3 = -6 - 3 \qquad \text{Subtract 3 from both sides.}$$
$$x = -9 \qquad \text{Simplify.}$$

4. INTERPRET the results. First, *check* the proposed solution in the stated problem. Twice "−9" is −18 and −18 + 3 is −15. This is equal to the number minus 6, or "−9" − 6, or −15. Then *state* your conclusion: The unknown number is −9.

■ Work Practice 2

✔**Concept Check** Suppose you have solved an equation involving perimeter to find the length of a rectangular table. Explain why you would want to recheck your math if you obtain the result of −5.

Example 3 Determining Distances

The distance by road from Chicago, Illinois, to Los Angeles, California, is 1091 miles *more* than the distance from Chicago to Boston, Massachusetts. If the total of these two distances is 3017 miles, find the distance from Chicago to Boston.
(*Source: World Almanac*)

Solution:

1. UNDERSTAND the problem. We read and reread the problem.

Let's propose and check a solution to help us better understand the problem. Suppose the distance from Chicago to Boston is 600 miles. Since the distance from Chicago to Los Angeles is 1091 miles *more*, then this distance is 600 + 1091 = 1691 miles. With these numbers, the total of the distances is 600 + 1691 = 2291 miles. This is less than the given total of 3017 miles, so we are incorrect. But not only do we have a better understanding of this exercise, we also know that the distance from Boston to Chicago is greater than 600 miles since this proposed solution led to a total too small. Now let's choose a variable to represent an unknown. Then we'll use this variable to represent any other unknown quantities. Let

x = distance from Chicago to Boston

Then

$x + 1091$ = distance from Chicago to Los Angeles

Since that distance is 1091 miles more.

2. TRANSLATE the problem into an equation.

In words:	Chicago to Boston distance	+	Chicago to Los Angeles distance	=	total miles
	↓		↓		↓
Translate:	x	+	$\overbrace{x + 1091}$	=	3017

(Continued on next page)

Practice 3

The distance by road from Cincinnati, Ohio, to Denver, Colorado, is 71 miles *less* than the distance from Denver to San Francisco, California. If the total of these two distances is 2399 miles, find the distance from Denver to San Francisco.

Answer
3. 1235 miles

✔**Concept Check Answer**
Length cannot be negative.

3. SOLVE the equation:

$$x + x + 1091 = 3017$$

$$2x + 1091 = 3017 \quad \text{Combine like terms.}$$

$$2x + 1091 - 1091 = 3017 - 1091 \quad \text{Subtract 1091 from both sides.}$$

$$2x = 1926 \quad \text{Simplify.}$$

$$\frac{2x}{2} = \frac{1926}{2} \quad \text{Divide both sides by 2.}$$

$$x = 963 \quad \text{Simplify.}$$

4. INTERPRET the results. First *check* the proposed solution in the stated problem. Since x represents the distance from Chicago to Boston, this is 963 miles. The distance from Chicago to Los Angeles is $x + 1091 = 963 + 1091 = 2054$ miles. To check, notice that the total number of miles is $963 + 2054 = 3017$ miles, the given total of miles. Also, 2054 is 1091 more miles than 963, so the solution checks. Then, *state* your conclusion: The distance from Chicago to Boston is 963 miles.

■ Work Practice 3

Practice 4

A woman's $57,000 estate is to be divided so that her husband receives twice as much as her son. How much will each receive?

Example 4 Calculating Separate Costs

A salesperson at an electronics store sold a computer system and software for $2100, receiving four times as much money for the computer system as for the software. Find the price of each.

Solution:

1. UNDERSTAND the problem. We read and reread the problem. Then we choose a variable to represent an unknown. We use this variable to represent any other unknown quantities. We let

$$x = \text{the software price}$$

Then

$$4x = \text{the computer system price}$$

2. TRANSLATE the problem into an equation.

In words:	software price	and	computer price	is	2100
	↓	↓	↓	↓	↓
Translate:	x	$+$	$4x$	$=$	2100

3. SOLVE the equation:

$$x + 4x = 2100$$

$$5x = 2100 \quad \text{Combine like terms.}$$

$$\frac{5x}{5} = \frac{2100}{5} \quad \text{Divide both sides by 5.}$$

$$x = 420 \quad \text{Simplify.}$$

4. INTERPRET the results. *Check* the proposed solution in the stated problem. The software sold for $420. The computer system sold for $4x = 4(\$420) = \$1680$. Since $\$420 + \$1680 = \$2100$, the total price, and $1680 is four times $420, the solution checks. *State* your conclusion: The software sold for $420, and the computer system sold for $1680.

■ Work Practice 4

Answer

4. husband: $38,000; son: $19,000

Vocabulary, Readiness & Video Check

Martin-Gay Interactive Videos *Watch the section lecture video and answer the following questions.*

See Video 3.4

Objective A 1. In ▸ Example 2, why does the left side of the equation translate to $-20 - x$ and not $x - (-20)$? ▸

Objective B 2. Why are parentheses used in the translation of the left side of the equation in ▸ Example 4? ▸

3. In ▸ Example 5, the solution to the equation is $x = 37$. Why is this not the solution to the application? ▸

3.4 Exercise Set MyMathLab®

Objective A Translating *Write each sentence as an equation. Use x to represent "a number." See Example 1.*

1. A number added to -5 is -7.

2. Five subtracted from a number equals 10.

3. Three times a number yields 27.

4. The quotient of 8 and a number is -2.

▸ 5. A number subtracted from -20 amounts to 104.

6. Two added to twice a number gives -14.

▸ 7. Twice a number gives 108.

8. Five times a number is equal to -75.

9. The product of 5 and the sum of -3 and a number is -20.

10. Twice the sum of -17 and a number is -14.

Objective B Translating *Translate each sentence into an equation. Then solve the equation. See Example 2.*

▸ 11. Three times a number, added to 9, is 33. Find the number.

12. Twice a number, subtracted from 60, is 20. Find the number.

13. The sum of 3, 4, and a number amounts to 16. Find the number.

14. The sum of 7, 9, and a number is 40. Find the number.

15. The difference of a number and 3 is equal to the quotient of 10 and 5. Find the number.

16. Eight decreased by a number equals the quotient of 15 and 5. Find the number.

17. Thirty less a number is equal to the product of 3 and the sum of the number and 6. Find the number.

18. The product of a number and 3 is twice the sum of that number and 5. Find the number.

19. 40 subtracted from five times a number is 8 more than the number. Find the number.

20. Five times the sum of a number and 2 is 11 less than the number times 8. Find the number.

21. Three times the difference of some number and 5 amounts to the quotient of 108 and 12. Find the number.

22. Seven times the difference of some number and 1 gives the quotient of 70 and 10. Find the number.

23. The product of 4 and a number is the same as 30 less twice that same number. Find the number.

24. Twice a number equals 25 less triple that same number. Find the number.

Solve. For Exercises 25 and 26, the solutions have been started for you. See Examples 3 and 4.

25. Florida has 28 fewer electoral votes for president than California. If the total number of electoral votes for these two states is 82, find the number for each state. (*Source: The World Almanac* 2013)

Start the solution:
1. UNDERSTAND the problem. Reread it as many times as needed. Let's let

   x = number of electoral votes for California
   Then
   $x - 28$ = number of electoral votes for Florida
2. TRANSLATE into an equation. (Fill in the blanks below.)

votes for California	+	votes for Florida	= 82
↓		↓	

   _____ + _____ = 82

   Now, you finish with
3. SOLVE the equation.
4. INTERPRET the results.

26. Texas has twice the number of electoral votes for president as Michigan. If the total number of electoral votes for these two states is 51, find the number for each state. (*Source: The World Almanac* 2013)

Start the solution:
1. UNDERSTAND the problem. Reread it as many times as needed. Let's let

   x = number of electoral votes for Michigan
   Then
   $2x$ = number of electoral votes for Texas
2. TRANSLATE into an equation. (Fill in the blanks below.)

votes for Michigan	+	votes for Texas	= 51
↓		↓	

   _____ + _____ = 51

   Now, you finish with
3. SOLVE the equation.
4. INTERPRET the results.

27. A falcon, when diving, can travel five times as fast as a pheasant's top speed. If the total speed for these two birds is 222 miles per hour, find the fastest speed of the falcon and the fastest speed of the pheasant.
(*Source: Fantastic Book of Comparisons*)

28. Norway has had three times as many rulers as Liechtenstein. If the total number of rulers for both countries is 56, find the number of rulers for Norway and the number for Liechtenstein.

Norway

Liechtenstein

29. The U.S. Sunday newspaper with the greatest circulation is *The New York Times*, followed by *The Los Angeles Times*. If the Sunday circulation for *The New York Times* is 384 thousand more than the circulation for *The Los Angeles Times*, and their combined circulation is 2494 thousand, find the circulation for each newspaper. (*Source: The Top Ten of Everything*, 2013)

30. The average life expectancy for an elephant is 24 years longer than the life expectancy for a chimpanzee. If the total of these life expectancies is 130 years, find the life expectancy of each.

31. Coca-Cola was recently named the Most Valuable Global Brand. It has a recognition value worth $43 billion more than Disney's. If the total value of these two global brands is $101 billion, find the value of each of the brands. (See the Chapter 3 Opener.)

32. The global brand Microsoft has a recognition value worth $26 billion more than Apple's. If the total value of these two global brands is $92 billion, find the value of each of the brands. (See the Chapter 3 Opener.)

33. An Xbox 360 game system and several games are sold for $440. The cost of the Xbox 360 is 3 times as much as the cost of the games. Find the cost of the Xbox 360 and the cost of the games.

34. The two top-selling PC games are *Call of Duty: Black Ops 2* and *Madden NFL 13*. A price for *Call of Duty: Black Ops 2* is $13 more than a price for *Madden NFL 13*. If the total of these two prices is $47, find the price of each game. (*Source:* Internet Research)

35. By air, the distance from New York City to London is 2001 miles *less* than the distance from Los Angeles to Tokyo. If the total of these two distances is 8939 miles, find the distance from Los Angeles to Tokyo.

36. By air, the distance from Melbourne, Australia, to Cairo, Egypt, is 2338 miles *more* than the distance from Madrid, Spain, to Bangkok, Thailand. If the total of these distances is 15,012 miles, find the distance from Madrid to Bangkok.

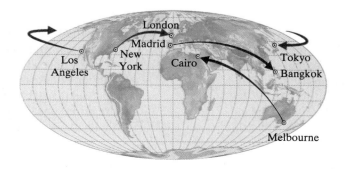

37. The two NCAA stadiums with the largest capacities are Beaver Stadium (Penn State) and Michigan Stadium (Univ. of Michigan). Beaver Stadium has a capacity of 1081 more than Michigan Stadium. If the combined capacity for the two stadiums is 213,483, find the capacity for each stadium. (*Source:* National Collegiate Athletic Association)

38. A National Hot Rod Association (NHRA) top fuel dragster has a top speed of 95 mph faster than an Indy Racing League car. If the top speed for these two cars combined is 565 mph, find the top speed of each car. (*Source:* USA Today)

39. In 2020, China is projected to be the country with the greatest number of visiting tourists. This number is twice the number of tourists projected for Spain. If the total number of tourists for these two countries is projected to be 210 million, find the number projected for each. (*Source: The State of the World Atlas* by Dan Smith)

40. California contains the largest state population of native Americans. This population is three times the native American population of Washington state. If the total of these two populations is 412 thousand, find the native American population in each of these two states. (*Source:* U.S. Census Bureau)

41. In Germany, about twice as many cars are manufactured per day than in the United States. If the total number of these cars manufactured per day is 24,258, find the number manufactured in the United States and the number manufactured in Germany. (Based on data from the International Organization of Motor Vehicle Manufacturers)

42. A Toyota Camry is traveling twice as fast as a Dodge truck. If their combined speed is 105 miles per hour, find the speed of the car and find the speed of the truck.

43. A biker sold his used mountain bike and accessories for $270. If he received five times as much money for the bike as he did for the accessories, find how much money he received for the bike.

44. A tractor and a plow attachment are worth $1200. The tractor is worth seven times as much money as the plow. Find the value of the tractor and the value of the plow.

45. During the 2013 Women's NCAA Division I basketball championship game, the Connecticut Huskies scored 33 points more than the Louisville Cardinals. Together, both teams scored a total of 153 points. How many points did the 2013 Champion Connecticut Huskies score during this game? (*Source:* National Collegiate Athletic Association)

46. During the 2013 Men's NCAA Division I basketball championship game, the Michigan Wolverines scored 6 points fewer than the Louisville Cardinals. Together, both teams scored 158 points. How many points did the 2013 Champion Louisville Cardinals score during the game? (*Source:* National Collegiate Athletic Association)

47. The USA is the country with the most personal computers in use, followed by China. If the USA has 115,500 thousand more computers than China and the total number of computers for both countries is 505,780 thousand, find the number of computers for each country. (*Source:* Computer Industry Almanac)

48. The total number of personal computers in use for Italy and Russia is 98,240 thousand. If Russia has 8800 thousand more computers than Italy, find the number of computers for each country. (*Source:* Computer Industry Almanac)

Review

Round each number to the given place value. See Section 1.4.

49. 586 to the nearest ten

50. 82 to the nearest ten

51. 1026 to the nearest hundred

52. 52,333 to the nearest thousand

53. 2986 to the nearest thousand

54. 101,552 to the nearest hundred

Concept Extensions

55. Solve Example 3 again, but this time let x be the distance from Chicago to Los Angeles. Did you get the same results? Explain why or why not.

56. Solve Exercise 25 again, but this time let x be the number of electoral votes for Florida. Did you get the same results? Explain why or why not.

In real estate, a house's selling price P is found by adding the real estate agent's commission C to the amount A that the seller of the house receives: $P = A + C$.

57. A house sold for $230,000. The owner's real estate agent received a commission of $13,800. How much did the seller receive? (*Hint:* Substitute the known values into the equation, then solve the equation for the remaining unknown.)

58. A homeowner plans to use a real estate agent to sell his house. He hopes to sell the house for $165,000 and keep $156,750 of that. If everything goes as he has planned, how much will his real estate agent receive as a commission?

In retailing, the retail price P of an item can be computed using the equation $P = C + M$, where C is the wholesale cost of the item and M is the amount of markup.

59. The retail price of a computer system is $999 after a markup of $450. What is the wholesale cost of the computer system? (*Hint:* Substitute the known values into the equation, then solve the equation for the remaining unknown.)

60. Slidell Feed and Seed sells a bag of cat food for $12. If the store paid $7 for the cat food, what is the markup on the cat food?

Chapter 3 Group Activity

Modeling Equation Solving with Addition and Subtraction

Sections 3.1–3.4

We can use positive counters ● and negative counters ● to help us model the equation-solving process. We also need to use an object that represents a variable. We use small slips of paper with the variable name written on them.

Recall that taking a ● and ● together creates a neutral or zero pair. After a neutral pair has been formed, it can be removed from or added to an equation model without changing the overall value. We also need to remember that we can add or remove the same number of positive or negative counters from both sides of an equation without changing the overall value.

We can represent the equation $x + 5 = 2$ as follows:

To get the variable by itself, we must remove 5 black counters from both sides of the model. Because there are only 2 counters on the right side, we must add 5 negative counters to both sides of the model. Then we can remove neutral pairs: 5 from the left side and 2 from the right side.

We are left with the following model, which represents the solution, $x = -3$.

Similarly, we can represent the equation $x - 4 = -6$ as follows:

To get the variable by itself, we must remove 4 red counters from both sides of the model.

We are left with the following model, which represents the solution, $x = -2$.

Use the counter model to solve each equation.

1. $x - 3 = -7$ 2. $x - 1 = -9$
3. $x + 2 = 8$ 4. $x + 4 = 5$
5. $x + 8 = 3$ 6. $x - 5 = -1$
7. $x - 2 = 1$ 8. $x - 5 = 10$
9. $x + 3 = -7$ 10. $x + 8 = -2$

Chapter 3 Vocabulary Check

Fill in each blank with one of the words or phrases listed below.

variable	addition	constant
terms	simplified	multiplication
like	combined	numerical coefficient

algebraic expression	equation
evaluating the expression	solution
distributive	

1. An algebraic expression is _____ when all like terms have been _____.

2. Terms that are exactly the same, except that they may have different numerical coefficients, are called _____ terms.

3. A letter used to represent a number is called a(n) _____.

4. A combination of operations on variables and numbers is called a(n) _____.

5. The addends of an algebraic expression are called the _____ of the expression.

6. The number factor of a variable term is called the _____.

7. Replacing a variable in an expression by a number and then finding the value of the expression is called _____ for the variable.

8. A term that is a number only is called a(n) _____.

9. A(n) _____ is of the form expression = expression.

10. A(n) _____ of an equation is a value for the variable that makes the equation a true statement.

11. To multiply $-3(2x + 1)$, we use the _____ property.

12. By the _____ property of equality, we may multiply or divide both sides of an equation by any nonzero number without changing the solution of the equation.

13. By the _____ property of equality, the same number may be added to or subtracted from both sides of an equation without changing the solution of the equation.

Helpful Hint
▶ Are you preparing for your test? Don't forget to take the Chapter 3 Test on page 207. Then check your answers at the back of the text and use the Chapter Test Prep Videos to see the fully worked-out solutions to any of the exercises you want to review.

3 Chapter Highlights

Definitions and Concepts	Examples
Section 3.1 Simplifying Algebraic Expressions	

The addends of an algebraic expression are called the **terms** of the expression.

$5x^2 + (-4x) + (-2)$

                3 terms

The number factor of a variable term is called the **numerical coefficient.**

Term	Numerical Coefficient
$7x$	7
$-6y$	-6
x or $1x$	1

Terms that are exactly the same, except that they may have different numerical coefficients, are called **like terms.**

An algebraic expression is **simplified** when all like terms have been **combined.**

$5x + 11x = (5 + 11)x = 16x$

like terms

$y - 6y = (1 - 6)y = -5y$

Use the **distributive property** to multiply an algebraic expression by a term.

Simplify: $-4(x + 2) + 3(5x - 7)$
$= -4 \cdot x + (-4) \cdot 2 + 3 \cdot 5x - 3 \cdot 7$
$= -4x + (-8) + 15x + (-21)$
$= 11x + (-29)$ or $11x - 29$

Section 3.2 Solving Equations: Review of the Addition and Multiplication Properties	

Addition Property of Equality

Let a, b, and c represent numbers. Then

$a = b$	Also, $a = b$
and $a + c = b + c$	and $a - c = b - c$
are equivalent equations.	are equivalent equations.

In other words, the same number may be added to or subtracted from both sides of an equation without changing the solution of the equation.

Solve for x:

$x + 8 = 2 + (-1)$
$x + 8 = 1$ Combine like terms.
$x + 8 - 8 = 1 - 8$ Subtract 8 from both sides.
$x = -7$ Simplify.

The solution is -7.

(continued)

Definitions and Concepts	Examples

Section 3.2 Solving Equations: Review of the Addition and Multiplication Properties (*continued*)

Multiplication Property of Equality

Let a, b, and c represent numbers and let $c \neq 0$. Then

$$a = b$$
and $a \cdot c = b \cdot c$
are equivalent equations.

Also, $a = b$
and $\dfrac{a}{c} = \dfrac{b}{c}$
are equivalent equations.

In other words, both sides of an equation may be multiplied or divided by the same nonzero number without changing the solution of the equation.

Solve: $y - 7y = 30$

$-6y = 30$ Combine like terms.

$\dfrac{-6y}{-6} = \dfrac{30}{-6}$ Divide both sides by -6.

$y = -5$ Simplify.

The solution is -5.

Section 3.3 Solving Linear Equations in One Variable

Steps for Solving an Equation

Step 1: If parentheses are present, use the distributive property.

Step 2: Combine any like terms on each side of the equation.

Step 3: Use the addition property of equality to rewrite the equation so that variable terms are on one side of the equation and constant terms are on the other side.

Step 4: Use the multiplication property of equality to divide both sides by the numerical coefficient of the variable to solve.

Step 5: Check the solution in the *original equation*.

Solve for x: $5(3x - 1) + 15 = -5$

Step 1: $15x - 5 + 15 = -5$ Apply the distributive property.

Step 2: $15x + 10 = -5$ Combine like terms.

Step 3: $15x + 10 - 10 = -5 - 10$ Subtract 10 from both sides.

$15x = -15$

Step 4: $\dfrac{15x}{15} = \dfrac{-15}{15}$ Divide both sides by 15.

$x = -1$

Step 5: Check to see that -1 is the solution.

Section 3.4 Linear Equations in One Variable and Problem Solving

Problem-Solving Steps

1. UNDERSTAND the problem. Some ways of doing this are

Read and reread the problem.

Construct a drawing.

Choose a variable to represent an unknown in the problem.

The incubation period for a golden eagle is three times the incubation period for a hummingbird. If the total of their incubation periods is 60 days, find the incubation period for each bird. (*Source: Wildlife Fact File,* International Masters Publishers)

1. UNDERSTAND the problem. Then choose a variable to represent an unknown. Let

x = incubation period of a hummingbird

Then

$3x$ = incubation period of a golden eagle

2. TRANSLATE the problem into an equation.

2. TRANSLATE.

incubation of hummingbird	+	incubation of golden eagle	is	60
$\downarrow$		$\downarrow$	$\downarrow$	$\downarrow$
x	+	$3x$	=	60

Definitions and Concepts	Examples
Section 3.4 Linear Equations in One Variable and Problem Solving (*continued*)	
3. SOLVE the equation.	**3.** SOLVE: $$x + 3x = 60$$ $$4x = 60$$ $$\frac{4x}{4} = \frac{60}{4}$$ $$x = 15$$
4. INTERPRET the results. *Check* the proposed solution in the stated problem and *state* your conclusion.	**4.** INTERPRET the solution in the stated problem. The incubation period for a hummingbird is 15 days. The incubation period for a golden eagle is $3x = 3 \cdot 15 = 45$ days. Since 15 days + 45 days = 60 days and 45 is 3(15), the solution checks. *State* your conclusion: The incubation period for a hummingbird is 15 days. The incubation period for a golden eagle is 45 days.

Chapter 3 Review

(3.1) *Simplify each expression by combining like terms.*

1. $3y + 7y - 15$

2. $2y - 10 - 8y$

3. $8a + a - 7 - 15a$

4. $y + 3 - 9y - 1$

Multiply.

5. $2(x + 5)$

6. $-3(y + 8)$

Simplify.

7. $7x + 3(x - 4) + x$

8. $-(3m + 2) - m - 10$

9. $3(5a - 2) - 20a + 10$

10. $6y + 3 + 2(3y - 6)$

11. $6y - 7 + 11y - y + 2$

12. $10 - x + 5x - 12 - 3x$

Find the perimeter of each figure.

△ **13.**

2x yards

3 yards

Rectangle

△ **14.**

Square   5y meters

Find the area of each figure.

△ **15.**

(2x − 1) yards

3 yards

Rectangle

△ **16.**

(x − 2) centimeters

(5x + 4) centimeters

10 centimeters

Rectangle

Rectangle

7 centimeters

(3.2) *Solve each equation.*

17. $z - 5 = -7$

18. $3x + 10 = 4x$

19. $3y = -21$

20. $-3a = -15$

21. $\dfrac{x}{-6} = 2$

22. $\dfrac{y}{-15} = -3$

23. $n + 18 = 10 - (-2)$

24. $c - 5 = -13 + 7$

25. $7x + 5 - 6x = -20$

26. $17x = 2(8x - 4)$

27. $5x + 7 = -3$

28. $-14 = 9y + 4$

29. $\dfrac{z}{4} = -8 - (-6)$

30. $-1 + (-8) = \dfrac{x}{5}$

31. $6y - 7y = 100 - 105$

32. $19x - 16x = 45 - 60$

33. $9(2x - 7) = 19x$

34. $-5(3x + 3) = -14x$

35. $3x - 4 = 11$

36. $6y + 1 = 73$

37. $2(x + 4) - 10 = -2(7)$

38. $-3(x - 6) + 13 = 20 - 1$

Translating *Translate each phrase into an algebraic expression. Let x represent "a number."*

39. The product of −5 and a number

40. Three subtracted from a number

41. The sum of −5 and a number

42. The quotient of −2 and a number

43. The product of −5 and a number, decreased by 50

44. Eleven added to twice a number

45. The quotient of 70 and the sum of a number and 6

46. Twice the difference of a number and 13

(3.3) *Solve each equation.*

47. $2x + 5 = 7x - 100$

48. $-6x - 4 = x + 66$

49. $2x + 7 = 6x - 1$

50. $5x - 18 = -4x$

51. $5(n - 3) = 7 + 3n$

52. $7(2 + x) = 4x - 1$

53. $6x + 3 - (-x) = -20 + 5x - 7$

54. $x - 25 + 2x = -5 + 2x - 10$

55. $3(x - 4) = 5x - 8$

56. $4(x - 3) = -2x - 48$

57. $6(2n - 1) + 18 = 0$

58. $7(3y - 2) - 7 = 0$

59. $95x - 14 = 20x - 10 + 10x - 4$

60. $32z + 11 - 28z = 50 + 2z - (-1)$

Translating *Write each sentence as an equation.*

61. The difference of 20 and −8 is 28.

62. Nineteen subtracted from −2 amounts to −21.

63. The quotient of −75 and the sum of 5 and 20 is equal to −3.

64. Five times the sum of 2 and −6 yields −20.

(3.4) Translating *Write each sentence as an equation using x as the variable.*

65. Twice a number minus 8 is 40.

66. The product of a number and 6 is equal to the sum of the number and 20.

67. Twelve subtracted from the quotient of a number and 2 is 10.

68. The difference of a number and 3 is the quotient of 8 and 4.

Solve.

69. Five times a number subtracted from 40 is the same as three times the number. Find the number.

70. The product of a number and 3 is twice the difference of that number and 8. Find the number.

71. In an election, the incumbent received 14,000 votes of the 18,500 votes cast. Of the remaining votes, the Democratic candidate received 272 more than the Independent candidate. Find how many votes the Democratic candidate received.

72. Rajiv Puri has twice as many movies on DVD as he has on Blu-ray Disc. Find the number of DVDs if he has a total of 126 movie recordings.

Mixed Review

Simplify.

73. $9x - 20x$

74. $-5(7x)$

75. $12x + 5(2x - 3) - 4$

76. $-7(x + 6) - 2(x - 5)$

Solve.

77. $c - 5 = -13 + 7$

78. $7x + 5 - 6x = -20$

79. $-7x + 3x = -50 - 2$

80. $-x + 8x = -38 - 4$

81. $9x + 12 - 8x = -6 + (-4)$

82. $-17x + 14 + 20x - 2x = 5 - (-3)$

83. $5(2x - 3) = 11x$

84. $\dfrac{y}{-3} = -1 - 5$

85. $12y - 10 = -70$

86. $4n - 8 = 2n + 14$

87. $-6(x - 3) = x + 4$

88. $9(3x - 4) + 63 = 0$

89. $-5z + 3z - 7 = 8z - 1 - 6$

90. $4x - 3 + 6x = 5x - 3 - 30$

91. Three times a number added to twelve is 27. Find the number.

92. Twice the sum of a number and four is ten. Find the number.

93. Out of the 50 states, Hawaii has the least number of roadway miles, followed by Delaware. If Delaware has 1931 more roadway miles than Hawaii and the total number of roadway miles for both states is 10,673, find the number of roadway miles for each state. (*Source:* U.S. Federal Highway Administration)

94. North and South Dakota both have over 80,000 roadway miles. North Dakota has 4489 more miles and the total number of roadway miles for both states is 169,197. Find the number of roadway miles for North Dakota and for South Dakota. (*Source:* U.S. Federal Highway Administration)

1. Simplify $7x - 5 - 12x + 10$ by combining like terms.

2. Multiply: $-2(3y + 7)$

Answers

3. Simplify: $-(3z + 2) - 5z - 18$

△ **4.** Write an expression that represents the perimeter of the equilateral triangle (a triangle with three sides of equal length). Simplify the expression.

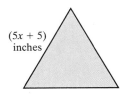

$(5x + 5)$ inches

△ **5.** Write an expression that represents the area of the rectangle. Simplify the expression.

4 meters

Rectangle $(3x - 1)$ meters

Solve each equation.

6. $12 = y - 3y$

7. $\dfrac{x}{2} = -5 - (-2)$

8. $5x + 12 - 4x - 14 = 22$

9. $-4x + 7 = 15$

10. $2(x - 6) = 0$

11. $-4(x - 11) - 34 = 10 - 12$

12. $5x - 2 = x - 10$

13. $4(5x + 3) = 2(7x + 6)$

14. $6 + 2(3n - 1) = 28$

Translate the following phrases into mathematical expressions. If needed, use x to represent "a number."

15. The sum of -23 and a number

16. Three times a number, subtracted from -2

1. _____

2. _____

3. _____

4. _____

5. _____

6. _____

7. _____

8. _____

9. _____

10. _____

11. _____

12. _____

13. _____

14. _____

15. _____

16. _____

17. _____

18. _____

19. _____

20. _____

21. _____

Translate each sentence into an equation. If needed, use x to represent "a number."

17. The sum of twice 5 and −15 is −5.

18. Six added to three times a number equals −30.

Solve.

19. The difference of three times a number and five times the same number is 4. Find the number.

20. In a championship basketball game, Paula made twice as many free throws as Maria. If the total number of free throws made by both women was 12, find how many free throws Paula made.

21. In a 10-kilometer race, there are 112 more men entered than women. Find the number of female runners if the total number of runners in the race is 600.

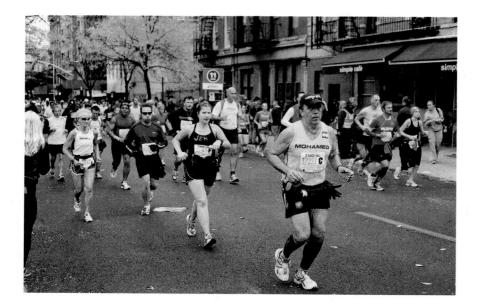

1. Write 308,063,557 in words.

2. Write 276,004 in words.

Answers

△ 3. Find the perimeter of the polygon shown.

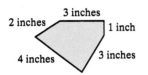

2 inches
3 inches
1 inch
4 inches
3 inches

△ 4. Find the perimeter of the rectangle shown.

6 inches
3 inches

1. _____

2. _____

3. _____

4. _____

5. Subtract: $900 - 174$. Check by adding.

6. Subtract: $17,801 - 8216$. Check by adding.

5. _____

6. _____

7. _____

7. Round 248,982 to the nearest hundred.

8. Round 844,497 to the nearest thousand.

8. _____

9. _____

9. Multiply: 25×8

10. Multiply: 395×74

10. _____

11. _____

11. Divide and check: $1872 \div 9$

12. Divide and check: $3956 \div 46$

12. _____

13. _____

13. Simplify: $2 \cdot 4 - 3 \div 3$

14. Simplify: $8 \cdot 4 + 9 \div 3$

14. _____

15. _____

15. Evaluate $x^2 + z - 3$ for $x = 5$ and $z = 4$.

16. Evaluate $2a^2 + 5 - c$ for $a = 2$ and $c = 3$.

16. _____

17. _____

17. Determine which numbers in the set $\{26, 40, 20\}$ are solutions of the equation $2n - 30 = 10$.

18. Insert $<$ or $>$ to make a true statement.

   a. -14 \qquad 0

   b. $-(-7)$ \qquad -8

18. a. _____

   b. _____

19. _____

19. Add using a number line: $5 + (-2)$

20. Add using a number line: $-3 + (-4)$

20. _____

21. _____

22. _____

23. _____

24. _____

25. _____

26. _____

27. _____

28. _____

29. _____

30. _____

31. _____

32. _____

33. _____

34. _____

35. _____

36. _____

37. _____

38. _____

39. _____

40. _____

41. _____

42. _____

43. _____

44. _____

45. _____

46. _____

47. _____

48. _____

49. _____

50. _____

Add.

21. $-15 + (-10)$

22. $3 + (-7)$

23. $-2 + 25$

24. $21 + 15 + (-19)$

Subtract.

25. $-4 - 10$

26. $-2 - 3$

27. $6 - (-5)$

28. $19 - (-10)$

29. $-11 - (-7)$

30. $-16 - (-13)$

Divide.

31. $\dfrac{-12}{6}$

32. $\dfrac{-30}{-5}$

33. $-20 \div (-4)$

34. $26 \div (-2)$

35. $\dfrac{48}{-3}$

36. $\dfrac{-120}{12}$

Find the value of each expression.

37. $(-3)^2$

38. -2^5

39. -3^2

40. $(-5)^2$

41. Simplify: $2y - 6 + 4y + 8$

42. Simplify: $6x + 2 - 3x + 7$

43. Determine whether -1 is a solution of the equation $3y + 1 = 3$.

44. Determine whether 2 is a solution of $5x - 3 = 7$.

45. Solve: $-12x = -36$

46. Solve: $-3y = 15$

47. Solve: $2x - 6 = 18$

48. Solve: $3a + 5 = -1$

49. A salesperson at an electronics store sold a computer system and software for $2100, receiving four times as much money for the computer system as for the software. Find the price of each.

50. Rose Daunis is thinking of a number. Two times the number plus four is the same amount as three times the number minus seven. Find Rose's number.

Fractions and Mixed Numbers

The following graph is called a circle graph or a pie chart. Each sector (shaped like a piece of pie) shows the fraction of entering college freshmen who choose to major in each discipline shown. Can you find your current choice of major in this graph? In Section 4.2, Exercises 93–96, we show this same circle graph, but in 3-D design. We simplify some of the fractions in it and also study sector size versus fraction value.

Fractions are numbers and, like whole numbers and integers, they can be added, subtracted, multiplied, and divided. Fractions are very useful and appear frequently in everyday language, in common phrases such as "half an hour," "quarter of a pound," and "third of a cup." This chapter reviews the concepts of fractions and mixed numbers and demonstrates how to add, subtract, multiply, and divide these numbers.

College Freshman Majors

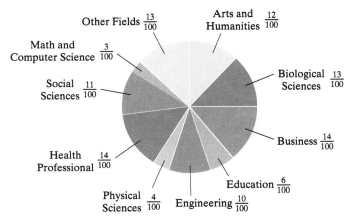

Source: The Higher Education Research Institute

4.1 Introduction to Fractions and Mixed Numbers

Objectives

A Identify the Numerator and the Denominator of a Fraction.

B Write a Fraction to Represent Parts of Figures or Real-Life Data.

C Graph Fractions on a Number Line.

D Review Division Properties of 0 and 1.

E Write Mixed Numbers as Improper Fractions.

F Write Improper Fractions as Mixed Numbers or Whole Numbers.

Objective A Identifying Numerators and Denominators

Whole numbers are used to count whole things or units, such as cars, horses, dollars, and people. To refer to a part of a whole, fractions can be used. Here are some examples of **fractions.** Study these examples for a moment.

a cup — 1 part considered, 2 equal parts — $\frac{1}{2}$ of a cup

a foot — 2 parts considered, 3 equal parts — $\frac{2}{3}$ of a foot

5 parts considered, 6 equal parts — $\frac{5}{6}$ of a pizza

In a fraction, the top number is called the **numerator** and the bottom number is called the **denominator.** The bar between the numbers is called the **fraction bar.**

Name	Fraction	Meaning
numerator ⟶	$\frac{5}{6}$	⟵ number of parts being considered
denominator ⟶		⟵ number of equal parts in the whole

Examples Identify the numerator and the denominator of each fraction.

1. $\frac{3}{7}$ ← numerator
      ← denominator

2. $\frac{13}{5x}$ ← numerator
      ← denominator

■ Work Practice 1–2

Practice 1–2

Identify the numerator and the denominator of each fraction.

1. $\frac{11}{2}$

2. $\frac{10y}{17}$

Helpful Hint

$\frac{3}{7}$ ← Remember that the bar in a fraction means division. Since division by 0 is undefined, a fraction with a denominator of 0 is undefined. For example, $\frac{3}{0}$ is undefined.

Objective B Writing Fractions to Represent Parts of Figures or Real-Life Data

One way to become familiar with the concept of fractions is to visualize fractions with shaded figures. We can then write a fraction to represent the shaded area of the figure (or diagram).

Answers
1. numerator = 11, denominator = 2
2. numerator = 10y, denominator = 17

Examples   Write a fraction to represent the shaded part of each figure.

3. In this figure, 2 of the 5 equal parts are shaded. Thus, the fraction is $\frac{2}{5}$.

$\frac{2}{5}$ ← number of parts shaded
← number of equal parts

4. In this figure, 3 of the 10 rectangles are shaded. Thus, the fraction is $\frac{3}{10}$.

$\frac{3}{10}$ ← number of parts shaded
← number of equal parts

■ Work Practice 3–4

Examples   Write a fraction to represent the shaded part of the diagram.

5.
The fraction is $\frac{3}{10}$.

10 equal parts

3 shaded parts

6.
The fraction is $\frac{1}{3}$.

3 equal parts

1 part shaded

■ Work Practice 5–6

Examples   Draw a figure and then shade a part of it to represent each fraction.

7. $\frac{5}{6}$ of a figure

We will use a geometric figure such as a rectangle. Since the denominator is 6, we divide it into 6 equal parts. Then we shade 5 of the equal parts.

5 parts shaded

$\frac{5}{6}$ of the rectangle is shaded

6 equal parts

(Continued on next page)

Practice 3–4

Write a fraction to represent the shaded part of each figure.

3.

4.

Practice 5–6

Write a fraction to represent the part of the whole shown.

5. Just consider this part of the syringe

6. ← Whole part →

Practice 7

Draw and shade a part of a figure to represent the fraction.

7. $\frac{2}{3}$ of a figure

Answers

3. $\frac{3}{8}$ **4.** $\frac{1}{6}$ **5.** $\frac{7}{10}$ **6.** $\frac{9}{16}$

7. answers may vary; for example,

Practice 8

Draw and shade a part of a figure to represent the fraction.

8. $\frac{7}{11}$ of a figure

8. $\frac{3}{8}$ of a figure

If you'd like, our figure can consist of 8 triangles of the same size. We will shade 3 of the triangles.

3 triangles shaded

8 triangles

$\frac{3}{8}$ of the figure or diagram is shaded

■ Work Practice 7–8

✔**Concept Check** If represents $\frac{6}{7}$ of a whole diagram, sketch the whole diagram.

Example 9 Writing Fractions from Real-Life Data

Of the eight planets in our solar system (Pluto is now a dwarf planet), three are closer to the Sun than Mars. What fraction of the planets are closer to the Sun than Mars?

Solution: The fraction of planets closer to the Sun than Mars is:

$\frac{3}{8}$ ← number of planets closer
        ← number of planets in our solar system

Thus, $\frac{3}{8}$ of the planets in our solar system are closer to the Sun than Mars.

■ Work Practice 9

Practice 9

Of the eight planets in our solar system, five are farther from the Sun than Earth is. What fraction of the planets are farther from the Sun than Earth is?

Answers

8. answers may vary; for example,

9. $\frac{5}{8}$

✔**Concept Check Answer**

The definitions and statements below apply to positive fractions.

A **proper fraction** is a fraction whose numerator is less than its denominator. Proper fractions are less than 1. For example, the shaded portion of the triangle is represented by $\frac{2}{3}$.

An **improper fraction** is a fraction whose numerator is greater than or equal to its denominator. Improper fractions are greater than or equal to 1.

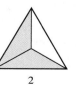

$\frac{2}{3}$

The shaded part of the group of circles below is $\frac{9}{4}$. The shaded part of the rectangle is $\frac{6}{6}$. Recall that $\frac{6}{6}$ simplifies to 1 and notice that the entire rectangle (1 whole figure) is shaded below.

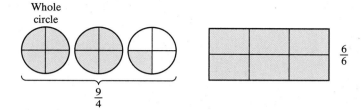

A **mixed number** contains a whole number and a fraction. Mixed numbers are greater than 1. Above, we wrote the shaded part of the group of circles below as the improper fraction $\frac{9}{4}$. Now let's write the shaded part as a mixed number. The shaded part of the group of circles' area is $2\frac{1}{4}$. Read this as "two and one-fourth."

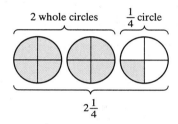

Note: The mixed number $2\frac{1}{4}$, diagrammed above, represents $2 + \frac{1}{4}$.

The mixed number $-3\frac{1}{5}$ represents $-\left(3 + \frac{1}{5}\right)$ or $-3 - \frac{1}{5}$. We review this later in this chapter.

Examples Represent the shaded part of each figure group as both an improper fraction and a mixed number.

10.

Whole object

improper fraction: $\frac{4}{3}$

mixed number: $1\frac{1}{3}$

11.

improper fraction: $\frac{11}{4}$

mixed number: $2\frac{3}{4}$

 Work Practice 10–11

✓**Concept Check** If you were to round $2\frac{3}{4}$, shown in Example 11 above, to the nearest whole number, would you choose 2 or 3? Why?

Practice 10–11

Represent the shaded part of each figure group as both an improper fraction and a mixed number.

10.

11.

Answers

10. $\frac{8}{3}, 2\frac{2}{3}$ **11.** $\frac{5}{4}, 1\frac{1}{4}$

✓**Concept Check Answer**

3; answers may vary

Objective C Graphing Fractions on a Number Line

Another way to visualize fractions is to graph them on a number line. To do this, think of 1 unit on the number line as a whole. To graph $\frac{2}{5}$, for example, divide the distance from 0 to 1 into 5 equal parts. Then start at 0 and count 2 parts to the right.

Notice that the graph of $\frac{2}{5}$ lies between 0 and 1. This means

$$0 < \frac{2}{5} \left(\text{or } \frac{2}{5} > 0 \right) \text{ and also } \frac{2}{5} < 1$$

Practice 12

Graph each proper fraction on a number line.

a. $\frac{5}{7}$ **b.** $\frac{2}{3}$ **c.** $\frac{4}{6}$

Example 12   Graph each proper fraction on a number line.

a. $\frac{3}{4}$ **b.** $\frac{1}{2}$ **c.** $\frac{3}{6}$

Solution:

a. To graph $\frac{3}{4}$, divide the distance from 0 to 1 into 4 parts. Then start at 0 and count over 3 parts.

b.

c.

Work Practice 12

The statements below apply to positive fractions.

The fractions in Example 12 are all proper fractions. Notice that the value of each is less than 1. This is always true for proper fractions since the numerator of a proper fraction is less than the denominator.

On the next page, we graph improper fractions. Notice that improper fractions are greater than or equal to 1. This is always true since the numerator of an improper fraction is greater than or equal to the denominator.

Copyright 2015 Pearson Education, Inc.

Answers

12. **a.**

b.

c.

Example 13 Graph each improper fraction on a number line.

a. $\frac{7}{6}$ **b.** $\frac{9}{5}$ **c.** $\frac{6}{6}$ **d.** $\frac{3}{1}$

Solution:

a.

b.

c.

d. Each 1-unit distance has 1 equal part. Count over 3 parts.

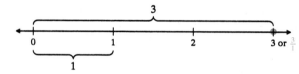

Work Practice 13

Note: We will graph mixed numbers at the end of this chapter.

Objective D Reviewing Division Properties of 0 and 1

Before we continue further, don't forget from Section 1.6 that a fraction bar indicates division. Let's review some division properties of 1 and 0.

$$\frac{9}{9} = 1 \text{ because } 1 \cdot 9 = 9 \qquad \frac{-11}{1} = -11 \text{ because } -11 \cdot 1 = -11$$

$$\frac{0}{6} = 0 \text{ because } 0 \cdot 6 = 0 \qquad \frac{6}{0} \text{ is } \textit{undefined} \text{ because there is no number that when multiplied by 0 gives 6.}$$

In general, we can say the following.

Let n be any integer except 0.

$$\frac{n}{n} = 1 \qquad \frac{0}{n} = 0$$

$$\frac{n}{1} = n \qquad \frac{n}{0} \text{ is undefined.}$$

Answers

13. **a.**
b.
c.

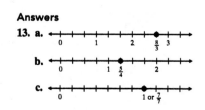

Practice 14–19

Simplify.

14. $\dfrac{9}{9}$ **15.** $\dfrac{-6}{-6}$

16. $\dfrac{0}{-1}$ **17.** $\dfrac{4}{1}$

18. $\dfrac{-13}{0}$ **19.** $\dfrac{-13}{1}$

Helpful Hint
Remember, for example, that

$$-\dfrac{2}{3} = \dfrac{-2}{3} = \dfrac{2}{-3}$$

Examples Simplify.

14. $\dfrac{5}{5} = 1$ **15.** $\dfrac{-2}{-2} = 1$ **16.** $\dfrac{0}{-5} = 0$

17. $\dfrac{-5}{1} = -5$ **18.** $\dfrac{41}{1} = 41$ **19.** $\dfrac{19}{0}$ is undefined

Work Practice 14–19

Notice from Example 17 that we can have negative fractions. In fact,

$$\dfrac{-5}{1} = -5, \qquad \dfrac{5}{-1} = -5, \qquad \text{and} \qquad -\dfrac{5}{1} = -5$$

Because all of the fractions equal -5, we have

$$\dfrac{-5}{1} = \dfrac{5}{-1} = -\dfrac{5}{1}$$

This means that the negative sign in a fraction can be written in the numerator, in the denominator, or in front of the fraction. Remember this as we work with negative fractions.

Objective E Writing Mixed Numbers as Improper Fractions

Earlier in this section, mixed numbers and improper fractions were both used to represent the shaded part of figure groups. For example,

$1\frac{2}{3}$ or $\frac{5}{3}$ Thus, $1\frac{2}{3} = \frac{5}{3}$.

The following steps may be used to write a mixed number as an improper fraction:

Writing a Mixed Number as an Improper Fraction

To write a mixed number as an improper fraction:

Step 1: Multiply the denominator of the fraction by the whole number.

Step 2: Add the numerator of the fraction to the product from Step 1.

Step 3: Write the sum from Step 2 as the numerator of the improper fraction over the original denominator.

For example,

$$1\frac{2}{3} = \overset{\text{Step 1}\;\;\text{Step 2}}{\dfrac{3 \cdot 1 + 2}{3}} = \dfrac{3 + 2}{3} = \dfrac{5}{3} \quad \text{or} \quad 1\frac{2}{3} = \dfrac{5}{3}, \text{ as stated above.}$$

Step 3

Practice 20

Write each as an improper fraction.

a. $5\dfrac{2}{7}$ **b.** $6\dfrac{2}{3}$ **c.** $10\dfrac{9}{10}$ **d.** $4\dfrac{1}{5}$

Example 20 Write each as an improper fraction.

a. $4\dfrac{2}{9} = \dfrac{9 \cdot 4 + 2}{9} = \dfrac{36 + 2}{9} = \dfrac{38}{9}$ **b.** $1\dfrac{8}{11} = \dfrac{11 \cdot 1 + 8}{11} = \dfrac{11 + 8}{11} = \dfrac{19}{11}$

Work Practice 20

Answers
14. 1 **15.** 1 **16.** 0 **17.** 4
18. undefined **19.** −13
20. a. $\dfrac{37}{7}$ **b.** $\dfrac{20}{3}$ **c.** $\dfrac{109}{10}$ **d.** $\dfrac{21}{5}$

Objective F Writing Improper Fractions as Mixed Numbers or Whole Numbers

Just as there are times when an improper fraction is preferred, sometimes a mixed or a whole number better suits a situation. To write improper fractions as mixed or whole numbers, we use division. Recall once again from Section 1.6 that the fraction bar means division. This means that the fraction

$\dfrac{5}{3}$ numerator
denominator

means $3\overline{)5}$
numerator
denominator

Writing an Improper Fraction as a Mixed Number or a Whole Number

To write an improper fraction as a mixed number or a whole number:

Step 1: Divide the denominator into the numerator.

Step 2: The whole number part of the mixed number is the quotient. The fraction part of the mixed number is the remainder over the original denominator.

$$\text{quotient} \dfrac{\text{remainder}}{\text{original denominator}}$$

For example,

Step 1

$\dfrac{5}{3} : 3\overline{)5}$
$\underline{-3}$
$\quad 2$

Step 2

$\dfrac{5}{3} = 1\dfrac{2}{3}$ ← remainder
← original denominator
↑
quotient

Example 21 Write each as a mixed number or a whole number.

a. $\dfrac{30}{7}$ **b.** $\dfrac{16}{15}$ **c.** $\dfrac{84}{6}$

Helpful Hint When the remainder is 0, the improper fraction is a whole number. For example, $\dfrac{92}{4} = 23$.

Solution:

a. $\dfrac{30}{7} : 7\overline{)30}$ $\dfrac{30}{7} = 4\dfrac{2}{7}$
$\quad\ \underline{-28}$
$\quad\quad\ 2$

$\quad\quad\quad 23$
$4\overline{)92}$
$\underline{-8}$
$\ \ 12$
$\underline{-12}$
$\quad\ 0$

b. $\dfrac{16}{15} : 15\overline{)16}$ $\dfrac{16}{15} = 1\dfrac{1}{15}$
$\quad\quad \underline{-15}$
$\quad\quad\quad 1$

c. $\dfrac{84}{6} : 6\overline{)84}$ $\dfrac{84}{6} = 14$ Since the remainder is 0, the result is the whole number 14.
$\quad\ \underline{-6}$
$\quad\ \ 24$
$\quad \underline{-24}$
$\quad\quad 0$

■ Work Practice 21

Practice 21

Write each as a mixed number or a whole number.

a. $\dfrac{9}{5}$ **b.** $\dfrac{23}{9}$ **c.** $\dfrac{48}{4}$

d. $\dfrac{62}{13}$ **e.** $\dfrac{51}{7}$ **f.** $\dfrac{21}{20}$

Answers

21. a. $1\dfrac{4}{5}$ **b.** $2\dfrac{5}{9}$ **c.** 12 **d.** $4\dfrac{10}{13}$
e. $7\dfrac{2}{7}$ **f.** $1\dfrac{1}{20}$

Vocabulary, Readiness & Video Check

Use the choices below to fill in each blank.

improper	fraction	proper	is undefined	mixed number	= 0
≥ 1	denominator	= 1	< 1	numerator	

1. The number $\frac{17}{31}$ is called a(n) _____ . The number 31 is called its _____ and 17 is called its _____ .

2. If we simplify each fraction, $\frac{-9}{-9}$ _____ , $\frac{0}{-4}$ _____ , and we say $\frac{-4}{0}$ _____ .

3. The fraction $\frac{8}{3}$ is called a(n) _____ fraction, the fraction $\frac{3}{8}$ is called a(n) _____ fraction, and $10\frac{3}{8}$ is called a(n) _____ .

4. The value of an improper fraction is always _____ , and the value of a proper fraction is always _____ .

Martin-Gay Interactive Videos

See Video 4.1

Watch the section lecture video and answer the following questions.

Objective A 5. Complete this statement based on ▣ Example 1: When the numerator is greater than or _____ to the denominator, you have a(n) _____ fraction. ▶

Objective B 6. In ▣ Example 4, there are two shapes in the diagram, so why do the representative fractions have a denominator 3? ▶

Objective C 7. From ▣ Examples 6 and 7, when graphing a positive fraction on a number line, how does the denominator help? What does the denominator tell you? ▶

Objective D 8. From ▣ Example 10, what can you conclude about any fraction where the numerator and denominator are the same nonzero number? ▶

Objective E 9. Complete this statement based on the lecture before ▣ Example 13: The operation of _____ is understood in a mixed number notation; for example, $1\frac{1}{3}$ means 1 _____ $\frac{1}{3}$. ▶

Objective F 10. From the lecture before ▣ Example 16, what operation is used to write an improper fraction as a mixed number? ▶

4.1 **Exercise Set** MyMathLab®

Objectives **A B** *Identify the numerator and the denominator of each fraction and identify each fraction as proper or improper. See Examples 1, 2, 10, and 11.*

1. $\frac{1}{2}$

2. $\frac{1}{4}$

3. $\frac{10}{3}$

4. $\frac{53}{21}$

5. $\frac{15}{15}$

6. $\frac{26}{26}$

Objective **B** *Write a proper or improper fraction to represent the shaded part of each diagram. If an improper fraction is appropriate, write the shaded part of the diagram as (**a**) an improper fraction and (**b**) a mixed number. (Note to students: In case you know how to simplify fractions, none of the fractions in this section are simplified.) See Examples 3 through 6 and 10 and 11.*

7.

8.

9.

10.

11.

12.

13.

14.

○ **15.**

16.

17.

18.

○ **19.**

20.

21.

22.

23.

24.

25.

1 whole mile

26.

1 whole inch

Objective B *Draw and shade a part of a diagram to represent each fraction. See Examples 7 and 8.*

27. $\frac{1}{5}$ of a diagram

28. $\frac{1}{16}$ of a diagram

29. $\frac{6}{7}$ of a diagram

30. $\frac{7}{9}$ of a diagram

31. $\frac{4}{4}$ of a diagram

32. $\frac{6}{6}$ of a diagram

Write each fraction. (Note to students: In case you know how to simplify fractions, none of the fractions in this section are simplified.) See Example 9.

33. Of the 131 students at a small private school, 42 are freshmen. What fraction of the students are freshmen?

34. Of the 63 employees at a new biomedical engineering firm, 22 are men. What fraction of the employees are men?

35. Use Exercise 33 to answer **a** and **b.**
   a. How many students are *not* freshmen?
   b. What fraction of the students are *not* freshmen?

36. Use Exercise 34 to answer **a** and **b.**
   a. How many of the employees are women?
   b. What fraction of the employees are women?

37. As of 2013, the United States has had 44 different presidents. A total of seven U.S. presidents were born in the state of Ohio, second only to the state of Virginia in producing U.S. presidents. What fraction of U.S. presidents were born in Ohio? (*Source: World Almanac,* 2013)

38. Of the eight planets in our solar system, four have days that are longer than the 24-hour Earth day. What fraction of the planets have longer days than Earth has? (*Source:* National Space Science Data Center)

39. The Atlantic hurricane season of 2005 rewrote the record books. There were 28 tropical storms, 15 of which turned into hurricanes. What fraction of the 2005 Atlantic tropical storms escalated to hurricanes?

40. There are 12 inches in a foot. What fractional part of a foot do 5 inches represent?

41. There are 31 days in the month of March. What fraction of the month do 11 days represent?

Mon.	Tue.	Wed.	Thu.	Fri.	Sat.	Sun.
					1	2
3	4	5	6	7	8	9
10	11	12	13	14	15	16
17	18	19	20	21	22	23
24	25	26	27	28	29	30
31						

42. There are 60 minutes in an hour. What fraction of an hour do 37 minutes represent?

43. In a prealgebra class containing 31 students, there are 18 freshmen, 10 sophomores, and 3 juniors. What fraction of the class is sophomores?

44. In a sports team with 20 children, there are 9 boys and 11 girls. What fraction of the team is boys?

45. Thirty-three out of the fifty total states in the United States contain federal Indian reservations.
  a. What fraction of the states contain federal Indian reservations?
  b. How many states do not contain federal Indian reservations?
  c. What fraction of the states do not contain federal Indian reservations? (*Source:* Tiller Research, Inc., Albuquerque, NM)

46. Consumer fireworks are legal in 44 out of the 50 total states in the United States.
  a. In what fraction of the states are consumer fireworks legal?
  b. In how many states are consumer fireworks illegal?
  c. In what fraction of the states are consumer fireworks illegal? (*Source:* United States Fireworks Safety Council)

47. A bag contains 50 red or blue marbles. If 21 marbles are blue, answer each question.
  a. What fraction of the marbles are blue?
  b. How many marbles are red?
  c. What fraction of the marbles are red?

48. An art dealer is taking inventory. His shop contains a total of 37 pieces, which are all sculptures, watercolor paintings, or oil paintings. If there are 15 watercolor paintings and 17 oil paintings, answer each question.
  a. What fraction of the inventory is watercolor paintings?
  b. What fraction of the inventory is oil paintings?
  c. How many sculptures are there?
  d. What fraction of the inventory is sculptures?

Objective C *Graph each fraction on a number line. See Examples 12 and 13.*

49. $\dfrac{1}{4}$

50. $\dfrac{1}{3}$

51. $\dfrac{4}{7}$

52. $\dfrac{5}{6}$

53. $\dfrac{8}{5}$

54. $\dfrac{9}{8}$

55. $\dfrac{7}{3}$

56. $\dfrac{13}{7}$

Objective D *Simplify by dividing. See Examples 14 through 19.*

57. $\dfrac{12}{12}$

58. $\dfrac{-3}{-3}$

59. $\dfrac{-5}{1}$

60. $\dfrac{-20}{1}$

61. $\dfrac{0}{-2}$ **62.** $\dfrac{0}{-8}$ **63.** $\dfrac{-8}{-8}$ **64.** $\dfrac{-14}{-14}$

65. $\dfrac{-9}{0}$ **66.** $\dfrac{-7}{0}$ **67.** $\dfrac{3}{1}$ **68.** $\dfrac{5}{5}$

Objective **E** *Write each mixed number as an improper fraction. See Example 20.*

69. $2\dfrac{1}{3}$ **70.** $1\dfrac{13}{17}$ **71.** $3\dfrac{3}{5}$ **72.** $2\dfrac{5}{9}$

73. $6\dfrac{5}{8}$ **74.** $7\dfrac{3}{8}$ **75.** $11\dfrac{6}{7}$ **76.** $12\dfrac{2}{5}$

77. $9\dfrac{7}{20}$ **78.** $10\dfrac{14}{27}$ **79.** $166\dfrac{2}{3}$ **80.** $114\dfrac{2}{7}$

Objective **F** *Write each improper fraction as a mixed number or a whole number. See Example 21.*

81. $\dfrac{17}{5}$ **82.** $\dfrac{13}{7}$ **83.** $\dfrac{37}{8}$ **84.** $\dfrac{64}{9}$

85. $\dfrac{47}{15}$ **86.** $\dfrac{65}{12}$ **87.** $\dfrac{225}{15}$ **88.** $\dfrac{196}{14}$

89. $\dfrac{182}{175}$ **90.** $\dfrac{149}{143}$ **91.** $\dfrac{737}{112}$ **92.** $\dfrac{901}{123}$

Review

Simplify. See Section 1.7.

93. 3^2 **94.** 4^3 **95.** 5^3 **96.** 3^4

Concept Extensions

Write each fraction in two other equivalent ways by inserting the negative sign in different places.

97. $-\dfrac{11}{2} = \qquad = $

99. $\dfrac{-13}{15} = \qquad = $

98. $-\dfrac{21}{4} = \qquad = $

100. $\dfrac{45}{-57} = \qquad = $

101. In your own words, explain why $\dfrac{0}{10} = 0$ and $\dfrac{10}{0}$ is undefined.

102. In your own words, explain why $\dfrac{0}{-3} = 0$ and $\dfrac{-3}{0}$ is undefined.

Solve. See the Concept Checks in this section.

103. If ◯◯◯◯ represents $\frac{4}{9}$ of a whole diagram, sketch the whole diagram.

104. If △△ represents $\frac{1}{3}$ of a whole diagram, sketch the whole diagram.

105. Round the mixed number $7\frac{1}{8}$ to the nearest whole number.

106. Round the mixed number $5\frac{11}{12}$ to the nearest whole number.

107. The Gap Corporation owns stores with six different brand names, with the three most popular shown on the bar graph. What fraction of the total stores shown on the graph are named "Banana Republic"?

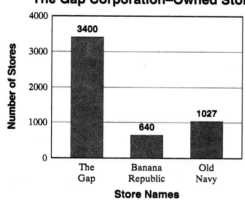

The Gap Corporation–Owned Stores

108. The Public Broadcasting Service (PBS) provides programming to the noncommercial public TV stations of the United States. The bar graph shows a breakdown of the public television licensees by type. Each licensee operates one or more PBS member TV stations. What fraction of the public television licensees are universities or colleges? (*Source:* The Public Broadcasting Service)

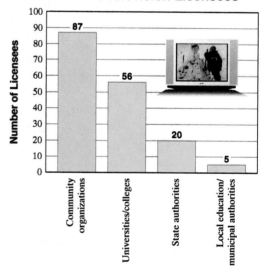

109. Habitat for Humanity is a nonprofit organization that helps provide affordable housing to families in need. Habitat for Humanity does its work of building and renovating houses through 1500 local affiliates in the United States and 80 international affiliates. What fraction of the total Habitat for Humanity affiliates are located in the United States? (*Hint:* First find the total number of affiliates.) (*Source:* Habitat for Humanity International)

110. The United States Marine Corps (USMC) has five principal training centers in California, three in North Carolina, two in South Carolina, one in Arizona, one in Hawaii, and one in Virginia. What fraction of the total USMC principal training centers are located in California? (*Hint:* First find the total number of USMC training centers.) (*Source:* U.S. Department of Defense)

Objectives

A Write a Number as a Product of Prime Numbers.

B Write a Fraction in Simplest Form.

C Determine Whether Two Fractions Are Equivalent.

D Solve Problems by Writing Fractions in Simplest Form.

Objective A Writing a Number as a Product of Prime Numbers

Recall from Section 1.5 that since $12 = 2 \cdot 2 \cdot 3$, the numbers 2 and 3 are called *factors* of 12. A **factor** is any number that divides a number evenly (with a remainder of 0).

To perform operations on fractions, it is necessary to be able to factor a number. Remember that factoring a number means writing a number as a product. We first practice writing a number as a product of prime numbers.

> A **prime number** is a natural number greater than 1 whose only factors are 1 and itself. The first few prime numbers are 2, 3, 5, 7, 11, 13, 17, 19, 23, 29, ...
> A **composite number** is a natural number greater than 1 that is not prime.

Helpful Hint

The natural number 1 is neither prime nor composite.

When a composite number is written as a product of prime numbers, this product is called the **prime factorization** of the number. For example, the prime factorization of 12 is $2 \cdot 2 \cdot 3$ because

$$12 = \underbrace{2 \cdot 2 \cdot 3}$$

This product is 12 and each number is a prime number.

Because multiplication is commutative, the order of the factors is not important. We can write the factorization $2 \cdot 2 \cdot 3$ as $2 \cdot 3 \cdot 2$ or $3 \cdot 2 \cdot 2$. Any of these is called the prime factorization of 12.

> Every whole number greater than 1 has exactly one prime factorization.

One method for finding the prime factorization of a number is by using a factor tree, as shown in the next example.

Practice 1

Use a factor tree to find the prime factorization of each number.

a. 30 **b.** 56 **c.** 72

Example 1 Write the prime factorization of 45.

Solution: We can begin by writing 45 as the product of two numbers, say, 5 and 9.

```
    45
   /  \
  5  ·  9
```

The number 5 is prime but 9 is not, so we write 9 as $3 \cdot 3$.

A factor tree

Each factor is now a prime number, so the prime factorization of 45 is $3 \cdot 3 \cdot 5$ or $3^2 \cdot 5$.

■ Work Practice 1

Answers

1. a. $2 \cdot 3 \cdot 5$ **b.** $2^3 \cdot 7$ **c.** $2^3 \cdot 3^2$

226

✓**Concept Check** True or false? Two different numbers can have exactly the same prime factorization. Explain your answer.

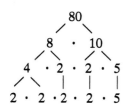

Example 2 Write the prime factorization of 80.

Solution: Write 80 as a product of two numbers. Continue this process until all factors are prime.

```
              80
            /    \
          8   ·   10
        /  \     /  \
      4  · 2 · 2 · 5
    /  \    |   |   |
  2 · 2 · 2 · 2 · 5
```

All factors are now prime, so the prime factorization of 80 is

$2 \cdot 2 \cdot 2 \cdot 2 \cdot 5$ or $2^4 \cdot 5$.

■ Work Practice 2

Practice 2

Write the prime factorization of 60.

Helpful Hint

It makes no difference which factors you start with. The prime factorization of a number will be the same.

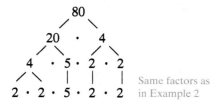

```
              80
            /    \
         20   ·   4
        /  \     /  \
      4  · 5 · 2 · 2
    /  \    |   |   |
  2 · 2 · 5 · 2 · 2
```
Same factors as in Example 2

There are a few quick **divisibility tests** to determine whether a number is divisible by the primes 2, 3, or 5. (A number is divisible by 2, for example, if 2 divides it evenly so that the remainder is 0.)

Divisibility Tests

A whole number is divisible by:

- 2 if the last digit is 0, 2, 4, 6, or 8.

  13**2** is divisible by 2 since the last digit is a 2.

- 3 if the sum of the digits is divisible by 3.

  144 is divisible by 3 since $1 + 4 + 4 = 9$ is divisible by 3.

- 5 if the last digit is 0 or 5.

  111**5** is divisible by 5 since the last digit is a 5.

Answer
2. $2^2 \cdot 3 \cdot 5$

✓**Concept Check Answer**
false; answers may vary

> **Helpful Hint**
>
> Here are a few other divisibility tests you may want to use. A whole number is divisible by:
> - 4 if its last two digits are divisible by 4.
>
>   1712 is divisible by 4.
> - 6 if it's divisible by 2 and 3.
>
>   9858 is divisible by 6.
> - 9 if the sum of its digits is divisible by 9.
>
>   5238 is divisible by 9 since $5 + 2 + 3 + 8 = 18$ is divisible by 9.

When finding the prime factorization of larger numbers, you may want to use the procedure shown in Example 3.

Practice 3

Write the prime factorization of 297.

Example 3   Write the prime factorization of 252.

Solution: For this method, we divide prime numbers into the given number. Since the ones digit of 252 is 2, we know that 252 is divisible by 2.

$$\begin{array}{r} 126 \\ 2\overline{)252} \end{array}$$

126 is divisible by 2 also.

$$\begin{array}{r} 63 \\ 2\overline{)126} \\ 2\overline{)252} \end{array}$$

63 is not divisible by 2 but is divisible by 3. Divide 63 by 3 and continue in this same manner until the quotient is a prime number.

$$\begin{array}{r} 7 \\ 3\overline{)\;21} \\ 3\overline{)\;63} \\ 2\overline{)126} \\ 2\overline{)252} \end{array}$$

> **Helpful Hint**   The order of choosing prime numbers does not matter. For consistency, we use the order $2, 3, 5, 7, \ldots$.

The prime factorization of 252 is $2 \cdot 2 \cdot 3 \cdot 3 \cdot 7$ or $2^2 \cdot 3^2 \cdot 7$.

■ Work Practice 3

In this text, we will write the factorization of a number from the smallest factor to the largest factor.

✔ **Concept Check**   True or false? The prime factorization of 117 is $9 \cdot 13$. Explain your reasoning.

Objective B Writing Fractions in Simplest Form

Fractions that represent the same portion of a whole or the same point on a number line are called **equivalent fractions.** Study the table on the next page to see two ways to visualize equivalent fractions.

Answer
3. $3^3 \cdot 11$

✔ **Concept Check Answer**
False; 9 is not prime.

Equivalent Fractions	
Figures	**Number Line**
When we shade $\frac{1}{3}$ and $\frac{2}{6}$ on the same-sized figures, 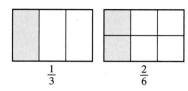 $\frac{1}{3}$ $\frac{2}{6}$ notice that both $\frac{1}{3}$ and $\frac{2}{6}$ represent the same portion of a whole. These fractions are called **equivalent fractions** and we write $\frac{1}{3} = \frac{2}{6}$.	When we graph $\frac{1}{3}$ and $\frac{2}{6}$ on a number line, notice that both $\frac{1}{3}$ and $\frac{2}{6}$ correspond to the same point. These fractions are called **equivalent fractions,** and we write $\frac{1}{3} = \frac{2}{6}$.
Thus, $\frac{1}{3} = \frac{2}{6}$ and $\frac{1}{3}$ and $\frac{2}{6}$ are equivalent.	

$\frac{2}{3}$ $\frac{4}{6}$ $\frac{8}{12}$

For example, $\frac{2}{3}, \frac{4}{6}$, and $\frac{8}{12}$ all represent the same shaded portion of the rectangle's area, so they are equivalent fractions. To show that these fractions are equivalent, we place an equal sign between them. In other words,

$$\frac{2}{3} = \frac{4}{6} = \frac{8}{12}$$

There are many equivalent forms of a fraction. A special equivalent form of a fraction is called **simplest form.**

Simplest Form of a Fraction

A fraction is written in **simplest form** or **lowest terms** when the numerator and the denominator have no common factors other than 1.

For example, the fraction $\frac{2}{3}$ *is* in simplest form because 2 and 3 have no common factor other than 1. The fraction $\frac{4}{6}$ *is not* in simplest form because 4 and 6 both have a factor of 2. That is, 2 is a common factor of 4 and 6. The process of writing a fraction in simplest form is called **simplifying** the fraction.

To simplify $\frac{4}{6}$ and write it as $\frac{2}{3}$, let's first study a few properties. Recall from Section 4.1 that any nonzero whole number n divided by itself is 1.

Any nonzero number n divided by itself is 1.

$$\frac{5}{5} = 1, \quad \frac{17}{17} = 1, \quad \frac{24}{24} = 1, \text{ or, in general, } \frac{n}{n} = 1$$

Also, in general, if $\dfrac{a}{b}$ and $\dfrac{c}{d}$ are fractions (with b and d not 0), the following is true.

$$\frac{a \cdot c}{b \cdot d} = \frac{a}{b} \cdot \frac{c}{d}*$$

Helpful Hint These two properties together are called the Fundamental Property of Fractions

$$\frac{a \cdot c}{b \cdot c} = \frac{a}{b} \cdot \frac{c}{c} = \frac{a}{b}$$

These properties allow us to do the following:

$$\frac{4}{6} = \frac{2 \cdot 2}{2 \cdot 3} = \frac{2}{2} \cdot \frac{2}{3} = 1 \cdot \frac{2}{3} = \frac{2}{3}$$

When 1 is multiplied by a number, the result is the same number.

⎣ This is 1.

Practice 4

Write in simplest form: $\dfrac{30}{45}$

Example 4 Write in simplest form: $\dfrac{12}{20}$

Solution: Notice that 12 and 20 have a common factor of 4.

$$\frac{12}{20} = \frac{4 \cdot 3}{4 \cdot 5} = \frac{4}{4} \cdot \frac{3}{5} = 1 \cdot \frac{3}{5} = \frac{3}{5}$$

Since 3 and 5 have no common factors (other than 1), $\dfrac{3}{5}$ is in simplest form.

■ Work Practice 4

If you have trouble finding common factors, write the prime factorization of the numerator and the denominator.

Practice 5

Write in simplest form: $\dfrac{39x}{51}$

Example 5 Write in simplest form: $\dfrac{42x}{66}$

Solution: Let's write the prime factorizations of 42 and 66. Remember that $42x$ means $42 \cdot x$.

$$\frac{42x}{66} = \frac{2 \cdot 3 \cdot 7 \cdot x}{2 \cdot 3 \cdot 11} = \frac{2}{2} \cdot \frac{3}{3} \cdot \frac{7x}{11} = 1 \cdot 1 \cdot \frac{7x}{11} = \frac{7x}{11}$$

■ Work Practice 5

In the example above, you may have saved time by noticing that 42 and 66 have a common factor of 6.

$$\frac{42x}{66} = \frac{6 \cdot 7x}{6 \cdot 11} = \frac{6}{6} \cdot \frac{7x}{11} = 1 \cdot \frac{7x}{11} = \frac{7x}{11}$$

Helpful Hint

Writing the prime factorizations of the numerator and the denominator is helpful in finding any common factors.

The method for simplifying negative fractions is the same as for positive fractions.

Practice 6

Write in simplest form: $-\dfrac{9}{50}$

Example 6 Write in simplest form: $-\dfrac{10}{27}$

Solution:

$$-\frac{10}{27} = -\frac{2 \cdot 5}{3 \cdot 3 \cdot 3}$$

Prime factorizations of 10 and 27

Since 10 and 27 have no common factors, $-\dfrac{10}{27}$ is already in simplest form.

■ Work Practice 6

Answers

4. $\dfrac{2}{3}$ **5.** $\dfrac{13x}{17}$ **6.** $-\dfrac{9}{50}$

Note: We will study this concept further in the next section.

Example 7 Write in simplest form: $\dfrac{30}{108}$

Solution:

$$\dfrac{30}{108} = \dfrac{2 \cdot 3 \cdot 5}{2 \cdot 2 \cdot 3 \cdot 3 \cdot 3} = \dfrac{\cancel{2}}{\cancel{2}} \cdot \dfrac{\cancel{3}}{\cancel{3}} \cdot \dfrac{5}{2 \cdot 3 \cdot 3} = 1 \cdot 1 \cdot \dfrac{5}{18} = \dfrac{5}{18}$$

■ Work Practice 7

Practice 7
Write in simplest form: $\dfrac{49}{112}$

We can use a shortcut procedure with common factors when simplifying.

$$\dfrac{4}{6} = \dfrac{\overset{1}{\cancel{2}} \cdot 2}{\underset{1}{\cancel{2}} \cdot 3} = \dfrac{1 \cdot 2}{1 \cdot 3} = \dfrac{2}{3}$$ Divide out the common factor of 2 in the numerator and denominator.

This procedure is possible because dividing out a common factor in the numerator and denominator is the same as removing a factor of 1 in the product.

Writing a Fraction in Simplest Form

To write a fraction in simplest form, write the prime factorization of the numerator and the denominator and then divide both by all common factors.

Example 8 Write in simplest form: $-\dfrac{72}{26}$

Solution:

$$-\dfrac{72}{26} = -\dfrac{\overset{1}{\cancel{2}} \cdot 2 \cdot 2 \cdot 3 \cdot 3}{\underset{1}{\cancel{2}} \cdot 13} = -\dfrac{1 \cdot 2 \cdot 2 \cdot 3 \cdot 3}{1 \cdot 13} = -\dfrac{36}{13}$$

■ Work Practice 8

Practice 8
Write in simplest form: $-\dfrac{64}{20}$

✓**Concept Check** Which is the correct way to simplify the fraction $\dfrac{15}{25}$? Or are both correct? Explain.

a. $\dfrac{15}{25} = \dfrac{3 \cdot \overset{1}{\cancel{5}}}{5 \cdot \underset{1}{\cancel{5}}} = \dfrac{3}{5}$ **b.** $\dfrac{1\cancel{5}}{2\cancel{5}} = \dfrac{11}{21}$

In this chapter, we will simplify and perform operations on fractions containing variables. When the denominator of a fraction contains a variable, such as $\dfrac{6x^2}{60x^3}$, we will assume that the variable does not represent 0. Recall that the denominator of a fraction cannot be 0.

Example 9 Write in simplest form: $\dfrac{6x^2}{60x^3}$

Solution: Notice that 6 and 60 have a common factor of 6. Let's also use the definition of an exponent to factor x^2 and x^3.

$$\dfrac{6x^2}{60x^3} = \dfrac{\overset{1}{\cancel{6}} \cdot \overset{1}{\cancel{x}} \cdot \overset{1}{\cancel{x}}}{\underset{1}{\cancel{6}} \cdot 10 \cdot \underset{1}{\cancel{x}} \cdot \underset{1}{\cancel{x}} \cdot x} = \dfrac{1 \cdot 1 \cdot 1}{1 \cdot 10 \cdot 1 \cdot 1 \cdot x} = \dfrac{1}{10x}$$

■ Work Practice 9

Practice 9
Write in simplest form: $\dfrac{7a^3}{56a^2}$

Answers

7. $\dfrac{7}{16}$ 8. $-\dfrac{16}{5}$ 9. $\dfrac{a}{8}$

✓**Concept Check Answers**
a. correct **b.** incorrect

Helpful Hint

Be careful when all factors of the numerator or denominator are divided out. In Example 9, the numerator was $1 \cdot 1 \cdot 1 = 1$, so the final result was $\dfrac{1}{10x}$.

Objective C Determining Whether Two Fractions Are Equivalent ▶

Recall from Objective **B** that two fractions are equivalent if they represent the same part of a whole. One way to determine whether two fractions are equivalent is to see whether they simplify to the same fraction.

Practice 10

Determine whether $\dfrac{7}{9}$ and $\dfrac{21}{27}$ are equivalent.

Example 10 Determine whether $\dfrac{16}{40}$ and $\dfrac{10}{25}$ are equivalent.

Solution: Simplify each fraction.

$$\frac{16}{40} = \frac{\overset{1}{\cancel{8}} \cdot 2}{\underset{1}{\cancel{8}} \cdot 5} = \frac{1 \cdot 2}{1 \cdot 5} = \frac{2}{5}$$

$$\frac{10}{25} = \frac{2 \cdot \overset{1}{\cancel{5}}}{5 \cdot \underset{1}{\cancel{5}}} = \frac{2 \cdot 1}{5 \cdot 1} = \frac{2}{5}$$

Since these fractions are the same, $\dfrac{16}{40} = \dfrac{10}{25}$.

■ Work Practice 10

There is a shortcut method you may use to check or test whether two fractions are equivalent. In the example above, we learned that the fractions are equivalent, or

$$\frac{16}{40} = \frac{10}{25}$$

In this example above, we call $25 \cdot 16$ and $40 \cdot 10$ **cross products** because they are the products one obtains by multiplying diagonally across the equal sign, as shown below.

Cross Products

$$25 \cdot 16 \qquad\qquad 40 \cdot 10$$

$$\frac{16}{40} = \frac{10}{25}$$

Notice that these cross products are equal:

$$25 \cdot 16 = 400, \quad 40 \cdot 10 = 400$$

In general, this is true for equivalent fractions.

Equality of Fractions

$$8 \cdot 6 \qquad\qquad 24 \cdot 2$$

$$\frac{6}{24} \overset{?}{=} \frac{2}{8}$$

Since the cross products ($8 \cdot 6 = 48$ and $24 \cdot 2 = 48$) are equal, the fractions are equal.

Note: If the cross products are not equal, the fractions are not equal.

Answer

10. equivalent

Example 11 Determine whether $\frac{8}{11}$ and $\frac{19}{26}$ are equivalent.

Solution: Let's check cross products.

$$26 \cdot 8$$
$$= 208 \qquad \frac{8}{11} \stackrel{?}{=} \frac{19}{26} \qquad = 209$$
$$11 \cdot 19$$

Since $208 \neq 209$, then $\frac{8}{11} \neq \frac{19}{26}$.

 "Not equal to" symbol

■ Work Practice 11

Practice 11

Determine whether $\frac{4}{13}$ and $\frac{5}{18}$ are equivalent.

Objective D Solving Problems by Writing Fractions in Simplest Form ▶

Many real-life problems can be solved by writing fractions. To make the answers clearer, these fractions should be written in simplest form.

Example 12 Calculating Fraction of Parks in Wyoming

There are currently 58 national parks in the United States. Two of these parks are located in the state of Wyoming. What fraction of the United States' national parks can be found in Wyoming? Write the fraction in simplest form. (*Source: World Almanac*, 2013)

Practice 12

There are eight national parks in Alaska. See Example 12 and determine what fraction of the United States' national parks are located in Alaska. Write the fraction in simplest form.

Solution: First we determine the fraction of parks found in Wyoming state.

$$\frac{2}{58} \quad \leftarrow \text{national parks in Wyoming}$$
$$\quad \leftarrow \text{total national parks}$$

Next we simplify the fraction.

$$\frac{2}{58} = \frac{\overset{1}{\cancel{2}}}{\underset{1}{\cancel{2}} \cdot 29} = \frac{1}{1 \cdot 29} = \frac{1}{29}$$

Thus, $\frac{1}{29}$ of the United States' national parks are in Wyoming state.

■ Work Practice 12

Answers

11. not equivalent   **12.** $\frac{4}{29}$

Calculator Explorations **Simplifying Fractions**

Scientific Calculator

Many calculators have a fraction key, such as $\boxed{a^b/c}$, that allows you to simplify a fraction on the calculator. For example, to simplify $\dfrac{324}{612}$, enter

$\boxed{324}$ $\boxed{a^b/c}$ $\boxed{612}$ $\boxed{=}$

The display will read

$\boxed{\quad 9 \mid 17 \quad}$

which represents $\dfrac{9}{17}$, the original fraction simplified.

Graphing Calculator

Graphing calculators also allow you to simplify fractions. The fraction option on a graphing calculator may be found under the $\boxed{\text{MATH}}$ menu.

To simplify $\dfrac{324}{612}$, enter

$\boxed{324}$ $\boxed{\div}$ $\boxed{612}$ $\boxed{\text{MATH}}$ $\boxed{\text{ENTER}}$ $\boxed{\text{ENTER}}$

The display will read

$\boxed{324/612 \blacktriangleright \text{Frac } 9/17}$

> **Helpful Hint**
> The Calculator Explorations boxes in this chapter provide only an introduction to fraction keys on calculators. Any time you use a calculator, there are both advantages and limitations to its use. Never rely solely on your calculator. It is very important that you understand how to perform all operations on fractions by hand in order to progress through later topics. For further information, talk to your instructor.

Use your calculator to simplify each fraction.

1. $\dfrac{128}{224}$ 2. $\dfrac{231}{396}$ 3. $\dfrac{340}{459}$

4. $\dfrac{999}{1350}$ 5. $\dfrac{432}{810}$ 6. $\dfrac{225}{315}$

7. $\dfrac{54}{243}$ 8. $\dfrac{455}{689}$

Vocabulary, Readiness & Video Check

Use the choices below to fill in each blank.

cross products	equivalent	composite
simplest form	prime factorization	prime

1. The number 40 equals $2 \cdot 2 \cdot 2 \cdot 5$. Since each factor is prime, we call $2 \cdot 2 \cdot 2 \cdot 5$ the _____ of 40.

2. A natural number, other than 1, that is not prime is called a(n) _____ number.

3. A natural number that has exactly two different factors, 1 and itself, is called a(n) _____ number.

4. In $\dfrac{11}{48}$, since 11 and 48 have no common factors other than 1, $\dfrac{11}{48}$ is in _____.

5. Fractions that represent the same portion of a whole are called _____ fractions.

6. In the statement $\dfrac{5}{12} = \dfrac{15}{36}$, $5 \cdot 36$ and $12 \cdot 15$ are called _____.

Watch the section lecture video and answer the following questions.

Objective A **7.** From ⊞ Example 1, what two things should you check to make sure your prime factorization of a number is correct? ▶

Objective B **8.** From the lecture before ⊞ Example 3, when you have a common factor in the numerator and denominator of a fraction, essentially you have what? ▶

Objective C **9.** Describe another way to solve ⊞ Example 7 besides using cross products. ▶

Objective D **10.** Why isn't $\dfrac{10}{24}$ the final answer to ⊞ Example 8? What is the final answer? ▶

4.2 Exercise Set MyMathLab® ▶

Objective A *Write the prime factorization of each number. See Examples 1 through 3.*

1. 20   **2.** 12   ▶ **3.** 48   **4.** 75

5. 81   **6.** 64   **7.** 162   **8.** 128

9. 110   **10.** 130   **11.** 85   **12.** 93

▶ **13.** 240   **14.** 836   **15.** 828   **16.** 504

Objective B *Write each fraction in simplest form. See Examples 4 through 9.*

17. $\dfrac{3}{12}$ **18.** $\dfrac{5}{30}$ **19.** $\dfrac{4x}{42}$ **20.** $\dfrac{9y}{48}$ **21.** $\dfrac{14}{16}$

22. $\dfrac{22}{34}$ **23.** $\dfrac{20}{30}$ **24.** $\dfrac{70}{80}$ **25.** $\dfrac{35a}{50a}$ **26.** $\dfrac{25z}{55z}$

▶ **27.** $-\dfrac{63}{81}$ **28.** $-\dfrac{21}{49}$ ▶ **29.** $\dfrac{30x^2}{36x}$ **30.** $\dfrac{45b}{80b^2}$ **31.** $\dfrac{27}{64}$

32. $\dfrac{32}{63}$ **33.** $\dfrac{25xy}{40y}$ **34.** $\dfrac{36y}{42yz}$ **35.** $-\dfrac{40}{64}$ **36.** $-\dfrac{28}{60}$

37. $\dfrac{36x^3y^2}{24xy}$ **38.** $\dfrac{60a^2b}{36ab^3}$ **39.** $\dfrac{90}{120}$ **40.** $\dfrac{60}{150}$ ▶ **41.** $\dfrac{40xy}{64xyz}$

42. $\dfrac{28abc}{60ac}$ **43.** $\dfrac{66}{308}$ **44.** $\dfrac{65}{234}$ **45.** $-\dfrac{55}{85y}$ **46.** $-\dfrac{78}{90x}$

47. $\dfrac{189z}{216z}$ **48.** $\dfrac{144y}{162y}$ **49.** $\dfrac{224a^3b^4c^2}{16ab^4c^2}$ **50.** $\dfrac{270x^4y^3z^3}{15x^3y^3z^3}$

Objective C *Determine whether each pair of fractions is equivalent. See Examples 10 and 11.*

51. $\dfrac{2}{6}$ and $\dfrac{4}{12}$ **52.** $\dfrac{3}{6}$ and $\dfrac{5}{10}$ ▸ **53.** $\dfrac{7}{11}$ and $\dfrac{5}{8}$

54. $\dfrac{2}{5}$ and $\dfrac{4}{11}$ **55.** $\dfrac{10}{15}$ and $\dfrac{6}{9}$ **56.** $\dfrac{4}{10}$ and $\dfrac{6}{15}$

▸ **57.** $\dfrac{3}{9}$ and $\dfrac{6}{18}$ **58.** $\dfrac{2}{8}$ and $\dfrac{7}{28}$ **59.** $\dfrac{10}{13}$ and $\dfrac{13}{15}$

60. $\dfrac{16}{20}$ and $\dfrac{9}{16}$ **61.** $\dfrac{8}{18}$ and $\dfrac{12}{24}$ **62.** $\dfrac{6}{21}$ and $\dfrac{14}{35}$

Objective D *Solve. Write each fraction in simplest form. See Example 12.*

63. A work shift for an employee at Starbucks consists of 8 hours. What fraction of the employee's work shift is represented by 2 hours?

64. Two thousand baseball caps were sold one year at the U.S. Open Golf Tournament. What fractional part of this total do 200 caps represent?

65. There are 5280 feet in a mile. What fraction of a mile is represented by 2640 feet?

66. There are 100 centimeters in 1 meter. What fraction of a meter is 20 centimeters?

67. Sixteen out of the total fifty states in the United States have Ritz-Carlton hotels. (*Source:* Ritz-Carlton Hotel Company, LLC)
  a. What fraction of states can claim at least one Ritz-Carlton hotel?
  b. How many states do not have a Ritz-Carlton hotel?
  c. Write the fraction of states without a Ritz-Carlton hotel.

68. There are 75 national monuments in the United States. Ten of these monuments are located in New Mexico. (*Source: World Almanac,* 2013)
  a. What fraction of the national monuments in the United States can be found in New Mexico?
  b. How many of the national monuments in the United States are found outside New Mexico?
  c. Write the fraction of national monuments found in states other than New Mexico.

▸ **69.** The outer wall of the Pentagon is 24 inches thick. Ten inches is concrete, 8 inches is brick, and 6 inches is limestone. What fraction of the wall is concrete?

70. There are 35 students in a biology class. If 10 students made an A on the first test, what fraction of the students made an A?

Limestone (6 in.)

Brick (8 in.)

Concrete (10 in.)

71. As Internet usage grows in the United States, more and more state governments are placing services online. Forty-two out of the total fifty states have Web sites that allow residents to file their federal and state income tax electronically at the same time.

   a. How many states do not have this type of Web site?

   b. What fraction of states do not have this type of Web site? (*Source:* MeF Federal/State Program)

72. Katy Biagini just bought a brand-new 2013 Toyota Camry hybrid for $24,200. Her old car was traded in for $12,000.

   a. How much of her purchase price was not covered by her trade-in?

   b. What fraction of the purchase price was not covered by the trade-in?

73. As of this writing, a total of 464 individuals from the United States are or have been astronauts. Of these, 26 were born in Texas. What fraction of U.S. astronauts were born in Texas? (*Source:* Spacefacts Web site)

74. Worldwide, Hallmark employs nearly 12,000 full-time employees. About 3200 employees work at the Hallmark headquarters in Kansas City, Missouri. What fraction of Hallmark employees work in Kansas City? (*Source:* Hallmark Cards, Inc.)

Review

Evaluate each expression using the given replacement numbers. See Section 2.5.

75. $\dfrac{x^3}{9}$ when $x = -3$

76. $\dfrac{y^3}{5}$ when $y = -5$

77. $2y$ when $y = -7$

78. $-5a$ when $a = -4$

Concept Extensions

79. In your own words, define equivalent fractions.

80. Given a fraction, say $\dfrac{15}{40}$, how many fractions are there that are equivalent to it, but in simplest form or lowest terms? Explain your answer.

Write each fraction in simplest form.

81. $\dfrac{3975}{6625}$

82. $\dfrac{9506}{12{,}222}$

There are generally considered to be eight basic blood types. The table shows the number of people with the various blood types in a typical group of 100 blood donors. Use the table to answer Exercises 83 through 86. Write each answer in simplest form.

Distribution of Blood Types in Blood Donors	
Blood Type	**Number of People**
O Rh-positive	37
O Rh-negative	7
A Rh-positive	36
A Rh-negative	6
B Rh-positive	9
B Rh-negative	1
AB Rh-positive	3
AB Rh-negative	1
(*Source:* American Red Cross Biomedical Services)	

83. What fraction of blood donors have blood type A Rh-positive?

84. What fraction of blood donors have an O blood type?

85. What fraction of blood donors have an AB blood type?

86. What fraction of blood donors have a B blood type?

Find the prime factorization of each number.

87. 34,020

88. 131,625

89. In your own words, define a prime number.

90. The number 2 is a prime number. All other even natural numbers are composite numbers. Explain why.

91. Two students have different prime factorizations for the same number. Is this possible? Explain.

92. Two students work to prime factor 120. One student starts by writing 120 as 12×10. The other student writes 120 as 24×5. Finish each prime factorization. Are they the same? Why or why not?

The following graph is called a circle graph or pie chart. Each sector (shaped like a piece of pie) shows the fraction of entering college freshmen who choose to major in each discipline shown. The whole circle represents the entire class of college freshmen. Use this graph to answer Exercises 93 through 96. Write each fraction answer in simplest form.

College Freshmen Majors

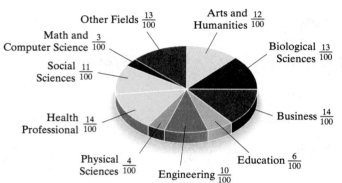

Other Fields $\frac{13}{100}$

Math and Computer Science $\frac{3}{100}$

Social Sciences $\frac{11}{100}$

Health Professional $\frac{14}{100}$

Physical Sciences $\frac{4}{100}$

Engineering $\frac{10}{100}$

Education $\frac{6}{100}$

Business $\frac{14}{100}$

Biological Sciences $\frac{13}{100}$

Arts and Humanities $\frac{12}{100}$

Source: The Higher Education Research Institute

93. What fraction of entering college freshmen plan to major in education?

94. What fraction of entering college freshmen plan to major in engineering?

95. Why is the Business sector the same size as the Health Professional sector?

96. Why is the Physical Sciences sector smaller than the Business sector?

Use this circle graph to answer Exercises 97 through 100. Write each fraction answer in simplest form.

Areas Maintained by the National Park Service

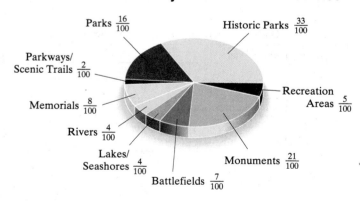

Parks $\frac{16}{100}$

Parkways/ Scenic Trails $\frac{2}{100}$

Memorials $\frac{8}{100}$

Rivers $\frac{4}{100}$

Lakes/ Seashores $\frac{4}{100}$

Battlefields $\frac{7}{100}$

Monuments $\frac{21}{100}$

Recreation Areas $\frac{5}{100}$

Historic Parks $\frac{33}{100}$

Source: National Park Service

97. What fraction of National Park Service areas are National Memorials?

98. What fraction of National Park Service areas are National Parks?

99. Why is the National Battlefields sector smaller than the National Monuments sector?

100. Why is the National Lakes/National Seashores sector the same size as the National Rivers sector?

Use the following numbers for Exercises 101 through 104.

8691   786   1235   2235   85   105   22   222   900   1470

101. List the numbers divisible by both 2 and 3.

102. List the numbers that are divisible by both 3 and 5.

103. The answers to Exercise 101 are also divisible by what number? Tell why.

104. The answers to Exercise 102 are also divisible by what number? Tell why.

Multiplying and Dividing Fractions

Objective A Multiplying Fractions

Let's use a diagram to discover how fractions are multiplied. For example, to multiply $\frac{1}{2}$ and $\frac{3}{4}$, we find $\frac{1}{2}$ of $\frac{3}{4}$. To do this, we begin with a diagram showing $\frac{3}{4}$ of a rectangle's area shaded.

$\frac{3}{4}$ of the rectangle's area is shaded.

To find $\frac{1}{2}$ of $\frac{3}{4}$, we heavily shade $\frac{1}{2}$ of the part that is already shaded.

By counting smaller rectangles, we see that $\frac{3}{8}$ of the larger rectangle is now heavily shaded, so that

$$\frac{1}{2} \text{ of } \frac{3}{4} \text{ is } \frac{3}{8}, \text{ or } \frac{1}{2} \cdot \frac{3}{4} = \frac{3}{8}$$ Notice that $\frac{1}{2} \cdot \frac{3}{4} = \frac{1 \cdot 3}{2 \cdot 4} = \frac{3}{8}$.

Objectives

A Multiply Fractions ▶

B Evaluate Exponential Expressions with Fractional Bases. ▶

C Divide Fractions. ▶

D Multiply and Divide Given Fractional Replacement Values. ▶

E Solve Applications That Require Multiplication of Fractions. ▶

Multiplying Fractions

To multiply two fractions, multiply the numerators and multiply the denominators. If a, b, c, and d represent numbers, and b and d are not 0, we have

$$\frac{a}{b} \cdot \frac{c}{d} = \frac{a \cdot c}{b \cdot d}$$

Examples Multiply.

1. $\frac{2}{3} \cdot \frac{5}{11} = \frac{2 \cdot 5}{3 \cdot 11} = \frac{10}{33}$ Multiply numerators.
Multiply denominators.

This fraction is in simplest form since 10 and 33 have no common factors other than 1.

2. $\frac{1}{4} \cdot \frac{1}{2} = \frac{1 \cdot 1}{4 \cdot 2} = \frac{1}{8}$ This fraction is in simplest form.

■ Work Practice 1–2

Practice 1–2

Multiply.

1. $\frac{3}{7} \cdot \frac{5}{11}$ **2.** $\frac{1}{3} \cdot \frac{1}{9}$

Example 3 Multiply and simplify: $\frac{6}{7} \cdot \frac{14}{27}$

Solution:

$$\frac{6}{7} \cdot \frac{14}{27} = \frac{6 \cdot 14}{7 \cdot 27}$$

We can simplify by finding the prime factorizations and using our shortcut procedure of dividing out common factors in the numerator and denominator.

$$\frac{6 \cdot 14}{7 \cdot 27} = \frac{2 \cdot \overset{1}{\cancel{3}} \cdot 2 \cdot \overset{1}{\cancel{7}}}{\underset{1}{\cancel{7}} \cdot \underset{1}{\cancel{3}} \cdot 3 \cdot 3} = \frac{2 \cdot 2}{3 \cdot 3} = \frac{4}{9}$$

■ Work Practice 3

Practice 3

Multiply and simplify: $\frac{6}{77} \cdot \frac{7}{8}$

Answers

1. $\frac{15}{77}$ **2.** $\frac{1}{27}$ **3.** $\frac{3}{44}$

Helpful Hint

Remember that the shortcut procedure in Example 3 is the same as removing factors of 1 in the product.

$$\frac{6 \cdot 14}{7 \cdot 27} = \frac{2 \cdot 3 \cdot 2 \cdot 7}{7 \cdot 3 \cdot 3 \cdot 3} = \frac{7}{7} \cdot \frac{3}{3} \cdot \frac{2 \cdot 2}{3 \cdot 3} = 1 \cdot 1 \cdot \frac{4}{9} = \frac{4}{9}$$

Practice 4

Multiply and simplify: $\dfrac{4}{27} \cdot \dfrac{3}{8}$

Helpful Hint   Don't forget that we may identify common factors that are not prime numbers.

Example 4 Multiply and simplify: $\dfrac{23}{32} \cdot \dfrac{4}{7}$

Solution: Notice that 4 and 32 have a common factor of 4.

$$\frac{23}{32} \cdot \frac{4}{7} = \frac{23 \cdot 4}{32 \cdot 7} = \frac{23 \cdot \overset{1}{\cancel{4}}}{\cancel{4} \cdot 8 \cdot 7} = \frac{23}{8 \cdot 7} = \frac{23}{56}$$

⬛ Work Practice 4

After multiplying two fractions, always check to see whether the product can be simplified.

Practice 5

Multiply.

$\dfrac{1}{2} \cdot \left(-\dfrac{11}{28}\right)$

Example 5 Multiply: $-\dfrac{1}{4} \cdot \dfrac{1}{2}$

Solution: Recall that the product of a negative number and a positive number is a negative number.

$$-\frac{1}{4} \cdot \frac{1}{2} = -\frac{1 \cdot 1}{4 \cdot 2} = -\frac{1}{8}$$

⬛ Work Practice 5

Practice 6–7

Multiply.

6. $\left(-\dfrac{4}{11}\right)\left(-\dfrac{33}{16}\right)$

7. $\dfrac{1}{6} \cdot \dfrac{3}{10} \cdot \dfrac{25}{16}$

Examples Multiply.

6. $\left(-\dfrac{6}{13}\right)\left(-\dfrac{26}{30}\right) = \dfrac{6 \cdot 26}{13 \cdot 30} = \dfrac{\overset{1}{\cancel{6}} \cdot \overset{1}{\cancel{13}} \cdot 2}{\cancel{13} \cdot \cancel{6} \cdot 5} = \dfrac{2}{5}$ The product of two negative numbers is a positive number.

7. $\dfrac{1}{3} \cdot \dfrac{2}{5} \cdot \dfrac{9}{16} = \dfrac{1 \cdot 2 \cdot 9}{3 \cdot 5 \cdot 16} = \dfrac{1 \cdot \overset{1}{\cancel{2}} \cdot \overset{1}{\cancel{3}} \cdot 3}{\cancel{3} \cdot 5 \cdot \cancel{2} \cdot 8} = \dfrac{3}{40}$

⬛ Work Practice 6–7

We multiply fractions in the same way if variables are involved.

Practice 8

Multiply: $\dfrac{2}{3} \cdot \dfrac{3y}{2}$

Example 8 Multiply: $\dfrac{3x}{4} \cdot \dfrac{8}{5x}$

Solution: Notice that 8 and 4 have a common factor of 4.

$$\frac{3x}{4} \cdot \frac{8}{5x} = \frac{3 \cdot \overset{1}{\cancel{x}} \cdot \overset{1}{\cancel{4}} \cdot 2}{\cancel{4} \cdot 5 \cdot \cancel{x}} = \frac{3 \cdot 1 \cdot 1 \cdot 2}{1 \cdot 5 \cdot 1} = \frac{6}{5}$$

⬛ Work Practice 8

Helpful Hint

Recall that when the denominator of a fraction contains a variable, such as $\dfrac{8}{5x}$, we assume that the variable does not represent 0.

Answers

4. $\dfrac{1}{18}$ **5.** $-\dfrac{11}{56}$ **6.** $\dfrac{3}{4}$ **7.** $\dfrac{5}{64}$ **8.** y

Example 9   Multiply: $\dfrac{x^2}{y} \cdot \dfrac{y^3}{x}$

Solution:

$$\frac{x^2}{y} \cdot \frac{y^3}{x} = \frac{x^2 \cdot y^3}{y \cdot x} = \frac{\overset{1}{\cancel{x}} \cdot x \cdot \overset{1}{\cancel{y}} \cdot y \cdot y}{\underset{1}{\cancel{y}} \cdot \underset{1}{\cancel{x}}} = \frac{x \cdot y \cdot y}{1} = xy^2$$

■ Work Practice 9

Practice 9

Multiply: $\dfrac{a^3}{b^2} \cdot \dfrac{b}{a^2}$

Objective B   Evaluating Expressions with Fractional Bases ▶

The base of an exponential expression can also be a fraction.

$$\left(\frac{1}{3}\right)^4 = \underbrace{\frac{1}{3} \cdot \frac{1}{3} \cdot \frac{1}{3} \cdot \frac{1}{3}}_{\frac{1}{3} \text{ is a factor 4 times.}} = \frac{1 \cdot 1 \cdot 1 \cdot 1}{3 \cdot 3 \cdot 3 \cdot 3} = \frac{1}{81}$$

Example 10   Evaluate.

a. $\left(\dfrac{2}{5}\right)^4 = \dfrac{2}{5} \cdot \dfrac{2}{5} \cdot \dfrac{2}{5} \cdot \dfrac{2}{5} = \dfrac{2 \cdot 2 \cdot 2 \cdot 2}{5 \cdot 5 \cdot 5 \cdot 5} = \dfrac{16}{625}$

b. $\left(-\dfrac{1}{4}\right)^2 = \left(-\dfrac{1}{4}\right) \cdot \left(-\dfrac{1}{4}\right) = \dfrac{1 \cdot 1}{4 \cdot 4} = \dfrac{1}{16}$ The product of two negative numbers is a positive number.

■ Work Practice 10

Practice 10

Evaluate.

a. $\left(\dfrac{3}{4}\right)^3$ **b.** $\left(-\dfrac{4}{5}\right)^2$

Objective C   Dividing Fractions ▶

Before we can divide fractions, we need to know how to find the **reciprocal** of a fraction.

> ### Reciprocal of a Fraction
>
> Two numbers are **reciprocals** of each other if their product is 1. The reciprocal of the fraction $\dfrac{a}{b}$ is $\dfrac{b}{a}$ because $\dfrac{a}{b} \cdot \dfrac{b}{a} = \dfrac{a \cdot b}{b \cdot a} = 1$.

Helpful Hint

Every number has a reciprocal except 0. The number 0 has no reciprocal because there is no number such that $0 \cdot a = 1$.

For example,

The reciprocal of $\dfrac{2}{5}$ is $\dfrac{5}{2}$ because $\dfrac{2}{5} \cdot \dfrac{5}{2} = \dfrac{10}{10} = 1$.

The reciprocal of 5 is $\dfrac{1}{5}$ because $5 \cdot \dfrac{1}{5} = \dfrac{5}{1} \cdot \dfrac{1}{5} = \dfrac{5}{5} = 1$.

The reciprocal of $-\dfrac{7}{11}$ is $-\dfrac{11}{7}$ because $-\dfrac{7}{11} \cdot -\dfrac{11}{7} = \dfrac{77}{77} = 1$.

Answers

9. $\dfrac{a}{b}$ **10. a.** $\dfrac{27}{64}$ **b.** $\dfrac{16}{25}$

Division of fractions has the same meaning as division of whole numbers. For example,

$10 \div 5$ means: How many 5s are there in 10?

There are two 5s in 10, so
$10 \div 5 = 2$.

$\frac{3}{4} \div \frac{1}{8}$ means: How many $\frac{1}{8}$s are there in $\frac{3}{4}$?

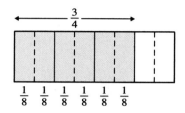

There are six $\frac{1}{8}$s in $\frac{3}{4}$, so $\frac{3}{4} \div \frac{1}{8} = 6$.

We use reciprocals to divide fractions.

Dividing Fractions

To divide two fractions, multiply the first fraction by the reciprocal of the second fraction.

    If $a, b, c,$ and d represent numbers, and $b, c,$ and d are not 0, then

$$\frac{a}{b} \div \frac{c}{d} = \frac{a}{b} \cdot \frac{d}{c} = \frac{a \cdot d}{b \cdot c}$$

              reciprocal

For example,

multiply by reciprocal

$$\frac{3}{4} \div \frac{1}{8} = \frac{3}{4} \cdot \frac{8}{1} = \frac{3 \cdot 8}{4 \cdot 1} = \frac{3 \cdot 2 \cdot \cancel{4}^{1}}{\cancel{4}_{1} \cdot 1} = \frac{6}{1} \text{ or } 6$$

After dividing fractions, *always* check to see whether the result can be simplified.

Practice 11–12

Divide and simplify.

11. $\frac{8}{7} \div \frac{2}{9}$ **12.** $\frac{4}{9} \div \frac{1}{2}$

Answers

11. $\frac{36}{7}$ **12.** $\frac{8}{9}$

Examples   Divide and simplify.

11. $\frac{5}{16} \div \frac{3}{4} = \frac{5}{16} \cdot \frac{4}{3} = \frac{5 \cdot 4}{16 \cdot 3} = \frac{5 \cdot \cancel{4}^{1}}{\cancel{4}_{1} \cdot 4 \cdot 3} = \frac{5}{12}$

12. $\frac{2}{5} \div \frac{1}{2} = \frac{2}{5} \cdot \frac{2}{1} = \frac{2 \cdot 2}{5 \cdot 1} = \frac{4}{5}$

■ Work Practice 11–12

Helpful Hint

When dividing by a fraction, do not look for common factors to divide out until you rewrite the division as multiplication.

Do not try to divide out these two 2s.

$$\frac{1}{2} \div \frac{2}{3} = \frac{1}{2} \cdot \frac{3}{2} = \frac{3}{4}$$

Example 13   Divide: $-\dfrac{7}{12} \div -\dfrac{5}{6}$

Solution: Recall that the quotient (or product) of two negative numbers is a positive number.

$$-\frac{7}{12} \div -\frac{5}{6} = -\frac{7}{12} \cdot -\frac{6}{5} = \frac{7 \cdot \overset{1}{\cancel{6}}}{2 \cdot \cancel{6} \cdot 5} = \frac{7}{10}$$

■ Work Practice 13

Practice 13

Divide: $-\dfrac{10}{4} \div \dfrac{2}{9}$

Example 14   Divide: $\dfrac{2x}{3} \div 3x^2$

Solution:

$$\frac{2x}{3} \div 3x^2 = \frac{2x}{3} \div \frac{3x^2}{1} = \frac{2x}{3} \cdot \frac{1}{3x^2} = \frac{2 \cdot \overset{1}{\cancel{x}} \cdot 1}{3 \cdot 3 \cdot \underset{1}{\cancel{x}} \cdot x} = \frac{2}{9x}$$

■ Work Practice 14

Practice 14

Divide: $\dfrac{3y}{4} \div 5y^3$

Example 15   Simplify: $\left(\dfrac{4}{7} \cdot \dfrac{3}{8}\right) \div -\dfrac{3}{4}$

Solution: Remember to perform the operations inside the ( ) first.

$$\left(\frac{4}{7} \cdot \frac{3}{8}\right) \div -\frac{3}{4} = \left(\frac{\overset{1}{\cancel{4}} \cdot 3}{7 \cdot 2 \cdot \underset{1}{\cancel{4}}}\right) \div -\frac{3}{4} = \frac{3}{14} \div -\frac{3}{4}$$

Now divide.

$$\frac{3}{14} \div -\frac{3}{4} = \frac{3}{14} \cdot -\frac{4}{3} = -\frac{\overset{1}{\cancel{3}} \cdot \overset{1}{\cancel{2}} \cdot 2}{\underset{1}{\cancel{2}} \cdot 7 \cdot \underset{1}{\cancel{3}}} = -\frac{2}{7}$$

■ Work Practice 15

Practice 15

Simplify: $\left(-\dfrac{2}{3} \cdot \dfrac{9}{14}\right) \div \dfrac{7}{15}$

Answers

13. $-\dfrac{45}{4}$ 14. $\dfrac{3}{20y^2}$ 15. $-\dfrac{45}{49}$

✓ **Concept Check Answers**

a. incorrect   **b.** correct

✓**Concept Check** Which is the correct way to divide $\dfrac{3}{5}$ by $\dfrac{5}{12}$? Explain.

a. $\dfrac{3}{5} \div \dfrac{5}{12} = \dfrac{5}{3} \cdot \dfrac{5}{12}$ **b.** $\dfrac{3}{5} \div \dfrac{5}{12} = \dfrac{3}{5} \cdot \dfrac{12}{5}$

Objective D Multiplying and Dividing with Fractional Replacement Values ▶

Recall the difference between an expression and an equation. For example, xy and $x \div y$ are expressions. They contain no equal signs. In Example 16, we practice *simplifying* expressions given fractional replacement values.

Practice 16

If $x = -\dfrac{3}{4}$ and $y = \dfrac{9}{2}$, evaluate **(a)** xy and **(b)** $x \div y$.

Example 16 If $x = \dfrac{7}{8}$ and $y = -\dfrac{1}{3}$, evaluate **(a)** xy and **(b)** $x \div y$.

Solution: Replace x with $\dfrac{7}{8}$ and y with $-\dfrac{1}{3}$.

a.
$$xy = \frac{7}{8} \cdot -\frac{1}{3}$$
$$= -\frac{7 \cdot 1}{8 \cdot 3}$$
$$= -\frac{7}{24}$$

b.
$$x \div y = \frac{7}{8} \div -\frac{1}{3}$$
$$= \frac{7}{8} \cdot -\frac{3}{1}$$
$$= -\frac{7 \cdot 3}{8 \cdot 1}$$
$$= -\frac{21}{8}$$

■ Work Practice 16

Practice 17

Is $-\dfrac{9}{8}$ a solution of the equation $2x = -\dfrac{9}{4}$?

Example 17 Is $-\dfrac{2}{3}$ a solution of the equation $-\dfrac{1}{2}x = \dfrac{1}{3}$?

Solution: To check whether a number is a solution of an equation, recall that we replace the variable with the given number and see if a true statement results.

$$-\frac{1}{2} \cdot x = \frac{1}{3} \qquad \text{Recall that } -\frac{1}{2}x \text{ means } -\frac{1}{2} \cdot x.$$

$$-\frac{1}{2} \cdot -\frac{2}{3} \stackrel{?}{=} \frac{1}{3} \qquad \text{Replace } x \text{ with } -\frac{2}{3}.$$

$$\frac{1 \cdot \overset{1}{2}}{2 \cdot 3} \stackrel{?}{=} \frac{1}{3} \qquad \text{The product of two negative numbers is a positive number.}$$

$$\frac{1}{3} = \frac{1}{3} \qquad \text{True}$$

Since we have a true statement, $-\dfrac{2}{3}$ is a solution.

■ Work Practice 17

Helpful Hint "of" usually translates to multiplication.

Objective E Solving Problems by Multiplying Fractions ▶

To solve real-life problems that involve multiplying fractions, we use our four problem-solving steps from Chapter 3. In Example 18, a new key word that implies multiplication is used. That key word is "**of.**"

Answers

16. a. $-\dfrac{27}{8}$ **b.** $-\dfrac{1}{6}$ **17.** yes

Example 18   Finding the Number of Roller Coasters
in an Amusement Park

Cedar Point is an amusement park located in
Sandusky, Ohio. Its collection of 72 rides is the
largest in the world. Of the rides, $\frac{2}{9}$ are roller
coasters. How many roller coasters are in Cedar
Point's collection of rides? (*Source:* Wikipedia)

Practice 18

Hershey Park is an amusement
park in Hershey, Pennsylvania.
Of its 66 rides, $\frac{1}{6}$ of these are
roller coasters. How many
roller coasters are in Hershey
Park?

Solution:

1. UNDERSTAND the problem. To do so, read and reread the problem. We are
told that $\frac{2}{9}$ of Cedar Point's rides are roller coasters. The word "of" here means
multiplication.

2. TRANSLATE.

In words:	number of roller coasters	is	$\frac{2}{9}$	of	total rides at Cedar Point
	↓	↓	↓	↓	↓
Translate:	number of roller coasters	=	$\frac{2}{9}$	·	72

3. SOLVE: Before we solve, let's estimate a reasonable answer. The fraction $\frac{2}{9}$
is less than $\frac{1}{4}$ (draw a diagram, if needed), and $\frac{1}{4}$ of 72 rides is 18 rides, so the
number of roller coasters should be less than 18.

$$\frac{2}{9} \cdot 72 = \frac{2}{9} \cdot \frac{72}{1} = \frac{2 \cdot 72}{9 \cdot 1} = \frac{2 \cdot \overset{1}{\cancel{9}} \cdot 8}{\underset{1}{\cancel{9}} \cdot 1} = \frac{16}{1} \quad \text{or} \quad 16$$

4. INTERPRET. *Check* your work. From our estimate, our answer is reasonable.
State your conclusion: The number of roller coasters at Cedar Point is 16.

◼ Work Practice 18

Helpful Hint

To help visualize a fractional part of a whole number, look at the diagram below.

$\frac{1}{5}$ of 60 = ?

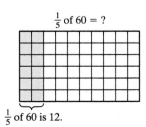

$\frac{1}{5}$ of 60 is 12.

Answer
18. 11 roller coasters

Vocabulary, Readiness & Video Check

Use the choices below to fill in each blank. Not all choices will be used.

multiplication	$\dfrac{a \cdot d}{b \cdot c}$	$\dfrac{a \cdot c}{b \cdot d}$	$\dfrac{2 \cdot 2 \cdot 2}{7}$	$\dfrac{2}{7} \cdot \dfrac{2}{7} \cdot \dfrac{2}{7}$
division	0	reciprocals		

1. To multiply two fractions, we write $\dfrac{a}{b} \cdot \dfrac{c}{d} =$ _____ .

2. Two numbers are _____ of each other if their product is 1.

3. The expression $\dfrac{2^3}{7} =$ _____ while $\left(\dfrac{2}{7}\right)^3 =$ _____ .

4. Every number has a reciprocal except _____ .

5. To divide two fractions, we write $\dfrac{a}{b} \div \dfrac{c}{d} =$ _____ .

6. The word "of" indicates _____ .

Martin-Gay Interactive Videos

See Video 4.3

Watch the section lecture video and answer the following questions.

Objective A 7. In ▣ Example 2, how do we know that the answer is negative? ▶

Objective B 8. In ▣ Example 4, does the exponent apply to the negative sign? Why or why not? ▶

Objective C 9. Complete this statement based on ▣ Example 5: When writing the reciprocal of a fraction, the denominator becomes the _____, and the numerator becomes the _____ . ▶

Objective D 10. In ▣ Example 11a, why don't we write out the prime factorizations of 4 and 9 in the numerator? ▶

Objective E 11. What formula is used to solve ▣ Example 12? ▶

4.3 Exercise Set MyMathLab® ▶

Objective A *Multiply. Write the product in simplest form. See Examples 1 through 9.*

1. $\dfrac{6}{11} \cdot \dfrac{3}{7}$

2. $\dfrac{5}{9} \cdot \dfrac{7}{4}$

 3. $-\dfrac{2}{7} \cdot \dfrac{5}{8}$

4. $\dfrac{4}{15} \cdot -\dfrac{1}{20}$

5. $-\dfrac{1}{2} \cdot -\dfrac{2}{15}$

6. $-\dfrac{3}{11} \cdot -\dfrac{11}{12}$

7. $\dfrac{18x}{20} \cdot \dfrac{36}{99}$

8. $\dfrac{5}{32} \cdot \dfrac{64y}{100}$

9. $3a^2 \cdot \dfrac{1}{4}$

10. $-\dfrac{2}{3} \cdot 6y^3$

11. $\dfrac{x^3}{y^3} \cdot \dfrac{y^2}{x}$

12. $\dfrac{a}{b^3} \cdot \dfrac{b}{a^3}$

13. $0 \cdot \dfrac{8}{9}$

14. $\dfrac{11}{12} \cdot 0$

15. $-\dfrac{17y}{20} \cdot \dfrac{4}{5y}$

16. $-\dfrac{13x}{20} \cdot \dfrac{5}{6x}$

17. $\dfrac{11}{20} \cdot \dfrac{1}{7} \cdot \dfrac{5}{22}$

18. $\dfrac{27}{32} \cdot \dfrac{10}{13} \cdot \dfrac{16}{30}$

Objective **B** *Evaluate. See Example 10.*

19. $\left(\dfrac{1}{5}\right)^3$ **20.** $\left(\dfrac{8}{9}\right)^2$ **21.** $\left(-\dfrac{2}{3}\right)^2$

22. $\left(-\dfrac{1}{2}\right)^4$ **23.** $\left(-\dfrac{2}{3}\right)^3 \cdot \dfrac{1}{2}$ **24.** $\left(-\dfrac{3}{4}\right)^3 \cdot \dfrac{1}{3}$

Objective **C** *Divide. Write all quotients in simplest form. See Examples 11 through 14.*

25. $\dfrac{2}{3} \div \dfrac{5}{6}$ **26.** $\dfrac{5}{8} \div \dfrac{3}{4}$ **27.** $-\dfrac{6}{15} \div \dfrac{12}{5}$ **28.** $-\dfrac{4}{15} \div -\dfrac{8}{3}$

29. $-\dfrac{8}{9} \div \dfrac{x}{2}$ **30.** $\dfrac{10}{11} \div -\dfrac{4}{5x}$ **31.** $\dfrac{11y}{20} \div \dfrac{3}{11}$ **32.** $\dfrac{9z}{20} \div \dfrac{2}{9}$

33. $-\dfrac{2}{3} \div 4$ **34.** $-\dfrac{5}{6} \div 10$ **35.** $\dfrac{1}{5x} \div \dfrac{5}{x^2}$ **36.** $\dfrac{3}{y^2} \div \dfrac{9}{y^3}$

Objectives **A** **B** **C** **Mixed Practice** *Perform each indicated operation. See Examples 1 through 15.*

37. $\dfrac{2}{3} \cdot \dfrac{5}{9}$ **38.** $\dfrac{8}{15} \cdot \dfrac{5}{32}$ **39.** $\dfrac{3x}{7} \div \dfrac{5}{6x}$ **40.** $\dfrac{2}{5y} \div \dfrac{5y}{11}$

41. $\dfrac{16}{27y} \div \dfrac{8}{15y}$ **42.** $\dfrac{12y}{21} \div \dfrac{4y}{7}$ **43.** $-\dfrac{5}{28} \cdot \dfrac{35}{25}$ **44.** $\dfrac{24}{45} \cdot -\dfrac{5}{8}$

45. $\left(-\dfrac{3}{4}\right)^2$ **46.** $\left(-\dfrac{1}{2}\right)^5$ **47.** $\dfrac{x^2}{y} \cdot \dfrac{y^3}{x}$ **48.** $\dfrac{b}{a^2} \cdot \dfrac{a^3}{b^3}$

49. $7 \div \dfrac{2}{11}$ **50.** $-100 \div \dfrac{1}{2}$ **51.** $-3x \div \dfrac{x^2}{12}$ **52.** $-7x^2 \div \dfrac{14x}{3}$

53. $\left(\dfrac{2}{7} \div \dfrac{7}{2}\right) \cdot \dfrac{3}{4}$ **54.** $\dfrac{1}{2} \cdot \left(\dfrac{5}{6} \div \dfrac{1}{12}\right)$ **55.** $-\dfrac{19}{63y} \cdot 9y^2$ **56.** $16a^2 \cdot -\dfrac{31}{24a}$

57. $-\dfrac{2}{3} \cdot -\dfrac{6}{11}$ **58.** $-\dfrac{1}{5} \cdot -\dfrac{6}{7}$ **59.** $\dfrac{4}{8} \div \dfrac{3}{16}$ **60.** $\dfrac{9}{2} \div \dfrac{16}{15}$

61. $\dfrac{21x^2}{10y} \div \dfrac{14x}{25y}$ **62.** $\dfrac{17y^2}{24x} \div \dfrac{13y}{18x}$ **63.** $\left(1 \div \dfrac{3}{4}\right) \cdot \dfrac{2}{3}$ **64.** $\left(33 \div \dfrac{2}{11}\right) \cdot \dfrac{5}{9}$

65. $\dfrac{a^3}{2} \div 30a^3$ **66.** $15c^3 \div \dfrac{3c^2}{5}$ **67.** $\dfrac{ab^2}{c} \cdot \dfrac{c}{ab}$ **68.** $\dfrac{ac}{b} \cdot \dfrac{b^3}{a^2c}$

69. $\left(\dfrac{1}{2} \cdot \dfrac{2}{3}\right) \div \dfrac{5}{6}$ **70.** $\left(\dfrac{3}{4} \cdot \dfrac{8}{9}\right) \div \dfrac{2}{5}$ **71.** $-\dfrac{4}{7} \div \left(\dfrac{4}{5} \cdot \dfrac{3}{7}\right)$ **72.** $\dfrac{5}{8} \div \left(\dfrac{4}{7} \cdot -\dfrac{5}{16}\right)$

Objective D *Given the following replacement values, evaluate (a) xy and (b) x ÷ y. See Example 16.*

73. $x = \frac{2}{5}$ and $y = \frac{5}{6}$ **74.** $x = \frac{8}{9}$ and $y = \frac{1}{4}$ ▶ **75.** $x = -\frac{4}{5}$ and $y = \frac{9}{11}$ **76.** $x = \frac{7}{6}$ and $y = -\frac{1}{2}$

Determine whether the given replacement values are solutions of the given equations. See Example 17.

77. Is $-\frac{5}{18}$ a solution to $3x = -\frac{5}{6}$?

78. Is $\frac{9}{11}$ a solution to $\frac{2}{3}y = \frac{6}{11}$?

79. Is $\frac{2}{5}$ a solution to $-\frac{1}{2}z = \frac{1}{10}$?

80. Is $\frac{3}{5}$ a solution to $5x = \frac{1}{3}$?

Objective E Translating *Solve. Write each answer in simplest form. For Exercises 81 through 84, recall that "of" translates to multiplication. See Example 18.*

81. Find $\frac{1}{4}$ of 200.

82. Find $\frac{1}{5}$ of 200.

83. Find $\frac{5}{6}$ of 24.

84. Find $\frac{5}{8}$ of 24.

Solve. For Exercises 85 and 86, the solutions have been started for you. See Example 18.

85. In the United States, $\frac{7}{50}$ of college freshmen major in business. A community college in Pennsylvania has a freshman enrollment of approximately 800 students. How many of these freshmen might we project are majoring in business?

Start the solution:

1. UNDERSTAND the problem. Reread it as many times as needed.
2. TRANSLATE into an equation. (Fill in the blank below.)

freshmen majoring in business	is	$\frac{7}{50}$	of	community college freshmen enrollment
↓	↓	↓	↓	↓

freshmen majoring in business $= \frac{7}{50} \cdot$ _____

Finish with:
3. SOLVE
4. INTERPRET

86. A patient was told that, at most, $\frac{1}{5}$ of his calories should come from fat. If his diet consists of 3000 calories a day, find the maximum number of calories that can come from fat.

Start the solution:

1. UNDERSTAND the problem. Reread it as many times as needed.
2. TRANSLATE into an equation. (Fill in the blank below.)

patient's fat calories	is	$\frac{1}{5}$	of	his daily calories
↓	↓	↓	↓	↓

patient's fat calories $= \frac{1}{5} \cdot$ _____

Finish with:
3. SOLVE
4. INTERPRET

87. In 2012, there were approximately 225 million moviegoers in the United States and Canada. Of these, about $\frac{12}{25}$ viewed at least one 3-D movie. Find the approximate number of people who viewed at least one 3-D movie. (*Source:* Motion Picture Association of America)

88. In a recent year, movie theater owners received a total of $7660 million in movie admission tickets. About $\frac{7}{10}$ of this amount was for R-rated movies. Find the amount of money received from R-rated movies. (*Source:* Motion Picture Association of America)

89. The Oregon National Historic Trail is 2170 miles long. It begins in Independence, Missouri, and ends in Oregon City, Oregon. Manfred Coulon has hiked $\frac{2}{5}$ of the trail before. How many miles has he hiked? (*Source:* National Park Service)

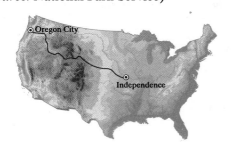

90. Each turn of a screw sinks it $\frac{3}{16}$ of an inch deeper into a piece of wood. Find how deep the screw is after 8 turns.

$\frac{3}{16}$ inch

91. The radius of a circle is one-half of its diameter, as shown. If the diameter of a circle is $\frac{3}{8}$ of an inch, what is its radius?

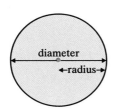

diameter
◄─radius─►

92. The diameter of a circle is twice its radius, as shown in the Exercise 91 illustration. If the radius of a circle is $\frac{7}{20}$ of a foot, what is its diameter?

93. A special on a cruise to the Bahamas is advertised to be $\frac{2}{3}$ of the regular price. If the regular price is $2757, what is the sale price?

94. A family recently sold their house for $102,000, but $\frac{3}{50}$ of this amount goes to the real estate companies that helped them sell their house. How much money does the family pay to the real estate companies?

95. The state of Mississippi houses $\frac{1}{184}$ of the total U.S. libraries. If there are about 9200 libraries in the United States, how many libraries are in Mississippi?

96. There have been about 410 contestants on the reality television show *Survivor* over 27 seasons. Some of these contestants have appeared in multiple seasons. If the number of repeat contestants is $\frac{6}{41}$ of the total number of participants in the first 27 seasons, how many contestants have participated more than once? (*Source:* Survivor.com)

Find the area of each rectangle. Recall that area = length · width.

97.

$\frac{1}{5}$ foot

$\frac{5}{14}$ foot

98.

$\frac{1}{2}$ mile

$\frac{3}{8}$ mile

*Recall from Section 4.2 that the following graph is called a **circle graph** or **pie chart**. Each sector (shaped like a piece of pie) shows the fractional part of a car's total mileage that falls into a particular category. The whole circle represents a car's total mileage.*

Shopping $\frac{3}{25}$

Vacation/other $\frac{3}{50}$

Work $\frac{8}{25}$

Social/recreational $\frac{13}{100}$

Medical $\frac{1}{100}$

Family business $\frac{1}{5}$

Visit friends $\frac{3}{25}$

School/church $\frac{2}{50}$

Source: The American Automobile Manufacturers Association and The National Automobile Dealers Association

In one year, a family drove 12,000 miles in the family car. Use the circle graph to determine how many of these miles might be expected to fall in the categories shown in Exercises 99 through 102.

99. Work

100. Shopping

101. Family business

102. Medical

Review

Perform each indicated operation. See Section 1.3.

103.
$$\begin{array}{r} 27 \\ 76 \\ + 98 \\ \hline \end{array}$$

104.
$$\begin{array}{r} 811 \\ 42 \\ + 69 \\ \hline \end{array}$$

105.
$$\begin{array}{r} 968 \\ - 772 \\ \hline \end{array}$$

106.
$$\begin{array}{r} 882 \\ - 773 \\ \hline \end{array}$$

Concept Extensions

107. In your own words, describe how to divide fractions.

108. In your own words, explain how to multiply fractions.

Simplify.

109. $\frac{42}{25} \cdot \frac{125}{36} \div \frac{7}{6}$

110. $\left(\frac{8}{13} \cdot \frac{39}{16} \cdot \frac{8}{9}\right)^2 \div \frac{1}{2}$

111. Approximately $\frac{1}{8}$ of the U.S. population lives in the state of California. If the U.S. population is approximately 313,914,000, find the approximate population of California. (*Source:* U.S. Census Bureau)

112. In 2012, there were approximately 11,430 commercial radio stations broadcasting in the United States. Of these, approximately $\frac{9}{51}$ were country stations. How many radio stations were country stations in 2012? (Round to the nearest whole.) (*Source:* Federal Communications Commission)

113. The National Park Service is charged with maintaining 27,000 historic structures. Monuments and statues make up $\frac{63}{200}$ of these historic structures. How many monuments and statues is the National Park Service charged with maintaining? (*Source:* National Park Service)

114. If $\frac{3}{4}$ of 36 students on a first bus are girls and $\frac{2}{3}$ of the 30 students on a second bus are *boys*, how many students on the two buses are girls?

4.4 ## Adding and Subtracting Like Fractions, Least Common Denominator, and Equivalent Fractions

Fractions with the same denominator are called **like fractions.** Fractions that have different denominators are called **unlike fractions.**

Like Fractions	Unlike Fractions
$\dfrac{2}{5}$ and $\dfrac{3}{5}$ same denominator	$\dfrac{2}{5}$ and $\dfrac{3}{4}$ different denominators
$\dfrac{5}{21}, \dfrac{16}{21},$ and $\dfrac{7}{21}$ same denominator	$\dfrac{5}{7}$ and $\dfrac{5}{9}$ different denominators

Objectives

A Add or Subtract Like Fractions.

B Add or Subtract Given Fractional Replacement Values.

C Solve Problems by Adding or Subtracting Like Fractions.

D Find the Least Common Denominator of a List of Fractions.

E Write Equivalent Fractions.

Objective A Adding or Subtracting Like Fractions

To see how we add like fractions (fractions with the same denominator), study one or both illustrations below.

Add: $\dfrac{1}{5} + \dfrac{3}{5}$	
Figures	**Number Line**
$\dfrac{1}{5}$ + $\dfrac{3}{5}$ $\dfrac{1}{5} + \dfrac{3}{5} = \dfrac{4}{5}$	To add $\dfrac{1}{5} + \dfrac{3}{5}$, start at 0 and draw an arrow $\dfrac{1}{5}$ of a unit long pointing to the right. From the tip of this arrow, draw an arrow $\dfrac{3}{5}$ of a unit long also pointing to the right. The tip of the second arrow ends at their sum, $\dfrac{4}{5}$. Start End $\dfrac{1}{5}$ $\dfrac{3}{5}$ 0 $\dfrac{4}{5}$ 1 $\dfrac{1}{5} + \dfrac{3}{5} = \dfrac{4}{5}$
Thus, $\dfrac{1}{5} + \dfrac{3}{5} = \dfrac{4}{5}$.	

Notice that the numerator of the sum is the sum of the numerators. Also, the denominator of the sum is the **common denominator.** This is how we add fractions. Similar illustrations can be shown for subtracting fractions.

> **Adding or Subtracting Like Fractions (Fractions with the Same Denominator)**
>
> If a, b, and c are numbers and b is not 0, then
>
> $$\frac{a}{b} + \frac{c}{b} = \frac{a+c}{b} \qquad \text{and also} \qquad \frac{a}{b} - \frac{c}{b} = \frac{a-c}{b}$$

In other words, to add or subtract fractions with the same denominator, add or subtract their numerators and write the sum or difference over the **common** denominator.

251

For example,

$$\frac{1}{4} + \frac{2}{4} = \frac{1+2}{4} = \frac{3}{4}$$ Add the numerators.
Keep the denominator.

$$\frac{4}{5} - \frac{2}{5} = \frac{4-2}{5} = \frac{2}{5}$$ Subtract the numerators.
Keep the denominator.

Helpful Hint

As usual, don't forget to write all answers in simplest form.

Practice 1–3

Add and simplify.

1. $\dfrac{6}{13} + \dfrac{2}{13}$

2. $\dfrac{5}{8x} + \dfrac{1}{8x}$

3. $\dfrac{20}{11} + \dfrac{6}{11} + \dfrac{7}{11}$

Examples Add and simplify.

1. $\dfrac{2}{7} + \dfrac{3}{7} = \dfrac{2+3}{7} = \dfrac{5}{7}$ ← Add the numerators.
← Keep the common denominator.

2. $\dfrac{3}{16x} + \dfrac{7}{16x} = \dfrac{3+7}{16x} = \dfrac{10}{16x} = \dfrac{\overset{1}{\cancel{2}} \cdot 5}{\underset{1}{\cancel{2}} \cdot 8 \cdot x} = \dfrac{5}{8x}$

3. $\dfrac{7}{8} + \dfrac{6}{8} + \dfrac{3}{8} = \dfrac{7+6+3}{8} = \dfrac{16}{8}$ or 2

Work Practice 1–3

✓Concept Check Find and correct the error in the following:

$$\frac{1}{5} + \frac{1}{5} = \frac{2}{10}$$

Practice 4–5

Subtract and simplify.

4. $\dfrac{11}{12} - \dfrac{6}{12}$

5. $\dfrac{7}{15} - \dfrac{2}{15}$

Examples Subtract and simplify.

4. $\dfrac{8}{9} - \dfrac{1}{9} = \dfrac{8-1}{9} = \dfrac{7}{9}$ ← Subtract the numerators.
← Keep the common denominator.

5. $\dfrac{7}{8} - \dfrac{5}{8} = \dfrac{7-5}{8} = \dfrac{2}{8} = \dfrac{\overset{1}{\cancel{2}}}{\underset{1}{\cancel{2}} \cdot 4} = \dfrac{1}{4}$

Work Practice 4–5

From our earlier work, we know that

$$\frac{-12}{6} = \frac{12}{-6} = -\frac{12}{6}$$ since these all simplify to −2.

In general, the following is true:

$$\frac{-a}{b} = \frac{a}{-b} = -\frac{a}{b}$$ as long as b is not 0.

Practice 6

Add: $-\dfrac{8}{17} + \dfrac{4}{17}$

Example 6 Add: $-\dfrac{11}{8} + \dfrac{6}{8}$

Solution: $-\dfrac{11}{8} + \dfrac{6}{8} = \dfrac{-11+6}{8}$

$$= \frac{-5}{8} \text{ or } -\frac{5}{8}$$

Work Practice 6

Answers

1. $\dfrac{8}{13}$ 2. $\dfrac{3}{4x}$ 3. 3 4. $\dfrac{5}{12}$ 5. $\dfrac{1}{3}$

6. $-\dfrac{4}{17}$

✓Concept Check Answer

We don't add denominators together;

correct solution: $\dfrac{1}{5} + \dfrac{1}{5} = \dfrac{2}{5}$.

Example 7 Subtract: $\dfrac{3x}{4} - \dfrac{7}{4}$

Solution: $\dfrac{3x}{4} - \dfrac{7}{4} = \dfrac{3x - 7}{4}$

Recall from Section 3.1 that the terms in the numerator are unlike terms and cannot be combined.

■ Work Practice 7

Example 8 Subtract: $\dfrac{3}{7} - \dfrac{6}{7} - \dfrac{3}{7}$

Solution: $\dfrac{3}{7} - \dfrac{6}{7} - \dfrac{3}{7} = \dfrac{3 - 6 - 3}{7} = \dfrac{-6}{7}$ or $-\dfrac{6}{7}$

■ Work Practice 8

Helpful Hint

Recall that $\dfrac{-6}{7} = -\dfrac{6}{7}$ $\left(\text{Also, } \dfrac{6}{-7} = -\dfrac{6}{7}, \text{if needed.}\right)$

Objective B Adding or Subtracting Given Fractional Replacement Values ▶

Example 9 Evaluate $y - x$ if $x = -\dfrac{3}{10}$ and $y = -\dfrac{8}{10}$.

Solution: Be very careful when replacing x and y with replacement values.

$y - x = -\dfrac{8}{10} - \left(-\dfrac{3}{10}\right)$ Replace x with $-\dfrac{3}{10}$ and y with $-\dfrac{8}{10}$.

$= \dfrac{-8 - (-3)}{10}$

$= \dfrac{-5}{10} = \dfrac{-1 \cdot 5}{2 \cdot 5} = \dfrac{-1}{2}$ or $-\dfrac{1}{2}$

■ Work Practice 9

✔**Concept Check** Fill in each blank with the best choice given.

expression   equation   simplified   solved

A(n) _____ contains an equal sign and may be _____ for the variable.

A(n) _____ does not contain an equal sign but may be _____.

Objective C Solving Problems by Adding or Subtracting Like Fractions ▶

Many real-life problems involve finding the perimeters of square or rectangular-shaped figures such as pastures, swimming pools, and so on. We can use our knowledge of adding fractions to find perimeters.

Practice 7

Subtract: $\dfrac{2}{5} - \dfrac{7y}{5}$

Practice 8

Subtract: $\dfrac{4}{11} - \dfrac{6}{11} - \dfrac{3}{11}$

Practice 9

Evaluate $x + y$ if $x = -\dfrac{10}{12}$ and $y = \dfrac{5}{12}$.

Answers

7. $\dfrac{2 - 7y}{5}$ 8. $-\dfrac{5}{11}$ 9. $-\dfrac{5}{12}$

✔**Concept Check Answer**

equation; solved; expression; simplified

Practice 10

Find the perimeter of the square.

$\frac{3}{20}$ mile

△ **Example 10** Find the perimeter of the rectangle.

$\frac{2}{15}$ inch

$\frac{4}{15}$ inch

Solution: Recall that perimeter means distance around and that opposite sides of a rectangle are the same length.

$\frac{4}{15}$ inch

$\frac{2}{15}$ inch $\frac{2}{15}$ inch

$\frac{4}{15}$ inch

$$\text{Perimeter} = \frac{2}{15} + \frac{4}{15} + \frac{2}{15} + \frac{4}{15} = \frac{2+4+2+4}{15}$$

$$= \frac{12}{15} = \frac{\cancel{3} \cdot 4}{\cancel{3} \cdot 5} = \frac{4}{5}$$

The perimeter of the rectangle is $\frac{4}{5}$ inch.

■ Work Practice 10

We can combine our skills in adding and subtracting fractions with our four problem-solving steps from Section 3.4 to solve many kinds of real-life problems.

Practice 11

A jogger ran $\frac{13}{4}$ miles on Monday and $\frac{11}{4}$ miles on Wednesday. How much farther did he run on Monday than on Wednesday?

Example 11 Calculating Distance

The distance from home to the World Gym is $\frac{7}{8}$ of a mile and from home to the post office is $\frac{3}{8}$ of a mile. How much farther is it from home to the World Gym than from home to the post office?

Home

$\frac{7}{8}$ mile

WORLD GYM

$\frac{3}{8}$ mile   Post office

Solution:

1. **UNDERSTAND.** Read and reread the problem. The phrase "How much farther" tells us to subtract distances.

2. **TRANSLATE.**

In words:	distance farther	is	home to World Gym distance	minus	home to post office distance
	↓	↓	↓	↓	↓
Translate:	distance farther	=	$\frac{7}{8}$	−	$\frac{3}{8}$

3. **SOLVE:** $\frac{7}{8} - \frac{3}{8} = \frac{7-3}{8} = \frac{4}{8} = \frac{\cancel{4}}{2 \cdot \cancel{4}} = \frac{1}{2}$

4. **INTERPRET.** *Check* your work. *State* your conclusion: The distance from home to the World Gym is $\frac{1}{2}$ mile farther than from home to the post office.

■ Work Practice 11

Answers

10. $\frac{3}{5}$ mi   **11.** $\frac{1}{2}$ mi

Objective D Finding the Least Common Denominator

In the next section, we will add and subtract fractions that have different, or unlike, denominators. To do so, we first write them as equivalent fractions with a common denominator.

Although any common denominator can be used to add or subtract unlike fractions, we will use the **least common denominator (LCD).** The LCD of a list of fractions is the same as the **least common multiple (LCM)** of the denominators. Why do we use this number as the common denominator? Since the LCD is the *smallest* of all common denominators, operations are usually less tedious with this number.

> The **least common denominator (LCD)** of a list of fractions is the smallest positive number divisible by all the denominators in the list. (The least common denominator is also the **least common multiple (LCM) of the denominators.)**

For example, the LCD of $\frac{1}{4}$ and $\frac{3}{10}$ is 20 because 20 is the smallest positive number divisible by both 4 and 10.

Finding the LCD: Method 1

One way to find the LCD is to see whether the larger denominator is divisible by the smaller denominator. If so, the larger number is the LCD. If not, then check consecutive multiples of the larger denominator until the LCD is found.

> **Method 1: Finding the LCD of a List of Fractions Using Multiples of the Largest Number**
>
> **Step 1:** Write the multiples of the largest denominator (starting with the number itself) until a multiple common to all denominators in the list is found.
>
> **Step 2:** The multiple found in Step 1 is the LCD.

Example 12 Find the LCD of $\frac{3}{7}$ and $\frac{5}{14}$.

Solution: We write the multiples of 14 until we find one that is also a multiple of 7.

$14 \cdot 1 = 14$ A multiple of 7

The LCD is 14.

■ Work Practice 12

Example 13 Find the LCD of $\frac{11}{12}$ and $\frac{7}{20}$.

Solution: We write the multiples of 20 until we find one that is also a multiple of 12.

$20 \cdot 1 = 20$ Not a multiple of 12

$20 \cdot 2 = 40$ Not a multiple of 12

$20 \cdot 3 = 60$ A multiple of 12

The LCD is 60.

■ Work Practice 13

Practice 12

Find the LCD of $\frac{7}{8}$ and $\frac{11}{16}$.

Practice 13

Find the LCD of $\frac{23}{25}$ and $\frac{1}{30}$.

Answers

12. 16   **13.** 150

Method 1 for finding multiples works fine for smaller numbers, but may get tedious for larger numbers. For this reason, let's study a second method, which uses prime factorization.

Finding the LCD: Method 2

For example, to find the LCD of $\frac{11}{12}$ and $\frac{7}{20}$, such as in Example 13, let's look at the prime factorization of each denominator.

$$12 = 2 \cdot 2 \cdot 3$$
$$20 = 2 \cdot 2 \cdot 5$$

Recall that the LCD must be a multiple of both 12 and 20. Thus, to build the LCD, we will circle the greatest number of factors for each different prime number. The LCD is the product of the circled factors.

Prime Number Factors

$12 = \boxed{2 \cdot 2} \quad \boxed{3}$
$20 = 2 \cdot 2 \qquad \boxed{5}$ — Circle either pair of 2s, but not both.
$\text{LCD} = 2 \cdot 2 \cdot 3 \cdot 5 = 60$

The number 60 is the smallest number that both 12 and 20 divide into evenly. This method is summarized below:

> **Method 2: Finding the LCD of a List of Denominators Using Prime Factorization**
>
> **Step 1:** Write the prime factorization of each denominator.
>
> **Step 2:** For each different prime factor in Step 1, circle the *greatest* number of times that factor occurs in any one factorization.
>
> **Step 3:** The LCD is the product of the circled factors.

Practice 14

Find the LCD of $-\frac{3}{40}$ and $\frac{11}{108}$.

Helpful Hint If you prefer working with exponents, circle the factor with the greatest exponent.

Example 14:
$72 = \boxed{2^3} \cdot \boxed{3^2}$
$60 = 2^2 \cdot 3 \cdot \boxed{5}$
$\text{LCD} = 2^3 \cdot 3^2 \cdot 5 = 360$

Answer
14. 1080

Example 14 Find the LCD of $-\frac{23}{72}$ and $\frac{17}{60}$.

Solution: First we write the prime factorization of each denominator.

$$72 = 2 \cdot 2 \cdot 2 \cdot 3 \cdot 3$$
$$60 = 2 \cdot 2 \cdot 3 \cdot 5$$

For the prime factors shown, we circle the greatest number of factors found in either factorization.

$72 = \boxed{2 \cdot 2 \cdot 2} \cdot \boxed{3 \cdot 3}$
$60 = 2 \cdot 2 \cdot 3 \cdot \boxed{5}$

The LCD is the product of the circled factors.

$$\text{LCD} = 2 \cdot 2 \cdot 2 \cdot 3 \cdot 3 \cdot 5 = 360$$

The LCD is 360.

Work Practice 14

Helpful Hint

If the number of factors of a prime number is equal, circle either one, but not both. For example,

$12 = \boxed{2 \cdot 2} \cdot \boxed{3}$

$15 = 3 \cdot \boxed{5}$ — Circle either 3 but not both.

The LCD is $2 \cdot 2 \cdot 3 \cdot 5 = 60$.

Example 15 Find the LCD of $\dfrac{1}{15}, \dfrac{5}{18}$, and $\dfrac{53}{54}$.

Solution: $15 = 3 \cdot \boxed{5}$

$18 = \boxed{2} \cdot 3 \cdot 3$

$54 = 2 \cdot \boxed{3 \cdot 3 \cdot 3}$

The LCD is $2 \cdot 3 \cdot 3 \cdot 3 \cdot 5$ or 270.

🔲 Work Practice 15

Practice 15

Find the LCD of $\dfrac{7}{20}, \dfrac{1}{24}$, and $\dfrac{13}{45}$.

Example 16 Find the LCD of $\dfrac{3}{5}, \dfrac{2}{x}$, and $\dfrac{7}{x^3}$.

Solution: $5 = \boxed{5}$

$x = x$

$x^3 = \boxed{x \cdot x \cdot x}$

$LCD = 5 \cdot x \cdot x \cdot x = 5x^3$

🔲 Work Practice 16

Practice 16

Find the LCD of $\dfrac{7}{y}$ and $\dfrac{6}{11}$.

✔**Concept Check** True or false? The LCD of the fractions $\dfrac{1}{6}$ and $\dfrac{1}{8}$ is 48.

Objective E Writing Equivalent Fractions ▶

To add or subtract unlike fractions in the next section, we first write equivalent fractions with the LCD as the denominator.

To write $\dfrac{1}{3}$ as an equivalent fraction with a denominator of 6, we multiply by 1 in the form of $\dfrac{2}{2}$. Why? Because $3 \cdot 2 = 6$, so the new denominator will become 6, as shown below.

$$\frac{1}{3} = \frac{1}{3} \cdot 1 = \frac{1}{3} \cdot \frac{2}{2} = \frac{1 \cdot 2}{3 \cdot 2} = \frac{2}{6}$$

$$\frac{2}{2} = 1$$

So $\dfrac{1}{3} = \dfrac{2}{6}$.

Helpful Hint Recall from the Helpful Hint on p. 230, that this is also called the Fundamental Property of Fractions.

$$\frac{a}{b} = \frac{a}{b} \cdot \frac{c}{c} = \frac{a \cdot c}{b \cdot c}$$

To write an equivalent fraction,

$$\frac{a}{b} = \frac{a}{b} \cdot \frac{c}{c} = \frac{a \cdot c}{b \cdot c}$$

where a, b, and c are nonzero numbers.

Answers

15. 360   **16.** 11y

✔**Concept Check Answer**

false; it is 24

✓**Concept Check** Which of the following is *not* equivalent to $\frac{3}{4}$?

a. $\frac{6}{8}$ b. $\frac{18}{24}$ c. $\frac{9}{14}$ d. $\frac{30}{40}$

Practice 17

Write $\frac{7}{8}$ as an equivalent fraction with a denominator of 56.

$$\frac{7}{8} = \frac{}{56}$$

Example 17 Write $\frac{3}{4}$ as an equivalent fraction with a denominator of 20.

$$\frac{3}{4} = \frac{}{20}$$

Solution: In the denominators, since $4 \cdot 5 = 20$, we will multiply by 1 in the form of $\frac{5}{5}$.

$$\frac{3}{4} = \frac{3}{4} \cdot \frac{5}{5} = \frac{3 \cdot 5}{4 \cdot 5} = \frac{15}{20}$$

Thus, $\frac{3}{4} = \frac{15}{20}$.

■ Work Practice 17

Helpful Hint

To check Example 17, write $\frac{15}{20}$ in simplest form.

$$\frac{15}{20} = \frac{3 \cdot \cancel{5}^{1}}{4 \cdot \cancel{5}_{1}} = \frac{3}{4},\text{ the original fraction.}$$

If the original fraction is in lowest terms, we can check our work by writing the new, equivalent fraction in simplest form. This form should be the original fraction.

✓**Concept Check** True or false? When the fraction $\frac{2}{9}$ is rewritten as an equivalent fraction with 27 as the denominator, the result is $\frac{2}{27}$.

Practice 18

Write an equivalent fraction with the given denominator.

$$\frac{1}{4} = \frac{}{20}$$

Answers

17. $\frac{49}{56}$ 18. $\frac{5}{20}$

✓**Concept Check Answers**

c

false; the correct result would be $\frac{6}{27}$

Example 18 Write an equivalent fraction with the given denominator.

$$\frac{2}{5} = \frac{}{15}$$

Solution: Since $5 \cdot 3 = 15$, we multiply by 1 in the form of $\frac{3}{3}$.

$$\frac{2}{5} = \frac{2}{5} \cdot \frac{3}{3} = \frac{2 \cdot 3}{5 \cdot 3} = \frac{6}{15}$$

Then $\frac{2}{5}$ is equivalent to $\frac{6}{15}$. They both represent the same part of a whole.

■ Work Practice 18

Example 19 Write an equivalent fraction with the given denominator.

$$\frac{9x}{11} = \frac{}{44}$$

Solution: Since $11 \cdot 4 = 44$, we multiply by 1 in the form of $\frac{4}{4}$.

$$\frac{9x}{11} = \frac{9x}{11} \cdot \frac{4}{4} = \frac{9x \cdot 4}{11 \cdot 4} = \frac{36x}{44}$$

Then $\frac{9x}{11}$ is equivalent to $\frac{36x}{44}$.

■ Work Practice 19

Practice 19

Write an equivalent fraction with the given denominator.

$$\frac{3x}{7} = \frac{}{42}$$

Example 20 Write an equivalent fraction with the given denominator.

$$3 = \frac{}{7}$$

Solution: Recall that $3 = \frac{3}{1}$. Since $1 \cdot 7 = 7$, multiply by 1 in the form $\frac{7}{7}$.

$$\frac{3}{1} = \frac{3}{1} \cdot \frac{7}{7} = \frac{3 \cdot 7}{1 \cdot 7} = \frac{21}{7}$$

■ Work Practice 20

Practice 20

Write an equivalent fraction with the given denominator.

$$4 = \frac{}{6}$$

Don't forget that when the denominator of a fraction contains a variable, such as $\frac{8}{3x}$, we will assume that the variable does not represent 0. Recall that the denominator of a fraction cannot be 0.

Example 21 Write an equivalent fraction with the given denominator.

$$\frac{8}{3x} = \frac{}{24x}$$

Solution: Since $3x \cdot 8 = 24x$, multiply by 1 in the form $\frac{8}{8}$.

$$\frac{8}{3x} = \frac{8}{3x} \cdot \frac{8}{8} = \frac{8 \cdot 8}{3x \cdot 8} = \frac{64}{24x}$$

■ Work Practice 21

Practice 21

Write an equivalent fraction with the given denominator.

$$\frac{9}{4x} = \frac{}{36x}$$

✓**Concept Check** What is the first step in writing $\frac{3}{10}$ as an equivalent fraction whose denominator is 100?

Answers

19. $\frac{18x}{42}$ **20.** $\frac{24}{6}$ **21.** $\frac{81}{36x}$

✓**Concept Check Answer**
answers may vary

Vocabulary, Readiness & Video Check

Use the choices below to fill in each blank. Not all choices will be used.

least common denominator (LCD)   like $-\dfrac{a}{b}$ $\dfrac{a-c}{b}$ $\dfrac{a+c}{b}$ $-\dfrac{a}{-b}$

perimeter   unlike

equivalent

1. The fractions $\dfrac{9}{11}$ and $\dfrac{13}{11}$ are called _____ fractions while $\dfrac{3}{4}$ and $\dfrac{1}{3}$ are called _____ fractions.

2. $\dfrac{a}{b} + \dfrac{c}{b} =$ _____ and $\dfrac{a}{b} - \dfrac{c}{b} =$ _____.

3. As long as b is not 0, $\dfrac{-a}{b} = \dfrac{a}{-b} =$ _____.

4. The distance around a figure is called its _____.

5. The smallest positive number divisible by all the denominators of a list of fractions is called the

_____.

6. Fractions that represent the same portion of a whole are called _____ fractions.

Martin-Gay Interactive Videos   Watch the section lecture video and answer the following questions.

See Video 4.4

Objective A 7. Complete this statement based on the lecture before ⊞ Example 1: To add like fractions, we add the _____ and keep the same _____ ▷.

Objective B 8. In ⊞ Example 6, why are we told to be careful when substituting the replacement value for y? ▷

Objective C 9. What is the perimeter equation used to solve ⊞ Example 7? What is the final answer? ▷

Objective D 10. In ⊞ Example 8, the LCD is found to be 45. What does this mean in terms of the specific fractions in the problem? ▷

Objective E 11. From ⊞ Example 10, why can we multiply a fraction by a form of 1 to get an equivalent fraction? ▷

4.4 Exercise Set MyMathLab®

Objective A *Add and simplify. See Examples 1 through 3, and 6.*

▷ **1.** $\dfrac{5}{11} + \dfrac{2}{11}$ **2.** $\dfrac{9}{17} + \dfrac{2}{17}$ **3.** $\dfrac{2}{9} + \dfrac{4}{9}$ **4.** $\dfrac{3}{10} + \dfrac{2}{10}$

▷ **5.** $-\dfrac{6}{20} + \dfrac{1}{20}$ **6.** $-\dfrac{3}{8} + \dfrac{1}{8}$ **7.** $-\dfrac{3}{14} + \left(-\dfrac{4}{14}\right)$ **8.** $-\dfrac{5}{24} + \left(-\dfrac{7}{24}\right)$

9. $\dfrac{2}{9x} + \dfrac{4}{9x}$ **10.** $\dfrac{3}{10y} + \dfrac{2}{10y}$ **11.** $-\dfrac{7x}{18} + \dfrac{3x}{18} + \dfrac{2x}{18}$ **12.** $-\dfrac{7z}{15} + \dfrac{3z}{15} + \dfrac{1z}{15}$

Subtract and simplify. See Examples 4, 5, 7, and 8.

13. $\dfrac{10}{11} - \dfrac{4}{11}$

14. $\dfrac{9}{13} - \dfrac{5}{13}$

15. $\dfrac{7}{8} - \dfrac{1}{8}$

16. $\dfrac{5}{6} - \dfrac{1}{6}$

17. $\dfrac{1}{y} - \dfrac{4}{y}$

18. $\dfrac{4}{z} - \dfrac{7}{z}$

19. $-\dfrac{27}{33} - \left(-\dfrac{8}{33}\right)$

20. $-\dfrac{37}{45} - \left(-\dfrac{18}{45}\right)$

21. $\dfrac{20}{21} - \dfrac{10}{21} - \dfrac{17}{21}$

22. $\dfrac{27}{28} - \dfrac{5}{28} - \dfrac{28}{28}$

23. $\dfrac{7a}{4} - \dfrac{3}{4}$

24. $\dfrac{18b}{5} - \dfrac{3}{5}$

Mixed Practice *Perform the indicated operation. See Examples 1 through 8.*

25. $-\dfrac{9}{100} + \dfrac{99}{100}$

26. $-\dfrac{15}{200} + \dfrac{85}{200}$

27. $-\dfrac{13x}{28} - \dfrac{13x}{28}$

28. $-\dfrac{15}{26y} - \dfrac{15}{26y}$

29. $\dfrac{9x}{15} + \dfrac{1}{15}$

30. $\dfrac{2x}{15} + \dfrac{7}{15}$

31. $\dfrac{7x}{16} - \dfrac{15x}{16}$

32. $\dfrac{3}{16z} - \dfrac{15}{16z}$

33. $\dfrac{9}{12} - \dfrac{7}{12} - \dfrac{10}{12}$

34. $\dfrac{1}{8} - \dfrac{15}{8} + \dfrac{2}{8}$

35. $\dfrac{x}{4} + \dfrac{3x}{4} - \dfrac{2x}{4} + \dfrac{x}{4}$

36. $\dfrac{9y}{8} + \dfrac{2y}{8} + \dfrac{5y}{8} - \dfrac{4y}{8}$

Objective B *Evaluate each expression for the given replacement values. See Example 9.*

37. $x + y;\ x = \dfrac{3}{4},\ y = \dfrac{2}{4}$

38. $x - y;\ x = \dfrac{7}{8},\ y = \dfrac{9}{8}$

39. $x - y;\ x = -\dfrac{1}{5},\ y = -\dfrac{3}{5}$

40. $x + y;\ x = -\dfrac{1}{6},\ y = \dfrac{5}{6}$

Objective C *Find the perimeter of each figure. (Hint: Recall that perimeter means distance around.) See Example 10.*

△ **41.**

$\frac{4}{20}$ inch, $\frac{7}{20}$ inch, Triangle, $\frac{9}{20}$ inch

△ **42.**

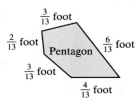

$\frac{3}{13}$ foot, $\frac{2}{13}$ foot, Pentagon, $\frac{6}{13}$ foot, $\frac{3}{13}$ foot, $\frac{4}{13}$ foot

43.

$\frac{5}{12}$ meter | Rectangle | $\frac{7}{12}$ meter

△ **44.**

Square | $\frac{1}{6}$ centimeter

Solve. For Exercises 45 and 46, the solutions have been started for you. Write each answer in simplest form. See Example 11.

45. A railroad inspector must inspect $\frac{19}{20}$ of a mile of railroad track. If she has already inspected $\frac{5}{20}$ of a mile, how much more does she need to inspect?

Start the solution:

1. UNDERSTAND the problem. Reread it as many times as needed.
2. TRANSLATE into an equation. (Fill in the blanks.)

distance left to inspect	is	distance needed to inspect	minus	distance already inspected
↓	↓	↓	↓	↓

$$\text{distance left to inspect} = \underline{\qquad} - \underline{\qquad}$$

Finish with:

3. SOLVE. and 4. INTERPRET.

46. Scott Davis has run $\frac{11}{8}$ miles already and plans to complete $\frac{16}{8}$ miles. To do this, how much farther must he run?

Start the solution:

1. UNDERSTAND the problem. Reread it as many times as needed.
2. TRANSLATE into an equation. (Fill in the blanks.)

distance left to run	is	distance planned to run	minus	distance already run
↓	↓	↓	↓	↓

$$\text{distance left to run} = \underline{\qquad} - \underline{\qquad}$$

Finish with:

3. SOLVE. and 4. INTERPRET.

47. As of 2013, the fraction of states in the United States with maximum interstate highway speed limits up to and including 70 mph was $\frac{33}{50}$. The fraction of states with 70 mph speed limits was $\frac{20}{50}$. What fraction of states had speed limits that were less than 70 mph? (*Source:* Insurance Institute for Highway Safety)

48. When people take aspirin, $\frac{31}{50}$ of the time it is used to treat some type of pain. Approximately $\frac{7}{50}$ of all aspirin use is for treating headaches. What fraction of aspirin use is for treating pain other than headaches? (*Source:* Bayer Market Research)

The map of the world below shows the fraction of the world's surface land area taken up by each continent. In other words, the continent of Africa, for example, makes up $\frac{20}{100}$ of the land in the world. Use this map to solve Exercises 49 through 52. Write answers in simplest form.

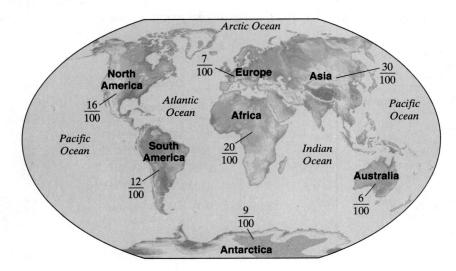

49. Find the fractional part of the world's land area within the continents of North America and South America.

50. Find the fractional part of the world's land area within the continents of Asia and Africa.

51. How much greater is the fractional part of the continent of Antarctica than the fractional part of the continent of Europe?

52. How much greater is the fractional part of the continent of Asia than the continent of Australia?

Objective D *Find the LCD of each list of fractions. See Examples 12 through 16.*

53. $\dfrac{2}{9}, \dfrac{6}{15}$

54. $\dfrac{7}{12}, \dfrac{3}{20}$

55. $-\dfrac{1}{36}, \dfrac{1}{24}$

56. $-\dfrac{1}{15}, \dfrac{1}{90}$

57. $\dfrac{2}{25}, \dfrac{3}{15}, \dfrac{5}{6}$

58. $\dfrac{3}{4}, \dfrac{1}{14}, \dfrac{13}{20}$

59. $-\dfrac{7}{24}, -\dfrac{5}{x}$

60. $-\dfrac{11}{y}, -\dfrac{13}{70}$

61. $\dfrac{23}{18}, \dfrac{1}{21}$

62. $\dfrac{45}{24}, \dfrac{2}{45}$

63. $\dfrac{4}{3}, \dfrac{8}{21}, \dfrac{3}{56}$

64. $\dfrac{12}{11}, \dfrac{20}{33}, \dfrac{12}{121}$

Objective E *Write each fraction as an equivalent fraction with the given denominator. See Examples 17 through 21.*

65. $\dfrac{2}{3} = \dfrac{}{21}$

66. $\dfrac{5}{6} = \dfrac{}{24}$

67. $\dfrac{4}{7} = \dfrac{}{35}$

68. $\dfrac{3}{5} = \dfrac{}{100}$

69. $\dfrac{1}{2} = \dfrac{}{50}$

70. $\dfrac{1}{5} = \dfrac{}{50}$

71. $\dfrac{14x}{17} = \dfrac{}{68}$

72. $\dfrac{19z}{21} = \dfrac{}{126}$

73. $\dfrac{2y}{3} = \dfrac{}{12}$

74. $\dfrac{3x}{2} = \dfrac{}{12}$

75. $\dfrac{5}{9} = \dfrac{}{36a}$

76. $\dfrac{7}{6} = \dfrac{}{36a}$

The table on the next page shows the fraction of goods sold online by type of goods in a particular year. Use this table to answer Exercises 77 through 80.

77. Complete the table by writing each fraction as an equivalent fraction with a denominator of 100.

78. Which of these types of goods has the largest fraction sold online?

79. Which of these types of goods has the smallest fraction sold online?

80. Which of the types of goods has **more than** $\frac{3}{5}$ of the goods sold online? (*Hint:* Write $\frac{3}{5}$ as an equivalent fraction with a denominator of 100.)

Type of Goods	Fraction of All Goods That Are Sold Online	Equivalent Fraction with a Denominator of 100
books and magazines	$\frac{27}{50}$	
clothing and accessories	$\frac{1}{2}$	
computer hardware	$\frac{23}{50}$	
computer software	$\frac{1}{2}$	
drugs, health and beauty aids	$\frac{3}{20}$	
electronics and appliances	$\frac{13}{20}$	
food, beer, and wine	$\frac{9}{20}$	
home furnishings	$\frac{13}{25}$	
music and videos	$\frac{3}{5}$	
office equipment and supplies	$\frac{61}{100}$	
sporting goods	$\frac{12}{25}$	
toys, hobbies, and games	$\frac{1}{2}$	

(*Source:* Fedstats.gov)

Review

Simplify. See Section 1.7.

81. 3^2

82. 4^3

83. 5^3

84. 3^4

85. 7^2

86. 5^4

87. $2^3 \cdot 3$

88. $4^2 \cdot 5$

Concept Extensions

Find and correct the error. See the first Concept Check in this section.

89. $\frac{2}{7} + \frac{9}{7} = \frac{11}{14}$

90. $\frac{3}{4} - \frac{1}{4} = \frac{2}{8} = \frac{1}{4}$

Solve.

91. In your own words, explain how to add like fractions.

92. In your own words, explain how to subtract like fractions.

93. Use the map of the world for Exercises 49 through 52 and find the sum of all the continents' fractions. Explain your answer.

94. Mike Cannon jogged $\frac{3}{8}$ of a mile from home and then rested. Then he continued jogging farther from home for another $\frac{3}{8}$ of a mile until he discovered his watch had fallen off. He walked back along the same path for $\frac{4}{8}$ of a mile until he found his watch. Find how far he was from his home.

Write each fraction as an equivalent fraction with the indicated denominator.

95. $\dfrac{37x}{165} = \dfrac{}{3630}$

96. $\dfrac{108}{215y} = \dfrac{}{4085y}$

 97. In your own words, explain how to find the LCD of two fractions.

98. In your own words, explain how to write a fraction as an equivalent fraction with a given denominator.

Solve. See the fourth and fifth Concept Checks in this section.

99. Which of the following are equivalent to $\frac{2}{3}$?

   a. $\dfrac{10}{15}$ **b.** $\dfrac{40}{60}$

   c. $\dfrac{16}{20}$ **d.** $\dfrac{200}{300}$

100. True or false? When the fraction $\frac{7}{12}$ is rewritten with a denominator of 48, the result is $\frac{11}{48}$. If false, give the correct fraction.

4.5 Adding and Subtracting Unlike Fractions

Objective A Adding and Subtracting Unlike Fractions

In this section we add and subtract fractions with unlike denominators. To add or subtract these unlike fractions, we first write the fractions as equivalent fractions with a common denominator and then add or subtract the like fractions. Recall from the previous section that the common denominator we use is called the **least common denominator (LCD).**

   To begin, let's add the unlike fractions $\frac{3}{4} + \frac{1}{6}$.

   The LCD of these fractions is 12. So we write each fraction as an equivalent fraction with a denominator of 12, then add as usual. This addition process is shown next and also illustrated by figures.

Objectives

A Add or Subtract Unlike Fractions.

B Write Fractions in Order.

C Evaluate Expressions Given Fractional Replacement Values.

D Solve Problems by Adding or Subtracting Unlike Fractions.

Add: $\frac{3}{4} + \frac{1}{6}$	The LCD is 12.
Figures	**Algebra**
$\frac{3}{4}$ $+$ $\frac{1}{6}$ $\frac{9}{12}$ $+$ $\frac{2}{12}$ $\frac{9}{12} + \frac{2}{12} = \frac{11}{12}$	$\frac{3}{4} = \frac{3}{4} \cdot \frac{3}{3} = \frac{9}{12}$ and $\frac{1}{6} = \frac{1}{6} \cdot \frac{2}{2} = \frac{2}{12}$ Remember $\frac{3}{3} = 1$ and $\frac{2}{2} = 1$. **Now we can add just as we did in Section 4.4.** $\frac{3}{4} + \frac{1}{6} = \frac{9}{12} + \frac{2}{12} = \frac{11}{12}$
Thus, the sum is $\frac{11}{12}$.	

Adding or Subtracting Unlike Fractions

Step 1: Find the least common denominator (LCD) of the fractions.

Step 2: Write each fraction as an equivalent fraction whose denominator is the LCD.

Step 3: Add or subtract the like fractions.

Step 4: Write the sum or difference in simplest form.

Practice 1

Add: $\frac{2}{7} + \frac{8}{21}$

Example 1 Add: $\frac{2}{5} + \frac{4}{15}$

Solution:

Step 1: The LCD of the fractions is 15. In later examples, we shall simply say, for example, that the LCD of the denominators 5 and 15 is 15.

Step 2: $\frac{2}{5} = \frac{2}{5} \cdot \frac{3}{3} = \frac{6}{15}$, $\frac{4}{15} = \frac{4}{15}$ ← This fraction already has a denominator of 15.

└ Multiply by 1 in the form $\frac{3}{3}$.

Step 3: $\frac{2}{5} + \frac{4}{15} = \frac{6}{15} + \frac{4}{15} = \frac{10}{15}$

Step 4: Write in simplest form.

$$\frac{10}{15} = \frac{2 \cdot \overset{1}{\cancel{5}}}{3 \cdot \underset{1}{\cancel{5}}} = \frac{2}{3}$$

■ Work Practice 1

When the fractions contain variables, we add and subtract the same way.

Answer

1. $\frac{2}{3}$

Example 2 Add: $\dfrac{2x}{15} + \dfrac{3x}{10}$

Solution:

Step 1: The LCD of the denominators 15 and 10 is 30.

Step 2: $\dfrac{2x}{15} = \dfrac{2x}{15} \cdot \dfrac{2}{2} = \dfrac{4x}{30} \qquad \dfrac{3x}{10} = \dfrac{3x}{10} \cdot \dfrac{3}{3} = \dfrac{9x}{30}$

Step 3: $\dfrac{2x}{15} + \dfrac{3x}{10} = \dfrac{4x}{30} + \dfrac{9x}{30} = \dfrac{13x}{30}$

Step 4: $\dfrac{13x}{30}$ is in simplest form.

■ Work Practice 2

Practice 2

Add: $\dfrac{5y}{6} + \dfrac{2y}{9}$

Example 3 Add: $-\dfrac{1}{6} + \dfrac{1}{2}$

Solution: The LCD of the denominators 6 and 2 is 6.

$$-\dfrac{1}{6} + \dfrac{1}{2} = \dfrac{-1}{6} + \dfrac{1 \cdot 3}{2 \cdot 3}$$

$$= \dfrac{-1}{6} + \dfrac{3}{6}$$

$$= \dfrac{2}{6}$$

Helpful Hint

Recall that

$$-\dfrac{1}{6} = \dfrac{-1}{6} = \dfrac{1}{-6}$$

Next, simplify $\dfrac{2}{6}$.

$$\dfrac{2}{6} = \dfrac{\overset{1}{\cancel{2}}}{\underset{1}{\cancel{2}} \cdot 3} = \dfrac{1}{3}$$

■ Work Practice 3

Practice 3

Add: $-\dfrac{1}{5} + \dfrac{9}{20}$

✓**Concept Check** Find and correct the error in the following:

$$\dfrac{2}{9} + \dfrac{4}{11} = \dfrac{6}{20} = \dfrac{3}{10}$$

Example 4 Subtract: $\dfrac{2}{3} - \dfrac{10}{11}$

Solution:

Step 1: The LCD of the denominators 3 and 11 is 33.

Step 2: $\dfrac{2}{3} = \dfrac{2}{3} \cdot \dfrac{11}{11} = \dfrac{22}{33} \qquad \dfrac{10}{11} = \dfrac{10}{11} \cdot \dfrac{3}{3} = \dfrac{30}{33}$

Step 3: $\dfrac{2}{3} - \dfrac{10}{11} = \dfrac{22}{33} - \dfrac{30}{33} = \dfrac{-8}{33}$ or $-\dfrac{8}{33}$

Step 4: $-\dfrac{8}{33}$ is in simplest form.

■ Work Practice 4

Practice 4

Subtract: $\dfrac{5}{7} - \dfrac{9}{10}$

Answers

2. $\dfrac{19y}{18}$ **3.** $\dfrac{1}{4}$ **4.** $-\dfrac{13}{70}$

✓**Concept Check Answer**

When adding fractions, we don't add the denominators. Correct solution:

$$\dfrac{2}{9} + \dfrac{4}{11} = \dfrac{22}{99} + \dfrac{36}{99} = \dfrac{58}{99}$$

Practice 5

Find: $\dfrac{5}{8} - \dfrac{1}{3} - \dfrac{1}{12}$

Example 5 Find: $-\dfrac{3}{4} - \dfrac{1}{14} + \dfrac{6}{7}$

Solution: The LCD of 4, 14, and 7 is 28.

$$-\frac{3}{4} - \frac{1}{14} + \frac{6}{7} = -\frac{3 \cdot 7}{4 \cdot 7} - \frac{1 \cdot 2}{14 \cdot 2} + \frac{6 \cdot 4}{7 \cdot 4}$$

$$= -\frac{21}{28} - \frac{2}{28} + \frac{24}{28}$$

$$= \frac{1}{28}$$

■ Work Practice 5

✓**Concept Check** Find and correct the error in the following:

$$\frac{7}{12} - \frac{3}{4} = \frac{4}{8} = \frac{1}{2}$$

Practice 6

Subtract: $5 - \dfrac{y}{4}$

Example 6 Subtract: $2 - \dfrac{x}{3}$

Solution: Recall that $2 = \dfrac{2}{1}$. The LCD of the denominators 1 and 3 is 3.

$$\frac{2}{1} - \frac{x}{3} = \frac{2 \cdot 3}{1 \cdot 3} - \frac{x}{3}$$

$$= \frac{6}{3} - \frac{x}{3}$$

$$= \frac{6 - x}{3}$$

> **Helpful Hint**
>
> The expression $\dfrac{6 - x}{3}$ from Example 6 *does not simplify* to $2 - x$. The number 3 must be a factor of both terms in the numerator (not just 6) in order to simplify.

The numerator $6 - x$ cannot be simplified further since 6 and $-x$ are unlike terms.

■ Work Practice 6

Practice 7

Insert < or > to form a true sentence.

$$\frac{5}{8} \qquad \frac{11}{20}$$

Answers

5. $\dfrac{5}{24}$ 6. $\dfrac{20 - y}{4}$ 7. >

✓**Concept Check Answers**

When adding fractions, we don't add the denominators. Correct solutions:

$$\frac{7}{12} - \frac{3}{4} = \frac{7}{12} - \frac{9}{12} = -\frac{2}{12} = -\frac{1}{6}$$

Objective B Writing Fractions in Order ▶

One important application of the least common denominator is to use the LCD to help order or compare fractions.

Example 7 Insert < or > to form a true sentence.

$$\frac{3}{4} \qquad \frac{9}{11}$$

Solution: The LCD for these fractions is 44. Let's write each fraction as an equivalent fraction with a denominator of 44.

$$\frac{3}{4} = \frac{3 \cdot 11}{4 \cdot 11} = \frac{33}{44} \qquad\qquad \frac{9}{11} = \frac{9 \cdot 4}{11 \cdot 4} = \frac{36}{44}$$

Since $33 < 36$, then

$$\frac{33}{44} < \frac{36}{44} \text{ or }$$

$$\frac{3}{4} < \frac{9}{11}$$

■ Work Practice 7

Example 8   Insert $<$ or $>$ to form a true sentence.

$$-\frac{2}{7} \qquad -\frac{1}{3}$$

Solution: The LCD is 21.

$$-\frac{2}{7} = -\frac{2 \cdot 3}{7 \cdot 3} = -\frac{6}{21} \text{ or } \frac{-6}{21} \qquad -\frac{1}{3} = -\frac{1 \cdot 7}{3 \cdot 7} = -\frac{7}{21} \text{ or } \frac{-7}{21}$$

Since $-6 > -7$, then

$$-\frac{6}{21} > -\frac{7}{21} \text{ or }$$

$$-\frac{2}{7} > -\frac{1}{3}$$

■ Work Practice 8

Practice 8

Insert $<$ or $>$ to form a true sentence.

$$-\frac{17}{20} \qquad -\frac{4}{5}$$

Objective C   Evaluating Expressions Given Fractional Replacement Values ▶

Example 9   Evaluate $x - y$ if $x = \frac{7}{18}$ and $y = \frac{2}{9}$.

Solution: Replace x with $\frac{7}{18}$ and y with $\frac{2}{9}$ in the expression $x - y$.

$$x - y = \frac{7}{18} - \frac{2}{9}$$

The LCD of the denominators 18 and 9 is 18. Then

$$\frac{7}{18} - \frac{2}{9} = \frac{7}{18} - \frac{2 \cdot 2}{9 \cdot 2}$$

$$= \frac{7}{18} - \frac{4}{18}$$

$$= \frac{3}{18} = \frac{1}{6} \qquad \text{Simplified}$$

■ Work Practice 9

Practice 9

Evaluate $x - y$ if $x = \frac{5}{11}$ and $y = \frac{4}{9}$.

Objective D   Solving Problems by Adding or Subtracting Unlike Fractions ▶

Very often, real-world problems involve adding or subtracting unlike fractions.

Answers

8. $<$ **9.** $\frac{1}{99}$

Practice 10

To repair her sidewalk, a home-owner must pour cement in three different locations. She needs $\frac{3}{5}$ of a cubic yard, $\frac{3}{10}$ of a cubic yard, and $\frac{1}{15}$ of a cubic yard for these locations. Find the total amount of cement the homeowner needs.

Example 10   Finding Total Weight

A freight truck has $\frac{1}{4}$ of a ton of computers, $\frac{1}{3}$ of a ton of televisions, and $\frac{3}{8}$ of a ton of small appliances. Find the total weight of its load.

Solution:

1. **UNDERSTAND.** Read and reread the problem. The phrase "total weight" tells us to add.

2. **TRANSLATE.**

In words:	total weight	is	weight of computers	plus	weight of televisions	plus	weight of appliances
	↓	↓	↓	↓	↓	↓	↓
Translate:	total weight	=	$\frac{1}{4}$	+	$\frac{1}{3}$	+	$\frac{3}{8}$

3. **SOLVE:** The LCD is 24.

$$\frac{1}{4} + \frac{1}{3} + \frac{3}{8} = \frac{1}{4} \cdot \frac{6}{6} + \frac{1}{3} \cdot \frac{8}{8} + \frac{3}{8} \cdot \frac{3}{3}$$

$$= \frac{6}{24} + \frac{8}{24} + \frac{9}{24}$$

$$= \frac{23}{24}$$

4. **INTERPRET.** *Check* the solution. *State* your conclusion: The total weight of the truck's load is $\frac{23}{24}$ ton.

▶ Work Practice 10

Practice 11

Find the difference in length of two boards if one board is $\frac{3}{4}$ of a foot long and the other is $\frac{2}{3}$ of a foot long.

Answers

10. $\frac{29}{30}$ cu yd   11. $\frac{1}{12}$ ft

Example 11   Calculating Flight Time

A flight from Tucson to Phoenix, Arizona, requires $\frac{5}{12}$ of an hour. If the plane has been flying $\frac{1}{4}$ of an hour, find how much time remains before landing.

Solution:

1. **UNDERSTAND.** Read and reread the problem. The phrase "how much time remains" tells us to subtract.

2. TRANSLATE.

In words:	time remaining	is	flight time from Tucson to Phoenix	minus	flight time already passed
	↓	↓	↓	↓	↓
Translate:	time remaining	$=$	$\dfrac{5}{12}$	$-$	$\dfrac{1}{4}$

3. SOLVE: The LCD is 12.

$$\frac{5}{12} - \frac{1}{4} = \frac{5}{12} - \frac{1}{4} \cdot \frac{3}{3}$$

$$= \frac{5}{12} - \frac{3}{12}$$

$$= \frac{2}{12} = \frac{\overset{1}{\cancel{2}}}{\underset{1}{\cancel{2}} \cdot 6} = \frac{1}{6}$$

4. INTERPRET. *Check* the solution. *State* your conclusion: The remaining flight time is $\dfrac{1}{6}$ of an hour.

■ Work Practice 11

🖩 Calculator Explorations Performing Operations on Fractions

Scientific Calculator

Many calculators have a fraction key, such as $\boxed{a^b/_c}$, that allows you to enter fractions and perform operations on fractions, and gives the result as a fraction. If your calculator has a fraction key, use it to calculate

$$\frac{3}{5} + \frac{4}{7}$$

Enter the keystrokes

$\boxed{3}\ \boxed{a^b/_c}\ \boxed{5}\ \boxed{+}\ \boxed{4}\ \boxed{a^b/_c}\ \boxed{7}\ \boxed{=}$

The display should read $\boxed{1\_6\ |\ 35}$

which represents the mixed number $1\dfrac{6}{35}$. Let's write the result as a fraction. To convert from mixed number notation to fractional notation, press

$\boxed{2^{nd}}\ \boxed{d/c}$

The display now reads $\boxed{41\ |\ 35}$

which represents $\dfrac{41}{35}$, the sum in fractional notation.

Graphing Calculator

Graphing calculators also allow you to perform operations on fractions and will give exact fractional results. The fraction option on a graphing calculator may be found under the $\boxed{\text{MATH}}$ menu. To perform the addition in the first column, try the keystrokes

$\boxed{3}\ \boxed{\div}\ \boxed{5}\ \boxed{+}\ \boxed{4}\ \boxed{\div}\ \boxed{7}\ \boxed{\text{MATH}}\ \boxed{\text{ENTER}}$
$\boxed{\text{ENTER}}$

The display should read

$\boxed{3/5 + 4/7 \blacktriangleright \text{Frac } 41/35}$

Use a calculator to add the following fractions. Give each sum as a fraction.

1. $\dfrac{1}{16} + \dfrac{2}{5}$ **2.** $\dfrac{3}{20} + \dfrac{2}{25}$ **3.** $\dfrac{4}{9} + \dfrac{7}{8}$

4. $\dfrac{9}{11} + \dfrac{5}{12}$ **5.** $\dfrac{10}{17} + \dfrac{12}{19}$ **6.** $\dfrac{14}{31} + \dfrac{15}{21}$

Vocabulary, Readiness & Video Check

Use the choices below to fill in each blank. Any numerical answers are not listed. Not all choices may be used.

expression   least common denominator >

equation   equivalent   <

1. To add or subtract unlike fractions, we first write the fractions as _____ fractions with a common denominator. The common denominator we use is called the _____.

2. The LCD for $\frac{1}{6}$ and $\frac{5}{8}$ is _____.

3. $\frac{1}{6} + \frac{5}{8} = \frac{1}{6} \cdot \frac{4}{4} + \frac{5}{8} \cdot \frac{3}{3} = \underline{\quad} + \underline{\quad} = \underline{\quad}$

4. $\frac{1}{6} - \frac{5}{8} = \frac{1}{6} \cdot \frac{4}{4} - \frac{5}{8} \cdot \frac{3}{3} = \underline{\quad} - \underline{\quad} = \underline{\quad}.$

5. $x - y$ is a(n) _____ while $3x = \frac{1}{5}$ is a(n) _____.

6. Since $-10 < -1$, we know that $-\frac{10}{13}$ _____ $-\frac{1}{13}.$

Martin-Gay Interactive Videos

See Video 4.5

Watch the section lecture video and answer the following questions.

Objective **A** 7. In ⊟ Example 3, why can't we add the two terms in the numerator?

Objective **B** 8. In ⊟ Example 5, when comparing two fractions, how does writing each fraction with the same denominator help? ▶

Objective **C** 9. In ⊟ Example 6, if we had chosen to simplify the first fraction before adding, what would our addition problem have become and what would our LCD have been? ▶

Objective **D** 10. What are the two forms of the answer to ⊟ Example 7? ▶

4.5 **Exercise Set** MyMathLab® ▶

Objective **A** *Add or subtract as indicated. See Examples 1 through 6.*

1. $\frac{2}{3} + \frac{1}{6}$ 2. $\frac{5}{6} + \frac{1}{12}$ 3. $\frac{1}{2} - \frac{1}{3}$ 4. $\frac{2}{3} - \frac{1}{4}$

5. $-\frac{2}{11} + \frac{2}{33}$ 6. $-\frac{5}{9} + \frac{1}{3}$ 7. $\frac{3}{14} - \frac{3}{7}$ 8. $\frac{2}{15} - \frac{2}{5}$

9. $\frac{11x}{35} + \frac{2x}{7}$ 10. $\frac{2y}{5} + \frac{3y}{25}$ 11. $2 - \frac{y}{12}$ 12. $5 - \frac{y}{20}$

13. $\frac{5}{12} - \frac{1}{9}$ 14. $\frac{7}{12} - \frac{5}{18}$ 15. $-7 + \frac{5}{7}$ 16. $-10 + \frac{7}{10}$

17. $\dfrac{5a}{11} + \dfrac{4a}{9}$

18. $\dfrac{7x}{18} + \dfrac{2x}{9}$

19. $\dfrac{2y}{3} - \dfrac{1}{6}$

20. $\dfrac{5z}{6} - \dfrac{1}{12}$

21. $\dfrac{1}{2} + \dfrac{3}{x}$

22. $\dfrac{2}{5} + \dfrac{3}{x}$

23. $-\dfrac{2}{11} - \dfrac{2}{33}$

24. $-\dfrac{5}{9} - \dfrac{1}{3}$

25. $\dfrac{9}{14} - \dfrac{3}{7}$

26. $\dfrac{4}{5} - \dfrac{2}{15}$

27. $\dfrac{11y}{35} - \dfrac{2}{7}$

28. $\dfrac{2b}{5} - \dfrac{3}{25}$

29. $\dfrac{1}{9} - \dfrac{5}{12}$

30. $\dfrac{5}{18} - \dfrac{7}{12}$

31. $\dfrac{7}{15} - \dfrac{5}{12}$

32. $\dfrac{5}{8} - \dfrac{3}{20}$

33. $\dfrac{5}{7} - \dfrac{1}{8}$

34. $\dfrac{10}{13} - \dfrac{7}{10}$

35. $\dfrac{7}{8} + \dfrac{3}{16}$

36. $\dfrac{7}{18} + \dfrac{2}{9}$

37. $\dfrac{3}{9} - \dfrac{5}{9}$

38. $\dfrac{1}{13} - \dfrac{4}{13}$

39. $-\dfrac{2}{5} + \dfrac{1}{3} - \dfrac{3}{10}$

40. $-\dfrac{1}{3} - \dfrac{1}{4} + \dfrac{2}{5}$

41. $\dfrac{5}{11} + \dfrac{y}{3}$

42. $\dfrac{5z}{13} + \dfrac{3}{26}$

43. $-\dfrac{5}{6} - \dfrac{3}{7}$

44. $-\dfrac{1}{2} - \dfrac{3}{29}$

45. $\dfrac{x}{2} + \dfrac{x}{4} + \dfrac{2x}{16}$

46. $\dfrac{z}{4} + \dfrac{z}{8} + \dfrac{2z}{16}$

47. $\dfrac{7}{9} - \dfrac{1}{6}$

48. $\dfrac{9}{16} - \dfrac{3}{8}$

49. $\dfrac{2a}{3} + \dfrac{6a}{13}$

50. $\dfrac{3y}{4} + \dfrac{y}{7}$

51. $\dfrac{7}{30} - \dfrac{5}{12}$

52. $\dfrac{7}{30} - \dfrac{3}{20}$

53. $\dfrac{5}{9} + \dfrac{1}{y}$

54. $\dfrac{1}{12} - \dfrac{5}{x}$

55. $\dfrac{6}{5} - \dfrac{3}{4} + \dfrac{1}{2}$

56. $\dfrac{6}{5} + \dfrac{3}{4} - \dfrac{1}{2}$

57. $\dfrac{4}{5} + \dfrac{4}{9}$

58. $\dfrac{11}{12} - \dfrac{7}{24}$

59. $\dfrac{5}{9x} + \dfrac{1}{8}$

60. $\dfrac{3}{8} + \dfrac{5}{12x}$

61. $-\dfrac{9}{12} + \dfrac{17}{24} - \dfrac{1}{6}$

62. $-\dfrac{5}{14} + \dfrac{3}{7} - \dfrac{1}{2}$

63. $\dfrac{3x}{8} + \dfrac{2x}{7} - \dfrac{5}{14}$

64. $\dfrac{9x}{10} - \dfrac{1}{2} + \dfrac{x}{5}$

Objective B *Insert < or > to form a true sentence. See Examples 7 and 8.*

65. $\dfrac{2}{7}$ $\dfrac{3}{10}$

66. $\dfrac{5}{9}$ $\dfrac{6}{11}$

67. $-\dfrac{5}{6}$ $-\dfrac{13}{15}$

68. $-\dfrac{7}{8}$ $-\dfrac{5}{6}$

69. $-\dfrac{3}{4}$ $-\dfrac{11}{14}$

70. $-\dfrac{2}{9}$ $-\dfrac{3}{13}$

Objective C *Evaluate each expression if $x = \dfrac{1}{3}$ and $y = \dfrac{3}{4}$. See Example 9.*

71. $x + y$

72. $x - y$

73. xy

74. $x \div y$

75. $2y + x$

76. $2x + y$

Objective D *Find the perimeter of each geometric figure. (Hint: Recall that perimeter means distance around.)*

▶ **77.**

$\frac{4}{5}$ cm

$\frac{1}{3}$ cm / Parallelogram / $\frac{1}{3}$ cm

$\frac{4}{5}$ cm

△ **78.**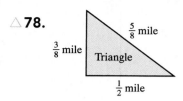

$\frac{3}{8}$ mile   Triangle $\frac{5}{8}$ mile

$\frac{1}{2}$ mile

△ **79.**

$\frac{1}{4}$ meter $\frac{1}{5}$ meter

Quadrilateral $\frac{1}{2}$ meter

$\frac{3}{4}$ meter

△ **80.**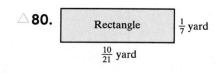

Rectangle $\frac{1}{7}$ yard

$\frac{10}{21}$ yard

Translating *Translate each phrase into an algebraic expression. Use "x" to represent "a number." See Examples 10 and 11.*

81. The sum of a number and $\frac{1}{2}$

82. A number increased by $-\frac{2}{5}$

83. A number subtracted from $-\frac{3}{8}$

84. The difference of a number and $\frac{7}{20}$

Solve. For Exercises 85 and 86, the solutions have been started for you. See Examples 10 and 11.

85. The slowest mammal is the three-toed sloth from South America. The sloth has an average ground speed of $\frac{1}{10}$ mph. In trees, it can accelerate to $\frac{17}{100}$ mph. How much faster can a sloth travel in trees? (*Source: The Guinness Book of World Records*)

Start the solution:
1. UNDERSTAND the problem. Reread it as many times as needed.
2. TRANSLATE into an equation. (Fill in the blanks.)

how much faster sloth travels in trees	is	sloth speed in trees	minus	sloth speed on ground
↓	↓	↓	↓	↓

how much faster sloth travels in trees = _____ − _____

Finish with:
3. SOLVE. and
4. INTERPRET.

86. Killer bees have been known to chase people for up to $\frac{1}{4}$ of a mile, while domestic European honeybees will normally chase a person for no more than 100 feet, or $\frac{5}{264}$ of a mile. How much farther will a killer bee chase a person than a domestic honeybee? (*Source:* Coachella Valley Mosquito & Vector Control District)

Start the solution:
1. UNDERSTAND the problem. Reread it as many times as needed.
2. TRANSLATE into an equation. (Fill in the blanks.)

how much farther killer bee will chase than honeybee	is	distance killer bee chases	minus	distance honeybee chases
↓	↓	↓	↓	↓

how much farther killer bee will chase than honeybee = _____ − _____

Finish with
3. SOLVE. and
4. INTERPRET.

87. Find the inner diameter of the washer.

$\frac{3}{16}$ inch $\frac{3}{16}$ inch

1 inch

88. Find the inner diameter of the tubing.

Inner diameter

$\frac{1}{8}$ inch $\frac{1}{8}$ inch

$\frac{3}{4}$ inch

89. About $\frac{13}{20}$ of American students ages 10 to 17 name math, science, or art as their favorite subject in school. Art is the favorite subject for about $\frac{4}{25}$ of the American students ages 10 to 17. For what fraction of students this age is math or science their favorite subject? (*Source:* Peter D. Hart Research Associates for the National Science Foundation)

90. In the 2012 FIA Formula One World Championship, the Red Bull Racing–Renault team won $\frac{7}{20}$ of all races. If the Red Bull driver Sebastian Vettel won $\frac{1}{4}$ of the races, how many did Red Bull driver Mark Webber win? (*Source:* Formula1.com)

91. Given the following diagram, find its total length.

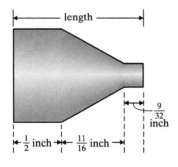

length

$\frac{9}{32}$ inch

$\frac{1}{2}$ inch $\frac{11}{16}$ inch

92. Given the following diagram, find its total width.

width

$\frac{11}{16}$ inch

$\frac{5}{8}$ inch

$\frac{11}{16}$ inch

The table below shows the fraction of the Earth's water area taken up by each ocean. Use this table for Exercises 93 and 94.

Fraction of Earth's Water Area per Ocean	
Ocean	**Fraction**
Arctic	$\frac{1}{25}$
Atlantic	$\frac{13}{50}$
Pacific	$\frac{1}{2}$
Indian	$\frac{1}{5}$

93. What fraction of the world's water surface area is accounted for by the Pacific and Atlantic Oceans?

94. What fraction of the world's water surface area is accounted for by the Arctic and Indian Oceans?

Use this circle graph to answer Exercises 95 through 98.

Areas Maintained by the National Park Service

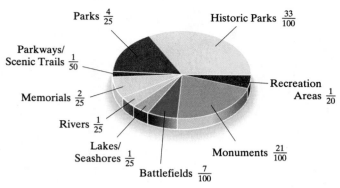

Parks $\frac{4}{25}$ Historic Parks $\frac{33}{100}$

Parkways/Scenic Trails $\frac{1}{50}$

Memorials $\frac{2}{25}$

Rivers $\frac{1}{25}$

Lakes/Seashores $\frac{1}{25}$

Battlefields $\frac{7}{100}$

Recreation Areas $\frac{1}{20}$

Monuments $\frac{21}{100}$

Source: National Park Service

95. What fraction of areas maintained by the National Park Service are designated as National Lakes or National Seashores?

96. What fraction of areas maintained by the National Park Service are designated as National Recreation Areas?

97. What fraction of areas maintained by the National Park Service are NOT National Monuments?

98. What fraction of areas maintained by the National Park Service are NOT National Parkways or Scenic Trails?

Review

Use order of operations to simplify. See Section 2.5.

99. $-50 \div 5 \cdot 2$

100. $8 - 6 \cdot 4 - 7$

101. $(8 - 6) \cdot (4 - 7)$

102. $50 \div (5 \cdot 2)$

Concept Extensions

For Exercises 103 and 104 below, do the following:

a) *Draw three rectangles of the same size and represent each fraction in the sum or difference, one fraction per rectangle, by shading.*

b) *Using these rectangles as estimates, determine whether there is an error in the sum or difference.*

c) *If there is an error, correctly calculate the sum or difference.*

See the Concept Checks in this section.

103. $\frac{3}{5} + \frac{4}{5} \stackrel{?}{=} \frac{7}{10}$

104. $\frac{5}{8} - \frac{3}{4} \stackrel{?}{=} \frac{2}{4}$

Subtract from left to right.

105. $\frac{2}{3} - \frac{1}{4} - \frac{2}{540}$

106. $\frac{9}{10} - \frac{7}{200} - \frac{1}{3}$

Perform each indicated operation.

107. $\frac{30}{55} + \frac{1000}{1760}$

108. $\frac{19}{26} - \frac{968}{1352}$

109. In your own words, describe how to add or subtract two fractions with different denominators.

110. Find the sum of the fractions in the circle graph above. Did the sum surprise you? Why or why not?

111. In 2012, about $\frac{69}{160}$ of the total number of pieces of mail delivered by the United States Postal Service was first-class mail. That same year, about $\frac{1}{2}$ of the total number of pieces of mail delivered by the United States Postal Service was standard mail. Which of these two categories account for a greater portion of the mail handled by volume? (*Source:* United States Postal Service)

Summary on Fractions and Operations on Fractions

Answers

Use a fraction to represent the shaded area of each figure. If the fraction is improper, also write the fraction as a mixed number.

1.

2.

Solve.

3. In a survey, 73 people out of 85 get fewer than 8 hours of sleep each night. What fraction of people in the survey get fewer than 8 hours of sleep?

4. Sketch a diagram to represent $\dfrac{9}{13}$.

Simplify.

5. $\dfrac{11}{-11}$

6. $\dfrac{17}{1}$

7. $\dfrac{0}{-3}$

8. $\dfrac{7}{0}$

Write the prime factorization of each composite number. Write any repeated factors using exponents.

9. 65

10. 70

11. 315

12. 441

Write each fraction in simplest form.

13. $\dfrac{2}{14}$

14. $\dfrac{24}{20}$

15. $-\dfrac{56}{60}$

16. $-\dfrac{72}{80}$

17. $\dfrac{54x}{135}$

18. $\dfrac{90}{240y}$

19. $\dfrac{165z^3}{210z}$

20. $\dfrac{245ab}{385a^2b^3}$

Determine whether each pair of fractions is equivalent.

21. $\dfrac{7}{8}$ and $\dfrac{9}{10}$

22. $\dfrac{10}{12}$ and $\dfrac{15}{18}$

23. Of the 50 states, 2 states are not adjacent to any other states.

  a. What fraction of the states are not adjacent to other states?

  b. How many states are adjacent to other states?

  c. What fraction of the states are adjacent to other states?

24. There are approximately 90,000 digital movie screens in the world. Of these, about 36,000 are in the U.S./Canada. (*Source:* Motion Picture Association of America)

  a. What fraction of digital movie screens are in the U.S./Canada?

  b. How many digital movie screens are not in the U.S./Canada?

  c. What fraction of digital movie screens are not in the U.S./Canada?

1. _____

2. _____

3. _____

4. _____

5. _____

6. _____

7. _____

8. _____

9. _____

10. _____

11. _____

12. _____

13. _____

14. _____

15. _____

16. _____

17. _____

18. _____

19. _____

20. _____

21. _____

22. _____

23. a.   b.   c.

24. a.   b.   c.

25. _____ 26. _____

Find the LCM of each list of numbers.

25. $5, 6$ **26.** $2, 14$ **27.** $6, 18, 30$

27. _____ 28. _____

Write each fraction as an equivalent fraction with the indicated denominator.

28. $\dfrac{7}{9} = \dfrac{}{36}$ **29.** $\dfrac{11}{15} = \dfrac{}{75}$ **30.** $\dfrac{5}{6} = \dfrac{}{48}$

29. _____ 30. _____

31. _____ 32. _____

The following summary will help you with the following review of operations on fractions.

33. _____ 34. _____

Operations on Fractions

Let $a, b, c,$ and d be integers.

35. _____ 36. _____

Addition: $\dfrac{a}{b} + \dfrac{c}{b} = \dfrac{a+c}{b}$ Subtraction: $\dfrac{a}{b} - \dfrac{c}{b} = \dfrac{a-c}{b}$

37. _____

$b \neq 0$ ↑ ↑
common denominator $(b \neq 0)$ ↑ ↑
common denominator

38. _____

Multiplication: $\dfrac{a}{b} \cdot \dfrac{c}{d} = \dfrac{a \cdot c}{b \cdot d}$ Division: $\dfrac{a}{b} \div \dfrac{c}{d} = \dfrac{a}{b} \cdot \dfrac{d}{c} = \dfrac{a \cdot d}{b \cdot c}$

$(b \neq 0, d \neq 0)$ $(b \neq 0, d \neq 0, c \neq 0)$

39. _____

40. _____

Perform each indicated operation.

31. $\dfrac{1}{5} + \dfrac{3}{5}$ **32.** $\dfrac{1}{5} - \dfrac{3}{5}$ **33.** $\dfrac{1}{5} \cdot \dfrac{3}{5}$ **34.** $\dfrac{1}{5} \div \dfrac{3}{5}$

41. _____

35. $\dfrac{2}{3} \div \dfrac{5}{6}$ **36.** $\dfrac{2a}{3} \cdot \dfrac{5}{6a}$ **37.** $\dfrac{2}{3y} - \dfrac{5}{6y}$ **38.** $\dfrac{2x}{3} + \dfrac{5x}{6}$

42. _____

39. $-\dfrac{1}{7} \cdot -\dfrac{7}{18}$ **40.** $-\dfrac{4}{9} \cdot -\dfrac{3}{7}$ **41.** $-\dfrac{7z}{8} \div 6z^2$ **42.** $-\dfrac{9}{10} \div 5$

43. _____

43. $\dfrac{7}{8} + \dfrac{1}{20}$ **44.** $\dfrac{5}{12} - \dfrac{1}{9}$ **45.** $\dfrac{2}{9} + \dfrac{1}{18} + \dfrac{1}{3}$ **46.** $\dfrac{3y}{10} + \dfrac{y}{5} + \dfrac{6}{25}$

44. _____

Translating *Translate each to an expression. Use x to represent "a number."*

45. _____

47. $\dfrac{2}{3}$ of a number   **48.** The quotient of a number and $-\dfrac{1}{5}$

46. _____

49. A number subtracted from $-\dfrac{8}{9}$ **50.** $\dfrac{6}{11}$ increased by a number

47. _____

Solve.

48. _____

51. Find $\dfrac{2}{3}$ of 1530.   **52.** A contractor is using 18 acres of his land to sell $\dfrac{3}{4}$-acre lots. How many lots can he sell?

49. _____

50. _____

53. Suppose that the cross-section of a piece of pipe looks like the diagram shown. What is the inner diameter?

51. _____

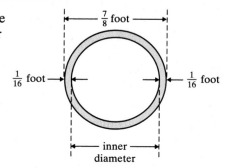

52. _____

53. _____

4.6 Complex Fractions and Review of Order of Operations

Objective A Simplifying Complex Fractions

Thus far, we have studied operations on fractions. We now practice simplifying fractions whose numerators or denominators themselves contain fractions. These fractions are called **complex fractions.**

Objectives

A Simplify Complex Fractions.

B Review the Order of Operations.

C Evaluate Expressions Given Replacement Values.

> **Complex Fraction**
>
> A fraction whose numerator or denominator or both numerator and denominator contain fractions is called a **complex fraction.**

Examples of complex fractions are

$$\dfrac{\dfrac{x}{4}}{\dfrac{3}{2}} \qquad \dfrac{\dfrac{1}{2}+\dfrac{3}{8}}{\dfrac{3}{4}-\dfrac{1}{6}} \qquad \dfrac{\dfrac{y}{5}-2}{\dfrac{3}{10}} \qquad \dfrac{-4z}{\dfrac{3}{5}}$$

Method 1 for Simplifying Complex Fractions

Two methods are presented to simplify complex fractions. The first method makes use of the fact that a fraction bar means division.

Example 1 Simplify: $\dfrac{\dfrac{x}{4}}{\dfrac{3}{2}}$

Solution: Since a fraction bar means division, the complex fraction $\dfrac{\dfrac{x}{4}}{\dfrac{3}{2}}$ can be written as $\dfrac{x}{4} \div \dfrac{3}{2}$. Then divide as usual to simplify.

$$\dfrac{x}{4} \div \dfrac{3}{2} = \dfrac{x}{4} \cdot \dfrac{2}{3} \qquad \text{Multiply by the reciprocal.}$$

$$= \dfrac{x \cdot \overset{1}{\cancel{2}}}{\underset{1}{\cancel{2}} \cdot 2 \cdot 3}$$

$$= \dfrac{x}{6}$$

Practice 1

Simplify: $\dfrac{\dfrac{7y}{10}}{\dfrac{1}{5}}$

■ Work Practice 1

Example 2 Simplify: $\dfrac{\dfrac{1}{2}+\dfrac{3}{8}}{\dfrac{3}{4}-\dfrac{1}{6}}$

Solution: Recall the order of operations. Since the fraction bar is considered a grouping symbol, we simplify the numerator and the denominator of the complex fraction separately. Then we divide.

$$\dfrac{\dfrac{1}{2}+\dfrac{3}{8}}{\dfrac{3}{4}-\dfrac{1}{6}} = \dfrac{\dfrac{1\cdot4}{2\cdot4}+\dfrac{3}{8}}{\dfrac{3\cdot3}{4\cdot3}-\dfrac{1\cdot2}{6\cdot2}} = \dfrac{\dfrac{4}{8}+\dfrac{3}{8}}{\dfrac{9}{12}-\dfrac{2}{12}} = \dfrac{\dfrac{7}{8}}{\dfrac{7}{12}}$$

Practice 2

Simplify: $\dfrac{\dfrac{1}{2}+\dfrac{1}{6}}{\dfrac{3}{4}-\dfrac{2}{3}}$

Answers

1. $\dfrac{7y}{2}$ **2.** $\dfrac{8}{1}$ or 8

(Continued on next page)

279

Thus,

$$\frac{\dfrac{1}{2} + \dfrac{3}{8}}{\dfrac{3}{4} - \dfrac{1}{6}} = \frac{\dfrac{7}{8}}{\dfrac{7}{12}}$$

$$= \frac{7}{8} \div \frac{7}{12} \qquad \text{Rewrite the quotient using the } \div \text{ sign.}$$

$$= \frac{7}{8} \cdot \frac{12}{7} \qquad \text{Multiply by the reciprocal.}$$

$$= \frac{7 \cdot 3 \cdot \overset{1}{\cancel{4}}}{2 \cdot \underset{1}{\cancel{4}} \cdot \underset{1}{\cancel{7}}} \qquad \text{Multiply.}$$

$$= \frac{3}{2} \qquad \text{Simplify.}$$

■ Work Practice 2

Method 2 for Simplifying Complex Fractions

The second method for simplifying complex fractions is to multiply the numerator and the denominator of the complex fraction by the LCD of all the fractions in its numerator and its denominator. This has the effect of leaving sums and differences of integers in the numerator and the denominator, as we shall see in the example below.

Let's use this second method to simplify the complex fraction in Example 2 again.

Practice 3

Use Method 2 to simplify:

$$\frac{\dfrac{1}{2} + \dfrac{1}{6}}{\dfrac{3}{4} - \dfrac{2}{3}}$$

Example 3   Simplify: $\dfrac{\dfrac{1}{2} + \dfrac{3}{8}}{\dfrac{3}{4} - \dfrac{1}{6}}$

Solution: The complex fraction contains fractions with denominators 2, 8, 4, and 6. The LCD is 24. By the fundamental property of fractions (See the Helpful Hints on p. 230 and p. 257), we can multiply the numerator and the denominator of the complex fraction by 24. Notice below that by the distributive property, this means that we multiply each term in the numerator and denominator by 24.

$$\frac{\dfrac{1}{2} + \dfrac{3}{8}}{\dfrac{3}{4} - \dfrac{1}{6}} = \frac{24\left(\dfrac{1}{2} + \dfrac{3}{8}\right)}{24\left(\dfrac{3}{4} - \dfrac{1}{6}\right)}$$

$$= \frac{\left(\overset{12}{\cancel{24}} \cdot \dfrac{1}{\underset{1}{\cancel{2}}}\right) + \left(\overset{3}{\cancel{24}} \cdot \dfrac{3}{\underset{1}{\cancel{8}}}\right)}{\left(\overset{6}{\cancel{24}} \cdot \dfrac{3}{\underset{1}{\cancel{4}}}\right) - \left(\overset{4}{\cancel{24}} \cdot \dfrac{1}{\underset{1}{\cancel{6}}}\right)} \qquad \begin{array}{l}\text{Apply the distributive property. Then divide out} \\ \text{common factors to aid in multiplying.}\end{array}$$

$$= \frac{12 + 9}{18 - 4} \qquad \text{Multiply.}$$

$$= \frac{21}{14}$$

$$= \frac{\overset{1}{\cancel{7}} \cdot 3}{\underset{1}{\cancel{7}} \cdot 2} = \frac{3}{2} \qquad \text{Simplify.}$$

■ Work Practice 3

Answer

3. $\dfrac{8}{1}$ or 8

The simplified result is the same, of course, no matter which method is used.

Example 4 Simplify: $\dfrac{\dfrac{y}{5} - 2}{\dfrac{3}{10}}$

Solution: Use the second method and multiply the numerator and the denominator of the complex fraction by the LCD of all fractions. Recall that $2 = \dfrac{2}{1}$. The LCD of the denominators 5, 1, and 10 is 10.

$$\dfrac{\dfrac{y}{5} - \dfrac{2}{1}}{\dfrac{3}{10}} = \dfrac{10\left(\dfrac{y}{5} - \dfrac{2}{1}\right)}{10\left(\dfrac{3}{10}\right)}$$

Multiply the numerator and denominator by 10.

$$= \dfrac{\left(\overset{2}{\cancel{10}} \cdot \dfrac{y}{\cancel{5}_1}\right) - \left(10 \cdot \dfrac{2}{1}\right)}{\overset{1}{\cancel{10}} \cdot \dfrac{3}{\cancel{10}_1}}$$

Apply the distributive property. Then divide out common factors to aid in multiplying.

$$= \dfrac{2y - 20}{3}$$

Multiply.

■ Work Practice 4

Practice 4

Simplify: $\dfrac{\dfrac{3}{4}}{\dfrac{x}{5} - 1}$

Helpful Hint

Don't forget to multiply the numerator and the denominator of the complex fraction by the same number—the LCD.

Objective B Reviewing the Order of Operations

At this time, it is probably a good idea to review the order of operations on expressions containing fractions. Before we do so, let's review how we perform operations on fractions.

	Review of Operations on Fractions	
Operation	**Procedure**	**Example**
Multiply	Multiply the numerators and multiply the denominators.	$\dfrac{5}{9} \cdot \dfrac{1}{2} = \dfrac{5 \cdot 1}{9 \cdot 2} = \dfrac{5}{18}$
Divide	Multiply the first fraction by the reciprocal of the second fraction.	$\dfrac{2}{3} \div \dfrac{11}{13} = \dfrac{2}{3} \cdot \dfrac{13}{11} = \dfrac{2 \cdot 13}{3 \cdot 11} = \dfrac{26}{33}$
Add or Subtract	1. Write each fraction as an equivalent fraction whose denominator is the LCD. 2. Add or subtract numerators and write the result over the common denominator.	$\dfrac{3}{4} + \dfrac{1}{8} = \dfrac{3}{4} \cdot \dfrac{2}{2} + \dfrac{1}{8} = \dfrac{6}{8} + \dfrac{1}{8} = \dfrac{7}{8}$

Now let's review order of operations.

Order of Operations

1. Perform all operations within parentheses ( ), brackets [ ], or other grouping symbols such as fraction bars, starting with the innermost set.
2. Evaluate any expressions with exponents.
3. Multiply or divide in order from left to right.
4. Add or subtract in order from left to right.

Example 5 Simplify: $\left(\dfrac{4}{5}\right)^2 - 1$

Solution: According to the order of operations, first evaluate $\left(\dfrac{4}{5}\right)^2$.

$$\left(\dfrac{4}{5}\right)^2 - 1 = \dfrac{16}{25} - 1 \quad \text{Write } \left(\dfrac{4}{5}\right)^2 \text{ as } \dfrac{16}{25}.$$

(*Continued on next page*)

Practice 5

Simplify: $\left(\dfrac{2}{3}\right)^3 - 2$

Answers

4. $\dfrac{15}{4x - 20}$ **5.** $-\dfrac{46}{27}$

Next, combine the fractions. The LCD of 25 and 1 is 25.

$$\frac{16}{25} - 1 = \frac{16}{25} - \frac{25}{25} \qquad \text{Write 1 as } \frac{25}{25}.$$

$$= \frac{-9}{25} \text{ or } -\frac{9}{25} \qquad \text{Subtract.}$$

■ Work Practice 5

Practice 6

Simplify: $\left(-\frac{1}{2} + \frac{1}{5}\right)\left(\frac{7}{8} + \frac{1}{8}\right)$

Example 6 Simplify: $\left(\frac{1}{4} + \frac{2}{3}\right)\left(\frac{11}{12} + \frac{1}{4}\right)$

Solution: First perform operations inside parentheses. Then multiply.

$$\left(\frac{1}{4} + \frac{2}{3}\right)\left(\frac{11}{12} + \frac{1}{4}\right) = \left(\frac{1 \cdot 3}{4 \cdot 3} + \frac{2 \cdot 4}{3 \cdot 4}\right)\left(\frac{11}{12} + \frac{1 \cdot 3}{4 \cdot 3}\right) \quad \text{Each LCD is 12.}$$

$$= \left(\frac{3}{12} + \frac{8}{12}\right)\left(\frac{11}{12} + \frac{3}{12}\right)$$

$$= \left(\frac{11}{12}\right)\left(\frac{14}{12}\right) \qquad \text{Add.}$$

$$= \frac{11 \cdot \overset{1}{\cancel{2}} \cdot 7}{\underset{1}{\cancel{2}} \cdot 6 \cdot 12} \qquad \text{Multiply.}$$

$$= \frac{77}{72} \qquad \text{Simplify.}$$

■ Work Practice 6

> **Helpful Hint** If you find it difficult replacing a variable with a number, try the following. First, replace the variable with a set of parentheses, then place the replacement number between the parentheses.
>
> If $x = \frac{4}{5}$, find $2x + x^2$.
>
> $2x + x^2 = 2(\ ) + (\ )^2$
>
> $\qquad = 2\left(\frac{4}{5}\right) + \left(\frac{4}{5}\right)^2 \cdots$
>
> then continue simplifying.

✓**Concept Check** What should be done first to simplify the expression $\frac{1}{5} \cdot \frac{5}{2} - \left(\frac{2}{3} + \frac{4}{5}\right)^2$?

Objective C Evaluating Algebraic Expressions

Example 7 Evaluate $2x + y^2$ if $x = -\frac{1}{2}$ and $y = \frac{1}{3}$.

Solution: Replace x and y with the given values and simplify.

$$2x + y^2 = 2\left(-\frac{1}{2}\right) + \left(\frac{1}{3}\right)^2 \quad \text{Replace } x \text{ with } -\frac{1}{2} \text{ and } y \text{ with } \frac{1}{3}.$$

$$= 2\left(-\frac{1}{2}\right) + \frac{1}{9} \qquad \text{Write } \left(\frac{1}{3}\right)^2 \text{ as } \frac{1}{9}.$$

$$= -1 + \frac{1}{9} \qquad \text{Multiply.}$$

$$= -\frac{9}{9} + \frac{1}{9} \qquad \text{The LCD is 9.}$$

$$= -\frac{8}{9} \qquad \text{Add.}$$

■ Work Practice 7

Practice 7

Evaluate $-\frac{3}{5} - xy$ if $x = \frac{3}{10}$ and $y = \frac{2}{3}$.

Answers

6. $-\frac{3}{10}$ 7. $-\frac{4}{5}$

✓ **Concept Check Answer**

Add inside parentheses.

Vocabulary, Readiness & Video Check

Use the choices below to fill in each blank.

addition   multiplication   evaluate the exponential expression

subtraction   division   complex

1. A fraction whose numerator or denominator or both numerator and denominator contain fractions is called a(n) _____ fraction.

2. To simplify $-\dfrac{1}{2} + \dfrac{2}{3} \cdot \dfrac{7}{8}$, which operation do we perform first? _____

3. To simplify $-\dfrac{1}{2} \div \dfrac{2}{3} \cdot \dfrac{7}{8}$, which operation do we perform first? _____

4. To simplify $\dfrac{7}{8} \cdot \left(\dfrac{1}{2} - \dfrac{2}{3} \right)$, which operation do we perform first? _____

5. To simplify $\dfrac{1}{3} \div \dfrac{1}{4} \cdot \left(\dfrac{9}{11} + \dfrac{3}{8} \right)^3$, which operation do we perform first? _____

6. To simplify $9 - \left(-\dfrac{3}{4} \right)^2$, which operation do we perform first? _____

Martin-Gay Interactive Videos   *Watch the section lecture video and answer the following questions.*

Objective A 7. In ⊞ Example 2, what property is used to simplify the denominator of the complex fraction? ▶

Objective B 8. In ⊞ Example 3, why can we add the fractions in the first set of parentheses right away? ▶

Objective C 9. In ⊞ Example 4, why do we use parentheses when substituting the replacement value for *x*? What would happen if we didn't use parentheses? ▶

See Video 4.6

4.6 **Exercise Set** MyMathLab® ▶

Objective A *Simplify each complex fraction. See Examples 1 through 4.*

▶ 1. $\dfrac{\frac{1}{8}}{\frac{3}{4}}$

2. $\dfrac{\frac{5}{12}}{\frac{15}{12}}$

3. $\dfrac{\frac{2}{3}}{\frac{2}{7}}$

4. $\dfrac{\frac{9}{25}}{\frac{6}{25}}$

5. $\dfrac{\frac{2x}{27}}{\frac{4}{9}}$

6. $\dfrac{\frac{3y}{11}}{\frac{1}{2}}$

7. $\dfrac{\frac{3}{4} + \frac{2}{5}}{\frac{1}{2} + \frac{3}{5}}$

8. $\dfrac{\frac{7}{6} + \frac{2}{3}}{\frac{3}{2} - \frac{8}{9}}$

▶ 9. $\dfrac{\frac{3x}{4}}{5 - \frac{1}{8}}$

10. $\dfrac{\frac{3}{10} + 2}{\frac{2}{5y}}$

Objective B *Use the order of operations to simplify each expression. See Examples 5 and 6.*

11. $\dfrac{1}{5} + \dfrac{1}{3} \cdot \dfrac{1}{4}$

12. $\dfrac{1}{2} + \dfrac{1}{6} \cdot \dfrac{1}{3}$

13. $\dfrac{5}{6} \div \dfrac{1}{3} \cdot \dfrac{1}{4}$

14. $\dfrac{7}{8} \div \dfrac{1}{4} \cdot \dfrac{1}{7}$

15. $2^2 - \left(\dfrac{1}{3}\right)^2$

16. $3^2 - \left(\dfrac{1}{2}\right)^2$

▶**17.** $\left(\dfrac{2}{9} + \dfrac{4}{9}\right)\left(\dfrac{1}{3} - \dfrac{9}{10}\right)$

18. $\left(\dfrac{1}{5} - \dfrac{1}{10}\right)\left(\dfrac{1}{5} + \dfrac{1}{10}\right)$

19. $\left(\dfrac{7}{8} - \dfrac{1}{2}\right) \div \dfrac{3}{11}$

20. $\left(-\dfrac{2}{3} - \dfrac{7}{3}\right) \div \dfrac{4}{9}$

21. $2 \cdot \left(\dfrac{1}{4} + \dfrac{1}{5}\right) + 2$

22. $\dfrac{2}{5} \cdot \left(5 - \dfrac{1}{2}\right) - 1$

23. $\left(\dfrac{3}{4}\right)^2 \div \left(\dfrac{3}{4} - \dfrac{1}{12}\right)$

24. $\left(\dfrac{8}{9}\right)^2 \div \left(2 - \dfrac{2}{3}\right)$

25. $\left(\dfrac{2}{5} - \dfrac{3}{10}\right)^2$

26. $\left(\dfrac{3}{2} - \dfrac{4}{3}\right)^3$

27. $\left(\dfrac{3}{4} + \dfrac{1}{8}\right)^2 - \left(\dfrac{1}{2} + \dfrac{1}{8}\right)$

28. $\left(\dfrac{1}{6} + \dfrac{1}{3}\right)^3 + \left(\dfrac{2}{5} \cdot \dfrac{3}{4}\right)^2$

Objective C *Evaluate each expression if $x = -\dfrac{1}{3}$, $y = \dfrac{2}{5}$, and $z = \dfrac{5}{6}$. See Example 7.*

29. $5y - z$

30. $2z - x$

31. $\dfrac{x}{z}$

32. $\dfrac{y + x}{z}$

▶**33.** $x^2 - yz$

34. $x^2 - z^2$

35. $(1 + x)(1 + z)$

36. $(1 - x)(1 - z)$

Objectives A B Mixed Practice *Simplify the following. See Examples 1 through 6.*

37. $\dfrac{\frac{5a}{24}}{\frac{1}{12}}$

38. $\dfrac{\frac{7}{10}}{\frac{14z}{25}}$

39. $\left(\dfrac{3}{2}\right)^3 + \left(\dfrac{1}{2}\right)^3$

40. $\left(\dfrac{5}{21} \div \dfrac{1}{2}\right) + \left(\dfrac{1}{7} \cdot \dfrac{1}{3}\right)$

41. $\left(-\dfrac{1}{2}\right)^2 + \dfrac{1}{5}$

42. $\left(-\dfrac{3}{4}\right)^2 + \dfrac{3}{8}$

43. $\dfrac{2 + \dfrac{1}{6}}{1 - \dfrac{4}{3}}$

44. $\dfrac{3 - \dfrac{1}{2}}{4 + \dfrac{1}{5}}$

45. $\left(1 - \dfrac{2}{5}\right)^2$

46. $\left(-\dfrac{1}{2}\right)^2 - \left(\dfrac{3}{4}\right)^2$

47. $\left(\dfrac{3}{4} - 1\right)\left(\dfrac{1}{8} + \dfrac{1}{2}\right)$

48. $\left(\dfrac{1}{10} + \dfrac{3}{20}\right)\left(\dfrac{1}{5} - 1\right)$

49. $\left(-\dfrac{2}{9} - \dfrac{7}{9}\right)^4$

50. $\left(\dfrac{5}{9} - \dfrac{2}{3}\right)^2$

51. $\dfrac{\dfrac{1}{3} - \dfrac{5}{6}}{\dfrac{3}{4} + \dfrac{1}{2}}$

52. $\dfrac{\dfrac{7}{10} + \dfrac{1}{2}}{\dfrac{4}{5} + \dfrac{3}{4}}$

53. $\left(\dfrac{3}{4} \div \dfrac{6}{5}\right) - \left(\dfrac{3}{4} \cdot \dfrac{6}{5}\right)$

54. $\left(\dfrac{1}{2} \cdot \dfrac{2}{7}\right) - \left(\dfrac{1}{2} \div \dfrac{2}{7}\right)$

55. $\dfrac{\dfrac{x}{3} + 2}{5 + \dfrac{1}{3}}$

56. $\dfrac{1 - \dfrac{x}{4}}{2 + \dfrac{3}{8}}$

Review

Perform each indicated operation. If the result is an improper fraction, also write the improper fraction as a mixed number. See Sections 4.1 and 4.5.

57. $3 + \dfrac{1}{2}$

58. $2 + \dfrac{2}{3}$

59. $9 - \dfrac{5}{6}$

60. $4 - \dfrac{1}{5}$

Concept Extensions

61. Calculate $\dfrac{2^3}{3}$ and $\left(\dfrac{2}{3}\right)^3$. Do both of these expressions simplify to the same number? Explain why or why not.

62. Calculate $\left(\dfrac{1}{2}\right)^2 \cdot \left(\dfrac{3}{4}\right)^2$ and $\left(\dfrac{1}{2} \cdot \dfrac{3}{4}\right)^2$. Do both of these expressions simplify to the same number? Explain why or why not.

Recall that to find the average of two numbers, we find their sum and divide by 2. For example, the average of $\dfrac{1}{2}$ and $\dfrac{3}{4}$ is $\dfrac{\dfrac{1}{2} + \dfrac{3}{4}}{2}$. Find the average of each pair of numbers.

63. $\dfrac{1}{2}, \dfrac{3}{4}$

64. $\dfrac{3}{5}, \dfrac{9}{10}$

65. $\dfrac{1}{4}, \dfrac{2}{14}$

66. $\dfrac{5}{6}, \dfrac{7}{9}$

67. Two positive numbers, a and b, are graphed below. Where should the graph of their average lie?

68. Study Exercise 67. Without calculating, can $\frac{1}{3}$ be the average of $\frac{1}{2}$ and $\frac{8}{9}$? Explain why or why not.

Answer true or false for each statement.

69. It is possible for the average of two numbers to be greater than both numbers.

70. It is possible for the average of two numbers to be less than both numbers.

71. The sum of two negative fractions is always a negative number.

72. The sum of a negative fraction and a positive fraction is always a positive number.

73. It is possible for the sum of two fractions to be a whole number.

74. It is possible for the difference of two fractions to be a whole number.

75. What operation should be performed first to simplify

$$\frac{1}{5} \cdot \frac{5}{2} - \left(\frac{2}{3} + \frac{4}{5}\right)^2 ?$$

Explain your answer.

76. A student is to evaluate $x - y$ when $x = \frac{1}{5}$ and $y = -\frac{1}{7}$. This student is asking you if he should evaluate $\frac{1}{5} - \frac{1}{7}$. What do you tell this student and why?

Each expression contains one addition, one subtraction, one multiplication, and one division. Write the operations in the order that they should be performed. Do not actually simplify. See the Concept Check in this section.

77. $[9 + 3(4 - 2)] \div \dfrac{10}{21}$

78. $[30 - 4(3 + 2)] \div \dfrac{5}{2}$

79. $\dfrac{1}{3} \div \left(\dfrac{2}{3}\right)\left(\dfrac{4}{5}\right) - \dfrac{1}{4} + \dfrac{1}{2}$

80. $\left(\dfrac{5}{6} - \dfrac{1}{3}\right) \cdot \dfrac{1}{3} + \dfrac{1}{2} \div \dfrac{9}{8}$

Evaluate each expression if $x = \dfrac{3}{4}$ and $y = -\dfrac{4}{7}$.

81. $\dfrac{2 + x}{y}$

82. $4x + y$

83. $x^2 + 7y$

84. $\dfrac{\frac{9}{14}}{x + y}$

Objective A Graphing Fractions and Mixed Numbers

Let's review graphing fractions and practice graphing mixed numbers on a number line. This will help us visualize rounding and estimating operations with mixed numbers.

Recall that $5\frac{2}{3}$ means $5 + \frac{2}{3}$ and

$-4\frac{1}{6}$ means $-\left(4 + \frac{1}{6}\right)$ or $-4 - \frac{1}{6}$ or $-4 + \left(-\frac{1}{6}\right)$

Example 1 Graph the numbers on a number line:

$\frac{1}{2}, -\frac{3}{4}, 2\frac{2}{3}, -3, -3\frac{1}{8}$

Solution: Remember that $2\frac{2}{3}$ means $2 + \frac{2}{3}$.

Also, $-3\frac{1}{8}$ means $-3 - \frac{1}{8}$, so $-3\frac{1}{8}$ lies to the left of -3.

■ Work Practice 1

Objectives

A Graph Positive and Negative Fractions and Mixed Numbers

B Multiply or Divide Mixed or Whole Numbers.

C Add or Subtract Mixed Numbers.

D Solve Problems Containing Mixed Numbers.

E Perform Operations on Negative Mixed Numbers.

Practice 1

Graph the numbers on a number line.

$-5, -4\frac{1}{2}, 2\frac{3}{4}, \frac{1}{8}, -\frac{1}{2}$

✓**Concept Check** Which of the following is/are equivalent to 9?

a. $7\frac{6}{3}$ **b.** $8\frac{4}{4}$ **c.** $8\frac{9}{9}$ **d.** $\frac{18}{2}$ **e.** all of these

Objective B Multiplying or Dividing with Mixed Numbers or Whole Numbers

When multiplying or dividing a fraction and a mixed or a whole number, remember that mixed and whole numbers can be written as improper fractions.

> **Multiplying or Dividing Fractions and Mixed Numbers or Whole Numbers**
>
> To multiply or divide with mixed numbers or whole numbers, first write any mixed or whole numbers as improper fractions and then multiply or divide as usual.

(*Note:* If an exercise contains a mixed number, we will write the answer as a mixed number, if possible.)

Answer

1.

✓**Concept Check Answer**
e

Practice 2

Multiply and simplify: $1\frac{2}{3} \cdot \frac{11}{15}$

Example 2 Multiply: $3\frac{1}{3} \cdot \frac{7}{8}$

Solution: Recall from Section 4.1 that the mixed number $3\frac{1}{3}$ can be written as the fraction $\frac{10}{3}$. Then

$$3\frac{1}{3} \cdot \frac{7}{8} = \frac{10}{3} \cdot \frac{7}{8} = \frac{\overset{1}{2} \cdot 5 \cdot 7}{3 \cdot \underset{1}{2} \cdot 4} = \frac{35}{12} \quad \text{or} \quad 2\frac{11}{12}$$

■ **Work Practice 2**

Don't forget that a whole number can be written as a fraction by writing the whole number over 1. For example,

$$20 = \frac{20}{1} \quad \text{and} \quad 7 = \frac{7}{1}$$

Practice 3

Multiply: $\frac{5}{6} \cdot 18$

Example 3 Multiply: $\frac{3}{4} \cdot 20$

Solution: $\frac{3}{4} \cdot 20 = \frac{3}{4} \cdot \frac{20}{1} = \frac{3 \cdot 20}{4 \cdot 1} = \frac{3 \cdot \overset{1}{4} \cdot 5}{\underset{1}{4} \cdot 1} = \frac{15}{1}$ or 15

■ **Work Practice 3**

When both numbers to be multiplied are mixed or whole numbers, it is a good idea to estimate the product to see if your answer is reasonable. To do this, we first practice rounding mixed numbers to the nearest whole. If the fraction part of the mixed number is $\frac{1}{2}$ or greater, we round the whole number part up. If the fraction part of the mixed number is less than $\frac{1}{2}$, then we do not round the whole number part up. Study the table below for examples.

Mixed Number	Rounding
$5\frac{1}{4}$ $\frac{1}{4}$ is less than $\frac{1}{2}$ $\frac{1}{4}$ $\frac{1}{2}$	Thus, $5\frac{1}{4}$ rounds to 5.
$3\frac{9}{16}$ ← 9 is greater than 8. → Half of 16 is 8.	Thus, $3\frac{9}{16}$ rounds to 4.
$1\frac{3}{7}$ ← 3 is less than $3\frac{1}{2}$. → Half of 7 is $3\frac{1}{2}$.	Thus, $1\frac{3}{7}$ rounds to 1.

Practice 4

Multiply. Check by estimating.

$3\frac{1}{5} \cdot 2\frac{3}{4}$

Example 4 Multiply $1\frac{2}{3} \cdot 2\frac{1}{4}$. Check by estimating.

Solution: $1\frac{2}{3} \cdot 2\frac{1}{4} = \frac{5}{3} \cdot \frac{9}{4} = \frac{5 \cdot 9}{3 \cdot 4} = \frac{5 \cdot \overset{1}{3} \cdot 3}{\underset{1}{3} \cdot 4} = \frac{15}{4}$ or $3\frac{3}{4}$ *Exact*

Let's check by estimating.

$1\frac{2}{3}$ rounds to 2, $2\frac{1}{4}$ rounds to 2, and $2 \cdot 2 = 4$ *Estimate*

The estimate is close to the exact value, so our answer is reasonable.

Answers

2. $1\frac{2}{9}$ **3.** 15 **4.** $8\frac{4}{5}$

■ **Work Practice 4**

Example 5 Multiply: $7 \cdot 2\frac{11}{14}$. Check by estimating.

Solution: $7 \cdot 2\frac{11}{14} = \frac{7}{1} \cdot \frac{39}{14} = \frac{7 \cdot 39}{1 \cdot 14} = \frac{\overset{1}{7} \cdot 39}{1 \cdot 2 \cdot 7} = \frac{39}{2}$ or $19\frac{1}{2}$ Exact

To estimate,

$2\frac{11}{14}$ rounds to 3 and $7 \cdot 3 = 21$.   Estimate

The estimate is close to the exact value, so our answer is reasonable.

■ Work Practice 5

✔**Concept Check** Find the error.

$2\frac{1}{4} \cdot \frac{1}{2} = 2\frac{1 \cdot 1}{4 \cdot 2} = 2\frac{1}{8}$

Examples Divide.

6. $\frac{3}{4} \div 5 = \frac{3}{4} \div \frac{5}{1} = \frac{3}{4} \cdot \frac{1}{5} = \frac{3 \cdot 1}{4 \cdot 5} = \frac{3}{20}$

7. $\frac{11}{18} \div 2\frac{5}{6} = \frac{11}{18} \div \frac{17}{6} = \frac{11}{18} \cdot \frac{6}{17} = \frac{11 \cdot 6}{18 \cdot 17} = \frac{11 \cdot \overset{1}{6}}{\underset{1}{6} \cdot 3 \cdot 17} = \frac{11}{51}$

8. $5\frac{2}{3} \div 2\frac{5}{9} = \frac{17}{3} \div \frac{23}{9} = \frac{17}{3} \cdot \frac{9}{23} = \frac{17 \cdot 9}{3 \cdot 23} = \frac{17 \cdot \overset{1}{3} \cdot 3}{\underset{1}{3} \cdot 23} = \frac{51}{23}$ or $2\frac{5}{23}$

■ Work Practice 6–8

Objective C Adding or Subtracting Mixed Numbers ▶

We can add or subtract mixed numbers, too, by first writing each mixed number as an improper fraction. But it is often easier to add or subtract the whole-number parts and add or subtract the proper-fraction parts vertically.

> **Adding or Subtracting Mixed Numbers**
>
> To add or subtract mixed numbers, add or subtract the fraction parts and then add or subtract the whole number parts.

Example 9 Add: $2\frac{1}{3} + 5\frac{3}{8}$. Check by estimating.

Solution: The LCD of the denominators 3 and 8 is 24.

$$2\frac{1 \cdot 8}{3 \cdot 8} = 2\frac{8}{24}$$
$$+5\frac{3 \cdot 3}{8 \cdot 3} = +5\frac{9}{24}$$
$$= 7\frac{17}{24}$$
← Add the fractions.
Add the whole numbers.

To check by estimating, we round as usual. The fraction $2\frac{1}{3}$ rounds to 2, $5\frac{3}{8}$ rounds to 5, and $2 + 5 = 7$, our estimate.
Our exact answer is close to 7, so our answer is reasonable.

■ Work Practice 9

Practice 5

Multiply. Check by estimating.

$3 \cdot 6\frac{7}{15}$

Practice 6–8

Divide.

6. $\frac{4}{9} \div 7$ 7. $\frac{8}{15} \div 3\frac{4}{5}$

8. $3\frac{2}{7} \div 2\frac{3}{14}$

Practice 9

Add: $2\frac{1}{6} + 4\frac{2}{5}$.
Check by estimating.

Answers
5. $19\frac{2}{5}$ 6. $\frac{4}{63}$ 7. $\frac{8}{57}$ 8. $1\frac{15}{31}$
9. $6\frac{17}{30}$

✔**Concept Check Answer**
forgot to change mixed number to improper fraction

When adding or subtracting mixed numbers and whole numbers, it is a good idea to estimate to see if your answer is reasonable.

For the rest of this section, we leave most of the checking by estimating to you.

Practice 10

Add: $3\frac{5}{14} + 2\frac{6}{7}$

Example 10   Add: $3\frac{4}{5} + 1\frac{4}{15}$

Solution: The LCD of the denominators 5 and 15 is 15.

$$
\begin{array}{rcl}
3\dfrac{4}{5} &=& 3\dfrac{12}{15}\\[2mm]
+1\dfrac{4}{15} &=& +1\dfrac{4}{15}\\[2mm]
\hline
&& 4\dfrac{16}{15}
\end{array}
$$

Add the fractions; then add the whole numbers.

Notice that the fraction part is improper.

Since $\frac{16}{15}$ is $1\frac{1}{15}$ we can write the sum as

$$4\frac{16}{15} + 4 + 1\frac{1}{15} = 5\frac{1}{15}$$

■ Work Practice 10

✓**Concept Check** Explain how you could estimate the following sum:

$$5\frac{1}{9} + 14\frac{10}{11}.$$

Practice 11

Add: $12 + 3\frac{6}{7} + 2\frac{1}{5}$

Example 11   Add: $2\frac{4}{5} + 5 + 1\frac{1}{2}$

Solution: The LCD of the denominators 5 and 2 is 10.

$$
\begin{array}{rcl}
2\dfrac{4}{5} &=& 2\dfrac{8}{10}\\[2mm]
5 &=& 5\\[2mm]
+1\dfrac{1}{2} &=& +1\dfrac{5}{10}\\[2mm]
\hline
&& 8\dfrac{13}{10} = 8 + 1\dfrac{3}{10} = 9\dfrac{3}{10}
\end{array}
$$

■ Work Practice 11

Practice 12

Subtract: $32\frac{7}{9} - 16\frac{5}{18}$

Example 12   Subtract: $8\frac{3}{7} - 5\frac{2}{21}$. Check by estimating.

Solution: The LCD of the denominators 7 and 21 is 21.

$$
\begin{array}{rcl}
8\dfrac{3}{7} &=& 8\dfrac{9}{21} \quad \leftarrow \text{The LCD of 7 and 21 is 21.}\\[2mm]
-5\dfrac{2}{21} &=& -5\dfrac{2}{21}\\[2mm]
\hline
&& 3\dfrac{7}{21} \quad \leftarrow \text{Subtract the fractions.}
\end{array}
$$

↑ Subtract the whole numbers.

Answers

10. $6\frac{3}{14}$ **11.** $18\frac{2}{35}$ **12.** $16\frac{1}{2}$

✓**Concept Check Answer**

Round each mixed number to the nearest whole number and add. $5\frac{1}{9}$ rounds to 5 and $14\frac{10}{11}$ rounds to 15, and the estimated sum is $5 + 15 = 20$.

Then $3\frac{7}{21}$ simplifies to $3\frac{1}{3}$. The difference is $3\frac{1}{3}$.

To check, $8\frac{3}{7}$ rounds to 8, $5\frac{2}{21}$ rounds to 5, and $8 - 5 = 3$, our estimate.

Our exact answer is close to 3, so our answer is reasonable.

■ Work Practice 12

When subtracting mixed numbers, borrowing may be needed, as shown in the next example.

Example 13   Subtract: $7\frac{3}{14} - 3\frac{6}{7}$

Solution: The LCD of the denominators 7 and 14 is 14.

$$7\frac{3}{14} = \quad 7\frac{3}{14} \qquad \text{Notice that we cannot subtract } \frac{12}{14} \text{ from } \frac{3}{14}, \text{ so we borrow}$$
$$-3\frac{6}{7} = -3\frac{12}{14} \qquad \text{from the whole number 7.}$$

borrow 1 from 7

$$7\frac{3}{14} = 6 + 1\frac{3}{14} = 6 + \frac{17}{14} \text{ or } 6\frac{17}{14}$$

Now subtract.

$$7\frac{3}{14} = \quad 7\frac{3}{14} = \quad 6\frac{17}{14}$$
$$-3\frac{6}{7} = -3\frac{12}{14} = -3\frac{12}{14}$$
$$\overline{\qquad\qquad 3\frac{5}{14}} \leftarrow \text{Subtract the fractions.}$$
$$\uparrow$$
$$\text{Subtract the whole numbers.}$$

■ Work Practice 13

✓**Concept Check** In the subtraction problem $5\frac{1}{4} - 3\frac{3}{4}$, $5\frac{1}{4}$ must be rewritten because $\frac{3}{4}$ cannot be subtracted from $\frac{1}{4}$. Why is it incorrect to rewrite $5\frac{1}{4}$ as $5\frac{5}{4}$?

Example 14   Subtract: $14 - 8\frac{3}{7}$

Solution:
$$14 = \quad 13\frac{7}{7} \qquad \text{Borrow 1 from 14 and write it as } \frac{7}{7}.$$
$$-8\frac{3}{7} = -8\frac{3}{7}$$
$$\overline{\qquad\qquad 5\frac{4}{7}} \leftarrow \text{Subtract the fractions.}$$
$$\uparrow$$
$$\text{Subtract the whole numbers.}$$

■ Work Practice 14

Practice 13

Subtract: $9\frac{7}{15} - 4\frac{3}{5}$

Practice 14

Subtract: $25 - 10\frac{2}{9}$

Answers

13. $4\frac{13}{15}$ **14.** $14\frac{7}{9}$

✓**Concept Check Answer**

Rewrite $5\frac{1}{4}$ as $4\frac{5}{4}$ by borrowing from the 5.

Objective D Solving Problems Containing Mixed Numbers ▶

Now that we know how to perform operations on mixed numbers, we can solve real-life problems.

Practice 15

The measurement around the trunk of a tree just below shoulder height is called its girth. The largest known American beech tree in the United States has a girth of $23\frac{1}{4}$ feet. The largest known sugar maple tree in the United States has a girth of $19\frac{5}{12}$ feet. How much larger is the girth of the largest known American beech tree than the girth of the largest known sugar maple tree? (*Source: American Forests*)

Girth

Example 15 Finding Legal Lobster Size

Lobster fishermen must measure the upper body shells of the lobsters they catch. Lobsters that are too small are thrown back into the ocean. Each state has its own size standard for lobsters to help control the breeding stock. Massachusetts divides its waters into four Lobster Conservation Management Areas, with a different minimum lobster size permitted in each area. In area three, the legal lobster size increased from $3\frac{13}{32}$ inches to $3\frac{1}{2}$ inches. How much of an increase was this? (*Source: Massachusetts Division of Marine Fisheries*)

Solution:

1. **UNDERSTAND.** Read and reread the problem carefully. The word "increase" found in the problem might make you think that we add to solve the problem. But the phrase "how much of an increase" tells us to subtract to find the increase.

2. **TRANSLATE.**

In words:	increase	is	new lobster size	minus	old lobster size
	↓	↓	↓	↓	↓
Translate:	increase	=	$3\frac{1}{2}$	−	$3\frac{13}{32}$

3. **SOLVE.** Before we solve, let's estimate by rounding to the nearest wholes. The fraction $3\frac{1}{2}$ can be rounded up to 4, $3\frac{13}{32}$ rounds to 3, and $4 - 3 = 1$. The increase is not 1, but will be smaller since we rounded $3\frac{1}{2}$ up and rounded $3\frac{13}{32}$ down.

$$3\frac{1}{2} = 3\frac{16}{32}$$
$$-3\frac{13}{32} = -3\frac{13}{32}$$
$$\overline{\frac{3}{32}}$$

4. **INTERPRET.** *Check* your work. Our estimate tells us that the exact increase of $\frac{3}{32}$ is reasonable. *State* your conclusion: The increase in lobster size was $\frac{3}{32}$ of an inch.

■ Work Practice 15

Answer

15. $3\frac{5}{6}$ ft

| Example 16 | Calculating Manufacturing Materials Needed |

In a manufacturing process, a metal-cutting machine cuts strips $1\frac{3}{5}$ inches long from a piece of metal stock. How many such strips can be cut from a 48-inch piece of stock?

Solution:

48 inches

1. UNDERSTAND the problem. To do so, read and reread the problem. Then draw a diagram:

We want to know how many $1\frac{3}{5}$s there are in 48.

↑↑↑↑↑↑ ···
$1\frac{3}{5}$ inches

2. TRANSLATE.

| In words: | number of strips | is | 48 | divided by | $1\frac{3}{5}$ |

↓ ↓ ↓ ↓ ↓

| Translate: | number of strips | = | 48 | ÷ | $1\frac{3}{5}$ |

3. SOLVE: Let's estimate a reasonable answer. The mixed number $1\frac{3}{5}$ rounds to 2 and $48 \div 2 = 24$.

$$48 \div 1\frac{3}{5} = 48 \div \frac{8}{5} = \frac{48}{1} \cdot \frac{5}{8} = \frac{48 \cdot 5}{1 \cdot 8} = \frac{\overset{1}{\cancel{8}} \cdot 6 \cdot 5}{1 \cdot \cancel{8}} = \frac{30}{1} \quad \text{or} \quad 30$$

4. INTERPRET. *Check* your work. Since the exact answer of 30 is close to our estimate of 24, our answer is reasonable. *State* your conclusion: Thirty strips can be cut from the 48-inch piece of stock.

📖 Work Practice 16

Objective E Operating on Negative Mixed Numbers ▶

To perform operations on negative mixed numbers, let's first practice writing these numbers as negative fractions and negative fractions as negative mixed numbers.

To understand negative mixed numbers, we simply need to know that, for example,

$$-3\frac{2}{5} \text{ means } -\left(3\frac{2}{5}\right)$$

Thus, to write a negative mixed number as a fraction, we do the following.

$$-3\frac{2}{5} = -\left(3\frac{2}{5}\right) = -\left(\frac{5 \cdot 3 + 2}{5}\right) = -\left(\frac{17}{5}\right) \quad \text{or} \quad -\frac{17}{5}$$

| Examples | Write each as a fraction. |

17. $-1\frac{7}{8} = -\frac{8 \cdot 1 + 7}{8} = -\frac{15}{8}$ Write $1\frac{7}{8}$ as an improper fraction and keep the negative sign.

18. $-23\frac{1}{2} = -\frac{2 \cdot 23 + 1}{2} = -\frac{47}{2}$ Write $23\frac{1}{2}$ as an improper fraction and keep the negative sign.

📖 Work Practice 17–18

Practice 16

A designer of women's clothing designs a woman's dress that requires $3\frac{1}{7}$ yards of material. How many dresses can be made from a 44-yard bolt of material?

Practice 17–18

Write each as a fraction.

17. $-9\frac{3}{7}$ **18.** $-5\frac{10}{11}$

Answers

16. 14 dresses   **17.** $-\frac{66}{7}$

18. $-\frac{65}{11}$

To write a negative fraction as a negative mixed number, we use a similar procedure. We simply disregard the negative sign, convert the improper fraction to a mixed number, and then reinsert the negative sign.

Practice 19–20

Write each as a mixed number.

19. $-\dfrac{37}{8}$ **20.** $-\dfrac{46}{5}$

Examples Write each as a mixed number.

19. $-\dfrac{22}{5} = -4\dfrac{2}{5}$

$$\begin{array}{r} 4 \\ 5\overline{)22} \\ -20 \\ \hline 2 \end{array} \qquad \dfrac{22}{5} = 4\dfrac{2}{5}$$

20. $-\dfrac{9}{4} = -2\dfrac{1}{4}$

$$\begin{array}{r} 2 \\ 4\overline{)9} \\ -8 \\ \hline 1 \end{array} \qquad \dfrac{9}{4} = 2\dfrac{1}{4}$$

◼ Work Practice 19–20

We multiply or divide with negative mixed numbers the same way that we multiply or divide with positive mixed numbers. We first write each mixed number as a fraction.

Practice 21–22

21. $2\dfrac{3}{4} \cdot \left(-3\dfrac{3}{5}\right)$

22. $-4\dfrac{2}{7} \div 1\dfrac{1}{4}$

Examples Perform the indicated operations.

21. $-4\dfrac{2}{5} \cdot 1\dfrac{3}{11} = -\dfrac{22}{5} \cdot \dfrac{14}{11} = -\dfrac{22 \cdot 14}{5 \cdot 11} = -\dfrac{2 \cdot \overset{1}{\cancel{11}} \cdot 14}{5 \cdot \underset{1}{\cancel{11}}} = -\dfrac{28}{5}$ or $-5\dfrac{3}{5}$

22. $-2\dfrac{1}{3} \div \left(-2\dfrac{1}{2}\right) = -\dfrac{7}{3} \div \left(-\dfrac{5}{2}\right) = -\dfrac{7}{3} \cdot \left(-\dfrac{2}{5}\right) = \dfrac{7 \cdot 2}{3 \cdot 5} = \dfrac{14}{15}$

◼ Work Practice 21–22

Helpful Hint Recall that $(-) \cdot (-) = +$

To add or subtract with negative mixed numbers, we must be very careful! Problems arise because recall that

$$-3\dfrac{2}{5} \text{ means } -\left(3\dfrac{2}{5}\right)$$

This means that

$$-3\dfrac{2}{5} = -\left(3\dfrac{2}{5}\right) = -\left(3 + \dfrac{2}{5}\right) = -3 - \dfrac{2}{5} \quad \text{This can sometimes be easily overlooked.}$$

Answers

19. $-4\dfrac{5}{8}$ **20.** $-9\dfrac{1}{5}$

21. $-9\dfrac{9}{10}$ **22.** $-3\dfrac{3}{7}$

To avoid problems, we will add or subtract negative mixed numbers by rewriting as addition and recalling how to add signed numbers.

Example 23   Add: $6\frac{3}{5} + \left(-9\frac{7}{10}\right)$

Solution: Here we are adding two numbers with different signs. Recall that we then subtract the absolute values and keep the sign of the larger absolute value.

Since $-9\frac{7}{10}$ has the larger absolute value, the answer is negative.

First, subtract absolute values:

$$9\frac{7}{10} = 9\frac{7}{10}$$
$$-6\frac{3\cdot2}{5\cdot2} = -6\frac{6}{10}$$
$$\overline{\phantom{-6\frac{3\cdot2}{5\cdot2}}3\frac{1}{10}}$$

Thus,

$$6\frac{3}{5} + \left(-9\frac{7}{10}\right) = -3\frac{1}{10}$$ The result is negative since $-9\frac{7}{10}$ has the larger absolute value.

■ Work Practice 23

Practice 23

Add: $6\frac{2}{3} + \left(-12\frac{3}{4}\right)$

Example 24   Subtract: $-11\frac{5}{6} - 20\frac{4}{9}$

Solution: Let's write as an equivalent addition: $-11\frac{5}{6} + \left(-20\frac{4}{9}\right)$. Here, we are adding two numbers with like signs. Recall that we add their absolute values and keep the common negative sign.

First, add absolute values:

$$11\frac{5\cdot3}{6\cdot3} = 11\frac{15}{18}$$
$$+20\frac{4\cdot2}{9\cdot2} = +20\frac{8}{18}$$
$$\overline{\phantom{+20\frac{4\cdot2}{9\cdot2}}31\frac{23}{18}\text{ or }32\frac{5}{18}}$$
$$\text{Since }\frac{23}{18} = 1\frac{5}{18}$$

Thus,

$$-11\frac{5}{6} - 20\frac{4}{9} = -32\frac{5}{18}$$
Keep the common sign.

■ Work Practice 24

Practice 24

Subtract: $-9\frac{2}{7} - 30\frac{11}{14}$

Answers

23. $-6\frac{1}{12}$ **24.** $-40\frac{1}{14}$

Calculator Explorations Converting Between Mixed Number and Fraction Notation

If your calculator has a fraction key, such as $\boxed{a^b/_c}$, you can use it to convert between mixed number notation and fraction notation.

To write $13\frac{7}{16}$ as an improper fraction, press

$\boxed{13}\ \boxed{a^b/_c}\ \boxed{7}\ \boxed{a^b/_c}\ \boxed{16}\ \boxed{2nd}\ \boxed{d/c}$

The display will read

$\boxed{215\,|\,16}$

which represents $\frac{215}{16}$. Thus $13\frac{7}{16} = \frac{215}{16}$.

To convert $\frac{190}{13}$ to a mixed number, press

$\boxed{190}\ \boxed{a^b/_c}\ \boxed{13}\ =$

The display will read

$\boxed{14\_8/13}$

which represents $14\frac{8}{13}$. Thus $\frac{190}{13} = 14\frac{8}{13}$.

Write each mixed number as a fraction and each fraction as a mixed number.

1. $25\frac{5}{11}$ 2. $67\frac{14}{15}$ 3. $107\frac{31}{35}$

4. $186\frac{17}{21}$ 5. $\frac{365}{14}$ 6. $\frac{290}{13}$

7. $\frac{2769}{30}$ 8. $\frac{3941}{17}$

Vocabulary, Readiness & Video Check

Use the choices below to fill in each blank.

round   fraction   whole number
improper   mixed number

1. The number $5\frac{3}{4}$ is called a(n) _____.

2. For $5\frac{3}{4}$, the 5 is called the _____ part and $\frac{3}{4}$ is called the _____ part.

3. To estimate operations on mixed numbers, we _____ mixed numbers to the nearest whole number.

4. The mixed number $2\frac{5}{8}$ written as a(n) _____ fraction is $\frac{21}{8}$.

Martin-Gay Interactive Videos

See Video 4.7

Watch the section lecture video and answer the following questions.

Objective A 5. In ⊞Example 1, why is the unit distance between −4 and −3 on the number line split into 5 equal parts? ▶

Objective B 6. Why do we need to know how to multiply fractions to solve ⊞Example 2? ▶

Objective C 7. In ⊞Example 4, why is the first form of the answer not an appropriate form? ▶

Objective D 8. Why do we need to know how to subtract fractions to solve ⊞Example 5? ▶

Objective E 9. In ⊞Example 6, how is it determined whether the answer is positive or negative? ▶

4.7 Exercise Set MyMathLab®

Objective A *Graph each list of numbers on the given number line. See Example 1.*

1. $-2, -2\frac{2}{3}, 0, \frac{7}{8}, -\frac{1}{3}$

2. $-1, -1\frac{1}{4}, -\frac{1}{4}, 3\frac{1}{4}, 3$

3. $4, \frac{1}{3}, -3, -3\frac{4}{5}, 1\frac{1}{3}$

4. $3, \frac{3}{8}, -4, -4\frac{1}{3}, -\frac{9}{10}$

Objective B *Choose the best estimate for each product or quotient. See Examples 4 and 5.*

5. $2\frac{11}{12} \cdot 1\frac{1}{4}$

   a. 2 **b.** 3 **c.** 1 **d.** 12

6. $5\frac{1}{6} \cdot 3\frac{5}{7}$

   a. 9 **b.** 15 **c.** 8 **d.** 20

7. $12\frac{2}{11} \div 3\frac{9}{10}$

   a. 3 **b.** 4 **c.** 36 **d.** 9

8. $20\frac{3}{14} \div 4\frac{8}{11}$

   a. 5 **b.** 80 **c.** 4 **d.** 16

Multiply or divide. For Exercises 13 through 16, find an exact answer and an estimated answer. See Examples 2 through 8.

9. $2\frac{2}{3} \cdot \frac{1}{7}$

10. $\frac{5}{9} \cdot 4\frac{1}{5}$

11. $7 \div 1\frac{3}{5}$

12. $9 \div 1\frac{2}{3}$

13. $2\frac{1}{5} \cdot 3\frac{1}{2}$

   Exact:

   Estimate:

14. $2\frac{1}{4} \cdot 7\frac{1}{8}$

   Exact:

   Estimate:

15. $3\frac{4}{5} \cdot 6\frac{2}{7}$

   Exact:

   Estimate:

16. $5\frac{5}{6} \cdot 7\frac{3}{5}$

   Exact:

   Estimate:

17. $5 \cdot 2\frac{1}{2}$

18. $6 \cdot 3\frac{1}{3}$

19. $3\frac{2}{3} \cdot 1\frac{1}{2}$

20. $2\frac{4}{5} \cdot 2\frac{5}{8}$

21. $2\frac{2}{3} \div \frac{1}{7}$

22. $\frac{5}{9} \div 4\frac{1}{5}$

Objective C *Choose the best estimate for each sum or difference. See Examples 9 and 12.*

23. $3\frac{7}{8} + 2\frac{1}{5}$

    a. 6 **b.** 5 **c.** 1 **d.** 2

24. $3\frac{7}{8} - 2\frac{1}{5}$

    a. 6 **b.** 5 **c.** 1 **d.** 2

25. $8\frac{1}{3} + 1\frac{1}{2}$

    a. 4 **b.** 10 **c.** 6 **d.** 16

26. $8\frac{1}{3} - 1\frac{1}{2}$

    a. 4 **b.** 10 **c.** 6 **d.** 16

Add. For Exercises 27 through 30, find an exact sum and an estimated sum. See Examples 9 through 11.

27. $\quad 4\frac{7}{12}$
$\quad + 2\frac{1}{12}$

Exact:

Estimate:

28. $\quad 7\frac{4}{11}$
$\quad + 3\frac{2}{11}$

Exact:

Estimate:

29. $\quad 10\frac{3}{14}$
$\quad + \ 3\frac{4}{7}$

Exact:

Estimate:

30. $\quad 12\frac{5}{12}$
$\quad + \ 4\frac{1}{6}$

Exact:

Estimate:

31. $\quad 9\frac{1}{5}$
$\quad + 8\frac{2}{25}$

32. $\quad 6\frac{2}{13}$
$\quad + 8\frac{7}{26}$

33. $\quad 12\frac{3}{14}$
$\quad\quad 10$
$\quad + 25\frac{5}{12}$

34. $\quad 8\frac{2}{9}$
$\quad\quad 32$
$\quad + \ 9\frac{10}{21}$

35. $\quad 15\frac{4}{7}$
$\quad + 9\frac{11}{14}$

36. $\quad 23\frac{3}{5}$
$\quad + 8\frac{8}{15}$

37. $\quad 3\frac{5}{8}$
$\quad\quad 2\frac{1}{6}$
$\quad + 7\frac{3}{4}$

38. $\quad 4\frac{1}{3}$
$\quad\quad 9\frac{2}{5}$
$\quad + 3\frac{1}{6}$

Subtract. For Exercises 39 through 42, find an exact difference and an estimated difference. See Examples 12 through 14.

39. $\quad 4\frac{7}{10}$
$\quad - 2\frac{1}{10}$

Exact:

Estimate:

40. $\quad 7\frac{4}{9}$
$\quad - 3\frac{2}{9}$

Exact:

Estimate:

41. $\quad 10\frac{13}{14}$
$\quad - \ 3\frac{4}{7}$

Exact:

Estimate:

42. $\quad 12\frac{5}{12}$
$\quad - \ 4\frac{1}{6}$

Exact:

Estimate:

43.
$$9\tfrac{1}{5}$$
$$-8\tfrac{6}{25}$$

44.
$$5\tfrac{2}{13}$$
$$-4\tfrac{7}{26}$$

45.
$$6$$
$$-2\tfrac{4}{9}$$

46.
$$8$$
$$-1\tfrac{7}{10}$$

47.
$$63\tfrac{1}{6}$$
$$-47\tfrac{5}{12}$$

48.
$$86\tfrac{2}{15}$$
$$-27\tfrac{3}{10}$$

Objectives B C Mixed Practice *Perform each indicated operation. See Examples 2 through 14.*

49.
$$2\tfrac{3}{4}$$
$$+1\tfrac{1}{4}$$

50.
$$5\tfrac{5}{8}$$
$$+2\tfrac{3}{8}$$

51.
$$15\tfrac{4}{7}$$
$$-9\tfrac{11}{14}$$

52.
$$23\tfrac{8}{15}$$
$$-8\tfrac{3}{5}$$

53. $3\tfrac{1}{9} \cdot 2$

54. $4\tfrac{1}{2} \cdot 3$

55. $1\tfrac{2}{3} \div 2\tfrac{1}{5}$

56. $5\tfrac{1}{5} \div 3\tfrac{1}{4}$

57. $22\tfrac{4}{9} + 13\tfrac{5}{18}$

58. $15\tfrac{3}{25} + 5\tfrac{2}{5}$

59. $5\tfrac{2}{3} - 3\tfrac{1}{6}$

60. $5\tfrac{3}{8} - 2\tfrac{3}{16}$

61.
$$15\tfrac{1}{5}$$
$$20\tfrac{3}{10}$$
$$+37\tfrac{2}{15}$$

62.
$$3\tfrac{7}{16}$$
$$6\tfrac{1}{2}$$
$$+9\tfrac{3}{8}$$

63. $6\tfrac{4}{7} - 5\tfrac{11}{14}$

64. $47\tfrac{5}{12} - 23\tfrac{19}{24}$

65. $4\tfrac{2}{7} \cdot 1\tfrac{3}{10}$

66. $6\tfrac{2}{3} \cdot 2\tfrac{3}{4}$

67.
$$6\tfrac{2}{11}$$
$$3$$
$$+4\tfrac{10}{33}$$

68.
$$7\tfrac{3}{7}$$
$$15$$
$$+20\tfrac{1}{2}$$

Objective D Translating *Translate each phrase into an algebraic expression. Use x to represent "a number." See Examples 15 and 16.*

69. $-5\frac{2}{7}$ decreased by a number

70. The sum of $8\frac{3}{4}$ and a number

71. Multiply $1\frac{9}{10}$ by a number.

72. Divide a number by $-6\frac{1}{11}$.

Solve. For Exercises 73 and 74, the solutions have been started for you. Write each answer in simplest form. See Examples 15 and 16.

73. A heart attack patient in rehabilitation walked on a treadmill $12\frac{3}{4}$ miles over 4 days. How many miles is this per day on average?

Start the solution:
1. UNDERSTAND the problem. Reread it as many times as needed.
2. TRANSLATE into an equation. (Fill in the blanks.)

miles per day	is	total miles	divided by	number of days
↓	↓	↓	↓	↓
miles per day	=	____	÷	____

Finish with:
3. SOLVE and 4. INTERPRET

74. A local restaurant is selling hamburgers from a booth on Memorial Day. A total of $27\frac{3}{4}$ pounds of hamburger have been ordered. How many quarter-pound hamburgers can this make?

Start the solution:
1. UNDERSTAND the problem. Reread it as many times as needed.
2. TRANSLATE into an equation. (Fill in the blanks.)

how many quarter-pound hamburgers	is	total pounds of hamburger	divided by	a quarter pound
↓	↓	↓	↓	↓
how many quarter-pound hamburgers	=	____	÷	____

Finish with:
3. SOLVE and 4. INTERPRET

75. The Gauge Act of 1846 set the standard gauge for U.S. railroads at $56\frac{1}{2}$ inches. (See figure.) If the standard gauge in Spain is $65\frac{9}{10}$ inches, how much wider is Spain's standard gauge than the U.S. standard gauge? (*Source:* San Diego Railroad Museum)

76. The standard railroad track gauge (see figure) in Spain is $65\frac{9}{10}$ inches, while in neighboring Portugal it is $65\frac{11}{20}$ inches. Which gauge is wider and by how much? (*Source:* San Diego Railroad Museum)

Track gauge (U.S. $56\frac{1}{2}$ inches)

Point of measurement of gauge

$\frac{5}{8}$ inch

77. If Tucson's average rainfall is $11\frac{1}{4}$ inches and Yuma's is $3\frac{3}{5}$ inches, how much more rain, on the average, does Tucson get than Yuma?

78. A pair of crutches needs adjustment. One crutch is 43 inches and the other is $41\frac{5}{8}$ inches. Find how much the shorter crutch should be lengthened to make both crutches the same length.

For Exercises 79 and 80, find the area of each figure.

79.

$1\frac{3}{4}$ yards

2 yards

80.

5 inches

$3\frac{1}{2}$ inches

81. A model for a proposed computer chip measures $\frac{3}{4}$ inch by $1\frac{1}{4}$ inches. Find its area.

$1\frac{1}{4}$ inches

$\frac{3}{4}$ inch

82. The Saltalamachios are planning to build a deck that measures $4\frac{1}{2}$ yards by $6\frac{1}{3}$ yards. Find the area of their proposed deck.

$4\frac{1}{2}$ yards

$6\frac{1}{3}$ yards

For Exercises 83 and 84, find the perimeter of each figure.

83.

$5\frac{1}{3}$ meters

5 meters

3 meters

$7\frac{7}{8}$ meters

84.

$3\frac{1}{4}$ yards $3\frac{1}{4}$ yards

$3\frac{1}{4}$ yards $3\frac{1}{4}$ yards

$3\frac{1}{4}$ yards

85. A homeowner has $15\frac{2}{3}$ feet of plastic pipe. She cuts off a $2\frac{1}{2}$-foot length and then a $3\frac{1}{4}$-foot length. If she now needs a 10-foot piece of pipe, will the remaining piece do? If not, by how much will the piece be short?

$3\frac{1}{4}$ feet

?

$2\frac{1}{2}$ feet

$15\frac{2}{3}$ feet

86. A trim carpenter cuts a board $3\frac{3}{8}$ feet long from one 6 feet long. How long is the remaining piece?

?

$3\frac{3}{8}$ feet

6 feet

△ **87.** The area of the rectangle below is 12 square meters. If its width is $2\frac{4}{7}$ meters, find its length.

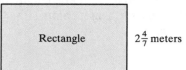

Rectangle $2\frac{4}{7}$ meters

△ **88.** The perimeter of the square below is $23\frac{1}{2}$ feet. Find the length of each side.

Square

The following table lists three upcoming total eclipses of the Sun that will be visible in North America. The duration of each eclipse is listed in the table. Use the table to answer Exercises 89 through 92.

Total Solar Eclipses Visible from North America	
Date of Eclipse	**Duration (in minutes)**
August 21, 2017	$2\frac{2}{3}$
April 8, 2024	$4\frac{7}{15}$
March 30, 2033	$2\frac{37}{60}$
(*Source:* NASA/Goddard Space Flight Center)	

89. What is the total duration for the three eclipses?

90. What is the total duration for the two eclipses occurring in odd-numbered years?

91. How much longer will the April 8, 2024, eclipse be than the August 21, 2017, eclipse?

92. How much longer will the April 8, 2024, eclipse be than the March 30, 2033, eclipse?

Objective E *Perform the indicated operations. See Examples 17 through 24.*

93. $-4\frac{2}{5} \cdot 2\frac{3}{10}$

94. $-3\frac{5}{6} \div \left(-3\frac{2}{3}\right)$

95. $-5\frac{1}{8} - 19\frac{3}{4}$

96. $17\frac{5}{9} + \left(-14\frac{2}{3}\right)$

97. $-31\frac{2}{15} + 17\frac{3}{20}$

98. $-31\frac{7}{8} - \left(-26\frac{5}{12}\right)$

99. $-1\frac{5}{7} \cdot \left(-2\frac{1}{2}\right)$

100. $1\frac{3}{4} \div \left(-3\frac{1}{2}\right)$

101. $11\frac{7}{8} - 13\frac{5}{6}$

102. $-20\frac{2}{5} + \left(-30\frac{3}{10}\right)$

103. $-7\frac{3}{10} \div (-100)$

104. $-4\frac{1}{4} \div 2\frac{3}{8}$

Review

Multiply. See Section 4.3.

105. $\frac{1}{3}(3x)$

106. $\frac{1}{5}(5y)$

107. $\frac{2}{3}\left(\frac{3}{2}a\right)$

108. $-\frac{9}{10}\left(-\frac{10}{9}m\right)$

Concept Extensions

Solve. See the first Concept Check in this section.

109. Which of the following are equivalent to 10?

    a. $9\frac{5}{5}$ **b.** $9\frac{100}{100}$ **c.** $6\frac{44}{11}$ **d.** $8\frac{13}{13}$

110. Which of the following are equivalent to $7\frac{3}{4}$?

    a. $6\frac{7}{4}$ **b.** $5\frac{11}{4}$ **c.** $7\frac{12}{16}$ **d.** all of them

Solve. See the second Concept Check in this section.

111. A student asked you to check her work below. Is it correct? If not, where is the error?

$$20\frac{2}{3} \div 10\frac{1}{2} \overset{?}{=} 2\frac{1}{3}$$

112. A student asked you to check his work below. Is it correct? If not, where is the error?

$$3\frac{2}{3} \cdot 1\frac{1}{7} \overset{?}{=} 3\frac{2}{21}$$

113. In your own words, describe how to divide mixed numbers.

114. In your own words, explain how to multiply
    a. fractions
    b. mixed numbers

Solve. See the third Concept Check in this section.

115. In your own words, explain how to round a mixed number to the nearest whole number.

116. Use rounding to estimate the best sum for
$$11\frac{19}{20} + 9\frac{1}{10}.$$
    a. 2 **b.** 3 **c.** 20 **d.** 21

Solve.

117. Explain in your own words why $9\frac{13}{9}$ is equal to $10\frac{4}{9}$.

118. In your own words, explain
    a. when to borrow when subtracting mixed numbers, and
    b. how to borrow when subtracting mixed numbers.

Objectives

A Solve Equations Containing Fractions.

B Solve Equations by Multiplying by the LCD.

C Review Adding and Subtracting Fractions.

Objective **A** Solving Equations Containing Fractions

In Chapter 3, we solved linear equations in one variable. In this section, we practice this skill by solving linear equations containing fractions. To help us solve these equations, let's review the properties of equality.

Addition Property of Equality

Let a, b, and c represent numbers. Then

$$a = b$$

and $a + c = b + c$

are equivalent equations.

Also, $a = b$

and $a - c = b - c$

are equivalent equations.

Multiplication Property of Equality

Let a, b, and c represent numbers and let $c \neq 0$. Then

$$a = b$$

and $a \cdot c = b \cdot c$

are equivalent equations.

Also, $a = b$

and $\dfrac{a}{c} = \dfrac{b}{c}$

are equivalent equations.

In other words, the same number may be added to or subtracted from both sides of an equation without changing the solution of the equation. Also, both sides of an equation may be multiplied or divided by the same nonzero number without changing the solution.

Also, don't forget that to solve an equation in x, our goal is to use properties of equality to write simpler equations, all equivalent to the original equation, until the final equation has the form

$x = $ **number** or **number** $= x$

Practice 1

Solve: $y - \dfrac{2}{3} = \dfrac{5}{12}$

Answer

1. $\dfrac{13}{12}$

Example 1 Solve: $x - \dfrac{3}{4} = \dfrac{1}{20}$

Solution: To get x by itself, add $\dfrac{3}{4}$ to both sides.

$$x - \frac{3}{4} = \frac{1}{20}$$

$$x - \frac{3}{4} + \frac{3}{4} = \frac{1}{20} + \frac{3}{4} \qquad \text{Add } \frac{3}{4} \text{ to both sides.}$$

$$x = \frac{1}{20} + \frac{3 \cdot 5}{4 \cdot 5} \qquad \text{The LCD of the denominators 20 and 4 is 20.}$$

$$x = \frac{1}{20} + \frac{15}{20}$$

$$x = \frac{16}{20}$$

$$x = \frac{\overset{1}{\cancel{4}} \cdot 4}{\underset{1}{\cancel{4}} \cdot 5} = \frac{4}{5} \qquad \text{Write } \frac{16}{20} \text{ in simplest form.}$$

Check: To check, replace x with $\frac{4}{5}$ in the original equation.

$$x - \frac{3}{4} = \frac{1}{20}$$

$$\frac{4}{5} - \frac{3}{4} \stackrel{?}{=} \frac{1}{20} \quad \text{Replace } x \text{ with } \frac{4}{5}.$$

$$\frac{4 \cdot 4}{5 \cdot 4} - \frac{3 \cdot 5}{4 \cdot 5} \stackrel{?}{=} \frac{1}{20} \quad \text{The LCD of 5 and 4 is 20.}$$

$$\frac{16}{20} - \frac{15}{20} \stackrel{?}{=} \frac{1}{20}$$

$$\frac{1}{20} = \frac{1}{20} \quad \text{True}$$

Thus $\frac{4}{5}$ is the solution of $x - \frac{3}{4} = \frac{1}{20}$.

■ Work Practice 1

Example 2 Solve: $\frac{1}{3}x = 7$

Practice 2

Solve: $\frac{1}{5}y = 2$

Solution: Recall that isolating x means that we want the coefficient of x to be 1. To do so, we use the multiplication property of equality and multiply both sides of the equation by the reciprocal of $\frac{1}{3}$, or 3. Since $\frac{1}{3} \cdot 3 = 1$, we will have isolated x.

$$\frac{1}{3}x = 7$$

$$3 \cdot \frac{1}{3}x = 3 \cdot 7 \quad \text{Multiply both sides by 3.}$$

$$1 \cdot x = 21 \text{ or } x = 21 \quad \text{Simplify.}$$

Check: To check, replace x with 21 in the original equation.

$$\frac{1}{3}x = 7 \quad \text{Original equation}$$

$$\frac{1}{3} \cdot 21 \stackrel{?}{=} 7 \quad \text{Replace } x \text{ with 21.}$$

$$7 = 7 \quad \text{True}$$

Since $7 = 7$ is a true statement, 21 is the solution of $\frac{1}{3}x = 7$.

■ Work Practice 2

Example 3 Solve: $\frac{3}{5}a = 9$

Practice 3

Solve: $\frac{5}{7}b = 25$

Solution: Multiply both sides by $\frac{5}{3}$, the reciprocal of $\frac{3}{5}$, so that the coefficient of a is 1.

$$\frac{3}{5}a = 9$$

$$\frac{5}{3} \cdot \frac{3}{5}a = \frac{5}{3} \cdot 9 \quad \text{Multiply both sides by } \frac{5}{3}.$$

$$1a = \frac{5 \cdot 9}{3} \quad \text{Multiply.}$$

$$a = 15 \quad \text{Simplify.}$$

Answers
2. 10 **3.** 35

(Continued on next page)

Check: To check, replace a with 15 in the original equation.

$$\frac{3}{5}a = 9$$

$$\frac{3}{5} \cdot 15 \stackrel{?}{=} 9 \quad \text{Replace } a \text{ with 15.}$$

$$\frac{3 \cdot 15}{5} \stackrel{?}{=} 9 \quad \text{Multiply.}$$

$$9 = 9 \quad \text{True}$$

Since $9 = 9$ is true, 15 is the solution of $\frac{3}{5}a = 9$.

■ Work Practice 3

Practice 4

Solve: $-\frac{7}{10}x = \frac{2}{5}$

Example 4 Solve: $\frac{3}{4}x = -\frac{1}{8}$

Solution: Multiply both sides of the equation by $\frac{4}{3}$, the reciprocal of $\frac{3}{4}$.

$$\frac{3}{4}x = -\frac{1}{8}$$

$$\frac{4}{3} \cdot \frac{3}{4}x = \frac{4}{3} \cdot -\frac{1}{8} \quad \text{Multiply both sides by } \frac{4}{3}.$$

$$1x = -\frac{4 \cdot 1}{3 \cdot 8} \quad \text{Multiply.}$$

$$x = -\frac{1}{6} \quad \text{Simplify.}$$

Check: To check, replace x with $-\frac{1}{6}$ in the original equation.

$$\frac{3}{4}x = -\frac{1}{8} \quad \text{Original equation}$$

$$\frac{3}{4} \cdot -\frac{1}{6} \stackrel{?}{=} -\frac{1}{8} \quad \text{Replace } x \text{ with } -\frac{1}{6}.$$

$$-\frac{1}{8} = -\frac{1}{8} \quad \text{True}$$

Since we arrived at a true statement, $-\frac{1}{6}$ is the solution of $\frac{3}{4}x = -\frac{1}{8}$.

■ Work Practice 4

Practice 5

Solve: $5x = -\frac{3}{4}$

Example 5 Solve: $3y = -\frac{2}{11}$

Solution: We can either divide both sides by 3 or multiply both sides by the reciprocal of 3, which is $\frac{1}{3}$.

$$3y = -\frac{2}{11}$$

$$\frac{1}{3} \cdot 3y = \frac{1}{3} \cdot -\frac{2}{11} \quad \text{Multiply both sides by } \frac{1}{3}.$$

$$1y = -\frac{1 \cdot 2}{3 \cdot 11} \quad \text{Multiply.}$$

$$y = -\frac{2}{33} \quad \text{Simplify.}$$

Check to see that the solution is $-\frac{2}{33}$.

■ Work Practice 5

Answers

4. $-\frac{4}{7}$ **5.** $-\frac{3}{20}$

Objective B Solving Equations by Multiplying by the LCD

Solving equations with fractions can be tedious. If an equation contains fractions, it is often helpful to first multiply both sides of the equation by the LCD of the fractions. This has the effect of eliminating the fractions in the equation, as shown in the next example.

Let's solve the equation in Example 4 again. This time, we will multiply both sides by the LCD.

Example 6 Solve: $\frac{3}{4}x = -\frac{1}{8}$ (Example 4 solved an alternate way.)

Solution: First, multiply both sides of the equation by the LCD of the fractions $\frac{3}{4}$ and $-\frac{1}{8}$. The LCD of the denominators is 8.

$$\frac{3}{4}x = -\frac{1}{8}$$

$$8 \cdot \frac{3}{4}x = 8 \cdot -\frac{1}{8} \quad \text{Multiply both sides by 8.}$$

$$\frac{8 \cdot 3}{1 \cdot 4}x = -\frac{\overset{1}{\cancel{8}} \cdot 1}{1 \cdot \cancel{8}} \quad \text{Multiply the fractions.}$$

$$\frac{2 \cdot \overset{1}{\cancel{4}} \cdot 3}{1 \cdot \underset{1}{\cancel{4}}}x = -\frac{1 \cdot 1}{1 \cdot 1} \quad \text{Simplify.}$$

$$6x = -1$$

$$\frac{6x}{6} = \frac{-1}{6} \quad \text{Divide both sides by 6.}$$

$$x = \frac{-1}{6} \text{ or } -\frac{1}{6} \quad \text{Simplify.}$$

As seen in Example 4, the solution is $-\frac{1}{6}$.

■ Work Practice 6

Practice 6

Solve: $\frac{11}{15}x = -\frac{3}{5}$

Example 7 Solve: $\frac{x}{6} + 1 = \frac{4}{3}$

Solution:

Solve by multiplying by the LCD:	**Solve with fractions:**	
The LCD of the denominators 6 and 3 is 6.	$\frac{x}{6} + 1 = \frac{4}{3}$	
$\frac{x}{6} + 1 = \frac{4}{3}$	$\frac{x}{6} + 1 - 1 = \frac{4}{3} - 1$	Subtract 1 from both sides.
$6\left(\frac{x}{6} + 1\right) = 6\left(\frac{4}{3}\right)$ Multiply both sides by 6.	$\frac{x}{6} = \frac{4}{3} - \frac{3}{3}$	Write 1 as $\frac{3}{3}$.
$\overset{1}{\cancel{6}}\left(\frac{x}{\underset{1}{\cancel{6}}}\right) + 6(1) = \overset{2}{\cancel{6}}\left(\frac{4}{\underset{1}{\cancel{3}}}\right)$ Apply the distributive property.	$\frac{x}{6} = \frac{1}{3}$	Subtract.
$x + 6 = 8$ Simplify.	$6 \cdot \frac{x}{6} = 6 \cdot \frac{1}{3}$	Multiply both sides by 6.
$x + 6 + (-6) = 8 + (-6)$ Add -6 to both sides.		
$x = 2$ Simplify.	$6 \cdot \frac{1}{6} \cdot x = \frac{\overset{2}{\cancel{6}} \cdot 1}{1 \cdot \cancel{3}}$	
	$1x = 2 \quad \text{or} \quad x = 2$	

Practice 7

Solve: $\frac{y}{8} + \frac{3}{4} = 2$

Answers

6. $-\frac{9}{11}$ **7.** 10

(Continued on next page)

Check: To check, replace x with 2 in the original equation.

$$\frac{x}{6} + 1 = \frac{4}{3} \qquad \text{Original equation}$$

$$\frac{2}{6} + 1 \stackrel{?}{=} \frac{4}{3} \qquad \text{Replace } x \text{ with 2.}$$

$$\frac{1}{3} + \frac{3}{3} \stackrel{?}{=} \frac{4}{3} \qquad \text{Simplify } \frac{2}{6}. \text{ The LCD of 3 and 1 is 3.}$$

$$\frac{4}{3} = \frac{4}{3} \qquad \text{True}$$

Since we arrived at a true statement, 2 is the solution of $\frac{x}{6} + 1 = \frac{4}{3}$.

🔳 Work Practice 7

Let's review the steps for solving equations in x. An extra step is now included to handle equations containing fractions.

Solving an Equation in x

Step 1: If fractions are present, multiply both sides of the equation by the LCD of the fractions.

Step 2: If parentheses are present, use the distributive property.

Step 3: Combine any like terms on each side of the equation.

Step 4: Use the addition property of equality to rewrite the equation so that variable terms are on one side of the equation and constant terms are on the other side.

Step 5: Divide both sides of the equation by the numerical coefficient of x to solve.

Step 6: Check the answer in the **original equation.**

Practice 8

Solve: $\dfrac{x}{5} - x = \dfrac{1}{5}$

> **Helpful Hint**   Don't forget to multiply *both* sides of the equation by the LCD.

Example 8   Solve: $\dfrac{z}{5} - \dfrac{z}{3} = 6$

Solution:

$$\frac{z}{5} - \frac{z}{3} = 6$$

$$15\left(\frac{z}{5} - \frac{z}{3}\right) = 15(6) \qquad \text{Multiply both sides by the LCD, 15.}$$

$$\cancel{15}^{3}\left(\frac{z}{\cancel{5}}\right) - \cancel{15}^{5}\left(\frac{z}{\cancel{3}}\right) = 15(6) \qquad \text{Apply the distributive property.}$$

$$3z - 5z = 90 \qquad \text{Simplify.}$$

$$-2z = 90 \qquad \text{Combine like terms.}$$

$$\frac{-2z}{-2} = \frac{90}{-2} \qquad \text{Divide both sides by } -2, \text{ the coefficient of } z.$$

$$z = -45 \qquad \text{Simplify.}$$

To check, replace z with -45 in the **original equation** to see that a true statement results.

🔳 Work Practice 8

Answer

8. $-\dfrac{1}{4}$

Example 9   Solve: $\dfrac{x}{2} = \dfrac{x}{3} + \dfrac{1}{2}$

Solution: First multiply both sides by the LCD, 6.

$$\frac{x}{2} = \frac{x}{3} + \frac{1}{2}$$

$$6\left(\frac{x}{2}\right) = 6\left(\frac{x}{3} + \frac{1}{2}\right) \qquad \text{Multiply both sides by the LCD, 6.}$$

$$\overset{3}{\cancel{6}}\left(\frac{x}{2}\right)_{1} = \overset{2}{\cancel{6}}\left(\frac{x}{3}\right)_{1} + \overset{3}{\cancel{6}}\left(\frac{1}{2}\right)_{1} \qquad \text{Apply the distributive property.}$$

$$3x = 2x + 3 \qquad \text{Simplify.}$$

$$3x - 2x = 2x + 3 - 2x \qquad \text{Subtract } 2x \qquad\qquad \text{from both sides.}$$

$$x = 3 \qquad \text{Simplify.}$$

To check, replace x with 3 in the original equation to see that a true statement results.

■ Work Practice 9

Practice 9

Solve: $\dfrac{y}{2} = \dfrac{y}{5} + \dfrac{3}{2}$

Objective C Review of Adding and Subtracting Fractions

Make sure you understand the difference between **solving an equation** containing fractions and **adding or subtracting two fractions.** To solve an equation containing fractions, we use the multiplication property of equality and multiply both sides by the LCD of the fractions, thus eliminating the fractions. This method does not apply to adding or subtracting fractions. The multiplication property of equality applies only to equations. To add or subtract unlike fractions, we write each fraction as an equivalent fraction using the LCD of the fractions as the denominator. See the next example for a review.

Example 10   Add: $\dfrac{x}{3} + \dfrac{2}{5}$

Solution: This is an expression, not an equation. Here, we are adding two unlike fractions. To add unlike fractions, we need to find the LCD. The LCD of the denominators 3 and 5 is 15. Write each fraction as an equivalent fraction with a denominator of 15.

$$\frac{x}{3} + \frac{2}{5} = \frac{x}{3} \cdot \frac{5}{5} + \frac{2}{5} \cdot \frac{3}{3} = \frac{x \cdot 5}{3 \cdot 5} + \frac{2 \cdot 3}{5 \cdot 3}$$

$$= \frac{5x}{15} + \frac{6}{15}$$

$$= \frac{5x + 6}{15}$$

■ Work Practice 10

Practice 10

Subtract: $\dfrac{9}{10} - \dfrac{y}{3}$

✓**Concept Check** Which of the following are equations and which are expressions?

a. $\dfrac{1}{2} + 3x = 5$ **b.** $\dfrac{2}{3}x - \dfrac{x}{5}$

c. $\dfrac{x}{12} + \dfrac{5x}{24}$ **d.** $\dfrac{x}{5} = \dfrac{1}{10}$

Answers

9. 5   **10.** $\dfrac{27 - 10y}{30}$

✓**Concept Check Answers**

equations: a, d; expressions: b, c

Vocabulary, Readiness & Video Check

Fill in the blank with the least common denominator (LCD). Do not solve these equations.

1. Equation: $\frac{2}{3} + x = \frac{5}{6}$; LCD = ____

2. Equation: $\frac{x}{21} - 1 = \frac{1}{7}$; LCD = ____

3. Equation: $\frac{y}{5} + \frac{1}{3} = 2$; LCD = ____

4. Equation: $\frac{-2n}{11} + \frac{1}{2} = 5$; LCD = ____

Martin-Gay Interactive Videos

See Video 4.8

Watch the section lecture video and answer the following questions.

Objective A **5.** In Example 1, what property is used to get x by itself on one side of the equation?

6. Explain how a reciprocal is used to solve Example 2.

Objective B **7.** Why are both sides of the equation multiplied by 12 in Example 3? What effect does this have on the fractions in the equation?

Objective C **8.** In Example 5, why can't we multiply by the LCD of all fractions?

4.8 Exercise Set MyMathLab®

Objective A *Solve each equation. Check your proposed solution. See Example 1.*

1. $x + \frac{1}{3} = -\frac{1}{3}$

2. $x + \frac{1}{9} = -\frac{7}{9}$

3. $y - \frac{3}{13} = -\frac{2}{13}$

4. $z - \frac{5}{14} = \frac{4}{14}$

5. $3x - \frac{1}{5} - 2x = \frac{1}{5} + \frac{2}{5}$

6. $5x + \frac{1}{11} - 4x = \frac{2}{11} - \frac{5}{11}$

 7. $x - \frac{1}{12} = \frac{5}{6}$

8. $y - \frac{8}{9} = \frac{1}{3}$

9. $\frac{2}{5} + y = -\frac{3}{10}$

10. $\frac{1}{2} + a = -\frac{3}{8}$

11. $7z + \frac{1}{16} - 6z = \frac{3}{4}$

12. $9x - \frac{2}{7} - 8x = \frac{11}{14}$

13. $-\frac{2}{9} = x - \frac{5}{6}$

14. $-\frac{1}{4} = y - \frac{7}{10}$

Solve each equation. See Examples 2 through 5.

15. $7x = 2$

16. $-5x = 4$

17. $\frac{1}{4}x = 3$

18. $\frac{1}{3}x = 6$

19. $\frac{2}{9}y = -6$

20. $\frac{4}{7}x = -8$

◐ 21. $-\frac{4}{9}z = -\frac{3}{2}$

22. $-\frac{11}{10}x = -\frac{2}{7}$

23. $7a = \frac{1}{3}$

24. $2z = -\frac{5}{12}$

25. $-3x = -\frac{6}{11}$

26. $-4z = -\frac{12}{25}$

Objective **B** *Solve each equation. See Examples 6 through 9.*

27. $\frac{5}{9}x = -\frac{3}{18}$

28. $\frac{3}{5}y = -\frac{7}{20}$

29. $\frac{x}{3} + 2 = \frac{7}{3}$

30. $\frac{x}{5} - 1 = \frac{7}{5}$

31. $\frac{x}{5} - x = -8$

32. $\frac{x}{3} - x = -6$

33. $\frac{1}{2} - \frac{3}{5} = \frac{x}{10}$

34. $\frac{2}{3} - \frac{1}{4} = \frac{x}{12}$

35. $\frac{x}{3} = \frac{x}{5} - 2$

36. $\frac{a}{2} = \frac{a}{7} + \frac{5}{2}$

Objective **C** *Add or subtract as indicated. See Example 10.*

37. $\frac{x}{7} - \frac{4}{3}$

38. $-\frac{5}{9} + \frac{y}{8}$

39. $\frac{y}{2} + 5$

40. $2 + \frac{7x}{3}$

▶ 41. $\frac{3x}{10} + \frac{x}{6}$

42. $\frac{9x}{8} - \frac{5x}{6}$

Objectives **A** **B** **C** **Mixed Practice** *Solve. If no equation is given, perform the indicated operation. See Examples 1 through 10.*

43. $\frac{3}{8}x = \frac{1}{2}$

44. $\frac{2}{5}y = \frac{3}{10}$

45. $\frac{2}{3} - \frac{x}{5} = \frac{4}{15}$

46. $\frac{4}{5} + \frac{x}{4} = \frac{21}{20}$

47. $\frac{9}{14}z = \frac{27}{20}$

48. $\frac{5}{16}a = \frac{5}{6}$

49. $-3m - 5m = \frac{4}{7}$

50. $30n - 34n = \frac{3}{20}$

51. $\dfrac{x}{4} + 1 = \dfrac{1}{4}$

52. $\dfrac{y}{7} - 2 = \dfrac{1}{7}$

53. $\dfrac{5}{9} - \dfrac{2}{3}$

54. $\dfrac{8}{11} - \dfrac{1}{2}$

55. $\dfrac{1}{5}y = 10$

56. $\dfrac{1}{4}x = -2$

57. $\dfrac{5}{7}y = -\dfrac{15}{49}$

58. $-\dfrac{3}{4}x = \dfrac{9}{2}$

59. $\dfrac{x}{2} - x = -2$

60. $\dfrac{y}{3} = -4 + y$

61. $-\dfrac{5}{8}y = \dfrac{3}{16} - \dfrac{9}{16}$

62. $-\dfrac{7}{9}x = -\dfrac{5}{18} - \dfrac{4}{18}$

63. $17x - 25x = \dfrac{1}{3}$

64. $27x - 30x = \dfrac{4}{9}$

65. $\dfrac{7}{6}x = \dfrac{1}{4} - \dfrac{2}{3}$

66. $\dfrac{5}{4}y = \dfrac{1}{2} - \dfrac{7}{10}$

67. $\dfrac{b}{4} = \dfrac{b}{12} + \dfrac{2}{3}$

68. $\dfrac{a}{6} = \dfrac{a}{3} + \dfrac{1}{2}$

69. $\dfrac{x}{3} + 2 = \dfrac{x}{2} + 8$

70. $\dfrac{y}{5} - 2 = \dfrac{y}{3} - 4$

Review

Round each number to the given place value. See Section 1.4.

71. 57,236 to the nearest hundred

72. 576 to the nearest hundred

73. 327 to the nearest ten

74. 2333 to the nearest ten

Concept Extensions

75. Explain why the method for eliminating fractions in an **equation** does not apply to simplifying **expressions** containing fractions.

76. Think about which exercise (part **a** or part **b**)may be completed by multiplying by 6. Now complete each exercise.

    a. Solve: $\dfrac{x}{6} - \dfrac{5}{3} = 2$

    b. Subtract: $\dfrac{x}{6} - \dfrac{5}{3}$

Solve.

77. $\dfrac{14}{11} + \dfrac{3x}{8} = \dfrac{x}{2}$

78. $\dfrac{19}{53} = \dfrac{353x}{1431} + \dfrac{23}{27}$

79. Find the area and the perimeter of the rectangle. Remember to attach proper units.

$\frac{1}{4}$ inch

$\frac{3}{4}$ inch

80. The area of the rectangle is $\dfrac{5}{12}$ square inch. Find its length, x.

x

$\frac{3}{4}$ inch

Chapter 4 Group Activity

Lobster Classification

Sections 4.1, 4.7, 4.8

This activity may be completed by working in groups or individually.

Lobsters are normally classified by weight. Use the weight classification table to answer the questions in this activity.

Classification of Lobsters	
Class	**Weight (in pounds)**
Chicken	1 to $1\frac{1}{8}$
Quarter	$1\frac{1}{4}$
Half	$1\frac{1}{2}$ to $1\frac{3}{4}$
Select	$1\frac{3}{4}$ to $2\frac{1}{2}$
Large select	$2\frac{1}{2}$ to $3\frac{1}{2}$
Jumbo	Over $3\frac{1}{2}$

(*Source:* The Maine Lobster Promotion Council)

1. A lobster fisher has kept four lobsters from a lobster trap. Classify each lobster if they have the following weights:

    a. $1\frac{7}{8}$ pounds

    b. $1\frac{9}{16}$ pounds

    c. $2\frac{3}{4}$ pounds

    d. $2\frac{3}{8}$ pounds

2. A recipe requires 5 pounds of lobster. Using the minimum weight for each class, decide whether a chicken, half, and select lobster will be enough for the recipe, and explain your reasoning. If not, suggest a better choice of lobsters to meet the recipe requirements.

3. A lobster market customer has selected two chickens, a select, and a large select. What is the most that these four lobsters could weigh? What is the least that these four lobsters could weigh?

4. A lobster market customer wishes to buy three quarters. If lobsters sell for $7 per pound, how much will the customer owe for her purchase?

5. Why do you think there is no classification for lobsters weighing under 1 pound?

Chapter 4 Vocabulary Check

Fill in each blank with one of the words or phrases listed below.

mixed number   complex fraction   like   numerator   prime factorization

composite number   equivalent   cross products   least common denominator   denominator

prime number   improper fraction   simplest form   undefined   0

reciprocals   proper fraction

1. Two numbers are _____ of each other if their product is 1.

2. A(n) _____ is a natural number greater than 1 that is not prime.

3. Fractions that represent the same portion of a whole are called _____ fractions.

4. A(n) _____ is a fraction whose numerator is greater than or equal to its denominator.

5. A(n) _____ is a natural number greater than 1 whose only factors are 1 and itself.

6. A fraction is in _____ when the numerator and the denominator have no factors in common other than 1.

7. A(n) _____ is one whose numerator is less than its denominator.

8. A(n) _____ contains a whole number part and a fraction part.

9. In the fraction $\frac{7}{9}$, the 7 is called the _____ and the 9 is called the _____.

10. The _____ of a number is the factorization in which all the factors are prime numbers.

11. The fraction $\frac{3}{0}$ is _____.

12. The fraction $\frac{0}{5}$ = _____.

13. Fractions that have the same denominator are called _____ fractions.

14. The LCM of the denominators in a list of fractions is called the _____.

15. A fraction whose numerator or denominator or both numerator and denominator contain fractions is called a(n) _____.

16. In $\frac{a}{b} = \frac{c}{d}$, $a \cdot d$ and $b \cdot c$ are called _____.

Helpful Hint

▶ Are you preparing for your test? Don't forget to take the Chapter 4 Test on page 318. Then check your answers at the back of the text and use the Chapter Test Prep Videos to see the fully worked-out solutions to any of the exercises you want to review.

4 Chapter Highlights

Definitions and Concepts	Examples
Section 4.1 Introduction to Fractions and Mixed Numbers	

A **fraction** is of the form

$$\frac{\text{numerator}}{\text{denominator}}$$

numerator ← number of parts being considered
denominator ← number of equal parts in the whole

Write a fraction to represent the shaded part of the figure.

$\frac{3}{8}$ ← number of parts shaded
   ← number of equal parts

A fraction is called a **proper fraction** if its numerator is less than its denominator.

A fraction is called an **improper fraction** if its numerator is greater than or equal to its denominator.

A **mixed number** contains a whole number and a fraction.

Proper Fractions: $\frac{1}{3}, \frac{2}{5}, \frac{7}{8}, \frac{100}{101}$

Improper Fractions: $\frac{5}{4}, \frac{2}{2}, \frac{9}{7}, \frac{101}{100}$

Mixed Numbers: $1\frac{1}{2}, 5\frac{7}{8}, 25\frac{9}{10}$

To Write a Mixed Number As an Improper Fraction

1. Multiply the denominator of the fraction by the whole number.

2. Add the numerator of the fraction to the product from Step 1.

3. Write the sum from Step 2 as the numerator of the improper fraction over the original denominator.

$$5\frac{2}{7} = \frac{7 \cdot 5 + 2}{7} = \frac{35 + 2}{7} = \frac{37}{7}$$

To Write an Improper Fraction As a Mixed Number or a Whole Number

1. Divide the denominator into the numerator.

2. The whole number part of the mixed number is the quotient. The fraction is the remainder over the original denominator.

$$\text{quotient} \frac{\text{remainder}}{\text{original denominator}}$$

$$\frac{17}{3} = 5\frac{2}{3}$$

$$\begin{array}{r} 5 \\ 3\overline{)17} \\ -15 \\ \hline 2 \end{array}$$

Definitions and Concepts	Examples

Section 4.2   Factors and Simplest Form

A **prime number** is a natural number that has exactly two different factors, 1 and itself.	$2, 3, 5, 7, 11, 13, 17,\ldots$
A **composite number** is any natural number other than 1 that is not prime.	$4, 6, 8, 9, 10, 12, 14, 15, 16,\ldots$
The **prime factorization** of a number is the factorization in which all the factors are prime numbers.	Write the prime factorization of 60. $60 = 6 \cdot 10$ $\quad = 2 \cdot 3 \cdot 2 \cdot 5 \quad \text{or} \quad 2^2 \cdot 3 \cdot 5$
Fractions that represent the same portion of a whole are called **equivalent fractions.**	 $\dfrac{3}{4} \quad = \quad \dfrac{12}{16}$
A fraction is in **simplest form** or **lowest terms** when the numerator and the denominator have no common factors other than 1.	The fraction $\dfrac{2}{3}$ is in simplest form.
To write a fraction in simplest form, write the prime factorizations of the numerator and the denominator and then divide both by all common factors.	Write in simplest form: $\dfrac{30}{36}$ $\dfrac{30}{36} = \dfrac{2 \cdot 3 \cdot 5}{2 \cdot 2 \cdot 3 \cdot 3} = \dfrac{2}{2} \cdot \dfrac{3}{3} \cdot \dfrac{5}{2 \cdot 3} = 1 \cdot 1 \cdot \dfrac{5}{6} = \dfrac{5}{6}$ or $\dfrac{30}{36} = \dfrac{2 \cdot 3 \cdot 5}{2 \cdot 2 \cdot 3 \cdot 3} = \dfrac{5}{6}$
Two fractions are equivalent if **Method 1.** They simplify to the same fraction. **Method 2.** Their cross products are equal. $\begin{array}{c} 24 \cdot 7 \\ = 168 \end{array} \quad \dfrac{7}{8} = \dfrac{21}{24} \quad \begin{array}{c} 8 \cdot 21 \\ = 168 \end{array}$ Since $168 = 168, \dfrac{7}{8} = \dfrac{21}{24}.$	Determine whether $\dfrac{7}{8}$ and $\dfrac{21}{24}$ are equivalent. $\dfrac{7}{8}$ is in simplest form. $\dfrac{21}{24} = \dfrac{3 \cdot 7}{3 \cdot 8} = \dfrac{1 \cdot 7}{1 \cdot 8} = \dfrac{7}{8}$ Since both simplify to $\dfrac{7}{8}$, then $\dfrac{7}{8} = \dfrac{21}{24}.$

Section 4.3   Multiplying and Dividing Fractions

To multiply two fractions, multiply the numerators and multiply the denominators.	Multiply. $\dfrac{2x}{3} \cdot \dfrac{5}{7} = \dfrac{2x \cdot 5}{3 \cdot 7} = \dfrac{10x}{21}$ $\dfrac{3}{4} \cdot \dfrac{1}{6} = \dfrac{3 \cdot 1}{4 \cdot 6} = \dfrac{3 \cdot 1}{4 \cdot 3 \cdot 2} = \dfrac{1}{8}$
To find the **reciprocal** of a fraction, interchange its numerator and denominator.	The reciprocal of $\dfrac{3}{5}$ is $\dfrac{5}{3}$.
To divide two fractions, multiply the first fraction by the reciprocal of the second fraction.	Divide. $-\dfrac{3}{10} \div \dfrac{7}{9} = -\dfrac{3}{10} \cdot \dfrac{9}{7} = -\dfrac{3 \cdot 9}{10 \cdot 7} = -\dfrac{27}{70}$

Definitions and Concepts	Examples

Section 4.4   Adding and Subtracting Like Fractions, Least Common Denominator, and Equivalent Fractions

Fractions that have the same denominator are called **like fractions**.	$-\dfrac{1}{3}$ and $\dfrac{2}{3}$; $\dfrac{5x}{7}$ and $\dfrac{6}{7}$
To add or subtract like fractions, combine the numerators and place the sum or difference over the common denominator.	$\dfrac{2}{7} + \dfrac{3}{7} = \dfrac{5}{7}$ ← Add the numerators. ← Keep the common denominator. $\dfrac{7}{8} - \dfrac{4}{8} = \dfrac{3}{8}$ ← Subtract the numerators. ← Keep the common denominator.
The **least common denominator (LCD)** of a list of fractions is the smallest positive number divisible by all the denominators in the list.	The LCD of $\dfrac{1}{2}$ and $\dfrac{5}{6}$ is 6 because 6 is the smallest positive number that is divisible by both 2 and 6.
Method 1 for finding the LCD of a list of fractions using multiples	Find the LCD of $\dfrac{1}{4}$ and $\dfrac{5}{6}$ using Method 1.
Step 1: Write the multiples of the largest denominator (starting with the number itself) until a multiple common to all denominators in the list is found.	$6 \cdot 1 = 6$ Not a multiple of 4 $6 \cdot 2 = 12$ A multiple of 4
Step 2: The multiple found in Step 1 is the LCD.	The LCD is 12.
Method 2 for finding the LCD of a list of a fractions using prime factorization	Find the LCD of $\dfrac{5}{6}$ and $\dfrac{11}{20}$ using Method 2.
Step 1: Write the prime factorization of each denominator.	$6 = 2 \cdot ③$ $20 = ②\cdot②\cdot ⑤$
Step 2: For each different prime factor in Step 1, circle the greatest number of times that factor occurs in any one factorization.	The LCD is
Step 3: The LCD is the product of the circled factors.	$2 \cdot 2 \cdot 3 \cdot 5 = 60$
Equivalent fractions represent the same portion of a whole.	Write an equivalent fraction with the indicated denominator. $\dfrac{2}{8} = \dfrac{}{16}$ $\dfrac{2 \cdot 2}{8 \cdot 2} = \dfrac{4}{16}$

Section 4.5   Adding and Subtracting Unlike Fractions

To add or subtract fractions with unlike denominators	Add: $\dfrac{3}{20} + \dfrac{2}{5}$
Step 1: Find the LCD.	**Step 1:** The LCD of the denominators 20 and 5 is 20.
Step 2: Write each fraction as an equivalent fraction whose denominator is the LCD.	**Step 2:** $\dfrac{3}{20} = \dfrac{3}{20}$; $\dfrac{2}{5} = \dfrac{2}{5} \cdot \dfrac{4}{4} = \dfrac{8}{20}$
Step 3: Add or subtract the like fractions.	**Step 3:** $\dfrac{3}{20} + \dfrac{2}{5} = \dfrac{3}{20} + \dfrac{8}{20} = \dfrac{11}{20}$
Step 4: Write the sum or difference in simplest form.	**Step 4:** $\dfrac{11}{20}$ is in simplest form.

Definitions and Concepts	Examples

Section 4.6 Complex Fractions and Review of Order of Operations

A fraction whose numerator or denominator or both contain fractions is called a **complex fraction.**

Complex Fractions:

$$\frac{\frac{11}{4}}{\frac{7}{10}}, \quad \frac{\frac{y}{6} - 11}{\frac{4}{3}}$$

One method for simplifying complex fractions is to multiply the numerator and the denominator of the complex fraction by the LCD of all fractions in its numerator and its denominator.

$$\frac{\frac{y}{6} - 11}{\frac{4}{3}} = \frac{6\left(\frac{y}{6} - 11\right)}{6\left(\frac{4}{3}\right)} = \frac{6\left(\frac{y}{6}\right) - 6(11)}{6\left(\frac{4}{3}\right)}$$

$$= \frac{y - 66}{8}$$

Section 4.7   Operations on Mixed Numbers

To multiply with mixed numbers or whole numbers, first write any mixed or whole numbers as improper fractions and then multiply as usual.

$$2\frac{1}{3} \cdot \frac{1}{9} = \frac{7}{3} \cdot \frac{1}{9} = \frac{7 \cdot 1}{3 \cdot 9} = \frac{7}{27}$$

To divide with mixed numbers or whole numbers, first write any mixed or whole numbers as fractions and then divide as usual.

$$2\frac{5}{8} \div 3\frac{7}{16} = \frac{21}{8} \div \frac{55}{16} = \frac{21}{8} \cdot \frac{16}{55} = \frac{21 \cdot 16}{8 \cdot 55}$$

$$= \frac{21 \cdot 2 \cdot \overset{1}{8}}{\underset{1}{8} \cdot 55} = \frac{42}{55}$$

To add or subtract with mixed numbers, add or subtract the fractions and then add or subtract the whole numbers.

Add: $2\frac{1}{2} + 5\frac{7}{8}$

$$2\frac{1}{2} = \quad 2\frac{4}{8}$$

$$+5\frac{7}{8} = +5\frac{7}{8}$$

$$7\frac{11}{8} = 7 + 1\frac{3}{8} = 8\frac{3}{8}$$

Section 4.8   Solving Equations Containing Fractions

To Solve an Equation in *x*

Step 1: If fractions are present, multiply both sides of the equation by the LCD of the fractions.

Step 2: If parentheses are present, use the distributive property.

Step 3: Combine any like terms on each side of the equation.

Step 4: Use the addition property of equality to rewrite the equation so that variable terms are on one side of the equation and constant terms are on the other side.

Step 5: Divide both sides by the numerical coefficient of *x* to solve.

Step 6: Check the answer in the *original equation.*

Solve: $\dfrac{x}{15} + 2 = \dfrac{7}{3}$

$$15\left(\frac{x}{15} + 2\right) = 15\left(\frac{7}{3}\right) \quad \text{Multiply by the LCD 15.}$$

$$15\left(\frac{x}{15}\right) + 15 \cdot 2 = 15\left(\frac{7}{3}\right)$$

$$x + 30 = 35$$

$$x + 30 - 30 = 35 - 30$$

$$x = 5$$

Check to see that 5 is the solution.

(4.1) *Write a fraction to represent the shaded area. If the fraction is improper, write the shaded area as a mixed number also. Do not simplify these answers.*

1.

2.

3.

4.

Solve.

5. A basketball player made 11 free throws out of 12 tries during a game. What fraction of free throws did the player make?

6. A new car lot contains 23 blue cars out of a total of 131 cars.
   a. How many cars on the lot are not blue?
   b. What fraction of cars on the lot are not blue?

Simplify by dividing.

7. $-\dfrac{3}{3}$

8. $\dfrac{-20}{-20}$

9. $\dfrac{0}{-1}$

10. $\dfrac{4}{0}$

Graph each fraction on a number line.

11. $\dfrac{7}{9}$

12. $\dfrac{4}{7}$

13. $\dfrac{5}{4}$

14. $\dfrac{7}{5}$

Write each improper fraction as a mixed number or a whole number.

15. $\dfrac{15}{4}$

16. $\dfrac{39}{13}$

Write each mixed number as an improper fraction.

17. $2\frac{1}{5}$

18. $3\frac{8}{9}$

(4.2) *Write each fraction in simplest form.*

19. $\frac{12}{28}$

20. $\frac{15}{27}$

21. $-\frac{25x}{75x^2}$

22. $-\frac{36y^3}{72y}$

23. $\frac{29ab}{32abc}$

24. $\frac{18xyz}{23xy}$

25. $\frac{45x^2y}{27xy^3}$

26. $\frac{42ab^2c}{30abc^3}$

27. There are 12 inches in a foot. What fractional part of a foot does 8 inches represent?

28. Six out of 15 cars are white. What fraction of the cars are *not* white?

Determine whether each two fractions are equivalent.

29. $\frac{10}{34}$ and $\frac{4}{14}$

30. $\frac{30}{50}$ and $\frac{9}{15}$

(4.3) *Multiply.*

31. $\frac{3}{5} \cdot \frac{1}{2}$

32. $-\frac{6}{7} \cdot \frac{5}{12}$

33. $-\frac{24x}{5} \cdot -\frac{15}{8x^3}$

34. $\frac{27y^3}{21} \cdot \frac{7}{18y^2}$

35. $\left(-\frac{1}{3}\right)^3$

36. $\left(-\frac{5}{12}\right)^2$

Divide.

37. $-\frac{3}{4} \div \frac{3}{8}$

38. $\frac{21a}{4} \div \frac{7a}{5}$

39. $-\frac{9}{2} \div -\frac{1}{3}$

40. $-\frac{5}{3} \div 2y$

41. Evaluate $x \div y$ if $x = \frac{9}{7}$ and $y = \frac{3}{4}$.

42. Evaluate ab if $a = -7$ and $b = \frac{9}{10}$.

Find the area of each figure.

△ **43.**

Rectangle $\frac{7}{8}$ foot

$\frac{11}{6}$ foot

△ **44.**

Square $\frac{2}{3}$ meter

(4.4) *Add or subtract as indicated.*

45. $\dfrac{7}{11} + \dfrac{3}{11}$

46. $\dfrac{4}{9} + \dfrac{2}{9}$

47. $\dfrac{1}{12} - \dfrac{5}{12}$

48. $\dfrac{11x}{15} + \dfrac{x}{15}$

49. $\dfrac{4y}{21} - \dfrac{3}{21}$

50. $\dfrac{4}{15} - \dfrac{3}{15} - \dfrac{2}{15}$

Find the LCD of each list of fractions.

51. $\dfrac{2}{3}, \dfrac{5}{x}$

52. $\dfrac{3}{4}, \dfrac{3}{8}, \dfrac{7}{12}$

Write each fraction as an equivalent fraction with the given denominator.

53. $\dfrac{2}{3} = \dfrac{?}{30}$

54. $\dfrac{5}{8} = \dfrac{?}{56}$

55. $\dfrac{7a}{6} = \dfrac{?}{42}$

56. $\dfrac{9b}{4} = \dfrac{?}{20}$

57. $\dfrac{4}{5x} = \dfrac{?}{50x}$

58. $\dfrac{5}{9y} = \dfrac{?}{18y}$

Solve.

59. One evening Mark Alorenzo did $\dfrac{3}{8}$ of his homework before supper, another $\dfrac{2}{8}$ of it while his children did their homework, and $\dfrac{1}{8}$ after his children went to bed. What part of his homework did he do that evening?

△ **60.** The Simpsons will be fencing in their land, which is in the shape of a rectangle. In order to do this, they need to find its perimeter. Find the perimeter of their land.

$\frac{3}{16}$ mile

$\frac{9}{16}$ mile

(4.5) *Add or subtract as indicated.*

61. $\dfrac{7}{18} + \dfrac{2}{9}$

62. $\dfrac{4}{13} - \dfrac{1}{26}$

63. $-\dfrac{1}{3} + \dfrac{1}{4}$

64. $-\dfrac{2}{3} + \dfrac{1}{4}$

65. $\dfrac{5x}{11} + \dfrac{2}{55}$

66. $\dfrac{4}{15} + \dfrac{b}{5}$

67. $\dfrac{5y}{12} - \dfrac{2y}{9}$

68. $\dfrac{7x}{18} + \dfrac{2x}{9}$

69. $\dfrac{4}{9} + \dfrac{5}{y}$

70. $-\dfrac{9}{14} - \dfrac{3}{7}$

71. $\dfrac{4}{25} + \dfrac{23}{75} + \dfrac{7}{50}$

72. $\dfrac{2}{3} - \dfrac{2}{9} - \dfrac{1}{6}$

Find the perimeter of each figure.

 73.

$\frac{2}{9}$ meter   Rectangle

$\frac{5}{6}$ meter

△ **74.** $\frac{1}{5}$ foot $\frac{3}{5}$ foot

$\frac{7}{10}$ foot

75. In a group of 100 blood donors, typically $\frac{9}{25}$ have type A Rh-positive blood and $\frac{3}{50}$ have type A Rh-negative blood. What fraction have type A blood?

76. Find the difference in length of two scarves if one scarf is $\frac{5}{12}$ of a yard long and the other is $\frac{2}{3}$ of a yard long.

$\frac{2}{3}$ of a yard

$\frac{5}{12}$ of a yard

(4.6) *Simplify each complex fraction.*

77. $\dfrac{\dfrac{2x}{5}}{\dfrac{7}{10}}$

78. $\dfrac{\dfrac{3y}{7}}{\dfrac{11}{7}}$

79. $\dfrac{\dfrac{2}{5} - \dfrac{1}{2}}{\dfrac{3}{4} - \dfrac{7}{10}}$

80. $\dfrac{\dfrac{5}{6} - \dfrac{1}{4}}{\dfrac{-1}{12y}}$

Evaluate each expression if $x = \dfrac{1}{2}$, $y = -\dfrac{2}{3}$, and $z = \dfrac{4}{5}$.

81. $\dfrac{x}{y + z}$

82. $\dfrac{x + y}{z}$

Evaluate each expression. Use the order of operations to simplify.

83. $\dfrac{5}{13} \div \dfrac{1}{2} \cdot \dfrac{4}{5}$

84. $\dfrac{2}{27} - \left(\dfrac{1}{3}\right)^2$

85. $\dfrac{9}{10} \cdot \dfrac{1}{3} - \dfrac{2}{5} \cdot \dfrac{1}{11}$

86. $-\dfrac{2}{7} \cdot \left(\dfrac{1}{5} + \dfrac{3}{10}\right)$

(4.7) *Perform operations as indicated. Simplify your answers. Estimate where noted.*

87.
$$7\dfrac{3}{8}$$
$$9\dfrac{5}{6}$$
$$+\ 3\dfrac{1}{12}$$

88.
$$8\dfrac{1}{5}$$
$$-\ 5\dfrac{3}{11}$$

Exact:

Estimate:

89. $1\dfrac{5}{8} \cdot 3\dfrac{1}{5}$

Exact:

Estimate:

90. $6\dfrac{3}{4} \div 1\dfrac{2}{7}$

91. A truck traveled 341 miles on $15\frac{1}{2}$ gallons of gas. How many miles might we expect the truck to travel on 1 gallon of gas?

92. There are $7\frac{1}{3}$ grams of fat in each ounce of hamburger. How many grams of fat are in a 5-ounce hamburger patty?

Find the unknown measurements.

△ **93.**

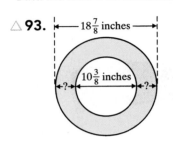

$18\frac{7}{8}$ inches

$10\frac{3}{8}$ inches

?   ?

△ **94.**

$\frac{1}{2}$ yard

$\frac{3}{5}$ yard

$1\frac{1}{30}$ yard

$1\frac{3}{10}$ yard

?

$1\frac{8}{15}$ yard

Perform the indicated operations.

95. $-12\frac{1}{7} + \left(-15\frac{3}{14}\right)$

96. $23\frac{7}{8} - 24\frac{7}{10}$

97. $-3\frac{1}{5} \div \left(-2\frac{7}{10}\right)$

98. $-2\frac{1}{4} \cdot 1\frac{3}{4}$

(4.8) *Solve each equation.*

99. $a - \frac{2}{3} = \frac{1}{6}$

100. $9x + \frac{1}{5} - 8x = -\frac{7}{10}$

101. $-\frac{3}{5}x = 6$

102. $\frac{2}{9}y = -\frac{4}{3}$

103. $\frac{x}{7} - 3 = -\frac{6}{7}$

104. $\frac{y}{5} + 2 = \frac{11}{5}$

105. $\frac{1}{6} + \frac{x}{4} = \frac{17}{12}$

106. $\frac{x}{5} - \frac{5}{4} = \frac{x}{2} - \frac{1}{20}$

Mixed Review

Perform the indicated operations. Write each answer in simplest form. Estimate where noted.

107. $\frac{6}{15} \cdot \frac{5}{8}$

108. $\frac{5x^2}{y} \div \frac{10x^3}{y^3}$

109. $\frac{3}{10} - \frac{1}{10}$

110. $\frac{7}{8x} \cdot -\frac{2}{3}$

111. $\frac{2x}{3} + \frac{x}{4}$

112. $-\frac{5}{11} + \frac{2}{55}$

113. $-1\frac{3}{5} \div \frac{1}{4}$

114. $2\frac{7}{8}$
$+ 9\frac{1}{2}$ Exact: _____

Estimate: _____

115. $12\frac{1}{7}$
$- 9\frac{3}{5}$

Exact: _____

Estimate: _____

116. Simplify: $\dfrac{2 + \frac{3}{4}}{1 - \frac{1}{8}}$

117. Evaluate: $-\frac{3}{8} \cdot \left(\frac{2}{3} - \frac{4}{9}\right)$

Solve.

118. $11x - \dfrac{2}{7} - 10x = -\dfrac{13}{14}$

119. $-\dfrac{3}{5}x = \dfrac{4}{15}$

120. $\dfrac{x}{12} + \dfrac{5}{6} = -\dfrac{3}{4}$

121. A ribbon $5\dfrac{1}{2}$ yards long is cut from a reel of ribbon with 50 yards on it. Find the length of the piece remaining on the reel.

△ **122.** A slab of natural granite is purchased and a rectangle with length $7\dfrac{4}{11}$ feet and width $5\dfrac{1}{2}$ feet is cut from it. Find the area of the rectangle.

$7\dfrac{4}{11}$ feet

$5\dfrac{1}{2}$ feet

Chapter 4 | Test

Step-by-step test solutions are found on the Chapter Test Prep Videos. Where available: **MyMathLab®** or **You Tube™**

Answers

Write a fraction to represent the shaded area.

1.

1. _____

2. _____

3. _____

Write the mixed number as an improper fraction.

2. $7\dfrac{2}{3}$

Write the improper fraction as a mixed number.

3. $\dfrac{75}{4}$

4. _____

5. _____

6. _____

Write each fraction in simplest form.

4. $\dfrac{24}{210}$

5. $-\dfrac{42x}{70}$

7. _____

8. _____

9. _____

Determine whether these fractions are equivalent.

6. $\dfrac{5}{7}$ and $\dfrac{8}{11}$

7. $\dfrac{6}{27}$ and $\dfrac{14}{63}$

10. _____

11. _____

12. _____

Find the prime factorization of each number.

8. 84

9. 495

13. _____

14. _____

Perform each indicated operation and write the answers in simplest form.

15. _____

10. $\dfrac{4}{4} \div \dfrac{3}{4}$

11. $-\dfrac{4}{3} \cdot \dfrac{4}{4}$

12. $\dfrac{7x}{9} + \dfrac{x}{9}$

13. $\dfrac{1}{7} - \dfrac{3}{x}$

16. _____

17. _____

14. $\dfrac{xy^3}{z} \cdot \dfrac{z}{xy}$

15. $-\dfrac{2}{3} \cdot -\dfrac{8}{15}$

16. $\dfrac{9a}{10} + \dfrac{2}{5}$

17. $-\dfrac{8}{15y} - \dfrac{2}{15y}$

18. _____

19. _____

18. $\dfrac{3a}{8} \cdot \dfrac{16}{6a^3}$

19. $\dfrac{11}{12} - \dfrac{3}{8} + \dfrac{5}{24}$

20.
$$3\dfrac{7}{8}$$
$$7\dfrac{2}{5}$$
$$+\,2\dfrac{3}{4}$$

21.
$$19$$
$$-2\dfrac{3}{11}$$

20. _____

21. _____

324

22. $-\dfrac{16}{3} \div -\dfrac{3}{12}$ **23.** $3\dfrac{1}{3} \cdot 6\dfrac{3}{4}$ **24.** $-\dfrac{2}{7} \cdot \left(6 - \dfrac{1}{6}\right)$ **25.** $\dfrac{1}{2} \div \dfrac{2}{3} \cdot \dfrac{3}{4}$

26. $\left(-\dfrac{3}{4}\right)^2 \div \left(\dfrac{2}{3} + \dfrac{5}{6}\right)$ **27.** Find the average of $\dfrac{5}{6}, \dfrac{4}{3}$, and $\dfrac{7}{12}$.

Simplify each complex fraction.

28. $\dfrac{\dfrac{5x}{7}}{\dfrac{20x^2}{21}}$ **29.** $\dfrac{5 + \dfrac{3}{7}}{2 - \dfrac{1}{2}}$

Solve.

30. $-\dfrac{3}{8}x = \dfrac{3}{4}$ **31.** $\dfrac{x}{5} + x = -\dfrac{24}{5}$ **32.** $\dfrac{2}{3} + \dfrac{x}{4} = \dfrac{5}{12} + \dfrac{x}{2}$

Evaluate each expression for the given replacement values.

33. $-5x; x = -\dfrac{1}{2}$ **34.** $x \div y; x = \dfrac{1}{2}, y = 3\dfrac{7}{8}$

Solve.

35. A carpenter cuts a piece $2\dfrac{3}{4}$ feet long from a cedar plank that is $6\dfrac{1}{2}$ feet long. How long is the remaining piece?

The circle graph below shows us how the average consumer spends money. For example, $\dfrac{7}{50}$ of spending goes for food. Use this information for Exercises 36 through 38.

Consumer Spending

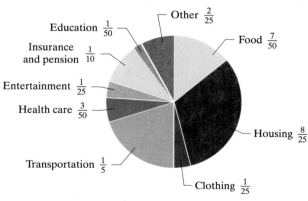

Other $\frac{2}{25}$
Education $\frac{1}{50}$
Insurance and pension $\frac{1}{10}$
Entertainment $\frac{1}{25}$
Health care $\frac{3}{50}$
Transportation $\frac{1}{5}$
Food $\frac{7}{50}$
Housing $\frac{8}{25}$
Clothing $\frac{1}{25}$

Source: U.S. Bureau of Labor Statistics; based on survey

36. What fraction of spending goes for housing and food combined?

37. What fraction of spending goes for education, transportation, and clothing?

38. Suppose your family spent $47,000 on the items in the graph. How much might we expect was spent on health care?

Find the perimeter and area of the figure.

△**39.**

Rectangle $\frac{2}{3}$ foot
1 foot

40. During a 258-mile trip, a car used $10\dfrac{3}{4}$ gallons of gas. How many miles would we expect the car to travel on 1 gallon of gas?

22. _____

23. _____

24. _____

25. _____

26. _____

27. _____

28. _____

29. _____

30. _____

31. _____

32. _____

33. _____

34. _____

35. _____

36. _____

37. _____

38. _____

39. _____

40. _____

Answers

Write each number in words.

1. 546

2. 115

3. 27,034

4. 6573

5. Add: 46 + 713

6. Add: 587 + 44

7. Subtract: 543 − 29. Check by adding.

8. Subtract: 995 − 62. Check by adding.

9. Round 278,362 to the nearest thousand.

10. Round 1436 to the nearest ten.

11. A digital video disc (DVD) can hold about 4800 megabytes (MB) of information. How many megabytes can 12 DVDs hold?

12. On a trip across the country, Daniel Daunis travels 435 miles per day. How many total miles does he travel in 3 days?

13. Divide and check: 56,717 ÷ 8

14. Divide and check: 4558 ÷ 12

Write using exponential notation.

15. $7 \cdot 7 \cdot 7$

16. $7 \cdot 7$

17. $3 \cdot 3 \cdot 3 \cdot 3 \cdot 9 \cdot 9 \cdot 9$

18. $9 \cdot 9 \cdot 9 \cdot 9 \cdot 5 \cdot 5$

19. Evaluate $2(x - y)$ for $x = 6$ and $y = 3$.

20. Evaluate $8a + 3(b - 5)$ for $a = 5$ and $b = 9$.

21. The world's deepest cave is Krubera (or Voronja), in the country of Georgia, located by the Black Sea in Asia. It has been explored to a depth of 7188 feet below the surface of Earth. Represent this position using an integer. (*Source:* messagetoeagle.com and Wikipedia)

22. The temperature on a cold day in Minneapolis, MN, was 21°F below zero. Represent this temperature using an integer.

1. _____

2. _____

3. _____

4. _____

5. _____

6. _____

7. _____

8. _____

9. _____

10. _____

11. _____

12. _____

13. _____

14. _____

15. _____

16. _____

17. _____

18. _____

19. _____

20. _____

21. _____

22. _____

23. Add using a number line: $-7 + 3$

24. Add using a number line: $-3 + 8$

25. Simplify: $7 - 8 - (-5) - 1$

26. Simplify: $6 + (-8) - (-9) + 3$

27. Evaluate: $(-5)^2$

28. Evaluate: -2^4

29. Simplify: $3(4 - 7) + (-2) - 5$

30. Simplify: $(20 - 5^2)^2$

31. Simplify: $2y - 6 + 4y + 8$

32. Simplify: $5x - 1 + x + 10$

Solve.

33. $5x + 2 - 4x = 7 - 19$

34. $9y + 1 - 8y = 3 - 20$

35. $17 - 7x + 3 = -3x + 21 - 3x$

36. $9x - 2 = 7x - 24$

37. Write a fraction to represent the shaded part of the figure.

38. Write the prime factorization of 156.

39. Write each as an improper fraction.

  a. $4\frac{2}{9}$ **b.** $1\frac{8}{11}$

40. Write $\frac{39}{5}$ as a mixed number.

41. Write in simplest form: $\frac{42x}{66}$

42. Write in simplest form: $\frac{70}{105y}$

43. Multiply: $3\frac{1}{3} \cdot \frac{7}{8}$

44. Multiply: $\frac{2}{3} \cdot 4$

45. Divide and simplify: $\frac{5}{16} \div \frac{3}{4}$

46. Divide: $1\frac{1}{10} \div 5\frac{3}{5}$

23. _____
24. _____
25. _____
26. _____
27. _____
28. _____
29. _____
30. _____
31. _____
32. _____
33. _____
34. _____
35. _____
36. _____
37. _____
38. _____
39. a. _____ b. _____
40. _____
41. _____
42. _____
43. _____
44. _____
45. _____
46. _____

5

Decimals

Decimal numbers represent parts of a whole, just like fractions. For example, one penny is 0.01 or $\frac{1}{100}$ of a dollar. In this chapter, we learn to perform arithmetic operations on decimals and to analyze the relationship between fractions and decimals. We also learn how decimals are used in the real world.

The graph below shows the age group distribution for average daily texting. (Check your age group and see if the data are accurate based on your own experiences.) While we have practiced calculating averages before in this text, an average certainly does not usually simplify to a whole number. While fractions are useful, decimals are also an important system of numbers that can be used to show values between whole numbers. Data are easy to round when they are in the form of a decimal. In Section 5.2, Exercises 83 and 84, we continue to study text messaging and how it is increasing each year.

Average Number of Texts Sent/Received per Day
(based on adults who use cell phone text messaging)

Number of Texts (per person, per day)

- 18–24: 109.5
- 25–34: 41.8
- 35–44: 25.9
- 45–54: 14.0
- 55–64: 9.8
- 65+: 4.7

Age Groups

Source: The Pew Research Center, 2011

Objective A Decimal Notation and Writing Decimals
in Words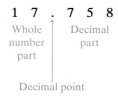

Like fractional notation, decimal notation is used to denote a part of a whole. Numbers written in decimal notation are called **decimal numbers,** or simply **decimals.** The decimal 17.758 has three parts.

$$1\ 7\ .\ 7\ 5\ 8$$

Whole   Decimal
number   part
part

Decimal point

In Section 1.2, we introduced place value for whole numbers. Place names and place values for the whole number part of a decimal number are exactly the same. Place names and place values for the decimal part are shown below.

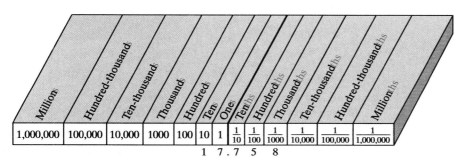

Notice that the value of each place is $\frac{1}{10}$ of the value of the place to its left. For example,

$$1 \cdot \frac{1}{10} = \frac{1}{10} \quad \text{and} \quad \frac{1}{10} \cdot \frac{1}{10} = \frac{1}{100}$$

   ↑   ↑   ↑   ↑

ones   tenths   tenths   hundredths

The decimal number 17.758 means

1 ten	+	7 ones	+	7 tenths	+	5 hundredths	+	8 thousandths

or $1 \cdot 10 \ + \ 7 \cdot 1 \ + \ 7 \cdot \dfrac{1}{10} \ + \ 5 \cdot \dfrac{1}{100} \ + \ 8 \cdot \dfrac{1}{1000}$

or $10 \ + \ 7 \ + \ \dfrac{7}{10} \ + \ \dfrac{5}{100} \ + \ \dfrac{8}{1000}$

Writing (or Reading) a Decimal in Words

Step 1: Write the whole number part in words.

Step 2: Write "and" for the decimal point.

Step 3: Write the decimal part in words as though it were a whole number, followed by the place value of the last digit.

Objectives

A Know the Meaning of Place Value for a Decimal Number and Write Decimals in Words.

B Write Decimals in Standard Form.

C Write Decimals as Fractions.

D Compare Decimals.

E Round Decimals to Given Place Values.

Helpful Hint   Notice that place values to the left of the decimal point end in "s." Place values to the right of the decimal point end in "ths."

Practice 1

Write each decimal in words.
a. 0.06
b. −200.073
c. 0.0829

> **Example 1** Write each decimal in words.
>
> **a.** 0.7   **b.** −50.82   **c.** 21.093
>
> **Solution:**
>
> **a.** seven tenths
> **b.** negative fifty and eighty-two hundredths
> **c.** twenty-one and ninety-three thousandths

■ Work Practice 1

Practice 2

Write the decimal 87.31 in words.

> **Example 2** Write the decimal in the following sentence in words: The Golden Jubilee Diamond is a 545.67-carat cut diamond. (*Source: The Guinness Book of Records*)
>
> **Solution:** five hundred forty-five and sixty-seven hundredths

■ Work Practice 2

Practice 3

Write the decimal 52.1085 in words.

> **Example 3** Write the decimal in the following sentence in words: The oldest known fragments of the Earth's crust are Zircon crystals; they were discovered in Australia and are thought to be 4.276 billion years old. (*Source: The Guinness Book of Records*)
>
> **Solution:** four and two hundred seventy-six thousandths

■ Work Practice 3

Suppose that you are paying for a purchase of $368.42 at Circuit City by writing a check. Checks are usually written using the following format.

Answers

1. a. six hundredths **b.** negative two hundred and seventy-three thousandths **c.** eight hundred twenty-nine ten-thousandths

2. eighty-seven and thirty-one hundredths

3. fifty-two and one thousand eighty-five ten-thousandths

Example 4 Fill in the check to Camelot Music to pay for your purchase of $92.98.

Solution:

Work Practice 4

Fill in the check to CLECO (Central Louisiana Electric Company) to pay for your monthly electric bill of $207.40.

Objective B Writing Decimals in Standard Form

A decimal written in words can be written in standard form by reversing the procedure in Objective A.

Examples Write each decimal in standard form.

5. Forty-eight and twenty-six hundredths is

48.26
— hundredths place

6. Six and ninety-five thousandths is

6.095
— thousandths place

Work Practice 5–6

Practice 5–6

Write each decimal in standard form.

5. Five hundred and ninety-six hundredths

6. Thirty-nine and forty-two thousandths

> **Helpful Hint**
>
> When converting a decimal from words to decimal notation, make sure the last digit is in the correct place by inserting 0s if necessary. For example,
>
> Two and thirty-eight thousandths is 2.038
>
> thousandths place

Objective C Writing Decimals as Fractions

Once you master reading and writing decimals, writing a decimal as a fraction follows naturally.

Decimal	In Words	Fraction
0.7	**seven** tenths	$\dfrac{7}{10}$
0.51	**fifty-one** hundredths	$\dfrac{51}{100}$
0.009	**nine** thousandths	$\dfrac{9}{1000}$
0.05	**five** hundredths	$\dfrac{5}{100} = \dfrac{1}{20}$

Answers

4.

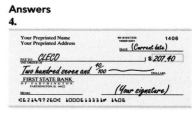

5. 500.96

6. 39.042

Notice that the number of decimal places in a decimal number is the same as the number of zeros in the denominator of the equivalent fraction. We can use this fact to write decimals as fractions.

$$0.31 = \frac{31}{100} \qquad 0.007 = \frac{7}{1000}$$

2 decimal   2 zeros   3 decimal   3 zeros
places   places

Practice 7

Write 0.051 as a fraction.

Example 7 Write 0.47 as a fraction.

Solution: $0.47 = \frac{47}{100}$

2   2 zeros
decimal places

◼ Work Practice 7

Practice 8

Write 29.97 as a mixed number.

Example 8 Write 5.9 as a mixed number.

Solution: $5.9 = 5\frac{9}{10}$

1   1 zero
decimal place

◼ Work Practice 8

Practice 9–11

Write each decimal as a fraction or mixed number. Write your answer in simplest form.

9. 0.12

10. 64.8

11. −209.986

Examples Write each decimal as a fraction or a mixed number. Write your answer in simplest form.

9. $0.125 = \frac{125}{1000} = \frac{\overset{1}{\cancel{125}}}{8 \cdot \cancel{125}} = \frac{1}{8}$

10. $43.5 = 43\frac{5}{10} = 43\frac{\cancel{5}}{2 \cdot \cancel{5}} = 43\frac{1}{2 \cdot 1} = 43\frac{1}{2}$

11. $-105.083 = -105\frac{83}{1000}$

◼ Work Practice 9–11

Later in the chapter, we write fractions as decimals. If you study Examples 7–11, you already know how to write fractions with denominators of 10, 100, 1000, and so on, as decimals.

Objective D Comparing Decimals ▶

One way to compare positive decimals is by comparing digits in corresponding places. To see why this works, let's compare 0.5 or $\frac{5}{10}$ and 0.8 or $\frac{8}{10}$. We know

$$\frac{5}{10} < \frac{8}{10} \text{ since } 5 < 8, \text{ so}$$

$$0.5 < 0.8 \text{ since } 5 < 8$$

This leads to the following.

Answers

7. $\frac{51}{1000}$ **8.** $29\frac{97}{100}$ **9.** $\frac{3}{25}$

10. $64\frac{4}{5}$ **11.** $-209\frac{493}{500}$

Comparing Two Positive Decimals

Compare digits in the same places from left to right. When two digits are not equal, the number with the larger digit is the larger decimal. If necessary, insert 0s after the last digit to the right of the decimal point to continue comparing.

Compare hundredths place digits

28.253   28.263
  ↑   ↑
  5   <   6

so 28.253   <   28.263

Helpful Hint

For any decimal, writing 0s after the last digit to the right of the decimal point does not change the value of the number.

7.6 = 7.60 = 7.600, and so on

When a whole number is written as a decimal, the decimal point is placed to the right of the ones digit.

25 = 25.0 = 25.00, and so on

Example 12 Insert <, >, or = to form a true statement.

0.378   0.368

Solution:

0.3 78   0.3 68   The tenths places are the same.

0.3 7 8   0.3 6 8   The hundredths places are different.

Since 7 > 6, then 0.378 > 0.368.

■ Work Practice 12

Practice 12

Insert <, >, or = to form a true statement.

26.208   26.28

Example 13 Insert <, >, or = to form a true statement.

0.052   0.236

Solution: 0. 0 52 < 0. 2 36   0 is smaller than 2 in the tenths place.
                ↑   ↑

■ Work Practice 13

Practice 13

Insert <, >, or = to form a true statement.

0.12   0.026

We can also use a number line to compare decimals. This is especially helpful when comparing negative decimals. Remember, the number whose graph is to the left is smaller, and the number whose graph is to the right is larger.

−1.7 < −1.2   0.5 < 0.8

Answers

12. <   **13.** >

Helpful Hint

If you have trouble comparing two negative decimals, try the following: Compare their absolute values. Then to correctly compare the negative decimals, reverse the direction of the inequality symbol.

$$0.568 < 0.586 \qquad \text{so} \qquad -0.568 > -0.586$$

Practice 14

Insert $<$, $>$, or $=$ to form a true statement.

   -0.039 ___ -0.0309

Example 14   Insert $<$, $>$, or $=$ to form a true statement.

   -0.0101 ___ -0.00109

Solution: Since $0.0101 > 0.00109$, then $-0.0101 < -0.00109$.

■ Work Practice 14

Objective E Rounding Decimals

We **round the decimal part** of a decimal number in nearly the same way as we round whole numbers. The only difference is that we drop digits to the right of the rounding place, instead of replacing these digits with 0s. For example,

   36.954   rounded to the nearest hundredth is   36.95.

Rounding Decimals to a Place Value to the Right of the Decimal Point

Step 1: Locate the digit to the right of the given place value.

Step 2: If this digit is 5 or greater, add 1 to the digit in the given place value and drop all digits to its right. If this digit is less than 5, drop all digits to the right of the given place.

Practice 15

Round 482.7817 to the nearest thousandth.

Example 15   Round 736.2359 to the nearest tenth.

Solution:

Step 1: We locate the digit to the right of the tenths place.

   tenths place

   736.2 3 59

   digit to the right

Step 2: Since the digit to the right is less than 5, we drop it and all digits to its right.

Thus, 736.2359 rounded to the nearest tenth is 736.2.

■ Work Practice 15

Answers
14. $<$ **15.** 482.782

The same steps for rounding can be used when the decimal is negative.

Example 16 Round −0.027 to the nearest hundredth.

Solution:

Step 1: Locate the digit to the right of the hundredths place.

hundredths place

− 0.02 7

digit to the right

Step 2: Since the digit to the right is 5 or greater, we add 1 to the hundredths digit and drop all digits to its right.

Thus, −0.027 is −0.03 rounded to the nearest hundredth.

■ Work Practice 16

Practice 16

Round −0.032 to the nearest hundredth.

The following number line illustrates the rounding of negative decimals.

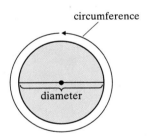

In Section 5.3, we will introduce a formula for the distance around a circle. The distance around a circle is given the special name **circumference.**

The symbol π is the Greek letter pi, pronounced "pie." We use π to denote the following constant:

$$\pi = \frac{\text{circumference of a circle}}{\text{diameter of a circle}}$$

circumference

diameter

The value π is an **irrational number.** This means if we try to write it as a decimal, it neither ends nor repeats in a pattern.

Example 17 $\pi \approx 3.14159265$. Round π to the nearest hundredth.

Solution:

hundredths place — 1 is less than 5.

3.14159265

Delete these digits.

Thus, 3.14159265 rounded to the nearest hundredth is 3.14. In other words, $\pi \approx 3.14$.

■ Work Practice 17

Practice 17

$\pi \approx 3.14159265$. Round π to the nearest ten-thousandth.

Rounding often occurs with money amounts. Since there are 100 cents in a dollar, each cent is $\frac{1}{100}$ of a dollar. This means that if we want to round to the nearest cent, we round to the nearest hundredth of a dollar.

✓**Concept Check** 1756.0894 rounded to the nearest *ten* is
a. 1756.1   **b.** 1760.0894   **c.** 1760   **d.** 1750

Answers
16. −0.03   **17.** $\pi \approx 3.1416$

✓**Concept Check Answer**
c

Practice 18

Water bills in Mexia are always rounded to the nearest dollar. Round a water bill of $24.62 to the nearest dollar.

Answer
18. $25

Example 18 Determining State Taxable Income

A high school teacher's taxable income is $41,567.72. The tax tables in the teacher's state use amounts rounded to the nearest dollar. Round the teacher's income to the nearest whole dollar.

Solution: Rounding to the nearest whole dollar means rounding to the ones place.

```
once place          7 is greater than 5.
        $41,567.72
          Add 1.   Delete these digits.
```

Thus, the teacher's income rounded to the nearest dollar is $41,568.

■ Work Practice 18

Vocabulary, Readiness & Video Check

Use the choices below to fill in each blank.

words	decimals	tenths	after
tens	circumference	and	standard form

1. The number "twenty and eight hundredths" is written in _____ and "20.08" is written in _____.
2. Another name for the distance around a circle is its _____.
3. Like fractions, _____ are used to denote part of a whole.
4. When writing a decimal number in words, the decimal point is written as _____.
5. The place value _____ is to the right of the decimal point while _____ is to the left of the decimal point.
6. The decimal point in a whole number is _____ the last digit.

Martin-Gay Interactive Videos

See Video 5.1

Watch the section lecture video and answer the following questions.

Objective A **7.** In ▣ Example 1, how is the decimal point written? ▶

Objective B **8.** Why is 9.8 not the correct answer to ▣ Example 3? What is the correct answer? ▶

Objective C **9.** From ▣ Example 5, why does reading a decimal number correctly help you write it as an equivalent fraction? ▶

Objective D **10.** In ▣ Example 7, we compare place value by place value in which direction? ▶

Objective E **11.** ▣ Example 8 is being rounded to the nearest tenth, so why is the digit 7, which is not in the tenths place, looked at? ▶

5.1 Exercise Set MyMathLab®

Objective A *Write each decimal number in words. See Examples 1 through 3.*

1. 5.62

2. 9.57

▶ **3.** 16.23

4. 47.65

5. −0.205

6. −0.495

7. 167.009

8. 233.056

9. 3000.04

10. 5000.02

11. 105.6

12. 410.3

13. The Akashi Kaikyo Bridge, between Kobe and Awaji-Shima, Japan, is approximately 2.43 miles long.

14. The English Channel Tunnel is a 31.04 miles long undersea rail tunnel connecting England and France. (*Source: Railway Directory & Year Book*)

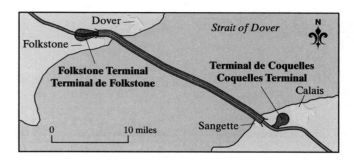

Fill in each check for the described purchase. See Example 4.

15. Your monthly car loan of $321.42 to R. W. Financial.

16. Your part of the monthly apartment rent, which is $213.70. You pay this to Amanda Dupre.

17. Your bill of $91.68 to Verizon wireless.

18. Your grocery bill of $387.49 at Kroger.

Objective B *Write each decimal number in standard form. See Examples 5 and 6.*

19. Two and eight tenths

20. Five and one tenth

21. Nine and eight hundredths

22. Twelve and six hundredths

23. Negative seven hundred five and six hundred twenty-five thousandths

24. Negative eight hundred four and three hundred ninety-nine thousandths

25. Forty-six ten-thousandths

26. Eighty-three ten-thousandths

Objective C *Write each decimal as a fraction or a mixed number. Write your answer in simplest form. See Examples 7 through 11.*

27. 0.7   **28.** 0.9   ● **29.** 0.27   **30.** 0.39

31. 0.4   **32.** 0.8   **33.** 5.4   **34.** 6.8

35. −0.058   **36.** −0.024   ● **37.** 7.008   **38.** 9.005

39. 15.802   **40.** 11.406   **41.** 0.3005   **42.** 0.2006

Objectives A B C Mixed Practice *Fill in the chart. The first row is completed for you. See Examples 1 through 11.*

	Decimal Number in Standard Form	In Words	Fraction
	0.37	thirty-seven hundredths	$\frac{37}{100}$
43.		eight tenths	
44.		five tenths	
45.	0.077		
46.	0.019		

Objective D *Insert <, >, or = between each pair of numbers to form a true statement. See Examples 12 through 14.*

47. 0.15   0.16   **48.** 0.12   0.15   **49.** −0.57   −0.54   **50.** −0.59   −0.52

51. 0.098   0.1   **52.** 0.0756   0.2   **53.** 0.54900   0.549   **54.** 0.98400   0.984

● **55.** 167.908   167.980   **56.** 519.3405   519.3054   **57.** −1.062   −1.07   **58.** −18.1   −18.01

59. −7.052   7.0052   **60.** 0.01   −0.1   **61.** −0.023   −0.024   **62.** −0.562   −0.652

Objective E *Round each decimal to the given place value. See Examples 15 through 18.*

● **63.** 0.57, nearest tenth   **64.** 0.64, nearest tenth   **65.** 98,207.23, nearest ten

66. 68,934.543, nearest ten   **67.** −0.234, nearest hundredth   **68.** −0.892, nearest hundredth

● **69.** 0.5942, nearest thousandth   **70.** 63.4523, nearest thousandth

Recall that the number π, written as a decimal, neither ends nor repeats in a pattern. Given that π ≈ 3.14159265, round π to the given place values below. (We study π further in Section 5.3.) See Example 17.

71. tenth   **72.** ones   **73.** thousandth   **74.** hundred-thousandth

Round each monetary amount to the nearest cent or dollar as indicated. See Example 18.

75. $26.95, to the nearest dollar

76. $14,769.52, to the nearest dollar

77. $0.1992, to the nearest cent

78. $0.7633, to the nearest cent

Round each number to the given place value. See Example 18.

79. At the time of this writing, the Apple MacBook Air is the thinnest Mac in production. At its thickest point, it measures 0.68 in. Round this number to the nearest tenth. (*Source:* Apple, Inc.)

13-inch MacBook Air

0.68 in.

80. A large tropical cockroach of the family Dictyoptera is the fastest-moving insect. This insect was clocked at a speed of 3.36 miles per hour. Round this number to the nearest tenth. (*Source:* University of California, Berkeley)

81. Missy Franklin of the United States won the gold medal for the 200 m backstroke in the 2012 London Summer Olympics with a record time of 2.0677 minutes. Round this time to the nearest hundredth of a minute.

82. The population density of the state of Utah is 34.745 people per square mile. Round this population density to the nearest tenth. (*Source:* U.S. Census Bureau)

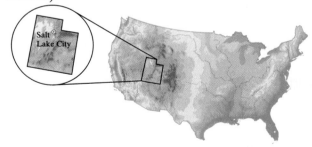

83. A used biology textbook is priced at $67.89. Round this price to the nearest dollar.

84. A used office desk is advertised at $19.95 by Drawley's Office Furniture. Round this price to the nearest dollar.

85. Venus makes a complete orbit around the Sun every 224.695 days. Round this figure to the nearest whole day. (*Source:* National Space Science Data Center)

86. The length of a day on Mars, a full rotation about its axis, is 24.6229 hours. Round this figure to the nearest thousandth. (*Source:* National Space Science Data Center)

Review

Perform each indicated operation. See Section 1.3.

87. 3452 + 2314   **88.** 8945 + 4536   **89.** 82 − 47   **90.** 4002 − 3897

Concept Extensions

Solve. See the Concept Check in this section.

91. 2849.1738 rounded to the nearest hundred is
   a. 2849.17   **b.** 2800   **c.** 2850   **d.** 2849.174

92. 146.059 rounded to the nearest ten is
   a. 146.0   **b.** 146.1   **c.** 140   **d.** 150

93. 2849.1738 rounded to the nearest hundredth is
   a. 2849.17   **b.** 2800   **c.** 2850   **d.** 2849.18

94. 146.059 rounded to the nearest tenth is
   a. 146.0   **b.** 146.1   **c.** 140   **d.** 150

95. In your own words, describe how to write a decimal as a fraction or a mixed number.

96. Explain how to identify the value of the 9 in the decimal 486.3297.

97. Write $7\frac{12}{100}$ as a decimal.

98. Write $17\frac{268}{1000}$ as a decimal.

99. Write 0.00026849577 as a fraction.

100. Write 0.00026849576 in words.

101. Write a 5-digit number that rounds to 1.7.

102. Write a 4-digit number that rounds to 26.3.

103. Write a decimal number that is greater than 8 but less than 9.

104. Write a decimal number that is greater than 48.1, but less than 48.2.

105. Which number(s) rounds to 0.26?
   0.26559   0.26499   0.25786   0.25186

106. Which number(s) rounds to 0.06?
   0.0612   0.066   0.0586   0.0506

Write these numbers from smallest to largest.

107. 0.9
   0.1038
   0.10299
   0.1037

108. 0.01
   0.0839
   0.09
   0.1

109. The all-time top six movies (those that have earned the most money in the United States) along with the approximate amount of money they have earned are listed in the table. Estimate the total amount of money that these movies have earned by first rounding each earning to the nearest hundred-million. (*Source:* The Internet Movie Database)

Top All-Time American Movies	
Movie	**Gross Domestic Earnings**
Avatar (2009)	$760.5 million
Titanic (1997)	$658.7 million
The Avengers (2012)	$623.3 million
The Dark Knight (2008)	$533.3 million
Star Wars: The Phantom Menace (1999)	$474.5 million
Star Wars (1977)	$460.9 million

110. In 2012, there were 1392.2 million singles downloaded at an average price of $1.20 each. Find an estimate of the total revenue from downloaded singles by answering parts **a–c**. (*Source:* Recording Industry Association of America)
   a. Round 1392.2 million to the nearest ten million.

   b. Multiply the rounded value in part **a** by 12.

   c. Move the decimal point in the product from part **b** one place to the left. This number is the total revenue in million dollars.

5.2 Adding and Subtracting Decimals

Objective A Adding or Subtracting Decimals

Adding or subtracting decimals is similar to adding or subtracting whole numbers. We add or subtract digits in corresponding place values from right to left, carrying or borrowing if necessary. To make sure that digits in corresponding place values are added or subtracted, we line up the decimal points vertically.

Objectives

A Add or Subtract Decimals.

B Estimate when Adding or Subtracting Decimals.

C Evaluate Expressions with Decimal Replacement Values.

D Simplify Expressions Containing Decimals.

E Solve Problems That Involve Adding or Subtracting Decimals.

Adding or Subtracting Decimals

Step 1: Write the decimals so that the decimal points line up vertically.

Step 2: Add or subtract as with whole numbers.

Step 3: Place the decimal point in the sum or difference so that it lines up vertically with the decimal points in the problem.

In this section, we will insert zeros in decimal numbers so that place-value digits line up neatly. This is shown in Example 1.

Example 1 Add: $23.85 + 1.604$

Solution: First we line up the decimal points vertically.

$$
\begin{array}{r}
23.850 \\
+\ \ 1.604 \\
\end{array}
$$
Insert one 0 so that digits line up neatly.

Line up decimal points.

Then we add the digits from right to left as for whole numbers.

$$
\begin{array}{r}
23.850 \\
+\ \ 1.604 \\
\hline
25.454 \\
\end{array}
$$
Place the decimal point in the sum so that all decimal points line up.

■ Work Practice 1

Practice 1

Add.

a. $19.52 + 5.371$

b. $40.08 + 17.612$

c. $0.125 + 422.8$

Helpful Hint

Recall that 0s may be placed after the last digit to the right of the decimal point without changing the value of the decimal. This may be used to help line up place values when adding decimals.

$$
\begin{array}{ccc}
3.2 & \text{becomes} & 3.200 \quad \text{Insert two 0s.} \\
15.567 & & 15.567 \\
+\ 0.11 & & +\ 0.110 \quad \text{Insert one 0.} \\
& & \overline{18.877} \quad \text{Add.}
\end{array}
$$

Answers
1. a. 24.891 **b.** 57.692 **c.** 422.925

341

Practice 2

Add.

a. 34.567 + 129.43 + 2.8903

b. 11.21 + 46.013 + 362.526

Example 2   Add: 763.7651 + 22.001 + 43.89

Solution: First we line up the decimal points.

$$
\begin{array}{r}
\overset{1\ 1\ 1}{763.7651} \\
22.0010 \quad \text{Insert one 0.} \\
+\ \ 43.8900 \quad \text{Insert two 0s.} \\
\hline
829.6561 \quad \text{Add.}
\end{array}
$$

■ Work Practice 2

Helpful Hint

Don't forget that the decimal point in a whole number is positioned after the last digit.

Practice 3

Add: 19 + 26.072

Example 3   Add: 45 + 2.06

Solution:

$$
\begin{array}{r}
45.00 \quad \text{Insert a decimal point and two 0s.} \\
+\ \ 2.06 \quad \text{Line up decimal points.} \\
\hline
47.06 \quad \text{Add.}
\end{array}
$$

■ Work Practice 3

✓**Concept Check** What is wrong with the following calculation of the sum of 7.03, 2.008, 19.16, and 3.1415?

$$
\begin{array}{r}
7.03 \\
2.008 \\
19.16 \\
+\ 3.1415 \\
\hline
3.6042
\end{array}
$$

Practice 4

Add: 7.12 + (−9.92)

Example 4   Add: 3.62 + (−4.78)

Solution: Recall from Chapter 2 that to add two numbers with different signs, we find the difference of the larger absolute value and the smaller absolute value. The sign of the answer is the same as the sign of the number with the larger absolute value.

$$
\begin{array}{r}
4.78 \\
-\ 3.62 \\
\hline
1.16 \quad \text{Subtract the absolute values.}
\end{array}
$$

Thus, 3.62 + (−4.78) = −1.16

The sign of the number with the larger absolute value; −4.78 has the larger absolute value.

■ Work Practice 4

Answers

2. a. 166.8873   **b.** 419.749

3. 45.072   **4.** −2.8

✓**Concept Check Answer**

The decimal places are not lined up properly.

Subtracting decimals is similar to subtracting whole numbers. We line up digits and subtract from right to left, borrowing when needed.

Example 5 Subtract: $3.5 - 0.068$. Check your answer.

Solution:
$$\begin{array}{r} \overset{\;\;\;\;\;\;\;9}{\overset{4\;\cancel{10}\;10}{3.\cancel{5}\,0\,0}} \quad \text{Insert two 0s.} \\ -0.0\,6\,8 \quad \text{Line up decimal points.} \\ \hline 3.4\,3\,2 \quad \text{Subtract.} \end{array}$$

Check: Recall that we can check a subtraction problem by adding.

$$\begin{array}{r} 3.432 \quad \text{Difference} \\ +\,0.068 \quad \text{Subtrahend} \\ \hline 3.500 \quad \text{Minuend} \end{array}$$

■ Work Practice 5

Practice 5
Subtract. Check your answers.
a. $6.7 - 3.92$
b. $9.72 - 4.068$

Example 6 Subtract: $85 - 17.31$. Check your answer.

Solution:
$$\begin{array}{r} \overset{\;\;\;\;\;\;\;\;\;9}{\overset{7\;\;14\;\;\;\;9}{\overset{7\;\cancel{4}\;\cancel{10}\;10}{8\,\cancel{5}.\cancel{0}\,0}}} \\ -1\,7.3\,1 \\ \hline 6\,7.6\,9 \end{array}$$
Check:
$$\begin{array}{r} 67.69 \quad \text{Difference} \\ +17.31 \quad \text{Subtrahend} \\ \hline 85.00 \quad \text{Minuend} \end{array}$$

■ Work Practice 6

Practice 6
Subtract. Check your answers.
a. $73 - 29.31$
b. $210 - 68.22$

Example 7 Subtract 3 from 6.98.

Solution:
$$\begin{array}{r} 6.98 \\ -3.00 \quad \text{Insert two 0s.} \\ \hline 3.98 \end{array}$$
Check:
$$\begin{array}{r} 3.98 \quad \text{Difference} \\ +3.00 \quad \text{Subtrahend} \\ \hline 6.98 \quad \text{Minuend} \end{array}$$

■ Work Practice 7

Practice 7
Subtract 19 from 25.91

Example 8 Subtract: $-5.8 - 1.7$

Solution: Recall from Chapter 2 that to subtract 1.7, we add the opposite of 1.7, or -1.7. Thus

$$-5.8 - 1.7 = -5.8 + (-1.7) \quad \text{To subtract, add the opposite of 1.7, which is } -1.7.$$

Add the absolute values.

$$= -7.5.$$

Use the common negative sign.

■ Work Practice 8

Practice 8
Subtract: $-5.4 - 9.6$

Example 9 Subtract: $-2.56 - (-4.01)$

Solution: $-2.56 - (-4.01) = -2.56 + 4.01$ To subtract, add the opposite of -4.01, which is 4.01.

Subtract the absolute values.

$$= 1.45$$

The answer is positive since 4.01 has the larger absolute value.

■ Work Practice 9

Practice 9
Subtract: $-1.05 - (-7.23)$

Answers
5. a. 2.78 **b.** 5.652
6. a. 43.69 **b.** 141.78
7. 6.91 **8.** -15 **9.** 6.18

Objective B Estimating when Adding or Subtracting Decimals

To help avoid errors, we can also estimate to see if our answer is reasonable when adding or subtracting decimals. Although only one estimate is needed per operation, we show two for variety.

Practice 10

Add or subtract as indicated. Then estimate to see if the answer is reasonable by rounding the given numbers and adding or subtracting the rounded numbers.

a. 58.1 + 326.97

b. 16.08 − 0.925

Example 10   Add or subtract as indicated. Then estimate to see if the answer is reasonable by rounding the given numbers and adding or subtracting the rounded numbers.

a. 27.6 + 519.25

Exact		Estimate 1		Estimate 2
$\overset{1}{2}7.60$	rounds to	30		30
+ 519.25	rounds to	+ 500	or	+ 520
546.85		530		550

Since the exact answer is close to either estimate, it is reasonable. (In the first estimate, each number is rounded to the place value of the leftmost digit. In the second estimate, each number is rounded to the nearest ten.)

b. 11.01 − 0.862

Exact		Estimate 1		Estimate 2
$1\overset{0}{\cancel{1}}.\overset{9}{\cancel{0}}\overset{10}{\cancel{1}}\overset{10}{\cancel{0}}$	rounds to	10		11
− 0 .8 6 2	rounds to	− 1	or	− 1
10 .1 4 8		9		10

In the first estimate, we rounded the first number to the nearest ten and the second number to the nearest one. In the second estimate, we rounded both numbers to the nearest one. Both estimates show us that our answer is reasonable.

■ Work Practice 10

Helpful Hint   Remember that estimates are used for our convenience to quickly check the reasonableness of an answer.

✓**Concept Check** Why shouldn't the sum 21.98 + 42.36 be estimated as 30 + 50 = 80?

Objective C Using Decimals as Replacement Values

Let's review evaluating expressions with given replacement values. This time the replacement values are decimals.

Practice 11

Evaluate $y - z$ for $y = 11.6$ and $z = 10.8$.

Example 11   Evaluate $x - y$ for $x = 2.8$ and $y = 0.92$.

Solution: Replace x with 2.8 and y with 0.92 and simplify.

$$x - y = 2.8 - 0.92$$
$$= 1.88$$

2.80
−0.92
1.88

■ Work Practice 11

Answers

10. a. Exact: 385.07; an Estimate: 390
b. Exact: 15.155; an Estimate: 15   **11.** 0.8

✓**Concept Check Answer**

Each number is rounded incorrectly. The estimate is too high.

Example 12 Is 2.3 a solution of the equation $6.3 = x + 4$?

Solution: Replace x with 2.3 in the equation $6.3 = x + 4$ to see if the result is a true statement.

$6.3 = x + 4$

$6.3 \stackrel{?}{=} 2.3 + 4$ Replace x with 2.3.

$6.3 = 6.3$ True

Since $6.3 = 6.3$ is a true statement, 2.3 is a solution of $6.3 = x + 4$.

Work Practice 12

Practice 12

Is 12.1 a solution of the equation $y - 4.3 = 7.8$?

Objective D Simplifying Expressions Containing Decimals ▶

Example 13 Simplify by combining like terms:

$11.1x - 6.3 + 8.9x - 4.6$

Solution:

$11.1x - 6.3 + 8.9x - 4.6 = 11.1x + 8.9x + (-6.3) + (-4.6)$
$= 20x + (-10.9)$
$= 20x - 10.9$

Work Practice 13

Practice 13

Simplify by combining like terms:

$-4.3y + 7.8 - 20.1y + 14.6$

Objective E Solving Problems by Adding or Subtracting Decimals ▶

Decimals are very common in real-life problems.

Example 14 Calculating the Cost of Owning an Automobile

Find the total monthly cost of owning and operating a certain automobile given the expenses shown.

Monthly car payment:	$256.63
Monthly insurance cost:	$47.52
Average gasoline bill per month:	$195.33

Solution:

1. UNDERSTAND. Read and reread the problem. The phrase "total monthly cost" tells us to add.
2. TRANSLATE.

In words:	total monthly cost	is	car payment	plus	insurance cost	plus	gasoline bill
	↓	↓	↓	↓	↓	↓	↓
Translate:	total monthly cost	=	$256.63	+	$47.52	+	$195.33

(*Continued on next page*)

Practice 14

Find the total monthly cost of owning and operating a certain automobile given the expenses shown.

Monthly car payment:	$563.52
Monthly insurance cost:	$52.68
Average gasoline bill per month:	$127.50

Answers

12. yes **13.** $-24.4y + 22.4$
14. $743.70

3. SOLVE: Let's also estimate by rounding each number to the nearest ten.

<table>
<tr><td>¹ ¹ ¹
256.63</td><td>rounds to</td><td>260</td><td></td></tr>
<tr><td>47.52</td><td>rounds to</td><td>50</td><td></td></tr>
<tr><td>+ 195.33</td><td>rounds to</td><td>200</td><td></td></tr>
<tr><td>499.48</td><td>Exact</td><td>510</td><td>Estimate</td></tr>
</table>

4. INTERPRET. *Check* your work. Since our estimate is close to our exact answer, our answer is reasonable. *State* your conclusion: The total monthly cost is $499.48.

■ Work Practice 14

The next bar graph has horizontal bars. To visualize the value represented by a bar, see how far it extends to the right. The value of each bar is labeled, and we will study bar graphs further in a later chapter.

Practice 15

Use the bar graph in Example 15. How much greater is the average height in the Netherlands than the average height in Czechoslovakia?

Example 15   Comparing Average Heights

The bar graph shows the current average heights for adults in various countries. How much greater is the average height in Denmark than the average height in the United States?

Average Adult Height

Country	Height
Netherlands	72.6 inches
Denmark	72.2 inches
Norway	71.9 inches
Sweden	71.8 inches
Germany	71.6 inches
USA	70.8 inches
Czechoslovakia[1]	70.8 inches

[1]Average for Czech Republic, Slovakia
Source: USA Today

* The ⌁ means that some numbers are purposefully missing on the axis.

Solution:

1. UNDERSTAND. Read and reread the problem. Since we want to know "how much greater," we subtract.

2. TRANSLATE.

In words:	How much greater	is	Denmark's average height	minus	U.S. average height
	↓	↓	↓	↓	↓
Translate:	How much greater	=	72.2	−	70.8

3. SOLVE: We estimate by rounding each number to the nearest whole.

<table>
<tr><td>¹ ¹²
7 2̶ . 2̶</td><td>rounds to</td><td>72</td><td></td></tr>
<tr><td>− 7 0 . 8</td><td>rounds to</td><td>− 71</td><td></td></tr>
<tr><td>1 . 4</td><td>Exact</td><td>1</td><td>Estimate</td></tr>
</table>

4. INTERPRET. *Check* your work. Since our estimate is close to our exact answer, 1.4 inches is reasonable. *State* your conclusion: The average height in Denmark is 1.4 inches greater than the average U.S. height.

■ Work Practice 15

Answer

15. 1.8 in.

Calculator Explorations Decimals

Entering Decimal Numbers

To enter a decimal number, find the key marked $\boxed{\,\cdot\,}$. To enter the number 2.56, for example, press the keys $\boxed{2}\,\boxed{\cdot}\,\boxed{56}$.
The display will read $\boxed{2.56}$.

Operations on Decimal Numbers

Operations on decimal numbers are performed in the same way as operations on whole or signed numbers. For example, to find $8.625 - 4.29$, press the keys $\boxed{8.625}\,\boxed{-}\,\boxed{4.29}$ then $\boxed{=}$ or $\boxed{\text{ENTER}}$.

The display will read $\boxed{4.335}$. (Although entering 8.625, for example, requires pressing more than one key, we group numbers together here for easier reading.)

Use a calculator to perform each indicated operation.

1. $315.782 + 12.96$ **2.** $29.68 + 85.902$

3. $6.249 - 1.0076$ **4.** $5.238 - 0.682$

5.
$$\begin{array}{r} 12.555 \\ 224.987 \\ 5.2 \\ +\,622.65 \\ \hline \end{array}$$

6.
$$\begin{array}{r} 47.006 \\ 0.17 \\ 313.259 \\ +\,139.088 \\ \hline \end{array}$$

Vocabulary, Readiness & Video Check

Use the choices below to fill in each blank. Not all choices will be used.

minuend	vertically	like	true
difference	subtrahend	last	false

1. The decimal point in a whole number is positioned after the _____ digit.

2. In $89.2 - 14.9 = 74.3$, the number 74.3 is called the _____, 89.2 is the _____, and 14.9 is the _____.

3. To simplify an expression, we combine any _____ terms.

4. To add or subtract decimals, we line up the decimal points _____.

5. True or false: If we replace x with 11.2 and y with -8.6 in the expression $x - y$, we have $11.2 - 8.6$. _____

6. True or false: If we replace x with -9.8 and y with -3.7 in the expression $x + y$, we have $-9.8 + 3.7$. _____

Martin-Gay Interactive Videos

See Video 5.2

Watch the section lecture video and answer the following questions.

Objective A   **7.** From ▦ Examples 1–3, why do you think we line up decimal points? ▶

Objective B   **8.** In ▦ Example 4, estimating is used to check whether the answer to the subtraction problem is reasonable, but what is the best way to fully check? ▶

Objective C   **9.** In ▦ Example 5, why is the actual subtraction performed to the side? ▶

Objective D   **10.** How many sets of like terms are there in ▦ Example 6? ▶

Objective E   **11.** In ▦ Example 7, to calculate the amount of border material needed, we are actually calculating the _____ of the triangle. ▶

Exercise Set MyMathLab®

Objectives A B Mixed Practice *Add. See Examples 1 through 4 and 10. For those exercises marked, also estimate to see if the answer is reasonable.*

1. 5.6 + 2.1

2. 3.6 + 4.1

3. 8.2 + 2.15

4. 5.17 + 3.7

5. 24.6 + 2.39 + 0.0678

6. 32.4 + 1.58 + 0.0934

7. −2.6 + (−5.97)

8. −18.2 + (−10.8)

9. 18.56 + (−8.23)

10. 4.38 + (−6.05)

11.   234.89
         + 230.67
     Exact: _____   Estimate: _____

12.   734.89
         + 640.56
     Exact: _____   Estimate: _____

13.   100.009
                6.08
         +   9.034
     Exact: _____   Estimate: _____

14.   200.89
                7.49
         +   62.83
     Exact: _____   Estimate: _____

15. Find the sum of 39, 3.006, and 8.403

16. Find the sum of 65, 5.0903, and 6.9003

Subtract and check. See Examples 5 through 10. For those exercises marked, also estimate to see if the answer is reasonable.

17. 12.6 − 8.2

18. 8.9 − 3.1

19. 18 − 2.7

20. 28 − 3.3

21.   654.9
         − 56.67

22.   863.23
         − 39.453

23. 5.9 − 4.07
     Exact:
     Estimate:

24. 6.4 − 3.04
     Exact:
     Estimate:

25.   1000
         −   123.4
     Exact:

     Estimate:

26.   2000
         −   327.47
     Exact:

     Estimate:

27. 200 − 5.6

28. 800 − 8.9

29. −1.12 − 5.2

30. −8.63 − 5.6

31. 5.21 − 11.36

32. 8.53 − 17.84

33. −2.6 − (−5.7)

34. −9.4 − (−10.4)

35. 3 − 0.0012

36. 7 − 0.097

37. Subtract 6.7 from 23.

38. Subtract 9.2 from 45.

Objective A *Perform the indicated operation. See Examples 1 through 9.*

39. $0.9 + 2.2$ **40.** $0.7 + 3.4$ **41.** $-6.06 + 0.44$ **42.** $-5.05 + 0.88$

43. $500.21 - 136.85$ **44.** $600.47 - 254.68$ **45.** $50.2 - 600$ **46.** $40.3 - 700$

47. Subtract 61.9 from 923.5.   **48.** Subtract 45.8 from 845.9.   **49.** Add 100.009 and 6.08 and 9.034.

50. Add 200.89 and 7.49 and 62.83.   **51.** $-0.003 + 0.091$ **52.** $-0.004 + 0.085$

53. $-102.4 - 78.04$ **54.** $-36.2 - 10.02$ **55.** $-2.9 - (-1.8)$ **56.** $-6.5 - (-3.3)$

Objective C *Evaluate each expression for $x = 3.6$, $y = 5$, and $z = 0.21$. See Example 11.*

57. $x + z$ **58.** $y + x$ ▶ **59.** $x - z$

60. $y - z$ **61.** $y - x + z$ **62.** $x + y + z$

Determine whether the given values are solutions to the given equations. See Example 12.

63. Is 7 a solution to $x + 2.7 = 9.3$?   **64.** Is 3.7 a solution to $x + 5.9 = 8.6$?

65. Is -11.4 a solution to $27.4 + y = 16$?   **66.** Is -22.9 a solution to $45.9 + z = 23$?

67. Is 1 a solution to $2.3 + x = 5.3 - x$?   **68.** Is 0.9 a solution to $1.9 - x = x + 0.1$?

Objective D *Simplify by combining like terms. See Example 13.*

▶ **69.** $30.7x + 17.6 - 23.8x - 10.7$ **70.** $14.2z + 11.9 - 9.6z - 15.2$

71. $-8.61 + 4.23y - 2.36 - 0.76y$ **72.** $-8.96x - 2.31 - 4.08x + 9.68$

Objective E *Solve. For Exercises 73 and 74, the solutions have been started for you. See Examples 14 and 15.*

73. Ann-Margaret Tober bought a book for $32.48. If she paid with two $20 bills, what was her change?

74. Phillip Guillot bought a car part for $18.26. If he paid with two $10 bills, what was his change?

Start the solution:

1. UNDERSTAND the problem. Reread it as many times as needed.
2. TRANSLATE into an equation. (Fill in the blank.)

change	is	two $20 bills	minus	cost of book
↓		↓	↓	↓
change	=	40	−	_____

Finish with

3. SOLVE and 4. INTERPRET

Start the solution:

1. UNDERSTAND the problem. Reread it as many times as needed.
2. TRANSLATE into an equation. (Fill in the blank.)

change	is	two $10 bills	minus	cost of car part
↓		↓	↓	↓
change	=	20	−	_____

Finish with

3. SOLVE and 4. INTERPRET

75. Microsoft stock opened the day at $35.17 per share, and the closing price the same day was $34.75. By how much did the price of each share change?

76. A pair of eyeglasses costs a total of $347.89. The frames of the glasses are $97.23. How much do the lenses of the eyeglasses cost?

△ **77.** Find the perimeter.

△ **78.** Find the perimeter.

79. The Apple iPhone 5 was released in 2012. It measures 4.87 inches by 2.31 inches. Find the perimeter of this phone. (*Source:* Apple.com)

80. The Google Nexus 4, released in 2012, is the newest Google phone (at this writing). It measures 5.27 inches by 2.7 inches. Find the perimeter of the phone. (*Source:* Google.com)

81. The average wind speed at the weather station on Mt. Washington in New Hampshire is 35.2 miles per hour. The highest speed ever recorded at the station is 231.0 miles per hour. How much faster is the highest speed than the average wind speed? (*Source:* National Climatic Data Center)

82. The average annual rainfall in Omaha, Nebraska, is 30.08 inches. The average annual rainfall in New Orleans, Louisiana, is 64.16 inches. On average, how much more rain does New Orleans receive annually than Omaha? (*Source:* National Climatic Data Center)

This bar graph shows the predicted increase in the total number of text messages per person per day in the United States. Use this graph for Exercises 83 and 84. (Source: Pew Research Center.)

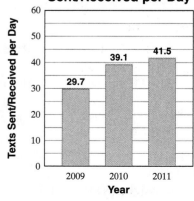

83. Find the increase in the number of texts sent or received per day from 2009 to 2011.

84. Find the increase in the number of texts sent or received per day from 2010 to 2011.

85. As of this writing, the top three U.S. movies that made the most money through movie ticket sales are *Avatar* (2009), $760.5 million; *Titanic* (1997), $658.7 million; and *The Avengers* (2012), $623.3 million. What was the total amount of ticket sales for these three movies? (*Source:* MovieWeb)

86. In 2010, the average credit card late fee was $35. In 2011, the average credit card late fee had decreased by about $11.85. Find the average credit card late fee in 2011. (*Source:* Consumer Financial Protection Bureau)

87. The snowiest city in the United States is Valdez, AK, which receives an average of 110.5 more inches of snow than the second snowiest city. The second snowiest city in the United States is Crested Butte, CO. Crested Butte receives an average of 215.8 inches annually. How much snow does Valdez receive on average each year?(*Source:* The Weather Channel)

88. The driest place in the world is the Atacama Desert in Chile, which receives an average of only 0.004 inch of rain per year. Yuma, Arizona, is the driest city in the United States. Yuma receives an average of 3.006 more inches of rain each year than the Atacama Desert. What is the average annual rainfall in Yuma? (*Source:* National Climatic Data Center)

89. A landscape architect is planning a border for a flower garden shaped like a triangle. The sides of the garden measure 12.4 feet, 29.34 feet, and 25.7 feet. Find the amount of border material needed.

90. A contractor purchased enough railing to completely enclose the newly built deck shown below. Find the amount of railing purchased.

The table shows the average speeds for the Daytona 500 winners for the years shown. Use this table to answer Exercises 91 and 92. (Source: Daytona International Speedway*)*

Daytona 500 Winners		
Year	Winner	Average Speed
1978	Bobby Allison	159.73
1988	Bobby Allison	137.531
1998	Dale Earnhardt	172.712
2008	Ryan Newman	152.672
2013	Jimmie Johnson	159.250

91. How much slower was the average Daytona 500 winning speed in 2013 than in 1998?

92. How much faster was Bobby Allison's average Daytona 500 winning speed in 1978 than his average Daytona 500 winning speed in 1988?

The bar graph shows the top five chocolate-consuming nations in the world. Use this table to answer Exercises 93 through 97.

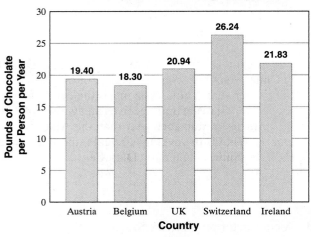

The World's Top Chocolate-Consuming Countries

Source: Confectionary News and Leatherhead Food Research

93. Which country in the table has the greatest chocolate consumption per person?

94. Which country in the table has the least chocolate consumption per person?

95. How much more is the greatest chocolate consumption than the least chocolate consumption shown in the table?

96. How much more chocolate does the average Irishman or woman consume per year than the average Austrian?

97. Make a new chart listing the countries and their corresponding chocolate consumptions in order from greatest to least.

Review

Multiply. See Sections 1.5 and 4.3.

98. $23 \cdot 2$

99. $46 \cdot 3$

100. $39 \cdot 3$

101. $\left(\dfrac{2}{3}\right)^2$

102. $\left(\dfrac{1}{5}\right)^3$

Concept Extensions

A friend asks you to check his calculations for Exercises 103 and 104. Are they correct? If not, explain your friend's errors and correct the calculations. See the first Concept Check in this section.

103.
$$
\begin{array}{r}
9.2 \\
8.63 \\
+\ 4.005 \\
\hline
4.960
\end{array}
$$

104.
$$
\begin{array}{r}
900.0 \\
-\ 96.4 \\
\hline
803.5
\end{array}
$$

Find the unknown length in each figure.

△**105.**

2.3 inches   ?   2.3 inches

10.68 inches

△**106.**

| ←5.26→ meters | ←7.82→ meters | ← ? → meters |

←17.67 meters→

Let's review the values of these common U.S. coins in order to answer the following exercises.

Penny Nickel Dime Quarter

$0.01 $0.05 $0.10 $0.25

For Exercises 107 and 108, write the value of each group of coins. To do so, it is usually easiest to start with the coin(s) of greatest value and end with the coin(s) of least value.

107.

108.

109. Name the different ways that coins can have a value of $0.17 given that you may use no more than 10 coins.

110. Name the different ways that coin(s) can have a value of $0.25 given that there are no pennies.

111. Why shouldn't the sum

  82.95 + 51.26

be estimated as 90 + 60 = 150?
See the second Concept Check in this section.

112. Laser beams can be used to measure the distance to the moon. One measurement showed the distance to the moon to be 256,435.235 miles. A later measurement showed that the distance is 256,436.012 miles. Find how much farther away the moon is in the second measurement as compared to the first.

113. Explain how adding or subtracting decimals is similar to adding or subtracting whole numbers.

114. Can the sum of two negative decimals ever be a positive decimal? Why or why not?

Combine like terms and simplify.

115. $-8.689 + 4.286x - 14.295 - 12.966x + 30.861x$

116. $14.271 - 8.968x + 1.333 - 201.815x + 101.239x$

Multiplying Decimals and Circumference of a Circle

Objectives

A Multiply Decimals.

B Estimate when Multiplying Decimals.

C Multiply Decimals by Powers of 10.

D Evaluate Expressions with Decimal Replacement Values.

E Find the Circumference of Circles.

F Solve Problems by Multiplying Decimals.

Objective A Multiplying Decimals

Multiplying decimals is similar to multiplying whole numbers. The only difference is that we place a decimal point in the product. To discover where a decimal point is placed in a product, let's multiply 0.6×0.03. We first write each decimal as an equivalent fraction and then multiply.

$$0.6 \quad \times \quad 0.03 \quad = \frac{6}{10} \times \frac{3}{100} = \frac{18}{1000} = 0.018$$

1 decimal place   2 decimal places   3 decimal places

Notice that $1 + 2 = 3$, the number of decimal places in the product. Now let's multiply 0.03×0.002.

$$0.03 \quad \times \quad 0.002 \quad = \frac{3}{100} \times \frac{2}{1000} = \frac{6}{100,000} = 0.00006$$

2 decimal place   3 decimal places   5 decimal places

Again, we see that $2 + 3 = 5$, the number of decimal places in the product.

Instead of writing decimals as fractions each time we want to multiply, we notice a pattern from these examples and state a rule that we can use:

Multiplying Decimals

Step 1: Multiply the decimals as though they are whole numbers.

Step 2: The decimal point in the product is placed so that the number of decimal places in the product is equal to the *sum* of the number of decimal places in the factors.

Practice 1

Multiply: 34.8×0.62

Example 1 Multiply: 23.6×0.78

Solution:

$$
\begin{array}{r}
23.6 \\
\times\ 0.78 \\
\hline
1888 \\
16520 \\
\hline
18.408
\end{array}
$$

23.6   1 decimal place
$\times$ 0.78   2 decimal places

Since $1 + 2 = 3$, insert the decimal point in the product so that there are 3 decimal places.

■ Work Practice 1

Practice 2

Multiply: 0.0641×27

Example 2 Multiply: 0.0531×16

Solution:

$$
\begin{array}{r}
0.0531 \\
\times\ \ \ \ 16 \\
\hline
3186 \\
5310 \\
\hline
0.8496
\end{array}
$$

0.0531   4 decimal places
$\times$ 16   0 decimal places

4 decimal places $(4 + 0 = 4)$

■ Work Practice 2

Answers

1. 21.576   **2.** 1.7307

✓**Concept Check** True or false? The number of decimal places in the product of 0.261 and 0.78 is 6. Explain.

Example 3 Multiply: $(-2.6)(0.8)$

Solution: Recall that the product of a negative number and a positive number is a negative number.

$$(-2.6)(0.8) = -2.08$$

■ Work Practice 3

Multiply: $(7.3)(-0.9)$

Objective B Estimating when Multiplying Decimals

Just as for addition and subtraction, we can estimate when multiplying decimals to check the reasonableness of our answer.

Example 4 Multiply: 28.06×1.95. Then estimate to see whether the answer is reasonable by rounding each factor, then multiplying the rounded numbers.

Solution:

Exact	**Estimate 1**	**or**	**Estimate 2**
28.06	28		30
× 1.95	× 2 Rounded to ones		× 2 Rounded to one nonzero digit
14030	56		60
252540			
280600			
54.7170			

The answer 54.7170 or 54.717 is reasonable.

■ Work Practice 4

Practice 4

Multiply: 30.26×2.89. Then estimate to see whether the answer is reasonable.

As shown in Example 4, estimated results will vary depending on what estimates are used. Notice that estimating results is a good way to see whether the decimal point has been correctly placed.

Objective C Multiplying Decimals by Powers of 10

There are some patterns that occur when we multiply a number by a power of 10 such as 10, 100, 1000, 10,000, and so on.

$23.6951 \times 10 = 236.951$ Move the decimal point *1 place* to the *right*.
⟍ 1 zero

$23.6951 \times 100 = 2369.51$ Move the decimal point *2 places* to the *right*.
⟍ 2 zeros

$23.6951 \times 100,000 = 2,369,510.$ Move the decimal point *5 places* to the *right* (insert a 0).
⟍ 5 zeros

Notice that we move the decimal point the same number of places as there are zeros in the power of 10.

Answers
3. -6.57 **4.** Exact: 87.4514; Estimate: $30 \cdot 3 = 90$

✓**Concept Check Answer**
false: 3 decimal places and 2 decimal places means 5 decimal places in the product

Multiplying Decimals by Powers of 10 Such as 10, 100, 1000, 10,000

Move the decimal point to the *right* the same number of places as there are *zeros* in the power of 10.

Practice 5–7

Practice 5–7

Multiply.

5. 46.8×10

6. 203.004×100

7. $(-2.33)(1000)$

Examples Multiply.

5. $7.68 \times 10 = 76.8$ 7.68

6. $23.702 \times 100 = 2370.2$ 23.702

7. $(-76.3)(1000) = -76,300$ 76.300

Work Practice 5–7

There are also powers of 10 that are less than 1. The decimals 0.1, 0.01, 0.001, 0.0001, and so on, are examples of powers of 10 less than 1. Notice the pattern when we multiply by these powers of 10:

$569.2 \times 0.1 = 56.92$ Move the decimal point *1 place* to the *left.*

1 decimal place

$569.2 \times 0.01 = 5.692$ Move the decimal point *2 places* to the *left.*

2 decimal places

$569.2 \times 0.0001 = 0.05692$ Move the decimal point *4 places* to the *left* (insert one 0).

4 decimal places

Multiplying Decimals by Powers of 10 Such as 0.1, 0.01, 0.001, 0.0001

Move the decimal point to the *left* the same number of places as there are *decimal places* in the power of 10.

Practice 8–10

Multiply.

8. 6.94×0.1

9. 3.9×0.01

10. $(-7682)(-0.001)$

Examples Multiply.

8. $42.1 \times 0.1 = 4.21$ 42.1

9. $76,805 \times 0.01 = 768.05$ 76,805.

10. $(-9.2)(-0.001) = 0.0092$ 0009.2

Work Practice 8–10

Answers

5. 468 **6.** 20,300.4 **7.** −2330
8. 0.694 **9.** 0.039 **10.** 7.682

Many times we see large numbers written, for example, in the form 297.9 million rather than in the longer standard notation. The next example shows us how to interpret these numbers.

Example 11 In 2050, the population of the United States is projected to be 420.3 million. Write this number in standard notation. (*Source:* U.S. Census Bureau)

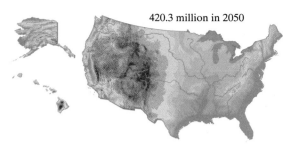

420.3 million in 2050

Solution: 420.3 million = 420.3 × 1 million

= 420.3 × 1,000,000 = 420,300,000

🔳 Work Practice 11

Practice 11

In 2012, there were 58.9 million married couples in the United States. Write this number in standard notation. (*Source:* U.S. Census Bureau)

Objective D Using Decimals as Replacement Values ▶

Now let's practice working with variables.

Example 12 Evaluate xy for $x = 2.3$ and $y = 0.44$.

Solution: Recall that xy means $x \cdot y$.

$xy = (2.3)(0.44)$

$$
\begin{array}{r}
2.3 \\
\times\, 0.44 \\
\hline
92 \\
920 \\
\hline
1.012
\end{array}
$$

$= 1.012 \longleftarrow 1.012$

🔳 Work Practice 12

Practice 12

Evaluate $7y$ for $y = -0.028$.

Example 13 Is -9 a solution of the equation $3.7y = -3.33$?

Solution: Replace y with -9 in the equation $3.7y = -3.33$ to see if a true equation results.

$$3.7y = -3.33$$
$$3.7(-9) \stackrel{?}{=} -3.33 \quad \text{Replace } y \text{ with } -9.$$
$$-33.3 = -3.33 \quad \text{False}$$

Since $-33.3 = -3.33$ is a false statement, -9 is **not** a solution of $3.7y = -3.33$.

🔳 Work Practice 13

Practice 13

Is -5.5 a solution of the equation $-6x = 33$?

Objective E Finding the Circumference of a Circle ▶

Recall from Section 1.3 that the distance around a polygon is called its perimeter. The distance around a circle is given the special name **circumference,** and this distance depends on the radius or the diameter of the circle.

Circumference of a Circle

Circumference = $2 \cdot \pi \cdot$ **r**adius or Circumference = $\pi \cdot$ **d**iameter

$$C = 2\pi r \quad \text{or} \quad C = \pi d$$

Answers
11. 58,900,000 **12.** −0.196 **13.** yes

In Section 5.1, we learned about the symbol π as the Greek letter pi, pronounced "pie." It is a constant between 3 and 4. A decimal approximation for π is 3.14. Also, a fraction approximation for π is $\frac{22}{7}$.

Practice 14

Find the circumference of a circle whose radius is 11 meters. Then use the approximation 3.14 for π to approximate this circumference.

△ **Example 14** Circumference of a Circle

Find the circumference of a circle whose radius is 5 inches. Then use the approximation 3.14 for π to approximate the circumference.

Solution: Let $r = 5$ in the formula $C = 2\pi r$.

$$C = 2\pi r$$
$$= 2\pi \cdot 5$$
$$= 10\pi$$

5 inches

Next, replace π with the approximation 3.14.

$$C = 10\pi$$
$$(\text{is approximately}) \longrightarrow \approx 10(3.14)$$
$$\approx 31.4$$

The **exact** circumference or distance around the circle is 10π inches, which is **approximately** 31.4 inches.

Work Practice 14

Objective F Solving Problems by Multiplying Decimals

The solutions to many real-life problems are found by multiplying decimals. We continue using our four problem-solving steps to solve such problems.

Practice 15

A biology major is fertilizing her personal garden. She uses 5.6 ounces of fertilizer per square yard. The garden measures 60.5 square yards. How much fertilizer does she need?

Example 15 Finding the Total Cost of Materials for a Job

A college student is hired to paint a billboard with paint costing $2.49 per quart. If the job requires 3 quarts of paint, what is the total cost of the paint?

Solution:

1. UNDERSTAND. Read and reread the problem. The phrase "total cost" might make us think addition, but since this problem requires repeated addition, let's multiply.

2. TRANSLATE.

In words:	total cost	is	cost per quart of paint	times	number of quarts
	↓	↓	↓	↓	↓
Translate:	total cost	=	2.49	×	3

3. SOLVE. We can estimate to check our calculations. The number 2.49 rounds to 2 and $2 \times 3 = 6$.

$$\begin{array}{r} 2.49 \\ \times \quad 3 \\ \hline 7.47 \end{array}$$

4. INTERPRET. *Check* your work. Since 7.47 is close to our estimate of 6, our answer is reasonable. *State* your conclusion: The total cost of the paint is $7.47.

Work Practice 15

Answers
14. 22π m $\approx$ 69.08 m   **15.** 338.8 oz

Vocabulary, Readiness & Video Check

Use the choices below to fill in each blank.

circumference	left	sum	zeros
decimal places	right	product	factor

1. When multiplying decimals, the number of decimal places in the product is equal to the _____ of the number of decimal places in the factors.
2. In $8.6 \times 5 = 43$, the number 43 is called the _____, while 8.6 and 5 are each called a _____.
3. When multiplying a decimal number by powers of 10 such as 10, 100, 1000, and so on, we move the decimal point in the number to the _____ the same number of places as there are _____ in the power of 10.
4. When multiplying a decimal number by powers of 10 such as 0.1, 0.01, and so on, we move the decimal point in the number to the _____ the same number of places as there are _____ in the power of 10.
5. The distance around a circle is called its _____.

Martin-Gay Interactive Videos

See Video 5.3

Watch the section lecture video and answer the following questions.

Objective A 6. From the lecture before ⊞ Example 1, what's the main difference between multiplying whole numbers and multiplying decimal numbers? ▶

Objective B 7. From ⊞ Example 3, what does estimating especially help us with? ▶

Objective C 8. Why don't we do any actual multiplying in ⊞ Example 5? ▶

Objective D 9. In ⊞ Example 8, once all replacement values are inserted in the variable expression, what is the resulting expression to evaluate? ▶

Objective E 10. Why is 31.4 cm not the exact answer to ⊞ Example 9? ▶

Objective F 11. In ⊞ Example 10, why is 24.8 not the complete answer? What is the complete answer? ▶

5.3 Exercise Set MyMathLab® ▶

Objectives A B Mixed Practice *Multiply. See Examples 1 through 4. For those exercises marked, also estimate to see if the answer is reasonable.*

1. 0.17×8

2. 0.23×9

3. $\begin{array}{r} 1.2 \\ \times\, 0.5 \\ \hline \end{array}$

4. $\begin{array}{r} 6.8 \\ \times\, 0.3 \\ \hline \end{array}$

▶ **5.** $(-2.3)(7.65)$

6. $(4.7)(-9.02)$

7. $(-5.73)(-9.6)$

8. $(-7.84)(-3.5)$

▶ **9.** 6.8×4.2
   Exact:
   Estimate:

10. 8.3×2.7
   Exact:
   Estimate:

11. $\begin{array}{r} 0.347 \\ \times\ \ 0.3 \\ \hline \end{array}$

12. $\begin{array}{r} 0.864 \\ \times\ \ 0.4 \\ \hline \end{array}$

13. 1.0047
$\times \quad 8.2$
Exact: _____ Estimate: _____

14. 2.0005
$\times \quad 5.5$
Exact: _____ Estimate: _____

15. 490.2
$\times 0.023$

16. 300.9
$\times 0.032$

Objective C Multiply. See Examples 5 through 10.

17. 6.5×10

18. 7.2×100

19. 8.3×0.1

20. 23.4×0.1

21. $(-7.093)(1000)$

22. $(-1.123)(1000)$

23. 0.7×100

24. 0.5×100

25. $(-9.83)(-0.01)$

26. $(-4.72)(-0.01)$

27. 25.23×0.001

28. 36.41×0.001

Objectives A B C Mixed Practice Multiply. See Examples 1 through 10.

29. 0.123×0.4

30. 0.216×0.3

31. $(147.9)(100)$

32. $(345.2)(100)$

33. 8.6×0.15

34. 0.42×5.7

35. $(937.62)(-0.01)$

36. $(-0.001)(562.01)$

37. 562.3×0.001

38. 993.5×0.001

39. 6.32
$\times 5.7$

40. 9.21
$\times 3.8$

Write each number in standard notation. See Example 11.

41. The cost of the Hubble Space Telescope at launch was $1.5 billion. (*Source:* NASA)

42. About 56.7 million American households own at least one dog. (*Source:* American Pet Products Manufacturers Association)

43. The Blue Streak is the oldest roller coaster at Cedar Point, an amusement park in Sandusky, Ohio. Since 1964, it has given more than 49.8 million rides. (*Source:* Cedar Fair, L.P.)

44. In 2013, the restaurant industry had projected sales of $660.5 billion. (*Source:* National Restaurant Association)

Objective D Evaluate each expression for $x = 3$, $y = -0.2$, and $z = 5.7$. See Example 12.

45. xy

46. yz

47. $xz - y$

48. $-5y + z$

Determine whether the given value is a solution of each given equation. See Example 13.

49. Is 14.2 a solution of $0.6x = 4.92$?

50. Is 1414 a solution of $100z = 14.14$?

51. Is -4 a solution of $3.5y = -14$?

52. Is -3.6 a solution of $0.7x = -2.52$?

Objective E Find the circumference of each circle. Then use the approximation 3.14 for π and approximate each circumference. See Example 14.

53.

10 centimeters

△ **54.**

22 inches

△ **55.**

9.1 yards

△ **56.**

5.9 kilometers

Objectives E F Mixed Practice *Solve. For Exercises 57 and 58, the solutions have been started for you. For circumference applications find the exact circumference and then use 3.14 for π to approximate the circumference. See Examples 14 and 15.*

57. An electrician for Central Power and Light worked 40 hours last week. Calculate his pay before taxes for last week if his hourly wage is $17.88.

Start the solution:

1. UNDERSTAND the problem. Reread it as many times as needed.
2. TRANSLATE into an equation. (Fill in the blanks.)

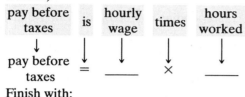

Finish with:

3. SOLVE and 4. INTERPRET.

58. An assembly line worker worked 20 hours last week. Her hourly rate is $19.52 per hour. Calculate her pay before taxes.

Start the solution:

1. UNDERSTAND the problem. Reread it as many times as needed.
2. TRANSLATE into an equation. (Fill in the blanks.)

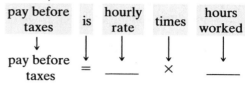

Finish with:

3. SOLVE and 4. INTERPRET.

59. A 1-ounce serving of cream cheese contains 6.2 grams of saturated fat. How much saturated fat is in 4 ounces of cream cheese? (*Source: Home and Garden Bulletin No. 72;* U.S. Department of Agriculture)

60. A 3.5-ounce serving of lobster meat contains 0.1 gram of saturated fat. How much saturated fat do 3 servings of lobster meat contain? (*Source:* The National Institutes of Health)

61. Recall that the face of the Apple iPhone 5 (see Section 5.2) measures 4.87 inches by 2.3 inches rounded. Find the approximate area of the face of the Apple iPhone 5.

62. Recall that the face of the Google Nexus 4 (see Section 5.2) measures 5.27 inches by 2.7 inches. Find the area of the face of the Google Nexus 4.

63. In 1893, the first ride called a Ferris wheel was constructed by Washington Gale Ferris. Its diameter was 250 feet. Find its circumference. Give an exact answer and an approximation using 3.14 for π. (*Source: The Handy Science Answer Book,* Visible Ink Press, 1994)

64. The radius of Earth is approximately 3950 miles. Find the distance around Earth at the equator. Give an exact answer and an approximation using 3.14 for π. (*Hint:* Find the circumference of a circle with radius 3950 miles.)

65. The London Eye, built for the millennium celebration in London, resembles a gigantic Ferris wheel with a diameter of 135 meters. If Adam Hawn rides the Eye for one revolution, find how far he travels. Give an exact answer and an approximation using 3.14 for π. (*Source:* Londoneye.com)

66. The world's longest suspension bridge is the Akashi Kaikyo Bridge in Japan. This bridge has two circular caissons, which are underwater foundations. If the diameter of a caisson is 80 meters, find its circumference. Give an exact answer and an approximation using 3.14 for π. (*Source: Scientific American;* How Things Work Today)

67. A meter is a unit of length in the metric system that is approximately equal to 39.37 inches. Sophia Wagner is 1.65 meters tall. Find her approximate height in inches.

68. The doorway to a room is 2.15 meters tall. Approximate this height in inches. (*Hint:* See Exercise **67.**)

△ **69. a.** Approximate the circumference of each circle.

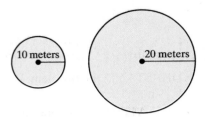

b. If radius of a circle is doubled, is its corresponding circumference doubled?

△ **70. a.** Approximate the circumference of each circle.

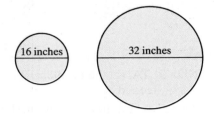

b. If the diameter of a circle is doubled, is its corresponding circumference doubled?

71. In 2011, the price of wheat was $7.30 per bushel. How much would 100 bushels of wheat cost at this price?(*Source:* National Agricultural Statistics Service)

72. In 2011, the price of soybeans was $11.70 per bushel. How much would a company pay for 10,000 bushels of soybeans?(*Source:* National Agricultural Statistics Service)

The table shows currency exchange rates for various countries on August 26, 2013. To find the amount of foreign currency equivalent to an amount of U.S. dollars, multiply the U.S. dollar amount by the exchange rate listed in the table. Use this table to answer Exercises 73 through 76. If needed, round answers to the nearest hundredth.

Foreign Currency Exchange Rates	
Country	**Exchange Rate**
Canadian dollar	1.04920
European Union euro	0.74697
New Zealand dollar	1.28084
Chinese yuan	6.15231
Japanese yen	98.68
Swiss franc	0.92090

73. How many Canadian dollars are equivalent to $750 U.S.?

74. Suppose you wish to exchange 300 American dollars for Chinese yuan. How much money, in Chinese yuan, would you receive?

75. The Scarpulla family is traveling to New Zealand. How many New Zealand dollars can they "buy" with 800 U.S. dollars?

76. A French tourist to the United States spent $130 for souvenirs at the *Head of the Charles Regatta* in Boston. How much money did he spend in euros? Round to the nearest hundredth.

Review

Divide. See Sections 1.6 and 4.3.

77. $2916 \div 6$

78. $2920 \div 365$

79. $-\dfrac{24}{7} \div \dfrac{8}{21}$

80. $\dfrac{162}{25} \div -\dfrac{9}{75}$

Concept Extensions

Mixed Practice (Sections 5.2, 5.3) *Perform the indicated operations.*

81. $3.6 + 0.04$

82. $7.2 + 0.14 + 98.6$

83. $3.6 - 0.04$

84. $100 - 48.6$

85. -0.221×0.5

86. -3.6×0.04

87. Find how far radio waves travel in 20.6 seconds. (Radio waves travel at a speed of 186,000 miles per second.)

88. If it takes radio waves approximately 8.3 minutes to travel from the sun to the earth, find approximately how far it is from the sun to the earth. (*Hint:* See Exercise **87.**)

89. In your own words, explain how to find the number of decimal places in a product of decimal numbers.

90. In your own words, explain how to multiply by a power of 10.

91. Write down two decimal numbers whose product will contain 5 decimal places. Without multiplying, explain how you know your answer is correct.

5.4 Dividing Decimals

Objective A Dividing Decimals

Dividing decimal numbers is similar to dividing whole numbers. The only difference is that we place a decimal point in the quotient. If the divisor is a whole number, we place the decimal point in the quotient directly above the decimal point in the dividend, and then divide as with whole numbers. Recall that division can be checked by multiplication.

Objectives

A Divide Decimals.

B Estimate when Dividing Decimals.

C Divide Decimals by Powers of 10.

D Evaluate Expressions with Decimal Replacement Values.

E Solve Problems by Dividing Decimals.

Example 1 Divide: $270.2 \div 7$. Check your answer.

Solution: We divide as usual. The decimal point in the quotient is directly above the decimal point in the dividend.

```
                  ┌─ Write the decimal point
                  ↓
              38.6   ← quotient
divisor →  7)270.2   ← dividend
             −21↓
              60
             −56↓
              4 2
             −4 2
                0
```

Check:
```
     6 4
    38.6
  ×    7
  ─────
   270.2
```

The quotient is 38.6.

■ Work Practice 1

Practice 1

Divide: $370.4 \div 8$. Check your answer.

Example 2 Divide: $32\overline{)8.32}$

Solution: We divide as usual. The decimal point in the quotient is directly above the decimal point in the dividend.

```
                     0.26   ← quotient
dividend → 32)8.32          ← divisor
            −64
            192
           −192
              0
```

Check:
```
    0.26   quotient
  ×  32    divisor
  ─────
    52
   7 80
   ─────
   8.32    dividend
```

Practice 2

Divide: $48\overline{)34.08}$. Check your answer.

■ Work Practice 2

Answers
1. 46.3   **2.** 0.71

Sometimes to continue dividing we need to insert zeros after the last digit in the dividend.

Practice 3

Divide and check.
a. $-15.89 \div 14$
b. $-2.808 \div (-104)$

Example 3 Divide: $-5.98 \div 115$

Solution: Recall that a negative number divided by a positive number gives a negative quotient.

$$
\begin{array}{r}
0.052 \\
115\overline{)5.980} \quad \leftarrow \text{Insert one 0.} \\
\underline{-575} \\
230 \\
\underline{-230} \\
0
\end{array}
$$

Thus $-5.98 \div 115 = -0.052$.

■ Work Practice 3

If the divisor is not a whole number, before we divide we need to move the decimal point to the right until the divisor is a whole number.

$$1.5\overline{)64.85}$$

divisor ↑   ↑ dividend

To understand how this works, let's rewrite

$1.5\overline{)64.85}$ as $\dfrac{64.85}{1.5}$

and then multiply by 1 in the form of $\dfrac{10}{10}$. We use the form $\dfrac{10}{10}$ so that the denominator (divisor) becomes a whole number.

$$\frac{64.85}{1.5} = \frac{64.85}{1.5} \cdot 1 = \frac{64.85}{1.5} \cdot \frac{10}{10} = \frac{64.85 \cdot 10}{1.5 \cdot 10} = \frac{648.5}{15},$$

which can be written as $15.\overline{)648.5}$. Notice that

$1.5\overline{)64.85}$ is equivalent to $15.\overline{)648.5}$

The decimal points in the dividend and the divisor were both moved one place to the right, and the divisor is now a whole number. This procedure is summarized next:

Dividing by a Decimal

Step 1: Move the decimal point in the divisor to the right until the divisor is a whole number.

Step 2: Move the decimal point in the dividend to the right the *same number of places* as the decimal point was moved in Step 1.

Step 3: Divide. Place the decimal point in the quotient directly over the moved decimal point in the dividend.

Answers
3. a. -1.135 **b.** 0.027

Example 4 Divide: $10.764 \div 2.3$

Solution: We move the decimal points in the divisor and the dividend one place to the right so that the divisor is a whole number.

$$2.3\overline{)10.764}$$

becomes

$$
\begin{array}{r}
4.68 \\
23\overline{)107.64} \\
-92 \\
\hline
15\,6 \\
-13\,8 \\
\hline
1\,84 \\
-1\,84 \\
\hline
0
\end{array}
$$

◼ Work Practice 4

Example 5 Divide: $5.264 \div 0.32$

Solution:

$$0.32\overline{)5.264}$$

becomes

$$
\begin{array}{r}
16.45 \\
32\overline{)526.40} \\
-32 \\
\hline
206 \\
-192 \\
\hline
14\,4 \\
-12\,8 \\
\hline
1\,60 \\
-1\,60 \\
\hline
0
\end{array}
$$

Insert one 0.

◼ Work Practice 5

✓**Concept Check** Is it always true that the number of decimal places in a quotient equals the sum of the decimal places in the dividend and divisor?

Example 6 Divide: $17.5 \div 0.48$. Round the quotient to the nearest hundredth.

Solution: First we move the decimal points in the divisor and the dividend two places. Then we divide and round the quotient to the nearest hundredth.

hundredths place

$$
\begin{array}{r}
36.458 \approx 36.46 \\
48\overline{)1750.000} \\
-144 \\
\hline
310 \\
-288 \\
\hline
22\,0 \\
-19\,2 \\
\hline
2\,80 \\
-2\,40 \\
\hline
400 \\
-384 \\
\hline
16
\end{array}
$$

"is approximately"

When rounding to the nearest hundredth, carry the division process out to one more decimal place, the thousandths place.

◼ Work Practice 6

Practice 4
Divide: $166.88 \div 5.6$

Practice 5
Divide: $1.976 \div 0.16$

Practice 6
Divide: $23.4 \div 0.57$. Round the quotient to the nearest hundredth.

Answers
4. 29.8 **5.** 12.35 **6.** 41.05

✓**Concept Check Answer**
no

✓**Concept Check** If a quotient is to be rounded to the nearest thousandth, to what place should the division be carried out? (Assume that the division carries out to your answer.)

Objective B Estimating when Dividing Decimals

Just as for addition, subtraction, and multiplication of decimals, we can estimate when dividing decimals to check the reasonableness of our answer.

Practice 7

Divide: $713.7 \div 91.5$. Then estimate to see whether the proposed answer is reasonable.

Example 7 Divide: $272.356 \div 28.4$. Then estimate to see whether the proposed result is reasonable.

Solution:

Exact:	**Estimate 1**		**Estimate 2**

$$\begin{array}{r} 9.59 \\ 284.\overline{)2723.56} \\ -2556 \\ \hline 167\,5 \\ -142\,0 \\ \hline 25\,56 \\ -25\,56 \\ \hline 0 \end{array}$$

$$\begin{array}{r} 9 \\ 30\overline{)270} \end{array} \quad \text{or} \quad \begin{array}{r} 10 \\ 30\overline{)300} \end{array}$$

The estimate is 9 or 10, so 9.59 is reasonable.

🔳 Work Practice 7

Objective C Dividing Decimals by Powers of 10

As with multiplication, there are patterns that occur when we divide decimals by powers of 10 such as 10, 100, 1000, and so on.

$$\frac{569.2}{10} = 56.92 \qquad \text{Move the decimal point } \textit{1 place} \text{ to the } \textit{left.}$$

  1 zero

$$\frac{569.2}{10,000} = 0.05692 \qquad \text{Move the decimal point } \textit{4 places} \text{ to the } \textit{left.}$$

  4 zeros

This pattern suggests the following rule:

> **Dividing Decimals by Powers of 10 Such as 10, 100, or 1000**
>
> Move the decimal point of the dividend to the *left* the same number of places as there are *zeros* in the power of 10.

Practice 8–9

Divide.

8. $\dfrac{362.1}{1000}$ **9.** $-\dfrac{0.49}{10}$

Answers

7. 7.8   **8.** 0.3621   **9.** −0.049

✓**Concept Check Answer**

ten-thousandths place

Examples Divide.

8. $\dfrac{786.1}{1000} = 0.7861$ Move the decimal point *3 places* to the *left.*

  3 zeros

9. $\dfrac{0.12}{10} = 0.012$ Move the decimal point *1 place* to the *left.*

  1 zero

🔳 Work Practice 8–9

Objective D Using Decimals as Replacement Values

Example 10 Evaluate $x \div y$ for $x = 2.5$ and $y = 0.05$.

Solution: Replace x with 2.5 and y with 0.05.

$$x \div y = 2.5 \div 0.05 \qquad 0.05\overline{)2.5} \text{ becomes } 5\overline{)250} \;\;{}^{50}$$
$$= 50$$

■ Work Practice 10

Practice 10

Evaluate $x \div y$ for $x = 0.035$ and $y = 0.02$.

Example 11 Is 720 a solution of the equation $\dfrac{y}{100} = 7.2$?

Solution: Replace y with 720 to see if a true statement results.

$$\frac{y}{100} = 7.2 \quad \text{Original equation}$$

$$\frac{720}{100} \overset{?}{=} 7.2 \quad \text{Replace } y \text{ with 720.}$$

$$7.2 = 7.2 \quad \text{True}$$

Since $7.2 = 7.2$ is a true statement, 720 is a solution of the equation.

■ Work Practice 11

Practice 11

Is 39 a solution of the equation

$$\frac{x}{100} = 3.9?$$

Objective E Solving Problems by Dividing Decimals

Many real-life problems involve dividing decimals.

△ **Example 12** Calculating Materials Needed for a Job

A gallon of paint covers a 250-square-foot area. If Betty Adkins wishes to paint a wall that measures 1450 square feet, how many gallons of paint does she need? If she can buy only gallon containers of paint, how many gallon containers does she need?

Solution:

1. UNDERSTAND. Read and reread the problem. We need to know how many 250s are in 1450, so we divide.
2. TRANSLATE.

In words:	number of gallons	is	square feet	divided by	square feet per gallon
	↓	↓	↓	↓	↓
Translate:	number of gallons	=	1450	÷	250

3. SOLVE. Let's see if our answer is reasonable by estimating. The dividend 1450 rounds to 1500 and the divisor 250 rounds to 300. Then $1500 \div 300 = 5$.

```
        5.8
250)1450.0
   -1250
     200 0
   - 200 0
           0
```

Practice 12

A bag of fertilizer covers 1250 square feet of lawn. Tim Parker's lawn measures 14,800 square feet. How many bags of fertilizer does he need? If he can buy only whole bags of fertilizer, how many whole bags does he need?

Answers
10. 1.75   **11.** no
12. 11.84 bags; 12 bags

(Continued on next page)

4. INTERPRET. *Check* your work. Since our estimate is close to our answer of 5, our answer is reasonable. *State* your conclusion: Betty needs 5.8 gallons of paint. If she can buy only gallon containers of paint, she needs 6 gallon containers of paint to complete the job.

■ Work Practice 12

 ## Calculator Explorations Estimation

Calculator errors can easily be made by pressing an incorrect key or by not pressing a correct key hard enough. Estimation is a valuable tool that can be used to check calculator results.

Example Use estimation to determine whether the calculator result is reasonable or not. (For example, a result that is not reasonable can occur if proper keys are not pressed.)

Divide: 82.064 ÷ 23
Calculator display: | 35.68 |

Solution: Round each number to the nearest 10. Since 80 ÷ 20 = 4, the calculator display 35.68 is not reasonable.

Use estimation to determine whether each result is reasonable or not.

1. 102.62 × 41.8; Result: 428.9516

2. 174.835 ÷ 47.9; Result: 3.65

3. 1025.68 − 125.42; Result: 900.26

4. 562.781 + 2.96; Result: 858.781

Vocabulary, Readiness & Video Check

Use the choices below to fill in each blank. Some choices may be used more than once, and some not used at all.

dividend	divisor	quotient	true
zeros	left	right	false

1. In 6.5 ÷ 5 = 1.3, the number 1.3 is called the _____ , 5 is the _____ , and 6.5 is the _____ .

2. To check a division exercise, we can perform the following multiplication: quotient · _____ = _____ .

3. To divide a decimal number by a power of 10 such as 10, 100, 1000, and so on, we move the decimal point in the number to the _____ the same number of places as there are _____ in the power of 10.

4. True or false: If we replace x with -12.6 and y with 0.3 in the expression $y \div x$, we have $0.3 \div (-12.6)$. _____

Martin-Gay Interactive Videos

See Video 5.4 ●

Watch the section lecture video and answer the following questions.

Objective A **5.** From the lecture before ▭ Example 1, what must we make sure the divisor is before dividing decimals? ▶

Objective B **6.** From ▭ Example 4, what does estimating especially help us with? ▶

Objective C **7.** Why don't we do any actual dividing in ▭ Example 5? ▶

Objective D **8.** In ▭ Example 6, 4 does not divide into 1. How does this affect the quotient? ▶

Objective E **9.** In ▭ Example 7, why is the division carried to the hundredths place? ▶

5.4 Exercise Set MyMathLab®

Objectives A B Mixed Practice *Divide. See Examples 1 through 5 and 7. For those exercises marked, also estimate to see if the answer is reasonable.*

1. $6\overline{)27.6}$

2. $4\overline{)23.6}$

3. $5\overline{)0.47}$

4. $6\overline{)0.51}$

5. $0.06\overline{)18}$

6. $0.04\overline{)20}$

7. $0.42\overline{)3.066}$

8. $0.36\overline{)1.764}$

9. $5.5\overline{)36.3}$
   Exact:
   Estimate:

10. $2.2\overline{)21.78}$
    Exact:
    Estimate:

11. $7.434 \div 18$

12. $8.304 \div 16$

13. $36 \div (-0.06)$

14. $36 \div (-0.04)$

15. Divide -4.2 by -0.6.

16. Divide -3.6 by -0.9.

17. $0.27\overline{)1.296}$

18. $0.34\overline{)2.176}$

19. $0.02\overline{)42}$

20. $0.03\overline{)24}$

21. $4.756 \div 0.82$

22. $3.312 \div 0.92$

23. $-36.3 \div (-6.6)$

24. $-21.78 \div (-9.9)$

25. $7.2\overline{)70.56}$
    Exact:
    Estimate:

26. $6.3\overline{)54.18}$
    Exact:
    Estimate:

27. $5.4\overline{)51.84}$

28. $7.7\overline{)33.88}$

29. $\dfrac{1.215}{0.027}$

30. $\dfrac{3.213}{0.051}$

31. $0.25\overline{)13.648}$

32. $0.75\overline{)49.866}$

33. $3.78\overline{)0.02079}$

34. $2.96\overline{)0.01332}$

Divide. Round the quotients as indicated. See Example 6.

35. Divide: $0.549 \div 0.023$. Round the quotient to the nearest hundredth.

36. Divide: $0.0453 \div 0.98$. Round the quotient to the nearest thousandth.

37. Divide: $68.39 \div 0.6$. Round the quotient to the nearest tenth.

38. Divide: $98.83 \div 3.5$. Round the quotient to the nearest tenth.

Objective C *Divide. See Examples 8 and 9.*

39. $\dfrac{83.397}{100}$

40. $\dfrac{64.423}{100}$

41. $\dfrac{26.87}{10}$

42. $\dfrac{13.49}{10}$

43. $12.9 \div (-1000)$

44. $13.49 \div (-10,000)$

Objectives A C Mixed Practice *Divide. See Examples 1 through 5, 8, and 9.*

45. $7\overline{)88.2}$

46. $9\overline{)130.5}$

47. $\dfrac{13.1}{10}$

48. $\dfrac{17.7}{10}$

49. $\dfrac{456.25}{10,000}$

50. $\dfrac{986.11}{10,000}$

51. $1.239 \div 3$

52. $0.54 \div 12$

53. Divide 4.8 by −0.6.   **54.** Divide 4.9 by −0.7.   **55.** −1.224 ÷ 0.17   **56.** −1.344 ÷ 0.42

57. Divide 42 by 0.03.   **58.** Divide 27 by 0.03.   **59.** Divide −18 by −0.6.   **60.** Divide 20 by 0.4.

61. Divide 87 by −0.0015.   **62.** Divide 35 by −0.0007.   **63.** −1.104 ÷ 1.6   **64.** −2.156 ÷ 0.98

65. −2.4 ÷ (−100)   **66.** −86.79 ÷ (−1000)   **67.** $\dfrac{4.615}{0.071}$ **68.** $\dfrac{23.8}{0.035}$

Objective D *Evaluate each expression for $x = 5.65$, $y = -0.8$, and $z = 4.52$. See Example 10.*

69. $z \div y$ **70.** $z \div x$ **71.** $x \div y$ **72.** $y \div 2$

Determine whether the given values are solutions of the given equations. See Example 11.

73. $\dfrac{x}{4} = 3.04$; $x = 12.16$ **74.** $\dfrac{y}{8} = 0.89$; $y = 7.12$ **75.** $\dfrac{z}{100} = 0.8$; $z = 8$ **76.** $\dfrac{x}{10} = 0.23$; $x = 23$

Objective E *Solve. For Exercises 77 and 78, the solutions have been started for you. See Example 12.*

77. A new homeowner is painting the walls of a room. The walls have a total area of 546 square feet. A quart of paint covers 52 square feet. If the paint is sold in whole quarts only, how many quarts are needed?

Start the solution:

1. UNDERSTAND the problem. Reread it as many times as needed.
2. TRANSLATE into an equation. (Fill in the blanks.)

number of quarts	is	square feet	divided by	square feet per quart
↓	↓	↓	↓	↓

number of quarts = _____ ÷ _____

3. SOLVE. Don't forget to round up your quotient.
4. INTERPRET.

78. A shipping box can hold 36 books. If 486 books must be shipped, how many boxes are needed?

Start the solution:

1. UNDERSTAND the problem. Reread it as many times as needed.
2. TRANSLATE into an equation. (Fill in the blanks.)

number of boxes	is	number of books	divided by	books per box
↓	↓	↓	↓	↓

number of boxes = _____ ÷ _____

3. SOLVE. Don't forget to round up your quotient.
4. INTERPRET.

79. There are approximately 39.37 inches in 1 meter. How many meters, to the nearest tenth of a meter, are there in 200 inches?

80. There are 2.54 centimeters in 1 inch. How many inches are there in 50 centimeters? Round to the nearest tenth.

← 1 inch →
← 2.54 cm →

81. In the United States, an average child will wear down 730 crayons by his or her tenth birthday. Find the number of boxes of 64 crayons this is equivalent to. Round to the nearest tenth. (*Source:* Binney & Smith Inc.)

82. In 2011, American farmers received an average of $68.20 per hundred pounds of turkey. What was the average price per pound for turkeys? Round to the nearest cent. (*Source:* National Agricultural Statistics Service)

A child is to receive a dose of 0.5 teaspoon of cough medicine every 4 hours. If the bottle contains 4 fluid ounces, answer Exercises 83 through 86.

83. A fluid ounce equals 6 teaspoons. How many teaspoons are in 4 fluid ounces?

84. The bottle of medicine contains how many doses for the child? (*Hint:* See Exercise **83**.)

85. If the child takes a dose every four hours, how many days will the medicine last?

86. If the child takes a dose every six hours, how many days will the medicine last?

87. Americans ages 16–19 drive, on average, 7624 miles per year. About how many miles each week is that? Round to the nearest tenth. (*Note:* There are 52 weeks in a year.) (*Source:* Federal Highway Administration)

88. Drake Saucier was interested in the gas mileage on his "new" used car. He filled the tank, drove 423.8 miles, and filled the tank again. When he refilled the tank, it took 19.35 gallons of gas. Calculate the miles per gallon for Drake's car. Round to the nearest tenth.

89. The book *Harry Potter and the Deathly Hallows* was released to the public on July 21, 2007. Booksellers in the United States sold approximately 8292 thousand copies in the first 24 hours after release. If the same number of books was sold each hour, calculate the number of books sold each hour in the United States for that first day.

90. The leading money winner in men's professional golf in 2012 was Rory McIlroy. He earned approximately $8,048,000. Suppose he had earned this working 40 hours each week for a year. Determine his hourly wage to the nearest cent. (*Note:* There are 52 weeks in a year.) (*Source:* Professional Golfers' Association)

Review

Perform the indicated operation. See Sections 4.3 and 4.5.

91. $\dfrac{3}{5} \cdot \dfrac{7}{10}$

92. $\dfrac{3}{5} \div \dfrac{7}{10}$

93. $\dfrac{3}{5} - \dfrac{7}{10}$

94. $-\dfrac{3}{4} - \dfrac{1}{14}$

Concept Extensions

Mixed Practice (Sections 5.2, 5.3, 5.4) *Perform the indicated operation.*

95. $1.278 \div 0.3$

96. 1.278×0.3

97. $1.278 + 0.3$

98. $1.278 - 0.3$

99. $(-8.6)(3.1)$

100. $7.2 + 0.05 + 49.1$

101. $\begin{array}{r} 1000 \\ -95.71 \\ \hline \end{array}$

102. $\dfrac{87.2}{-10{,}000}$

Choose the best estimate.

103. 8.62×41.7
  a. 36
  b. 32
  c. 360
  d. 3.6

104. $1.437 + 20.69$
  a. 34
  b. 22
  c. 3.4
  d. 2.2

105. $78.6 \div 97$
  a. 7.86
  b. 0.786
  c. 786
  d. 7860

106. $302.729 - 28.697$
  a. 270
  b. 20
  c. 27
  d. 300

Recall from Section 1.6 that the average of a list of numbers is their total divided by how many numbers there are in the list. Use this procedure to find the average of the test scores listed in Exercises 107 and 108. If necessary, round to the nearest tenth.

107. 86, 78, 91, 87

108. 56, 75, 80

△ **109.** The area of a rectangle is 38.7 square feet. If its width is 4.5 feet, find its length.

△ **110.** The perimeter of a square is 180.8 centimeters. Find the length of a side.

111. When dividing decimals, describe the process you use to place the decimal point in the quotient.

112. In your own words, describe how to quickly divide a number by a power of 10 such as 10, 100, 1000, etc.

To convert wind speeds in miles per hour to knots, divide by 1.15. Use this information and the Saffir-Simpson Hurricane Intensity chart below to answer Exercises 113 and 114. Round to the nearest tenth.

		Saffir-Simpson Hurricane Intensity Scale		
Category	**Wind Speed**	**Barometric Pressure [inches of mercury (Hg)]**	**Storm Surge**	**Damage Potential**
1 (Weak)	75–95 mph	≥28.94 in.	4–5 ft	Minimal damage to vegetation
2 (Moderate)	96–110 mph	28.50–28.93 in.	6–8 ft	Moderate damage to houses
3 (Strong)	111–130 mph	27.91–28.49 in.	9–12 ft	Extensive damage to small buildings
4 (Very Strong)	131–155 mph	27.17–27.90 in.	13–18 ft	Extreme structural damage
5 (Devastating)	>155 mph	<27.17 in.	>18 ft	Catastrophic building failures possible

113. The chart gives wind speeds in miles per hour. What is the range of wind speeds for a Category 1 hurricane in knots?

114. What is the range of wind speeds for a Category 4 hurricane in knots?

△ **115.** A rancher is building a horse corral that's shaped like a rectangle with a width of 24.3 meters. He plans to make a four-wire fence; that is, he will string four wires around the corral. If he plans to use all of his 412.8 meters of wire, find the length of the corral he can construct.

116. A college student signed up for a new credit card that guarantees her no interest charges on transferred balances for a year. She transferred over a $2523.86 balance from her old credit card. Her minimum payment is $185.35 per month. If she pays only the minimum, will she pay off her balance before interest charges start again?

Operations on Decimals

Perform the indicated operation.

Answers

1. $1.6 + 0.97$ **2.** $3.2 + 0.85$ **3.** $9.8 - 0.9$ **4.** $10.2 - 6.7$

1. _____

2. _____

3. _____

4. _____

5. $\begin{array}{r} 0.8 \\ \times\, 0.2 \\ \hline \end{array}$ **6.** $\begin{array}{r} 0.6 \\ \times\, 0.4 \\ \hline \end{array}$ **7.** $8\overline{)2.16}$ **8.** $6\overline{)3.12}$

5. _____

6. _____

7. _____

8. _____

9. $(9.6)(-0.5)$ **10.** $(-8.7)(-0.7)$ **11.** $\begin{array}{r} 123.6 \\ -\ 48.04 \\ \hline \end{array}$ **12.** $\begin{array}{r} 325.2 \\ -\ 36.08 \\ \hline \end{array}$

9. _____

10. _____

11. _____

12. _____

13. _____

13. $-25 + 0.026$ **14.** $0.125 + (-44)$ **15.** $29.24 \div (-3.4)$ **16.** $-10.26 \div (-1.9)$

14. _____

15. _____

16. _____

17. _____

17. -2.8×100 **18.** 1.6×1000 **19.** $\begin{array}{r} 96.21 \\ 7.028 \\ +\ 121.7 \\ \hline \end{array}$ **20.** $\begin{array}{r} 0.268 \\ 1.93 \\ +\ 142.881 \\ \hline \end{array}$

18. _____

19. _____

20. _____

21. _____

22. _____

23. _____

21. $-25.76 \div (-46)$ **22.** $-27.09 \div 43$ **23.** $\begin{array}{r} 12.004 \\ \times\ \ 2.3 \\ \hline \end{array}$ **24.** $\begin{array}{r} 28.006 \\ \times\ \ 5.2 \\ \hline \end{array}$

24. _____

25. _____

26. _____

27. _____

28. _____

29. _____

30. _____

31. _____

32. _____

33. _____

34. _____

35. _____

36. _____

37. _____

38. _____

39. _____

25. Subtract 4.6 from 10.   **26.** Subtract 18 from 0.26.   **27.** $-268.19 - 146.25$

28. $-860.18 - 434.85$ **29.** $\dfrac{2.958}{-0.087}$ **30.** $\dfrac{-1.708}{0.061}$

31. $160 - 43.19$ **32.** $120 - 101.21$ **33.** 15.62×10

34. $15.62 \div 10$ **35.** $15.62 + 10$ **36.** $15.62 - 10$

37. Find the distance in miles between Garden City, Kansas, and Wichita, Kansas. Next, estimate the distance by rounding each given distance to the nearest ten.

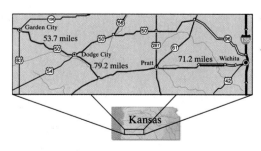

38. It costs $7.29 to send a 5-pound package locally via parcel post at a U.S. Post Office. To send the same package Priority Mail costs $8.10. How much more does it cost to send a package as Priority Mail? (*Source:* United States Postal Service)

39. In 2011, sales of Blu-ray Discs were $2 billion, but DVD sales dropped to $6.8 billion. Find the total spent to buy Blu-ray Discs or DVDs in 2011. Write the total in billions of dollars and also in standard notation. (*Source: USA Today*)

5.5 Fractions, Decimals, and Order of Operations

Objective A Writing Fractions as Decimals

To write a fraction as a decimal, we interpret the fraction bar to mean division and find the quotient.

Objectives

A Write Fractions as Decimals.

B Compare Decimals and Fractions.

C Simplify Expressions Containing Decimals and Fractions Using Order of Operations.

D Solve Area Problems Containing Fractions and Decimals.

E Evaluate Expressions Given Decimal Replacement Values.

> **Writing Fractions as Decimals**
>
> To write a fraction as a decimal, divide the numerator by the denominator.

Example 1 Write $\frac{1}{4}$ as a decimal.

Solution: $\frac{1}{4} = 1 \div 4$

$$
\begin{array}{r}
0.25 \\
4\overline{)1.00} \\
-8 \\
\hline
20 \\
-20 \\
\hline
0
\end{array}
$$

Thus, $\frac{1}{4}$ written as a decimal is 0.25.

■ Work Practice 1

Example 2 Write $-\frac{5}{8}$ as a decimal.

Solution: $-\frac{5}{8} = -(5 \div 8) = -0.625$

$$
\begin{array}{r}
0.625 \\
8\overline{)5.000} \\
-48 \\
\hline
20 \\
-16 \\
\hline
40 \\
-40 \\
\hline
0
\end{array}
$$

■ Work Practice 2

Example 3 Write $\frac{2}{3}$ as a decimal.

Solution:

$$
\begin{array}{r}
0.666\ldots \\
3\overline{)2.000} \\
-18 \\
\hline
20 \\
-18 \\
\hline
20 \\
-18 \\
\hline
2
\end{array}
$$

Remainder is 2, then 0 is brought down.

Remainder is 2, then 0 is brought down.

Remainder is 2.

(Continued on next page)

Practice 1

a. Write $\frac{2}{5}$ as a decimal.

b. Write $\frac{9}{40}$ as a decimal.

Practice 2

Write $-\frac{3}{8}$ as a decimal.

Practice 3

a. Write $\frac{5}{6}$ as a decimal.

b. Write $\frac{2}{9}$ as a decimal.

Answers

1. a. 0.4 **b.** 0.225 **2.** −0.375
3. a. $0.8\overline{3}$ **b.** $0.\overline{2}$

Notice that the digit 2 keeps occurring as the remainder. This will continue so that the digit 6 will keep repeating in the quotient. We place a bar over the digit 6 to indicate that it repeats.

$$\frac{2}{3} = 0.666\ldots = 0.\overline{6}$$

We can also write a decimal approximation for $\frac{2}{3}$. For example, $\frac{2}{3}$ rounded to the nearest hundredth is 0.67. This can be written as $\frac{2}{3} \approx 0.67$.

■ Work Practice 3

Practice 4

Write $\frac{28}{13}$ as a decimal. Round to the nearest thousandth.

Example 4 Write $\frac{22}{7}$ as a decimal. (Recall that the fraction $\frac{22}{7}$ is an approximation for π.) Round to the nearest hundredth.

Solution:

$$
\begin{array}{r}
3.142 \approx 3.14 \\
7\overline{)22.000} \\
-21 \\
\hline
10 \\
-7 \\
\hline
30 \\
-28 \\
\hline
20 \\
-14 \\
\hline
6
\end{array}
$$

Carry the division out to the thousandths place.

The fraction $\frac{22}{7}$ in decimal form is approximately 3.14.

■ Work Practice 4

Practice 5

Write $3\frac{5}{16}$ as a decimal.

Example 5 Write $2\frac{3}{16}$ as a decimal.

Solution:

Option 1. Write the fractional part only as a decimal.

$$\frac{3}{16} \longrightarrow
\begin{array}{r}
0.1875 \\
16\overline{)3.0000} \\
-1\,6 \\
\hline
1\,40 \\
-1\,28 \\
\hline
120 \\
-112 \\
\hline
80 \\
-80 \\
\hline
0
\end{array}
$$

Thus $2\frac{3}{16} = 2.1875$

Option 2. Write $2\frac{3}{16}$ as an improper fraction, and divide.

$$2\frac{3}{16} = \frac{35}{16} \longrightarrow
\begin{array}{r}
2.1875 \\
16\overline{)35.0000} \\
-32 \\
\hline
3\,0 \\
-1\,6 \\
\hline
1\,40 \\
-1\,28 \\
\hline
120 \\
-112 \\
\hline
80 \\
-80 \\
\hline
0
\end{array}
$$

■ Work Practice 5

Answers

4. 2.154   **5.** 3.3125

Some fractions may be written as decimals using our knowledge of decimals. From Section 5.1, we know that if the denominator of a fraction is 10, 100, 1000, or so on, we can immediately write the fraction as a decimal. For example,

$$\frac{4}{10} = 0.4, \qquad \frac{12}{100} = 0.12, \text{ and so on}$$

Example 6 Write $\frac{4}{5}$ as a decimal.

Solution: Let's write $\frac{4}{5}$ as an equivalent fraction with a denominator of 10.

$$\frac{4}{5} = \frac{4}{5} \cdot \frac{2}{2} = \frac{8}{10} = 0.8$$

■ Work Practice 6

Practice 6

Write $\frac{3}{5}$ as a decimal.

Example 7 Write $\frac{1}{25}$ as a decimal.

Solution: $\frac{1}{25} = \frac{1}{25} \cdot \frac{4}{4} = \frac{4}{100} = 0.04$

■ Work Practice 7

Practice 7

Write $\frac{3}{50}$ as a decimal.

✓**Concept Check** Suppose you are writing the fraction $\frac{9}{16}$ as a decimal. How do you know you have made a mistake if your answer is 1.735?

Objective B Comparing Decimals and Fractions ▶

Now we can compare decimals and fractions by writing fractions as equivalent decimals.

Example 8 Insert $<$, $>$, or $=$ to form a true statement.

$$\frac{1}{8} \qquad 0.12$$

Solution: First we write $\frac{1}{8}$ as an equivalent decimal. Then we compare decimal places.

$$\begin{array}{r} 0.125 \\ 8\overline{)1.000} \\ \underline{-8} \\ 20 \\ \underline{-16} \\ 40 \\ \underline{-40} \\ 0 \end{array}$$

Original numbers	$\frac{1}{8}$	0.12
Decimals	0.125	0.120
Compare	0.125 > 0.12	

Thus, $\frac{1}{8} > 0.12$

■ Work Practice 8

Practice 8

Insert $<$, $>$, or $=$ to form a true statement.

$$\frac{1}{5} \qquad 0.25$$

Answers
6. 0.6   **7.** 0.06   **8.** $<$

✓**Concept Check Answer**
$\frac{9}{16}$ is less than 1 while 1.735 is greater than 1.

Practice 9

Insert $<$, $>$, or $=$ to form a true statement.

a. $\dfrac{1}{2}$ 0.54   **b.** $0.\overline{5}$ $\dfrac{5}{9}$

c. $\dfrac{5}{7}$ 0.72

Example 9   Insert $<$, $>$, or $=$ to form a true statement.

$0.\overline{7}$ $\dfrac{7}{9}$

Solution: We write $\dfrac{7}{9}$ as a decimal and then compare.

$$\begin{array}{r} 0.77\ldots = 0.\overline{7} \\ 9\overline{)7.00} \\ -6.3 \\ \hline 70 \\ -63 \\ \hline 7 \end{array}$$

Original numbers	$0.\overline{7}$	$\dfrac{7}{9}$
Decimals	$0.\overline{7}$	$0.\overline{7}$
Compare	$0.\overline{7} = 0.\overline{7}$	

Thus, $0.\overline{7} = \dfrac{7}{9}$

■ Work Practice 9

Practice 10

Write the numbers in order from smallest to largest.

a. $\dfrac{1}{3}$, 0.302, $\dfrac{3}{8}$

b. 1.26, $1\dfrac{1}{4}$, $1\dfrac{2}{5}$

c. 0.4, 0.41, $\dfrac{3}{7}$

Example 10   Write the numbers in order from smallest to largest.

$\dfrac{9}{20}$, $\dfrac{4}{9}$, 0.456

Solution:

Original numbers	$\dfrac{9}{20}$	$\dfrac{4}{9}$	0.456
Decimals	0.450	$0.444\ldots$	0.456
Compare in order	2nd	1st	3rd

Written in order, we have

1st 2nd 3rd
↓   ↓   ↓

$\dfrac{4}{9}$, $\dfrac{9}{20}$, 0.456

■ Work Practice 10

Objective C Simplifying Expressions with Decimals and Fractions ▶

In the remaining examples, we will review the order of operations by simplifying expressions that contain decimals.

Order of Operations

1. Perform all operations within parentheses ( ), brackets [ ], or other grouping symbols such as fraction bars.
2. Evaluate any expressions with exponents.
3. Multiply or divide in order from left to right.
4. Add or subtract in order from left to right.

Answers

9. a. $<$ **b.** $=$ **c.** $<$

10. a. 0.302, $\dfrac{1}{3}$, $\dfrac{3}{8}$ **b.** $1\dfrac{1}{4}$, 1.26, $1\dfrac{2}{5}$

c. 0.4, 0.41, $\dfrac{3}{7}$

Example 11 Simplify: $723.6 \div 1000 \times 10$

Solution: Multiply or divide in order from left to right.

$$723.6 \div 1000 \times 10 = 0.7236 \times 10 \quad \text{Divide.}$$
$$= 7.236 \quad \text{Multiply.}$$

■ Work Practice 11

Practice 11
Simplify: $897.8 \div 100 \times 10$

Example 12 Simplify: $-0.5(8.6 - 1.2)$

Solution: According to the order of operations, we simplify inside the parentheses first.

$$-0.5(8.6 - 1.2) = -0.5(7.4) \quad \text{Subtract.}$$
$$= -3.7 \quad \text{Multiply.}$$

■ Work Practice 12

Practice 12
Simplify: $-8.69(3.2 - 1.8)$

Example 13 Simplify: $(-1.3)^2 + 2.4$

Solution: Recall the meaning of an exponent.

$$(-1.3)^2 + 2.4 = (-1.3)(-1.3) + 2.4 \quad \text{Use the definition of an exponent.}$$
$$= 1.69 + 2.4 \quad \text{Multiply. The product of two negative numbers is a positive number.}$$
$$= 4.09 \quad \text{Add.}$$

■ Work Practice 13

Practice 13
Simplify: $(-0.7)^2 + 2.1$

Example 14 Simplify: $\dfrac{5.68 + (0.9)^2 \div 100}{0.2}$

Solution: First we simplify the numerator of the fraction. Then we divide.

$$\frac{5.68 + (0.9)^2 \div 100}{0.2} = \frac{5.68 + 0.81 \div 100}{0.2} \quad \text{Simplify } (0.9)^2.$$
$$= \frac{5.68 + 0.0081}{0.2} \quad \text{Divide.}$$
$$= \frac{5.6881}{0.2} \quad \text{Add.}$$
$$= 28.4405 \quad \text{Divide.}$$

■ Work Practice 14

Practice 14
Simplify: $\dfrac{20.06 - (1.2)^2 \div 10}{0.02}$

Objective D Solving Area Problems Containing Fractions and Decimals ▶

Sometimes real-life problems contain both fractions and decimals. In the next example, we review the area of a triangle, and when values are substituted, the result may be an expression containing both fractions and decimals.

Answers
11. 89.78 **12.** −12.166
13. 2.59 **14.** 995.8

Practice 15

Find the area of the triangle.

2.1 meters
7 meters

 Example 15 The area of a triangle is Area $= \frac{1}{2} \cdot$ base $\cdot$ height. Find the area of the triangle shown.

3 feet
5.6 feet

Solution:

$$\text{Area} = \frac{1}{2} \cdot \text{base} \cdot \text{height}$$

$$= \frac{1}{2} \cdot 5.6 \cdot 3$$

$$= 0.5 \cdot 5.6 \cdot 3 \qquad \text{Write } \frac{1}{2} \text{ as the decimal } 0.5.$$

$$= 8.4$$

The area of the triangle is 8.4 square feet.

■ Work Practice 15

Objective E Using Decimals as Replacement Values ▶

Practice 16

Evaluate $1.7y - 2$ for $y = 2.3$.

Example 16 Evaluate $-2x + 5$ for $x = 3.8$.

Solution: Replace x with 3.8 in the expression $-2x + 5$ and simplify.

$$-2x + 5 = -2(3.8) + 5 \qquad \text{Replace } x \text{ with } 3.8.$$

$$= -7.6 + 5 \qquad \text{Multiply.}$$

$$= -2.6 \qquad \text{Add.}$$

■ Work Practice 16

Answers
15. 7.35 sq m   **16.** 1.91

Vocabulary, Readiness & Video Check

Answer each exercise "true" or "false."

1. The number $0.\overline{5}$ means 0.555. _____

2. To write $\dfrac{9}{19}$ as a decimal, perform the division $19\overline{)9}$. _____

3. $(-1.2)^2$ means $(-1.2)(-1.2)$ or -1.44. _____

4. To simplify $8.6(4.8 - 9.6)$, we first subtract. _____

Martin-Gay Interactive Videos Watch the section lecture video and answer the following questions.

See Video 5.5

Objective A 5. In ⊞ Example 2, why is the bar placed over just the 6? ⊳

Objective B 6. In ⊞ Example 3, why do we write the fraction as a decimal rather than the decimal as a fraction? ⊳

Objective C 7. In ⊞ Example 4, besides meaning division, what other purpose does the fraction bar serve? ⊳

Objective D 8. What formula is used to solve ⊞ Example 5? What is the final answer? ⊳

Objective E 9. In ⊞ Example 6, once all replacement values are put into the variable expression, what is the resulting expression to evaluate? ⊳

5.5 **Exercise Set** MyMathLab® ⊳

Objective A *Write each number as a decimal. See Examples 1 through 7.*

1. $\frac{1}{5}$ 2. $\frac{1}{20}$ 3. $\frac{17}{25}$ 4. $\frac{13}{25}$ ⊳ 5. $\frac{3}{4}$

6. $\frac{1}{8}$ 7. $-\frac{2}{25}$ 8. $-\frac{3}{25}$ 9. $\frac{9}{4}$ 10. $\frac{8}{5}$

⊳ 11. $\frac{11}{12}$ 12. $\frac{5}{12}$ 13. $\frac{17}{40}$ 14. $\frac{19}{25}$ 15. $\frac{18}{40}$

16. $\frac{31}{40}$ 17. $-\frac{1}{3}$ 18. $-\frac{7}{9}$ 19. $\frac{7}{16}$ 20. $\frac{9}{16}$

21. $\frac{7}{11}$ 22. $\frac{9}{11}$ 23. $5\frac{17}{20}$ 24. $4\frac{7}{8}$ 25. $\frac{78}{125}$ 26. $\frac{159}{375}$

Round each number as indicated. See Example 4.

27. Round your decimal answer to Exercise **17** to the nearest hundredth.

28. Round your decimal answer to Exercise **18** to the nearest hundredth.

29. Round your decimal answer to Exercise **19** to the nearest hundredth.

30. Round your decimal answer to Exercise **20** to the nearest hundredth.

31. Round your decimal answer to Exercise **21** to the nearest tenth.

32. Round your decimal answer to Exercise **22** to the nearest tenth.

Write each fraction as a decimal. If necessary, round to the nearest hundredth. See Examples 1 through 7.

33. Of the U.S. mountains that are over 14,000 feet in elevation, $\frac{56}{91}$ are located in Colorado. (*Source:* U.S. Geological Survey)

34. About $\frac{9}{20}$ of all U.S. citizens have type O blood. (*Source:* American Red Cross Biomedical Services)

35. About $\frac{43}{50}$ of Americans are Internet users. (*Source:* Digitalcenter)

36. About $\frac{14}{25}$ of Americans use the Internet through a wireless device. (*Source:* Digitalcenter)

37. When first launched, the Hubble Space Telescope's primary mirror was out of shape on the edges by $\frac{1}{50}$ of a human hair. This very small defect made it difficult to focus faint objects being viewed. Because the HST was in low Earth orbit, it was serviced by a shuttle and the defect was corrected.

38. The two mirrors currently in use in the Hubble Space Telescope were ground so that they do not deviate from a perfect curve by more than $\frac{1}{800,000}$ of an inch. Do not round this number.

Objective B *Insert* $<, >,$ *or* $=$ *to form a true statement. See Examples 8 and 9.*

39. 0.562   0.569

40. 0.983   0.988

41. 0.215 $\frac{43}{200}$

42. $\frac{29}{40}$ 0.725

43. -0.0932 -0.0923

44. -0.00563 -0.00536

45. $0.\overline{6}$ $\frac{5}{6}$

46. $0.\overline{1}$ $\frac{2}{17}$

47. $\frac{51}{91}$ $0.56\overline{4}$

48. $0.58\overline{3}$ $\frac{6}{11}$

49. $\frac{4}{7}$ 0.14

50. $\frac{5}{9}$ 0.557

51. 1.38 $\frac{18}{13}$

52. 0.372 $\frac{22}{59}$

53. 7.123 $\frac{456}{64}$

54. 12.713 $\frac{89}{7}$

Write the numbers in order from smallest to largest. See Example 10.

55. 0.34, 0.35, 0.32

56. 0.47, 0.42, 0.40

57. 0.49, 0.491, 0.498

58. 0.72, 0.727, 0.728

59. $5.23, \frac{42}{8}, 5.34$

60. $7.56, \frac{67}{9}, 7.562$

61. $\frac{5}{8}, 0.612, 0.649$

62. $\frac{5}{6}, 0.821, 0.849$

Objective C *Simplify each expression. See Examples 11 through 14.*

63. $(0.3)^2 + 0.5$

64. $(-2.5)(3) - 4.7$

65. $\frac{1 + 0.8}{-0.6}$

66. $(-0.05)^2 + 3.13$

67. $(-2.3)^2 (0.3 + 0.7)$

68. $(8.2)(100) - (8.2)(10)$

69. $(5.6 - 2.3)(2.4 + 0.4)$

70. $\frac{0.222 - 2.13}{12}$

71. $\frac{(4.5)^2}{100}$

72. $0.9(5.6 - 6.5)$

73. $\frac{7 + 0.74}{-6}$

74. $(1.5)^2 + 0.5$

Find the value of each expression. Give the result as a decimal. See Examples 11 through 14.

75. $\frac{1}{5} - 2(7.8)$

76. $\frac{3}{4} - (9.6)(5)$

77. $\frac{1}{4}(-9.6 - 5.2)$

78. $\frac{3}{8}(4.7 - 5.9)$

Objective D *Find the area of each triangle or rectangle. See Example 15.*

△ **79.**

9 inches

5.7 inches

△ **80.**

4.4 feet

←—— 17 feet ——→

▶ **81.**
△

0.62 yard

$\frac{2}{5}$ yard

△ **82.**

1.2 miles

$\frac{7}{8}$ mile

Objective E *Evaluate each expression for x = 6, y = 0.3, and z = −2.4. See Example 16.*

83. z^2 **84.** y^2 **85.** $x - y$ **86.** $x - z$ ▶ **87.** $4y - z$ **88.** $\frac{x}{y} + 2z$

Review

Simplify. See Sections 4.3 and 4.5.

89. $\frac{9}{10} + \frac{16}{25}$ **90.** $\frac{4}{11} - \frac{19}{22}$ **91.** $\left(\frac{2}{5}\right)\left(\frac{5}{2}\right)^2$ **92.** $\left(\frac{2}{3}\right)^2\left(\frac{3}{2}\right)^3$

Concept Extensions

Without calculating, describe each number as < 1, = 1, or > 1. See the Concept Check in this section.

93. 1.0 **94.** 1.0000 **95.** 1.00001 **96.** $\frac{101}{99}$ **97.** $\frac{99}{100}$ **98.** $\frac{99}{99}$

In 2012, there were 11,434 commercial radio stations in the United States. The most popular formats are listed in the table along with their counts. Use this graph to answer Exercises 99 through 102.

99. Write as a decimal the fraction of radio stations with a classic hits music format. Round to the nearest thousandth.

100. Write as a decimal the fraction of radio stations with a Spanish format. Round to the nearest hundredth.

101. Estimate, by rounding each number in the table to the nearest hundred, the total number of stations with the top six formats in 2012.

102. Use your estimate from Exercise **101** to write the fraction of radio stations accounted for by the top six formats as a decimal. Round to the nearest hundredth.

Top Commercial Radio Station Formats in 2012

Number of Stations

Country 2020; News/talk 1503; Classic Hits 657; Oldies 597; Spanish 816; Sports 692

Format (Total stations: 11,434)

103. Describe two ways to write fractions as decimals.

104. Describe two ways to write mixed numbers as decimals.

Objective

A Solve Equations Containing Decimals.

Objective A Solving Equations Containing Decimals

In this section, we continue our work with decimals and algebra by solving equations containing decimals. First, we review the steps given earlier for solving an equation.

> **Steps for Solving an Equation in x**
>
> **Step 1:** If fractions are present, multiply both sides of the equation by the LCD of the fractions.
>
> **Step 2:** If parentheses are present, use the distributive property.
>
> **Step 3:** Combine any like terms on each side of the equation.
>
> **Step 4:** Use the addition property of equality to rewrite the equation so that variable terms are on one side of the equation and constant terms are on the other side.
>
> **Step 5:** Divide both sides by the numerical coefficient of x to solve.
>
> **Step 6:** Check your answer in the **original equation**.

Practice 1

Solve: $z + 0.9 = 1.3$

Example 1 Solve: $x - 1.5 = 8$

Solution: Steps 1 through 3 are not needed for this equation, so we begin with Step 4. To get x alone on one side of the equation, add 1.5 to both sides.

$$x - 1.5 = 8 \qquad \text{Original equation}$$
$$x - 1.5 + 1.5 = 8 + 1.5 \qquad \text{Add 1.5 to both sides.}$$
$$x = 9.5 \qquad \text{Simplify.}$$

Check: To check, replace x with 9.5 in the *original equation*.

$$x - 1.5 = 8 \qquad \text{Original equation}$$
$$9.5 - 1.5 \stackrel{?}{=} 8 \qquad \text{Replace } x \text{ with 9.5.}$$
$$8 = 8 \qquad \text{True}$$

Since $8 = 8$ is a true statement, 9.5 is a solution of the equation.

■ Work Practice 1

Practice 2

Solve: $0.17x = -0.34$

Example 2 Solve: $-2y = 6.7$

Solution: Steps 1 through 4 are not needed for this equation, so we begin with Step 5. To solve for y, divide both sides by the coefficient of y, which is -2.

$$-2y = 6.7 \qquad \text{Original equation}$$
$$\frac{-2y}{-2} = \frac{6.7}{-2} \qquad \text{Divide both sides by } -2.$$
$$y = -3.35 \qquad \text{Simplify.}$$

Check: To check, replace y with -3.35 in the original equation.

$$-2y = 6.7 \qquad \text{Original equation}$$
$$-2(-3.35) \stackrel{?}{=} 6.7 \qquad \text{Replace } y \text{ with } -3.35.$$
$$6.7 = 6.7 \qquad \text{True}$$

Thus -3.35 is a solution of the equation $-2y = 6.7$.

■ Work Practice 2

Answers
1. 0.4 **2.** -2

Example 3   Solve: $1.2x + 5.8 = 8.2$

Solution: We begin with Step 4 and get the variable term alone by subtracting 5.8 from both sides.

$$1.2x + 5.8 = 8.2$$
$$1.2x + 5.8 - 5.8 = 8.2 - 5.8 \quad \text{Subtract 5.8 from both sides.}$$
$$1.2x = 2.4 \quad \text{Simplify.}$$
$$\frac{1.2x}{1.2} = \frac{2.4}{1.2} \quad \text{Divide both sides by 1.2.}$$
$$x = 2 \quad \text{Simplify.}$$

To check, replace x with 2 in the original equation. The solution is 2.

■ Work Practice 3

Practice 3

Solve: $2.9 = 1.7 + 0.3x$

Example 4   Solve: $7x + 3.2 = 4x - 1.6$

Solution: We start with Step 4 to get variable terms on one side and numerical terms on the other.

$$7x + 3.2 = 4x - 1.6$$
$$7x + 3.2 - 3.2 = 4x - 1.6 - 3.2 \quad \text{Subtract 3.2 from both sides.}$$
$$7x = 4x - 4.8 \quad \text{Simplify.}$$
$$7x - 4x = 4x - 4.8 - 4x \quad \text{Subtract } 4x \text{ from both sides.}$$
$$3x = -4.8 \quad \text{Simplify.}$$
$$\frac{3x}{3} = -\frac{4.8}{3} \quad \text{Divide both sides by 3.}$$
$$x = -1.6 \quad \text{Simplify.}$$

Check to see that -1.6 is the solution.

■ Work Practice 4

Practice 4

Solve: $8x + 4.2 = 10x + 11.6$

Example 5   Solve: $5(x - 0.36) = -x + 2.4$

Solution: First use the distributive property to distribute the factor 5.

$$5(x - 0.36) = -x + 2.4 \quad \text{Original equation}$$
$$5x - 1.8 = -x + 2.4 \quad \text{Apply the distributive property.}$$

Next, get the variable terms alone on the left side of the equation by adding 1.8 to both sides of the equation and then adding x to both sides of the equation.

$$5x - 1.8 + 1.8 = -x + 2.4 + 1.8 \quad \text{Add 1.8 to both sides.}$$
$$5x = -x + 4.2 \quad \text{Simplify.}$$
$$5x + x = -x + 4.2 + x \quad \text{Add } x \text{ to both sides.}$$
$$6x = 4.2 \quad \text{Simplify.}$$
$$\frac{6x}{6} = \frac{4.2}{6} \quad \text{Divide both sides by 6.}$$
$$x = 0.7 \quad \text{Simplify.}$$

To verify that 0.7 is the solution, replace x with 0.7 in the original equation.

■ Work Practice 5

Practice 5

Solve: $6.3 - 5x = 3(x + 2.9)$

Answers

3. 4   **4.** -3.7 **5.** -0.3

Instead of solving equations with decimals, sometimes it may be easier to first rewrite the equation so that it contains integers only. Recall that multiplying a decimal by a power of 10 such as 10, 100, or 1000 has the effect of moving the decimal point to the right. We can use the multiplication property of equality to multiply both sides of the equation by an appropriate power of 10. The resulting equivalent equation will contain integers only.

Practice 6

Solve: $0.2y + 2.6 = 4$

Example 6   Solve: $0.5y + 2.3 = 1.65$

Solution: Multiply both sides of the equation by 100. This will move the decimal point in each term two places to the right.

$$0.5y + 2.3 = 1.65 \qquad \text{Original equation}$$
$$100(0.5y + 2.3) = 100(1.65) \qquad \text{Multiply both sides by 100.}$$
$$100(0.5y) + 100(2.3) = 100(1.65) \qquad \text{Apply the distributive property.}$$
$$50y + 230 = 165 \qquad \text{Simplify.}$$

Now the equation contains integers only. Continue solving by subtracting 230 from both sides.

$$50y + 230 = 165$$
$$50y + 230 - 230 = 165 - 230 \qquad \text{Subtract 230 from both sides.}$$
$$50y = -65 \qquad \text{Simplify.}$$
$$\frac{50y}{50} = \frac{-65}{50} \qquad \text{Divide both sides by 50.}$$
$$y = -1.3 \qquad \text{Simplify.}$$

Check to see that -1.3 is the solution by replacing y with -1.3 in the original equation.

■ Work Practice 6

Answer

6. 7

✓ **Concept Check Answer**

Multiply by 1000.

✓ **Concept Check** By what number would you multiply both sides of the following equation to make calculations easier? Explain your choice.

$$1.7x + 3.655 = -14.2$$

Martin-Gay Interactive Videos

See Video 5.6

Watch the section lecture video and answer the following questions.

Objective A   **1.** In ▣ Example 3, why did we multiply both sides of the equation by 10? ▶

       2. In ▣ Example 4, we subtracted $3x$ from both sides, but what would have been a potential benefit of subtracting $2x$ instead?

5.6 Exercise Set MyMathLab®

Objective A *Solve each equation. See Examples 1 and 2.*

1. $x + 1.2 = 7.1$ **2.** $y - 0.5 = 9$ **3.** $-5y = 2.15$ **4.** $-0.4x = 50$

5. $6.2 = y - 4$ **6.** $9.7 = x + 11.6$ **7.** $3.1x = -13.95$ **8.** $3y = -25.8$

Solve each equation. See Examples 3 through 5.

9. $-3.5x + 2.8 = -11.2$ **10.** $7.1 - 0.2x = 6.1$ **11.** $6x + 8.65 = 3x + 10$

12. $7x - 9.64 = 5x + 2.32$ **13.** $2(x - 1.3) = 5.8$ **14.** $5(x + 2.3) = 19.5$

Solve each equation by first multiplying both sides by an appropriate power of 10 so that the equation contains integers only. See Example 6.

15. $0.4x + 0.7 = -0.9$ **16.** $0.7x + 0.1 = 1.5$ **17.** $7x - 10.8 = x$

18. $3y = 7y + 24.4$ **19.** $2.1x + 5 - 1.6x = 10$ **20.** $1.5x + 2 - 1.2x = 12.2$

Solve. See Examples 1 through 6.

21. $y - 3.6 = 4$ **22.** $x + 5.7 = 8.4$ **23.** $-0.02x = -1.2$

24. $-9y = -0.162$ **25.** $6.5 = 10x + 7.2$ **26.** $2x - 4.2 = 8.6$

27. $2.7x - 25 = 1.2x + 5$ **28.** $9y - 6.9 = 6y - 11.1$ **29.** $200x - 0.67 = 100x + 0.81$

30. $2.3 + 500x = 600x - 0.2$ **31.** $3(x + 2.71) = 2x$ **32.** $7(x + 8.6) = 6x$

33. $8x - 5 = 10x - 8$ **34.** $24y - 10 = 20y - 17$ **35.** $1.2 + 0.3x = 0.9$

36. $1.5 = 0.4x + 0.5$ **37.** $-0.9x + 2.65 = -0.5x + 5.45$ **38.** $-50x + 0.81 = -40x - 0.48$

39. $4x + 7.6 = 2(3x - 3.2)$ **40.** $4(2x - 1.6) = 5x - 6.4$ **41.** $0.7x + 13.8 = x - 2.16$

42. $y - 5 = 0.3y + 4.1$

Review

Simplify each expression by combining like terms. See Section 3.1.

43. $2x - 7 + x - 9$

44. $x + 14 - 5x - 17$

Perform the indicated operation. See Sections 4.3, 4.5, and 4.7.

45. $\dfrac{6x}{5} \cdot \dfrac{1}{2x^2}$

46. $5\dfrac{1}{3} \div 9\dfrac{1}{6}$

47. $\dfrac{x}{3} + \dfrac{2x}{7}$

48. $50 - 14\dfrac{9}{13}$

Concept Extensions

Mixed Practice (*Sections 5.2 and 5.6*) *This section of exercises contains equations and expressions. If the exercise contains an equation, solve it for the variable. If the exercise contains an expression, simplify it by combining any like terms.*

49. $b + 4.6 = 8.3$

50. $y - 15.9 = -3.8$

51. $2x - 0.6 + 4x - 0.01$

52. $-x - 4.1 - x - 4.02$

53. $5y - 1.2 - 7y + 8$

54. $9a - 5.6 - 3a + 6$

55. $2.8 = z - 6.3$

56. $9.7 = x + 4.3$

57. $4.7x + 8.3 = -5.8$

58. $2.8x + 3.4 = -13.4$

59. $7.76 + 8z - 12z + 8.91$

60. $9.21 + x - 4x + 11.33$

61. $5(x - 3.14) = 4x$

62. $6(x + 1.43) = 5x$

63. $2.6y + 8.3 = 4.6y - 3.4$

64. $8.4z - 2.6 = 5.4z + 10.3$

65. $9.6z - 3.2 - 11.7z - 6.9$

66. $-3.2x + 12.6 - 8.9x - 15.2$

67. Explain in your own words the property of equality that allows us to multiply both sides of an equation by a power of 10.

68. By what number would you multiply both sides of $8x - 7.6 = 4.23$ to make calculations easier? Explain your choice.

69. Construct an equation whose solution is 1.4.

70. Construct an equation whose solution is -8.6.

Solve.

71. $-5.25x = -40.33575$

72. $7.68y = -114.98496$

73. $1.95y + 6.834 = 7.65y - 19.8591$

74. $6.11x + 4.683 = 7.51x + 18.235$

5.7 **Decimal Applications: Mean, Median, and Mode**

Objective A Finding the Mean

Sometimes we want to summarize data by displaying them in a graph, but sometimes it is also desirable to be able to describe a set of data, or a set of numbers, by a single "middle" number. Three such **measures of central tendency** are the **mean,** the **median,** and the **mode.**

The most common measure of central tendency is the mean (sometimes called the "arithmetic mean" or the "average"). Recall that we first introduced finding the average of a list of numbers in Section 1.6.

> The **mean (average)** of a set of numbered items is the sum of the items divided by the number of items.
>
> $$\text{mean} = \frac{\text{sum of items}}{\text{number of items}}$$

 Objectives

A Find the Mean of a List of Numbers.

B Find the Median of a List of Numbers.

C Find the Mode of a List of Numbers.

Example 1 Finding the Mean Time in an Experiment

Seven students in a psychology class conducted an experiment on mazes. Each student was given a pencil and asked to successfully complete the same maze. The timed results are below:

Student	Ann	Thanh	Carlos	Jesse	Melinda	Ramzi	Dayni
Time (Seconds)	13.2	11.8	10.7	16.2	15.9	13.8	18.5

a. Who completed the maze in the shortest time? Who completed the maze in the longest time?

b. Find the mean time.

c. How many students took longer than the mean time? How many students took shorter than the mean time?

Solution:

a. Carlos completed the maze in 10.7 seconds, the shortest time. Dayni completed the maze in 18.5 seconds, the longest time.

b. To find the mean (or average), we find the sum of the items and divide by 7, the number of items.

$$\text{mean} = \frac{13.2 + 11.8 + 10.7 + 16.2 + 15.9 + 13.8 + 18.5}{7}$$

$$= \frac{100.1}{7} = 14.3$$

c. Three students, Jesse, Melinda, and Dayni, had times longer than the mean time. Four students, Ann, Thanh, Carlos, and Ramzi, had times shorter than the mean time.

■ Work Practice 1

Practice 1

Find the mean of the following test scores: 87, 75, 96, 91, and 78.

✓**Concept Check** Estimate the mean of the following set of data:

5, 10, 10, 10, 10, 15

Often in college, the calculation of a **grade point average** (GPA) is a **weighted mean** and is calculated as shown in Example 2.

Answer
1. 85.4

✓**Concept Check Answer**
10

389

Copyright 2015 Pearson Education, Inc.

Practice 2

Find the grade point average if the following grades were earned in one semester.

Grade	Credit Hours
A	2
B	4
C	5
D	2
A	2

Example 2   Calculating Grade Point Average (GPA)

The following grades were earned by a student during one semester. Find the student's grade point average.

Course	Grade	Credit Hours
College mathematics	A	3
Biology	B	3
English	A	3
PE	C	1
Social studies	D	2

Solution: To calculate the grade point average, we need to know the point values for the different possible grades. The point values of grades commonly used in colleges and universities are given below:

A: 4,   B: 3,   C: 2,   D: 1,   F: 0

Now, to find the grade point average, we multiply the number of credit hours for each course by the point value of each grade. The grade point average is the sum of these products divided by the sum of the credit hours.

Course	Grade	Point Value of Grade	Credit Hours	Point Value of Credit Hours
College mathematics	A	4	3	12
Biology	B	3	3	9
English	A	4	3	12
PE	C	2	1	2
Social studies	D	1	2	2
		Totals:	12	37

$$\text{grade point average} = \frac{37}{12} \approx 3.08 \text{ rounded to two decimal places}$$

The student earned a grade point average of 3.08.

■ Work Practice 2

Objective B   Finding the Median

You may have noticed that a very low number or a very high number can affect the mean of a list of numbers. Because of this, you may sometimes want to use another measure of central tendency. A second measure of central tendency is called the **median.** The median of a list of numbers is not affected by a low or high number in the list.

> The **median** of a set of numbers in numerical order is the middle number. If the number of items is odd, the median is the middle number. If the number of items is even, the median is the mean of the two middle numbers.

Practice 3

Find the median of the list of numbers: 5, 11, 14, 23, 24, 35, 38, 41, 43

Example 3   Find the median of the following list of numbers:

25, 54, 56, 57, 60, 71, 98

Solution: Because this list is in numerical order, the median is the middle number, 57.

■ Work Practice 3

Answers
2. 2.67   **3.** 24

Example 4 Find the median of the following list of scores: 67, 91, 75, 86, 55, 91

Solution: First we list the scores in numerical order and then we find the middle number.

55, 67, 75, 86, 91, 91

Since there is an even number of scores, there are two middle numbers, 75 and 86. The median is the mean of the two middle numbers.

$$\text{median} = \frac{75 + 86}{2} = 80.5$$

The median is 80.5.

Work Practice 4

Helpful Hint

Don't forget to write the numbers in order from smallest to largest before finding the median.

Practice 4

Find the median of the list of scores:
36, 91, 78, 65, 95, 95, 88, 71

Objective C Finding the Mode ▷

The last common measure of central tendency is called the **mode.**

The **mode** of a set of numbers is the number that occurs most often. (It is possible for a set of numbers to have more than one mode or to have no mode.)

Example 5 Find the mode of the list of numbers:

11, 14, 14, 16, 31, 56, 65, 77, 77, 78, 79

Solution: There are two numbers that occur the most often. They are 14 and 77. This list of numbers has two modes, 14 and 77.

Work Practice 5

Practice 5

Find the mode of the list of numbers:
14, 10, 10, 13, 15, 15, 15, 17, 18, 18, 20

Example 6 Find the median and the mode of the following set of numbers. These numbers were high temperatures for 14 consecutive days in a city in Montana.

76, 80, 85, 86, 89, 87, 82, 77, 76, 79, 82, 89, 89, 92

Solution: First we write the numbers in numerical order.

76, 76, 77, 79, 80, 82, 82, 85, 86, 87, 89, 89, 89, 92

Since there is an even number of items, the median is the mean of the two middle numbers, 82 and 85.

$$\text{median} = \frac{82 + 85}{2} = 83.5$$

The mode is 89, since 89 occurs most often.

Work Practice 6

Practice 6

Find the median and the mode of the list of numbers:
26, 31, 15, 15, 26, 30, 16, 18, 15, 35

Answers
4. 83 **5.** 15 **6.** median: 22; mode: 15

✓**Concept Check** True or false? Every set of numbers *must* have a mean, median, and mode. Explain your answer.

✓**Concept Check Answer**
false; a set of numbers may have no mode

> **Helpful Hint**
>
> Don't forget that it is possible for a list of numbers to have no mode. For example, the list
>
>   2, 4, 5, 6, 8, 9
>
> has no mode. There is no number or numbers that occur more often than the others.

Vocabulary, Readiness & Video Check

Use the choices below to fill in each blank. Some choices may be used more than once.

mean   mode   grade point average

median   average

1. Another word for "mean" is _____.

2. The number that occurs most often in a set of numbers is called the _____.

3. The _____ of a set of number items is $\dfrac{\text{sum of items}}{\text{number of items}}$.

4. The _____ of a set of numbers is the middle number. If the number of numbers is even, it is
   the _____ of the two middle numbers.

5. An example of weighted mean is a calculation of _____.

Martin-Gay Interactive Videos   Watch the section lecture video and answer the following questions.

Objective A 6. Why is the ≈ symbol used in ⊞ Example 1? ▶

Objective B 7. From ⊞ Example 3, what is always the first step when finding
   the median of a set of data numbers? ▶

Objective C 8. From ⊞ Example 4, why do you think it is helpful to have
   data numbers in numerical order when finding the mode? ▶

See Video 5.7 ●

5.7 Exercise Set MyMathLab® ▶

Objectives A B C Mixed Practice *For each set of numbers, find the mean, median, and mode. If necessary, round the mean to one decimal place. See Examples 1 and 3 through 6.*

1. 15, 23, 24, 18, 25

2. 45, 36, 28, 46, 52

▶ 3. 7.6, 8.2, 8.2, 9.6, 5.7, 9.1

4. 4.9, 7.1, 6.8, 6.8, 5.3, 4.9

5. 0.5, 0.2, 0.2, 0.6, 0.3, 1.3, 0.8, 0.1, 0.5

6. 0.6, 0.6, 0.8, 0.4, 0.5, 0.3, 0.7, 0.8, 0.1

7. 231, 543, 601, 293, 588, 109, 334, 268

8. 451, 356, 478, 776, 892, 500, 467, 780

The ten tallest buildings in the world, completed as of the start of 2012, are listed in the following table. Use this table to answer Exercises 9 through 14. If necessary, round results to one decimal place. See Examples 1 and 3 through 6.

9. Find the mean height of the five tallest buildings.

10. Find the median height of the five tallest buildings.

11. Find the median height of the eight tallest buildings.

12. Find the mean height of the eight tallest buildings.

Building	Height (in feet)
Burj Khalifa, Dubai	2717
Makkah Royal Clock Tower Hotel, Saudi Arabia	1972
Taipei 101	1667
Shanghai World Financial Center	1614
International Commerce Centre, Hong Kong	1588
Petronas Tower 1, Kuala Lumpur	1483
Petronas Tower 2, Kuala Lumpur	1483
Zifeng Tower, China	1476
Willis Tower, Chicago	1451
KK 100 Development, China	1449
(*Source:* Council on Tall Buildings and Urban Habitat)	

13. Given the building heights, explain how you know, without calculating, that the answer to Exercise **10** is greater than the answer to Exercise **11**.

14. Given the building heights, explain how you know, without calculating, that the answer to Exercise **12** is less than the answer to Exercise **9**.

For Exercises 15 through 18, the grades are given for a student for a particular semester. Find the grade point average. If necessary, round the grade point average to the nearest hundredth. See Example 2.

15.

Grade	Credit Hours
B	3
C	3
A	4
C	4

16.

Grade	Credit Hours
D	1
F	1
C	4
B	5

17.

Grade	Credit Hours
A	3
A	3
A	4
B	3
C	1

18.

Grade	Credit Hours
B	2
B	2
C	3
A	3
B	3

During an experiment, the following times (in seconds) were recorded:

7.8, 6.9, 7.5, 4.7, 6.9, 7.0.

19. Find the mean. Round to the nearest tenth.

20. Find the median.

21. Find the mode.

In a mathematics class, the following test scores were recorded for a student: 93, 85, 89, 79, 88, 91.

22. Find the mean. Round to the nearest hundredth.

23. Find the median.

24. Find the mode.

The following pulse rates were recorded for a group of 15 students:

78, 80, 66, 68, 71, 64, 82, 71, 70, 65, 70, 75, 77, 86, 72.

25. Find the mean.

26. Find the median.

27. Find the mode.

28. How many pulse rates were higher than the mean?

29. How many pulse rates were lower than the mean?

Review

Write each fraction in simplest form. See Section 4.2.

30. $\dfrac{12}{20}$

31. $\dfrac{6}{18}$

32. $\dfrac{4x}{36}$

33. $\dfrac{18}{30y}$

34. $\dfrac{35a^3}{100a^2}$

35. $\dfrac{55y^2}{75y^2}$

Concept Extensions

Find the missing numbers in each set of numbers.

36. 16, 18, _____, _____, _____. The mode is 21. The median is 20.

37. _____, _____, _____, 40, _____. The mode is 35. The median is 37. The mean is 38.

38. Write a list of numbers for which you feel the median would be a better measure of central tendency than the mean.

39. Without making any computations, decide whether the median of the following list of numbers will be a whole number. Explain your reasoning.

36, 77, 29, 58, 43

Chapter 5 Group Activity

Maintaining a Checking Account

(Sections 5.1, 5.2, 5.3, 5.4)

This activity may be completed by working in groups or individually.

A checking account is a convenient way of handling money and paying bills. To open a checking account, the bank or savings and loan association requires a customer to make a deposit. Then the customer receives a checkbook that contains checks, deposit slips, and a register for recording checks written and deposits made. It is important to record all payments and deposits that affect the account. It is also important to keep the checkbook balance current by subtracting checks written and adding deposits made.

About once a month, checking customers receive a statement from the bank listing all activity that the account has had in the last month. The statement lists a beginning balance, all checks and deposits, any service charges made against the account, and an ending balance. Because it may take several days for checks that a customer has written to clear the banking system, the check register may list checks that do not appear on the monthly bank statement. These checks are called **outstanding checks.** Deposits that are recorded in the check register but do not appear on the statement are called **deposits in transit.** Because of these differences, it is important to balance, or reconcile, the checkbook against the monthly statement. The steps for doing so are listed below.

Balancing or Reconciling a Checkbook

Step 1: Place a check mark in the checkbook register next to each check and deposit listed on the monthly bank statement. Any entries in the register without a check mark are outstanding checks or deposits in transit.

Step 2: Find the ending checkbook register balance and add to it any outstanding checks and any interest paid on the account.

Step 3: From the total in Step 2, subtract any deposits in transit and any service charges.

Step 4: Compare the amount found in Step 3 with the ending balance listed on the bank statement. If they are the same, the checkbook balances with the bank statement. Be sure to update the check register with service charges and interest.

Step 5: If the checkbook does not balance, recheck the balancing process. Next, make sure that the running checkbook register balance was calculated correctly. Finally, compare the checkbook register with the statement to make sure that each check was recorded for the correct amount.

For the checkbook register and monthly bank statement given:

a. *update the checkbook register*   **b.** *list the outstanding checks and their total, and deposits in transit*

c. *balance the checkbook—be sure to update the register with any interest or service fees*

Checkbook Register						
						Balance
#	Date	Description	Payment	✓	Deposit	**425.86**
114	4/1	Market Basket	30.27			
115	4/3	May's Texaco	8.50			
	4/4	Cash at ATM	50.00			
116	4/6	UNO Bookstore	121.38			
	4/7	Deposit			100.00	
117	4/9	MasterCard	84.16			
118	4/10	Redbox	6.12			
119	4/12	Kroger	18.72			
120	4/14	Parking sticker	18.50			
	4/15	Direct deposit			294.36	
121	4/20	Rent	395.00			
122	4/25	Student fees	20.00			
	4/28	Deposit			75.00	

First National Bank Monthly Statement 4/30		
BEGINNING BALANCE:		425.86
Date	Number	Amount
CHECKS AND ATM WITHDRAWALS		
4/3	114	30.27
4/4	ATM	50.00
4/11	117	84.16
4/13	115	8.50
4/15	119	18.72
4/22	121	395.00
DEPOSITS		
4/7		100.00
4/15	Direct deposit	294.36
SERVICE CHARGES		
Low balance fee		7.50
INTEREST		
Credited 4/30		1.15
ENDING BALANCE:		227.22

Chapter 5 Vocabulary Check

Fill in each blank with one of the choices listed below. Some choices may be used more than once and some not at all.

vertically	decimal	and	right triangle
standard form	mean	median	circumference
sum	denominator	numerator	mode

1. Like fractional notation, _____ notation is used to denote a part of a whole.

2. To write fractions as decimals, divide the _____ by the _____.

3. To add or subtract decimals, write the decimals so that the decimal points line up _____.

4. When writing decimals in words, write "_____" for the decimal point.

5. When multiplying decimals, the decimal point in the product is placed so that the number of decimal places in the product is equal to the _____ of the number of decimal places in the factors.

6. The _____ of a set of numbers is the number that occurs most often.

7. The distance around a circle is called the _____.

8. The _____ of a set of numbers in numerical order is the middle number. If there is an even number of numbers, the median is the _____ of the two middle numbers.

9. The _____ of a list of items with number values is $\dfrac{\text{sum of items}}{\text{number of items}}$.

10. When 2 million is written as 2,000,000, we say it is written in _____.

> **Helpful Hint**
>
> ▶ Are you preparing for your test? Don't forget to take the Chapter 5 Test on page 405. Then check your answers at the back of the text and use the Chapter Test Prep Videos to see the fully worked-out solutions to any of the exercises you want to review.

5 Chapter Highlights

Definitions and Concepts	Examples
Section 5.1 Introduction to Decimals	

Place-Value Chart

hundreds	tens	ones	decimal point	tenths	hundredths	thousandths	ten-thousandths	hundred-thousandths
		4	.	2	6	5		
100	10	1		$\dfrac{1}{10}$	$\dfrac{1}{100}$	$\dfrac{1}{1000}$	$\dfrac{1}{10,000}$	$\dfrac{1}{100,000}$

4.265 means

$$4 \cdot 1 + 2 \cdot \frac{1}{10} + 6 \cdot \frac{1}{100} + 5 \cdot \frac{1}{1000}$$

or

$$4 + \frac{2}{10} + \frac{6}{100} + \frac{5}{1000}$$

Definitions and Concepts	Examples

Section 5.1   Introduction to Decimals   (*continued*)

Writing (or Reading) a Decimal in Words

Step 1: Write the whole number part in words.

Step 2: Write "and" for the decimal point.

Step 3: Write the decimal part in words as though it were a whole number, followed by the place value of the last digit.

A decimal written in words can be written in standard form by reversing the above procedure.

Write 3.08 in words.
Three and eight hundredths

Write "negative four and twenty-one thousandths" in standard form.

$$-4.021$$

To Round a Decimal to a Place Value to the Right of the Decimal Point

Step 1: Locate the digit to the right of the given place value.

Step 2: If this digit is 5 or greater, add 1 to the digit in the given place value and drop all digits to its right. If this digit is less than 5, drop all digits to the right of the given place value.

Round 86.1256 to the nearest hundredth.

Step 1: 86.12 5 6   ⎡—hundredths place
                        ⎣—digit to the right

Step 2: Since the digit to the right is 5 or greater, we add 1 to the digit in the hundredths place and drop all digits to its right.

86.1256 rounded to the nearest hundredth is 86.13.

Section 5.2   Adding and Subtracting Decimals

To Add or Subtract Decimals

Step 1: Write the decimals so that the decimal points line up vertically.

Step 2: Add or subtract as with whole numbers.

Step 3: Place the decimal point in the sum or difference so that it lines up vertically with the decimal points in the problem.

Add: 4.6 + 0.28   Subtract: 2.8 − 1.04

$$\begin{array}{r} 4.60 \\ + 0.28 \\ \hline 4.88 \end{array} \qquad \begin{array}{r} 2.8\cancel{0} \\ - 1.04 \\ \hline 1.76 \end{array}$$

Section 5.3   Multiplying Decimals and Circumference of a Circle

To Multiply Decimals

Step 1: Multiply the decimals as though they are whole numbers.

Step 2: The decimal point in the product is placed so that the number of decimal places in the product is equal to the *sum* of the number of decimal places in the factors.

Multiply: 1.48 × 5.9

$$\begin{array}{r} 1.48 \\ \times\ 5.9 \\ \hline 1332 \\ 7400 \\ \hline 8.732 \end{array}$$

1.48 ← 2 decimal places
× 5.9 ← 1 decimal place

8.732 ← 3 decimal places

(continued)

Definitions and Concepts	Examples

Section 5.3   Multiplying Decimals and Circumference of a Circle   (*continued*)

The **circumference** of a circle is the distance around the circle.

$$C = \pi d \text{ or } C = 2\pi r$$

where $\pi \approx 3.14$ or $\pi \approx \dfrac{22}{7}$.

or

Find the exact circumference of a circle with radius 5 miles and an approximation by using 3.14 for π.

$$
\begin{aligned}
C &= 2\pi r \\
&= 2\pi(5) \\
&= 10\pi \\
&\approx 10(3.14) \\
&\approx 31.4
\end{aligned}
$$

The circumference is exactly 10π miles and approximately 31.4 miles.

Section 5.4   Dividing Decimals

To Divide Decimals

Step 1: If the divisor is not a whole number, move the decimal point in the divisor to the right until the divisor is a whole number.

Step 2: Move the decimal point in the dividend to the right the *same number of places* as the decimal point was moved in Step 1.

Step 3: Divide. The decimal point in the quotient is directly over the moved decimal point in the dividend.

Divide: $1.118 \div 2.6$

$$
\begin{array}{r}
0.43 \\
2.6\overline{)1.118} \\
-104 \\
\hline
78 \\
-78 \\
\hline
0
\end{array}
$$

Section 5.5   Fractions, Decimals, and Order of Operations

To **write fractions as decimals,** divide the numerator by the denominator.

Write $\dfrac{3}{8}$ as a decimal.

$$
\begin{array}{r}
0.375 \\
8\overline{)3.000} \\
-24 \\
\hline
60 \\
-56 \\
\hline
40 \\
-40 \\
\hline
0
\end{array}
$$

Order of Operations

1. Perform all operations within parentheses ( ), brackets [ ], or other grouping symbols such as fraction bars.
2. Evaluate any expressions with exponents.
3. Multiply or divide in order from left to right.
4. Add or subtract in order from left to right.

Simplify.

$$
\begin{aligned}
-1.9(12.8 - 4.1) &= -1.9(8.7) \quad \text{Subtract.} \\
&= -16.53 \quad \text{Multiply.}
\end{aligned}
$$

Definitions and Concepts	Examples
Section 5.6　Solving Equations Containing Decimals	

Steps for Solving an Equation in x

Step 1: If fractions are present, multiply both sides of the equation by the LCD of the fractions.

Step 2: If parentheses are present, use the distributive property.

Step 3: Combine any like terms on each side of the equation.

Step 4: Use the addition property of equality to rewrite the equation so that variable terms are on one side of the equation and constant terms are on the other side.

Step 5: Divide both sides by the numerical coefficient of x to solve.

Step 6: Check your answer in the *original equation*.

Solve:

$$3(x + 2.6) = 10.92$$
$$3x + 7.8 = 10.92 \quad \text{Apply the distributive property.}$$

$$3x + 7.8 - 7.8 = 10.92 - 7.8 \quad \text{Subtract 7.8 from both sides.}$$

$$3x = 3.12 \quad \text{Simplify.}$$
$$\frac{3x}{3} = \frac{3.12}{3} \quad \text{Divide both sides by 3.}$$
$$x = 1.04 \quad \text{Simplify.}$$

Check 1.04 in the original equation.

Section 5.7　Decimal Applications: Mean, Median, and Mode	

The **mean** (or **average**) of a set of number items is

$$\text{mean} = \frac{\text{sum of items}}{\text{number of items}}$$

The **median** of a set of numbers in numerical order is the middle number. If the number of items is even, the median is the mean of the two middle numbers.

The **mode** of a set of numbers is the number that occurs most often. (A set of numbers may have no mode or more than one mode.)

Find the mean, median, and mode of the following set of numbers: 33, 35, 35, 43, 68, 68

$$\text{mean} = \frac{33 + 35 + 35 + 43 + 68 + 68}{6} = 47$$

The median is the mean of the two middle numbers, 35 and 43

$$\text{median} = \frac{35 + 43}{2} = 39$$

There are two modes because there are two numbers that occur twice:

35 and 68

Chapter 5　Review

(5.1) *Determine the place value of the number 4 in each decimal.*

1. 23.45

2. 0.000345

Write each decimal in words.

3. −23.45

4. 0.00345

5. 109.23

6. 200.000032

Write each decimal in standard form.

7. Eight and six hundredths

8. Negative five hundred three and one hundred two thousandths

9. Sixteen thousand twenty-five and fourteen ten-thousandths

10. Fourteen and eleven thousandths

Write each decimal as a fraction or a mixed number.

11. 0.16

12. −12.023

Write each fraction or mixed number as a decimal.

13. $\dfrac{231}{100,000}$

14. $25\dfrac{1}{4}$

Insert $<$, $>$, or $=$ between each pair of numbers to make a true statement.

15. 0.49   0.43

16. 0.973   0.9730

17. −38.0027   −38.00056

18. −0.230505   −0.23505

Round each decimal to the given place value.

19. 0.623, nearest tenth

20. 0.9384, nearest hundredth

21. −42.895, nearest hundredth

22. 16.34925, nearest thousandth

Write each number in standard notation.

23. Saturn is a distance of about 887 million miles from the Sun.

24. The tail of a comet can be over 600 thousand miles long.

(5.2) *Add.*

25. 8.6 + 9.5

26. 3.9 + 1.2

27. −6.4 + (−0.88)

28. −19.02 + 6.98

29. 200.49 + 16.82 + 103.002

30. 0.00236 + 100.45 + 48.29

Subtract.

31. 4.9 − 3.2

32. 5.23 − 2.74

33. −892.1 − 432.4

34. 0.064 − 10.2

35. 100 − 34.98

36. 200 − 0.00198

Solve.

37. Find the total distance between Grove City and Jerome.

38. Evaluate $x - y$ for $x = 1.2$ and $y = 6.9$.

△ **39.** Find the perimeter.

△ **40.** Find the perimeter.

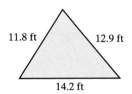

(5.3) *Multiply.*

41. 7.2×10

42. 9.345×1000

43. -34.02×2.3

44. $-839.02 \times (-87.3)$

Find the exact circumference of each circle. Then use the approximation 3.14 for π and approximate the circumference.

△ **45.**

△ **46.**

(5.4) *Divide. Round the quotient to the nearest thousandth if necessary.*

47. $3\overline{)0.2631}$

48. $20\overline{)316.5}$

49. $-21 \div (-0.3)$

50. $-0.0063 \div 0.03$

51. $0.34\overline{)2.74}$

52. $19.8\overline{)601.92}$

53. $\dfrac{23.65}{1000}$

54. $\dfrac{93}{-10}$

55. There are approximately 3.28 feet in 1 meter. Find how many meters are in 24 feet to the nearest tenth of a meter.

56. George Strait pays $69.71 per month to pay back a loan of $3136.95. In how many months will the loan be paid off?

(5.5) *Write each fraction or mixed number as a decimal. Round to the nearest thousandth if necessary.*

57. $\dfrac{4}{5}$

58. $-\dfrac{12}{13}$

59. $2\dfrac{1}{3}$

60. $\dfrac{13}{60}$

Insert $<, >,$ *or* $=$ *to make a true statement.*

61. 0.392   0.39200

62. −0.0231   −0.0221

63. $\dfrac{4}{7}$ 0.625

64. 0.293 $\dfrac{5}{17}$

Write the numbers in order from smallest to largest.

65. 0.837, 0.839, 0.832

66. 0.685, 0.626, $\dfrac{5}{8}$

67. $\dfrac{3}{7}$, 0.42, 0.43

68. $\dfrac{18}{11}$, 1.63, $\dfrac{19}{12}$

Simplify each expression.

69. $-7.6 \times 1.9 + 2.5$

70. $(-2.3)^2 - 1.4$

71. $0.0726 \div 10 \times 1000$

72. $0.9(6.5 - 5.6)$

73. $\dfrac{(1.5)^2 + 0.5}{0.05}$

74. $\dfrac{7 + 0.74}{-0.06}$

Find each area.

△ **75.**

3 feet

4.6 feet

△ **76.**

2.1 inches

5.2 inches

(5.6) *Solve.*

77. $x + 3.9 = 4.2$

78. $70 = y - 22.81$

79. $2x = 17.2$

80. $-1.1y = 88$

81. $3x - 0.78 = 1.2 + 2x$

82. $-x + 0.6 - 2x = -4x - 0.9$

83. $-1.3x - 9.4 = -0.4x + 8.6$

84. $3(x - 1.1) = 5x - 5.3$

(5.7) *Find the mean, median, and any mode(s) for each list of numbers. If necessary, round to the nearest tenth.*

85. 13, 23, 33, 14, 6

86. 45, 86, 21, 60, 86, 64, 45

87. 14,000, 20,000, 12,000, 20,000, 36,000, 45,000

88. 560, 620, 123, 400, 410, 300, 400, 780, 430, 450

For Exercises 89 and 90, the grades are given for a student for a particular semester. Find each grade point average. If necessary, round the grade point average to the nearest hundredth.

89.

Grade	Credit Hours
A	3
A	3
C	2
B	3
C	1

90.

Grade	Credit Hours
B	3
B	4
C	2
D	2
B	3

Mixed Review

91. Write 200.0032 in words.

92. Write negative sixteen and nine hundredths in standard form.

93. Write 0.0847 as a fraction or a mixed number.

94. Write the numbers $\frac{6}{7}, \frac{8}{9}, 0.75$ in order from smallest to largest.

Write each fraction as a decimal. Round to the nearest thousandth, if necessary.

95. $-\frac{7}{100}$

96. $\frac{9}{80}$ (Do not round.)

97. $\frac{8935}{175}$

Insert $<$, $>$, or $=$ to make a true statement.

98. $-402.000032 \qquad -402.00032$

99. $\frac{6}{11} \qquad 0.55$

Round each decimal to the given place value.

100. 86.905, nearest hundredth

101. 3.11526, nearest thousandth

Round each money amount to the nearest dollar.

102. $123.46

103. $3645.52

Add or subtract as indicated.

104. $3.2 - 4.9$

105. $9.12 - 3.86$

106. $-102.06 + 89.3$

107. $-4.021 + (-10.83) + (-0.056)$

Multiply or divide as indicated. Round to the nearest thousandth, if necessary.

108. $\begin{array}{r} 2.54 \\ \times\ 3.2 \\ \hline \end{array}$ **109.** $(-3.45)(2.1)$ **110.** $0.005\overline{)24.5}$ **111.** $2.3\overline{)54.98}$

Solve.

△ **112.** Tomaso is going to fertilize his lawn, a rectangle that measures 77.3 feet by 115.9 feet. Approximate the area of the lawn by rounding each measurement to the nearest ten feet.

113. Estimate the cost of the items to see whether the groceries can be purchased with a $10 bill.

Simplify each expression.

114. $\dfrac{(3.2)^2}{100}$

115. $(2.6 + 1.4)(4.5 - 3.6)$

Find the mean, median, and any mode(s) for each list of numbers. If needed, round answers to the nearest hundredth.

116. $73, 82, 95, 68, 54$

117. $952, 327, 566, 814, 327, 729$

Write each decimal as indicated.

1. 45.092, in words

2. Three thousand and fifty-nine thousandths, in standard form

Perform each indicated operation. Round the result to the nearest thousandth if necessary.

3. $2.893 + 4.21 + 10.492$ **4.** $-47.92 - 3.28$ **5.** $9.83 - 30.25$

6. 10.2×4.01 **7.** $-0.00843 \div (-0.23)$

Round each decimal to the indicated place value.

8. 34.8923, nearest tenth   **9.** 0.8623, nearest thousandth

Insert $<, >,$ or $=$ between each pair of numbers to form a true statement.

10. 25.0909   25.9090   **11.** $\dfrac{4}{9}$ 0.445

Write each decimal as a fraction or a mixed number.

12. 0.345   **13.** -24.73

Write each fraction as a decimal. If necessary, round to the nearest thousandth.

14. $-\dfrac{13}{26}$ **15.** $\dfrac{16}{17}$

Simplify.

16. $(-0.6)^2 + 1.57$ **17.** $\dfrac{0.23 + 1.63}{-0.3}$ **18.** $2.4x - 3.6 - 1.9x - 9.8$

Answers

1. _____

2. _____

3. _____

4. _____

5. _____

6. _____

7. _____

8. _____

9. _____

10. _____

11. _____

12. _____

13. _____

14. _____

15. _____

16. _____

17. _____

18. _____

405

19. _____

20. _____

21. _____

22. _____

23. _____

24. _____

25. _____

26. _____

27. a. _____

b. _____

28. _____

Solve.

19. $0.2x + 1.3 = 0.7$

20. $2(x + 5.7) = 6x - 3.4$

Find the mean, median, and mode of each list of numbers.

21. 26, 32, 42, 43, 49

22. 8, 10, 16, 16, 14, 12, 12, 13

Find the grade point average. If necessary, round to the nearest hundredth.

23.

Grade	Credit Hours
A	3
B	3
C	3
B	4
A	1

Solve.

24. At its farthest, Pluto is 4583 million miles from the Sun. Write this number using standard notation.

△ **25.** Find the area.

1.1 miles

4.2 miles

△ **26.** Find the exact circumference of the circle. Then use the approximation 3.14 for π and approximate the circumference.

9 miles

27. Vivian Thomas is going to put insecticide on her lawn to control grubworms. The lawn is a rectangle that measures 123.8 feet by 80 feet. The amount of insecticide required is 0.02 ounce per square foot.

a. Find the area of her lawn.

b. Find how much insecticide Vivian needs to purchase.

28. Find the total distance from Bayette to Center City.

Bayette   Crawford   16.1 miles
14.2 miles   23.7 miles   Center City
Atkinson

Write each number in words.

Answers

1. 72

2. 107

3. 546

4. 5026

5. Add: 46 + 713

6. Find the perimeter.

3 in.   7 in.

9 in.

7. Subtract: 543 − 29. Then check by adding.

8. Divide: 3268 ÷ 27

9. Round 278,362 to the nearest thousand.

10. Write the prime factorization of 30.

11. Multiply: 236 × 86

12. Multiply: 236 × 86 × 0

13. Find each quotient and then check the answer by multiplying.

　a. 1)7̄

　b. 12 ÷ 1

　c. $\dfrac{6}{6}$

　d. 9 ÷ 9

　e. $\dfrac{20}{1}$

　f. 18)18̄

14. Find the average of 25, 17, 19, and 39.

15. Simplify: 2 · 4 − 3 ÷ 3

16. Simplify: 77 ÷ 11 · 7

Evaluate.

17. 9^2

18. 5^3

Answers

1. _____

2. _____

3. _____

4. _____

5. _____

6. _____

7. _____

8. _____

9. _____

10. _____

11. _____

12. _____

13. a. _____

　　b. _____

　　c. _____

　　d. _____

　　e. _____

　　f. _____

14. _____

15. _____

16. _____

17. _____

18. _____

19. _____

20. _____

21. _____

22. _____

23. a. _____

    b. _____

    c. _____

24. a. _____

    b. _____

    c. _____

25. _____

26. _____

27. _____

28. _____

29. _____

30. _____

31. _____

32. _____

33. _____

34. _____

35. _____

36. _____

37. _____

38. _____

19. 3^4

20. 10^3

21. Evaluate $\dfrac{x - 5y}{y}$ for $x = 35$ and $y = 5$.

22. Evaluate $\dfrac{2a + 4}{c}$ for $a = 7$ and $c = 3$.

23. Find the opposite of each number.
   a. 13   **b.** -2 **c.** 0

24. Find the opposite of each number.
   a. -7 **b.** 4   **c.** -1

25. Add: $-2 + (-21)$

26. Add: $-7 + (-15)$

Find the value of each expression.

27. $5 \cdot 6^2$

28. $4 \cdot 2^3$

29. -7^2

30. $(-2)^5$

31. $(-5)^2$

32. -3^2

Represent the shaded part as an improper fraction and a mixed number.

33.

34.

35. ◯ ◯ ◯

36.

37. Write the prime factorization of 252.

38. Find the difference of 87 and 25.

39. Write $-\dfrac{72}{26}$ in simplest form.

40. Write $9\dfrac{7}{8}$ as an improper fraction.

41. Determine whether $\dfrac{16}{40}$ and $\dfrac{10}{25}$ are equivalent.

42. Insert $<$ or $>$ to form a true statement. $\dfrac{4}{7} \qquad \dfrac{5}{9}$

Multiply.

43. $\dfrac{2}{3} \cdot \dfrac{5}{11}$

44. $2\dfrac{5}{8} \cdot \dfrac{4}{7}$

45. $\dfrac{1}{4} \cdot \dfrac{1}{2}$

46. $7 \cdot 5\dfrac{2}{7}$

Solve.

47. $\dfrac{z}{-4} = 11 - 5$

48. $6x - 12 - 5x = -20$

49. Add: $763.7651 + 22.001 + 43.89$

50. Add: $89.27 + 14.361 + 127.2318$

51. Multiply: 23.6×0.78

52. Multiply: 43.8×0.645

39. _____

40. _____

41. _____

42. _____

43. _____

44. _____

45. _____

46. _____

47. _____

48. _____

49. _____

50. _____

51. _____

52. _____

6

Ratio, Proportion, and Percent

Check Your Progress

Vocabulary Check

Chapter Highlights

Chapter Review

Chapter Test

Cumulative Review

This chapter is devoted to ratio, proportion, and percent, concepts used virtually every day in ordinary and business life. Understanding percent and using it efficiently depend on understanding ratios, because a percent is a ratio whose denominator is 100. We present techniques to write percents as fractions and as decimals. We then solve percent problems by using equations and also with proportions. A proportion is an equation with two equal ratios. The rest of this chapter is devoted to select applications of percent—including interest rates, sales tax, discounts, and other real-life situations.

Is it "disk" or "disc"? Actually, either spelling can be used unless there is a trademark involved. Disk (or disc) storage is, then, a general category that includes various storage mechanisms where data are recorded and stored by various methods to a surface layer of a rotating disk(s). Disk storage has certainly changed or evolved over the years, and just a few examples are shown here.

In Section 6.1, Exercises 19–22, we find the ratios of diameters of certain disk storage mechanisms.

Disk or Disc?

8″ floppy disk

$5\frac{1}{4}$″ floppy disk

$3\frac{1}{2}$″ floppy disk

12 cm audio Compact Disc (CD)

8 cm mini CD

12 cm Digital Versatile Disc (DVD)

8 cm mini DVD

12 cm Blu-ray Disc (BD)

8 cm mini BD

12″ vinyl record

10″ vinyl record

7″ vinyl record

20 cm LaserDisc

30 cm LaserDisc

12 cm LaserDisc

6.1 Ratio and Proportion

Objective A Writing Ratios as Fractions

A **ratio** is the quotient of two numbers or two quantities. A ratio, in fact, is no different from a fraction, except that a ratio is sometimes written using notation other than fractional notation. For example, the ratio of 1 to 2 can be written as

$$1 \text{ to } 2 \quad \text{or} \quad \frac{1}{2} \quad \text{or} \quad 1:2$$

fractional notation   colon notation

These ratios are all read as, "the ratio of 1 to 2."

Objectives

A Write Ratios as Fractions.

B Solve Proportions.

C Solve Problems Modeled by Proportions.

> **Ratio**
>
> The ratio of a number a to a number b is their quotient. Ways of writing ratios are
>
> $$a \text{ to } b, \quad a{:}b, \quad \text{and} \quad \frac{a}{b}$$

Whenever possible, we will convert quantities in a ratio to the same unit of measurement.

Example 1 Write a ratio for each phrase. Use fractional notation.

a. The ratio of 2 parts salt to 5 parts water
b. The ratio of 18 inches to 2 feet

Solution:

a. The ratio of 2 parts salt to 5 parts water is $\frac{2}{5}$.

b. First we convert to the same unit of measurement. For example,

$$2 \text{ feet} = 2 \cdot 12 \text{ inches} = 24 \text{ inches}$$

The ratio of 18 inches to 2 feet is then $\frac{18}{24}$, or $\frac{3}{4}$ in lowest terms.

■ Work Practice 1

If a ratio compares two decimal numbers, we will write the simplified ratio as a ratio of whole numbers.

Example 2 Write the ratio of 2.5 to 3.15 as a fraction in simplest form.

Solution: The ratio is

$$\frac{2.5}{3.15}$$

Now let's clear the ratio of decimals.

$$\frac{2.5}{3.15} = \frac{2.5 \cdot 100}{3.15 \cdot 100} = \frac{250}{315} = \frac{50}{63} \quad \text{Simplest form}$$

■ Work Practice 2

Practice 1

Write a ratio for each phrase. Use fractional notation.

a. The ratio of 3 parts oil to 7 parts gasoline

b. The ratio of 40 minutes to 3 hours

Practice 2

Write the ratio of 1.68 to 4.8 as a fraction in simplest form.

Answers

1. a. $\frac{3}{7}$ **b.** $\frac{2}{9}$ **2.** $\frac{7}{20}$

Practice 3

Given the triangle shown:

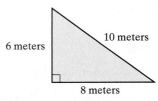

a. Find the ratio of the length of the shortest side to the length of the longest side in simplest form.

b. Find the ratio of the length of the longest side to the perimeter of the triangle in simplest form.

 Example 3   Given the rectangle shown:

a. Find the ratio of its width (shorter side) to its length (longer side).

b. Find the ratio of its length to its perimeter.

Solution:

a. The ratio of its width to its length is

$$\frac{\text{width}}{\text{length}} = \frac{5 \text{ feet}}{7 \text{ feet}} = \frac{5}{7}$$

b. Recall that the perimeter of a rectangle is the distance around the rectangle: $7 + 5 + 7 + 5 = 24$ feet. The ratio of its length to its perimeter is

$$\frac{\text{length}}{\text{perimeter}} = \frac{7 \text{ feet}}{24 \text{ feet}} = \frac{7}{24}$$

■ **Work Practice 3**

✓**Concept Check** Explain why the answer $\frac{7}{5}$ would be incorrect for part (a) of Example 3.

Objective B Solving Proportions

Ratios can be used to form proportions. A **proportion** is a mathematical statement that two ratios are equal.

For example, the equation

$$\frac{1}{2} = \frac{4}{8}$$

is a proportion that says that the ratios $\frac{1}{2}$ and $\frac{4}{8}$ are equal.

Notice that a proportion contains four numbers. If any three numbers are known, we can solve and find the fourth number. One way to do so is to use cross products. To understand cross products, which were introduced in Section 4.2, let's start with the proportion

$$\frac{a}{b} = \frac{c}{d}$$

and multiply both sides by the LCD, bd.

$$\frac{a}{b} = \frac{c}{d}$$

$$bd\left(\frac{a}{b}\right) = bd\left(\frac{c}{d}\right) \quad \text{Multiply both sides by the LCD, } bd.$$

$$ad = bc \quad \text{Simplify.}$$

cross product   cross product

Answers

3. **a.** $\frac{3}{5}$ **b.** $\frac{5}{12}$

✓**Concept Check Answer**

$\frac{7}{5}$ is the ratio of the rectangle's length to its width.

Notice why *ad* and *bc* are called cross products.

$$ad \qquad\qquad\qquad bc$$
$$\frac{a}{b} = \frac{c}{d}$$

Cross Products

If $\dfrac{a}{b} = \dfrac{c}{d}$, then $ad = bc$.

Example 4   Solve for *x*: $\dfrac{45}{x} = \dfrac{5}{7}$

Solution: To solve, we set cross products equal.

$$\frac{45}{x} = \frac{5}{7}$$

$$
\begin{aligned}
45 \cdot 7 &= x \cdot 5 && \text{Set cross products equal.}\\
315 &= 5x && \text{Multiply.}\\
\frac{315}{5} &= \frac{5x}{5} && \text{Divide both sides by 5.}\\
63 &= x && \text{Simplify.}
\end{aligned}
$$

Check: To check, substitute 63 for *x* in the original proportion. The solution is 63.

■ Work Practice 4

Practice 4

Solve for *x*: $\dfrac{3}{8} = \dfrac{63}{x}$

Example 5   Solve for *x*: $\dfrac{x-5}{3} = \dfrac{x+2}{5}$

Solution:

$$\frac{x-5}{3} = \frac{x+2}{5}$$

$$
\begin{aligned}
5(x-5) &= 3(x+2) && \text{Set cross products equal.}\\
5x - 25 &= 3x + 6 && \text{Multiply.}\\
5x &= 3x + 31 && \text{Add 25 to both sides.}\\
2x &= 31 && \text{Subtract } 3x \text{ from both sides.}\\
\frac{2x}{2} &= \frac{31}{2} && \text{Divide both sides by 2.}\\
x &= \frac{31}{2}
\end{aligned}
$$

Check: Verify that $\dfrac{31}{2}$ is the solution.

■ Work Practice 5

Practice 5

Solve for *x*: $\dfrac{2x+1}{7} = \dfrac{x-3}{5}$

✓**Concept Check**   For which of the following equations can we immediately use cross products to solve for *x*?

a. $\dfrac{2-x}{5} = \dfrac{1+x}{3}$ **b.** $\dfrac{2}{5} - x = \dfrac{1+x}{3}$

Answers

4. $x = 168$ **5.** $x = -\dfrac{26}{3}$

✓**Concept Check Answer**

a

Objective C Solving Problems Modeled by Proportions ▶

Writing proportions is a powerful tool for solving problems in almost every field, including business, chemistry, biology, health sciences, and engineering, as well as in daily life. Given a specified ratio (or rate) of two quantities, a proportion can be used to determine an unknown quantity.

Practice 6

On an architect's blueprint, 1 inch corresponds to 4 feet. How long is a wall represented by a $4\frac{1}{4}$-inch line on the blueprint?

Example 6 Determining Distances from a Map

On a Chamber of Commerce map of Abita Springs, 5 miles corresponds to 2 inches. How many miles correspond to 7 inches?

Solution:

1. **UNDERSTAND.** Read and reread the problem. You may want to draw a diagram.

			between 15 and 20 miles
	15 miles		20 miles
5 miles	5 miles	5 miles	5 miles = a little over 15 miles
2 inches	2 inches	2 inches	2 inches = 7 inches
	6 inches		8 inches
		7 inches	

From the diagram we can see that a reasonable solution should be between 15 and 20 miles.

2. **TRANSLATE.** We will let x be our unknown number. Since 5 miles corresponds to 2 inches as x miles corresponds to 7 inches, we have the proportion

$$\begin{array}{rccl} \text{miles} & \rightarrow & \dfrac{5}{2} = \dfrac{x}{7} & \leftarrow \quad \text{miles} \\ \text{inches} & \rightarrow & & \leftarrow \quad \text{inches} \end{array}$$

3. **SOLVE:** In earlier sections, we estimated to obtain a reasonable answer. Notice we did this in Step 1 above.

$$\frac{5}{2} \diagup\!\!\!\!\diagdown \frac{x}{7}$$

$$5 \cdot 7 = 2 \cdot x \qquad \text{Set the cross products equal to each other.}$$

$$35 = 2x \qquad \text{Multiply.}$$

$$\frac{35}{2} = \frac{2x}{2} \qquad \text{Divide both sides by 2.}$$

$$17\frac{1}{2} = x \text{ or } x = 17.5 \qquad \text{Simplify.}$$

4. **INTERPRET.** *Check* your work. This result is reasonable since it is between 15 and 20 miles. *State* your conclusion: 7 inches corresponds to 17.5 miles.

Answer

6. 17 ft

◼ Work Practice 6

Helpful Hint

We can also solve Example 6 by writing the proportion

$$\frac{2 \text{ inches}}{5 \text{ miles}} = \frac{7 \text{ inches}}{x \text{ miles}}$$

Although other proportions may be used to solve Example 6, we will solve by writing proportions so that the numerators have the same unit measures and the denominators have the same unit measures.

Example 7   Finding Medicine Dosage

The standard dose of an antibiotic is 4 cc (cubic centimeters) for every 25 pounds (lb) of body weight. At this rate, find the standard dose for a 140-lb woman.

Solution:

1. UNDERSTAND. Read and reread the problem. You may want to draw a diagram to estimate a reasonable solution.

140-pound woman

25 pounds ⟶ 4 cc
25 pounds ⟶ 4 cc
25 pounds ⟶ 4 cc
25 pounds ⟶ 4 cc
25 pounds ⟶ 4 cc
15 pounds ⟶ ?

140 pounds   over   20 cc

From the diagram, we can see that a reasonable solution is a little over 20 cc.

2. TRANSLATE. We will let x be the unknown number. From the problem, we know that 4 cc is to 25 pounds as x cc is to 140 pounds, or

cubic centimeters $\rightarrow$ $\dfrac{4}{25} = \dfrac{x}{140}$ $\leftarrow$ cubic centimeters
pounds $\rightarrow$ $\leftarrow$ pounds

3. SOLVE:

$$\frac{4}{25} = \frac{x}{140}$$

$4 \cdot 140 = 25 \cdot x$ Set the cross products equal to each other.

$560 = 25x$ Multiply.

$\dfrac{560}{25} = \dfrac{25x}{25}$ Divide both sides by 25.

$22\dfrac{2}{5} = x$ or $x = 22.4$ Simplify.

4. INTERPRET. *Check* your work. This result is reasonable since it is a little over 20 cc. *State* your conclusion: The standard dose for a 140-lb woman is 22.4 cc.

■ Work Practice 7

Practice 7

An auto mechanic recommends that 5 ounces of isopropyl alcohol be mixed with a tankful of gas (16 gallons) to increase the octane of the gasoline for better engine performance. At this rate, how many gallons of gas can be treated with an 8-ounce bottle of alcohol?

Answer

7. $25\dfrac{3}{5}$ or 25.6 gal

Vocabulary, Readiness & Video Check

Use the words and phrases below to fill in each blank.

ratio   cross products   proportion

1. $\frac{4.2}{8.4} = \frac{1}{2}$ is called a _____ while the fraction $\frac{7}{8}$ may also be called a _____ .

2. In $\frac{a}{b} = \frac{c}{d}$, $a \cdot d$ and $b \cdot c$ are called _____ .

Martin-Gay Interactive Videos

See Video 6.1 ●

Watch the section lecture video and answer the following questions.

Objective A 3. In ⊨ Example 2, why are dollars converted to nickels? ▶

Objective B 4. Based on ⊨ Examples 3 and 4, can proportions only be solved by using cross products? Explain. ▶

Objective C 5. In ⊨ Example 5 we are told there are many ways to set up a correct proportion. Why does this fact make it even more important to check that your solution is reasonable? ▶

6.1 Exercise Set MyMathLab® ▶

Objective A *Write each ratio in fractional notation in lowest terms. See Examples 1 through 3.*

1. 2 megabytes to 15 megabytes

2. 18 disks to 41 disks

▶ 3. 10 inches to 12 inches

4. 15 miles to 40 miles

▶ 5. 4 nickels to 2 dollars

6. 12 quarters to 2 dollars

7. 190 minutes to 3 hours

8. 60 hours to 2 days

9. 7.7 to 10

10. 8.1 to 10

11. 3.5 to 12.25

12. 1.5 to 9.75

△ 13. Find the ratio of the length to the width of a regulation size basketball court.

△ 14. Find the ratio of the base to the height of the triangular mainsail.

50 feet (width)

94 feet (length)

18 feet (height)

6 feet (base)

△ **15.** Find the ratio of the longest side to the perimeter of the right-triangular-shaped billboard.

8 feet   **Ski**
15 feet
Whitetop
17 feet

△ **16.** Find the ratio of the width to the perimeter of the rectangular vegetable garden.

4.5 meters   2 meters

Blood contains three types of cells: red blood cells, white blood cells, and platelets. For approximately every 600 red blood cells in healthy humans, there are 40 platelets and 1 white blood cell. Use this for Exercises 17 and 18. (Source: American Red Cross Biomedical Services)

17. Write the ratio of red blood cells to platelet cells.

18. Write the ratio of white blood cells to red blood cells.

Exercises 19–22 have to do with disk storage. See the Chapter Opener for more information on disk storage.

19. A standard DVD has a diameter of 12 centimeters while a miniDVD has a diameter of 8 centimeters. Write the ratio of the miniDVD diameter to the standard DVD diameter.

20. LaserDiscs have a diameter of 12 centimeters and 20 centimeters. Write the ratio of the smaller diameter to the larger diameter.

21. Hard drives come in many diameters. Find the ratio of a $2\frac{1}{2}''$ diameter to a $5\frac{1}{4}''$ diameter hard drive. (Note: If you choose to work with mixed numbers, find $2\frac{1}{2} \div 5\frac{1}{4}$, or write each mixed number as an equivalent decimal number.)

22. Floppy disks come in many diameters. Find the ratio of a $3\frac{1}{2}''$ diameter to a $5\frac{1}{4}''$ diameter floppy disk. (See the note for the previous exercise.)

Objective B *Solve each proportion. See Examples 4 and 5.*

23. $\dfrac{2}{3} = \dfrac{x}{6}$

24. $\dfrac{x}{2} = \dfrac{16}{6}$

25. $\dfrac{x}{10} = \dfrac{5}{9}$

26. $\dfrac{9}{4x} = \dfrac{6}{2}$

27. $\dfrac{4x}{6} = \dfrac{7}{2}$

28. $\dfrac{a}{5} = \dfrac{3}{2}$

29. $\dfrac{x-3}{x} = \dfrac{4}{7}$

30. $\dfrac{y}{y-16} = \dfrac{5}{3}$

31. $\dfrac{x+1}{2x+3} = \dfrac{2}{3}$

32. $\dfrac{x+1}{x+2} = \dfrac{5}{3}$

33. $\dfrac{9}{5} = \dfrac{12}{3x+2}$

34. $\dfrac{6}{11} = \dfrac{27}{3x-2}$

35. $\dfrac{3}{x+1} = \dfrac{5}{2x}$

36. $\dfrac{7}{x-3} = \dfrac{8}{2x}$

37. $\dfrac{16}{3x-4} = \dfrac{5}{x}$

38. $\dfrac{x}{3} = \dfrac{2x-5}{7}$

Objective C *Solve. See Examples 6 and 7.*

39. The ratio of the weight of an object on Earth to the weight of the same object on Pluto is 100 to 3. If an elephant weighs 4100 pounds on Earth, find the elephant's weight on Pluto.

40. If a 170-pound person weighs approximately 65 pounds on Mars, how much does a 9000-pound satellite weigh on Mars? Round to the nearest pound.

41. There are 110 calories per 28.4 grams of Crispy Rice cereal. Find how many calories are in 42.6 grams of this cereal.

42. On an architect's blueprint, 1 inch corresponds to 4 feet. Find the length of a wall represented by a line that is $3\frac{7}{8}$ inches long on the blueprint.

43. A 16-oz grande Shaken Sweet Tea at Starbucks has 100 calories. How many calories are there in a 24-oz venti Shaken Sweet Tea? (*Source:* Starbucks Coffee Company)

44. A 16-oz nonfat Skinny Mocha at Starbucks has 140 calories. How many calories are there in a 12-oz nonfat Skinny Mocha? (*Source:* Starbucks Coffee Company)

45. Mosquitos are annoying insects. To eliminate mosquito larvae, a certain granular substance can be applied to standing water in a ratio of 1 tsp per 25 sq ft of standing water.
   a. At this rate, find how many teaspoons of granules must be used for 450 square feet.
   b. If 3 tsp = 1 tbsp, how many tablespoons of granules must be used?

46. Another type of mosquito control is liquid, where 3 oz of pesticide is mixed with 100 oz of water. This mixture is sprayed on roadsides to control mosquito breeding grounds hidden by tall grass.
   a. If one mixture of water with this pesticide can treat 150 feet of roadway, how many ounces of pesticide are needed to treat one mile? (*Hint:* 1 mile = 5280 feet)
   b. If 8 liquid ounces equals one cup, write your answer to part **a** in cups. Round to the nearest cup.

47. The daily supply of oxygen for one person is provided by 625 square feet of lawn. A total of 3750 square feet of lawn would provide the daily supply of oxygen for how many people? (*Source:* Professional Lawn Care Association of America)

48. In 2013, approximately 96 million of the 136 million U.S. employees worked in service industries. In a town of 6800 workers, how many would be expected to work in service-industry jobs? (*Source:* U.S. Bureau of Labor Statistics)

49. A student would like to estimate the height of the Statue of Liberty in New York City's harbor. The length of the Statue of Liberty's right arm is 42 feet. The student's right arm is 2 feet long and her height is $5\frac{1}{3}$ feet. Use this information to estimate the height of the Statue of Liberty. How close is your estimate to the statue's actual height of 111 feet, 1 inch from heel to top of head? (*Source:* National Park Service)

42 feet

$5\frac{1}{3}$ feet

2 feet

50. The length of the Statue of Liberty's index finger is 8 feet while the height to the top of the head is about 111 feet. Suppose your measurements are proportionaly the same as this statue and that your height is 5 feet.

    a. Use this information to find the proposed length of your index finger. Give an exact measurement and then a decimal rounded to the nearest hundredth.

    b. Measure your index finger and write it as decimal in feet rounded to the nearest hundredth. How close is the length of your index finger to the answer to **a**? Explain why.

51. There are 72 milligrams of cholesterol in a 3.5-ounce serving of lobster. How much cholesterol is in 5 ounces of lobster? Round to the nearest tenth of a milligram. (*Source:* The National Institutes of Health)

52. There are 76 milligrams of cholesterol in a 3-ounce serving of skinless chicken. How much cholesterol is in 8 ounces of chicken? (*Source:* USDA)

53. Trump World Tower in New York City is 881 feet tall and contains 72 stories. The Empire State Building contains 102 stories. If the Empire State Building has the same number of feet per floor as the Trump World Tower, approximate its height rounded to the nearest foot. (*Source:* Skyscrapers.com)

54. In 2012, 9 out of 10 American preschool-aged children had received a measles vaccine. In a preschool with 130 students, how many students would be expected to have received a measles vaccine? (*Source:* Centers for Disease Control and Prevention)

55. In 2012, nearly one out of every four autos sold in the United States was a crossover utility vehicle (CUV). If an auto dealership sold 4500 vehicles in total that year, how many of these sales would you expect involved a CUV? (*Source:* Alliance of Automobile Manufacturers)

56. In the United States in 2013, 1 in every 17 private-sector jobs depended on the auto industry. In a group of 595 private-sector U.S. workers, how many would you expect to have worked in a job that depended on the auto industry? (*Source:* Alliance of Automobile Manufacturers)

57. In 2012, two out of every three wireless phones sold in the United States were smartphones. Approximately 170 million wireless phones were sold in the United States in 2012. How many of them were smartphones? Round to the nearest million. (*Source:* Consumer Electronics Association)

58. One pound of firmly packed brown sugar yields $2\frac{1}{4}$ cups. How many pounds of brown sugar will be required in a recipe that calls for 6 cups of firmly packed brown sugar? (*Source:* Based on data from *Family Circle* magazine)

When making homemade ice cream in an electric or a hand-cranked freezer, the tub containing the ice cream mix is surrounded by a brine (water/salt) solution. To freeze the ice cream mix rapidly so that smooth and creamy ice cream results, the brine solution should combine crushed ice and rock salt in a ratio of 5 to 1. Use this for Exercises 59 and 60. (Source: White Mountain Freezers, The Rival Company)

59. A small ice cream freezer requires 12 cups of crushed ice. How much rock salt should be mixed with the ice to create the necessary brine solution?

60. A large ice cream freezer requires $18\frac{3}{4}$ cups of crushed ice. How much rock salt will be needed?

61. The gas/oil ratio for a certain chainsaw is 50 to 1.
   a. How much oil (in gallons) should be mixed with 5 gallons of gasoline?
   b. If 1 gallon equals 128 fluid ounces, write the answer to part **a** in fluid ounces. Round to the nearest whole ounce.

62. The gas/oil ratio for a certain tractor mower is 20 to 1.
   a. How much oil (in gallons) should be mixed with 10 gallons of gas?
   b. If 1 gallon equals 4 quarts, write the answer to part **a** in quarts.

63. The adult daily dosage for a certain medicine is 150 mg (milligrams) of medicine for every 20 pounds of body weight.
   a. At this rate, find the daily dose for a man who weighs 275 pounds.
   b. If the man is to receive 500 mg of this medicine every 8 hours, is he receiving the proper dosage?

64. The adult daily dosage for a certain medicine is 80 mg (milligrams) for every 25 pounds of body weight.
   a. At this rate, find the daily dose for a woman who weighs 190 pounds.
   b. If she is to receive this medicine every 6 hours, find the amount to be given every 6 hours.

Review

Find the prime factorization of each number. See Section 4.2.

65. 200   **66.** 300   **67.** 32   **68.** 81

Concept Extensions

69. Suppose someone tells you that the ratio of 11 inches to 2 feet is $\frac{11}{2}$. How would you correct that person and explain the error?

70. Write a real-life example of a ratio that can be written in fractional notation as $\frac{3}{2}$.

As we have seen earlier, proportions are often used in medicine dosage calculations. The exercises below have to do with liquid drug preparations, where the weight of the drug is contained in a volume of solution. The description of mg and ml below will help. We will study metric units further in Chapter 8.

mg means milligrams (A paper clip weighs about a gram. A milligram is about the weight of $\frac{1}{1000}$ of a paper clip.)

ml means milliliters (A liter is about a quart. A milliliter is about the amount of liquid in $\frac{1}{1000}$ of a quart.)

One way to solve the applications below is to set up the proportion $\frac{mg}{ml} = \frac{mg}{ml}$.

A solution strength of 15 mg of medicine in 1 ml of solution is available.

71. If a patient needs 12 mg of medicine, how many ml do you administer?

72. If a patient needs 33 mg of medicine, how many ml do you administer?

A solution strength of 8 mg of medicine in 1 ml of solution is available.

73. If a patient needs 10 mg of medicine, how many ml do you administer?

74. If a patient needs 6 mg of medicine, how many ml do you administer?

Percents, Decimals, and Fractions

Objective A Understanding Percent

The word **percent** comes from the Latin phrase *per centum*, which means **"per 100."** For example, 53% (53 percent) means 53 per 100. In the square below, 53 of the 100 squares are shaded. Thus, 53% of the figure is shaded.

53 of 100 squares
are shaded
or
53% is shaded.

Objectives

A Understand Percent.

B Write Percents as Decimals or Fractions.

C Write Decimals or Fractions as Percents.

D Applications with Percents, Decimals, and Fractions.

Since 53% means 53 per 100, 53% is the ratio of 53 to 100, or $\frac{53}{100}$.

$$53\% = \frac{53}{100}$$

Also,

$7\% = \frac{7}{100}$ 7 parts per 100 parts

$73\% = \frac{73}{100}$ 73 parts per 100 parts

$109\% = \frac{109}{100}$ 109 parts per 100 parts

Percent

Percent means **per one hundred.** The "%" symbol is used to denote percent.

Percent is used in a variety of everyday situations. For example,

- 84.1% of the U.S. population uses the Internet.
- The store is having a 20%-off sale.
- For the past two years, the enrollment in community colleges increased 15%.
- The South is the home of 49% of all frequent paintball participants.
- 50% of the cinema screens in the United States are digital non-3D.

Example 1 In a survey of 100 people, 17 people drive blue cars. What percent of people drive blue cars?

Solution: Since 17 people out of 100 drive blue cars, the fraction is $\frac{17}{100}$. Then

$$\frac{17}{100} = 17\%$$

Work Practice 1

Practice 1

Of 100 students in a club, 27 are freshmen. What percent of the students are freshmen?

Answer
1. 27%

421

Practice 2

31 out of 100 executives are in their forties. What percent of executives are in their forties?

Example 2 45 out of every 100 young college graduates return home to live (at least temporarily). What percent of college graduates is this? (*Source:* Independent Insurance Agents of America)

Solution:

$$\frac{45}{100} = 45\%$$

■ Work Practice 2

Objective B Writing Percents as Decimals or Fractions

Since percent means "per hundred," we have that

$$1\% = \frac{1}{100} = 0.01$$

In other words, the percent symbol means "per hundred" or, equivalently, "$\frac{1}{100}$" or "0.01." Thus

Write 87% as a fraction: $87\% = 87 \times \frac{1}{100} = \frac{87}{100}$

or

Write 87% as a decimal: $87\% = 87 \times (0.01) = 0.87$

> Results are the same.

Of course, we know that the end results are the same; that is,

$$\frac{87}{100} = 0.87$$

The above gives us two options for converting percents. We can replace the percent symbol, %, by $\frac{1}{100}$ or by 0.01 and then multiply.

For consistency, when we
- convert from a percent to a *decimal,* we will drop the % symbol and multiply by 0.01.
- convert from a percent to a *fraction,* we will drop the % symbol and multiply by $\frac{1}{100}$.

Let's practice writing percents as decimals, then writing percents as fractions.

Writing a Percent as a Decimal

Replace the percent symbol with its decimal equivalent, 0.01; then multiply.

$$43\% = 43(0.01) = 0.43$$

Helpful Hint

If it helps, think of writing a percent as a decimal by

Percent → | Remove the % symbol and move the decimal point 2 places to the left. | → Decimal

Answer

2. 31%

Examples Write each percent as a decimal.

3. $23\% = 23(0.01) = 0.23$ Replace the percent symbol with 0.01. Then multiply.

4. $4.6\% = 4.6(0.01) = 0.046$ Replace the percent symbol with 0.01. Then multiply.

5. $190\% = 190(0.01) = 1.90$ or 1.9

6. $0.74\% = 0.74(0.01) = 0.0074$

7. $100\% = 100(0.01) = 1.00$ or 1

> **Helpful Hint**
> We just learned that $100\% = 1$.

■ Work Practice 3–7

Practice 3–7

Write each percent as a decimal.

3. 49%

4. 3.1%

5. 175%

6. 0.46%

7. 600%

✓**Concept Check** Why is it incorrect to write the percent 0.033% as 3.3 in decimal form?

Now let's write percents as fractions.

Writing a Percent as a Fraction

Replace the percent symbol with its fraction equivalent, $\frac{1}{100}$; then multiply. Don't forget to simplify the fraction if possible.

$$43\% = 43 \cdot \frac{1}{100} = \frac{43}{100}$$

Examples Write each percent as a fraction or mixed number in simplest form.

8. $40\% = 40 \cdot \frac{1}{100} = \frac{40}{100} = \frac{2 \cdot 20}{5 \cdot 20} = \frac{2}{5}$

9. $1.9\% = 1.9 \cdot \frac{1}{100} = \frac{1.9}{100}$. We don't want the numerator of the fraction to contain a decimal, so we multiply by 1 in the form of $\frac{10}{10}$.

$$= \frac{1.9}{100} \cdot \frac{10}{10} = \frac{1.9 \cdot 10}{100 \cdot 10} = \frac{19}{1000}$$

10. $125\% = 125 \cdot \frac{1}{100} = \frac{125}{100} = \frac{5 \cdot 25}{4 \cdot 25} = \frac{5}{4}$ or $1\frac{1}{4}$

11. $33\frac{1}{3}\% = 33\frac{1}{3} \cdot \frac{1}{100} = \frac{100}{3} \cdot \frac{1}{100} = \frac{100 \cdot 1}{3 \cdot 100} = \frac{1}{3}$

$\underbrace{}$ → Write as an improper fraction.

> **Helpful Hint**
> Just as in Example 7, we confirm that $100\% = 1$.

12. $100\% = 100 \cdot \frac{1}{100} = \frac{100}{100} = 1$

■ Work Practice 8–12

Practice 8–12

Write each percent as a fraction or mixed number in simplest form.

8. 50%

9. 2.3%

10. 150%

11. $66\frac{2}{3}\%$

12. 12%

Objective C Writing Decimals or Fractions as Percents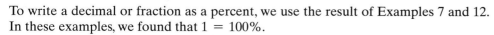

To write a decimal or fraction as a percent, we use the result of Examples 7 and 12. In these examples, we found that $1 = 100\%$.

Write 0.38 as a percent: $0.38 = 0.38(1) = 0.38(100\%) = 38.\%$

Write $\frac{1}{5}$ as a percent: $\frac{1}{5} = \frac{1}{5}(1) = \frac{1}{5} \cdot 100\% = \frac{100}{5}\% = 20\%$

First, let's practice writing decimals as percents.

Answers

3. 0.49   **4.** 0.031   **5.** 1.75   **6.** 0.0046

7. 6   **8.** $\frac{1}{2}$ **9.** $\frac{23}{1000}$ **10.** $\frac{3}{2}$ or $1\frac{1}{2}$

11. $\frac{2}{3}$ **12.** $\frac{3}{25}$

✓**Concept Check Answers**

To write a percent as a decimal, the decimal point should be moved two places to the left, not to the right. So the correct answer is 0.00033.

Writing a Decimal as a Percent

Multiply by 1 in the form of 100%.

$$0.27 = 0.27(100\%) = 27.\%$$

Helpful Hint

If it helps, think of writing a decimal as a percent by reversing the steps in the Helpful Hint on page 422.

Percent ← │ Move the decimal point 2 places to the right and attach a % symbol. │ ← Decimal

---

Practice 13–16

Write each decimal as a percent.
13. 0.14   **14.** 1.75
15. 0.057   **16.** 0.5

Examples Write each decimal as a percent.

13. $0.65 = 0.65(100\%) = 65.\%$ or 65% Multiply by 100%.

14. $1.25 = 1.25(100\%) = 125.\%$ or 125%

15. $0.012 = 0.012(100\%) = 001.2\%$ or 1.2%

16. $0.6 = 0.6(100\%) = 060.\%$ or 60%

Helpful Hint A zero was inserted as a placeholder.

■ Work Practice 13–16

✓**Concept Check** Why is it incorrect to write the decimal 0.0345 as 34.5% in percent form?

Now let's write fractions as percents.

Writing a Fraction as a Percent

Multiply by 1 in the form of 100%.

$$\frac{1}{8} = \frac{1}{8} \cdot 100\% = \frac{1}{8} \cdot \frac{100}{1}\% = \frac{100}{8}\% = 12\frac{1}{2}\%   \text{or}   12.5\%$$

Answers

13. 14%   **14.** 175%   **15.** 5.7%
16. 50%

✓**Concept Check Answer**

To change a decimal to a percent, multiply by 100%, or move the decimal point *only* two places to the right. So the correct answer is 3.45%.

Helpful Hint

From Examples 7 and 12, we know that

$$100\% = 1$$

Recall that when we multiply a number by 1, we are not changing the value of that number. This means that when we multiply a number by 100%, we are not changing its value but rather writing the number as an equivalent percent.

Examples Write each fraction or mixed number as a percent.

17. $\dfrac{7}{20} = \dfrac{7}{20} \cdot 100\% = \dfrac{7}{20} \cdot \dfrac{100}{1}\% = \dfrac{700}{20}\% = 35\%$

18. $\dfrac{2}{3} = \dfrac{2}{3} \cdot 100\% = \dfrac{2}{3} \cdot \dfrac{100}{1}\% = \dfrac{200}{3}\% = 66\dfrac{2}{3}\%$

19. $2\dfrac{1}{4} = \dfrac{9}{4} \cdot 100\% = \dfrac{9}{4} \cdot \dfrac{100}{1}\% = \dfrac{900}{4}\% = 225\%$

Helpful Hint

$\dfrac{200}{3} = 66.\overline{6}.$

Thus, another way to write $\dfrac{200}{3}\%$ is $66.\overline{6}\%.$

Practice 17–19

Write each fraction or mixed number as a percent.

17. $\dfrac{3}{25}$ **18.** $\dfrac{9}{40}$ **19.** $5\dfrac{1}{2}$

■ Work Practice 17–19

✓**Concept Check** Which digit in the percent 76.4582% represents

a. A tenth percent?

b. A thousandth percent?

c. A hundredth percent?

d. A ten percent?

Example 20 Write $\dfrac{1}{12}$ as a percent. Round to the nearest hundredth percent.

Solution:

$\dfrac{1}{12} = \dfrac{1}{12} \cdot 100\% = \dfrac{1}{12} \cdot \dfrac{100\%}{1} = \dfrac{100}{12}\%$ ≈ 8.33%   ← "approximately"

$$\begin{array}{r} 8.333 \approx 8.33 \\ 12\overline{)100.000} \\ -96 \\ \hline 4\,0 \\ -3\,6 \\ \hline 40 \\ -36 \\ \hline 40 \\ -36 \\ \hline 4 \end{array}$$

Thus, $\dfrac{1}{12}$ is approximately 8.33%.

Practice 20

Write $\dfrac{3}{17}$ as a percent. Round to the nearest hundredth percent.

■ Work Practice 20

Objective D Applications with Percents, Decimals, and Fractions ▶

Let's summarize what we have learned so far about percents, decimals, and fractions:

Summary of Converting Percents, Decimals, and Fractions

- *To write a percent as a decimal,* replace the % symbol with its decimal equivalent, 0.01; then multiply.
- *To write a percent as a fraction,* replace the % symbol with its fraction equivalent, $\dfrac{1}{100}$; then multiply.
- *To write a decimal or fraction as a percent,* multiply by 100%.

Answers

17. 12%   **18.** $22\dfrac{1}{2}\%$ **19.** 550%

20. 17.65%

✓**Concept Check Answers**

a. 4   **b.** 8   **c.** 5   **d.** 7

If we let x represent a number, below we summarize using symbols.

Write a percent as a decimal:	Write a percent as a fraction:	Write a number as a percent:
$x\% = x(0.01)$	$x\% = x \cdot \dfrac{1}{100}$	$x = x \cdot 100\%$

Practice 21

A family decides to spend no more than 27.5% of its monthly income on rent. Write 27.5% as a decimal and as a fraction.

Example 21   In the last ten years, automobile thefts in the continental United States have decreased 39.8%. Write this percent as a decimal and as a fraction. (*Source:* The American Automobile Manufacturers Association)

Solution:

As a decimal: $39.8\% = 39.8(0.01) = 0.398$.

As a fraction: $39.8\% = 39.8 \cdot \dfrac{1}{100} = \dfrac{39.8}{100} = \dfrac{39.8}{100} \cdot \dfrac{10}{10} = \dfrac{398}{1000} = \dfrac{\cancel{2} \cdot 199}{\cancel{2} \cdot 500} = \dfrac{199}{500}$.

Thus, 39.8% written as a decimal is 0.398, and written as a fraction is $\dfrac{199}{500}$.

■ Work Practice 21

Practice 22

Provincetown's budget for waste disposal increased by $1\frac{3}{4}$ times over the budget from last year. What percent increase is this?

Example 22   An advertisement for a stereo system reads "$\frac{1}{4}$ off." What percent off is this?

Solution: Write $\dfrac{1}{4}$ as a percent.

$$\frac{1}{4} = \frac{1}{4} \cdot 100\% = \frac{1}{4} \cdot \frac{100\%}{1} = \frac{100}{4}\% = 25\%$$

Thus, "$\frac{1}{4}$ off" is the same as "25% off."

■ Work Practice 22

Answers

21. $0.275, \dfrac{11}{40}$ **22.** 175%

Note: It is helpful to know a few basic percent conversions. Appendix A.2 contains a handy reference of percent, decimal, and fraction equivalencies.
    Also, Appendix A.3 shows how to find common percents of a number.

Vocabulary, Readiness & Video Check

Use the choices below to fill in each blank. Some choices may be used more than once.

$\frac{1}{100}$ 0.01   100%   percent

1. _____ means "per hundred."

2. _____ = 1.

3. The % symbol is read as _____.

4. To write a decimal or a fraction as a percent, multiply by 1 in the form of _____.

5. To write a percent as a *decimal,* drop the % symbol and multiply by _____.

6. To write a percent as a *fraction,* drop the % symbol and multiply by _____.

Martin-Gay Interactive Videos   *Watch the section lecture video and answer the following questions.*

See Video 6.2

Objective A **7.** From the lecture before ⊞ Example 1, what is the most important thing to remember about percent? ⊙

Objective B **8.** From ⊞ Example 4, what is the percent equivalent of 1? ⊙

Objective C **9.** Complete this statement based on ⊞ Example 9: Multiplying by 100% is the same as multiplying by _____. ⊙

Objective D **10.** From ⊞ Example 15, what is the main difference between writing a percent as a decimal and writing a percent as a fraction? ⊙

6.2 Exercise Set MyMathLab® ⊙

Objective A *Solve. See Examples 1 and 2.*

⊙ **1.** In a survey of 100 college students, 96 use the Internet. What percent use the Internet?

2. A basketball player makes 81 out of 100 attempted free throws. What percent of free throws are made?

One hundred adults were asked to name their favorite sport, and the results are shown in the circle graph.

3. What sport was preferred by most adults? What percent preferred this sport?

4. What sport was preferred by the least number of adults? What percent preferred this sport?

5. What percent of adults preferred football or soccer?

6. What percent of adults preferred basketball or baseball?

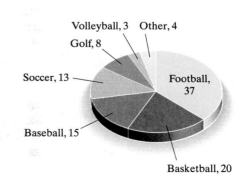

Volleyball, 3   Other, 4
Golf, 8
Soccer, 13
Football, 37
Baseball, 15
Basketball, 20

Objective B *Write each percent as a decimal. See Examples 3 through 7.*

▶ **7.** 41%   **8.** 62%   ▶ **9.** 6%   **10.** 3%

▶ **11.** 100%   **12.** 136%   **13.** 73.6%   **14.** 45.7%

▶ **15.** 2.8%   **16.** 1.4%   **17.** 0.6%   **18.** 0.9%

19. 300%   **20.** 500%   **21.** 32.58%   **22.** 72.18%

Write each percent as a fraction or mixed number in simplest form. See Examples 8 through 12.

▶ **23.** 8%   **24.** 22%   **25.** 4%   **26.** 2%

27. 4.5%   **28.** 7.5%   ▶ **29.** 175%   **30.** 275%

31. 6.25%   **32.** 8.75%   ▶ **33.** $10\frac{1}{3}$ %   **34.** $7\frac{3}{4}$ %

35. $22\frac{3}{8}$ %   **36.** $21\frac{7}{8}$ %

Objective C *Write each decimal as a percent. See Examples 13 through 16.*

▶ **37.** 0.22   **38.** 0.44   ▶ **39.** 0.006   **40.** 0.008

41. 5.3   **42.** 2.7   **43.** 0.056   **44.** 0.019

45. 0.2228   **46.** 0.1115   ▶ **47.** 3.00   **48.** 9.00

49. 0.7   **50.** 0.8

Write each fraction or mixed number as a percent. See Examples 17 through 19.

51. $\frac{7}{10}$ **52.** $\frac{9}{10}$ ▶ **53.** $\frac{4}{5}$ **54.** $\frac{2}{5}$

55. $\frac{34}{50}$ **56.** $\frac{41}{50}$ **57.** $\frac{3}{8}$ **58.** $\frac{5}{16}$

▶ **59.** $\frac{1}{3}$ **60.** $\frac{5}{6}$ **61.** $4\frac{1}{2}$ **62.** $6\frac{1}{5}$

63. $1\frac{9}{10}$ **64.** $2\frac{7}{10}$

Write each fraction as a percent. Round to the nearest hundredth percent. See Example 20.

65. $\frac{9}{11}$ **66.** $\frac{11}{12}$ ▶ **67.** $\frac{4}{15}$ **68.** $\frac{10}{11}$

Objectives A B C Mixed Practice *Complete each table. See Examples 1 through 20.*

69.

Percent	Decimal	Fraction
60%		
	0.235	
		$\frac{4}{5}$
$33\frac{1}{3}$%		
		$\frac{7}{8}$
7.5%		

70.

Percent	Decimal	Fraction
	0.525	
		$\frac{3}{4}$
$66\frac{1}{2}$%		
		$\frac{5}{6}$
100%		
		$\frac{7}{50}$

71.

Percent	Decimal	Fraction
200%		
	2.8	
705%		
		$4\frac{27}{50}$

72.

Percent	Decimal	Fraction
800%		
	3.2	
608%		
		$9\frac{13}{50}$

Objective D *Write each percent as a decimal and a fraction. See Examples 21 and 22.*

73. People take aspirin for a variety of reasons. A common use of aspirin is to prevent heart disease, accounting for 38% of all aspirin use. (*Source:* Bayer Market Research)

74. Japan exports 80.5% of all motorcycles manufactured there. (*Source:* Japan Automobile Manufacturers Association)

75. In the United States recently, 35.8% of households had no landlines, just cell phones. (*Source:* CTIA— The Wireless Association)

76. From 2000 to 2011, use of smoked tobacco products in the United States decreased by 27.5%. (*Source:* Centers for Disease Control and Prevention)

77. Approximately 91% of all eighth-grade students in public schools recently reported that they use a computer at home. (*Source:* National Center for Education Statistics)

78. Approximately 15.7% of the American population is not covered by health insurance. (*Source:* U.S. Census Current Population Study)

In Exercises 79 through 82, write the percent from the circle graph as a decimal and a fraction.

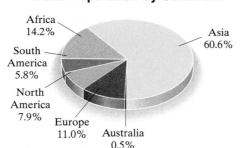

World Population by Continent

Africa 14.2%
South America 5.8%
North America 7.9%
Europe 11.0%
Australia 0.5%
Asia 60.6%

79. Australia: 0.5%

80. Europe: 11%

81. Africa: 14.2%

82. Asia: 60.6%

Solve. See Examples 21 and 22.

83. In a particular year, 0.781 of all electricity produced in France was nuclear generated. Write this decimal as a percent.

84. The United States' share of the total world motor vehicle production is 0.123. Write this decimal as a percent. (*Source:* OICA)

85. The mirrors on the Hubble Space Telescope are able to lock onto a target without deviating more than $\frac{7}{1000}$ of an arc-second. Write this fraction as a percent. (*Source:* NASA)

86. In a recent year, $\frac{1}{4}$ of light trucks sold in the United States were white. Write this fraction as a percent.

87. In 2012, the U.S. Postal Service handled 40% of the world's card and letter mail volume. Write this percent as a decimal. (*Source:* U.S. Postal Service)

88. In 2013, 20% of viewers bought a high-definition television to watch the Super Bowl. Write this percent as a fraction. (*Source:* Nielsen Media)

Review

Perform the indicated operations. See Sections 4.6 and 4.7.

89. $\frac{3}{4} - \frac{1}{2} \cdot \frac{8}{9}$

90. $\left(\frac{2}{11} + \frac{5}{11}\right)\left(\frac{2}{11} - \frac{5}{11}\right)$

91. $6\frac{2}{3} - 4\frac{5}{6}$

92. $6\frac{2}{3} \div 4\frac{5}{6}$

Concept Extensions

Solve. See the Concept Checks in this section.

93. Given the percent 52.8647%, round as indicated.
   a. Round to the nearest tenth percent.
   b. Round to the nearest hundredth percent.

94. Given the percent 0.5269%, round as indicated.
   a. Round to the nearest tenth percent.
   b. Round to the nearest hundredth percent.

95. Which of the following are correct?
   a. 6.5% = 0.65
   b. 7.8% = 0.078
   c. 120% = 0.12
   d. 0.35% = 0.0035

96. Which of the following are correct?
   a. 0.231 = 23.1%
   b. 5.12 = 0.0512%
   c. 3.2 = 320%
   d. 0.0175 = 0.175%

Recall that 1 = 100%. This means that 1 whole is 100%. Use this for Exercises 97 and 98. (Source: Some Body! by Dr. Pete Rowen)

97. The four blood types are A, B, O, and AB. (Each blood type can also be further classified as Rh-positive or Rh-negative depending upon whether your blood contains protein or not.) Given the percent blood types for people in the United States below, calculate the percent of the U.S. population with AB blood type.

45%   40%   11%   ?%

98. The top four components of bone are below. Find the missing percent.
   1. Minerals—45%
   2. Living tissue—30%
   3. Water—20%
   4. Other—?

What percent of the figure is shaded?

99.

100.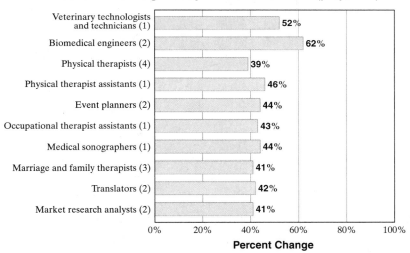

Fill in the blanks.

101. A fraction written as a percent is greater than 100% when the numerator is _____ than the denominator. (greater/less)

102. A decimal written as a percent is less than 100% when the decimal is _____ than 1. (greater/less)

Write each fraction as a decimal and then write each decimal as a percent. Round the decimal to three decimal places (nearest thousandth) and the percent to the nearest tenth percent.

103. $\dfrac{21}{79}$

104. $\dfrac{56}{102}$

The bar graph shows the predicted fastest-growing occupations by percent that require an associate degree or more education. Use this graph for Exercises 105 through 108.

Fastest-Growing Occupations 2010–2020 (projected)

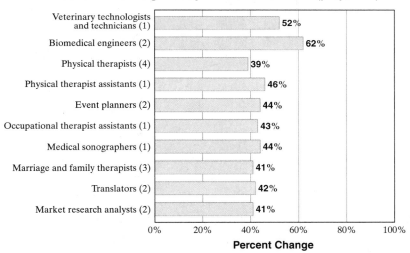

Veterinary technologists and technicians (1) — 52%
Biomedical engineers (2) — 62%
Physical therapists (4) — 39%
Physical therapist assistants (1) — 46%
Event planners (2) — 44%
Occupational therapist assistants (1) — 43%
Medical sonographers (1) — 44%
Marriage and family therapists (3) — 41%
Translators (2) — 42%
Market research analysts (2) — 41%

Percent Change

(*Note:* (1) = associate degree; (2) = bachelor degree; (3) = master degree; (4) = doctoral or professional degree)
Source: Bureau of Labor Statistics

105. What occupation is predicted to be the fastest growing?

106. What occupation is predicted to be the second fastest growing?

107. Write the percent change for physical therapists as a decimal.

108. Write the percent change for event planners as a decimal.

109. In your own words, explain how to write a percent as a decimal.

110. In your own words, explain how to write a decimal as a percent.

Solving Percent Problems with Equations

Objectives

A Write Percent Problems as Equations.

B Solve Percent Problems.

Sections 6.3 and 6.4 introduce two methods for solving percent problems. It may not be necessary for you to study both sections. You may want to check with your instructor for further advice.

To solve percent problems in this section, we will translate the problems into mathematical statements, or equations.

Objective A Writing Percent Problems as Equations

Recognizing key words in a percent problem is helpful in writing the problem as an equation. Three key words in the statement of a percent problem and their meanings are as follows:

> **of** means **multiplication** (·)
>
> **is** means **equal** (=)
>
> **what** (or some equivalent) means **the unknown number**

In our examples, we will let the letter x stand for the unknown number.

Practice 1

Translate: 8 is what percent of 48?

Example 1 Translate to an equation:

5 is what percent of 20?

Solution: 5   is   what percent of   20?
            ↓   ↓   ↓   ↓   ↓
            5   = x ·   20

■ Work Practice 1

Helpful Hint

Remember that an equation is simply a mathematical statement that contains an equal sign (=).

$$5 = 20x$$
  ↑
equal sign

Practice 2

Translate: 2.6 is 40% of what number?

Example 2 Translate to an equation:

1.2 is 30% of what number?

Solution: 1.2   is   30%   of   what number?
            ↓   ↓   ↓   ↓   ↓
            1.2   =   30%   · x

■ Work Practice 2

Practice 3

Translate: What number is 90% of 0.045?

Example 3 Translate to an equation:

What number is 25% of 0.008?

Solution: What number   is   25%   of   0.008?
                ↓   ↓   ↓   ↓   ↓
                x =   25%   ·   0.008

■ Work Practice 3

Answers

1. $8 = x \cdot 48$ **2.** $2.6 = 40\% \cdot x$
3. $x = 90\% \cdot 0.045$

432

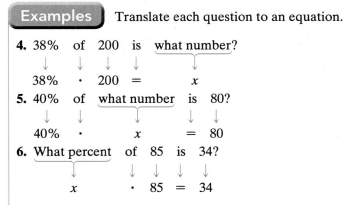

Examples Translate each question to an equation.

4. 38%   of   200   is   what number?
    ↓   ↓   ↓   ↓   ↓
   38% · 200   =   x

5. 40%   of   what number   is   80?
    ↓   ↓   ↓   ↓   ↓
   40% ·   x   =   80

6. What percent   of   85   is   34?
        ↓   ↓   ↓   ↓
        x   · 85 = 34

◼ Work Practice 4–6

Practice 4–6

Translate each question to an equation.

4. 56% of 180 is what number?
5. 12% of what number is 21?
6. What percent of 95 is 76?

✔**Concept Check** In the equation $2x = 10$, what step is taken to solve the equation?

Objective B Solving Percent Problems ▶

You may have noticed by now that each percent problem has contained three numbers—in our examples, two are known and one is unknown. Each of these numbers is given a special name.

15%   of   60   is   9
 ↓   ↓   ↓   ↓   ↓
15%   ·   60   =   9
percent   base   amount

We call this equation the **percent equation.**

Percent Equation

percent · base = amount

Once a percent problem has been written as a percent equation, we can use the equation to find the unknown number, whether it is the percent, the base, or the amount.

Example 7 Solving Percent Equations for the Amount

        What number   is   35%   of   60?
            ↓   ↓   ↓   ↓   ↓
Solution: x   =   35% · 60   Translate to an equation.

            x   =   0.35 · 60   Write 35% as 0.35.

            x   =   21   Multiply: 60
                                                    × 0.35
                                                      300
                                                     1800
                                                    21.00

Then 21 is 35% of 60. Is this reasonable? To see, round 35% to 40%. Then 40% of 60 or 0.40(60) is 24. Our result is reasonable since 21 is close to 24.

◼ Work Practice 7

Practice 7

What number is 25% of 90?

Answers

4. $56\% \cdot 180 = x$ 5. $12\% \cdot x = 21$
6. $x \cdot 95 = 76$ 7. 22.5

✔**Concept Check Answer**

Divide both sides of the equation by 2.

Helpful Hint

When solving a percent equation, write the percent as a decimal or fraction.

Practice 8

95% of 400 is what number?

Example 8   85% of 300 is what number?

Solution:
$$85\% \cdot 300 = x \quad \text{Translate to an equation.}$$
$$0.85 \cdot 300 = x \quad \text{Write 85\% as 0.85.}$$
$$255 = x \quad \text{Multiply: } 0.85 \cdot 300 = 255.$$

Then 85% of 300 is 255. Is this result reasonable? To see, round 85% to 90%. Then 90% of 300 or $0.90(300) = 270$, which is close to 255.

■ Work Practice 8

Practice 9

15% of what number is 2.4?

Example 9   Solving Percent Equations for the Base

12% of what number is 0.6?

Solution:
$$12\% \cdot x = 0.6 \quad \text{Translate to an equation.}$$
$$0.12 \cdot x = 0.6 \quad \text{Write 12\% as 0.12.}$$
$$\frac{0.12 \cdot x}{0.12} = \frac{0.6}{0.12} \quad \text{Divide both sides by 0.12.}$$
$$x = 5$$

$$\begin{array}{r} 5. \\ 0.12\overline{)0.60} \\ \underline{60} \\ 0 \end{array}$$

Then 12% of 5 is 0.6. Is this reasonable? To see, round 12% to 10%. Then 10% of 5 or $0.10(5) = 0.5$, which is close to 0.6.

■ Work Practice 9

Practice 10

18 is $4\frac{1}{2}$% of what number?

Example 10   13 is $6\frac{1}{2}$% of what number?

Solution:
$$13 = 6\frac{1}{2}\% \cdot x \quad \text{Translate to an equation.}$$
$$13 = 0.065 \cdot x \qquad 6\frac{1}{2}\% = 6.5\% = 0.065$$
$$\frac{13}{0.065} = \frac{0.065 \cdot x}{0.065} \quad \text{Divide both sides by 0.065.}$$
$$200 = x$$

$$\begin{array}{r} 200. \\ 0.065\overline{)13.000} \\ \underline{130} \\ 0 \end{array}$$

Then 13 is $6\frac{1}{2}$% of 200. Check to see if this result is reasonable.

■ Work Practice 10

Answers

8. 380   **9.** 16   **10.** 400

Example 11 Solving Percent Equations for the Percent

What percent of 12 is 9?

Solution:

$x \cdot 12 = 9$ Translate to an equation.

$\dfrac{x \cdot 12}{12} = \dfrac{9}{12}$ Divide both sides by 12.

or $x = 0.75$

Next, since we are looking for a percent, we can write $\dfrac{9}{12}$ or 0.75 as a percent.

$x = 75\%$

Then 75% of 12 is 9. To check, see that $75\% \cdot 12 = 9$.

▓ Work Practice 11

Practice 11

What percent of 90 is 27?

Helpful Hint

If your unknown in the percent equation is a percent, don't forget to convert your answer to a percent.

Example 12 78 is what percent of 65?

Solution:

$78 = x \cdot 65$ Translate to an equation.

$\dfrac{78}{65} = \dfrac{x \cdot 65}{65}$ Divide both sides by 65.

$1.2 = x$

$120\% = x$ Write 1.2 as a percent.

Then 78 is 120% of 65. Check this result.

▓ Work Practice 12

Practice 12

63 is what percent of 45?

✓**Concept Check** Consider these problems

1. 75% of $50 =$
   a. 50   **b.** a number greater than 50   **c.** a number less than 50
2. 40% of a number is 10. Is the number
   a. 10?   **b.** less than 10?   **c.** greater than 10?
3. 800 is 120% of what number? Is the number
   a. 800?   **b.** less than 800?   **c.** greater than 800?

Helpful Hint

Use the following to see if your answers are reasonable.

(100%) of a number $=$ the number

$\begin{pmatrix} \text{a percent} \\ \text{greater than} \\ 100\% \end{pmatrix}$ of a number $= \begin{matrix} \text{a number greater} \\ \text{than the original number} \end{matrix}$

$\begin{pmatrix} \text{a percent} \\ \text{less than } 100\% \end{pmatrix}$ of a number $= \begin{matrix} \text{a number less} \\ \text{than the original number} \end{matrix}$

Answers
11. 30%   **12.** 140%

✓**Concept Check Answers**
1. c   **2.** c   **3.** b

Vocabulary, Readiness & Video Check

Use the choices below to fill in each blank.

percent	amount	of	less
base	the number	is	greater

1. The word _____ translates to "=" .
2. The word _____ usually translates to "multiplication."
3. In the statement "10% of 90 is 9," the number 9 is called the _____ , 90 is called the _____, and 10 is called the _____ .
4. 100% of a number = _____ .
5. Any "percent greater than 100%" of "a number" = "a number _____ than the original number."
6. Any "percent less than 100%" of "a number" = "a number _____ than the original number."

Martin-Gay Interactive Videos Watch the section lecture video and answer the following questions.

See Video 6.3

Objective A 7. What are the three translations we need to remember from the lecture before ▣ Example 1? ▶

Objective B 8. What is different about the translated equation in ▣ Example 5? ▶

6.3 Exercise Set MyMathLab®

Objective A Translating *Translate each to an equation. Do not solve. See Examples 1 through 6.*

▶ **1.** 18% of 81 is what number?

2. 36% of 72 is what number?

3. 20% of what number is 105?

4. 40% of what number is 6?

5. 0.6 is 40% of what number?

6. 0.7 is 20% of what number?

▶ **7.** What percent of 80 is 3.8?

8. 9.2 is what percent of 92?

9. What number is 9% of 43?

10. What number is 25% of 55?

11. What percent of 250 is 150?

12. What percent of 375 is 300?

Objective B *Solve. See Examples 7 and 8.*

▶ **13.** 10% of 35 is what number?

14. 25% of 68 is what number?

15. What number is 14% of 205?

16. What number is 18% of 425?

Solve. See Examples 9 and 10.

▶ **17.** 1.2 is 12% of what number?

18. 0.22 is 44% of what number?

19. $8\frac{1}{2}$% of what number is 51?

20. $4\frac{1}{2}$% of what number is 45?

Solve. See Examples 11 and 12.

21. What percent of 80 is 88?

22. What percent of 40 is 60?

23. 17 is what percent of 50?

24. 48 is what percent of 50?

Objectives A B Mixed Practice *Solve. See Examples 1 through 12.*

25. 0.1 is 10% of what number?

26. 0.5 is 5% of what number?

27. 150% of 430 is what number?

28. 300% of 56 is what number?

29. 82.5 is $16\frac{1}{2}$% of what number?

30. 7.2 is $6\frac{1}{4}$% of what number?

▶ **31.** 2.58 is what percent of 50?

32. 2.64 is what percent of 25?

33. What number is 42% of 60?

34. What number is 36% of 80?

35. What percent of 184 is 64.4?

36. What percent of 120 is 76.8?

37. 120% of what number is 42?

38. 160% of what number is 40?

39. 2.4% of 26 is what number?

40. 4.8% of 32 is what number?

41. What percent of 600 is 3?

42. What percent of 500 is 2?

43. 6.67 is 4.6% of what number?

44. 9.75 is 7.5% of what number?

45. 1575 is what percent of 2500?

46. 2520 is what percent of 3500?

47. 2 is what percent of 50?

48. 2 is what percent of 40?

Review

Find the value of x in each proportion. See Section 6.1.

49. $\dfrac{27}{x} = \dfrac{9}{10}$

50. $\dfrac{35}{x} = \dfrac{7}{5}$

51. $\dfrac{x}{5} = \dfrac{8}{11}$

52. $\dfrac{x}{3} = \dfrac{6}{13}$

Write each sentence as a proportion. See Section 6.1.

53. 17 is to 12 as x is to 20.   **54.** 20 is to 25 as x is to 10.   **55.** 8 is to 9 as 14 is to x.   **56.** 5 is to 6 as 15 is to x.

Concept Extensions

For each equation, determine the next step taken to find the value of n. See the first Concept Check in this section.

57. $5 \cdot n = 32$

    a. $n = 5 \cdot 32$ **b.** $n = \dfrac{5}{32}$ **c.** $n = \dfrac{32}{5}$ **d.** none of these

58. $68 = 8 \cdot n$

    a. $n = 8 \cdot 68$ **b.** $n = \dfrac{68}{8}$ **c.** $n = \dfrac{8}{68}$ **d.** none of these

59. $0.06 = n \cdot 7$

    a. $n = 0.06 \cdot 7$ **b.** $n = \dfrac{0.06}{7}$ **c.** $n = \dfrac{7}{0.06}$ **d.** none of these

60. $n = 0.7 \cdot 12$

    a. $n = 8.4$ **b.** $n = \dfrac{12}{0.7}$ **c.** $n = \dfrac{0.7}{12}$ **d.** none of these

61. Write a word statement for the equation $20\% \cdot x = 18.6$. Use the phrase "what number" for "x."

62. Write a word statement for the equation $x = 33\dfrac{1}{3}\% \cdot 24$. Use the phrase "what number" for "x."

For each exercise, determine whether the percent, x, is (a) 100%, (b) greater than 100%, or (c) less than 100%. See the second Concept Check in this section.

63. $x\%$ of 20 is 30   **64.** $x\%$ of 98 is 98   **65.** $x\%$ of 120 is 85   **66.** $x\%$ of 35 is 50

For each exercise, determine whether the number, y, is (a) equal to 45, (b) greater than 45, or (c) less than 45.

67. 55% of 45 is y **68.** 230% of 45 is y **69.** 100% of 45 is y

70. 30% of y is 45   **71.** 100% of y is 45   **72.** 180% of y is 45

73. In your own words, explain how to solve a percent equation.

74. Write a percent problem that uses the percent 50%.

Solve.

75. 1.5% of 45,775 is what number?   **76.** What percent of 75,528 is 27,945.36?

77. 22,113 is 180% of what number?

There is more than one method that can be used to solve percent problems. (See the note at the beginning of Section 6.3.) In the last section, we used the percent equation. In this section, we will use proportions.

Objective A Writing Percent Problems as Proportions

Objectives

A Write Percent Problems as Proportions.

B Solve Percent Problems.

To understand the proportion method, recall that 70% means the ratio of 70 to 100, or $\frac{70}{100}$.

$$\frac{7}{10} \text{ shaded}$$

$$70\% = \frac{70}{100} = \frac{7}{10}$$

70% or $\frac{70}{100}$ shaded

Since the ratio $\frac{70}{100}$ is equal to the ratio $\frac{7}{10}$, we have the proportion

$$\frac{7}{10} = \frac{70}{100}$$

We call this proportion the **percent proportion.** In general, we can name the parts of this proportion as follows:

Percent Proportion

$$\frac{\text{amount}}{\text{base}} = \frac{\text{percent}}{100} \quad \leftarrow \text{always 100}$$

or

$$\text{amount} \rightarrow \frac{a}{b} = \frac{p}{100} \quad \leftarrow \text{percent}$$
$$\text{base} \rightarrow$$

When we translate percent problems to proportions, the **percent,** p, can be identified by looking for the symbol % or the word *percent*. The **base,** b, usually follows the word *of*. The **amount,** a, is the part compared to the whole.

Helpful Hint

This table may be useful when identifying the parts of a proportion.

Part of Proportion	How It's Identified
Percent	% or *percent*
Base	Appears after *of*
Amount	Part compared to whole

Practice 1

Translate to a proportion.
27% of what number is 54?

Example 1 Translate to a proportion.

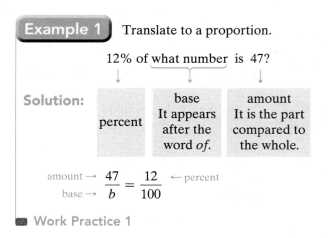

12% of what number is 47?

Solution:

percent | base — It appears after the word *of*. | amount — It is the part compared to the whole.

$$\text{amount} \rightarrow \frac{47}{b} = \frac{12}{100} \leftarrow \text{percent} \quad \text{base} \rightarrow$$

■ Work Practice 1

Practice 2

Translate to a proportion.
30 is what percent of 90?

Example 2 Translate to a proportion.

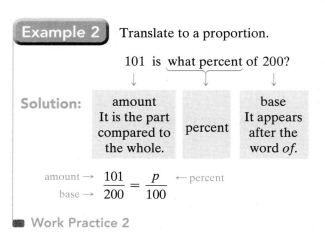

101 is what percent of 200?

Solution:

amount — It is the part compared to the whole. | percent | base — It appears after the word *of*.

$$\text{amount} \rightarrow \frac{101}{200} = \frac{p}{100} \leftarrow \text{percent} \quad \text{base} \rightarrow$$

■ Work Practice 2

Practice 3

Translate to a proportion.
What number is 25% of 116?

Example 3 Translate to a proportion.

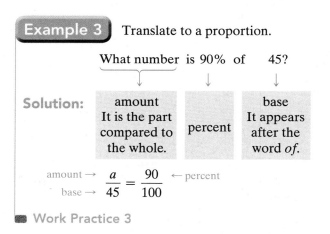

What number is 90% of 45?

Solution:

amount — It is the part compared to the whole. | percent | base — It appears after the word *of*.

$$\text{amount} \rightarrow \frac{a}{45} = \frac{90}{100} \leftarrow \text{percent} \quad \text{base} \rightarrow$$

■ Work Practice 3

Practice 4

Translate to a proportion.
680 is 65% of what number?

Example 4 Translate to a proportion.

238 is 40% of what number?

Solution: amount   percent   base

$$\frac{238}{b} = \frac{40}{100}$$

■ Work Practice 4

Answers

1. $\dfrac{54}{b} = \dfrac{27}{100}$ 2. $\dfrac{30}{90} = \dfrac{p}{100}$

3. $\dfrac{a}{116} = \dfrac{25}{100}$ 4. $\dfrac{680}{b} = \dfrac{65}{100}$

Translate to a proportion.

$$\underbrace{\text{What percent}}_{} \quad \text{of} \quad \underset{\downarrow}{30} \quad \text{is} \quad \underset{\downarrow}{75?}$$

Solution: percent   base   amount

$$\frac{75}{30} = \frac{p}{100}$$

■ Work Practice 5

Practice 5

Translate to a proportion.
What percent of 40 is 75?

Example 6 Translate to a proportion.

$$\underset{\downarrow}{45\%} \quad \text{of} \quad \underset{\downarrow}{105} \quad \text{is} \quad \underbrace{\text{what number?}}_{\downarrow}$$

Solution: percent   base   amount

$$\frac{a}{105} = \frac{45}{100}$$

■ Work Practice 6

Practice 6

Translate to a proportion.
46% of 80 is what number?

✓**Concept Check** Consider the statement "78 is what percent of 350?" Which part of the percent proportion is unknown?

a. the amount
b. the base
c. the percent

Consider another statement: "14 is 10% of some number."
Which part of the percent proportion is unknown?

a. the amount
b. the base
c. the percent

Objective B Solving Percent Problems ▶

The proportions that we have written in this section contain three values that can change: the percent, the base, and the amount. If any two of these values are known, we can find the third (the unknown value). To do this, we write a percent proportion and find the unknown value as we did in Section 6.1.

Example 7 Solving Percent Proportions for the Amount

$$\underbrace{\text{What number}}_{\downarrow} \quad \text{is} \quad \underset{\downarrow}{30\%} \quad \text{of} \quad \underset{\downarrow}{9?}$$

Solution: amount   percent   base

$$\frac{a}{9} = \frac{30}{100}$$

Practice 7

What number is 8% of 120?

Answers

5. $\frac{75}{40} = \frac{p}{100}$ **6.** $\frac{a}{80} = \frac{46}{100}$ **7.** 9.6

✓**Concept Check Answers**
c, b

Helpful Hint   The proportion in Example 7 contains the ratio $\frac{30}{100}$. A ratio in a proportion may be simplified before solving the proportion. The unknown number in both

$$\frac{a}{9} = \frac{30}{100} \text{ and } \frac{a}{9} = \frac{3}{10} \text{ is 2.7.}$$

To solve, we set cross products equal to each other.

$$\frac{a}{9} = \frac{30}{100}$$

$$a \cdot 100 = 9 \cdot 30 \quad \text{Set cross products equal.}$$

$$100a = 270 \quad \text{Multiply.}$$

$$\frac{100a}{100} = \frac{270}{100} \quad \text{Divide both sides by 100, the coefficient of } a.$$

$$a = 2.7 \quad \text{Simplify.}$$

Thus, 2.7 is 30% of 9.

■ Work Practice 7

Practice 8

65% of what number is 52?

Example 8   Solving Percent Problems for the Base

150% of what number is 30?

Solution: percent   base   amount

$$\frac{30}{b} = \frac{150}{100} \quad \text{Write the proportion.}$$

$$\frac{30}{b} = \frac{3}{2} \quad \text{Simplify } \frac{150}{100} \text{ and write as } \frac{3}{2}.$$

$$30 \cdot 2 = b \cdot 3 \quad \text{Set cross products equal.}$$

$$60 = 3b \quad \text{Multiply.}$$

$$\frac{60}{3} = \frac{3b}{3} \quad \text{Divide both sides by 3.}$$

$$20 = b \quad \text{Simplify.}$$

Thus, 150% of 20 is 30.

■ Work Practice 8

✓**Concept Check** When solving a percent problem by using a proportion, describe how you can check the result.

Practice 9

15.4 is 5% of what number?

Example 9

20.8 is 40% of what number?

Solution: amount   percent   base

$$\frac{20.8}{b} = \frac{40}{100} \quad \text{or} \quad \frac{20.8}{b} = \frac{2}{5} \quad \text{Write the proportion and simplify } \frac{40}{100}.$$

$$20.8 \cdot 5 = b \cdot 2 \quad \text{Set cross products equal.}$$

$$104 = 2b \quad \text{Multiply.}$$

$$\frac{104}{2} = \frac{2b}{2} \quad \text{Divide both sides by 2.}$$

$$52 = b \quad \text{Simplify.}$$

So, 20.8 is 40% of 52.

■ Work Practice 9

Answers

8. 80   **9.** 308

✓**Concept Check Answer**

by putting the result into the proportion and checking that the proportion is true

Example 10 Solving Percent Problems for the Percent

What percent of 50 is   8?

Solution: percent   base   amount

$$\frac{8}{50} = \frac{p}{100} \quad \text{or} \quad \frac{4}{25} = \frac{p}{100}$$ Write the proportion and simplify $\frac{8}{50}$.

$$4 \cdot 100 = 25 \cdot p$$ Set cross products equal.

$$400 = 25p$$ Multiply.

$$\frac{400}{25} = \frac{25p}{25}$$ Divide both sides by 25.

$$16 = p$$ Simplify.

So, 16% of 50 is 8.

🔲 Work Practice 10

Helpful Hint Recall from our percent proportion that this number already is a percent. Just keep the number as is and attach a % symbol.

Practice 10
What percent of 40 is 8?

Example 11

504 is what percent of 360?

Solution: amount   percent   base

$$\frac{504}{360} = \frac{p}{100}$$

Let's choose not to simplify the ratio $\frac{504}{360}$.

$$504 \cdot 100 = 360 \cdot p$$ Set cross products equal.

$$50,400 = 360p$$ Multiply.

$$\frac{50,400}{360} = \frac{360p}{360}$$ Divide both sides by 360.

$$140 = p$$ Simplify.

Notice that by choosing not to simplify $\frac{504}{360}$, we had larger numbers in our equation. Either way, we find that 504 is 140% of 360.

🔲 Work Practice 11

Practice 11
414 is what percent of 180?

Helpful Hint

Use the following to see whether your answers to the above examples and practice problems are reasonable.

100% of a number = the greater

$$\left(\begin{array}{c} \text{a percent} \\ \text{greater than} \\ 100\% \end{array} \right) \text{of a number} = \begin{array}{c} \text{a number greater} \\ \text{than the original number} \end{array}$$

$$\left(\begin{array}{c} \text{a percent} \\ \text{less than } 100\% \end{array} \right) \text{of a number} = \begin{array}{c} \text{a number less} \\ \text{than the original number} \end{array}$$

Answers
10. 20% **11.** 230%

Vocabulary, Readiness & Video Check

Use the choices below to fill in each blank. These choices will be used more than once.

    amount   base   percent

1. When translating the statement "20% of 15 is 3" to a proportion, the number 3 is called the _____,
   15 is the _____, and 20 is the _____.
2. In the question "50% of what number is 28?", which part of the percent proportion is unknown? _____
3. In the question "What number is 25% of 200?", which part of the percent proportion is unknown? _____
4. In the question "38 is what percent of 380?", which part of the percent proportion is unknown? _____

Martin-Gay Interactive Videos   *Watch the section lecture video and answer the following questions.*

Objective A 5. In ▤ Example 1, how did we identify what part of the percent proportion 45 is? ▶

Objective B 6. From ▤ Examples 4–6, what number is *always* part of the cross product equation of a percent proportion? ▶

See Video 6.4

6.4   Exercise Set MyMathLab®

Objective A Translating *Translate each to a proportion. Do not solve. See Examples 1 through 6.*

▶ **1.** 98% of 45 is what number?

2. 92% of 30 is what number?

3. What number is 4% of 150?

4. What number is 7% of 175?

5. 14.3 is 26% of what number?

6. 1.2 is 47% of what number?

7. 35% of what number is 84?

8. 85% of what number is 520?

▶ **9.** What percent of 400 is 70?

10. What percent of 900 is 216?

11. 8.2 is what percent of 82?

12. 9.6 is what percent of 96?

Objective B *Solve. See Example 7.*

13. 40% of 65 is what number?

14. 25% of 84 is what number?

15. What number is 18% of 105?

16. What number is 60% of 29?

Solve. See Examples 8 and 9.

17. 15% of what number is 90?

18. 55% of what number is 55?

19. 7.8 is 78% of what number?

20. 1.1 is 44% of what number?

Solve. See Examples 10 and 11.

21. What percent of 35 is 42?

22. What percent of 98 is 147?

23. 14 is what percent of 50?

24. 24 is what percent of 50?

Objectives A B Mixed Practice *Solve. See Examples 1 through 11.*

25. 3.7 is 10% of what number?

26. 7.4 is 5% of what number?

27. 2.4% of 70 is what number?

28. 2.5% of 90 is what number?

29. 160 is 16% of what number?

30. 30 is 6% of what number?

31. 394.8 is what percent of 188?

32. 550.4 is what percent of 172?

33. What number is 89% of 62?

34. What number is 53% of 130?

35. What percent of 6 is 2.7?

36. What percent of 5 is 1.6?

37. 140% of what number is 105?

38. 170% of what number is 221?

39. 1.8% of 48 is what number?

40. 7.8% of 24 is what number?

41. What percent of 800 is 4?

42. What percent of 500 is 3?

43. 3.5 is 2.5% of what number?

44. 9.18 is 6.8% of what number?

45. 20% of 48 is what number?

46. 75% of 14 is what number?

47. 2486 is what percent of 2200?

48. 9310 is what percent of 3800?

Review

Add or subtract the fractions. See Sections 4.4, 4.5, and 4.7.

49. $-\dfrac{11}{16} + \left(-\dfrac{3}{16}\right)$ **50.** $\dfrac{7}{12} - \dfrac{5}{8}$ **51.** $3\dfrac{1}{2} - \dfrac{11}{30}$ **52.** $2\dfrac{2}{3} + 4\dfrac{1}{2}$

Add or subtract the decimals. See Section 5.2.

53. $\begin{array}{r} 0.41 \\ +\,0.29 \\ \hline \end{array}$ **54.** $\begin{array}{r} 10.78 \\ 4.3 \\ +\ 0.21 \\ \hline \end{array}$ **55.** $\begin{array}{r} 2.38 \\ -\,0.19 \\ \hline \end{array}$ **56.** $\begin{array}{r} 16.37 \\ -\ 2.61 \\ \hline \end{array}$

Concept Extensions

57. Write a word statement for the proportion $\dfrac{x}{28} = \dfrac{25}{100}$. Use the phrase "what number" for "*x*."

58. Write a percent statement that translates to $\dfrac{16}{80} = \dfrac{20}{100}$.

Suppose you have finished solving four percent problems using proportions that you set up correctly. Check each answer to see if each makes the proportion a true proportion. If any proportion is not true, solve it to find the correct solution. See the Concept Checks in this section.

59. $\dfrac{a}{64} = \dfrac{25}{100}$
Is the amount equal to 17?

60. $\dfrac{520}{b} = \dfrac{65}{100}$
Is the base equal to 800?

61. $\dfrac{p}{100} = \dfrac{13}{52}$
Is the percent equal to 25 (25%)?

62. $\dfrac{36}{12} = \dfrac{p}{100}$
Is the percent equal to 50 (50%)?

63. In your own words, describe how to identify the percent, the base, and the amount in a percent problem.

64. In your own words, explain how to use a proportion to solve a percent problem.

Solve. Round to the nearest tenth, if necessary.

65. What number is 22.3% of 53,862?

66. What percent of 110,736 is 88,542?

67. 8652 is 119% of what number?

Ratio, Proportion, and Percent

Answers

Write each ratio as a ratio of whole numbers using fractional notation. Write the fraction in simplest form.

1. 18 to 20   **2.** 36 to 100   **3.** 8.6 to 10   **4.** 1.6 to 4.6

Find the ratio described in each problem.

5. Find the ratio of the width to the length of the sign below.

← 12 inches →

18 inches

6. At the end of fiscal year 2012, Apple Inc. had approximately $180 billion in assets and approximately $40 billion in debts. Find the ratio of assets to debts. (*Source*: Apple Inc.)

Solve.

7. $\dfrac{3.5}{12.5} = \dfrac{7}{z}$

8. $\dfrac{x + 7}{3} = \dfrac{2x}{5}$

An office uses 5 boxes of envelopes every 3 weeks.

9. Find how long a gross of envelope boxes is likely to last. (A gross of boxes is 144 boxes.) Round to the nearest week.

10. Find how many boxes should be purchased to last a month. Round to the nearest box.

Write each number as a percent.

11. 0.94   **12.** 0.17   **13.** $\dfrac{3}{8}$ **14.** $\dfrac{7}{2}$

15. 4.7   **16.** 8   **17.** $\dfrac{9}{20}$ **18.** $\dfrac{53}{50}$

19. $6\dfrac{3}{4}$ **20.** $3\dfrac{1}{4}$ **21.** 0.02   **22.** 0.06

1. _____

2. _____

3. _____

4. _____

5. _____

6. _____

7. _____

8. _____

9. _____

10. _____

11. _____

12. _____

13. _____

14. _____

15. _____

16. _____

17. _____

18. _____

19. _____

20. _____

21. _____

22. _____

23. _____ 24. _____

25. _____ 26. _____

27. _____ 28. _____

29. _____ 30. _____

31. _____

32. _____

33. _____

34. _____

35. _____

36. _____

37. _____

38. _____

39. _____ 40. _____

41. _____ 42. _____

43. _____ 44. _____

45. _____ 46. _____

47. _____ 48. _____

49. _____ 50. _____

Write each percent as a decimal.

23. 71%   **24.** 31%   **25.** 3%   **26.** 4%

27. 224%   **28.** 700%   **29.** 2.9%   **30.** 6.6%

Write each percent as a decimal and as a fraction or mixed number in simplest form. (If necessary when writing as a decimal, round to the nearest thousandth.)

31. 7%   **32.** 5%   **33.** 6.8%   **34.** 11.25%

35. 74%   **36.** 45%   **37.** $16\frac{1}{3}$%   **38.** $12\frac{2}{3}$%

Solve each percent problem.

39. 15% of 90 is what number?

40. 78 is 78% of what number?

41. 297.5 is 85% of what number?

42. 78 is what percent of 65?

43. 23.8 is what percent of 85?

44. 38% of 200 is what number?

45. What number is 40% of 85?

46. What percent of 99 is 128.7?

47. What percent of 250 is 115?

48. What number is 45% of 84?

49. 42% of what number is 63?

50. 95% of what number is 58.9?

Objective A Solving Applications Involving Percent

Objectives

A Solve Applications Involving Percent.

B Find Percent Increase and Percent Decrease.

Percent is used in a variety of everyday situations. The next examples show just a few ways that percent occurs in real-life settings. (Each of these examples shows two ways of solving these problems. If you studied Section 6.3 only, see *Method 1*. If you studied Section 6.4 only, see *Method 2*.)

The next example has to do with the Appalachian Trail, a hiking trail conceived by a forester in 1921 and diagrammed to the right. (*Note:* The trail mileage changes from year to year as maintenance groups reroute the trail as needed.)

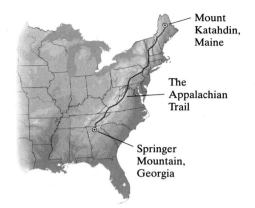

Mount Katahdin, Maine

The Appalachian Trail

Springer Mountain, Georgia

Example 1 The circle graph in the margin shows the Appalachian Trail mileage by state. If the total mileage of the trail is 2174, use the circle graph to determine the number of miles in the state of New York. Round to the nearest whole mile.

Solution: *Method 1.* First, we state the problem in words.

In words: What number is 4% of 2174?

Translate: $x = 4\% \cdot 2174$

To solve for x, we find $4\% \cdot 2174$.

$x = 0.04 \cdot 2174$ Write 4% as a decimal.

$x = 86.96$ Multiply.

$x \approx 87$ Round to the nearest whole.

Rounded to the nearest whole mile, we have that approximately 87 miles of the Appalachian Trail are in New York state.

Method 2. State the problem in words; then translate.

In words: What number is 4% of 2174?

amount   percent   base

Translate: amount → $\dfrac{a}{2174} = \dfrac{4}{100}$ ← percent
base →

Next, we solve for a.

$a \cdot 100 = 2174 \cdot 4$ Set cross products equal.

$100a = 8696$ Multiply.

$\dfrac{100a}{100} = \dfrac{8696}{100}$ Divide both sides by 100.

$a = 86.96$ Simplify.

$a \approx 87$ Round to the nearest whole.

Rounded to the nearest whole mile, we have that approximately 87 miles of the Appalachian Trail are in New York state.

Practice 1

If the total mileage of the Appalachian Trail is 2174, use the circle graph to determine the number of miles in the state of Virginia.

Appalachian Trail Mileage by State Percent

Maine 13%
Georgia 4%
North Carolina 4%
Tennessee 14%
New Hampshire 7%
Vermont 7%
Virginia 25%
Massachusetts 4%
Connecticut 2%
New York 4%
New Jersey 3%
Pennsylvania 11%
West Virginia 0.2%
Maryland 2%

Total miles: 2174
Source: purebound.com

Answer
1. 543.5 mi

■ Work Practice 1

Practice 2

From 2010 to 2020, it is projected that the number of employed nurses will grow by 710,000. If the number of nurses employed in 2010 was 2,740,000, find the percent increase in nurses employed from 2010 to 2020. Round to the nearest percent. (*Source:* Bureau of Labor Statistics)

Example 2 Finding Percent of Nursing School Applications Accepted

There continues to be a shortage of nursing school facilities. Recently, of the 256,000 applications for bachelor degree nursing schools, 101,000 of these were accepted. What percent of these applications were accepted? Round to the nearest percent. (*Source:* Bureau of Labor Statistics)

Solution: *Method 1.* First, we state the problem in words.

In words: 101   is   what percent   of   256?

Translate: 101   = x ·   256
       or   101   = $256x$

Next, solve for x.

$$\frac{101}{256} = \frac{256x}{256}$$ Divide both sides by 256.

$$0.39 \approx x$$ Divide and round to the nearest hundredth.

$$39\% \approx x$$ Write as a percent.

About 39% of nursing school applications were accepted.

Method 2.

In words: 101   is   what percent   of   256?
             amount   percent   base

Translate: amount → $\dfrac{101}{256} = \dfrac{p}{100}$ ← percent
             base →

Next, solve for p.

$$101 \cdot 100 = 256 \cdot p$$ Set cross products equal.

$$10{,}100 = 256p$$ Multiply.

$$\frac{10{,}100}{256} = \frac{256p}{256}$$ Divide both sides by 256.

$$39 \approx p$$

About 39% of nursing school applications were accepted.

■ Work Practice 2

Practice 3

The freshmen class of 864 students is 32% of all students at Euclid University. How many students go to Euclid University?

Example 3 Finding the Base Number of Absences

Mr. Percy, the principal at Slidell High School, counted 31 freshmen absent during a particular day. If this is 4% of the total number of freshmen, how many freshmen are there at Slidell High School?

Solution: *Method 1.*   First we state the problem in words; then we translate.

In words: 31   is   4%   of   what number?

Translate: 31   =   4%   · x

Next, we solve for x.

$$31 = 0.04 \cdot x$$ Write 4% as a decimal.

$$\frac{31}{0.04} = \frac{0.04x}{0.04}$$ Divide both sides by 0.04.

$$775 = x$$ Simplify.

There are 775 freshmen at Slidell High School.

Answers

2. 26%   **3.** 2700

Method 2. First we state the problem in words; then we translate.

In words: 31   is   4%   of   what number?

amount   percent   base

Translate: amount → $\dfrac{31}{b} = \dfrac{4}{100}$ ← percent
            base →

Next, we solve for *b*.

$31 \cdot 100 = b \cdot 4$ Set cross products equal.

$3100 = 4b$ Multiply.

$\dfrac{3100}{4} = \dfrac{4b}{4}$ Divide both sides by 4.

$775 = b$ Simplify.

There are 775 freshmen at Slidell High School.

Work Practice 3

Example 4   Finding the Base Increase in Licensed Drivers

From 2000 to 2011, the number of licensed drivers on the road in the United States increased by 11.6%. In 2000, there were about 190 million licensed drivers on the road.

a. Find the increase in licensed drivers from 2000 to 2011.

b. Find the number of licensed drivers on the road in 2011. (*Source:* Federal Highway Administration)

Solution: *Method 1.*   First we find the increase in licensed drivers.

In words: What number   is   11.6%   of   190?

Translate: x =   11.6%   ·   190

Next, we solve for *x*.

$x = 0.116 \cdot 190$ Write 11.6 as a decimal.

$x = 22.04$ Multiply.

a. The increase in licensed drivers is 22.04 million.

b. This means that the number of licensed drivers in 2011 was

$$\begin{array}{ccc} \text{Number of} & \text{Number of} & \text{Increase} \\ \text{licensed drivers} = \text{licensed drivers} + \text{in number of} \\ \text{in 2000} & \text{in 2000} & \text{licensed drivers} \end{array}$$

= 190 million + 22.04 million

= 212.04 million

(Continued on next page)

Practice 4

From 2000 to 2011, the number of registered vehicles on the road in the United States increased by 11.4%. In 2000, the number of vehicles on the road was 220 million.

a. Find the increase in the number of vehicles on the road in 2011.

b. Find the total number of registered vehicles on the road in 2011.

(*Source:* Federal Highway Administration)

Answers

4. a. 25.08 million   **b.** 245.08 million

Method 2. First we find the increase in licensed drivers.

In words: What number is 11.6% of 190?

amount   percent   base

Translate: amount → $\dfrac{a}{190} = \dfrac{11.6}{100}$ ← percent
             base →

Next, we solve for a.

$$a \cdot 100 = 190 \cdot 11.6 \quad \text{Set cross products equal.}$$
$$100a = 2204 \quad \text{Multiply.}$$
$$\dfrac{100a}{100} = \dfrac{2204}{100} \quad \text{Divide both sides by 100.}$$
$$a = 22.04 \quad \text{Simplify.}$$

a. The increase in licensed drivers is 22.04 million.

b. This means that the number of licensed drivers in 2011 was

Number of   Number of   Increase
licensed drivers = licensed drivers + in number of
in 2011   in 2000   licensed drivers

$$= 190 \text{ million} + 22.04 \text{ million}$$
$$= 212.04 \text{ million}$$

▇ Work Practice 4

Objective B Finding Percent Increase and Percent Decrease ▶

We often use percents to show how much an amount has increased or decreased.
   Suppose that the population of a town is 10,000 people and then it increases by 2000 people. The **percent of increase** is

amount of increase → $\dfrac{2000}{10{,}000} = 0.2 = 20\%$
original amount →

In general, we have the following.

> **Percent of Increase**
>
> $$\text{percent of increase} = \frac{\text{amount of increase}}{\text{original amount}}$$
>
> Then write the quotient as a percent.

Example 5 Finding Percent Increase

The number of applications for a mathematics scholarship at Yale increased from 34 to 45 in one year. What is the percent increase? Round to the nearest whole percent.

Solution: First we find the amount of increase by subtracting the original number of applicants from the new number of applicants.

amount of increase = 45 − 34 = 11

The amount of increase is 11 applicants. To find the percent of increase,

$$\text{percent of increase} = \frac{\text{amount of increase}}{\text{original amount}} = \frac{11}{34} \approx 0.32 = 32\%$$

The number of applications increased by about 32%.

Helpful Hint

Make sure that this number is the original number and not the new number.

■ Work Practice 5

✔**Concept Check** A student is calculating the percent increase in enrollment from 180 students one year to 200 students the next year. Explain what is wrong with the following calculations:

$$\frac{\text{Amount}}{\text{of increase}} = 200 - 180 = 20$$

$$\frac{\text{Percent of}}{\text{increase}} = \frac{20}{200} = 0.1 = 10\%$$

Suppose that your income was $300 a week and then it decreased by $30. The **percent of decrease** is

$$\text{amount of decrease} \rightarrow \frac{\$30}{\$300} = 0.1 = 10\%$$
$$\text{original amount} \rightarrow$$

Percent of Decrease

$$\text{percent of decrease} = \frac{\text{amount of decrease}}{\text{original amount}}$$

Then write the quotient as a percent.

Example 6 Finding Percent Decrease

In response to a decrease in sales, a company with 1500 employees reduces the number of employees to 1230. What is the percent decrease?

Solution: First we find the amount of decrease by subtracting 1230 from 1500.

amount of decrease = 1500 − 1230 = 270

The amount of decrease is 270. To find the percent of decrease,

$$\frac{\text{percent of}}{\text{decrease}} = \frac{\text{amount of decrease}}{\text{original amount}} = \frac{270}{1500} = 0.18 = 18\%$$

The number of employees decreased by 18%.

■ Work Practice 6

✔**Concept Check** An ice cream stand sold 6000 ice cream cones last summer. This year the same stand sold 5400 cones. Was there a 10% increase, a 10% decrease, or neither? Explain.

Practice 6

A town with a population of 20,200 in 2003 decreased to 18,483 in 2013. What was the percent decrease?

Answer
6. 8.5%

✔**Concept Check Answers**
To find the percent of increase, you have to divide the amount of increase (20) by the original amount (180); 10% decrease.

Martin-Gay Interactive Videos   *Watch the section lecture video and answer the following questions.*

Objective A 1. How do we interpret the answer 175,000 in ▣ Example 1? ⊙

Objective B 2. In ▣ Example 3, what does the improper fraction tell us? ⊙

See Video 6.5 ●

6.5 Exercise Set MyMathLab®

Objective A *Solve. For Exercises 1 and 2, the solutions have been started for you. See Examples 1 through 4. If necessary, round percents to the nearest tenth and all other answers to the nearest whole.*

1. An inspector found 24 defective bolts during an inspection. If this is 1.5% of the total number of bolts inspected, how many bolts were inspected?

Start the solution:

1. UNDERSTAND the problem. Reread it as many times as needed.
Go to Method 1 or Method 2.

Method 1.
2. TRANSLATE into an equation. (Fill in the boxes.)

$$24 \quad \text{is} \quad 1.5\% \quad \text{of} \quad \overbrace{\text{what number}}$$
$$\downarrow \quad \downarrow \quad \downarrow \quad \downarrow \qquad \downarrow$$
$$24 \quad \Box \quad 1.5\% \quad \Box \qquad x$$

3. SOLVE for *x*. (See Example 3, Method 1, for help.)
4. INTERPRET. The total number of bolts inspected was _____.

Method 2.
2. TRANSLATE into a proportion. (Fill in the blanks with "amount" or "base.")

$$24 \quad \text{is} \quad 1.5\% \quad \text{of} \quad \overbrace{\text{what number}}$$
$$\downarrow \qquad \searrow \qquad \qquad \downarrow$$
$$\underline{\quad\quad} \qquad \boxed{\text{percent}} \qquad \underline{\quad\quad}$$

$$\text{amount} \rightarrow \frac{\underline{\quad\quad}}{\underline{\quad\quad}} = \frac{1.5}{100} \leftarrow \text{percent}$$
$$\text{base} \rightarrow$$

3. SOLVE the proportion. (See Example 3, Method 2, for help.)
4. INTERPRET. The total number of bolts inspected was _____.

2. A day care worker found 28 children absent one day during an epidemic of chicken pox. If this was 35% of the total number of children attending the day care center, how many children attend this day care center?

Start the solution:

1. UNDERSTAND the problem. Reread it as many times as needed.
Go to Method 1 or Method 2.

Method 1.
2. TRANSLATE into an equation. (Fill in the boxes.)

$$28 \quad \text{is} \quad 35\% \quad \text{of} \quad \overbrace{\text{what number}}$$
$$\downarrow \quad \downarrow \quad \downarrow \quad \downarrow \qquad \downarrow$$
$$28 \quad \Box \quad 35\% \quad \Box \qquad x$$

3. SOLVE for *x*. (See Example 3, Method 1, for help.)
4. INTERPRET. The total number of children attending the day care center is _____.

Method 2.
2. TRANSLATE into a proportion. (Fill in the blanks with "amount" or "base.")

$$28 \quad \text{is} \quad 35\% \quad \text{of} \quad \overbrace{\text{what number}}$$
$$\downarrow \qquad \searrow \qquad \qquad \downarrow$$
$$\underline{\quad\quad} \qquad \boxed{\text{percent}} \qquad \underline{\quad\quad}$$

$$\text{amount} \rightarrow \frac{\underline{\quad\quad}}{\underline{\quad\quad}} = \frac{35}{100} \leftarrow \text{percent}$$
$$\text{base} \rightarrow$$

3. SOLVE the proportion. (See Example 3, Method 2, for help.)
4. INTERPRET. The total number of children attending the day care center is _____.

3. One model of Total Gym® provides weight resistance through adjustments of incline. The minimum weight resistance is 4% of the weight of the person using the Total Gym. Find the minimum weight resistance possible for a 220-pound man. (*Source:* Total Gym)

4. The maximum weight resistance for one model of Total Gym is 60% of the weight of the person using it. Find the maximum weight resistance possible for a 220-pound man. (See Exercise **3** if needed.)

5. A student's cost for last semester at her community college was $2700. She spent $378 of that on books. What percent of last semester's college costs was spent on books?

6. Pierre Sampeau belongs to his local food cooperative, where he receives a percentage of what he spends each year as a dividend. He spent $3850 last year at the food cooperative store and received a dividend of $154. What percent of his total spending at the food cooperative did he receive as a dividend?

In 2012, there were about 40,000 cinema screens in the United States. Use this information for Exercises 7 and 8.

7. If about 34% of the total screens in the United States are digital 3-D screens, find the number of digital 3-D screens.

8. If about 16% of the total screens in the United States are analog screens, find the number of analog screens.

Solve.

9. Approximately 160,650 of America's 945,000 restaurants are pizza restaurants. Determine the percent of restaurants in America that are pizza restaurants. (*Source:* Pizza Marketplace, National Restaurant Association)

10. Of the 97,100 veterinarians in private practice in the United States, approximately 52,434 are female. Determine the percent of female veterinarians in private practice in the United States. (*Source:* American Veterinary Medical Association)

11. A furniture company currently produces 6200 chairs per month. If production decreases by 8%, find the decrease and the new number of chairs produced each month.

12. The enrollment at a local college decreased by 5% over last year's enrollment of 7640. Find the decrease in enrollment and the current enrollment.

13. From 2010 to 2020, the number of people employed as physician assistants in the United States is expected to increase by 30%. The number of people employed as physician assistants in 2010 was 83,600. Find the predicted number of physician assistants in 2020. (*Source:* Bureau of Labor Statistics)

14. From 2007 to 2012, the number of households owning turtles increased by 19.3%. The number of households owning turtles in 2007 was 1,106,000. Find the number of households owning turtles in 2012. (*Source:* American Veterinary Medical Association)

Two states, Michigan and Rhode Island, decreased in population from 2010 to 2012. Their locations are shown on the partial U.S. map below. (Source: U.S. Dept. of Commerce)

15. In 2010, the population of Rhode Island was approximately 1,053,000. If the population decrease was 0.3%, find the population of Rhode Island in 2012.

16. In 2010, the population in Michigan was approximately 9938 thousand. If the population decrease was about 0.6%, find the population of Michigan in 2012.

A popular extreme sport is snowboarding. Ski trails are marked with difficulty levels of easy ●, intermediate ■, difficult ◆, expert ◆◆, and other variations. Use this information for Exercises 17 and 18. Round each percent to the nearest whole.

17. At Keystone ski area in Colorado, approximately 41 of the 135 total ski runs are rated intermediate. What percent of the runs are intermediate?

18. At Telluride ski area in Colorado, about 28 of the 115 total ski runs are rated easy. What percent of the runs are easy?

For each food described, find the percent of total calories from fat. If necessary, round to the nearest tenth percent. See Example 2.

19. Ranch dressing, serving size of 2 tablespoons

	Calories
Total	40
From fat	20

20. Unsweetened cocoa powder, serving size of 1 tablespoon

	Calories
Total	20
From fat	5

21.

Nutrition Facts
Serving Size 1 pouch (20g)
Servings Per Container 6

Amount Per Serving

Calories 80
    Calories from fat 10

% Daily Value*

Total Fat 1g	**2%**
Sodium 45mg	**2%**
Total Carbohydrate 17g	**6%**
Sugars 9g	
Protein 0g	

Vitamin C   25%

Not a significant source of saturated fat, cholesterol, dietary fiber, vitamin A, calcium and iron.

*Percent Daily Values are based on a 2,000 calorie diet.

Artificial Fruit Snacks

22.

Nutrition Facts
Serving Size $\frac{1}{4}$ cup (33g)
Servings Per Container About 9

Amount Per Serving

Calories 190 Calories from Fat 130

% Daily Value

Total Fat 16g	**24%**
Saturated Fat 3g	**16%**
Cholesterol 0mg	**0%**
Sodium 135mg	**6%**
Total Carbohydrate 9g	**3%**
Dietary Fiber 1g	**5%**
Sugars 2g	
Protein 5g	

Vitamin A 0% • Vitamin C 0%
Calcium 0%   •   Iron 8%

Peanut Mixture

23.

Nutrition Facts
Serving Size 18 crackers (29g)
Servings Per Container About 9

Amount Per Serving

Calories 120 Calories from Fat 35

% Daily Value*

Total Fat 4g	**6%**
Saturated Fat 0.5g	**3%**
Polyunsaturated Fat 0g	
Monounsaturated Fat 1.5g	
Cholesterol 0mg	**0%**
Sodium 220mg	**9%**
Total Carbohydrate 21g	**7%**
Dietary Fiber 2g	**7%**
Sugars 3g	
Protein 2g	

Vitamin A 0% • Vitamin C 0%
Calcium 2%   •   Iron 4%
Phosphorus 10%

Snack Crackers

24.

Nutrition Facts
Serving Size 28 crackers (31g)
Servings Per Container About 6

Amount Per Serving

Calories 130 Calories from Fat 35

% Daily Value*

Total Fat 4g	**6%**
Saturated Fat 2g	**10%**
Polyunsaturated Fat 1g	
Monounsaturated Fat 1g	
Cholesterol 0mg	**0%**
Sodium 470mg	**20%**
Total Carbohydrate 23g	**8%**
Dietary Fiber 1g	**4%**
Sugars 4g	
Protein 2g	

Vitamin A 0% • Vitamin C 0%
Calcium 0%   •   Iron 2%

Snack Crackers

Solve. If necessary, round money amounts to the nearest cent and all other amounts to the nearest tenth. See Examples 1 through 4.

25. A family paid $26,250 as a down payment for a home. If this represents 15% of the price of the home, find the price of the home.

26. A banker learned that $842.40 is withheld from his monthly check for taxes and insurance. If this represents 18% of his total pay, find the total pay.

27. An owner of a repair service company estimates that for every 40 hours a repairperson is on the job, he can bill for only 78% of the hours. The remaining hours, the repairperson is idle or driving to or from a job. Determine the number of hours per 40-hour week the owner can bill for a repairperson.

28. A manufacturer of electronic components expects 1.04% of its products to be defective. Determine the number of defective components expected in a batch of 28,350 components. Round to the nearest whole component.

29. A car manufacturer announced that next year, the price of a certain model of car will increase by 4.5%. This year the price is $19,286. Find the increase in price and the new price.

30. A union contract calls for a 6.5% salary increase for all employees. Determine the increase and the new salary that a worker currently making $58,500 under this contract can expect.

A popular extreme sport is artificial wall climbing. The photo shown is an artificial climbing wall. Exercises 31–32 are about the Footsloggers Climbing Tower in Boone, North Carolina.

31. A climber is resting at a height of 21 feet while on the Footsloggers Climbing Tower. If this is 60% of the tower's total height, find the height of the tower.

32. A group plans to climb the Footsloggers Climbing Tower at the group rate, once they save enough money. Thus far, $126 has been saved. If this is 70% of the total amount needed for the group, find the total price.

33. Tuition for an Ohio resident at the Columbus campus of Ohio State University was $8679 in 2008. The tuition increased by 15.3% during the period from 2008 to 2013. Find the increase, and the tuition for the 2013–2014 school year. Round the increase to the nearest whole dollar. (*Source:* Ohio State University)

34. The population of Americans aged 65 and older was 40 million in 2010. That population is projected to increase by 80.5% by 2030. Find the increase and the projected 2030 population. (*Source:* Bureau of the Census)

35. From 2013–2014 to 2020–2021, the number of associate degrees awarded is projected to increase by 17.4%. If the number of associate degrees awarded in 2013–2014 was 943,000, find the increase and the projected number of associate degrees awarded in the 2020–2021 school year. (*Source:* National Center for Education Statistics)

36. From 2013–2014 to 2020–2021, the number of bachelor degrees awarded is projected to increase by 7.6%. If the number of bachelor degrees awarded in 2013–2014 was 1,836,000, find the increase and the projected number of bachelor degrees awarded in the 2020–2021 school year. (*Source:* National Center for Education Statistics)

Objective B *Find the amount of increase and the percent increase. See Example 5.*

	Original Amount	New Amount	Amount of Increase	Percent Increase
37.	50	80		
38.	8	12		
39.	65	117		
40.	68	170		

Find the amount of decrease and the percent decrease. See Example 6.

	Original Amount	New Amount	Amount of Decrease	Percent Decrease
41.	8	6		
42.	25	20		
43.	160	40		
44.	200	162		

Solve. Round percents to the nearest tenth, if necessary. See Examples 5 and 6.

45. There are 150 calories in a cup of whole milk and only 84 in a cup of skim milk. In switching to skim milk, find the percent decrease in number of calories per cup.

46. In reaction to a slow economy, the number of employees at a soup company decreased from 530 to 477. What was the percent decrease in the number of employees?

47. Before taking a typing course, Geoffry Landers could type 32 words per minute. By the end of the course, he was able to type 76 words per minute. Find the percent increase.

48. The number of cable TV systems recently decreased from 10,845 to 10,700. Find the percent decrease.

49. The number of cell sites in the United States was 178,025 in 2005. By 2012, the number of cell sites had increased to 301,779. What was the percent increase? (*Source:* CTIA—The Wireless Association)

50. The population of Japan is expected to decrease from 127,799 thousand in 2011 to 97,076 thousand in 2050. Find the percent decrease. (*Source:* International Programs Center, Bureau of the Census, U.S. Dept. of Commerce)

51. In 2010, there were 3725 thousand elementary and secondary teachers employed in the United States. This number is expected to increase to 4205 thousand teachers in 2018. What is the percent increase? (*Source:* National Center for Education Statistics)

52. In 2010, approximately 493 thousand correctional officers were employed in the United States. By 2020, this number is expected to increase to 518 thousand correctional officers. What is the percent increase? (*Source:* Bureau of Labor Statistics)

53. In a recent 10-year period, the number of indoor cinema sites in the United States decreased from 5813 to 5331. What is this percent decrease? (*Source:* National Association of Theater Owners)

54. As the largest health care occupation, registered nurses held about 2.7 million jobs in 2010. The number of registered nurses is expected to be 7.1 million by 2020. What is the percent increase? (*Source:* Bureau of Labor Statistics)

Semiconductors are the foundation for solid-state electronics, including digital televisions (DTV). Businesses measure the overall decline in the production of televisions by studying DTV semiconductor revenue. (Examples of semiconductor use in DTVs include the main board for DTVs, power, LED backlighting, flat-panel TVs, and integrated circuits used in remote controls, just to name a few.) Use this graph to answer Exercises 55 and 56.

Worldwide DTV Semiconductor Revenue

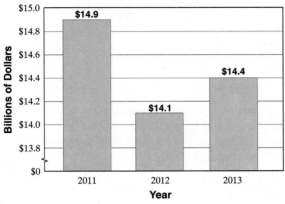

Source: IHS iSuppli Research, 2013

55. Find the percent decrease in DTV semiconductor revenue from 2011 to 2012.

56. Find the percent decrease in DTV semiconductor revenue from 2011 to 2013.

57. In 1940, the average size of a farm in the United States was 174 acres. In a recent year, the average size of a farm in the United States had increased to 420 acres. What is this percent increase? (*Source: National Agricultural Statistics Service*)

58. In 1994, there were 784 deaths from boating accidents in the United States. By 2012, the number of deaths from boating accidents had decreased to 651. What was the percent decrease? (*Source:* U.S. Coast Guard)

In 1999, Napster, a free online file-sharing service, debuted. iTunes, which debuted in 2003, is given credit for getting people to start paying for digital music. This 4-year gap between the starts of these two companies was only the beginning of the decline in music revenue.

59. In 1999, total revenue from U.S. music sales and licensing was $14.6 billion. It was forecasted that this number would continue to drop until it reached $5.5 billion in 2014. Find this percent decrease in music revenue.

60. By comparing prices, a particular music album downloads from a low of $2.99 to a high of $7.99. Find the percent increase from $2.99 to $7.99.

Review

Perform each indicated operation. See Sections 4.3 through 4.5, 4.7, and 5.2 through 5.4.

61. 0.12×38

62. $29.4 \div 0.7$

63. $9.20 + 1.98$

64. $78 - 19.46$

65. $-\dfrac{3}{8} + \dfrac{5}{12}$

66. $\left(-\dfrac{3}{8}\right)\left(-\dfrac{5}{12}\right)$

67. $2\dfrac{4}{5} \div 3\dfrac{9}{10}$

68. $2\dfrac{4}{5} - 3\dfrac{9}{10}$

Concept Extensions

69. If a number is increased by 100%, how does the increased number compare with the original number? Explain your answer.

70. In your own words, explain what is wrong with the following statement: "Last year we had 80 students attend. This year we have a 50% increase or a total of 160 students attend."

Use the bar and circle graphs below for Exercises 71 and 72.

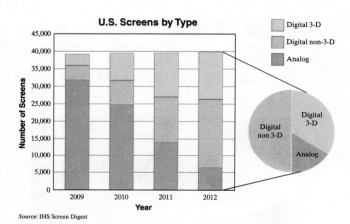

U.S. Screens by Type

Digital 3-D
Digital non-3-D
Analog

Source: IHS Screen Digest

71. Use the last bar in the bar graph, the 2012 bar. Are your answers for Exercises **7** and **8** reasonable? Explain why or why not.

72. Use the circle graph. If the 40,000 screens represent 100% of this circle graph, do the percents given and your answers in Exercises **7** and **8** seem reasonable? Explain why or why not.

Explain what errors were made by each student when solving percent of increase or decrease problems and then correct the errors. See the Concept Checks in this section. "The population of a certain rural town was 150 in 1990, 180 in 2000, and 150 in 2010."

73. Find the percent of increase in population from 1980 to 1990.

Miranda's solution: Percent of increase $= \dfrac{30}{180} = 0.1\overline{6} \approx 16.7\%$

74. Find the percent of decrease in population from 1990 to 2000.

Jeremy's solution: Percent of decrease $= \dfrac{30}{150} = 0.20 = 20\%$

75. The percent of increase from 1980 to 1990 is the same as the percent of decrease from 1990 to 2000. True or false?

Chris's answer: True because they had the same amount of increase as the amount of decrease.

6.6 Percent and Problem Solving: Sales Tax, Commission, and Discount

Objective A Calculating Sales Tax and Total Price

Percents are frequently used in the retail trade. For example, most states charge a tax on certain items when purchased. This tax is called a **sales tax,** and retail stores collect it for the state. Sales tax is almost always stated as a percent of the purchase price.

A 9% sales tax rate on a purchase of a $10 calculator gives a sales tax of

$$\text{sales tax} = 9\% \text{ of } \$10 = 0.09 \cdot \$10.00 = \$0.90$$

The total price to the customer would be

purchase price   plus   sales tax
↓   ↓   ↓
$10.00   + $0.90 = $10.90

This example suggests the following equations:

> **Sales Tax and Total Price**
>
> sales tax = tax rate · purchase price
> total price = purchase price + sales tax

In this section we round dollar amounts to the nearest cent.

Objectives

A Calculate Sales Tax and Total Price.

B Calculate Commissions.

C Calculate Discount and Sale Price.

Example 1   Finding Sales Tax and Purchase Price

Find the sales tax and the total price on the purchase of an $85.50 atlas in a city where the sales tax rate is 7.5%.

Solution: The purchase price is $85.50 and the tax rate is 7.5%.

sales tax = tax rate · purchase price
↓   ↓   ↙

sales tax = 7.5% · $85.50
     = 0.075 · $85.5   Write 7.5% as a decimal.
     ≈ $6.41   Rounded to the nearest cent

Thus, the sales tax is $6.41. Next find the total price.

total price = purchase price + sales tax
↓   ↓   ↙

total price = $85.50 + $6.41
     = $91.91

The sales tax on $85.50 is $6.41, and the total price is $91.91.

Work Practice 1

Practice 1

If the sales tax rate is 8.5%, what is the sales tax and the total amount due on a $59.90 Goodgrip tire? (Round the sales tax to the nearest cent.)

Answer
1. tax: $5.09; total: $64.99

✓**Concept Check** The purchase price of a textbook is $50 and sales tax is 10%. If you are told by the cashier that the total price is $75, how can you tell that a mistake has been made?

Practice 2

The sales tax on an $18,500 automobile is $1665. Find the sales tax rate.

Example 2 Finding a Sales Tax Rate

The sales tax on a $310 Sony flat-screen, digital 32-inch television is $26.35. Find the sales tax rate.

Solution: Let r represent the unknown sales tax rate. Then

$$\text{sales tax} = \text{tax rate} \cdot \text{purchase price}$$

$$\$26.35 = r \cdot \$310$$

$$\frac{26.35}{310} = \frac{r \cdot 310}{310} \qquad \text{Divide both sides by 310.}$$

$$0.085 = r \qquad \text{Simplify.}$$

$$8.5\% = r \qquad \text{Write 0.085 as a percent.}$$

The sales tax rate is 8.5%.

▪ Work Practice 2

Objective B Calculating Commissions ▶

A **wage** is payment for performing work. Hourly wage, commissions, and salary are some of the ways wages can be paid. Many people who work in sales are paid a commission. An employee who is paid a **commission** is paid a percent of his or her total sales.

> **Commission**
>
> commission = commission rate · sales

Practice 3

A sales representative for Office Product Copiers sold $47,632 worth of copy equipment and supplies last month. What is his commission for the month if he is paid a commission of 6.6% of his total sales for the month?

Example 3 Finding the Amount of Commission

Sherry Souter, a real estate broker for Wealth Investments, sold a house for $214,000 last week. If her commission is 1.5% of the selling price of the home, find the amount of her commission.

Solution:

$$\text{commission} = \text{commission rate} \cdot \text{sales}$$

$$\text{commission} = \quad 1.5\% \quad \cdot \$214,000$$

$$= \quad 0.015 \quad \cdot \$214,000 \qquad \text{Write 1.5\% as 0.015.}$$

$$= \quad \$3210 \qquad \text{Multiply.}$$

Her commission on the house is $3210.

▪ Work Practice 3

Answers

2. 9% **3.** $3143.71

✓**Concept Check Answer**

Since $10\% = \frac{1}{10}$, the sales tax is $\frac{\$50}{10} = \$5$. The total price should be $55.

Example 4 Finding a Commission Rate

A salesperson earned $1560 for selling $13,000 worth of electronics equipment. Find the commission rate.

Solution: Let r stand for the unknown commission rate. Then

$$\text{commission} = \text{commission rate} \cdot \text{sales}$$

$$\downarrow \qquad\qquad \downarrow \qquad\qquad \downarrow$$

$$\$1560 \quad = \qquad r \qquad \cdot \$13,000$$

$$\frac{1560}{13,000} \quad = r \quad \text{Divide 1560 by 13,000, the number multiplied by } r.$$

$$0.12 \quad\; = r \quad \text{Simplify.}$$

$$12\% \quad\; = r \quad \text{Write 0.12 as a percent.}$$

The commission rate is 12%.

Work Practice 4

Practice 4

A salesperson earns $645 for selling $4300 worth of appliances. Find the commission rate.

Objective C Calculating Discount and Sale Price

Suppose that an item that normally sells for $40 is on sale for 25% off. This means that the **original price** of $40 is reduced, or **discounted,** by 25% of $40, or $10. The **discount rate** is 25%, the **amount of discount** is $10, and the **sale price** is $40 − $10, or $30. Study the diagram below to visualize these terms.

To calculate discounts and sale prices, we can use the following equations:

Discount and Sale Price

> amount of discount = discount rate · original price
>
> sale price = original price − amount of discount

Example 5 Finding a Discount and a Sale Price

An electric rice cooker that normally sells for $65 is on sale for 25% off. What is the amount of discount and what is the sale price?

Solution: First we find the amount of discount, or simply the discount.

$$\text{amount of discount} = \text{discount rate} \cdot \text{original price}$$

$$\downarrow \qquad\qquad \downarrow \qquad\qquad \downarrow$$

$$\text{amount of discount} = \quad 25\% \quad\cdot \quad \$65$$

$$= 0.25 \cdot \$65 \quad \text{Write 25\% as 0.25.}$$

$$= \$16.25 \quad \text{Multiply.}$$

Practice 5

A discontinued washer and dryer combo is advertised on sale for 35% off the regular price of $700. Find the amount of discount and the sale price.

Answers
4. 15%   **5.** $245; $455

(Continued on next page)

The discount is $16.25. Next, find the sale price.

sale price = original price − discount

↓   ↓   ↓

sale price = $65   − $16.25

= $48.75   Subtract.

The sale price is $48.75.

■ Work Practice 5

Vocabulary, Readiness & Video Check

Use the choices below to fill in each blank.

amount of discount   sale price   sales tax
commission   total price

1. _____ = tax rate · purchase price

2. _____ = purchase price + sales tax

3. _____ = commission rate · sales

4. _____ = discount rate · original price

5. _____ = original price − amount of discount

Martin-Gay Interactive Videos   *Watch the section lecture video and answer the following questions.*

Objective A 6. In ⊞ Example 1, what is our first step after translating the problem into an equation? ▶

Objective B 7. What is our final step in solving ⊞ Example 2? ▶

Objective C 8. In the lecture before ⊞ Example 3, since both equations shown involve the "amount of discount," how can the two equations be combined into one equation? ▶

See Video 6.6 ●

6.6 Exercise Set MyMathLab®

Objective A *Solve. See Examples 1 and 2.*

1. What is the sales tax on a jacket priced at $150 if the sales tax rate is 5%?

2. If the sales tax rate is 6%, find the sales tax on a microwave oven priced at $188.

3. The purchase price of a camcorder is $799. What is the total price if the sales tax rate is 7.5%?

4. A stereo system has a purchase price of $426. What is the total price if the sales tax rate is 8%?

5. A new large-screen television has a purchase price of $4790. If the sales tax on this purchase is $335.30, find the sales tax rate.

6. The sales tax on the purchase of a $6800 used car is $374. Find the sales tax rate.

7. The sales tax on a table saw is $10.20.
   a. What is the purchase price of the table saw (before tax) if the sales tax rate is 8.5%? (*Hint:* Use the sales tax equation and insert the replacement values.)
   b. Find the total price of the table saw.

8. The sales tax on a one-half-carat diamond ring is $76.
   a. Find the purchase price of the ring (before tax) if the sales tax rate is 9.5%. (See the hint for Exercise **7a**.)
   b. Find the total price of the ring.

9. A gold and diamond bracelet sells for $1800. Find the sales tax and the total price if the sales tax rate is 6.5%.

10. The purchase price of a personal computer is $1890. If the sales tax rate is 8%, what is the sales tax and the total price?

11. The sales tax on the purchase of a futon is $24.25. If the tax rate is 5%, find the purchase price of the futon.

12. The sales tax on the purchase of a TV-DVD combination is $32.85. If the tax rate is 9%, find the purchase price of the TV-DVD.

13. The sales tax is $98.70 on a stereo sound system purchase of $1645. Find the sales tax rate.

14. The sales tax is $103.50 on a necklace purchase of $1150. Find the sales tax rate.

15. A cell phone costs $210, a battery recharger costs $15, and batteries cost $5. What is the sales tax and total price for purchasing these items if the sales tax rate is 7%?

16. Ms. Warner bought a blouse for $35, a skirt for $55, and a blazer for $95. Find the sales tax and the total price she paid, given a sales tax rate of 6.5%.

Objective B *Solve. See Examples 3 and 4.*

17. A sales representative for a large furniture warehouse is paid a commission rate of 4%. Find her commission if she sold $1,329,401 worth of furniture last year.

18. Rosie Davis-Smith is a beauty consultant for a home cosmetic business. She is paid a commission rate of 12.8%. Find her commission if she sold $1638 in cosmetics last month.

19. A salesperson earned a commission of $1380.40 for selling $9860 worth of paper products. Find the commission rate.

20. A salesperson earned a commission of $3575 for selling $32,500 worth of books to various bookstores. Find the commission rate.

21. How much commission will Jack Pruet make on the sale of a $325,900 house if he receives 1.5% of the selling price?

22. Frankie Lopez sold $9638 of jewelry this week. Find her commission for the week if she receives a commission rate of 5.6%.

23. A real estate agent earned a commission of $5565 for selling a house. If his rate is 3%, find the selling price of the house. (*Hint:* Use the commission equation and insert the replacement values.)

24. A salesperson earned $1750 for selling fertilizer. If her commission rate is 7%, find the selling price of the fertilizer. (See the hint for Exercise **23.**)

Objective C *Find the amount of discount and the sale price. See Example 5.*

	Original Price	Discount Rate	Amount of Discount	Sale Price
25.	$89	10%		
26.	$74	20%		
27.	$196.50	50%		
28.	$110.60	40%		
29.	$410	35%		
30.	$370	25%		
31.	$21,700	15%		
32.	$17,800	12%		

33. A $300 fax machine is on sale for 15% off. Find the amount of discount and the sale price.

34. A $4295 designer dress is on sale for 30% off. Find the amount of discount and the sale price.

Objectives A B Mixed Practice *Complete each table.*

	Purchase Price	Tax Rate	Sales Tax	Total Price
35.	$305	9%		
36.	$243	8%		
37.	$56	5.5%		
38.	$65	8.4%		

	Sale	Commission Rate	Commission
39.	$235,800	3%	
40.	$195,450	5%	
41.	$17,900		$1432
42.	$25,600		$2304

Review

Multiply. See Sections 4.3, 5.3, and 5.5.

43. $2000 \cdot \dfrac{3}{10} \cdot 2$

44. $500 \cdot \dfrac{2}{25} \cdot 3$

45. $400 \cdot \dfrac{3}{100} \cdot 11$

46. $1000 \cdot \dfrac{1}{20} \cdot 5$

47. $600 \cdot 0.04 \cdot \dfrac{2}{3}$

48. $6000 \cdot 0.06 \cdot \dfrac{3}{4}$

Concept Extensions

Solve. See the Concept Check in this section.

49. Your purchase price is $68 and the sales tax rate is 9.5%. Round each amount and use the rounded amounts to estimate the total price. Choose the best estimate.

a. $105   **b.** $58   **c.** $93   **d.** $77

50. Your purchase price is $200 and the tax rate is 10%. Choose the best estimate of the total price.

a. $190   **b.** $210   **c.** $220   **d.** $300

Tipping *One very useful application of percent is mentally calculating a tip. Recall that to find 10% of a number, simply move the decimal point one place to the left. To find 20% of a number, just double 10% of the number. To find 15% of a number, find 10% and then add to that number half of the 10% amount. Mentally fill in the chart below. To do so, start by rounding the bill amount to the nearest dollar.*

	Tipping Chart			
	Bill Amount	**10%**	**15%**	**20%**
51.	$40.21			
52.	$15.89			
53.	$72.17			
54.	$9.33			

55. Suppose that the original price of a shirt is $50. Which is better, a 60% discount or a discount of 30% followed by a discount of 35% of the reduced price? Explain your answer.

56. Which is better, a 30% discount followed by an additional 25% off or a 20% discount followed by an additional 40% off? To see, suppose an item costs $100 and calculate each discounted price. Explain your answer.

57. A diamond necklace sells for $24,966. If the tax rate is 7.5%, find the total price.

58. A house recently sold for $562,560. The commission rate on the sale is 5.5%. If the real estate agent is to receive 60% of the commission, find the amount received by the agent.

6.7 Percent and Problem Solving: Interest

Objective A Calculating Simple Interest

Interest is money charged for using other people's money. When you borrow money, you pay interest. When you loan or invest money, you earn interest. The money borrowed, loaned, or invested is called the **principal amount,** or simply **principal.** Interest is normally stated in terms of a percent of the principal for a given period of time. The **interest rate** is the percent used in computing the interest. Unless stated otherwise, *the rate is understood to be per year.* When the interest is computed on the original principal, it is called **simple interest.** Simple interest is calculated using the following equation:

Objectives

A Calculate Simple Interest.

B Calculate Compound Interest.

> ### Simple Interest
>
> Simple Interest = Principal · Rate · Time
>
> $$I = P \cdot R \cdot T$$
>
> where the rate is understood to be per year and time is in years.

Practice 1

Find the simple interest after 5 years on $875 at an interest rate of 7%.

Example 1 Finding Simple Interest

Find the simple interest after 2 years on $500 at an interest rate of 12%.

Solution: In this example, $P = \$500$, $R = 12\%$, and $T = 2$ years. Replace the variables with values in the formula $I = PRT$.

$$I = P \cdot R \cdot T$$
$$I = \$500 \cdot 12\% \cdot 2 \quad \text{Let } P = \$500, R = 12\%, \text{ and } T = 2.$$
$$= \$500 \cdot (0.12) \cdot 2 \quad \text{Write 12\% as a decimal.}$$
$$= \$120 \quad \text{Multiply.}$$

The simple interest is $120.

▪ Work Practice 1

If time is not given in years, we need to convert the given time to years.

Practice 2

A student borrowed $1500 for 9 months on her credit card at a simple interest rate of 20%. How much interest did she pay?

Example 2 Finding Simple Interest

A recent college graduate borrowed $2400 at 10% simple interest for 8 months to buy a used Toyota Corolla. Find the simple interest he paid.

Solution: Since there are 12 months in a year, we first find what part of a year 8 months is.

$$8 \text{ months} = \frac{8}{12} \text{ year} = \frac{2}{3} \text{ year}$$

Now we find the simple interest.

$$I = P \cdot R \cdot T$$
$$= \$2400 \cdot (0.10) \cdot \frac{2}{3} \quad \text{Let } P = \$2400, R = 10\% \text{ or } 0.10, \text{ and } T = \frac{2}{3}.$$
$$= \$160$$

The interest on his loan is $160.

▪ Work Practice 2

✓**Concept Check** Suppose in Example 2 you had obtained an answer of $16,000. How would you know that you had made a mistake in this problem?

When money is borrowed, the borrower pays the original amount borrowed, or the principal, as well as the interest. When money is invested, the investor receives the original amount invested, or the principal, as well as the interest. In either case, the **total amount** is the sum of the principal and the interest.

Answers

1. $306.25　**2.** $225

✓**Concept Check Answer**

$16,000 is too much interest

Finding the Total Amount of a Loan or Investment

total amount (paid or received) = principal + interest

Example 3 Finding the Total Amount of an Investment

An accountant invested $2000 at a simple interest rate of 10% for 2 years. What total amount of money will she have from her investment in 2 years?

Solution: First we find her interest.

$$I = P \cdot R \cdot T$$
$$= \$2000 \cdot (0.10) \cdot 2 \quad \text{Let } P = \$2000, R = 10\% \text{ or } 0.10, \text{ and } T = 2.$$
$$= \$400$$

The interest is $400.

Next, we add the interest to the principal.

total amount = principal + interest
↓   ↓   ↓
total amount = $2000 + $400
           = $2400

After 2 years, she will have a total amount of $2400.

■ Work Practice 3

✓**Concept Check** Which investment would earn more interest: an amount of money invested at 8% interest for 2 years, or the same amount of money invested at 8% for 3 years? Explain.

Objective B Calculating Compound Interest ▶

Recall that simple interest depends on the original principal only. Another type of interest is compound interest. **Compound interest** is computed on not only the principal, but also on the interest already earned in previous compounding periods. Compound interest is used more often than simple interest.

Let's see how compound interest differs from simple interest. Suppose that $2000 is invested at 7% interest **compounded annually** for 3 years. This means that interest is added to the principal at the end of each year and that next year's interest is computed on this new amount. In this section, we round dollar amounts to the nearest cent.

	Amount at Beginning of Year	Principal	·	Rate	·	Time	= Interest	Amount at End of Year
1st year	$2000	$2000	·	0.07	·	1	= $140	$2000 + 140 = $2140
2nd year	$2140	$2140	·	0.07	·	1	= $149.80	$2140 + 149.80 = $2289.80
3rd year	$2289.80	$2289.80	·	0.07	·	1	= $160.29	$2289.80 + 160.29 = $2450.09

The compound interest earned can be found by

total amount − original principal = compound interest
↓   ↓   ↓
$2450.09   − $2000   = $450.09

The simple interest earned would have been

principal · rate · time = interest
↓   ↓   ↓   ↓
$2000   · 0.07 · 3   = $420

Since compound interest earns "interest on interest," compound interest earns more than simple interest.

Computing compound interest using the method above can be tedious. We can use a calculator and the compound interest formula on the next page to compute compound interest more quickly.

Practice 3

If $2100 is borrowed at a simple interest rate of 13% for 6 months, find the total amount paid.

Answer
3. $2236.50

✓**Concept Check Answer**

8% for 3 years. Since the interest rate is the same, the longer you keep the money invested, the more interest you earn.

> ### Compound Interest Formula
>
> The total amount A in an account is given by
>
> $$A = P\left(1 + \frac{r}{n}\right)^{n \cdot t}$$
>
> where P is the principal, r is the interest rate written as a decimal, t is the length of time in years, and n is the number of times compounded per year.

Practice 4

$3000 is invested at 4% interest compounded annually. Find the total amount after 6 years.

Example 4

$1800 is invested at 2% interest compounded annually. Find the total amount after 3 years.

Solution: "Compounded annually" means 1 time a year, so

$n = 1$. Also, $P = \$1800$, $r = 2\% = 0.02$, and $t = 3$ years.

$$A = P\left(1 + \frac{r}{n}\right)^{n \cdot t}$$

$$= 1800\left(1 + \frac{0.02}{1}\right)^{1 \cdot 3}$$

$$= 1800(1.02)^3$$

$$\approx 1910.17 \qquad \text{Round to 2 decimal places.}$$

The total amount at the end of 3 years is $1910.17.

> **Helpful Hint**
> Remember order of operations. **First** evaluate $(1.02)^3$, then multiply by 1800.

■ Work Practice 4

Practice 5

$5500 is invested at $6\frac{1}{4}\%$ compounded *daily* for 5 years. Find the total amount at the end of 5 years. (Use 1 year = 365 days.)

Example 5 — Finding Total Amount Received from an Investment

$4000 is invested at 5.3% compounded quarterly for 10 years. Find the total amount at the end of 10 years.

Solution: "Compounded quarterly" means 4 times a year, so

$n = 4$. Also, $P = \$4000$, $r = 5.3\% = 0.053$, and $t = 10$ years.

$$A = P\left(1 + \frac{r}{n}\right)^{n \cdot t}$$

$$= 4000\left(1 + \frac{0.053}{4}\right)^{4 \cdot 10}$$

$$= 4000(1.01325)^{40}$$

$$\approx 6772.12$$

The total amount after 10 years is $6772.12.

Answers

4. $3795.96   5. $7517.41

■ Work Practice 5

🖩 Calculator Explorations Compound Interest Formula

For a review of using your calculator to evaluate compound interest, see this box.

Let's review the calculator keys pressed to evaluate the expression in Example 5,

$$4000\left(1 + \frac{0.053}{4}\right)^{40}$$

To evaluate, press the keys

4000 × (1 + 0.053 ÷ 4) y^x or ∧ 40 then = or ENTER . The display will read 6772.117549 . Rounded to 2 decimal places, this is 6772.12.

Find the compound interest.

1. $600, 5 years, 9%, compounded quarterly

2. $10,000, 15 years, 4%, compounded daily

3. $1200, 20 years, 11%, compounded annually

4. $5800, 1 year, 7%, compounded semiannually

5. $500, 4 years, 6%, compounded quarterly

6. $2500, 19 years, 5%, compounded daily

Vocabulary, Readiness & Video Check

Use the choices below to fill in each blank. Choices may be used more than once.

total amount   simple   principal amount   compound

1. To calculate _____ interest, use $I = P \cdot R \cdot T$.

2. To calculate _____ interest, use $A = P\left(1 + \dfrac{r}{n}\right)^{n \cdot t}$.

3. _____ interest is computed not only on the original principal, but also on interest already earned in previous compounding periods.

4. When interest is computed on the original principal only, it is called _____ interest.

5. _____ (paid or received) = principal + interest.

6. The _____ is the money borrowed, loaned, or invested.

Martin-Gay Interactive Videos   *Watch the section lecture video and answer the following questions.*

Objective A 7. Complete this statement based on the lecture before Example 1: Simple interest is charged on the _____ only.

Objective B 8. In Example 2, how often is the interest compounded, and what number does this translate to in the formula?

See Video 6.7

6.7 Exercise Set MyMathLab®

Objective A *Find the simple interest. See Examples 1 and 2.*

	Principal	Rate	Time
1.	$200	8%	2 years
3.	$160	11.5%	4 years
5.	$5000	10%	$1\frac{1}{2}$ years
7.	$375	18%	6 months
9.	$2500	16%	21 months

	Principal	Rate	Time
2.	$800	9%	3 years
4.	$950	12.5%	5 years
6.	$1500	14%	$2\frac{1}{4}$ years
8.	$775	15%	8 months
10.	$1000	10%	18 months

Solve. See Examples 1 through 3.

11. A company borrows $162,500 for 5 years at a simple interest rate of 12.5%. Find the interest paid on the loan and the total amount paid back.

12. $265,000 is borrowed to buy a house. If the simple interest rate on the 30-year loan is 8.25%, find the interest paid on the loan and the total amount paid back.

13. A money market fund advertises a simple interest rate of 9%. Find the total amount received on an investment of $5000 for 15 months.

14. The Real Service Company takes out a 270-day (9-month) short-term, simple interest loan of $4500 to finance the purchase of some new equipment. If the interest rate is 14%, find the total amount that the company pays back.

15. Marsha borrows $8500 and agrees to pay it back in 4 years. If the simple interest rate is 17%, find the total amount she pays back.

16. An 18-year-old is given a high school graduation gift of $2000. If this money is invested at 8% simple interest for 5 years, find the total amount.

Objective B *Find the total amount in each compound interest account. See Examples 4 and 5.*

17. $6150 is compounded semiannually at a rate of 14% for 15 years.

18. $2060 is compounded annually at a rate of 15% for 10 years.

19. $1560 is compounded daily at a rate of 8% for 5 years.

20. $1450 is compounded quarterly at a rate of 10% for 15 years.

21. $10,000 is compounded semiannually at a rate of 9% for 20 years.

22. $3500 is compounded daily at a rate of 8% for 10 years.

23. $2675 is compounded annually at a rate of 9% for 1 year.

24. $6375 is compounded semiannually at a rate of 10% for 1 year.

25. $2000 is compounded annually at a rate of 8% for 5 years.

26. $2000 is compounded semiannually at a rate of 8% for 5 years.

27. $2000 is compounded quarterly at a rate of 8% for 5 years.

28. $2000 is compounded daily at a rate of 8% for 5 years.

Review

Find the perimeter of each figure. See Section 1.3.

29.

30.

31.
Regular pentagon—All sides are same length / 7 meters

32.
Square | 21 miles

Perform the indicated operations. See Section 4.3 through 4.6.

33. $\dfrac{x}{4} + \dfrac{x}{5}$

34. $-\dfrac{x}{4} \div \left(-\dfrac{x}{5}\right)$

35. $\left(\dfrac{2}{3}\right)\left(-\dfrac{1}{3}\right) - \left(\dfrac{9}{10}\right)\left(\dfrac{2}{5}\right)$

36. $\dfrac{3}{11} \div \dfrac{9}{22} \cdot \dfrac{1}{3}$

Concept Extensions

37. Review Exercises **25** through **28**. As the number of compoundings increases per year, how is the total amount affected?

38. Explain how to find the amount of interest in a compounded account.

39. Compare the following accounts: Account 1: $1000 is invested for 10 years at a simple interest rate of 6%. Account 2: $1000 is compounded semiannually at a rate of 6% for 10 years. Discuss how the interest is computed for each account. Determine which account earns more interest. Why?

Chapter 6 Group Activity

Investigating Scale Drawings

Sections 6.1

Materials:

- ruler
- tape measure
- grid paper (optional)

This activity may be completed by working in groups or individually.

Scale drawings are used by architects, engineers, interior designers, shipbuilders, and others. In a scale drawing, each unit measurement on the drawing represents a fixed length on the object being drawn. For instance, in an architect's scale drawing, 1 inch on the drawing may represent 10 feet on a building. The scale describes the relationship between the measurements. If the measurements have the same units, the scale can be expressed as a ratio. In this case, the ratio would be 1 : 120, representing 1 inch to 120 inches (or 10 feet).

Use a ruler and the scale drawing of a college building below to answer the following questions.

1. How wide are each of the front doors of the college building?
2. How long is the front of the college building?
3. How tall is the front of the college building?

Now you will draw your own scale floor plan. First choose a room to draw—it can be your math classroom, your living room, your dormitory room, or any room that can be easily measured. Start by using a tape measure to measure the distances around the base of the walls in the room you are drawing.

4. Choose a scale for your floor plan.
5. Convert each measurement in the room you are drawing to the corresponding lengths needed for the scale drawing.
6. Complete your floor plan (you may find it helpful to use grid paper). Mark the locations of doors and windows on your floor plan. Be sure to indicate on the drawing the scale used in your floor plan.

Scale: 1 inch represents 10 feet

Chapter 6 Vocabulary Check

Fill in each blank with one of the words or phrases listed below. Some words may be used more than once.

percent	sales tax	is	0.01	$\dfrac{1}{100}$	amount of discount
percent of decrease	total price	ratio	proportion	base	of
amount	100%	compound interest	percent of increase	sale price	commission

1. In a mathematical statement, _____ usually means "multiplication."
2. In a mathematical statement, _____ means "equal."
3. _____ means "per hundred."

4. _____ is computed not only on the principal, but also on interest already earned in previous compounding periods.

5. In the percent proportion, $\dfrac{\rule{2cm}{0.4pt}}{\rule{2cm}{0.4pt}} = \dfrac{\text{percent}}{100}$.

6. To write a decimal or fraction as a percent, multiply by _____.

7. The decimal equivalent of the % symbol is _____.

8. The fraction equivalent of the % symbol is _____.

9. The percent equation is _____ · percent = _____.

10. _____ $= \dfrac{\text{amount of decrease}}{\text{original amount}}$

11. _____ $= \dfrac{\text{amount of increase}}{\text{original amount}}$.

12. _____ = tax rate · purchase price

13. _____ = purchase price + sales tax

14. _____ = commission rate · sales

15. _____ = discount rate · original price

16. _____ = original price − amount of discount

17. A(n) _____ is a mathematical statement that two ratios are equal.

18. A (n) _____ is the quotient of two numbers or two quantities

Helpful Hint ▶ Are you preparing for your test? Don't forget to take the Chapter 6 Test on page 481. Then check your answers at the back of the text and use the Chapter Test Prep Videos to see the fully worked-out solutions to any of the exercises you want to review.

6 Chapter Highlights

Definitions and Concepts	Examples
Section 6.1 Ratio and Proportion	
A **ratio** is the quotient of two numbers or two quantities.	Write the ratio of 5 hours to 1 day using fractional notation. $$\frac{5 \text{ hours}}{1 \text{ day}} = \frac{5 \text{ hours}}{24 \text{ hours}} = \frac{5}{24}$$
A **proportion** is a mathematical statement that two ratios are equal.	$\dfrac{2}{3} = \dfrac{8}{12} \qquad \dfrac{x}{7} = \dfrac{15}{35}$
In the proportion $\dfrac{a}{b} = \dfrac{c}{d}$, the products ad and bc are called **cross products.**	$\dfrac{2}{3} \diagdown \dfrac{8}{12} \quad \longrightarrow \quad 3 \cdot 8 \text{ or } 24$ $\phantom{\dfrac{2}{3}} \qquad\qquad \longrightarrow \quad 2 \cdot 12 \text{ or } 24$
If $\dfrac{a}{b} = \dfrac{c}{d}$, then $ad = bc$.	Solve: $\quad \dfrac{3}{4} = \dfrac{x}{x-1}$ $$\frac{3}{4} = \frac{x}{x-1}$$ $3(x-1) = 4x \quad \text{Set cross products equal.}$ $3x - 3 = 4x$ $-3 = x$
Section 6.2 Percents, Decimals, and Fractions	
Percent means "per hundred." The % symbol denotes percent.	$51\% = \dfrac{51}{100} \quad 51 \text{ per } 100$ $7\% = \dfrac{7}{100} \quad 7 \text{ per } 100$
To write a percent as a decimal, replace the % symbol with its decimal equivalent, 0.01, and multiply.	$32\% = 32(0.01) = 0.32$

Definitions and Concepts	Examples

Section 6.2   Percents, Decimals, and Fractions (*continued*)

To write a decimal as a percent, multiply by 100%.	$0.08 = 0.08(100\%) = 08.\% = 8\%$
To write a percent as a fraction, replace the % symbol with its fraction equivalent, $\frac{1}{100}$, and multiply.	$25\% = 25 \cdot \frac{1}{100} = \frac{25}{100} = \frac{\overset{1}{25}}{4 \cdot \underset{1}{25}} = \frac{1}{4}$
To write a fraction as a percent, multiply by 100%.	$\frac{1}{6} = \frac{1}{6} \cdot 100\% = \frac{1}{6} \cdot \frac{100}{1}\% = \frac{100}{6}\% = 16\frac{2}{3}\%$

Section 6.3   Solving Percent Problems with Equations

Three key words in the statement of a percent problem are
 	
  of, which means multiplication $(\cdot)$
  is, which means equal $(=)$
  what (or some equivalent word or phrase), which stands for the unknown (x)
	Solve:
	
	6 is 12% of what number?
	↓ ↓ ↓ ↓ ↓
	$6 = 12\% \cdot x$
	$6 = 0.12 \cdot x$ Write 12% as a decimal.
	$\dfrac{6}{0.12} = \dfrac{0.12 \cdot x}{0.12}$ Divide both sides by 0.12.
	$50 = x$
	
	Thus, 6 is 12% of 50.

Section 6.4   Solving Percent Problems with Proportions

Percent Proportion
 	
$\dfrac{\text{amount}}{\text{base}} = \dfrac{\text{percent}}{100}$ ← always 100
or
 	
amount → $\dfrac{a}{b} = \dfrac{p}{100}$ ← percent
base →
	Solve:
	
	20.4 is what percent of 85?
	  ↘ ↓ ↘
	  amount percent base
	
	amount → $\dfrac{20.4}{85} = \dfrac{p}{100}$ ← percent
	base →
	$20.4 \cdot 100 = 85 \cdot p$ Set cross products equal.
	$2040 = 85 \cdot p$ Multiply.
	$\dfrac{2040}{85} = \dfrac{85 \cdot p}{85}$ Divide both sides by 85.
	$24 = p$ Simplify.
	
	Thus, 20.4 is 24% of 85.

Section 6.5   Applications of Percent

Percent Increase $\text{percent increase} = \dfrac{\text{amount of increase}}{\text{original amount}}$ **Percent Decrease** $\text{percent decrease} = \dfrac{\text{amount of decrease}}{\text{original amount}}$	A town with a population of 16,480 decreased to 13,870 over a 12-year period. Find the percent decrease. Round to the nearest whole percent. $\text{amount of decrease} = 16{,}480 - 13{,}870$ $= 2610$ $\text{percent decrease} = \dfrac{\text{amount of decrease}}{\text{original amount}}$ $= \dfrac{2610}{16{,}480} \approx 0.16$ $\approx 16\%$ The town's population decreased by about 16%.

(*Continued*)

Definitions and Concepts	Examples

Section 6.6 Percent and Problem Solving: Sales Tax, Commission, and Discount	

Sales Tax $\quad$ sales tax = sales tax rate · purchase price $\quad$ total price = purchase price + sales tax	Find the sales tax and the total price of a purchase of $42.00 if the sales tax rate is 9%. $\quad$ sales tax $=$ sales tax rate $\cdot$ purchase price $\quad\quad\quad\downarrow\quad\quad\quad\quad\downarrow\quad\quad\quad\quad\downarrow$ $\quad$ sales tax $=\quad\quad$ 9% $\quad\cdot\quad\quad$ \$42 $\quad\quad\quad\quad\quad=\quad$ 0.09 · \$42 $\quad\quad\quad\quad\quad=\quad$ \$3.78 The total price is $\quad$ total price $=$ purchase price $+$ sales tax $\quad\quad\quad\downarrow\quad\quad\quad\quad\downarrow\quad\quad\quad\quad\downarrow$ $\quad$ total price $=\quad$ \$42.00 $\quad+\quad$ \$3.78 $\quad\quad\quad\quad\quad=\quad$ \$45.78 The total price is \$45.78.
Commission $\quad$ commission = commission rate · sales	A salesperson earns a commission of 3%. Find the commission from sales of \$12,500 worth of appliances. $\quad$ commission $=$ commission rate $\cdot$ sales $\quad\quad\quad\downarrow\quad\quad\quad\quad\downarrow\quad\quad\quad\downarrow$ $\quad$ commission $=\quad\quad$ 3% $\quad\quad\cdot$ \$12,500 $\quad\quad\quad\quad\quad\quad=\quad$ 0.03 · 12,500 $\quad\quad\quad\quad\quad\quad=\quad$ \$375 The commission is \$375.
Discount and Sale Price $\quad$ amount of discount = discount rate · original price $\quad$ sale price = original price − amount of discount	A suit is priced at \$320 and is on sale today for 25% off. What is the sale price? $\quad$ amount of discount $=$ discount rate $\cdot$ original price $\quad\quad\quad\quad\downarrow\quad\quad\quad\quad\downarrow\quad\quad\quad\quad\downarrow$ $\quad$ amount of discount $=\quad$ 25% $\quad\cdot\quad$ \$320 $\quad\quad\quad\quad\quad\quad\quad=\quad$ 0.25 · \$320 $\quad\quad\quad\quad\quad\quad\quad=\quad$ \$80 $\quad$ sale price $=$ original price $-$ amount of discount $\quad\quad\quad\downarrow\quad\quad\quad\quad\downarrow\quad\quad\quad\quad\downarrow$ $\quad$ sale price $=\quad$ \$320 $\quad-\quad$ \$80 $\quad\quad\quad\quad\quad=\quad$ \$240 The sale price is \$240.

Definitions and Concepts	Examples
Section 6.7 Percent and Problem Solving: Interest	

Definitions and Concepts	Examples
Simple Interest $\qquad$ interest = principal · rate · time where the rate is understood to be per year, unless told otherwise.	Find the simple interest after 3 years on $800 at an interest rate of 5%. $\begin{array}{ccccccc} \text{interest} & = & \text{principal} & \cdot & \text{rate} & \cdot & \text{time} \\ \downarrow & & \downarrow & & \downarrow & & \downarrow \\ \text{interest} & = & \$800 & \cdot & 5\% & \cdot & 3 \\ & = & \$800 \cdot 0.05 \cdot 3 & & \text{Write 5\% as 0.05.} \\ & = & \$120 & & \text{Multiply.} \end{array}$ The interest is $120.
Compound Interest Formula The total amount A in an account is $$A = P\left(1 + \frac{r}{n}\right)^{n \cdot t}$$ where P is the principal, r is the interest rate written as a decimal, t is time in years, and n is the number of times compounded per year.	$800 is invested at 5% compounded quarterly for 10 years. Find the total amount at the end of 10 years. "Compounded quarterly" means $n = 4$. Also, $P = \$800$, $r = 5\% = 0.05$, and $t = 10$ years. $$\begin{aligned} A &= P\left(1 + \frac{r}{n}\right)^{n \cdot t} \\ &= 800\left(1 + \frac{0.05}{4}\right)^{4 \cdot 10} \\ &= 800(1.0125)^{40} \\ &\approx 1314.90 \end{aligned}$$ The total amount is $1314.90.

Chapter 6   Review

(6.1) *Write each phrase as a ratio in fractional notation.*

1. 20 cents to 1 dollar

2. four parts red to six parts white

Solve each proportion.

3. $\dfrac{x}{2} = \dfrac{12}{4}$

4. $\dfrac{20}{1} = \dfrac{x}{25}$

5. $\dfrac{32}{100} = \dfrac{100}{x}$

6. $\dfrac{20}{2} = \dfrac{c}{5}$

7. $\dfrac{2}{x-1} = \dfrac{3}{x+3}$

8. $\dfrac{4}{y-3} = \dfrac{3}{y+2}$

9. $\dfrac{y+2}{y} = \dfrac{5}{3}$

10. $\dfrac{x-3}{3x+2} = \dfrac{2}{5}$

11. A machine can process 300 parts in 20 minutes. Find how many parts can be processed in 45 minutes.

12. As his consulting fee, Mr. Visconti charges $90.00 per day. Find how much he charges for 3 hours of consulting. Assume an 8-hour workday.

(6.2) *Solve.*

13. In a survey of 100 adults, 37 preferred pep-peroni on their pizzas. What percent preferred pepperoni?

14. A basketball player made 77 out 100 attempted free throws. What percent of free throws was made?

Write each percent as a decimal.

15. 26%

16. 75%

17. 3.5%

18. 1.5%

19. 275%

20. 400%

21. 47.85%

22. 85.34%

Write each decimal as a percent.

23. 1.6

24. 0.055

25. 0.076

26. 0.085

27. 0.71

28. 0.65

29. 6

30. 9

Write each percent as a fraction or mixed number in simplest form.

31. 7%

32. 15%

33. 25%

34. 8.5%

35. 10.2%

36. $16\frac{2}{3}\%$

37. $33\frac{1}{3}\%$

38. 110%

Write each fraction or mixed number as a percent.

39. $\frac{2}{5}$

40. $\frac{7}{10}$

41. $\frac{7}{12}$

42. $1\frac{2}{3}$

43. $1\frac{1}{4}$

44. $\frac{3}{5}$

45. $\frac{1}{16}$

46. $\frac{5}{8}$

(6.3) Translating *Translate each to an equation and solve.*

47. 1250 is 1.25% of what number?

48. What number is $33\frac{1}{3}\%$ of 24,000?

49. 124.2 is what percent of 540?

50. 22.9 is 20% of what number?

51. What number is 17% of 640?

52. 693 is what percent of 462?

(6.4) Translating *Translate each to a proportion and solve.*

53. 104.5 is 25% of what number?

54. 16.5 is 5.5% of what number?

55. What number is 30% of 532?

56. 63 is what percent of 35?

57. 93.5 is what percent of 85?

58. What number is 33% of 500?

(6.5) *Solve.*

59. In a survey of 2000 people, it was found that 1320 have a microwave oven. Find the percent of people who own microwaves.

60. Of the 12,360 freshmen entering County College, 2000 are enrolled in prealgebra. Find the percent of entering freshmen who are enrolled in prealgebra. Round to the nearest whole percent.

61. The number of violent crimes in a city decreased from 675 to 534. Find the percent decrease. Round to the nearest tenth percent.

62. The current charge for dumping waste in a local landfill is $16 per cubic foot. To cover new environmental costs, the charge will increase to $33 per cubic foot. Find the percent increase.

63. This year the fund drive for a charity collected $215,000. Next year, a 4% decrease is expected. Find how much is expected to be collected in next year's drive.

64. A local union negotiated a new contract that increases the hourly pay 15% over last year's pay. The old hourly rate was $11.50. Find the new hourly rate rounded to the nearest cent.

(6.6) *Solve.*

65. If the sales tax rate is 9.5%, what is the total amount charged for a $250 coat?

66. Find the sales tax paid on a $25.50 purchase if the sales tax rate is 8.5%. Round to the nearest cent.

67. Russ James is a sales representative for a chemical company and is paid a commission rate of 5% on all sales. Find his commission if he sold $100,000 worth of chemicals last month.

68. Carol Sell is a sales clerk in a clothing store. She receives a commission of 7.5% on all sales. Find her commission for the week if her sales for the week were $4005. Round to the nearest cent.

69. A $3000 mink coat is on sale for 30% off. Find the discount and the sale price.

70. A $90 calculator is on sale for 10% off. Find the discount and the sale price.

(6.7) *Solve.*

71. Find the simple interest due on $4000 loaned for 4 months at 12% interest.

72. Find the simple interest due on $6500 loaned for 3 months at 20%.

73. Find the total amount in an account if $5500 is compounded annually at 12% for 15 years.

74. Find the total amount in an account if $6000 is compounded semiannually at 11% for 10 years.

75. Find the total amount in an account if $100 is compounded quarterly at 12% for 5 years.

76. Find the total amount in an account if $1000 is compounded quarterly at 18% for 20 years.

Mixed Review

Write each percent as a decimal.

77. 3.8%

78. 124.5%

Write each decimal as a percent.

79. 0.54

80. 95.2

Write each percent as a fraction or mixed number in simplest form.

81. 47%

82. 5.6%

Write each fraction or mixed number as a percent.

83. $\dfrac{3}{8}$

84. $\dfrac{6}{5}$

Translating *Translate each into an equation and solve.*

85. 43 is 16% of what number?

86. 27.5 is what percent of 25?

87. What number is 36% of 1968?

88. 67 is what percent of 50?

Translating *Translate each into a proportion and solve.*

89. 75 is what percent of 25?

90. What number is 16% of 240?

91. 28 is 5% of what number?

92. 52 is what percent of 16?

Solve.

93. The total number of cans in a soft drink machine is 300. If 78 soft drinks have been sold, find the percent of soft drink cans that have been sold.

94. A home valued at $96,950 last year has lost 7% of its value this year. Find the loss in value.

95. A dinette set sells for $568.00. If the sales tax rate is 8.75%, find the total price of the dinette set.

96. The original price of a video game is $23.00. It is on sale for 15% off. What is the amount of the discount?

97. A candy salesman makes a commission of $1.60 from each case of candy he sells. If a case of candy costs $12.80, what is his rate of commission?

98. Find the total amount due on a 6-month loan of $1400 at a simple interest rate of 13%.

99. Find the total amount due on a loan of $5500 for 9 years at 12.5% simple interest.

Write each percent as a decimal.

1. 85%   **2.** 500%   **3.** 0.6%

Write each decimal as a percent.

4. 0.056   **5.** 6.1   **6.** 0.35

Write each percent as a fraction or a mixed number in simplest form.

7. 120%   **8.** 38.5%   **9.** 0.2%

Write each fraction or mixed number as a percent.

10. $\frac{11}{20}$ **11.** $\frac{3}{8}$ **12.** $1\frac{3}{4}$

13. Bottled water accounts for $\frac{1}{5}$ of the total noncarbonated beverage category in convenience stores. Write $\frac{1}{5}$ as a percent. (*Source:* Grocery Manufacturers of America)

14. In small firms in the United States, 64% of full-time employees receive medical insurance benefits. Write 64% as a fraction. (*Source:* U.S. Bureau of Labor Statistics)

Solve.

15. What number is 42% of 80?   **16.** 0.6% of what number is 7.5?

17. 567 is what percent of 756?

Answers

1. _____

2. _____

3. _____

4. _____

5. _____

6. _____

7. _____

8. _____

9. _____

10. _____

11. _____

12. _____

13. _____

14. _____

15. _____

16. _____

17. _____

18. _____

19. _____

20. _____

21. _____

22. _____

23. _____

24. _____

25. _____

26. _____

27. _____

28. _____

29. _____

30. _____

31. _____

Solve. If necessary, round percents to the nearest tenth, dollar amounts to the nearest cent, and all other numbers to the nearest whole.

18. An alloy is 12% copper. How much copper is contained in 320 pounds of this alloy?

19. A farmer in Nebraska estimates that 20% of his potential crop, or $11,350, has been lost to a hard freeze. Find the total value of his potential crop.

20. If the local sales tax rate is 8.25%, find the total amount charged for a stereo system priced at $354.

21. A town's population increased from 25,200 to 26,460. Find the percent increase.

22. A $120 framed picture is on sale for 15% off. Find the discount and the sale price.

23. Randy Nguyen is paid a commission rate of 4% on all sales. Find Randy's commission if his sales were $9875.

24. A sales tax of $13.77 is added to an item's price of $152.99. Find the sales tax rate. Round to the nearest whole percent.

25. Find the simple interest earned on $2000 saved for $3\frac{1}{2}$ years at an interest rate of 9.25%.

26. $1365 is compounded annually at 8%. Find the total amount in the account after 5 years.

27. A couple borrowed $400 from a bank at 13.5% simple interest for 6 months for car repairs. Find the total amount due the bank at the end of the 6-month period.

28. In a recent 5-year period, the number of major crimes reported in New York City decreased from 149,488 to 142,760. Find the percent decrease. (*Source:* New York State Division of Criminal Justice Services)

29. Write the ratio $75 to $10 as a fraction in simplest form.

30. Solve: $\dfrac{5}{y+1} = \dfrac{4}{y+2}$

31. In a sample of 85 fluorescent bulbs, 3 were found to be defective. At this rate, how many defective bulbs should be found in 510 bulbs?

1. Multiply: 236×86

2. Multiply: 409×76

3. Subtract 7 from -3.

4. Subtract -2 from 8.

5. Solve: $x - 2 = -1$

6. Solve: $x + 4 = 3$

7. Solve: $3(2x - 6) + 6 = 0$

8. Solve: $5(x - 2) = 3x$

9. Write an equivalent fraction with the given denominator.

$$3 = \frac{}{7}$$

10. Write an equivalent fraction with the given denominator.

$$8 = \frac{}{5}$$

11. Write in simplest form: $-\dfrac{10}{27}$

12. Write in simplest form: $\dfrac{10y}{32}$

13. Divide: $-\dfrac{7}{12} \div -\dfrac{5}{6}$

14. Divide: $-\dfrac{2}{5} \div \dfrac{7}{10}$

15. Evaluate $y - x$ if $x = -\dfrac{3}{10}$ and $y = -\dfrac{8}{10}$.

16. Evaluate $2x + 3y$ if $x = \dfrac{2}{5}$ and $y = -\dfrac{1}{5}$.

17. Find: $-\dfrac{3}{4} - \dfrac{1}{14} + \dfrac{6}{7}$

18. Find: $\dfrac{2}{9} + \dfrac{7}{15} - \dfrac{1}{3}$

19. Simplify: $\dfrac{\frac{1}{2} + \frac{3}{8}}{\frac{3}{4} - \frac{1}{6}}$

20. Simplify: $\dfrac{\frac{2}{3} + \frac{1}{6}}{\frac{3}{4} - \frac{3}{5}}$

21. Solve: $\dfrac{x}{2} = \dfrac{x}{3} + \dfrac{1}{2}$

22. Solve: $\dfrac{x}{2} + \dfrac{1}{5} = 3 - \dfrac{x}{5}$

Answers

1. _____

2. _____

3. _____

4. _____

5. _____

6. _____

7. _____

8. _____

9. _____

10. _____

11. _____

12. _____

13. _____

14. _____

15. _____

16. _____

17. _____

18. _____

19. _____

20. _____

21. _____

22. _____

23. a. _____

    b. _____

24. a. _____

    b. _____

25. _____

26. _____

27. _____

28. _____

29. _____

30. _____

31. _____

32. _____

33. _____

34. _____

35. _____

36. _____

37. _____

38. _____

39. _____

40. _____

41. _____

42. _____

43. _____

44. _____

45. _____

46. _____

47. _____

48. _____

49. _____

50. _____

23. Write each mixed number as an improper fraction.

    a. $4\dfrac{2}{9}$

    b. $1\dfrac{8}{11}$

24. Write each mixed number as an improper fraction.

    a. $3\dfrac{2}{5}$

    b. $6\dfrac{2}{7}$

Write each decimal as a fraction or mixed number. Write your answer in simplest form.

25. 0.125

26. 0.85

27. -105.083

28. 17.015

29. Subtract: $85 - 17.31$

30. Subtract: $38 - 10.06$

Multiply.

31. 7.68×10

32. 12.483×100

33. $(-76.3)(1000)$

34. -853.75×10

35. Evaluate $x \div y$ for $x = 2.5$ and $y = 0.05$.

36. Is 470 a solution of the equation
$$\dfrac{x}{100} = 4.75?$$

37. Find the median of the scores: $67, 91, 75, 86, 55, 91$

38. Find the mean of 36, 40, 86, and 30.

39. Write the ratio of 2.5 to 3.15 as a fraction in simplest form.

40. Write the ratio of 5.8 to 7.6 as a fraction in simplest form.

41. Solve for x: $\dfrac{45}{x} = \dfrac{5}{7}$

42. Solve for x: $\dfrac{x - 1}{3x + 1} = \dfrac{3}{8}$

43. On a chamber of commerce map of Abita Springs, 5 miles corresponds to 2 inches. How many miles correspond to 7 inches?

44. A student doing math homework can complete 7 problems in about 6 minutes. At this rate, how many problems can be completed in 30 minutes?

Write each percent as a fraction or mixed number in simplest form.

45. 1.9%

46. 2.3%

47. $33\dfrac{1}{3}\%$

48. 108%

49. What number is 35% of 60?

50. What number is 42% of 85?

Equations, Inequalities, and Problem Solving

9

Approximate map
of cranberry ranges:
—— Common cranberry
—— Small cranberry
—— American cranberry

Check Your Progress

Vocabulary Check

Chapter Highlights

Chapter Review

Chapter Test

Cumulative Review

The cranberry is one of only three fruits that are native to North America (the other two are the blueberry and the Concord grape). Native Americans pounded cranberries into a paste that they mixed with dried meat to create pemmican. American and Canadian sailors took cranberries on long sea voyages to combat scurvy, because of their high vitamin C content.

Americans consume 400 million pounds of cranberries annually, 20% of them during Thanksgiving week. They are available in many forms: fresh, jellied, dried, and in juice. They are high in antioxidants and beneficial to the health of gums and teeth. In Exercises 69–72, Section 9.1, we will explore information about cranberry crops from the top five cranberry-producing states. (*Source:* Cape Cod Cranberry Growers Association)

In this chapter, we review solving equations and introduce solving inequalities. Solving equations and inequalities is necessary in order to solve word problems. Of course, problem solving is an integral topic in algebra and its discussion is continued throughout this text.

Cranberry flower—named because of resemblance of Crane

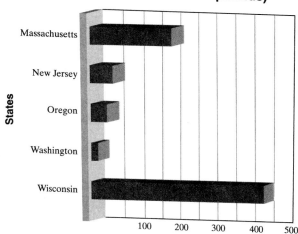

Top Cranberry-Producing States (in millions of pounds)

States: Massachusetts, New Jersey, Oregon, Washington, Wisconsin

Millions of lb of Cranberries 2012

Source: National Agricultural Statistics Service

Objectives

A Define the Meaning of the Symbols $=$, $\neq$, $<$, $>$, $\leq$, and $\geq$.

B Translate Sentences into Mathematical Statements.

C Identify Integers, Rational Numbers, Irrational Numbers, and Real Numbers.

Throughout the previous chapters, we have studied different sets of numbers. In this section, we review these sets of numbers. We also introduce a few new sets of numbers in order to show the relationships among these common sets of real numbers. We begin with a review of the set of natural numbers and the set of whole numbers and how we use symbols to compare these numbers. A **set** is a collection of objects, each of which is called a **member** or **element** of the set. A pair of brace symbols { } encloses the list of elements and is translated as "the set of" or "the set containing."

Natural numbers

$$\{1, 2, 3, 4, 5, 6, \ldots\}$$

Whole numbers

$$\{0, 1, 2, 3, 4, 5, 6, \ldots\}$$

> **Helpful Hint**
>
> The three dots (an ellipsis) at the end of the list of elements of a set means that the list continues in the same manner indefinitely.

Objective A Equality and Inequality Symbols

Picturing natural numbers and whole numbers on a number line helps us to see the order of the numbers. Symbols can be used to describe in writing the order of two quantities. We will use equality symbols and inequality symbols to compare quantities.

Below is a review of these symbols. The letters a and b are used to represent quantities. Letters such as a and b that are used to represent numbers or quantities are called **variables.**

Equality and Inequality Symbols

		Meaning
Equality symbol:	$a = b$	a is equal to b.
Inequality symbols:	$a \neq b$	a is not equal to b.
	$a < b$	a is less than b.
	$a > b$	a is greater than b.
	$a \leq b$	a is less than or equal to b.
	$a \geq b$	a is greater than or equal to b.

These symbols may be used to form **mathematical statements** such as

$$2 = 2 \quad \text{and} \quad 2 \neq 6$$

Recall that on a number line, we see that a number **to the right of** another number is **larger.** Similarly, a number **to the left of** another number is **smaller.** For example, 3 is to the left of 5 on the number line, which means that 3 is less than 5, or $3 < 5$. Similarly, 2 is to the right of 0 on the number line, which means that 2 is greater than 0, or $2 > 0$. Since 0 is to the left of 2, we can also say that 0 is less than 2, or $0 < 2$.

$$3 < 5$$

$$2 > 0 \text{ or } 0 < 2$$

Helpful Hint

Notice that $2 > 0$ has exactly the same meaning as $0 < 2$. Switching the order of the numbers and reversing the "direction" of the inequality symbol does not change the meaning of the statement.

$6 > 4$ has the same meaning as $4 < 6$.

Also notice that when the statement is true, the inequality arrow points to the smaller number.

Our discussion above can be generalized in the order property below.

Order Property for Real Numbers

For any two real numbers a and b, a is less than b if a is to the left of b on a number line.

$$a < b \text{ or also } b > a$$

Examples Determine whether each statement is true or false.

1. $2 < 3$ True.   Since 2 is to the left of 3 on a number line
2. $72 < 27$ False.   72 is to the right of 27 on a number line, so $72 > 27$.
3. $8 \geq 8$ True.   Since $8 = 8$ is true
4. $8 \leq 8$ True.   Since $8 = 8$ is true
5. $23 \leq 0$ False.   Since neither $23 < 0$ nor $23 = 0$ is true
6. $0 \leq 23$ True.   Since $0 < 23$ is true

■ Work Practice 1–6

Objective B Translating Sentences into Mathematical Statements

Now, let's use the symbols discussed on the previous page to translate sentences into mathematical statements.

Example 7 Translate each sentence into a mathematical statement.

a. Nine is less than or equal to eleven.   b. Eight is greater than one.

c. Three is not equal to four.

Solution:

a.
nine	is less than or equal to	eleven
↓	↓	↓
9	$\leq$	11

b.
eight	is greater than	one
↓	↓	↓
8	$>$	1

c.
three	is not equal to	four
↓	↓	↓
3	$\neq$	4

■ Work Practice 7

Practice 1–6

Determine whether each statement is true or false.

1. $8 < 6$ 2. $100 > 10$
3. $21 \leq 21$ 4. $21 \geq 21$
5. $0 \geq 5$ 6. $25 \geq 22$

Helpful Hint

If either $3 < 3$ or $3 = 3$ is true, then $3 \leq 3$ is true.

Practice 7

Translate each sentence into a mathematical statement.

a. Fourteen is greater than or equal to fourteen.

b. Zero is less than five.

c. Nine is not equal to ten.

Answers

1. false   2. true   3. true
4. true   5. false   6. true
7. a. $14 \geq 14$ b. $0 < 5$ c. $9 \neq 10$

Objective C Identifying Common Sets of Numbers

Whole numbers are not sufficient to describe many situations in the real world. For example, quantities smaller than zero must sometimes be represented, such as temperatures less than 0 degrees.

Recall that we can place numbers less than zero on a number line as follows: Numbers less than 0 are to the left of 0 and are labeled $-1, -2, -3$, and so on. The numbers we have labeled on the number line below are called the set of **integers.**

Integers to the left of 0 are called **negative integers;** integers to the right of 0 are called **positive integers.** The integer 0 is neither positive nor negative.

Integers

$$\{\ldots, -3, -2, -1, 0, 1, 2, 3, \ldots\}$$

Helpful Hint

A $-$ sign, such as the one in -2, tells us that the number is to the left of 0 on a number line.

-2 is read "negative two."

A $+$ sign or no sign tells us that the number lies to the right of 0 on a number line. For example, 3 and $+3$ both mean positive three.

Practice 8

Use an integer to express the number in the following: "The elevation of the city of New Orleans is 8 feet below sea level." (*Source: The World Almanac*)

Example 8 Use an integer to express the number in the following: "The lowest temperature ever recorded at South Pole Station, Antarctica, occurred during the month of June. The record-low temperature was 117 degrees below zero." (*Source:* The National Oceanic and Atmospheric Administration)

Solution: The integer -117 represents 117 degrees below zero.

■ Work Practice 8

Answer
8. -8

A problem with integers in real-life settings arises when quantities are smaller than some integer but greater than the next smallest integer. On a number line, these quantities may be visualized by points between integers. Some of these quantities between integers can be represented as quantities of integers. For example,

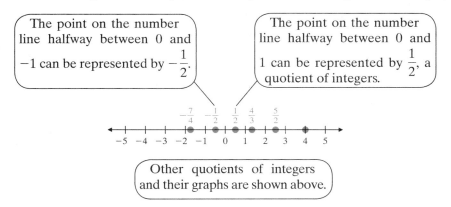

The point on the number line halfway between 0 and -1 can be represented by $-\frac{1}{2}$.

The point on the number line halfway between 0 and 1 can be represented by $\frac{1}{2}$, a quotient of integers.

Other quotients of integers and their graphs are shown above.

These numbers, each of which can be represented as a quotient of integers, are examples of **rational numbers.** It's not possible to list the set of rational numbers using the notation that we have been using. For this reason, we will use a different notation.

Rational Numbers

$$\left\{ \frac{a}{b} \,\middle|\, a \text{ and } b \text{ are integers and } b \neq 0 \right\}$$

We read this set as "the set of numbers $\frac{a}{b}$ such that a and b are integers and b **is not equal to 0.**"

Helpful Hint

We commonly refer to rational numbers as fractions.

Notice that every integer is also a rational number since each integer can be written as a quotient of integers. For example, the integer 5 is also a rational number since $5 = \frac{5}{1}$. For the rational number $\frac{5}{1}$, recall that the top number, 5, is called the numerator and the bottom number, 1, is called the denominator.

Let's practice **graphing** numbers on a number line.

Example 9 Graph the numbers on a number line.

$$-\frac{4}{3}, \quad \frac{1}{4}, \quad \frac{3}{2}, \quad -2\frac{1}{8}, \quad 3.5$$

Solution: To help graph the improper fractions in the list, we first write them as mixed numbers.

■ Work Practice 9

Every rational number has a point on the number line that corresponds to it. But not every point on the number line corresponds to a rational number. Those points that do not correspond to rational numbers correspond instead to **irrational numbers.**

Practice 9

Graph the numbers on the number line.

$$-2\frac{1}{2}, \quad -\frac{2}{3}, \quad \frac{1}{5}, \quad \frac{5}{4}, \quad 2.25$$

Answer

9.

Irrational Numbers

{Nonrational numbers that correspond to points on a number line}

An irrational number that you have probably seen is π. Also, $\sqrt{2}$, the length of the diagonal of the square shown below, is an irrational number.

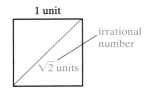

Both rational and irrational numbers can be written as decimal numbers. The decimal equivalent of a rational number will either terminate or repeat in a pattern. For example, upon dividing we find that

$$\frac{3}{4} = 0.75 \qquad \text{(Decimal number terminates or ends.)}$$

$$\frac{2}{3} = 0.66666\ldots \qquad \text{(Decimal number repeats in a pattern.)}$$

The decimal representation of an irrational number will neither terminate nor repeat. (For further review of decimals, see Chapter 5.)

The set of numbers, each of which corresponds to a point on a number line, is called the set of **real numbers.** One and only one point on a number line corresponds to each real number.

Real Numbers

{All numbers that correspond to points on a number line}

Several different sets of numbers have been discussed in this section. The following diagram shows the relationships among these sets of real numbers. Notice that, together, the rational numbers and the irrational numbers make up the real numbers.

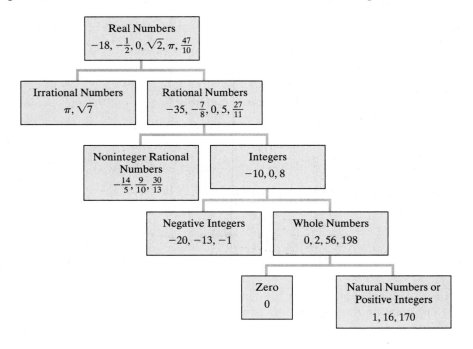

Now that other sets of numbers have been reviewed, let's continue our practice of comparing numbers.

Example 10 Insert $<, >,$ or $=$ between the pairs of numbers to form true statements.

a. $-5 \quad -6$ **b.** $3.195 \quad 3.2$ **c.** $\dfrac{1}{4} \quad \dfrac{1}{3}$

Solution:

a. $-5 > -6$ since -5 lies to the right of -6 on a number line.

b. By comparing digits in the same place values, we find that $3.195 < 3.2$, since $0.1 < 0.2$.

c. By dividing, we find that $\dfrac{1}{4} = 0.25$ and $\dfrac{1}{3} = 0.33\ldots$. Since $0.25 < 0.33\ldots$, $\dfrac{1}{4} < \dfrac{1}{3}$.

■ Work Practice 10

Practice 10

Insert $<, >,$ or $=$ between the pairs of numbers to form true statements.

a. $-11 \quad -9$

b. $4.511 \quad 4.151$

c. $\dfrac{7}{8} \quad \dfrac{2}{3}$

Example 11 Given the set $\left\{-3, -2, 0, \dfrac{1}{4}, \sqrt{2}, 11, 112\right\}$, list the numbers in this set that belong to the set of:

a. Natural numbers **b.** Whole numbers **c.** Integers
d. Rational numbers **e.** Irrational numbers **f.** Real numbers

Solution:

a. The natural numbers are 11 and 112.

b. The whole numbers are $0, 11,$ and 112.

c. The integers are $-3, -2, 0, 11,$ and 112.

d. Recall that integers are rational numbers also. The rational numbers are $-3, -2, 0, \dfrac{1}{4}, 11,$ and 112.

e. The only irrational number is $\sqrt{2}$.

f. All numbers in the given set are real numbers.

■ Work Practice 11

Practice 11

Given the set $\left\{-100, -\dfrac{2}{5}, 0, \pi, 6, 913\right\}$, list the numbers in this set that belong to the set of:

a. Natural numbers
b. Whole numbers
c. Integers
d. Rational numbers
e. Irrational numbers
f. Real numbers

Answers
10. a. $<$ **b.** $>$ **c.** $>$
11. a. $6, 913$ **b.** $0, 6, 913$
c. $-100, 0, 6, 913$
d. $-100, -\dfrac{2}{5}, 0, 6, 913$ **e.** π
f. all numbers in the given set

Vocabulary, Readiness & Video Check

Use the choices below to fill in each blank. Not all choices will be used.

real	natural	whole	$\dfrac{1}{2}$	$\dfrac{1}{4}$
rational	inequality	integers	0	1

1. The _____ numbers are $\{0, 1, 2, 3, 4, \ldots\}$.

2. The _____ numbers are $\{1, 2, 3, 4, 5, \ldots\}$.

3. The symbols $\neq, \leq,$ and $>$ are called _____ symbols.

4. The _____ are $\{\ldots, -3, -2, -1, 0, 1, 2, 3, \ldots\}$.

5. The _____ numbers are {all numbers that correspond to points on a number line}.

6. The _____ numbers are $\left\{ \dfrac{a}{b} \,\middle|\, a \text{ and } b \text{ are integers}, b \neq 0 \right\}$.

7. The integer _____ is neither positive nor negative.

8. The point on a number line halfway between 0 and $\dfrac{1}{2}$ can be represented by _____.

Martin-Gay Interactive Videos   *Watch the section lecture video and answer the following questions.*

See Video 9.1

Objective A 9. In ▯ Example 2, why is the symbol $<$ inserted between the two numbers? ◐

Objective B 10. Write the sentence given in ▯ Example 4 and translate it to a mathematical statement using symbols. ◐

Objective C 11. Which sets of numbers does the number in ▯ Example 6 belong to? Why is this number not an irrational number? ◐

9.1 Exercise Set MyMathLab®

Objectives Ⓐ Ⓒ **Mixed Practice** *Insert* $<, >,$ *or* $=$ *in the space between the paired numbers to make each statement true. See Examples 1 through 6 and 10.*

1. 4   10

2. 8   5

▷ **3.** 7   3

4. 9   15

5. 6.26   6.26

6. 1.13   1.13

▷ **7.** 0   7

8. 20   0

9. The freezing point of water is 32° Fahrenheit. The boiling point of water is 212° Fahrenheit. Write an inequality statement using $<$ or $>$ comparing the numbers 32 and 212.

10. The freezing point of water is 0° Celsius. The boiling point of water is 100° Celsius. Write an inequality statement using $<$ or $>$ comparing the numbers 0 and 100.

△**11.** An angle measuring 30° and an angle measuring 45° are shown. Write an inequality statement using $\leq$ or $\geq$ comparing the numbers 30 and 45.

△**12.** The sum of the measures of the angles of a parallelogram is 360°. The sum of the measures of the angles of a triangle is 180°. Write an inequality statement using $\leq$ or $\geq$ comparing the numbers 360 and 180.

30°   45°

Determine whether each statement is true or false. See Examples 1 through 6 and 10.

⊙ **13.** $11 \leq 11$ **14.** $8 \geq 9$ **15.** $-11 > -10$ **16.** $-16 > -17$

17. $5.092 < 5.902$ **18.** $1.02 > 1.021$ **19.** $\dfrac{9}{10} \leq \dfrac{8}{9}$ **20.** $\dfrac{4}{5} \leq \dfrac{9}{11}$

Rewrite each inequality so that the inequality symbol points in the opposite direction and the resulting statement has the same meaning as the given one. See Examples 1 through 6 and 10.

21. $25 \geq 20$ **22.** $-13 \leq 13$ **23.** $0 < 6$

24. $5 > 3$ **25.** $-10 > -12$ **26.** $-4 < -2$

Objectives B C Mixed Practice—Translating *Write each sentence as a mathematical statement. See Example 7.*

27. Seven is less than eleven.   **28.** Twenty is greater than two.

⊙ **29.** Five is greater than or equal to four.   **30.** Negative ten is less than or equal to thirty-seven.

⊙ **31.** Fifteen is not equal to negative two.   **32.** Negative seven is not equal to seven.

Use integers to represent the value(s) in each statement. See Example 8.

33. The highest elevation in California is Mt. Whitney, with an altitude of 14,494 feet. The lowest elevation in California is Death Valley, with an altitude of 282 feet below sea level. (*Source:* U.S. Geological Survey)

34. Driskill Mountain, in Louisiana, has an altitude of 535 feet. New Orleans, Louisiana, lies 8 feet below sea level. (*Source:* U.S. Geological Survey)

35. The number of graduate students at the University of Texas at Austin was 27,724 fewer than the number of undergraduate students. (*Source:* University of Texas at Austin, 2012)

36. The number of students admitted to the class of 2011 at UCLA was 56,715 fewer students than the number that had applied. (*Source:* UCLA, 2012)

37. A community college student deposited $475 in her savings account. She later withdrew $195.

38. A deep-sea diver ascended 17 feet and later descended 15 feet.

Graph each set of numbers on the number line. See Example 9.

39. $-4, 0, 2, -2$

40. $-3, 0, 1, -5$

41. $-2, 4, \dfrac{1}{3}, -\dfrac{1}{4}$

42. $-5, 3, -\dfrac{1}{3}, \dfrac{7}{8}$

43. $-4.5, \dfrac{7}{4}, 3.25, -\dfrac{3}{2}$

44. $4.5, -\dfrac{9}{4}, 1.75, -\dfrac{7}{2}$

Tell which set or sets each number belongs to: natural numbers, whole numbers, integers, rational numbers, irrational numbers, or real numbers. See Example 11.

45. 0

46. $\frac{1}{4}$

47. -7

48. $-\frac{1}{7}$

49. 265

50. 7941

51. $\frac{2}{3}$

52. $\sqrt{3}$

Determine whether each statement is true or false.

53. Every rational number is also an integer.

54. Every natural number is positive.

55. 0 is a real number.

56. $\frac{1}{2}$ is an integer.

57. Every negative number is also a rational number.

58. Every rational number is also a real number.

59. Every real number is also a rational number.

60. Every whole number is an integer.

Review

Insert $<$, $>$, or $=$ in the appropriate space to make each statement true. See Section 2.1.

61. $|-5|$ -4

62. $|-12|$ $|0|$

63. $\left|-\frac{5}{8}\right|$ $\left|\frac{5}{8}\right|$

64. $\left|\frac{2}{5}\right|$ $\left|-\frac{2}{5}\right|$

65. $|-2|$ $|-2.7|$

66. $|-5.01|$ $|-5|$

67. $|0|$ $|-8|$

68. $|-12|$ $\frac{-24}{2}$

Concept Extensions

The bar graph shows cranberry production from the top five cranberry-producing states. (Source: National Agricultural Statistics Service)

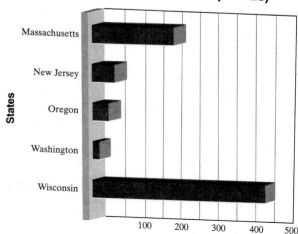

Top Cranberry-Producing States (in millions of pounds)

States

Massachusetts

New Jersey

Oregon

Washington

Wisconsin

100   200   300   400   500

Millions of lb of Cranberries 2012

Source: National Agricultural Statistics Service

69. Write an inequality comparing the 2012 cranberry production in Oregon with the 2012 cranberry production in Washington.

70. Write an inequality comparing the 2012 cranberry production in Massachusetts with the 2012 cranberry production in Wisconsin.

71. Determine the difference between the 2012 cranberry production in Washington and the 2012 cranberry production in New Jersey.

72. Determine the difference between the 2012 cranberry production in Massachusetts and the 2012 cranberry production in Wisconsin.

The apparent magnitude of a star is the measure of its brightness as seen by someone on Earth. The smaller the apparent magnitude, the brighter the star. Below, the apparent magnitudes of some stars are listed. Use this table to answer Exercises 73 through 78.

Star	Apparent Magnitude	Star	Apparent Magnitude
Arcturus	−0.04	Spica	0.98
Sirius	−1.46	Rigel	0.12
Vega	0.03	Regulus	1.35
Antares	0.96	Canopus	−0.72
Sun (Sol)	−26.7	Hadar	0.61

(*Source: Norton's 2000.0: Star Atlas and Reference Handbook,* 18th ed., Longman Group, UK, 1989)

73. The apparent magnitude of the sun is −26.7. The apparent magnitude of the star Arcturus is −0.04. Write an inequality statement comparing the numbers −0.04 and −26.7.

74. The apparent magnitude of Antares is 0.96. The apparent magnitude of Spica is 0.98. Write an inequality statement comparing the numbers 0.96 and 0.98.

75. Which is brighter, the sun or Arcturus?

76. Which is dimmer, Antares or Spica?

77. Which star listed is the brightest?

78. Which star listed is the dimmest?

79. In your own words, explain how to find the absolute value of a number.

80. Give an example of a real-life situation that can be described with integers but not with whole numbers.

9.2 Properties of Real Numbers

Objective A Using the Commutative and Associative Properties

In this section we review names of properties of real numbers with which we are already familiar. Throughout this section, the variables a, b, and c represent real numbers.

We know that order does not matter when adding numbers. For example, we know that $7 + 5$ is the same as $5 + 7$. This property is given a special name—the **commutative property of addition.** We also know that order does not matter when multiplying numbers. For example, we know that $-5(6) = 6(-5)$. This property means that multiplication is commutative also and is called the **commutative property of multiplication.**

Objectives

A Use the Commutative and Associative Properties.

B Use the Distributive Property.

C Use the Identity and Inverse Properties.

Commutative Properties

Addition:	$a + b = b + a$
Multiplication:	$a \cdot b = b \cdot a$

These properties state that the *order* in which any two real numbers are added or multiplied does not change their sum or product. For example, if we let $a = 3$ and $b = 5$, then the commutative properties guarantee that

$$3 + 5 = 5 + 3 \quad \text{and} \quad 3 \cdot 5 = 5 \cdot 3$$

Helpful Hint

Is subtraction also commutative? Try an example. Is $3 - 2 = 2 - 3$? **No!** The left side of this statement equals 1; the right side equals -1. There is no commutative property of subtraction. Similarly, there is no commutative property of division. For example, $10 \div 2$ does not equal $2 \div 10$.

Practice 1

Use a commutative property to complete each statement.

a. $7 \cdot y = $ _____

b. $4 + x = $ _____

Example 1 Use a commutative property to complete each statement.

a. $x + 5 = $ _____   **b.** $3 \cdot x = $ _____

Solution:

a. $x + 5 = 5 + x$ By the commutative property of addition

b. $3 \cdot x = x \cdot 3$ By the commutative property of multiplication

■ Work Practice 1

✓**Concept Check** Which of the following pairs of actions are commutative?

a. "raking the leaves" and "bagging the leaves"

b. "putting on your left glove" and "putting on your right glove"

c. "putting on your coat" and "putting on your shirt"

d. "reading a novel" and "reading a newspaper"

Let's now discuss grouping numbers. When we add three numbers, the way in which they are grouped or associated does not change their sum. For example, we know that $2 + (3 + 4) = 2 + 7 = 9$. This result is the same if we group the numbers differently. In other words, $(2 + 3) + 4 = 5 + 4 = 9$, also. Thus, $2 + (3 + 4) = (2 + 3) + 4$. This property is called the **associative property of addition.**

In the same way, changing the grouping of numbers when multiplying does not change their product. For example, $2 \cdot (3 \cdot 4) = (2 \cdot 3) \cdot 4$ (check it). This is the **associative property of multiplication.**

Associative Properties

Addition:	$(a + b) + c = a + (b + c)$
Multiplication:	$(a \cdot b) \cdot c = a \cdot (b \cdot c)$

Answers

1. a. $y \cdot 7$ **b.** $x + 4$

✓**Concept Check Answer**

b, d

These properties state that the way in which three numbers are *grouped* does not change their sum or their product.

Example 2 Use an associative property to complete each statement.

a. $5 + (4 + 6) = $ _____

b. $(-1 \cdot 2) \cdot 5 = $ _____

c. $(m + n) + 9 = $ _____

d. $(xy) \cdot 12 = $ _____

Solution:

a. $5 + (4 + 6) = (5 + 4) + 6$ By the associative property of addition

b. $(-1 \cdot 2) \cdot 5 = -1 \cdot (2 \cdot 5)$ By the associative property of multiplication

c. $(m + n) + 9 = m + (n + 9)$ By the associative property of addition

d. $(xy) \cdot 12 = x \cdot (y \cdot 12)$ Recall that xy means $x \cdot y$.

◼ Work Practice 2

Practice 2

Use an associative property to complete each statement.

a. $5 \cdot (-3 \cdot 6) = $ _____

b. $(-2 + 7) + 3 = $ _____

c. $(q + r) + 17 = $ _____

d. $(ab) \cdot 21 = $ _____

Helpful Hint

Remember the difference between the commutative properties and the associative properties. The commutative properties have to do with the *order* of numbers and the associative properties have to do with the *grouping* of numbers.

Examples Determine whether each statement is true by an associative property or a commutative property.

3. $(7 + 10) + 4 = (10 + 7) + 4$ Since the order of two numbers was changed and their grouping was not, this is true by the commutative property of addition.

4. $2 \cdot (3 \cdot 1) = (2 \cdot 3) \cdot 1$ Since the grouping of the numbers was changed and their order was not, this is true by the associative property of multiplication.

◼ Work Practice 3–4

Practice 3–4

Determine whether each statement is true by an associative property or a commutative property.

3. $5 \cdot (4 \cdot 7) = 5 \cdot (7 \cdot 4)$

4. $-2 + (4 + 9)$
$= (-2 + 4) + 9$

Let's now illustrate how these properties can help us simplify expressions.

Practice 5–6

Simplify each expression.

5. $(-3 + x) + 17$ **6.** $4(5x)$

Examples Simplify each expression.

5. $10 + (x + 12) = 10 + (12 + x)$ By the commutative property of addition

$= (10 + 12) + x$ By the associative property of addition

$= 22 + x$ Add.

6. $-3(7x) = (-3 \cdot 7)x$ By the associative property of multiplication

$= -21x$ Multiply.

◼ Work Practice 5–6

Objective B Using the Distributive Property

The **distributive property of multiplication over addition** is used repeatedly throughout algebra. It is useful because it allows us to write a product as a sum or a sum as a product.

We know that $7(2 + 4) = 7(6) = 42$. Compare that with

$7(2) + 7(4) = 14 + 28 = 42$

Since both original expressions equal 42, they must equal each other, or

$7(2 + 4) = 7(2) + 7(4)$

Answers

2. a. $(5 \cdot -3) \cdot 6$ **b.** $-2 + (7 + 3)$
c. $q + (r + 17)$ **d.** $a \cdot (b \cdot 21)$
3. commutative   **4.** associative
5. $14 + x$ **6.** $20x$

This is an example of the distributive property. The product on the left side of the equal sign is equal to the sum on the right side. We can think of the 7 as being distributed to each number inside the parentheses.

> ### Distributive Property of Multiplication Over Addition
>
> $$a(b + c) = ab + ac$$

Since multiplication is commutative, this property can also be written as

$$(b + c)a = ba + ca$$

The distributive property can also be extended to more than two numbers inside the parentheses. For example,

$$3(x + y + z) = 3(x) + 3(y) + 3(z)$$
$$= 3x + 3y + 3z$$

Since we define subtraction in terms of addition, the distributive property is also true for subtraction. For example,

$$2(x - y) = 2(x) - 2(y)$$
$$= 2x - 2y$$

Practice 7–12

Use the distributive property to write each expression without parentheses. Then simplify the result.

7. $5(x + y)$

8. $-3(2 + 7x)$

9. $4(x + 6y - 2z)$

10. $-1(3 - a)$

11. $-(8 + a - b)$

12. $\dfrac{1}{2}(2x + 4) + 9$

Answers

7. $5x + 5y$ **8.** $-6 - 21x$

9. $4x + 24y - 8z$ **10.** $-3 + a$

11. $-8 - a + b$ **12.** $x + 11$

Examples Use the distributive property to write each expression without parentheses. Then simplify the result.

7. $2(x + y) = 2(x) + 2(y)$
$$= 2x + 2y$$

8. $-5(-3 + 2z) = -5(-3) + (-5)(2z)$
$$= 15 - 10z$$

9. $5(x + 3y - z) = 5(x) + 5(3y) - 5(z)$
$$= 5x + 15y - 5z$$

10. $-1(2 - y) = (-1)(2) - (-1)(y)$
$$= -2 + y$$

11. $-(3 + x - w) = -1(3 + x - w)$
$$= (-1)(3) + (-1)(x) - (-1)(w)$$
$$= -3 - x + w$$

12. $\dfrac{1}{2}(6x + 14) + 10 = \dfrac{1}{2}(6x) + \dfrac{1}{2}(14) + 10$ Apply the distributive property.
$$= 3x + 7 + 10 \quad \text{Multiply.}$$
$$= 3x + 17 \quad \text{Add.}$$

> **Helpful Hint**
>
> Notice in Example 11 that $-(3 + x - w)$ can be rewritten as $-1(3 + x - w)$.

■ Work Practice 7–12

The distributive property can also be used to write a sum as a product.

Examples Use the distributive property to write each sum as a product.

13. $8 \cdot 2 + 8 \cdot x = 8(2 + x)$
14. $7s + 7t = 7(s + t)$

Work Practice 13–14

Practice 13–14

Use the distributive property to write each sum as a product.
13. $9 \cdot 3 + 9 \cdot y$
14. $4x + 4y$

Objective C Using the Identity and Inverse Properties

Next, we look at the **identity properties.**

The number 0 is called the identity for addition because when 0 is added to any real number, the result is the same real number. In other words, the *identity* of the real number is not changed.

The number 1 is called the identity for multiplication because when a real number is multiplied by 1, the result is the same real number. In other words, the *identity* of the real number is not changed.

Identities for Addition and Multiplication

0 is the identity element for addition.

$$a + 0 = a \quad \text{and} \quad 0 + a = a$$

1 is the identity element for multiplication.

$$a \cdot 1 = a \quad \text{and} \quad 1 \cdot a = a$$

Notice that 0 is the *only* number that can be added to any real number with the result that the sum is the same real number. Also, 1 is the *only* number that can be multiplied by any real number with the result that the product is the same real number.

Additive inverses or **opposites** were introduced in Section 2.1. Two numbers are called additive inverses or opposites if their sum is 0. The additive inverse or opposite of 6 is -6 because $6 + (-6) = 0$. The additive inverse or opposite of -5 is 5 because $-5 + 5 = 0$.

Reciprocals or **multiplicative inverses** were introduced in Section 4.3. Two non-zero numbers are called reciprocals or multiplicative inverses if their product is 1. The reciprocal or multiplicative inverse of $\frac{2}{3}$ is $\frac{3}{2}$ because $\frac{2}{3} \cdot \frac{3}{2} = 1$. Likewise, the reciprocal of -5 is $-\frac{1}{5}$ because $-5\left(\frac{1}{5}\right) = 1$.

Additive or Multiplicative Inverses

The numbers a and $-a$ are additive inverses or opposites of each other because their sum is 0; that is,

$$a + (-a) = 0$$

The numbers b and $\frac{1}{b}$ (for $b \neq 0$) are reciprocals or multiplicative inverses of each other because their product is 1; that is,

$$b \cdot \frac{1}{b} = 1$$

Answers
13. $9(3 + y)$ **14.** $4(x + y)$

Practice 15–21

Name the property illustrated by each true statement.

15. $7(a + b) = 7 \cdot a + 7 \cdot b$

16. $12 + y = y + 12$

17. $-4 \cdot (6 \cdot x) = (-4 \cdot 6) \cdot x$

18. $6 + (z + 2) = 6 + (2 + z)$

19. $3\left(\dfrac{1}{3}\right) = 1$

20. $(x + 0) + 23 = x + 23$

21. $(7 \cdot y) \cdot 10 = y \cdot (7 \cdot 10)$

Answers

15. distributive property

16. commutative property of addition

17. associative property of multiplication

18. commutative property of addition

19. multiplicative inverse property

20. identity element for addition

21. commutative and associative properties of multiplication

✓ **Concept Check Answers**

a. $\dfrac{3}{10}$ **b.** $-\dfrac{10}{3}$

✓ **Concept Check** Which of the following is the

a. opposite of $-\dfrac{3}{10}$, and which is the

b. reciprocal of $-\dfrac{3}{10}$?

$$1, -\dfrac{10}{3}, \dfrac{3}{10}, 0, \dfrac{10}{3}, -\dfrac{3}{10}$$

Examples   Name the property illustrated by each true statement.

15. $3(x + y) = 3 \cdot x + 3 \cdot y$ Distributive property

16. $(x + 7) + 9 = x + (7 + 9)$ Associative property of addition (grouping changed)

17. $(b + 0) + 3 = b + 3$ Identity element for addition

18. $2 \cdot (z \cdot 5) = 2 \cdot (5 \cdot z)$ Commutative property of multiplication (order changed)

19. $-2 \cdot \left(-\dfrac{1}{2}\right) = 1$ Multiplicative inverse property

20. $-2 + 2 = 0$ Additive inverse property

21. $-6 \cdot (y \cdot 2) = (-6 \cdot 2) \cdot y$ Commutative and associative properties of multiplication (order and grouping changed)

▪ **Work Practice 15–21**

Vocabulary, Readiness & Video Check

Use the choices below to fill in each blank.

distributive property   associative property of multiplication   commutative property of addition

opposites or additive inverses   associative property of addition

reciprocals or multiplicative inverses   commutative property of multiplication

1. $x + 5 = 5 + x$ is a true statement by the _____.

2. $x \cdot 5 = 5 \cdot x$ is a true statement by the _____.

3. $3(y + 6) = 3 \cdot y + 3 \cdot 6$ is true by the _____.

4. $2 \cdot (x \cdot y) = (2 \cdot x) \cdot y$ is a true statement by the _____.

5. $x + (7 + y) = (x + 7) + y$ is a true statement by the _____.

6. The numbers $-\dfrac{2}{3}$ and $-\dfrac{3}{2}$ are called _____.

7. The numbers $-\dfrac{2}{3}$ and $\dfrac{2}{3}$ are called _____.

Martin-Gay Interactive Videos

See Video 9.2

Watch the section lecture video and answer the following questions.

Objective A 8. The commutative properties are discussed in ⊞ Examples 1 and 2 and the associative properties are discussed in ⊞ Examples 3–7. What's the one word used again and again to describe the commutative property? The associative property? ▶

Objective B 9. In ⊞ Example 10, what point is made about the term 2? ▶

Objective C 10. Complete these statements based on the lecture given before ⊞ Example 12:
- The identity element for addition is _____because if we add _____ to any real number, the result is that real number.
- The identity element for multiplication is _____ because any real number times _____ gives a result of that original real number. ▶

9.2 Exercise Set MyMathLab® ▶

Objective A *Use a commutative property to complete each statement. See Examples 1 and 3.*

▶ **1.** $x + 16 =$ _____

2. $8 + y =$ _____

3. $-4 \cdot y =$ _____

4. $-2 \cdot x =$ _____

▶ **5.** $xy =$ _____

6. $ab =$ _____

7. $2x + 13 =$ _____

8. $19 + 3y =$ _____

Use an associative property to complete each statement. See Examples 2 and 4.

▶ **9.** $(xy) \cdot z =$ _____

10. $3 \cdot (x \cdot y) =$ _____

11. $2 + (a + b) =$ _____

12. $(y + 4) + z =$ _____

13. $4 \cdot (ab) =$ _____

14. $(-3y) \cdot z =$ _____

▶ **15.** $(a + b) + c =$ _____

16. $6 + (r + s) =$ _____

Use the commutative and associative properties to simplify each expression. See Examples 5 and 6.

▶ **17.** $8 + (9 + b)$

18. $(r + 3) + 11$

▶ **19.** $4(6y)$

20. $2(42x)$

21. $\frac{1}{5}(5y)$

22. $\frac{1}{8}(8z)$

23. $(13 + a) + 13$

24. $7 + (x + 4)$

25. $-9(8x)$

26. $-3(12y)$

27. $\frac{3}{4}\left(\frac{4}{3}s\right)$

28. $\frac{2}{7}\left(\frac{7}{2}r\right)$

29. $-\frac{1}{2}(5x)$

30. $-\frac{1}{3}(7x)$

Objective **B** *Use the distributive property to write each expression without parentheses. Then simplify the result, if possible. See Examples 7 through 12.*

31. $4(x + y)$

32. $7(a + b)$

33. $9(x - 6)$

34. $11(y - 4)$

35. $2(3x + 5)$

36. $5(7 + 8y)$

37. $7(4x - 3)$

38. $3(8x - 1)$

▶ **39.** $3(6 + x)$

40. $2(x + 5)$

41. $-2(y - z)$

42. $-3(z - y)$

43. $-\dfrac{1}{3}(3y + 5)$

44. $-\dfrac{1}{2}(2r + 11)$

45. $5(x + 4m + 2)$

46. $8(3y + z - 6)$

47. $-4(1 - 2m + n) + 4$

48. $-4(4 + 2p + 5) + 16$

49. $-(5x + 2)$

50. $-(9r + 5)$

▶ **51.** $-(r - 3 - 7p)$

52. $-(q - 2 + 6r)$

53. $\dfrac{1}{2}(6x + 7) + \dfrac{1}{2}$

54. $\dfrac{1}{4}(4x - 2) - \dfrac{7}{2}$

55. $-\dfrac{1}{3}(3x - 9y)$

56. $-\dfrac{1}{5}(10a - 25b)$

57. $3(2r + 5) - 7$

58. $10(4s + 6) - 40$

▶ **59.** $-9(4x + 8) + 2$

60. $-11(5x + 3) + 10$

61. $-0.4(4x + 5) - 0.5$

62. $-0.6(2x + 1) - 0.1$

Use the distributive property to write each sum as a product. See Examples 13 and 14.

63. $4 \cdot 1 + 4 \cdot y$

64. $14 \cdot z + 14 \cdot 5$

▶ **65.** $11x + 11y$

66. $9a + 9b$

67. $(-1) \cdot 5 + (-1) \cdot x$

68. $(-3)a + (-3)y$

69. $30a + 30b$

70. $25x + 25y$

Objectives **A** **C** **Mixed Practice** *Name the property illustrated by each true statement. See Examples 15 through 21.*

71. $3 \cdot 5 = 5 \cdot 3$

72. $4(3 + 8) = 4 \cdot 3 + 4 \cdot 8$

73. $2 + (x + 5) = (2 + x) + 5$

74. $9 \cdot (x \cdot 7) = (9 \cdot x) \cdot 7$

75. $(x + 9) + 3 = (9 + x) + 3$

▶ **76.** $1 \cdot 9 = 9$

77. $(4 \cdot y) \cdot 9 = 4 \cdot (y \cdot 9)$

78. $-4 \cdot (8 \cdot 3) = (8 \cdot 3) \cdot (-4)$

79. $0 + 6 = 6$

80. $(a + 9) + 6 = a + (9 + 6)$

81. $-4(y + 7) = -4 \cdot y + (-4) \cdot 7$

82. $(11 + r) + 8 = (r + 11) + 8$

83. $6 \cdot \dfrac{1}{6} = 1$

84. $r + 0 = r$

85. $-6 \cdot 1 = -6$

86. $-\dfrac{3}{4}\left(-\dfrac{4}{3}\right) = 1$

Review

Evaluate each expression for the given values. See Section 2.5.

87. If $x = -1$ and $y = 3$, find $y - x^2$.

88. If $g = 0$ and $h = -4$, find $gh - h^2$.

89. If $a = 2$ and $b = -5$, find $a - b^2$.

90. If $x = -3$, find $x^3 - x^2 + 4$.

91. If $y = -5$ and $z = 0$, find $yz - y^2$.

92. If $x = -2$, find $x^3 - x^2 - x$.

Concept Extensions

Fill in the table with the opposite (additive inverse), the reciprocal (multiplicative inverse), or the expression. Assume that the value of each expression is not 0.

	93.	94.	95.	96.	97.	98.
Expression	8	$-\dfrac{2}{3}$	x	$4y$		
Opposite						$7x$
Reciprocal					$\dfrac{1}{2x}$	

Decide whether each statement is true or false. See the second Concept Check in this section.

99. The opposite of $-\dfrac{a}{2}$ is $-\dfrac{2}{a}$.

100. The reciprocal of $-\dfrac{a}{2}$ is $\dfrac{a}{2}$.

Determine which pairs of actions are commutative. See the first Concept Check in this section.

101. "taking a test" and "studying for the test"

102. "putting on your shoes" and "putting on your socks"

103. "putting on your left shoe" and "putting on your right shoe"

104. "reading the sports section" and "reading the comics section"

105. "mowing the lawn" and "trimming the hedges"

106. "baking a cake" and "eating the cake"

107. "feeding the dog" and "feeding the cat"

108. "dialing a number" and "turning on the cell phone"

Name the property illustrated by each step.

109. a. $\triangle + (\square + \bigcirc) = (\square + \bigcirc) + \triangle$

b. $\qquad = (\bigcirc + \square) + \triangle$

c. $\qquad = \bigcirc + (\square + \triangle)$

110. a. $(x + y) + z = x + (y + z)$

b. $\qquad = (y + z) + x$

c. $\qquad = (z + y) + x$

111. Explain why 0 is called the identity element for addition.

112. Explain why 1 is called the identity element for multiplication.

113. Write an example that shows that division is not commutative.

114. Write an example that shows that subtraction is not commutative.

9.3 Further Solving Linear Equations

Objectives

A Apply the General Strategy for Solving a Linear Equation.

B Solve Equations Containing Fractions or Decimals.

C Recognize Identities and Equations with No Solution.

Objective A Solving Linear Equations

Since Chapter 2, we have been solving equations. In this section, we give a definition of a linear equation in one variable and review steps we may use to solve these equations.

Let's begin with a formal definition of a linear equation in one variable.

A **linear equation in one variable** can be written in the form

$$Ax + B = C$$

where A, B, and C are real numbers and $A \neq 0$.

We now combine our knowledge from the previous chapters and review solving linear equations.

To Solve Linear Equations in One Variable

Step 1: If an equation contains fractions or decimals, multiply both sides by the LCD to clear the equation of fractions or decimals.

Step 2: Use the distributive property to remove parentheses if they are present.

Step 3: Simplify each side of the equation by combining like terms.

Step 4: Get all variable terms on one side and all numbers on the other side by using the addition property of equality.

Step 5: Get the variable alone by using the multiplication property of equality.

Step 6: Check the solution by substituting it into the original equation.

Practice 1

Solve:

$5(3x - 1) + 2 = 12x + 6$

Answer

1. $x = 3$

Example 1 Solve: $4(2x - 3) + 7 = 3x + 5$

Solution: There are no fractions, so we begin with Step 2.

$$4(2x - 3) + 7 = 3x + 5$$

Step 2: $\quad 8x - 12 + 7 = 3x + 5 \quad$ Use the distributive property.

Step 3: $\qquad 8x - 5 = 3x + 5 \quad$ Combine like terms.

Step 4: Get all variable terms on one side of the equation and all numbers on the other side. One way to do this is by subtracting $3x$ from both sides and then adding 5 to both sides.

$$8x - 5 - 3x = 3x + 5 - 3x \qquad \text{Subtract } 3x \text{ from both sides.}$$
$$5x - 5 = 5 \qquad \text{Simplify.}$$
$$5x - 5 + 5 = 5 + 5 \qquad \text{Add 5 to both sides.}$$
$$5x = 10 \qquad \text{Simplify.}$$

Step 5: Use the multiplication property of equality to get x alone.

$$\frac{5x}{5} = \frac{10}{5} \qquad \text{Divide both sides by 5.}$$
$$x = 2 \qquad \text{Simplify.}$$

Step 6: Check.

$$4(2x - 3) + 7 = 3x + 5 \qquad \text{Original equation}$$
$$4[2(2) - 3] + 7 \stackrel{?}{=} 3(2) + 5 \qquad \text{Replace } x \text{ with 2.}$$
$$4(4 - 3) + 7 \stackrel{?}{=} 6 + 5$$
$$4(1) + 7 \stackrel{?}{=} 11$$
$$4 + 7 \stackrel{?}{=} 11$$
$$11 = 11 \qquad \text{True}$$

The solution is 2.

> **Helpful Hint** When checking solutions, use the original equation.

■ Work Practice 1

Example 2 Solve: $8(2 - t) = -5t$

Solution: First, we apply the distributive property.

$$8(2 - t) = -5t$$

Step 2: $\qquad 16 - 8t = -5t \qquad \text{Use the distributive property.}$

Step 4: $16 - 8t + 8t = -5t + 8t \qquad \text{Add } 8t \text{ to both sides.}$

$$16 = 3t \qquad \text{Combine like terms.}$$

Step 5: $\qquad \dfrac{16}{3} = \dfrac{3t}{3} \qquad \text{Divide both sides by 3.}$

$$\frac{16}{3} = t \qquad \text{Simplify.}$$

Step 6: Check.

$$8(2 - t) = -5t \qquad \text{Original equation}$$
$$8\left(2 - \frac{16}{3}\right) \stackrel{?}{=} -5\left(\frac{16}{3}\right) \qquad \text{Replace } t \text{ with } \frac{16}{3}.$$
$$8\left(\frac{6}{3} - \frac{16}{3}\right) \stackrel{?}{=} -\frac{80}{3} \qquad \text{The LCD is 3.}$$
$$8\left(-\frac{10}{3}\right) \stackrel{?}{=} -\frac{80}{3} \qquad \text{Subtract fractions.}$$
$$-\frac{80}{3} = -\frac{80}{3} \qquad \text{True}$$

The solution is $\dfrac{16}{3}$.

■ Work Practice 2

Practice 2

Solve: $9(5 - x) = -3x$

Answer

2. $x = \dfrac{15}{2}$

Objective B Solving Equations Containing Fractions or Decimals ▶

If an equation contains fractions, we can clear the equation of fractions by multiplying both sides by the LCD of all denominators. By doing this, we avoid working with time-consuming fractions.

Practice 3

Solve: $\dfrac{5}{2}x - 1 = \dfrac{3}{2}x - 4$

Example 3 Solve: $\dfrac{x}{2} - 1 = \dfrac{2}{3}x - 3$

Solution: We begin by clearing fractions. To do this, we multiply both sides of the equation by the LCD, which is 6.

$$\frac{x}{2} - 1 = \frac{2}{3}x - 3$$

Step 1: $6\left(\dfrac{x}{2} - 1\right) = 6\left(\dfrac{2}{3}x - 3\right)$ Multiply both sides by the LCD, 6.

Step 2: $6\left(\dfrac{x}{2}\right) - 6(1) = 6\left(\dfrac{2}{3}x\right) - 6(3)$ Use the distributive property.

> **Helpful Hint** Don't forget to multiply *each* term by the LCD.

$$3x - 6 = 4x - 18$$ Simplify.

There are no longer grouping symbols and no like terms on either side of the equation, so we continue with Step 4.

$$3x - 6 = 4x - 18$$

Step 4: $3x - 6 - 3x = 4x - 18 - 3x$ Subtract $3x$ from both sides.

$$-6 = x - 18$$ Simplify.

$$-6 + 18 = x - 18 + 18$$ Add 18 to both sides.

$$12 = x$$ Simplify.

Step 5: The variable is now alone, so there is no need to apply the multiplication property of equality.

Step 6: Check.

$$\frac{x}{2} - 1 = \frac{2}{3}x - 3$$ Original equation

$$\frac{12}{2} - 1 \stackrel{?}{=} \frac{2}{3} \cdot 12 - 3$$ Replace x with 12.

$$6 - 1 \stackrel{?}{=} 8 - 3$$ Simplify.

$$5 = 5$$ True

The solution is 12.

▪ **Work Practice 3**

Practice 4

Solve: $\dfrac{3(x - 2)}{5} = 3x + 6$

Example 4 Solve: $\dfrac{2(a + 3)}{3} = 6a + 2$

Solution: We clear the equation of fractions first.

$$\frac{2(a + 3)}{3} = 6a + 2$$

Step 1: $3 \cdot \dfrac{2(a + 3)}{3} = 3(6a + 2)$ Clear the fraction by multiplying both sides by the LCD, 3.

$$2(a + 3) = 3(6a + 2)$$ Simplify.

Answers

3. $x = -3$ **4.** $x = -3$

Step 2: Next, we use the distributive property to remove parentheses.

$$2a + 6 = 18a + 6 \qquad \text{Use the distributive property.}$$

Step 4: $2a + 6 - 18a = 18a + 6 - 18a \qquad$ Subtract $18a$ from both sides.

$$-16a + 6 = 6 \qquad \text{Simplify.}$$

$$-16a + 6 - 6 = 6 - 6 \qquad \text{Subtract 6 from both sides.}$$

$$-16a = 0$$

Step 5: $\dfrac{-16a}{-16} = \dfrac{0}{-16} \qquad$ Divide both sides by -16.

$$a = 0 \qquad \text{Simplify.}$$

Step 6: To check, replace a with 0 in the original equation. The solution is 0.

▨ Work Practice 4

Helpful Hint

Remember: When solving an equation, it makes no difference on which side of the equation variable terms lie. Just make sure that constant terms lie on the other side.

When solving a problem about money, you may need to solve an equation containing decimals. If you choose, you may multiply to clear the equation of decimals.

Example 5 Solve: $0.25x + 0.10(x - 3) = 1.1$

Solution: First we clear this equation of decimals by multiplying both sides of the equation by 100. Recall that multiplying a decimal number by 100 has the effect of moving the decimal point 2 places to the right.

$$0.25x + 0.10(x - 3) = 1.1$$

Step 1: $0.25x + 0.10(x - 3) = 1.10 \qquad$ Multiply both sides by 100.

$$25x + 10(x - 3) = 110$$

Step 2: $\quad 25x + 10x - 30 = 110 \qquad$ Apply the distributive property.

Step 3: $\qquad\qquad 35x - 30 = 110 \qquad$ Combine like terms.

Step 4: $\quad 35x - 30 + 30 = 110 + 30 \qquad$ Add 30 to both sides.

$$35x = 140 \qquad \text{Combine like terms.}$$

Step 5: $\qquad \dfrac{35x}{35} = \dfrac{140}{35} \qquad$ Divide both sides by 35.

$$x = 4$$

Step 6: To check, replace x with 4 in the original equation. The solution is 4.

▨ Work Practice 5

Practice 5

Solve:
$0.06x - 0.10(x - 2) = -0.16$

Helpful Hint If you have trouble with this step, try removing parentheses first.

$$0.25x + 0.10(x - 3) = 1.1$$
$$0.25x + 0.10x - 0.3 = 1.1$$
$$0.25x + 0.10x - 0.30 = 1.10$$
$$25x + 10x - 30 = 110$$

Then continue.

Objective C Recognizing Identities and Equations with No Solution ▶

So far, each equation that we have solved has had a single solution. However, not every equation in one variable has a single solution. Some equations have no solution, while others have an infinite number of solutions. For example,

$$x + 5 = x + 7$$

Answer
5. $x = 9$

has **no solution** since no matter which real number we replace x with, the equation is false.

real number $+ 5 =$ same real number $+ 7$ FALSE

On the other hand,

$x + 6 = x + 6$

has infinitely many solutions since x can be replaced by any real number and the equation will always be true.

real number $+ 6 =$ same real number $+ 6$ TRUE

The equation $x + 6 = x + 6$ is called an **identity.** The next two examples illustrate special equations like these.

Practice 6

Solve:
$5(2 - x) + 8x = 3(x - 6)$

Example 6 Solve: $-2(x - 5) + 10 = -3(x + 2) + x$

Solution:

$$-2(x - 5) + 10 = -3(x + 2) + x$$
$$-2x + 10 + 10 = -3x - 6 + x \quad \text{Apply the distributive property on both sides.}$$
$$-2x + 20 = -2x - 6 \quad \text{Combine like terms.}$$
$$-2x + 20 + 2x = -2x - 6 + 2x \quad \text{Add } 2x \text{ to both sides.}$$
$$20 = -6 \quad \text{Combine like terms.}$$

The final equation contains no variable terms, and the result is the false statement $20 = -6$. There is no value for x that makes $20 = -6$ a true equation. Thus, we conclude that there is **no solution** to this equation.

■ Work Practice 6

Practice 7

Solve:
$-6(2x + 1) - 14$
$= -10(x + 2) - 2x$

Example 7 Solve: $3(x - 4) = 3x - 12$

Solution: $3(x - 4) = 3x - 12$
$3x - 12 = 3x - 12 \quad \text{Apply the distributive property.}$

The left side of the equation is now identical to the right side. Every real number may be substituted for x and a true statement will result. We arrive at the same conclusion if we continue.

$$3x - 12 = 3x - 12$$
$$3x - 12 - 3x = 3x - 12 - 3x \quad \text{Subtract } 3x \text{ from both sides.}$$
$$-12 = -12 \quad \text{Combine like terms.}$$

Again, the final equation contains no variables, but this time the result is the true statement $-12 = -12$. This means that one side of the equation is identical to the other side. Thus, $3(x - 4) = 3x - 12$ is an **identity** and **all real numbers** are solutions.

■ Work Practice 7

Answers

6. no solution

7. All real numbers are solutions.

✓ Concept Check Answer

a. All real numbers are solutions.

b. The solution is 0.

c. There is no solution.

✓ Concept Check Suppose you have simplified several equations and obtained the following results. What can you conclude about the solutions to the original equation?

a. $7 = 7$ **b.** $x = 0$ **c.** $7 = -4$

Calculator Explorations Checking Equations

We can use a calculator to check possible solutions of equations. To do this, replace the variable by the possible solution and evaluate each side of the equation separately.

Equation: $3x - 4 = 2(x + 6)$ Solution: $x = 16$

$3x - 4 = 2(x + 6)$ Original equation

$3(16) - 4 \stackrel{?}{=} 2(16 + 6)$ Replace x with 16.

Now evaluate each side with your calculator.

Evaluate left side: ⎡3⎤ ⎡×⎤ ⎡16⎤ ⎡−⎤ ⎡4⎤ ⎡=⎤

or

⎡ENTER⎤

Display: ⎡44⎤

Evaluate right side: ⎡2⎤ ⎡(⎤ ⎡16⎤ ⎡+⎤ ⎡6⎤ ⎡)⎤ ⎡=⎤

or

⎡ENTER⎤

Display: ⎡44⎤

Since the left side equals the right side, the equation checks.

Use a calculator to check the possible solutions to each equation.

1. $2x = 48 + 6x;$ $x = -12$

2. $-3x - 7 = 3x - 1;$ $x = -1$

3. $5x - 2.6 = 2(x + 0.8);$ $x = 4.4$

4. $-1.6x - 3.9 = -6.9x - 25.6;$ $x = 5$

5. $\dfrac{564x}{4} = 200x - 11(649);$ $x = 121$

6. $20(x - 39) = 5x - 432;$ $x = 23.2$

Vocabulary, Readiness & Video Check

Throughout algebra, it is important to be able to distinguish between equations and expressions.

Remember,
- an equation contains an equal sign and
- an expression does not.

Among other things,
- we solve equations and
- we simplify or perform operations on expressions.

Identify each as an equation or an expression.

1. $x = -7$ _____

2. $x - 7$ _____

3. $4y - 6 + 9y + 1$ _____

4. $4y - 6 = 9y + 1$ _____

5. $\dfrac{1}{x} - \dfrac{x - 1}{8}$ _____

6. $\dfrac{1}{x} - \dfrac{x - 1}{8} = 6$ _____

7. $0.1x + 9 = 0.2x$ _____

8. $0.1x^2 + 9y - 0.2x^2$ _____

Martin-Gay Interactive Videos

See Video 9.3

Watch the section lecture video and answer the following questions.

Objective A **9.** The general strategy for solving linear equations in one variable is discussed after ▣ Example 1. How many properties (not steps) are mentioned in this strategy and what are they? ▶

Objective B **10.** In the first step for solving ▣ Example 2, both sides of the equation are multiplied by the LCD. Why is the distributive property mentioned? ▶

11. In ▣ Example 3, why is the number of decimal places in each term of the equation important? ▶

Objective C **12.** Complete each statement based on ▣ Examples 4 and 5. When solving an equation and all variable terms subtract out: ▶

  a. If we have a true statement, then the equation has _____ solution(s).

  b. If we have a false statement, then the equation has _____ solution(s).

9.3 Exercise Set MyMathLab® ▶

Objective A *Solve each equation. See Examples 1 and 2.*

1. $-4y + 10 = -2(3y + 1)$

2. $-3x + 1 = -2(4x + 2)$

3. $15x - 8 = 10 + 9x$

4. $15x - 5 = 7 + 12x$

5. $-2(3x - 4) = 2x$

6. $-(5x - 10) = 5x$

▶ **7.** $5(2x - 1) - 2(3x) = 1$

8. $3(2 - 5x) + 4(6x) = 12$

9. $-6(x - 3) - 26 = -8$

10. $-4(n - 4) - 23 = -7$

11. $8 - 2(a + 1) = 9 + a$

12. $5 - 6(2 + b) = b - 14$

13. $4x + 3 = -3 + 2x + 14$

14. $6y - 8 = -6 + 3y + 13$

15. $-2y - 10 = 5y + 18$

16. $-7n + 5 = 8n - 10$

Objective B *Solve each equation. See Examples 3 through 5.*

17. $\dfrac{2}{3}x + \dfrac{4}{3} = -\dfrac{2}{3}$

18. $\dfrac{4}{5}x - \dfrac{8}{5} = -\dfrac{16}{5}$

19. $\dfrac{3}{4}x - \dfrac{1}{2} = 1$

20. $\dfrac{2}{9}x - \dfrac{1}{3} = 1$

▶ **21.** $0.50x + 0.15(70) = 35.5$

22. $0.40x + 0.06(30) = 9.8$

23. $\dfrac{2(x + 1)}{4} = 3x - 2$

24. $\dfrac{3(y + 3)}{5} = 2y + 6$

25. $x + \dfrac{7}{6} = 2x - \dfrac{7}{6}$

26. $\dfrac{5}{2}x - 1 = x + \dfrac{1}{4}$

27. $0.12(y - 6) + 0.06y = 0.08y - 0.7$

28. $0.60(z - 300) + 0.05z = 0.70z - 205$

Objective C *Solve each equation. See Examples 6 and 7.*

29. $4(3x + 2) = 12x + 8$

30. $14x + 7 = 7(2x + 1)$

31. $\frac{x}{4} + 1 = \frac{x}{4}$

32. $\frac{x}{3} - 2 = \frac{x}{3}$

33. $3x - 7 = 3(x + 1)$

34. $2(x - 5) = 2x + 10$

35. $-2(6x - 5) + 4 = -12x + 14$

36. $-5(4y - 3) + 2 = -20y + 17$

Objectives A B C Mixed Practice *Solve. See Examples 1 through 7.*

37. $\frac{6(3 - z)}{5} = -z$

38. $\frac{4(5 - w)}{3} = -u$

39. $-3(2t - 5) + 2t = 5t - 4$

40. $-(4a - 7) - 5a = 10 + a$

41. $5y + 2(y - 6) = 4(y + 1) - 2$

42. $9x + 3(x - 4) = 10(x - 5) + 7$

43. $\frac{3(x - 5)}{2} = \frac{2(x + 5)}{3}$

44. $\frac{5(x - 1)}{4} = \frac{3(x + 1)}{2}$

45. $0.7x - 2.3 = 0.5$

46. $0.9x - 4.1 = 0.4$

▶ **47.** $5x - 5 = 2(x + 1) + 3x - 7$

48. $3(2x - 1) + 5 = 6x + 2$

49. $4(2n + 1) = 3(6n + 3) + 1$

50. $4(4y + 2) = 2(1 + 6y) + 8$

51. $x + \frac{5}{4} = \frac{3}{4}x$

52. $\frac{7}{8}x + \frac{1}{4} = \frac{3}{4}x$

▶ **53.** $\frac{x}{2} - 1 = \frac{x}{5} + 2$

54. $\frac{x}{5} - 7 = \frac{x}{3} - 5$

▶ **55.** $2(x + 3) - 5 = 5x - 3(1 + x)$

56. $4(2 + x) + 1 = 7x - 3(x - 2)$

57. $0.06 - 0.01(x + 1) = -0.02(2 - x)$

58. $-0.01(5x + 4) = 0.04 - 0.01(x + 4)$

59. $\frac{9}{2} + \frac{5}{2}y = 2y - 4$

60. $3 - \frac{1}{2}x = 5x - 8$

Review

Translating *Write each algebraic expression described. See Section 3.1.*

△ **61.** A plot of land is in the shape of a triangle. If one side is x meters, a second side is $(2x - 3)$ meters, and a third side is $(3x - 5)$ meters, express the perimeter of the lot as a simplified expression in x.

62. A portion of a board has length x feet. The other part has length $(7x - 9)$ feet. Express the total length of the board as a simplified expression in x.

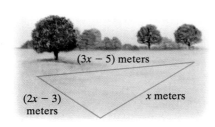

Translating *Write each phrase as an algebraic expression. Use x for the unknown number. See Section 3.2.*

63. A number subtracted from −8

64. Three times a number

65. The sum of −3 and twice a number

66. The difference of 8 and twice a number

67. The product of 9 and the sum of a number and 20

68. The quotient of −12 and the difference of a number and 3

Concept Extensions

See the Concept Check in this section.

69. a. Solve: $x + 3 = x + 3$

   b. If you simplify an equation (such as the one in part **a**) and get a true statement such as $3 = 3$ or $0 = 0$, what can you conclude about the solution(s) of the original equation?

   c. On your own, construct an equation for which every real number is a solution.

70. a. Solve: $x + 3 = x + 5$

   b. If you simplify an equation (such as the one in part **a**) and get a false statement such as $3 = 5$ or $10 = 17$, what can you conclude about the solution(s) of the original equation?

   c. On your own, construct an equation that has no solution.

Match each equation in the first column with its solution in the second column. Items in the second column may be used more than once.

71. $5x + 1 = 5x + 1$

72. $3x + 1 = 3x + 2$

73. $2x − 6x − 10 = −4x + 3 − 10$

74. $x − 11x − 3 = −10x − 1 − 2$

75. $9x − 20 = 8x − 20$

76. $−x + 15 = x + 15$

 a. all real numbers
 b. no solution
 c. 0

77. Explain the difference between simplifying an expression and solving an equation.

78. On your own, write an expression and then an equation. Label each.

For Exercises 79 and 80, **a.** *Write an equation for perimeter.* **b.** *Solve the equation in part (a).* **c.** *Find the length of each side.*

79. The perimeter of a geometric figure is the sum of the lengths of its sides. If the perimeter of the following pentagon (five-sided figure) is 28 centimeters, find the length of each side.

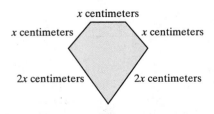

x centimeters
x centimeters   *x* centimeters
2*x* centimeters   2*x* centimeters

80. The perimeter of the following triangle is 35 meters. Find the length of each side.

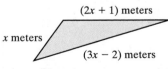

(2*x* + 1) meters
x meters
(3*x* − 2) meters

Fill in the blanks with numbers of your choice so that each equation has the given solution. Note: Each blank may be replaced by a different number.

81. $x +$ ____ $= 2x −$ ____; solution: 9

82. $−5x −$ ____ $=$ ____; solution: 2

Solve.

83. $1000(7x − 10) = 50(412 + 100x)$

84. $1000(x + 40) = 100(16 + 7x)$

85. $0.035x + 5.112 = 0.010x + 5.107$

86. $0.127x − 2.685 = 0.027x − 2.38$

Real Numbers and Solving Linear Equations

Tell which set or sets each number belongs to: natural numbers, whole numbers, integers, rational numbers, irrational numbers, or real numbers.

1. 0 **2.** 143 **3.** $\dfrac{3}{8}$ **4.** 1

5. -13 **6.** $\dfrac{9}{10}$ **7.** $-\dfrac{1}{9}$ **8.** $\sqrt{5}$

Remove parentheses and simplify each expression.

9. $7(d - 3) + 10$ **10.** $9(z + 7) - 15$

11. $-4(3y - 4) + 12y$ **12.** $-3(2x + 5) - 6x$

Solve. Feel free to use the steps given in Section 9.3.

13. $2x - 7 = 6x - 27$ **14.** $3 + 8y = 3y - 2$

15. $-3a + 6 + 5a = 7a - 8a$ **16.** $4b - 8 - b = 10b - 3b$

17. $-\dfrac{2}{3}x = \dfrac{5}{9}$ **18.** $-\dfrac{3}{8}y = -\dfrac{1}{16}$

19. $10 = -6n + 16$ **20.** $-5 = -2m + 7$

Answers

1. _____
2. _____
3. _____
4. _____
5. _____
6. _____
7. _____
8. _____
9. _____
10. _____
11. _____
12. _____
13. _____
14. _____
15. _____
16. _____
17. _____
18. _____
19. _____
20. _____

21. _____

22. _____

23. _____

24. _____

25. _____

26. _____

27. _____

28. _____

29. _____

30. _____

31. _____

32. _____

21. $3(5c - 1) - 2 = 13c + 3$

22. $4(3t + 4) - 20 = 3 + 5t$

23. $\dfrac{2(z + 3)}{3} = 5 - z$

24. $\dfrac{3(w + 2)}{4} = 2w + 3$

25. $-2(2x - 5) = -3x + 7 - x + 3$

26. $-4(5x - 2) = -12x + 4 - 8x + 4$

27. $0.02(6t - 3) = 0.04(t - 2) + 0.02$

28. $0.03(m + 7) = 0.02(5 - m) + 0.03$

29. $-3y = \dfrac{4(y - 1)}{5}$

30. $-4x = \dfrac{5(1 - x)}{6}$

31. $\dfrac{5}{3}x - \dfrac{7}{3} = x$

32. $\dfrac{7}{5}n + \dfrac{3}{5} = -n$

Further Problem Solving

In this section, we review our problem-solving steps first introduced in Section 3.4 and continue to solve problems that are modeled by linear equations.

General Strategy for Problem Solving

1. **UNDERSTAND** the problem. During this step, become comfortable with the problem. Some ways of doing this are:

   Read and reread the problem.
   Choose a variable to represent the unknown.
   Construct a drawing.
   Propose a solution and check. Pay careful attention to how you check your proposed solution. This will help when writing an equation to model the problem.

2. **TRANSLATE** the problem into an equation.
3. **SOLVE** the equation.
4. **INTERPRET** the results: *Check* the proposed solution in the stated problem and *state* your conclusion.

Objective A Solving Direct Translation Problems ▶

Much of problem solving involves a direct translation from a sentence to an equation.

Example 1 Finding an Unknown Number

Twice a number, added to seven, is the same as three subtracted from the number. Find the number.

Solution: Translate the sentence into an equation and solve.

In words:	twice a number	added to	seven	is the same as	three subtracted from the number
	↓	↓	↓	↓	↓
Translate:	$2x$	$+$	7	$=$	$x - 3$

To solve, begin by subtracting x from both sides to isolate the variable term.

$$2x + 7 = x - 3$$
$$2x + 7 - x = x - 3 - x \quad \text{Subtract } x \text{ from both sides.}$$
$$x + 7 = -3 \quad \text{Combine like terms.}$$
$$x + 7 - 7 = -3 - 7 \quad \text{Subtract 7 from both sides.}$$
$$x = -10 \quad \text{Combine like terms.}$$

Check the solution in the problem as it was originally stated. To do so, replace "number" in the sentence with -10. Twice "-10" added to 7 is the same as 3 subtracted from "-10."

$$2(-10) + 7 \stackrel{?}{=} -10 - 3$$
$$-13 = -13$$

The unknown number is -10.

■ Work Practice 1

Practice 1

Three times a number, minus 6, is the same as two times the number, plus 3. Find the number.

Answer
1. 9

Helpful Hint

When checking solutions, go back to the original stated problem, rather than to your equation in case errors have been made in translating to an equation.

Practice 2

Three times the difference of a number and 5 is the same as twice the number decreased by 3. Find the number.

Example 2   Finding an Unknown Number

Twice the sum of a number and 4 is the same as four times the number decreased by 12. Find the number.

Solution:

1. UNDERSTAND. Read and reread the problem. If we let x = the unknown number, then

   "the sum of a number and 4" translates to "$x + 4$" and

   "four times the number" translates to "$4x$"

2. TRANSLATE.

twice	sum of a number and 4	is the same as	four times the number	decreased by	12
↓	↓	↓	↓	↓	↓
2	$(x + 4)$	$=$	$4x$	$-$	12

3. SOLVE

$$2(x + 4) = 4x - 12$$
$$2x + 8 = 4x - 12 \qquad \text{Apply the distributive property.}$$
$$2x + 8 - 4x = 4x - 12 - 4x \qquad \text{Subtract } 4x \text{ from both sides.}$$
$$-2x + 8 = -12$$
$$-2x + 8 - 8 = -12 - 8 \qquad \text{Subtract 8 from both sides.}$$
$$-2x = -20$$
$$\frac{-2x}{-2} = \frac{-20}{-2} \qquad \text{Divide both sides by } -2.$$
$$x = 10$$

4. INTERPRET.

   Check: Check this solution in the problem as it was originally stated. To do so, replace "number" with 10. Twice the sum of "10" and 4 is 28, which is the same as 4 times "10" decreased by 12.

   State: The number is 10.

◼ Work Practice 2

Objective B Solving Problems Involving Relationships Among Unknown Quantities ▶

Practice 3

An 18-foot wire is to be cut so that the length of the longer piece is 5 times the length of the shorter piece. Find the length of each piece.

Answers

2. 12

3. shorter piece: 3 feet; longer piece: 15 feet

Example 3   Finding the Length of a Board

A 10-foot board is to be cut into two pieces so that the length of the longer piece is 4 times the length of the shorter. Find the length of each piece.

Solution:

1. UNDERSTAND the problem. To do so, read and reread the problem. You may also want to propose a solution. For example, if 3 feet represents the length of the shorter piece, then $4(3) = 12$ feet is the length of the longer piece, since it is 4 times the length of the shorter piece.

This guess gives a total board length of 3 feet + 12 feet = 15 feet, which is too long. However, the purpose of proposing a solution is not to guess correctly, but to help better understand the problem and how to model it.

In general, if we let

x = length of shorter piece, then

$4x$ = length of longer piece

2. TRANSLATE the problem. First, we write the equation in words.

length of shorter piece	added to	length of longer piece	equals	total length of board
↓	↓	↓	↓	↓
x	$+$	$4x$	$=$	10

3. SOLVE.

$$x + 4x = 10$$
$$5x = 10 \quad \text{Combine like terms.}$$
$$\frac{5x}{5} = \frac{10}{5} \quad \text{Divide both sides by 5.}$$
$$x = 2$$

4. INTERPRET.

Check: Check the solution in the stated problem. If the length of the shorter piece of board is 2 feet, the length of the longer piece is $4 \cdot (2 \text{ feet}) = 8$ feet and the sum of the lengths of the two pieces is 2 feet + 8 feet = 10 feet.

State: The shorter piece of board is 2 feet and the longer piece of board is 8 feet.

■ Work Practice 3

Helpful Hint

Make sure that units are included in your answer, if appropriate.

Example 4 Finding the Number of Republican Democratic Senators

As of July 2013, the total number of Democrats and Republicans in the U.S. House of Representatives was 440. There were 28 more Republican representatives than Democratic. Find the number of representatives from each party. (*Source:* Congressional Research Service)

Solution:

1. UNDERSTAND the problem. Read and re-read the problem. Let's suppose that there are 200 Democratic representatives. Since there are 28 more Republicans than Democrats, there must be $200 + 28 = 228$ Republicans. The total number of Democrats and Republicans is then $200 + 228 = 428$. This is incorrect since the total should be 440, but we now have a better understanding of the problem.

In general, if we let

x = number of Democrats, then

$x + 28$ = number of Republicans

(Continued on next page)

Practice 4

Through the year 2020, the state of California will have 17 more electoral votes for president than the state of Texas. If the total electoral votes for these two states is 93, find the number of electoral votes for each state.

Answer

4. Texas: 38 electoral votes; California: 55 electoral votes

2. TRANSLATE the problem. First, we write the equation in words.

number of Democrats	added to	number of Republicans	equals	440
↓	↓	↓	↓	↓
x	+	$(x + 28)$	=	440

3. SOLVE.

$$x + (x + 28) = 440$$
$$2x + 28 = 440 \qquad \text{Combine like terms.}$$
$$2x + 28 - 28 = 440 - 28 \qquad \text{Subtract 28 from both sides.}$$
$$2x = 412$$
$$\frac{2x}{2} = \frac{412}{2} \qquad \text{Divide both sides by 2.}$$
$$x = 206$$

4. INTERPRET.

Check: If there were 206 Democratic representatives, then there were $206 + 28 = 234$ Republican representatives. The total number of representatives is then $206 + 234 = 440$. The results check.

State: There were 206 Democratic and 234 Republican representatives in Congress in July 2013.

■ Work Practice 4

Practice 5

A car rental agency charges $28 a day and $0.15 a mile. If you rent a car for a day and your bill (before taxes) is $52, how many miles did you drive?

Example 5 Calculating Hours on the Job

A computer science major at a local university has a part-time job working on computers for his clients. He charges $20 to go to your home or office and then $25 per hour. During one month he visited 10 homes or offices and his total income was $575. How many hours did he spend working on computers?

Solution:

1. UNDERSTAND. Read and reread the problem. Let's propose that the student spent 20 hours working on computers. Pay careful attention as to how his income is calculated. For 20 hours and 10 visits, his income is $20(\$25) + 10(\$20) = \$700$, which is more than $575. We now have a better understanding of the problem and know that the time spent working on computers was less than 20 hours.

Let's let

$x =$ hours working on computers. Then

$25x =$ amount of money made while working on computers

2. TRANSLATE.

money made while working on computers	plus	money made for visits	is equal to	575
↓	↓	↓	↓	↓
$25x$	+	$10(20)$	=	575

3. SOLVE.

$$25x + 200 = 575$$
$$25x + 200 - 200 = 575 - 200 \qquad \text{Subtract 200 from both sides.}$$
$$25x = 375 \qquad \text{Simplify.}$$
$$\frac{25x}{25} = \frac{375}{25} \qquad \text{Divide both sides by 25.}$$
$$x = 15 \qquad \text{Simplify.}$$

Answer

5. 160 miles

4. INTERPRET.

Check: If the student works 15 hours and makes 10 visits, his income is
15($25) + 10($20) = $575.

State: The student spent 15 hours working on computers.

■ Work Practice 5

Example 6 Finding Angle Measures

If the two walls of the Vietnam Veterans Memorial in Washington, D.C., were connected, an isosceles triangle would be formed. The measure of the third angle is 97.5° more than the measure of either of the two equal angles. Find the measure of the third angle. (*Source:* National Park Service)

Solution:

1. UNDERSTAND. Read and reread the problem. We then draw a diagram (recall that an isosceles triangle has two angles with the same measure) and let

$$x = \text{degree measure of one angle}$$
$$x = \text{degree measure of the second, equal angle}$$
$$x + 97.5 = \text{degree measure of the third angle}$$

2. TRANSLATE. Recall that the sum of the measures of the angles of a triangle equals 180.

measure of first angle	+	measure of second angle	+	measure of third angle	equals	180
↓		↓		↓	↓	↓
x	+	x	+	$(x + 97.5)$	=	180

3. SOLVE.

$$x + x + (x + 97.5) = 180$$
$$3x + 97.5 = 180 \qquad \text{Combine like terms.}$$
$$3x + 97.5 - 97.5 = 180 - 97.5 \qquad \text{Subtract 97.5 from both sides.}$$
$$3x = 82.5$$
$$\frac{3x}{3} = \frac{82.5}{3} \qquad \text{Divide both sides by 3.}$$
$$x = 27.5$$

4. INTERPRET.

Check: If $x = 27.5$, then the measure of the third angle is $x + 97.5 = 125$. The sum of the angles is then $27.5 + 27.5 + 125 = 180$, the correct sum.

State: The third angle measures 125°.*

■ Work Practice 6

---

*The two walls actually meet at an angle of 125 degrees 12 minutes. The measurement of 97.5° given in the problem is an approximation.

Practice 6

The measure of the second angle of a triangle is twice the measure of the smallest angle. The measure of the third angle of the triangle is three times the measure of the smallest angle. Find the measures of the angles.

Answer
6. smallest: 30°; second: 60°; third: 90°

Objective C Solving Consecutive Integer Problems ▶

The next example has to do with consecutive integers. Recall what we have learned thus far about these integers.

	Example	*General Representation*	
Consecutive Integers	11, 12, 13 +1 +1	Let x be an integer.	x, $x+1$, $x+2$ +1 +1
Consecutive Even Integers	38, 40, 42 +2 +2	Let x be an even integer.	x, $x+2$, $x+4$ +2 +2
Consecutive Odd Integers	57, 59, 61 +2 +2	Let x be an odd integer.	x, $x+2$ $x+4$ +2 +2

Practice 7

The sum of three consecutive even integers is 144. Find the integers.

Helpful Hint Remember, the 2 here means that odd integers are 2 units apart—for example, the odd integers 13 and $13 + 2 = 15$.

Example 7 Some states have a single area code for the entire state. Two such states have area codes that are consecutive odd integers. If the sum of these integers is 1208, find the two area codes. (*Source: World Almanac*)

Solution:

1. **UNDERSTAND.** Read and reread the problem. If we let

   x = the first odd integer, then

   $x + 2$ = the next odd integer

2. **TRANSLATE.**

first odd integer	the sum of	next odd integer	is	1208
↓	↓	↓		
x	$+$	$(x + 2)$	$=$	1208

3. **SOLVE.**

$$x + x + 2 = 1208$$
$$2x + 2 = 1208$$
$$2x + 2 - 2 = 1208 - 2$$
$$2x = 1206$$
$$\frac{2x}{2} = \frac{1206}{2}$$
$$x = 603$$

4. **INTERPRET.**

   Check: If $x = 603$, then the next odd integer $x + 2 = 603 + 2 = 605$. Notice their sum, $603 + 605 = 1208$, as needed.

   State: The area codes are 603 and 605.

   Note: New Hampshire's area code is 603 and South Dakota's area code is 605.

■ Work Practice 7

Answer

7. 46, 48, 50

Vocabulary, Readiness & Video Check

Fill in the table.

	A number:		Double the number:		Double the number, decreased by 31:
1.	x	→		→	
2.	A number: x	→	Three times the number:	→	Three times the number, increased by 17:
3.	A number: x	→	The sum of the number and 5:	→	Twice the sum of the number and 5:
4.	A number: x	→	The difference of the number and 11:	→	Seven times the difference of the number and 11:
5.	A number: y	→	The difference of 20 and the number:	→	The difference of 20 and the number, divided by 3:
6.	A number: y	→	The sum of −10 and the number:	→	The sum of −10 and the number, divided by 9:

Martin-Gay Interactive Videos   Watch the section lecture video and answer the following questions.

See Video 9.4

Objective A 7. At the end of Example 1, where are we told is the best place to check the solution of an application problem?

Objective B 8. The solution of the equation for Example 3 is $x = 43$. Why is this not the solution to the application?

Objective C 9. What are two things that should be checked to make sure the solution of Example 4 is correct?

9.4 Exercise Set MyMathLab®

Objective A *Solve. See Examples 1 and 2. For Exercises 1 through 4, write each of the following as equations. Then solve.*

1. The sum of twice a number and 7 is equal to the sum of the number and 6. Find the number.

2. The difference of three times a number and 1 is the same as twice the number. Find the number.

3. Three times a number, minus 6, is equal to two times the number, plus 8. Find the number.

4. The sum of 4 times a number and −2 is equal to the sum of 5 times the number and −2. Find the number.

 5. Twice the difference of a number and 8 is equal to three times the sum of the number and 3. Find the number.

6. Five times the sum of a number and −1 is the same as 6 times the number. Find the number.

7. The product of twice a number and 3 is the same as the difference of five times the number and $\frac{3}{4}$. Find the number.

8. If the difference of a number and 4 is doubled, the result is $\frac{1}{4}$ less than the number. Find the number.

Objective B *Solve. See Examples 3 and 4.*

9. A 25-inch piece of steel is cut into three pieces so that the second piece is twice as long as the first piece, and the third piece is one inch more than five times the length of the first piece. Find the lengths of the pieces.

10. A 46-foot piece of rope is cut into three pieces so that the second piece is three times as long as the first piece, and the third piece is two feet more than seven times the length of the first piece. Find the lengths of the pieces.

11. A 40-inch board is to be cut into three pieces so that the second piece is twice as long as the first piece and the third piece is 5 times as long as the first piece. If x represents the length of the first piece, find the lengths of all three pieces.

12. A 21-foot beam is to be divided so that the longer piece is 1 foot more than 3 times the length of the shorter piece. If x represents the length of the shorter piece, find the lengths of both pieces.

13. In 2012, New York produced 226 million pounds more apples than Pennsylvania. Together, the two states produced 1214 million pounds of apples. Find the amount of apples grown in New York and Pennsylvania in 2012. (*Source:* National Agriculture Statistics Service)

14. In the 2012 Summer Olympics, the U.S. team won 8 more gold medals than the Chinese team. If the total number of gold medals won by both teams was 84, find the number of gold medals won by each team. (*Source:* International Olympic Committee)

Solve. See Example 5.

15. A car rental agency advertised renting a Buick Century for $24.95 per day and $0.29 per mile. If you rent this car for 2 days, how many whole miles can you drive on a $100 budget?

16. A plumber gave an estimate for the renovation of a kitchen. Her hourly pay is $27 per hour and the plumbing parts will cost $80. If her total estimate is $404, how many hours does she expect this job to take?

17. In one U.S. city, the taxi cost is $3 plus $0.80 per mile. If you are traveling from the airport, there is an additional charge of $4.50 for tolls. How far can you travel from the airport by taxi for $27.50?

18. A professional carpet cleaning service charges $30 plus $25.50 per hour to come to your home. If your total bill from this company is $119.25 before taxes, for how many hours were you charged?

Solve. See Example 6.

△ **19.** The flag of Equatorial Guinea contains an isosceles triangle. (Recall that an isosceles triangle contains two angles with the same measure.) If the measure of the third angle of the triangle is 30° more than twice the measure of either of the other two angles, find the measure of each angle of the triangle. (*Hint:* Recall that the sum of the measures of the angles of a triangle is 180°.)

△ **20.** The flag of Brazil contains a parallelogram. One angle of the parallelogram is 15° less than twice the measure of the angle next to it. Find the measure of each angle of the parallelogram. (*Hint:* Recall that opposite angles of a parallelogram have the same measure and that the sum of the measures of the angles is 360°.)

21. The sum of the measures of the angles of a parallelogram is 360°. In the parallelogram below, angles *A* and *D* have the same measure as angles *C* and *B*. If the measure of angle *C* is twice the measure of angle *A*, find the measure of each angle.

22. Recall that the sum of the measures of the angles of a triangle is 180°. In the triangle below, angle *C* has the same measure as angle *B*, and angle *A* measures 42° less than angle *B*. Find the measure of each angle.

Objective C *Solve. See Example 7. Fill in the table. Most of the first row has been completed for you.*

	First Integer →	Next Integers		→	Indicated Sum
23. Three consecutive integers:	Integer: x	$x + 1$	$x + 2$		Sum of the three consecutive integers, simplified:
24. Three consecutive integers:	Integer: x				Sum of the second and third consecutive integers, simplified:
25. Three consecutive even integers:	Even integer: x				Sum of the first and third even consecutive integers, simplified:
26. Three consecutive odd integers:	Odd integer: x				Sum of the three consecutive odd integers, simplified:
27. Four consecutive integers:	Integer: x				Sum of the four consecutive integers, simplified:
28. Four consecutive integers:	Integer: x				Sum of the first and fourth consecutive integers, simplified:
29. Three consecutive odd integers:	Odd integer: x				Sum of the second and third consecutive odd integers, simplified:
30. Three consecutive even integers:	Even integer: x				Sum of the three consecutive even integers, simplified:

Solve. See Example 7

31. The left and right page numbers of an open book are two consecutive integers whose sum is 469. Find these page numbers.

32. The room numbers of two adjacent classrooms are two consecutive even numbers. If their sum is 654, find the classroom numbers.

33. To make an international telephone call, you need the code for the country you are calling. The codes for Belgium, France, and Spain are three consecutive integers whose sum is 99. Find the code for each country. (Source: *The World Almanac and Book of Facts*)

34. The code to unlock a student's combination lock happens to be three consecutive odd integers whose sum is 51. Find the integers.

Objectives A B C Mixed Practice *Solve. See Examples 1 through 7.*

35. A 17-foot piece of string is cut into two pieces so that the longer piece is 2 feet longer than twice the length of the shorter piece. Find the lengths of both pieces.

36. A 25-foot wire is to be cut so that the longer piece is one foot longer than 5 times the length of the shorter piece. Find the length of each piece.

37. Currently, the two fastest trains are the Japanese Maglev and the French TGV. The sum of their fastest speeds is 718.2 miles per hour. If the speed of the Maglev is 3.8 mph faster than the speed of the TGV, find the speeds of each.

38. The Pentagon is the world's largest office building in terms of floor space. It has three times the amount of floor space as the Empire State Building. If the total floor space for these two buildings is approximately 8700 thousand square feet, find the floor space of each building.

39. Two angles are supplementary if their sum is 180°. The larger angle below measures eight degrees more than three times the measure of the smaller angle. If x represents the measure of the smaller angle and these two angles are supplementary, find the measure of each angle.

40. Two angles are complementary if their sum is 90°. Given the measures of the complementary angles shown, find the measure of each angle.

41. The measures of the angles of a triangle are 3 consecutive even integers. Find the measure of each angle.

42. A quadrilateral is a polygon with 4 sides. The sum of the measures of the 4 angles in a quadrilateral is 360°. If the measures of the angles of a quadrilateral are consecutive odd integers, find the measures.

43. The sum of $\frac{1}{5}$ and twice a number is equal to $\frac{4}{5}$ subtracted from three times the number. Find the number.

44. The sum of $\frac{2}{3}$ and four times a number is equal to $\frac{5}{6}$ subtracted from five times the number. Find the number.

45. Hertz Car Rental charges a daily rate of $39 plus $0.20 per mile for a certain car. Suppose that you rent that car for a day and your bill (before taxes) is $95. How many miles did you drive?

46. A woman's $15,000 estate is to be divided so that her husband receives twice as much as her son. Find the amount of money that her husband receives and the amount of money that her son receives.

47. During the 2013 Rose Bowl, Stanford University beat University of Wisconsin by 6 points. If their combined scores totaled 34, find the individual team scores.

48. In June 2013, there were 10 more Republican governors than Democratic governors in the United States. How many Democrats and how many Republicans held governors' offices after this election? (*Source:* National Governors Association)

49. The number of counties in California and the number of counties in Montana are consecutive even integers whose sum is 114. If California has more counties than Montana, how many counties does each state have? (*Source: The World Almanac and Book of Facts*)

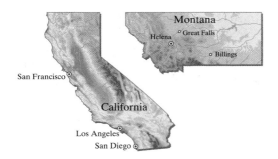

50. A student is building a bookcase with stepped shelves for her dorm room. She buys a 48-inch board and wants to cut the board into three pieces with lengths equal to three consecutive even integers. Find the three board lengths.

51. Scientists are continually updating information about the planets in our solar system, including the number of satellites orbiting each. Uranus is now believed to have 13 more satellites than Neptune. Also, Saturn is now believed to have 8 more than twice the number of satellites of Uranus. If the total number of satellites for these planets is 103, find the number of satellites for each planet. (*Source:* National Space Science Data Center)

52. Apple's iPad Mini tablet computer was launched in 2012. The height of each iPad Mini is 70 millimeters less than twice the width. If the sum of the height and width of an iPad Mini is 335 millimeters, find each dimension. (*Source:* Apple Inc.)

53. If the sum of a number and five is tripled, the result is one less than twice the number. Find the number.

54. Twice the sum of a number and six equals three times the sum of the number and four. Find the number.

55. The area of the Sahara Desert is 7 times the area of the Gobi Desert. If the sum of their areas is 4,000,000 square miles, find the area of each desert.

56. The largest meteorite in the world is the Hoba West, located in Namibia. Its weight is 3 times the weight of the Armanty meteorite, located in Outer Mongolia. If the sum of their weights is 88 tons, find the weight of each.

57. In the 2012 Summer Olympics, New Zealand won more gold medals than Cuba, which won more gold medals than Jamaica. If the number of gold medals won by these three countries is three consecutive integers whose sum is 15, find the number of gold medals won by each. (*Source:* International Olympic Committee)

58. To make an international telephone call, you need the code for the country you are calling. The codes for Mali Republic, Côte d'Ivoire, and Niger are three consecutive odd integers whose sum is 675. Find the code for each country.

59. In the fall of 2012, there were 1580 more female students enrolled at Rutgers University than male students. If the total student enrollment at Rutgers was 58,788 that fall, find the numbers of female students and male students who were enrolled. (*Source:* Rutgers, The State University of New Jersey)

60. In 2012, approximately 1.1 million fewer pickups were sold in the United States than middle-sized cars. If the total number of pickups and middle-sized cars sold was 4.9 million, find the number of vehicles sold in each category. (*Source:* Alliance of Automobile Manufacturers)

61. A geodesic dome, based on the design by Buckminster Fuller, is composed of two different types of triangular panels. One of these is an isosceles triangle. In one geodesic dome, the measure of the third angle is 76.5° more than the measure of either of the two equal angles. Find the measure of the three angles. (*Source:* Buckminster Fuller Institute)

62. The measures of the angles of a particular triangle are such that the second and third angles are each four times the measure of the smallest angle. Find the measures of the angles of this triangle.

smallest angle

The graph below shows the states with the highest provisional tourism budgets in 2012/2013. Use the graph for Exercises 63 through 66.

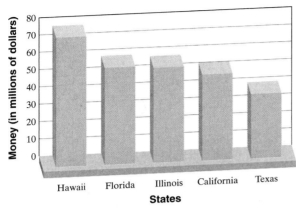

Source: U.S. Travel Association

63. Which state spent the most money on tourism?

64. Which state(s) spent between $30 and $40 million on tourism?

65. The states of Florida and California spent a total of $106.2 million on tourism. The state of Florida spent $6.2 million more than the state of California. Find the amount that each state spent on tourism.

66. The states of Illinois and Texas spent a total of $92.6 million on tourism. The state of Illinois spent $19.0 million less than twice the amount of money that the state of Texas. Find the amount that each state spent on tourism.

Compare the heights of the bars in the graph with your results of the exercises below. Are your answers reasonable?

67. Exercise **65**

68. Exercise **66**

Review

Evaluate each expression for the given values. See Section 1.8.

69. $2W + 2L$; $W = 7$ and $L = 10$

70. $\frac{1}{2} Bh$; $B = 14$ and $h = 22$

71. πr^2; $r = 15$

72. $r \cdot t$; $r = 15$ and $t = 2$

Concept Extensions

73. A golden rectangle is a rectangle whose length is approximately 1.6 times its width. The early Greeks thought that a rectangle with these dimensions was the most pleasing to the eye, and examples of the golden rectangle are found in many early works of art. For example, the Parthenon in Athens contains many examples of golden rectangles.

Mike Hallahan would like to plant a rectangular garden in the shape of a golden rectangle. If he has 78 feet of fencing available, find the dimensions of the garden.

74. Dr. Dorothy Smith gave the students in her geometry class at the University of New Orleans the following question: Is it possible to construct a triangle such that the second angle of the triangle has a measure that is twice the measure of the first angle and the measure of the third angle is 5 times the measure of the first? If so, find the measure of each angle. (*Hint:* Recall that the sum of the measures of the angles of a triangle is 180°.)

75. Only male crickets chirp. They chirp at different rates depending on their species and the temperature of their environment. Suppose a certain species is currently chirping at a rate of 90 chirps per minute. At this rate, how many chirps occur in one hour? In one 24-hour day? In one year?

76. The human eye blinks once every 5 seconds on average. How many times does the average eye blink in one hour? In one 16-hour day while awake? In one year while awake?

77. In your own words, explain why a solution of a word problem should be checked using the original wording of the problem and not the equation written from the wording.

78. Give an example of how you recently solved a problem using mathematics.

*Recall from Exercise **73** that a golden rectangle is a rectangle whose length is approximately 1.6 times its width.*

79. It is thought that for about 75% of adults, a rectangle in the shape of the golden rectangle is the most pleasing to the eye. Draw three rectangles, one in the shape of the golden rectangle, and poll your class. Do the results agree with the percentage given above?

80. Examples of golden rectangles can be found today in architecture and manufacturing packaging. Find an example of a golden rectangle in your home. A few suggestions: the front face of a book, the floor of a room, the front of a box of food.

For Exercises 81 and 82, measure the dimensions of each rectangle and decide which one best approximates the shape of a golden rectangle.

81.

(a)   (b)   (c)

82.

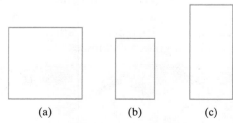

(a)   (b)   (c)

Formulas and Problem Solving

Objective A Using Formulas to Solve Problems

A **formula** describes a known relationship among quantities. Many formulas are given as equations. For example, the formula

$$d = r \cdot t$$

stands for the relationship

$$\text{distance} = \text{rate} \cdot \text{time}$$

Let's look at one way that we can use this formula.

If we know we traveled a distance of 100 miles at a rate of 40 miles per hour, we can replace the variables d and r in the formula $d = rt$ and find our travel time, t.

$$d = rt \quad \text{Formula}$$

$$100 = 40t \quad \text{Replace } d \text{ with 100 and } r \text{ with 40.}$$

To solve for t, we divide both sides of the equation by 40.

$$\frac{100}{40} = \frac{40t}{40} \quad \text{Divide both sides by 40.}$$

$$\frac{5}{2} = t \quad \text{Simplify.}$$

The travel time was $\frac{5}{2}$ hours, or $2\frac{1}{2}$ hours, or 2.5 hours.

In this section, we solve problems that can be modeled by known formulas. We use the same problem-solving strategy that was used in the previous section.

Objectives

A Use Formulas to Solve Problems.

B Solve a Formula or Equation for One of Its Variables.

> **Example 1** Finding Time Given Rate and Distance

A glacier is a giant mass of rocks and ice that flows downhill like a river. Portage Glacier in Alaska is about 6 miles, or 31,680 *feet,* long and moves 400 *feet* per year. Icebergs are created when the front end of the glacier flows into Portage Lake. How long does it take for ice at the head (beginning) of the glacier to reach the lake?

Solution:

1. UNDERSTAND. Read and reread the problem. The appropriate formula needed to solve this problem is the distance formula, $d = rt$. To become familiar with this formula, let's find the distance that ice traveling at a rate of 400 feet per year travels in 100 years. To do so, we let time t be 100 years and rate r be the given 400 feet per year, and substitute these values into the formula $d = rt$. We then have that distance $d = 400(100) = 40,000$ feet. Since we are interested in finding how long it takes ice to travel 31,680 feet, we now know that it is less than 100 years.

(Continued on next page)

Practice 1

A family is planning their vacation to visit relatives. They will drive from Cincinnati, Ohio, to Rapid City, South Dakota, a distance of 1180 miles. They plan to average a rate of 50 miles per hour. How much time will they spend driving?

Answer
1. 23.6 hours

Since we are using the formula $d = rt$, we let

t = the time in years for ice to reach the lake

r = rate or speed of ice

d = distance from beginning of glacier to lake

2. **TRANSLATE.** To translate to an equation, we use the formula $d = rt$ and let distance $d = 31{,}680$ feet and rate $r = 400$ feet per year.

$$d = r \cdot t$$
$$31{,}680 = 400 \cdot t \quad \text{Let } d = 31{,}680 \text{ and } r = 400.$$

3. **SOLVE.** Solve the equation for t. To solve for t, we divide both sides by 400.

$$\frac{31{,}680}{400} = \frac{400 \cdot t}{400} \quad \text{Divide both sides by 400.}$$
$$79.2 = t \quad \text{Simplify.}$$

4. **INTERPRET.**

Check: To check, substitute 79.2 for t and 400 for r in the distance formula and check to see that the distance is 31,680 feet.

State: It takes 79.2 years for the ice at the head of Portage Glacier to reach the lake.

> **Helpful Hint**
> Don't forget to include units, if appropriate.

■ Work Practice 1

Practice 2

A wood deck is being built behind a house. The width of the deck must be 18 feet because of the shape of the house. If there is 450 square feet of decking material, find the length of the deck.

> **Example 2**   Calculating the Length of a Garden

Charles Pecot can afford enough fencing to enclose a rectangular garden with a perimeter of 140 feet. If the width of his garden is to be 30 feet, find the length.

Solution:

1. **UNDERSTAND.** Read and reread the problem. The formula needed to solve this problem is the formula for the perimeter of a rectangle, $P = 2l + 2w$. Before continuing, let's become familar with this formula.

l = the length of the rectangular garden

w = the width of the rectangular garden

P = perimeter of the garden

2. **TRANSLATE.** To translate to an equation, we use the formula $P = 2l + 2w$ and let perimeter $P = 140$ feet and width $w = 30$ feet.

$$P = 2l + 2w \quad \text{Let } P = 140 \text{ and } w = 30.$$
$$140 = 2l + 2(30)$$

Answer

2. 25 feet

3. SOLVE.

$$140 = 2l + 2(30)$$
$$140 = 2l + 60 \qquad \text{Multiply 2(30).}$$
$$140 - 60 = 2l + 60 - 60 \qquad \text{Subtract 60 from both sides.}$$
$$80 = 2l \qquad \text{Combine like terms.}$$
$$40 = l \qquad \text{Divide both sides by 2.}$$

4. INTERPRET.

Check: Substitute 40 for l and 30 for w in the perimeter formula and check to see that the perimeter is 140 feet.

State: The length of the rectangular garden is 40 feet.

◼ Work Practice 2

Example 3 Finding an Equivalent Temperature

The average maximum temperature for January in Algiers, Algeria, is 59° Fahrenheit. Find the equivalent temperature in degrees Celsius.

Practice 3

Convert the temperature 5°C to Fahrenheit.

Solution:

1. UNDERSTAND. Read and reread the problem. A formula that can be used to solve this problem is the formula for converting degrees Celsius to degrees Fahrenheit, $F = \frac{9}{5}C + 32$. Before continuing, become familiar with this formula. Using this formula, we let

C = temperature in degrees Celsius, and

F = temperature in degrees Fahrenheit.

2. TRANSLATE. To translate to an equation, we use the formula $F = \frac{9}{5}C + 32$ and let degrees Fahrenheit F = 59.

Formula: $\qquad F = \frac{9}{5}C + 32$

Substitute: $\qquad 59 = \frac{9}{5}C + 32 \qquad \text{Let F = 59.}$

3. SOLVE.

$$59 = \frac{9}{5}C + 32$$

$$59 - 32 = \frac{9}{5}C + 32 - 32 \qquad \text{Subtract 32 from both sides.}$$

$$27 = \frac{9}{5}C \qquad \text{Combine like terms.}$$

$$\frac{5}{9} \cdot 27 = \frac{5}{9} \cdot \frac{9}{5}C \qquad \text{Multiply both sides by } \frac{5}{9}.$$

$$15 = C \qquad \text{Simplify.}$$

4. INTERPRET.

Check: To check, replace C with 15 and F with 59 in the formula and see that a true statement results.

State: Thus, 59° Fahrenheit is equivalent to 15° Celsius.

◼ Work Practice 3

Answer

3. 41°F

In the next example, we use the formula for perimeter of a rectangle as in Example 2. In Example 2, we knew the width of the rectangle. In this example, both the length and width are unknown.

Practice 4

The length of a rectangle is 1 meter more than 4 times its width. Find the dimensions if the perimeter is 52 meters.

Example 4 Finding Road Sign Dimensions

The length of a rectangular road sign is 2 feet less than three times its width. Find the dimensions if the perimeter is 28 feet.

Solution:

1. UNDERSTAND. Read and reread the problem. Recall that the formula for the perimeter of a rectangle is $P = 2l + 2w$. Draw a rectangle and guess the solution. If the width of the rectangular sign is 5 feet, its length is 2 feet less than 3 times the width, or $3(5 \text{ feet}) - 2 \text{ feet} = 13 \text{ feet}$. The perimeter P of the rectangle is then $2(13 \text{ feet}) + 2(5 \text{ feet}) = 36 \text{ feet}$, too large. We now know that the width is less than 5 feet.

Proposed rectangle:

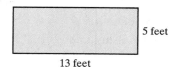

5 feet

13 feet

Let

w = the width of the rectangular sign; then

$3w - 2$ = the length of the sign.

w

$3w - 2$

Draw a rectangle and label it with the assigned variables.

2. TRANSLATE.

Formula: $P = 2l + 2w$

Substitute: $28 = 2(3w - 2) + 2w$

3. SOLVE.

$$28 = 2(3w - 2) + 2w$$
$$28 = 6w - 4 + 2w \qquad \text{Apply the distributive property.}$$
$$28 = 8w - 4$$
$$28 + 4 = 8w - 4 + 4 \qquad \text{Add 4 to both sides.}$$
$$32 = 8w$$
$$\frac{32}{8} = \frac{8w}{8} \qquad \text{Divide both sides by 8.}$$
$$4 = w$$

4. INTERPRET.

Check: If the width of the sign is 4 feet, the length of the sign is $3(4 \text{ feet}) - 2 \text{ feet} = 10 \text{ feet}$. This gives the rectangular sign a perimeter of $P = 2(4 \text{ feet}) + 2(10 \text{ feet}) = 28 \text{ feet}$, the correct perimeter.

State: The width of the sign is 4 feet and the length of the sign is 10 feet.

Answer

4. length: 21 m; width: 5 m

■ Work Practice 4

Objective B Solving a Formula for a Variable

We say that the formula

$$d = rt$$

is solved for d because d is alone on one side of the equation and the other side contains no d's. Suppose that we have a large number of problems to solve where we are given distance d and rate r and asked to find time t. In this case, it may be easier to first solve the formula $d = rt$ for t. To solve for t, we divide both sides of the equation by r.

$$d = rt$$

$$\frac{d}{r} = \frac{rt}{r} \qquad \text{Divide both sides by } r.$$

$$\frac{d}{r} = t \qquad \text{Simplify.}$$

To solve a formula or an equation for a specified variable, we use the same steps as for solving a linear equation except that we treat the specified variable as the only variable in the equation. These steps are listed next.

Solving Equations for a Specified Variable

Step 1: Multiply on both sides to clear the equation of fractions if they appear.

Step 2: Use the distributive property to remove parentheses if they appear.

Step 3: Simplify each side of the equation by combining like terms.

Step 4: Get all terms containing the specified variable on one side and all other terms on the other side by using the addition property of equality.

Step 5: Get the specified variable alone by using the multiplication property of equality.

Example 5 Solve $V = lwh$ for l.

Solution: This formula is used to find the volume of a box. To solve for l, we divide both sides by wh.

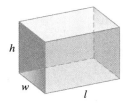

$$V = lwh$$

$$\frac{V}{wh} = \frac{lwh}{wh} \qquad \text{Divide both sides by } wh.$$

$$\frac{V}{wh} = l \qquad \text{Simplify.}$$

Since we have l alone on one side of the equation, we have solved for l in terms of V, w, and h. Remember that it does not matter on which side of the equation we get the variable alone.

▓ Work Practice 5

Practice 5

Solve $C = 2\pi r$ for r. (This formula is used to find the circumference, C, of a circle given its radius, r.)

Answer

5. $r = \dfrac{C}{2\pi}$

Practice 6

Solve $P = 2l + 2w$ for l.

Example 6   Solve $y = mx + b$ for x.

Solution: First we get mx alone by subtracting b from both sides.

$$y = mx + b$$
$$y - b = mx + b - b \quad \text{Subtract } b \text{ from both sides.}$$
$$y - b = mx \quad \text{Combine like terms.}$$

Next we solve for x by dividing both sides by m.

$$\frac{y - b}{m} = \frac{mx}{m}$$
$$\frac{y - b}{m} = x \quad \text{Simplify.}$$

◼ Work Practice 6

✓**Concept Check** Solve:

a. ⬤ = ▦ − ▦ for ▦

b. ⬤ = ▦ · ▲ − ▦ for ▦

Practice 7

Solve $P = 2a + b - c$ for a.

Example 7   Solve $P = 2l + 2w$ for w.

Solution: This formula relates the perimeter of a rectangle to its length and width. Find the term containing the variable w. To get this term, $2w$, alone, subtract $2l$ from both sides.

$$P = 2l + 2w$$
$$P - 2l = 2l + 2w - 2l \quad \text{Subtract } 2l \text{ from both sides.}$$
$$P - 2l = 2w \quad \text{Combine like terms.}$$
$$\frac{P - 2l}{2} = \frac{2w}{2} \quad \text{Divide both sides by 2.}$$
$$\frac{P - 2l}{2} = w \quad \text{Simplify.}$$

> **Helpful Hint**   The 2s may *not* be divided out here. Although 2 is a factor of the denominator, 2 is *not* a factor of the numerator since it is not a factor of both terms in the numerator.

◼ Work Practice 7

The next example has an equation containing a fraction. We will first clear the equation of fractions and then solve for the specified variable.

Practice 8

Solve $A = \dfrac{a + b}{2}$ for b.

Example 8   Solve $F = \dfrac{9}{5}C + 32$ for C.

Solution:

$$F = \frac{9}{5}C + 32$$
$$5(F) = 5\left(\frac{9}{5}C + 32\right) \quad \text{Clear the fraction by multiplying both sides by the LCD.}$$
$$5F = 9C + 160 \quad \text{Distribute the 5.}$$
$$5F - 160 = 9C + 160 - 160 \quad \text{To get the term containing the variable } C \text{ alone, subtract 160 from both sides.}$$
$$5F - 160 = 9C \quad \text{Combine like terms.}$$
$$\frac{5F - 160}{9} = \frac{9C}{9} \quad \text{Divide both sides by 9.}$$
$$\frac{5F - 160}{9} = C \quad \text{Simplify.}$$

◼ Work Practice 8

Answers

6. $l = \dfrac{P - 2w}{2}$ 7. $a = \dfrac{P - b + c}{2}$

8. $b = 2A - a$

✓**Concept Check Answer**

a. ⬤ + ▦   b.

Vocabulary, Readiness & Video Check

Martin-Gay Interactive Videos Watch the section lecture video and answer the following questions.

Objective A 1. Complete this statement based on the lecture given before ⊞ Example 1: A formula is an equation that describes known _____ among quantities.

2. In ⊞ Example 2, how are the units for the solution determined?

Objective B 3. In ⊞ Example 4, what is the equation $5x = 30$ used to show?

See Video 9.5

9.5 **Exercise Set** MyMathLab®

Objective A *Substitute the given values into each given formula and solve for the unknown variable. See Examples 1 through 4.*

1. $A = bh$; $A = 45, b = 15$ (Area of a parallelogram)

2. $d = rt$; $d = 195, t = 3$ (Distance formula)

3. $S = 4lw + 2wh$; $S = 102, l = 7, w = 3$ (Surface area of a special rectangular box)

4. $V = lwh$; $l = 14, w = 8, h = 3$ (Volume of a rectangular box)

5. $A = \frac{1}{2}h(B + b)$; $A = 180, B = 11, b = 7$ (Area of a trapezoid)

6. $A = \frac{1}{2}h(B + b)$; $A = 60, B = 7, b = 3$ (Area of a trapezoid)

7. $P = a + b + c$; $P = 30, a = 8, b = 10$ (Perimeter of a triangle)

8. $V = \frac{1}{3}Ah$; $V = 45, h = 5$ (Volume of a pyramid)

9. $C = 2\pi r$; $C = 15.7$ (Circumference of a circle) (Use the approximation 3.14 for π.)

10. $A = \pi r^2$; $r = 4$ (Area of a circle) (Use the approximation 3.14 for π.)

Objective B *Solve each formula for the specified variable. See Examples 5 through 8.*

11. $f = 5gh$ for h

12. $x = 4\pi y$ for y

13. $V = lwh$ for w

14. $T = mnr$ for n

15. $3x + y = 7$ for y

16. $-x + y = 13$ for y

17. $A = P + PRT$ for R

18. $A = P + PRT$ for T

19. $V = \dfrac{1}{3}Ah$ for A

20. $D = \dfrac{1}{4}fk$ for k

21. $P = a + b + c$ for a

22. $PR = x + y + z + w$ for z

◐ 23. $S = 2\pi rh + 2\pi r^2$ for h

△ 24. $S = 4lw + 2wh$ for h

Objective A *Solve. See Examples 1 through 4.*

25. For the purpose of purchasing new baseboard and carpet,
   a. Find the area and perimeter of the room below (neglecting doors).
   b. Identify whether baseboard has to do with area or perimeter and the same with carpet.

11.5 ft   9 ft

26. For the purpose of purchasing lumber for a new fence and seed to plant grass,
   a. Find the area and perimeter of the yard below.
   b. Identify whether a fence has to do with area or perimeter and the same with grass seed.

$$\left(A = \dfrac{1}{2}bh \right)$$

27 ft   45 ft   36 ft

27. A frame shop charges according to both the amount of framing needed to surround the picture and the amount of glass needed to cover the picture.
   a. Find the area and perimeter of the picture below.
   b. Identify whether the frame has to do with perimeter or area and the same with the glass.

24 in.
20 in.   12 in.   20 in.
56 in.

28. A decorator is painting and placing a border completely around a parallelogram-shaped wall.
   a. Find the area and perimeter of the wall below.
   b. Identify whether the border has to do with perimeter or area and the same with paint.

7 ft   11.7 ft   9.3 ft

29. The iconic NASDAQ sign in New York's Times Square has a width of 84 feet and an area of 10,080 square feet. Find the height of the sign. (*Source:* livedesignonline.com)

△ 30. The world's largest sign for Coca-Cola is located in Arica, Chile. The rectangular sign has a length of 400 feet and an area of 52,400 square feet. Find the width of the sign. (*Source:* Fabulous Facts about Coca-Cola, Atlanta, GA)

31. Convert Nome, Alaska's 14°F high temperature to Celsius.

32. Convert Paris, France's low temperature of −5°C to Fahrenheit.

33. The X-30 is a "space plane" that skims the edge of space at 4000 miles per hour. Neglecting altitude, if the circumference of the Earth is approximately 25,000 miles, how long does it take for the X-30 to travel around the Earth?

34. In the United States, a notable hang glider flight was a 303-mile, $8\frac{1}{2}$-hour flight from New Mexico to Kansas. What was the average rate during this flight?

35. An architect designs a rectangular flower garden such that the width is exactly two-thirds of the length. If 260 feet of antique picket fencing is to be used to enclose the garden, find the dimensions of the garden.

x feet

36. If the length of a rectangular parking lot is 10 meters less than twice its width, and the perimeter is 400 meters, find the length of the parking lot.

x meters

37. A flower bed is in the shape of a triangle with one side twice the length of the shortest side and the third side 30 feet more than the length of the shortest side. Find the dimensions if the perimeter is 102 feet.

?

x

?

38. The perimeter of a yield sign in the shape of an isosceles triangle is 22 feet. If the shortest side is 2 feet less than the other two sides, find the length of the shortest side. (*Hint:* An isosceles triangle has two sides the same length.)

?

YIELD

x feet   *x feet*

39. The Eurostar is a high-speed train that shuttles passengers between London, England, and Paris, France, via the Channel Tunnel. The Eurostar can make the trip in about $2\frac{1}{4}$ hours at an average speed of 136 mph. About how long is the Eurostar's route connecting London and Paris? (*Source:* Eurostar)

40. A family is planning their vacation to Disney World. They will drive from a small town outside New Orleans, Louisiana, to Orlando, Florida, a distance of 700 miles. They plan to average a rate of 56 mph. How long will this trip take?

Dolbear's Law states the relationship between the rate at which Snowy Tree Crickets chirp and the air temperature of their environment. The formula is

$$T = 50 + \frac{N - 40}{4}, \text{ where }$$

$T =$ temperature in degrees Fahrenheit and
$N =$ number of chirps per minute

41. If $N = 86$, find the temperature in degrees Fahrenheit, T.

42. If $N = 94$, find the temperature in degrees Fahrenheit, T.

43. If $T = 55°F$, find the number of chirps per minute.

44. If $T = 65°F$, find the number of chirps per minute.

Use the results of Exercises 41–44 to complete each sentence with "increases" or "decreases."

45. As the number of cricket chirps per minute increases, the air temperature of their environment _____.

46. As the air temperature of their environment decreases, the number of cricket chirps per minute _____.

Solve. See Examples 1 through 4.

△ **47.** Piranha fish require 1.5 cubic feet of water per fish to maintain a healthy environment. Find the maximum number of piranhas you could put in a tank measuring 8 feet by 3 feet by 6 feet.

6 feet
3 feet
8 feet

△ **48.** Find the maximum number of goldfish you can put in a cylindrical tank whose diameter is 8 meters and whose height is 3 meters, if each goldfish needs 2 cubic meters of water. ($V = \pi r^2 h$)

8 meters
3 meters

△ **49.** A lawn is in the shape of a trapezoid with a height of 60 feet and bases of 70 feet and 130 feet. How many bags of fertilizer must be purchased to cover the lawn if each bag covers 4000 square feet?

70 feet
60 feet
130 feet

△ **50.** If the area of a right-triangularly shaped sail is 20 square feet and its base is 5 feet, find the height of the sail. $\left(A = \dfrac{1}{2}bh \right)$

?
5 feet

△ **51.** Maria's Pizza sells one 16-inch cheese pizza or two 10-inch cheese pizzas for $9.99. Determine which size gives more pizza.

16 inches   10 inches   10 inches

△ **52.** Find how much rope is needed to wrap around the Earth at the equator, if the radius of the Earth is 4000 miles. (*Hint:* Use 3.14 for π and the formula for circumference.)

△ **53.** The perimeter of an equilateral triangle is 7 inches more than the perimeter of a square, and the side of the triangle is 5 inches longer than the side of the square. Find the side of the triangle. (*Hint:* An equilateral triangle has three sides the same length.)

△ **54.** A square animal pen and a pen shaped like an equilateral triangle have equal perimeters. Find the length of the sides of each pen if the sides of the triangular pen are 15 less than twice a side of the square pen. (*Hint:* An equilateral triangle has three sides the same length.)

55. Find how long it takes Tran Nguyen to drive 135 miles on I-10 if he merges onto I-10 at 10 a.m. and drives nonstop with his cruise control set on 60 mph.

56. Beaumont, Texas, is about 150 miles from Toledo Bend. If Leo Miller leaves Beaumont at 4 a.m. and averages 45 mph, when should he arrive at Toledo Bend?

△ **57.** The longest runway at Los Angeles International Airport has the shape of a rectangle and an area of 1,813,500 square feet. This runway is 150 feet wide. How long is the runway? (*Source:* Los Angeles World Airports)

58. The return stroke of a bolt of lightning can travel at a speed of 87,000 miles per second (almost half the speed of light). At this speed, how many times can an object travel around the world in one second? (See Exercise **52.**) Round to the nearest tenth. (*Source: The Handy Science Answer Book*)

59. The highest temperature ever recorded in Europe was 122°F in Seville, Spain, in August of 1881. Convert this record high temperature to Celsius. (*Source:* National Climatic Data Center)

60. The lowest temperature ever recorded in Oceania was −10°C at the Haleakala Summit in Maui, Hawaii, in January 1961. Convert this record low temperature to Fahrenheit. (*Source:* National Climatic Data Center)

61. The Eurostar high-speed train has a top speed of 186 mph. It travels beneath the English Channel through the Channel Tunnel, which is 31.35 miles long. If the Eurostar were able to travel at its top speed the entire length of the Channel Tunnel, how many *minutes* would the trip take? Round to the nearest tenth of a minute. (*Source:* Eurostar)

62. In 1983, the Hawaiian volcano Kilauea began erupting in a series of episodes still occurring at the time of this writing. At times, the lava flows have advanced at speeds of up to 0.5 kilometer per hour. In 1983 and 1984 lava flows destroyed 16 homes in the Royal Gardens subdivision, about 6 km away from the eruption site. Roughly how long did it take the lava to reach Royal Gardens? (*Source:* U.S. Geological Survey Hawaiian Volcano Observatory)

△ **63.** The IZOD IndyCar series is an open-wheeled race car competition based in the United States. An IndyCar car has a maximum length of 204 inches, a maximum width of 76.5 inches, and a maximum height of 44 inches. When the IZOD IndyCar series travels to another country for a grand prix, teams must ship their cars. Find the volume of the smallest shipping crate needed to ship an IndyCar car of maximum dimensions. (*Source:* Championship Auto Racing Teams, Inc.)

64. During a recent IndyCar road course race, the winner's average speed was 118 mph. Based on this speed, how long would it take an IndyCar driver to travel from Los Angeles to New York City, a distance of about 2810 miles by road, without stopping? Round to the nearest tenth of an hour.

IndyCar Racing Car

Max. height = 44 inches

Max. length = 204 inches

Max. width = 76.5 inches

65. The Hoberman Sphere is a toy ball that expands and contracts. When it is completely closed, it has a diameter of 9.5 inches. Find the volume of the Hoberman Sphere when it is completely closed. Use 3.14 for π. Round to the nearest whole cubic inch. (*Hint:* Volume of a sphere $= \frac{4}{3}\pi r^3$.) (*Source:* Hoberman Designs, Inc.)

66. When the Hoberman Sphere (see Exercise **65**) is completely expanded, its diameter is 30 inches. Find the volume of the Hoberman Sphere when it is completely expanded. Use 3.14 for π. (*Source:* Hoberman Designs, Inc.)

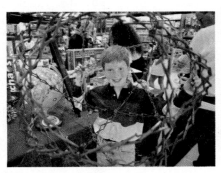

67. The average temperature on the planet Mercury is 167°C. Convert this temperature to degrees Fahrenheit. Round to the nearest degree. (*Source:* National Space Science Data Center)

68. The average temperature on the planet Jupiter is −227°F. Convert this temperature to degrees Celsius. Round to the nearest degree. (*Source:* National Space Science Data Center)

Review

Write each percent as a decimal. See Section 6.2.

69. 32%

70. 8%

71. 200%

72. 0.5%

Write each decimal as a percent. See Section 6.2.

73. 0.17

74. 0.03

75. 7.2

76. 5

Concept Extensions

Solve.

77. $N = R + \dfrac{V}{G}$ for V (Urban forestry: tree plantings per year)

78. $B = \dfrac{F}{P - V}$ for V (Business: break-even point)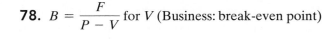

79. The formula $V = lwh$ is used to find the volume of a box. If the length of a box is doubled, the width is doubled, and the height is doubled, how does this affect the volume? Explain your answer.

80. The formula $A = bh$ is used to find the area of a parallelogram. If the base of a parallelogram is doubled and its height is doubled, how does this affect the area? Explain your answer.

81. Use the Dolbear's Law formula from Exercises **41–46** and calculate when the number of cricket chirps per minute is the same as the temperature in degrees Fahrenheit. (*Hint:* Replace T with N and solve for N, or replace N with T and solve for T.)

82. Find the temperature at which the Celsius measurement and the Fahrenheit measurement are the same number.

Solve. See the Concept Check in this section.

83. ▲ − ⬤ · ◼ = ▦ for ⬤

84. ⬢ · ◼ + ▲ = ⬤ for ◼

85. Flying fish do not *actually* fly, but glide. They have been known to travel a distance of 1300 feet at a rate of 20 miles per hour. How many seconds would it take to travel this distance? (*Hint:* First convert miles per hour to feet per second. Recall that 1 mile = 5280 feet.) Round to the nearest tenth of a second.

86. A glacier is a giant mass of rocks and ice that flows downhill like a river. Exit Glacier, near Seward, Alaska, moves at a rate of 20 inches a day. Find the distance in feet the glacier moves in a year. (Assume 365 days a year.) Round to two decimal places.

Substitute the given values into each given formula and solve for the unknown variable. If necessary, round to one decimal place.

87. $I = PRT$; $I = 1,056,000, R = 0.055, T = 6$ (Simple interest formula)

88. $I = PRT$; $I = 3750, P = 25,000, R = 0.05$ (Simple interest formula)

89. $V = \frac{4}{3}\pi r^3$; $r = 3$ (Volume of a sphere) (Use a calculator approximation for π.)

90. $V = \frac{1}{3}\pi r^2 h$; $V = 565.2, r = 6$ (Volume of a cone) (Use a calculator approximation for π.)

9.6 Linear Inequalities and Problem Solving

In Section 9.1, we reviewed these inequality symbols and their meanings:

> < means "is less than" ≤ means "is less than or equal to"
> > means "is greater than" ≥ means "is greater than or equal to"

An **inequality** is a statement that contains one of the symbols above.

Equations	Inequalities
$x = 3$	$x \leq 3$
$5n - 6 = 14$	$5n - 6 > 14$
$12 = 7 - 3y$	$12 \leq 7 - 3y$
$\frac{x}{4} - 6 = 1$	$\frac{x}{4} - 6 > 1$

Objectives

A Graph Inequalities on a Number Line.

B Use the Addition Property of Inequality to Solve Inequalities.

C Use the Multiplication Property of Inequality to Solve Inequalities.

D Use Both Properties to Solve Inequalities.

E Solve Problems Modeled by Inequalities.

Objective A Graphing Inequalities on a Number Line

Recall that the single solution to the equation $x = 3$ is 3. The solutions of the inequality $x \leq 3$ include 3 and *all real numbers less than 3* (for example, $-10, \frac{1}{2}, 2$, and 2.9). Because we can't list all numbers less than 3, we instead show a picture of the solutions by graphing them on a number line.

To graph the solutions of $x \leq 3$, we shade the numbers to the left of 3 since they are less than 3. Then we place a closed circle on the point representing 3. The closed circle indicates that 3 *is* a solution: 3 *is* less than or equal to 3.

To graph the solutions of $x < 3$, we shade the numbers to the left of 3. Then we place an open circle on the point representing 3. The open circle indicates that 3 *is not* a solution: 3 *is not* less than 3.

Practice 1

Graph: $x \geq -2$

Example 1   Graph: $x \geq -1$

Solution: To graph the solutions of $x \geq -1$, we place a closed circle at -1 since the inequality symbol is $\geq$ and -1 is greater than or equal to -1. Then we shade to the right of -1.

🔲 Work Practice 1

Practice 2

Graph: $5 > x$

Example 2   Graph: $-1 > x$

Solution: Recall from Section 9.1 that $-1 > x$ means the same as $x < -1$. The graph of the solutions of $x < -1$ is shown below.

🔲 Work Practice 2

Practice 3

Graph: $-3 \leq x < 1$

Example 3   Graph: $-4 < x \leq 2$

Solution: We read $-4 < x \leq 2$ as "-4 is less than x and x is less than or equal to 2," or as "x is greater than -4 and x is less than or equal to 2." To graph the solutions of this inequality, we place an open circle at -4 (-4 is not part of the graph), a closed circle at 2 (2 is part of the graph), and shade all numbers between -4 and 2. Why? All numbers between -4 and 2 are greater than -4 *and* also less than 2.

🔲 Work Practice 3

Objective B Using the Addition Property

When solutions of a linear inequality are not immediately obvious, they are found through a process similar to the one used to solve a linear equation. Our goal is to get the variable alone on one side of the inequality. We use properties of inequality similar to properties of equality.

> ### Addition Property of Inequality
>
> If a, b, and c are real numbers, then
> $$a < b \qquad \text{and} \qquad a + c < b + c$$
> are equivalent inequalities.

This property also holds true for subtracting values, since subtraction is defined in terms of addition. In other words, adding or subtracting the same quantity from both sides of an inequality does not change the solutions of the inequality.

Answers

1.

2.

3.

Example 4 Solve $x + 4 \leq -6$. Graph the solutions.

Solution: To solve for x, subtract 4 from both sides of the inequality.

$$x + 4 \leq -6 \qquad \text{Original inequality}$$
$$x + 4 - 4 \leq -6 - 4 \qquad \text{Subtract 4 from both sides.}$$
$$x \leq -10 \qquad \text{Simplify.}$$

The graph of the solutions is shown below.

Work Practice 4

Practice 4

Solve $x - 6 \geq -11$. Graph the solutions.

Helpful Hint

Notice that any number less than or equal to -10 is a solution to $x \leq -10$. For example, solutions include

$$-10, \quad -200, \quad -11\frac{1}{2}, \quad -\sqrt{130}, \quad \text{and} \quad -50.3$$

Objective C Using the Multiplication Property

An important difference between solving linear equations and solving linear inequalities is shown when we multiply or divide both sides of an inequality by a nonzero real number. For example, start with the true statement $6 < 8$ and multiply both sides by 2. As we see below, the resulting inequality is also true.

$$6 < 8 \qquad \text{True}$$
$$2(6) < 2(8) \qquad \text{Multiply both sides by 2.}$$
$$12 < 16 \qquad \text{True}$$

But if we start with the same true statement $6 < 8$ and multiply both sides by -2, the resulting inequality is not a true statement.

$$6 < 8 \qquad \text{True}$$
$$-2(6) < -2(8) \qquad \text{Multiply both sides by } -2.$$
$$-12 < -16 \qquad \text{False}$$

Notice, however, that if we reverse the direction of the inequality symbol, the resulting inequality is true.

$$-12 < -16 \qquad \text{False}$$
$$-12 > -16 \qquad \text{True}$$

This demonstrates the multiplication property of inequality.

Multiplication Property of Inequality

1. If a, b, and c are real numbers, and c is **positive,** then
   $$a < b \qquad \text{and} \qquad ac < bc$$
   are equivalent inequalities.
2. If a, b, and c are real numbers, and c is **negative,** then
   $$a < b \qquad \text{and} \qquad ac > bc$$
   are equivalent inequalities.

Answer

4. $x \geq -5$

Because division is defined in terms of multiplication, this property also holds true when dividing both sides of an inequality by a nonzero number: If we multiply or divide both sides of an inequality by a negative number, **the direction of the inequality sign must be reversed for the inequalities to remain equivalent.**

✓**Concept Check** Fill in each box with $<$, $>$, $\leq$, or $\geq$.

a. Since $-8 < -4$, then $3(-8) \,\square\, 3(-4)$.

b. Since $5 \geq -2$, then $\dfrac{5}{-7} \,\square\, \dfrac{-2}{-7}$.

c. If $a < b$, then $2a \,\square\, 2b$.

d. If $a \geq b$, then $\dfrac{a}{-3} \,\square\, \dfrac{b}{-3}$.

Practice 5

Solve $-3x \leq 12$. Graph the solutions.

Example 5 Solve $-2x \leq -4$. Graph the solutions.

Solution: Remember to reverse the direction of the inequality symbol when dividing by a negative number.

$$-2x \leq -4$$

$$\dfrac{-2x}{-2} \geq \dfrac{-4}{-2} \quad \text{Divide both sides by } -2 \text{ and reverse the inequality sign.}$$

$$x \geq 2 \quad \text{Simplify.}$$

The graph of the solutions is shown.

■ Work Practice 5

Practice 6

Solve $5x > -20$. Graph the solutions.

Example 6 Solve $2x < -4$. Graph the solutions.

Solution:

$$2x < -4$$

$$\dfrac{2x}{2} < \dfrac{-4}{2} \quad \text{Divide both sides by 2. Do not reverse the inequality sign.}$$

$$x < -2 \quad \text{Simplify.}$$

The graph of the solutions is shown.

■ Work Practice 6

Since we cannot list all solutions to an inequality such as $x < -2$, we will use the set notation $\{x \mid x < -2\}$. Recall from Section 9.1 that this is read "the set of all x such that x is less than -2." We will use this notation when solving inequalities.

Objective D Using Both Properties of Inequality

The following steps may be helpful when solving inequalities in one variable. Notice that these steps are similar to the ones given in Section 9.3 for solving equations.

Answers

5. $x \geq -4$

6. $x > -4$

✓**Concept Check Answers**

a. $<$ **b.** $\leq$ **c.** $<$ **d.** $\leq$

To Solve Linear Inequalities in One Variable

Step 1: If an inequality contains fractions or decimals, multiply both sides by the LCD to clear the inequality of fractions or decimals.

Step 2: Use the distributive property to remove parentheses if they appear.

Step 3: Simplify each side of the inequality by combining like terms.

Step 4: Get all variable terms on one side and all numbers on the other side by using the addition property of inequality.

Step 5: Get the variable alone by using the multiplication property of inequality.

Helpful Hint

Don't forget that if both sides of an inequality are multiplied or divided by a negative number, the direction of the inequality sign must be reversed.

Example 7 Solve $-4x + 7 \geq -9$. Graph the solution set.

Solution:

$$-4x + 7 \geq -9$$

$-4x + 7 - 7 \geq -9 - 7$ Subtract 7 from both sides.

$\qquad -4x \geq -16$ Simplify.

$\qquad \dfrac{-4x}{-4} \leq \dfrac{-16}{-4}$ Divide both sides by -4 and reverse the direction of the inequality sign.

$\qquad\qquad x \leq 4$ Simplify.

The graph of the solution set $\{x \mid x \leq 4\}$ is shown.

■ Work Practice 7

Practice 7

Solve $-3x + 11 \leq -13$. Graph the solution set.

Example 8 Solve $-5x + 7 < 2(x - 3)$. Graph the solution set.

Solution: $-5x + 7 < 2(x - 3)$

$\qquad -5x + 7 < 2x - 6$ Apply the distributive property.

$-5x + 7 - 2x < 2x - 6 - 2x$ Subtract $2x$ from both sides.

$\qquad -7x + 7 < -6$ Combine like terms.

$\qquad -7x + 7 - 7 < -6 - 7$ Subtract 7 from both sides.

$\qquad\qquad -7x < -13$ Combine like terms.

$\qquad\qquad \dfrac{-7x}{-7} > \dfrac{-13}{-7}$ Divide both sides by -7 and reverse the direction of the inequality sign.

$\qquad\qquad\qquad x > \dfrac{13}{7}$ Simplify.

The graph of the solution set $\left\{ x \mid x > \dfrac{13}{7} \right\}$ is shown.

■ Work Practice 8

Practice 8

Solve $2x - 3 > 4(x - 1)$. Graph the solution set.

Answers

7. $\{x \mid x \geq 8\}$

8. $\left\{ x \mid x < \dfrac{1}{2} \right\}$

Practice 9

Solve:
$3(x + 5) - 1 \geq 5(x - 1) + 7$

Example 9 Solve: $2(x - 3) - 5 \leq 3(x + 2) - 18$

Solution:

$$2(x - 3) - 5 \leq 3(x + 2) - 18$$

$$2x - 6 - 5 \leq 3x + 6 - 18 \qquad \text{Apply the distributive property.}$$

$$2x - 11 \leq 3x - 12 \qquad \text{Combine like terms.}$$

$$-x - 11 \leq -12 \qquad \text{Subtract } 3x \text{ from both sides.}$$

$$-x \leq -1 \qquad \text{Add 11 to both sides.}$$

$$\frac{-x}{-1} \geq \frac{-1}{-1} \qquad \text{Divide both sides by } -1 \text{ and reverse the direction of the inequality sign.}$$

$$x \geq 1 \qquad \text{Simplify.}$$

The solution set is $\{x \mid x \geq 1\}$.

■ Work Practice 9

Objective E Solving Problems Modeled by Inequalities

Problems containing words such as "at least," "at most," "between," "no more than," and "no less than" usually indicate that an inequality should be solved instead of an equation. In solving applications involving linear inequalities, we use the same procedure we used to solve applications involving linear equations.

Some Inequality Translations			
≥	≤	<	>
at least	at most	is less than	is greater than
no less than	no more than		

Practice 10

Twice a number, subtracted from 35 is greater than 15. Find all numbers that make this true.

Example 10 12 subtracted from 3 times a number is less than 21. Find all numbers that make this statement true.

Solution:

1. **UNDERSTAND.** Read and reread the problem. This is a direct translation problem, and let's let

   x = the unknown number

2. **TRANSLATE.**

12	subtracted from	three times a number	is less than	21

   $3x \qquad - \qquad 12 \qquad < \qquad 21$

3. **SOLVE.** $3x - 12 < 21$

   $$3x < 33 \qquad \text{Add 12 to both sides.}$$

   $$\frac{3x}{3} < \frac{33}{3} \qquad \text{Divide both sides by 3 and do not reverse the direction of the inequality sign.}$$

   $$x < 11 \qquad \text{Simplify.}$$

4. **INTERPRET.**

   Check: Check the translation; then let's choose a number less than 11 to see if it checks. For example, let's check 10. 12 subtracted from 3 times 10 is 12 subtracted from 30, or 18. Since 18 is less than 21, the number 10 checks.

   State: All numbers less than 11 make the original statement true.

■ Work Practice 10

Example 11 Budgeting for a Wedding

A couple are having their wedding reception at the Gallery reception hall. They may spend at most $1000 for the reception. If the reception hall charges a $100 cleanup fee plus $14 per person, find the greatest number of people that they can invite and still stay within their budget.

Solution:

1. **UNDERSTAND.** Read and reread the problem. Suppose that 50 people attend the reception. The cost is then $100 + $14(50) = $100 + $700 = $800.

   Let x = the number of people who attend the reception.

2. **TRANSLATE.**

cleanup fee	+	cost per person	times	number of people	must be less than or equal to	$1000
↓		↓	↓	↓	↓	↓
100	+	14	·	x	≤	1000

3. **SOLVE.**

   $$100 + 14x \leq 1000$$
   $$14x \leq 900 \quad \text{Subtract 100 from both sides.}$$
   $$x \leq 64\frac{2}{7} \quad \text{Divide both sides by 14.}$$

4. **INTERPRET.**

   Check: Since x represents the number of people, we round down to the nearest whole, or 64. Notice that if 64 people attend, the cost is $100 + $14(64) = $996. If 65 people attend, the cost is $100 + $14(65) = $1010, which is more than the given $1000.

   State: The couple can invite at most 64 people to the reception.

■ Work Practice 11

Practice 11

Alex earns $600 per month plus 4% of all his sales. Find the minimum sales that will allow Alex to earn at least $3000 per month.

Answer
11. $60,000

Vocabulary, Readiness & Video Check

Identify each as an equation, expression, or inequality.

1. $6x - 7(x + 9)$ _____

2. $6x = 7(x + 9)$ _____

3. $6x < 7(x + 9)$ _____

4. $5y - 2 \geq -38$ _____

5. $\dfrac{9}{7} = \dfrac{x + 2}{14}$ _____

6. $\dfrac{9}{7} - \dfrac{x + 2}{14}$ _____

Decide which number listed is not a solution to each given inequality.

7. $x \geq -3$; $-3, 0, -5, \pi$ _____

8. $x < 6$; $-6, |-6|, 0, -3.2$ _____

9. $x < 4.01$; $4, -4.01, 4.1, -4.1$ _____

10. $x \geq -3$; $-4, -3, -2, -(-2)$ _____

Martin-Gay Interactive Videos   *Watch the section lecture video and answer the following questions.*

See Video 9.6

Objective A 11. From ⊞ Example 1, when graphing an inequality, what inequality symbol(s) does an open circle indicate? What inequality symbol(s) does a closed circle indicate? ▶

Objective B 12. From the lecture before ⊞ Example 2, which property is the addition property of inequality very similar to? ▶

Objective C 13. What is the answer to ⊞ Example 3, written in solution set notation? ▶

Objective D 14. When solving ⊞ Example 4, why is special attention given to the coefficient of x in the last step? ▶

Objective E 15. What is the phrase in ⊞ Example 5 that tells us to translate to an inequality? What does this phrase translate to? ▶

9.6 Exercise Set MyMathLab® ▶

Objective A *Graph each inequality on the number line. See Examples 1 and 2.*

▶ **1.** $x \leq -1$

2. $y < 0$

3. $x > \dfrac{1}{2}$

4. $z \geq -\dfrac{2}{3}$

5. $y < 4$

6. $x > 3$

7. $-2 \leq m$

8. $-5 \geq x$

Graph each inequality on the number line. See Example 3.

9. $-1 < x < 3$

10. $-2 \leq x \leq 3$

11. $0 \leq y < 2$

12. $-4 < x \leq 0$

Objective B *Solve each inequality. Graph the solution set. Write each answer using set notation. See Example 4.*

▶ **13.** $x - 2 \geq -7$

14. $x + 4 \leq 1$

15. $-9 + y < 0$

16. $-3 + m > 5$

17. $3x - 5 > 2x - 8$

18. $3 - 7x \geq 10 - 8x$

19. $4x - 1 \leq 5x - 2x$

20. $7x + 3 < 9x - 3x$

Objective **C** *Solve each inequality. Graph the solution set. See Examples 5 and 6.*

21. $2x < -6$

22. $3x > -9$

23. $-8x \leq 16$

24. $-5x < 20$

25. $-x > 0$

26. $-y \geq 0$

27. $\dfrac{3}{4}y \geq -2$

28. $\dfrac{5}{6}x \leq -8$

29. $-0.6y < -1.8$

30. $-0.3x > -2.4$

Objectives **B** **C** **D** **Mixed Practice** *Solve each inequality. Write each answer using set notation.*
See Examples 4 through 9.

31. $-8 < x + 7$

32. $-11 > x + 4$

33. $7(x + 1) - 6x \geq -4$

34. $10(x + 2) - 9x \leq -1$

35. $4x > 1$

36. $6x < 5$

37. $-\dfrac{2}{3}y \leq 8$

38. $-\dfrac{3}{4}y \geq 9$

39. $4(2z + 1) < 4$

40. $6(2 - z) \geq 12$

41. $3x - 7 < 6x + 2$

42. $2x - 1 \geq 4x - 5$

43. $5x - 7x \leq x + 2$

44. $4 - x < 8x + 2x$

45. $-6x + 2 \geq 2(5 - x)$

46. $-7x + 4 > 3(4 - x)$

47. $3(x - 5) < 2(2x - 1)$

48. $5(x - 2) \leq 3(2x - 1)$

49. $4(3x - 1) \leq 5(2x - 4)$

50. $3(5x - 4) \leq 4(3x - 2)$

51. $3(x + 2) - 6 > -2(x - 3) + 14$

52. $7(x - 2) + x \leq -4(5 - x) - 12$

53. $-5(1 - x) + x \leq -(6 - 2x) + 6$

54. $-2(x - 4) - 3x < -(4x + 1) + 2x$

55. $\dfrac{1}{4}(x + 4) < \dfrac{1}{5}(2x + 3)$

56. $\dfrac{1}{2}(x - 5) < \dfrac{1}{3}(2x - 1)$

57. $-5x + 4 \leq -4(x - 1)$

58. $-6x + 2 < -3(x + 4)$

Objective E *Solve the following. See Examples 10 and 11.*

59. Six more than twice a number is greater than negative fourteen. Find all numbers that make this statement true.

60. One more than five times a number is less than or equal to ten. Find all such numbers.

61. The perimeter of a rectangle is to be no greater than 100 centimeters and the width must be 15 centimeters. Find the maximum length of the rectangle.

15 cm

x cm

62. One side of a triangle is four times as long as another side, and the third side is 12 inches long. If the perimeter can be no longer than 87 inches, find the maximum lengths of the other two sides.

12 in.   *x* in.

4*x* in.

63. Ben Holladay bowled 146 and 201 in his first two games. What must he bowl in his third game to have an average of at least 180? (*Hint:* The average of a list of numbers is their sum divided by the number of numbers in the list.)

64. On an NBA team the two forwards measure 6′8″ and 6′6″ tall and the two guards measure 6′0″ and 5′9″ tall. How tall should the center be if they wish to have a starting team average height of at least 6′5″?

65. Dennis and Nancy Wood are celebrating their 30th wedding anniversary by having a reception at Tiffany Oaks reception hall. They have budgeted $3000 for their reception. If the reception hall charges a $50.00 cleanup fee plus $34 per person, find the greatest number of people that they may invite and still stay within their budget.

66. A surprise retirement party is being planned for Pratap Puri. A total of $860 has been collected for the event, which is to be held at a local reception hall. This reception hall charges a cleanup fee of $40 and $15 per person for drinks and light snacks. Find the greatest number of people that may be invited and still stay within the $860 budget.

67. A 150-pound person uses 5.8 calories per minute when walking at a speed of 4 mph. How long must a person walk at this speed to use at least 200 calories? Round up to the nearest minute. (*Source: Home & Garden Bulletin* No. 72)

68. A 170-pound person uses 5.3 calories per minute when bicycling at a speed of 5.5 mph. How long must a person ride a bike at this speed in order to use at least 200 calories? Round up to the nearest minute. (*Source:* Same as Exercise **67**)

Review

Evaluate each expression. See Sections 1.7 and 4.3.

69. 3^4 **70.** 4^3 **71.** 1^8 **72.** 0^7 **73.** $\left(\dfrac{7}{8}\right)^2$ **74.** $\left(\dfrac{2}{3}\right)^3$

The graph shows the number of recreation visitors to Pecos National Historical Park in New Mexico from 2005 to 2012. Use this graph to answer Exercises 75 through 80. See Section 7.1.

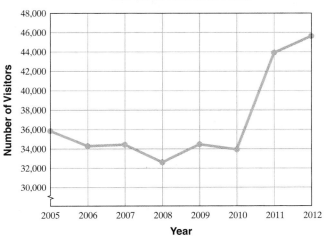

Annual Visitation to Pecos National Historic Park

Source: National Park Service

75. How many people visited Pecos National Historical Park in 2006?

76. How many people visited Pecos National Historical Park in 2011?

77. Between which two years did the greatest increase in the number of visitors to Pecos National Historical Park occur?

78. In what year were there approximately 35,800 visitors to Pecos National Historical Park?

79. In which year did the number of visitors to Pecos National Historical Park first fall below 34,000?

80. In which year did the number of visitors to Pecos National Historical Park first rise above 45,000?

Concept Extensions

Fill in the box with $<, >, \leq,$ or $\geq$. See the Concept Check in this section.

81. Since $3 < 5$, then $3(-4) \;\square\; 5(-4)$.

82. If $m \leq n$, then $2m \;\square\; 2n$.

83. If $m \leq n$, then $-2m \;\square\; -2n$.

84. If $-x < y$, then $x \;\square\; -y$.

85. When solving an inequality, when must you reverse the direction of the inequality symbol?

86. If both sides of the inequality $-3x < -30$ are divided by 3, do you reverse the direction of the inequality symbol? Why or why not?

Solve.

87. A history major has scores of 75, 83, and 85 on his history tests. Use an inequality to find the scores he can make on his final exam to receive a B in the class. The final exam counts as **two** tests, and a B is received if the final course average is greater than or equal to 80.

88. A mathematics major has scores of 85, 95, and 92 on her college geometry tests. Use an inequality to find the scores she can make on her final exam to receive an A in the course. The final exam counts as **three** tests, and an A is received if the final course average is greater than or equal to 90. Round to one decimal place.

Chapter 9 Group Activity

Investigating Averages

Sections 9.1–9.6

Materials:

- small rubber ball or crumpled paper ball
- bucket or waste can

This activity may be completed by working in groups or individually.

1. Try shooting the ball into the bucket or waste can 5 times. Record your results below.

   Shots Made   **Shots Missed**

2. Find your shooting percent for the 5 shots (that is, the percent of the shots you actually made out of the number you tried).

3. Suppose you are going to try an additional 5 shots. How many of the next 5 shots will you have to make to have a 50% shooting percent for all 10 shots? An 80% shooting percent?

4. Did you solve an equation in Question 3? If so, explain what you did. If not, explain how you could use an equation to find the answers.

5. Suppose instead of trying 5 additional shots, you try 22 additional shots. How many of the next 22 shots will you have to make to have at least a 50% shooting percent for all 27 shots? At least a 70% shooting percent?

6. Choose one of the sports played at your college that is currently in season. How many regular-season games are scheduled? What is the team's current percent of games won?

7. Suppose the team has a goal of finishing the season with a winning percent better than 110% of their current wins. At least how many of the remaining games must they win to achieve their goal?

Chapter 9 Vocabulary Check

Fill in each blank with one of the words or phrases listed below.

no solution	all real numbers	linear equation in one variable
reciprocals	formula	reversed
equivalent inequalities	opposites	
linear inequality in one variable	the same	

1. A(n) _____ can be written in the form $ax + b = c$.

2. Inequalities that have the same solution are called _____.

3. An equation that describes a known relationship among quantities is called a(n) _____.

4. A(n) _____ can be written in the form $ax + b < c$ (or $>, \leq, \geq$).

5. The solution(s) to the equation $x + 5 = x + 5$ is/are _____.

6. The solution(s) to the equation $x + 5 = x + 4$ is/are _____.

7. If both sides of an inequality are multiplied or divided by the same positive number, the direction of the inequality symbol is _____.

8. If both sides of an inequality are multiplied by the same negative number, the direction of the inequality symbol is _____.

9. Two numbers whose sum is 0 are called _____.

10. Two numbers whose product is 1 are called _____.

Helpful Hint ▶ Are you preparing for your test? Don't forget to take the Chapter 9 Test on page 718. Then check your answers at the back of the text and use the Chapter Test Prep Videos to see the fully worked-out solutions to any of the exercises you want to review.

Chapter Highlights

Definitions and Concepts	Examples
Section 9.1 Symbols and Sets of Numbers	

A **set** is a collection of objects, called **elements,** enclosed in braces.

A line used to picture numbers is called a **number line.**

$\{a, c, e\}$

$$\overset{\longleftrightarrow}{\underset{-5\ -4\ -3\ -2\ -1\ \ 0\ \ 1\ \ 2\ \ 3\ \ 4\ \ 5}{\mid\mid\mid\mid\mid\mid\mid\mid\mid\mid\mid}}$$

Natural numbers: $\{1, 2, 3, 4, \ldots\}$

Whole numbers: $\{0, 1, 2, 3, 4, \ldots\}$

Integers: $\{\ldots, -3, -2, -1, 0, 1, 2, 3, \ldots\}$

Rational numbers: {real numbers that can be expressed as quotients of integers}

Irrational numbers: {real numbers that cannot be expressed as quotients of integers}

Real numbers: {all numbers that correspond to points on a number line}

Given the set $\left\{-3.4, \sqrt{3}, 0, \dfrac{2}{3}, 5, -4\right\}$, list the numbers that belong to the set of

Natural numbers   5
Whole numbers   0, 5
Integers   −4, 0, 5
Rational numbers $-4, -3.4, 0, \dfrac{2}{3}, 5$
Irrational numbers $\sqrt{3}$
Real numbers   all numbers in the given set

Symbols:

$=$ is equal to
$\neq$ is not equal to
$>$ is greater than
$<$ is less than
$\leq$ is less than or equal to
$\geq$ is greater than or equal to

$-7 = -7$

$3 \neq -3$

$4 > 1$

$1 < 4$

$6 \leq 6$

$18 \geq -\dfrac{1}{3}$

| **Section 9.2   Properties of Real Numbers** | |

Commutative Properties

Addition: $a + b = b + a$
Multiplication: $a \cdot b = b \cdot a$

$3 + (-7) = -7 + 3$
$-8 \cdot 5 = 5 \cdot (-8)$

Associative Properties

Addition: $(a + b) + c = a + (b + c)$
Multiplication: $(a \cdot b) \cdot c = a \cdot (b \cdot c)$

$(5 + 10) + 20 = 5 + (10 + 20)$
$(-3 \cdot 2) \cdot 11 = -3 \cdot (2 \cdot 11)$

(continued)

Definitions and Concepts	Examples

Section 9.2   Properties of Real Numbers   (*continued*)

Two numbers whose product is 1 are called **multiplicative inverses** or **reciprocals.** The reciprocal of a nonzero number a is $\frac{1}{a}$ because $a \cdot \frac{1}{a} = 1$.

The reciprocal of 3 is $\frac{1}{3}$.

The reciprocal of $-\frac{2}{5}$ is $-\frac{5}{2}$.

Distributive Property

$$a(b + c) = a \cdot b + a \cdot c$$

$$5(6 + 10) = 5 \cdot 6 + 5 \cdot 10$$
$$-2(3 + x) = -2 \cdot 3 + (-2)(x)$$

Identities

$$a + 0 = a \quad 0 + a = a$$
$$a \cdot 1 = a \quad\quad 1 \cdot a = a$$

$$5 + 0 = 5 \quad\quad 0 + (-2) = -2$$
$$-14 \cdot 1 = -14 \quad\quad 1 \cdot 27 = 27$$

Inverses

Additive or opposite: $a + (-a) = 0$

$$7 + (-7) = 0$$

Multiplicative or reciprocal: $b \cdot \dfrac{1}{b} = 1, \quad b \neq 0$

$$3 \cdot \frac{1}{3} = 1$$

Section 9.3   Further Solving Linear Equations

To Solve Linear Equations

1. Clear the equation of fractions.

Solve: $\dfrac{5(-2x + 9)}{6} + 3 = \dfrac{1}{2}$

1. $6 \cdot \dfrac{5(-2x + 9)}{6} + 6 \cdot 3 = 6 \cdot \dfrac{1}{2}$

2. Remove any grouping symbols such as parentheses.

2. $5(-2x + 9) + 18 = 3$ Apply the distributive property.
$$-10x + 45 + 18 = 3$$

3. Simplify each side by combining like terms.

3. $\quad\quad -10x + 63 = 3$ Combine like terms.

4. Get all variable terms on one side and all numbers on the other side by using the addition property of equality.

4. $-10x + 63 - 63 = 3 - 63$ Subtract 63.
$$-10x = -60$$

5. Get the variable alone by using the multiplication property of equality.

5. $\quad \dfrac{-10x}{-10} = \dfrac{-60}{-10}$ Divide by -10.

6. Check the solution by substituting it into the original equation.

$$x = 6$$

Section 9.4   Further Problem Solving

Problem-Solving Steps

The height of the Hudson volcano in Chile is twice the height of the Kiska volcano in the Aleutian Islands. If the sum of their heights is 12,870 feet, find the height of each.

1. UNDERSTAND the problem.

1. Read and reread the problem. Guess a solution and check your guess.

Let x be the height of the Kiska volcano. Then $2x$ is the height of the Hudson volcano.

x $2x$

(continued)

Definitions and Concepts	Examples

Section 9.4   Further Problem Solving   (*continued*)

2. TRANSLATE the problem.

2.

height of Kiska	added to	height of Hudson	is	12,870
↓	↓	↓	↓	↓
x	$+$	$2x$	$=$	12,870

3. SOLVE the equation.

3. $x + 2x = 12{,}870$

$3x = 12{,}870$

$x = 4290$

4. INTERPRET the results.

4. *Check:* If x is 4290, then $2x$ is 2(4290) or 8580. Their sum is $4290 + 8580$ or 12,870, the required amount.

State: The Kiska volcano is 4290 feet tall, and the Hudson volcano is 8580 feet tall.

Section 9.5   Formulas and Problem Solving

An equation that describes a known relationship among quantities is called a **formula.**

To solve a formula for a specified variable, use the same steps as for solving a linear equation. Treat the specified variable as the only variable of the equation.

$A = lw$ (area of a rectangle)

$I = PRT$ (simple interest)

Solve: $P = 2l + 2w$ for l

$P = 2l + 2w$

$P - 2w = 2l + 2w - 2w$ Subtract $2w$.

$P - 2w = 2l$

$\dfrac{P - 2w}{2} = \dfrac{2l}{2}$ Divide by 2.

$\dfrac{P - 2w}{2} = l$

Section 9.6   Linear Inequalities and Problem Solving

Properties of inequalities are similar to properties of equations. However, if you multiply or divide both sides of an inequality by the same *negative* number, you must reverse the direction of the inequality symbol.

$-2x \le 4$

$\dfrac{-2x}{-2} \ge \dfrac{4}{-2}$ Divide by -2; reverse the inequality symbol.

$x \ge -2$

To Solve Linear Inequalities

1. Clear the inequality of fractions.
2. Remove grouping symbols.
3. Simplify each side by combining like terms.
4. Write all variable terms on one side and all numbers on the other side using the addition property of inequality.
5. Get the variable alone by using the multiplication property of inequality.

Solve: $3(x + 2) \le -2 + 8$

1. $3(x + 2) \le -2 + 8$ No fractions to clear.

2. $3x + 6 \le -2 + 8$ Apply the distributive property.

3. $3x + 6 \le 6$ Combine like terms.

4. $3x + 6 - 6 \le 6 - 6$ Subtract 6.

$3x \le 0$

5. $\dfrac{3x}{3} \le \dfrac{0}{3}$ Divide by 3.

$x \le 0$

The solution set is $\{x \mid x \le 0\}$.

Chapter 9   Review

(9.1) *Insert* <, >, *or* = *in the appropriate space to make each statement true. (See Section 2.1 for a review of absolute value.)*

1. 8   10

2. 7   2

3. −4   −5

4. $\dfrac{12}{2}$ −8

5. $|-7|$ $|-8|$

6. $|-9|$ −9

7. $-|-1|$ −1

8. $|-14|$ $-(-14)$

9. 1.2   1.02

10. $-\dfrac{3}{2}$ $-\dfrac{3}{4}$

Translating *Translate each statement into symbols.*

11. Four is greater than or equal to negative three.

12. Six is not equal to five.

13. 0.03 is less than 0.3.

14. For fiscal year 2012–2013, Massachusetts had a \$10.9 million tourism budget, and Louisiana had a \$13.2 million tourism budget. Write an inequality statement comparing the numbers 10.9 million and 13.2 million. (*Source:* U.S. Travel Association)

Given the sets of numbers below, list the numbers in each set that also belong to the set of:

a. Natural numbers
c. Integers
e. Irrational numbers

b. Whole numbers
d. Rational numbers
f. Real numbers

15. $\left\{ -6, 0, 1, 1\dfrac{1}{2}, 3, \pi, 9.62 \right\}$

16. $\left\{ -3, -1.6, 2, 5, \dfrac{11}{2}, 15.1, \sqrt{5}, 2\pi \right\}$

The following chart shows the gains and losses in dollars of Density Oil and Gas stock for a particular week. Use this chart to answer Exercises 17 and 18.

Day	Gain or Loss (in dollars)
Monday	+1
Tuesday	−2
Wednesday	+5
Thursday	+1
Friday	−4

17. Which day showed the greatest loss?

18. Which day showed the greatest gain?

(9.2) *Name the property illustrated in each equation.*

19. $-6 + 5 = 5 + (-6)$

20. $6 \cdot 1 = 6$

21. $3(8 - 5) = 3 \cdot 8 + 3 \cdot (-5)$

22. $4 + (-4) = 0$

23. $2 + (3 + 9) = (2 + 3) + 9$

24. $2 \cdot 8 = 8 \cdot 2$

25. $6(8 + 5) = 6 \cdot 8 + 6 \cdot 5$

26. $(3 \cdot 8) \cdot 4 = 3 \cdot (8 \cdot 4)$

27. $4 \cdot \dfrac{1}{4} = 1$

28. $8 + 0 = 8$

(9.3) *Solve each equation.*

29. $\dfrac{5}{3}x + 4 = \dfrac{2}{3}x$

30. $\dfrac{7}{8}x + 1 = \dfrac{5}{8}x$

31. $-(5x + 1) = -7x + 3$

32. $-4(2x + 1) = -5x + 5$

33. $-6(2x - 5) = -3(9 + 4x)$

34. $3(8y - 1) = 6(5 + 4y)$

35. $\dfrac{3(2 - z)}{5} = z$

36. $\dfrac{4(n + 2)}{5} = -n$

37. $0.5(2n - 3) - 0.1 = 0.4(6 + 2n)$

38. $1.72y - 0.04y = 0.42$

39. $\dfrac{5(c + 1)}{6} = 2c - 3$

40. $-9 - 5a = 3(6a - 1)$

(9.4) *Solve each of the following.*

41. The height of the Washington Monument is 50.5 inches more than 10 times the length of a side of its square base. If the sum of these two dimensions is 7327 inches, find the height of the Washington Monument. (*Source:* National Park Service)

42. A 12-foot board is to be divided into two pieces so that one piece is twice as long as the other. If x represents the length of the shorter piece, find the length of each piece.

43. The National Park System in the United States includes a variety of park unit types. In 2013, there were a total of 40 national battlefields and national memorials. The number of national memorials is four less than three times the number of national battlefields. How many of each park unit were there? (*Source:* National Park System)

44. Find three consecutive integers whose sum is -114.

45. The quotient of a number and 3 is the same as the difference of the number and 2. Find the number.

46. Double the sum of a number and 6 is the opposite of the number. Find the number.

(9.5) *Substitute the given values into the given formulas and solve for the unknown variable.*

47. $P = 2l + 2w$; $P = 46, l = 14$

48. $V = lwh$; $V = 192, l = 8, w = 6$

Solve each equation for the indicated variable.

49. $y = mx + b$ for m

50. $r = vst - 5$ for s

51. $2y - 5x = 7$ for x

52. $3x - 6y = -2$ for y

△ **53.** $C = \pi d$ for d

△ **54.** $C = 2\pi r$ for r

△ **55.** A swimming pool holds 900 cubic meters of water. If its length is 20 meters and its height is 3 meters, find its width.

56. The perimeter of a rectangular billboard is 60 feet and has a length 6 feet longer than its width. Find the dimensions of the billboard.

57. A charity 10K race is given annually to benefit a local hospice organization. How long would it take to run/walk a 10K race (10 kilometers or 10,000 meters) if your average pace is 125 **meters** per minute? Give your time in hours and minutes.

58. On September 14, 2013, the highest temperature recorded in the United States was 113°F, which occurred in Death Valley, California. Convert this temperature to degrees Celsius. (*Source:* National Weather Service)

(9.6) *Graph on the given number line.*

59. $x \le -2$

60. $0 < x \le 5$

Solve each inequality. Write each answer using set notation.

61. $x - 5 \le -4$

62. $x + 7 > 2$

63. $-2x \ge -20$

64. $-3x > 12$

65. $5x - 7 > 8x + 5$

66. $x + 4 \ge 6x - 16$

67. $\dfrac{2}{3}y > 6$

68. $-0.5y \leq 7.5$ **69.** $-2(x - 5) > 2(3x - 2)$ **70.** $4(2x - 5) \leq 5x - 1$

71. A part-time salesperson earns \$175 per week plus a 5% commission on all her sales. Find the minimum amount of sales she must make to ensure that she earns at least \$300 per week.

72. An amateur golfer shot rounds of 76, 82, and 79 golfing. What must he shoot on his next round so that his average will be below 80?

Mixed Review

Solve each equation.

73. $6x + 2x - 1 = 5x + 11$ **74.** $2(3y - 4) = 6 + 7y$ **75.** $4(3 - a) - (6a + 9) = -12a$

76. $\dfrac{x}{3} - 2 = 5$ **77.** $2(y + 5) = 2y + 10$ **78.** $7x - 3x + 2 = 2(2x - 1)$

Solve.

79. The sum of six and twice a number is equal to seven less than the number. Find the number.

80. A 23-inch piece of string is to be cut into two pieces so that the length of the longer piece is three more than four times the length of the shorter piece. Find the lengths of both pieces.

Solve for the specified variable.

81. $V = \dfrac{1}{3}Ah$ for h

Solve each inequality. Graph the solution set. Write each answer using set notation.

82. $4x - 7 > 3x + 2$

83. $-5x < 20$

84. $-3(1 + 2x) + x \geq -(3 - x)$

Chapter 9   Test

Step-by-step test solutions are found on the Chapter Test Prep Videos. Where available: MyMathLab® or YouTube™

Answers

Translate each statement into symbols.

1. The absolute value of negative seven is greater than five.

2. The sum of nine and five is greater than or equal to four.

3. Given

$$\left\{-5, -1, \frac{1}{4}, 0, 1, 7, 11.6, \sqrt{7}, 3\pi\right\},$$ list the numbers in this set that also belong to the set of:

    a. Natural numbers   **b.** Whole numbers
    c. Integers   **d.** Rational numbers
    e. Irrational numbers   **f.** Real numbers

1. _____

2. _____

3. a. _____

  b. _____

  c. _____

  d. _____

  e. _____

  f. _____

Identify the property illustrated by each expression.

4. $8 + (9 + 3) = (8 + 9) + 3$

5. $6 \cdot 8 = 8 \cdot 6$

6. $-6(2 + 4) = -6 \cdot 2 + (-6) \cdot 4$

7. $\frac{1}{6}(6) = 1$

8. Find the opposite of -9.

9. Find the reciprocal of $-\frac{1}{3}$.

4. _____

5. _____

6. _____

7. _____

8. _____

9. _____

Use the distributive property to write each expression without parentheses. Then simplify if possible.

10. $7 + 2(5y - 3)$

11. $4(x - 2) - 3(2x - 6)$

10. _____

Solve each equation.

12. $4(n - 5) = -(4 - 2n)$

13. $-2(x - 3) = x + 5 - 3x$

11. _____

12. _____

14. $4z + 1 - z = 1 + z$

15. $\frac{2(x + 6)}{3} = x - 5$

13. _____

14. _____

15. _____

16. $\frac{1}{2} - x + \frac{3}{2} = x - 4$

17. $-0.3(x - 4) + x = 0.5(3 - x)$

16. _____

17. _____

18. $-4(a + 1) - 3a = -7(2a - 3)$

18. _____

Solve each application.

19. A number increased by two-thirds of the number is 35. Find the number.

△ **20.** A gallon of water seal covers 200 square feet. How many gallons are needed to paint two coats of water seal on a deck that measures 20 feet by 35 feet?

20 feet   35 feet

21. Find the value of x if $y = -14$, $m = -2$, and $b = -2$ in the formula $y = mx + b$.

Solve the equation for the indicated variable.

22. $V = \pi r^2 h$ for h

23. $3x - 4y = 10$ for y

Solve the inequality. Graph the solution set. Write each answer using set notation.

24. $3x - 5 > 7x + 3$

<<-5 -4 -3 -2 -1 0 1 2 3 4 5>>

Solve each inequality. Write each answer using set notation.

25. $-0.3x \geq 2.4$

26. $-5(x - 1) + 6 \leq -3(x + 4) + 1$

27. $\dfrac{2(5x + 1)}{3} > 2$

28. California has more public libraries than any other state. It has 387 more public libraries than Ohio. If the total number of public libraries for these states is 1827, find the number of public libraries in California and the number in Ohio. (*Source:* Institute of Museum and Library Services)

19. _____

20. _____

21. _____

22. _____

23. _____

24. _____

25. _____

26. _____

27. _____

28. _____

Answers

1. a. _____

   b. _____

   c. _____

2. a. _____

   b. _____

   c. _____

   d. _____

   e. _____

3. _____

4. _____

5. _____

6. _____

7. _____

8. _____

9. _____

10. _____

11. _____

12. _____

13. _____

14. _____

15. _____

16. _____

17. _____

18. _____

19. _____

20. _____

21. _____

22. _____

Simplify.

1. a. $-(-4)$ **b.** $-|-5|$ **c.** $-|6|$

2. Insert $<$, $>$, or $=$ in the appropriate space to make each statement true.

   a. $|0|$ 2 **b.** $|-5|$ 5
   c. $|-3|$ $|-2|$ **d.** $|5|$ $|6|$
   e. $|-7|$ $|6|$

3. Simplify: $-2[-3 + 2(-1 + 6)] - 5$

4. Simplify: $\dfrac{3 + |4 - 3| + 2^2}{6 - 4}$

Add.

5. $-18 + 10$ **6.** $(-8) + (-11)$ **7.** $12 + (-8)$

8. $(-2) + 10$ **9.** $(-3) + 4 + (-11)$ **10.** $0.2 + (-0.5)$

Perform the indicated operation.

11. $\dfrac{2}{3} - \dfrac{10}{11}$ **12.** $\dfrac{2}{5} - \dfrac{39}{40}$ **13.** $2 - \dfrac{x}{3}$ **14.** $5 + \dfrac{x}{2}$

Evaluate. Let $x = -\dfrac{1}{2}$ and $y = \dfrac{1}{3}$.

15. $2x + y^2$ **16.** $2y + x^2$

Perform the indicated operation.

17. $-4\dfrac{2}{5} \cdot 1\dfrac{3}{11}$ **18.** $-2\dfrac{1}{2} \cdot \left(-2\dfrac{1}{2}\right)$ **19.** $-2\dfrac{1}{3} \div \left(-2\dfrac{1}{2}\right)$

20. $3\dfrac{3}{5} \div \left(-3\dfrac{1}{3}\right)$ **21.** $(-1.3)^2 + 2.4$ **22.** $1.2(7.3 - 9.3)$

23. $\sqrt{49}$ **24.** $\sqrt{64}$ **25.** $\sqrt{\dfrac{4}{25}}$ **26.** $\sqrt{\dfrac{9}{100}}$

Solve.

27. $1.2x + 5.8 = 8.2$ **28.** $1.3x - 2.6 = -9.1$

Determine whether each statement is true or false.

29. $8 \geq 8$ **30.** $-4 \leq -4$ **31.** $8 \leq 8$ **32.** $-4 \geq -4$

33. $23 \leq 0$ **34.** $-8 \leq 0$ **35.** $0 \leq 23$ **36.** $0 \leq -8$

Use the distributive property to write each expression without parentheses. Then simplify the result.

37. $-5(-3 + 2z)$ **38.** $-4(2x - 1)$ **39.** $\dfrac{1}{2}(6x + 14) + 10$ **40.** $9 + 2(5x + 6)$

Solve.

41. $\dfrac{2(a + 3)}{3} = 6a + 2$ **42.** $\dfrac{x}{2} + \dfrac{x}{5} = 3$

43. As of July 2013, the total number of Democrats and Republicans in the U.S. House of Representatives was 440. There were 28 more Republican representatives than Democratic. Find the number of representatives from each party.

44. Three times the sum of a number and 2 is the same as 9 times the number. Find the number.

45. A glacier is a giant mass of rocks and ice that flows downhill like a river. Portage Glacier in Alaska is about 6 miles, or 31,680 feet, long and moves 400 feet per year. Icebergs are created when the front end of the glacier flows into Portage Lake. How long does it take for ice at the head (beginning) of the glacier to reach the lake?

46. Solve $V = lwh$ for w.

47. Graph $-1 > x$.

48. Solve: $-3x < -30$

49. Solve: $2(x - 3) - 5 \leq 3(x + 2) - 18$

50. Solve: $10 + x < 6x - 10$

23. _____
24. _____
25. _____
26. _____
27. _____
28. _____
29. _____
30. _____
31. _____
32. _____
33. _____
34. _____
35. _____
36. _____
37. _____
38. _____
39. _____
40. _____
41. _____
42. _____
43. _____
44. _____
45. _____
46. _____
47. _____
48. _____
49. _____
50. _____

13 Graphing Equations and Inequalities

Check Your Progress

Vocabulary Check

Chapter Highlights

Chapter Review

Chapter Test

Cumulative Review

In Chapter 9 we learned to solve and graph the solutions of linear equations and inequalities in one variable on number lines. Now we define and present techniques for solving and graphing linear equations and inequalities in two variables on grids. Two-variable equations lead directly to the concept of *function*, perhaps the most important concept in all of mathematics. Functions are introduced in Section 13.6.

ourism 2020 Vision was the World Tourism Organization's long-term forecast and study of the growth and economic impact of world tourism through the year 2020. As the current year approaches 2020, the new World Tourism Organization's long-term study and forecast is entitled *Tourism Towards 2030*. The broken line graph below shows some actual trends and forecasts from 2000 to 2030. In Section 13.1, Exercises 45–50, we read a bar graph showing the top tourist destinations by country.

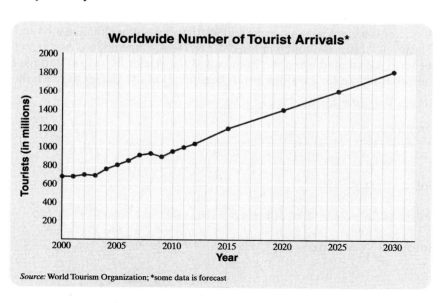

Source: World Tourism Organization; *some data is forecast

In Sections 7.1 and 7.2, we learned how to read graphs. The broken line graph below shows the relationship between the time before and after smoking a cigarette and pulse rate. The horizontal line or axis shows time in minutes and the vertical line or axis shows the pulse rate in heartbeats per minute. Notice that there are two numbers associated with each point of the graph. For example, the graph shows that 15 minutes after "lighting up," the pulse rate is 80 beats per minute. If we agree to write the time first and the pulse rate second, we can say there is a point on the graph corresponding to the **ordered pair** of numbers (15, 80). A few more ordered pairs are shown alongside their corresponding points.

Objectives

A Plot Ordered Pairs of Numbers on the Rectangular Coordinate System.

B Graph Paired Data to Create a Scatter Diagram.

C Find the Missing Coordinate of an Ordered Pair Solution, Given One Coordinate of the Pair.

Objective A Plotting Ordered Pairs of Numbers

In general, we use the idea of ordered pairs to describe the location of a point in a plane (such as a piece of paper). We start with a horizontal and a vertical axis. Each axis is a number line, and for the sake of consistency we construct our axes to intersect at the 0 coordinate of both. This point of intersection is called the **origin.** Notice that these two number lines or axes divide the plane into four regions called **quadrants.** The quadrants are usually numbered with Roman numerals as shown. The axes are not considered to be in any quadrant.

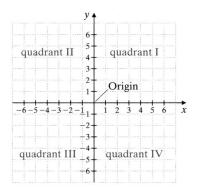

It is helpful to label axes, so we label the horizontal axis the ***x*-axis** and the vertical axis the ***y*-axis.** We call the system described above the **rectangular coordinate system,** or the **coordinate plane.** Just as with other graphs shown, we can then describe the locations of points by ordered pairs of numbers. We list the horizontal, ***x*-axis** measurement first and the vertical, ***y*-axis** measurement second.

Practice 1

On a single coordinate system, plot each ordered pair. State in which quadrant, or on which axis, each point lies.

a. $(4, 2)$ **b.** $(-1, -3)$

c. $(2, -2)$ **d.** $(-5, 1)$

e. $(0, 3)$ **f.** $(3, 0)$

g. $(0, -4)$ **h.** $\left(-2\frac{1}{2}, 0\right)$

i. $\left(1, -3\frac{3}{4}\right)$

Answers
1.

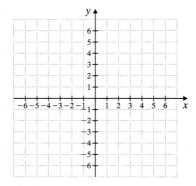

a. Point $(4, 2)$ lies in quadrant I.

b. Point $(-1, -3)$ lies in quadrant III.

c. Point $(2, -2)$ lies in quadrant IV.

d. Point $(-5, 1)$ lies in quadrant II.

e–h. Points $(3, 0)$ and $\left(-2\frac{1}{2}, 0\right)$ lie on the x-axis. Points $(0, 3)$ and $(0, -4)$ lie on the y-axis.

i. Point $\left(1, -3\frac{3}{4}\right)$ lies in quadrant IV.

✔Concept Check Answer

The graph of point $(-5, 1)$ lies in quadrant II and the graph of point $(1, -5)$ lies in quadrant IV. They are *not* in the same location.

To plot or graph the point corresponding to the ordered pair (a, b) we start at the origin. We then move a units left or right (right if a is positive, left if a is negative). From there, we move b units up or down (up if b is positive, down if b is negative). For example, to plot the point corresponding to the ordered pair $(3, 2)$, we start at the origin, move 3 units right, and from there move 2 units up. (See the figure below.) The x-value, 3, is also called the **x-coordinate** and the y-value, 2, is also called the **y-coordinate**. From now on, we will call the point with coordinates $(3, 2)$ simply the point $(3, 2)$. The point $(-2, 5)$ is also graphed below.

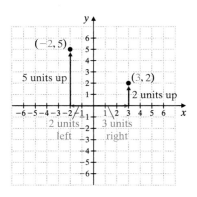

Helpful Hint

Don't forget that **each ordered pair corresponds to exactly one point in the plane and that each point in the plane corresponds to exactly one ordered pair.**

✔Concept Check Is the graph of the point $(-5, 1)$ in the same location as the graph of the point $(1, -5)$? Explain.

Example 1 On a single coordinate system, plot each ordered pair. State in which quadrant, or on which axis, each point lies.

a. $(5, 3)$ **b.** $(-2, -4)$ **c.** $(1, -2)$ **d.** $(-5, 3)$ **e.** $(0, 0)$

f. $(0, 2)$ **g.** $(-5, 0)$ **h.** $\left(0, -5\frac{1}{2}\right)$ **i.** $\left(4\frac{2}{3}, -3\right)$

Solution:

a. Point $(5, 3)$ lies in quadrant I.

b. Point $(-2, -4)$ lies in quadrant III.

c. Point $(1, -2)$ lies in quadrant IV.

d. Point $(-5, 3)$ lies in quadrant II.

e–h. Points $(0, 0)$, $(0, 2)$, and $\left(0, -5\frac{1}{2}\right)$ lie on the y-axis. Points $(0, 0)$ and $(-5, 0)$ lie on the x-axis.

i. Point $\left(4\frac{2}{3}, -3\right)$ lies in quadrant IV.

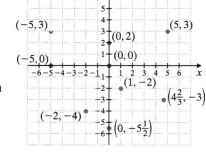

■ Work Practice 1

Helpful Hint

In Example 1, notice that the point $(0, 0)$ lies on both the x-axis and the y-axis. It is the only point in the entire rectangular coordinate system that has this feature. Why? It is the only point of intersection of the x-axis and the y-axis.

✓**Concept Check** For each description of a point in the rectangular coordinate system, write an ordered pair that represents it.

a. Point A is located three units to the left of the y-axis and five units above the x-axis.

b. Point B is located six units below the origin.

From Example 1, notice that the y-coordinate of any point on the x-axis is 0. For example, the point $(-5, 0)$ lies on the x-axis. Also, the x-coordinate of any point on the y-axis is 0. For example, the point $(0, 2)$ lies on the y-axis.

Objective B Creating Scatter Diagrams

Data that can be represented as ordered pairs are called **paired data.** Many types of data collected from the real world are paired data. For instance, the annual measurements of a child's height can be written as ordered pairs of the form (year, height in inches) and are paired data. The graph of paired data as points in the rectangular coordinate system is called a **scatter diagram.** Scatter diagrams can be used to look for patterns and trends in paired data.

Example 2 The table gives the annual net sales for PetSmart for the years shown. (*Source:* PetSmart)

Year	PetSmart Net Sales (in billions of dollars)
2007	4.7
2008	5.1
2009	5.3
2010	5.7
2011	6.1
2012	6.8

a. Write this paired data as a set of ordered pairs of the form (year, net sales in billions of dollars).

b. Create a scatter diagram of the paired data.

c. What trend in the paired data does the scatter diagram show?

Solution:

a. The ordered pairs are (2007, 4.7), (2008, 5.1), (2009, 5.3), (2010, 5.7), (2011, 6.1), and (2012, 6.8).

b. We begin by plotting the ordered pairs. Because the x-coordinate in each ordered pair is a year, we label the x-axis "Year" and mark the horizontal axis with the years given. Then we label the y-axis or vertical axis "Net Sales (in billions of dollars)." In this case, it is convenient to mark the vertical axis in increments of 1, starting with 0.

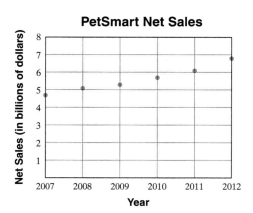

PetSmart Net Sales

c. The scatter diagram shows that PetSmart net sales steadily increased over the years 2007–2012.

🔲 Work Practice 2

The table gives the number of tornadoes that occurred in the United States for the years shown. (*Source:* Storm Prediction Center, National Weather Service)

Year	Tornadoes
2007	1096
2008	1692
2009	1156
2010	1282
2011	1693
2012	939

a. Write this paired data as a set of ordered pairs of the form (year, number of tornadoes).

b. Create a scatter diagram of the paired data.

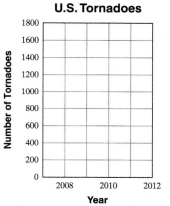

U.S. Tornadoes

c. What trend in the paired data, if any, does the scatter diagram show?

Answers

2. **a.** (2007, 1096), (2008, 1692), (2009, 1156), (2010, 1282), (2011, 1693), (2012, 939)

b.

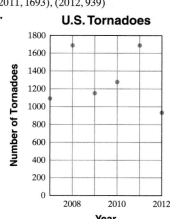

U.S. Tornadoes

c. The number of tornadoes varies greatly from year to year.

✓**Concept Check Answers**

a. $(-3, 5)$ **b.** $(0, -6)$

Objective C Completing Ordered Pair Solutions

Let's see how we can use ordered pairs to record solutions of equations containing two variables. An equation in one variable such as $x + 1 = 5$ has one solution, 4: The number 4 is the value of the variable x that makes the equation true.

An equation in two variables, such as $2x + y = 8$, has solutions consisting of two values, one for x and one for y. For example, $x = 3$ and $y = 2$ is a solution of $2x + y = 8$ because, if x is replaced with 3 and y with 2, we get a true statement.

$$2x + y = 8$$
$$2(3) + 2 \stackrel{?}{=} 8 \quad \text{Replace } x \text{ with 3 and } y \text{ with 2.}$$
$$8 = 8 \quad \text{True}$$

The solution $x = 3$ and $y = 2$ can be written as $(3, 2)$, an ordered pair of numbers.

> In general, an ordered pair is a **solution** of an equation in two variables if replacing the variables by the values of the ordered pair results in a *true statement*.

For example, another ordered pair solution of $2x + y = 8$ is $(5, -2)$. Replacing x with 5 and y with -2 results in a true statement.

$$2x + y = 8$$
$$2(5) + (-2) \stackrel{?}{=} 8 \quad \text{Replace } x \text{ with 5 and } y \text{ with } -2.$$
$$10 - 2 \stackrel{?}{=} 8$$
$$8 = 8 \quad \text{True}$$

Practice 3

Complete each ordered pair so that it is a solution to the equation $x + 2y = 8$.

a. $(0,)$
b. $(, 3)$
c. $(-4,)$

Example 3 Complete each ordered pair so that it is a solution to the equation $3x + y = 12$.

a. $(0,)$ **b.** $(, 6)$ **c.** $(-1,)$

Solution:

a. In the ordered pair $(0,)$, the x-value is 0. We let $x = 0$ in the equation and solve for y.

$$3x + y = 12$$
$$3(0) + y = 12 \quad \text{Replace } x \text{ with 0.}$$
$$0 + y = 12$$
$$y = 12$$

The completed ordered pair is $(0, 12)$.

b. In the ordered pair $(, 6)$, the y-value is 6. We let $y = 6$ in the equation and solve for x.

$$3x + y = 12$$
$$3x + 6 = 12 \quad \text{Replace } y \text{ with 6.}$$
$$3x = 6 \quad \text{Subtract 6 from both sides.}$$
$$x = 2 \quad \text{Divide both sides by 3.}$$

The ordered pair is $(2, 6)$.

c. In the ordered pair $(-1,)$, the x-value is -1. We let $x = -1$ in the equation and solve for y.

$$3x + y = 12$$
$$3(-1) + y = 12 \quad \text{Replace } x \text{ with } -1.$$
$$-3 + y = 12$$
$$y = 15 \quad \text{Add 3 to both sides.}$$

The ordered pair is $(-1, 15)$.

Answers

3. a. $(0, 4)$ **b.** $(2, 3)$ **c.** $(-4, 6)$

■ Work Practice 3

Solutions of equations in two variables can also be recorded in a **table of paired values,** as shown in the next example.

Example 4 Complete the table for the equation $y = 3x$.

	x	y
a.	-1	
b.		0
c.		-9

Solution:

a. We replace x with -1 in the equation and solve for y.

$$y = 3x$$
$$y = 3(-1) \quad \text{Let } x = -1.$$
$$y = -3$$

The ordered pair is $(-1, -3)$.

b. We replace y with 0 in the equation and solve for x.

$$y = 3x$$
$$0 = 3x \quad \text{Let } y = 0.$$
$$0 = x \quad \text{Divide both sides by 3.}$$

The ordered pair is $(0, 0)$.

c. We replace y with -9 in the equation and solve for x.

$$y = 3x$$
$$-9 = 3x \quad \text{Let } y = -9.$$
$$-3 = x \quad \text{Divide both sides by 3.}$$

The ordered pair is $(-3, -9)$. The completed table is shown to the right.

x	y
-1	-3
0	0
-3	-9

■ Work Practice 4

Practice 4

Complete the table for the equation $y = -2x$.

	x	y
a.	-3	
b.		0
c.		10

Example 5 Complete the table for the equation

$$y = \frac{1}{2}x - 5.$$

	x	y
a.	-2	
b.	0	
c.		0

Solution:

a. Let $x = -2$.

$$y = \frac{1}{2}x - 5$$
$$y = \frac{1}{2}(-2) - 5$$
$$y = -1 - 5$$
$$y = -6$$

b. Let $x = 0$.

$$y = \frac{1}{2}x - 5$$
$$y = \frac{1}{2}(0) - 5$$
$$y = 0 - 5$$
$$y = -5$$

c. Let $y = 0$.

$$y = \frac{1}{2}x - 5$$
$$0 = \frac{1}{2}x - 5 \quad \text{Now, solve for } x.$$
$$5 = \frac{1}{2}x \quad \text{Add 5.}$$
$$10 = x \quad \text{Multiply by 2.}$$

Ordered pairs: $(-2, -6)$ $(0, -5)$ $(10, 0)$

The completed table is

x	-2	0	10
y	-6	-5	0

■ Work Practice 5

Practice 5

Complete the table for the equation $y = \frac{1}{3}x - 1$.

	x	y
a.	-3	
b.	0	
c.		0

Answers

4.

	x	y
a.	-3	6
b.	0	0
c.	-5	10

5.

	x	y
a.	-3	-2
b.	0	-1
c.	3	0

By now, you have noticed that equations in two variables often have more than one solution. We discuss this more in the next section.

A table showing ordered pair solutions may be written vertically or horizontally, as shown in the next example.

Practice 6

A company purchased a fax machine for $400. The business manager of the company predicts that the fax machine will be used for 7 years and the value in dollars y of the machine in x years is $y = -50x + 400$. Complete the table.

x	1	2	3	4	5	6	7
y							

Example 6 A small business purchased a computer for $2000. The business predicts that the computer will be used for 5 years and the value in dollars y of the computer in x years is $y = -300x + 2000$. Complete the table.

x	0	1	2	3	4	5
y						

Solution:

To find the value of y when x is 0, we replace x with 0 in the equation. We use this same procedure to find y when x is 1 and when x is 2.

When $x = 0$,
$y = -300x + 2000$
$y = -300 \cdot 0 + 2000$
$y = 0 + 2000$
$y = 2000$

When $x = 1$,
$y = -300x + 2000$
$y = -300 \cdot 1 + 2000$
$y = -300 + 2000$
$y = 1700$

When $x = 2$,
$y = -300x + 2000$
$y = -300 \cdot 2 + 2000$
$y = -600 + 2000$
$y = 1400$

We have the ordered pairs $(0, 2000)$, $(1, 1700)$, and $(2, 1400)$. This means that in 0 years the value of the computer is $2000, in 1 year the value of the computer is $1700, and in 2 years the value is $1400. To complete the table of values, we continue the procedure for $x = 3$, $x = 4$, and $x = 5$.

When $x = 3$,
$y = -300x + 2000$
$y = -300 \cdot 3 + 2000$
$y = -900 + 2000$
$y = 1100$

When $x = 4$,
$y = -300x + 2000$
$y = -300 \cdot 4 + 2000$
$y = -1200 + 2000$
$y = 800$

When $x = 5$,
$y = -300x + 2000$
$y = -300 \cdot 5 + 2000$
$y = -1500 + 2000$
$y = 500$

The completed table is shown below.

x	0	1	2	3	4	5
y	2000	1700	1400	1100	800	500

■ Work Practice 6

The ordered pair solutions recorded in the completed table for Example 6 are another set of paired data. They are graphed next. Notice that this scatter diagram gives a visual picture of the decrease in value of the computer.

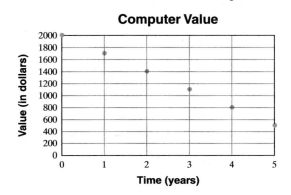

Answer

6.

x	1	2	3	4	5	6	7
y	350	300	250	200	150	100	50

Vocabulary, Readiness & Video Check

Use the choices below to fill in each blank. The exercises below all have to do with the rectangular coordinate system.

origin   *x*-coordinate   *x*-axis   scatter diagram   four

quadrants   *y*-coordinate   *y*-axis   solution   one

1. The horizontal axis is called the _____.

2. The vertical axis is called the _____.

3. The intersection of the horizontal axis and the vertical axis is a point called the _____.

4. The axes divide the plane into regions, called _____. There are _____ of these regions.

5. In the ordered pair of numbers $(-2, 5)$, the number -2 is called the _____ and the number 5 is called the _____.

6. Each ordered pair of numbers corresponds to _____ point in the plane.

7. An ordered pair is a(n) _____ of an equation in two variables if replacing the variables by the coordinates of the ordered pair results in a true statement.

8. The graph of paired data as points in a rectangular coordinate system is called a(n) _____.

Martin-Gay Interactive Videos   *Watch the section lecture video and answer the following questions.*

See Video 13.1

Objective A **9.** Several points are plotted in ▦ Examples 1–6. Where do we always start when plotting a point? How does the first coordinate tell us to move? How does the second coordinate tell us to move?

Objective B **10.** From ▦ Example 7, what kind of data can be graphed in a scatter diagram?

Objective C **11.** In ▦ Example 8, when finding the missing value in an ordered pair solution of a linear equation in two variables, how can we check our solution?

13.1 **Exercise Set** MyMathLab®

Objective A *Plot each ordered pair. State in which quadrant or on which axis each point lies. See Example 1.*

1. **a.** $(1, 5)$ **b.** $(-5, -2)$ **c.** $(-3, 0)$ **d.** $(0, -1)$
   e. $(2, -4)$ **f.** $\left(-1, 4\frac{1}{2}\right)$ **g.** $(3.7, 2.2)$ **h.** $\left(\frac{1}{2}, -3\right)$

2. **a.** $(2, 4)$ **b.** $(0, 2)$ **c.** $(-2, 1)$ **d.** $(-3, -3)$
   e. $\left(3\frac{3}{4}, 0\right)$ **f.** $(5, -4)$ **g.** $(-3.4, 4.8)$ **h.** $\left(\frac{1}{3}, -5\right)$

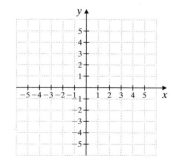

Find the x- and y-coordinates of each labeled point. See Example 1.

3. *A*

4. *B*

5. *C*

6. *D*

7. *E*

8. *F*

9. *G*

10. *A*

11. *B*

12. *C*

13. *D*

14. *E*

15. *F*

16. *G*

Objective B *Solve. See Example 2.*

17. The table shows the domestic box office (in billions of dollars) for the U.S. movie industry during the years shown. (*Source:* Motion Picture Association of America)

Year	Box Office (in billions of dollars)
2007	9.6
2008	9.6
2009	10.6
2010	10.6
2011	10.2
2012	10.8

a. Write this paired data as a set of ordered pairs of the form (year, box office).

b. In your own words, write the meaning of the ordered pair (2010, 10.6).

c. Create a scatter diagram of the paired data. Be sure to label the axes appropriately.

Domestic Box Office

d. What trend in the paired data does the scatter diagram show?

18. The table shows the amount of money (in billions of dollars) that Americans spent on their pets for the years shown. (*Source:* American Pet Products Association, Inc.)

Year	Pet-Related Expenditures (in billions of dollars)
2007	41
2008	43
2009	46
2010	48
2011	51
2012	53

a. Write this paired data as a set of ordered pairs of the form (year, pet-related expenditures).

b. In your own words, write the meaning of the ordered pair (2012, 53).

c. Create a scatter diagram of the paired data. Be sure to label the axes appropriately.

Pet-Related Expenditures

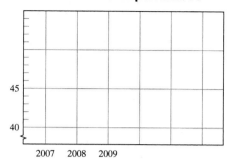

d. What trend in the paired data does the scatter diagram show?

19. Minh, a psychology student, kept a record of how much time she spent studying for each of her 20-point psychology quizzes and her score on each quiz.

Hours Spent Studying	0.50	0.75	1.00	1.25	1.50	1.50	1.75	2.00
Quiz Score	10	12	15	16	18	19	19	20

a. Write the data as ordered pairs of the form (hours spent studying, quiz score).

b. In your own words, write the meaning of the ordered pair (1.25, 16).

c. Create a scatter diagram of the paired data. Be sure to label the axes appropriately.

d. What might Minh conclude from the scatter diagram?

Minh's Chart for Psychology

20. A local lumberyard uses quantity pricing. The table shows the price per board for different amounts of lumber purchased.

Price per Board (in dollars)	Number of Boards Purchased
8.00	1
7.50	10
6.50	25
5.00	50
2.00	100

a. Write the data as ordered pairs of the form (price per board, number of boards purchased).

b. In your own words, write the meaning of the ordered pair (2.00, 100).

c. Create a scatter diagram of the paired data. Be sure to label the axes appropriately.

Lumberyard Board Pricing

d. What trend in the paired data does the scatter diagram show?

Objective C *Complete each ordered pair so that it is a solution to the given linear equation. See Example 3.*

21. $x - 4y = 4$; (, -2), (4,   )

22. $x - 5y = -1$; (, -2), (4,   )

23. $y = \dfrac{1}{4}x - 3$; (-8,   ), (, 1)

24. $y = \dfrac{1}{5}x - 2$; (-10,   ), (, 1)

Complete the table of ordered pairs for each linear equation. See Examples 4 and 5.

25. $y = -7x$

x	y
0	
-1	
	2

26. $y = -9x$

x	y
	0
-3	
	2

27. $x = -y + 2$

x	y
0	
	0
-3	5

28. $x = -y + 4$

x	y
	0
0	
	-3

29. $y = \dfrac{1}{2}x$

x	y
0	
-6	
	1

30. $y = \dfrac{1}{3}x$

x	y
0	
-6	
	1

31. $x + 3y = 6$

x	y
0	
	0
	1

32. $2x + y = 4$

x	y
0	
	0
	2

33. $y = 2x - 12$

x	y
0	
	-2
3	

34. $y = 5x + 10$

x	y
	0
	5
0	

35. $2x + 7y = 5$

x	y
0	
	0
	1

36. $x - 6y = 3$

x	y
0	
1	
	-1

Objectives A B C Mixed Practice *Complete the table of ordered pairs for each equation. Then plot the ordered pair solutions. See Examples 1 through 5.*

37. $x = -5y$

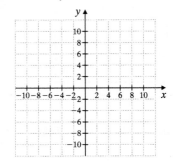

x	y
	0
	1
10	

38. $y = -3x$

x	y
0	
-2	
	9

39. $y = \dfrac{1}{3}x + 2$

x	y
0	
−3	
	0

40. $y = \dfrac{1}{2}x + 3$

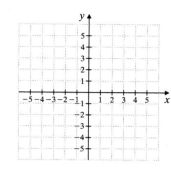

x	y
0	
−4	
	0

Solve. See Example 6.

41. The cost in dollars y of producing x computer desks is given by $y = 80x + 5000$.

  a. Complete the table.

x	100	200	300
y			

  b. Find the number of computer desks that can be produced for $8600. (*Hint:* Find x when $y = 8600$.)

42. The hourly wage y of an employee at a certain production company is given by $y = 0.25x + 9$, where x is the number of units produced by the employee in an hour.

  a. Complete the table.

x	0	1	5	10
y				

  b. Find the number of units that the employee must produce each hour to earn an hourly wage of $12.25. (*Hint:* Find x when $y = 12.25$.)

43. The average annual cinema admission price y (in dollars) from 2003 through 2012 is given by $y = 0.24x + 5.96$. In this equation, x represents the number of years after 2003. (*Source:* Motion Picture Association of America)

  a. Complete the table.

x	2	5	8
y			

  b. Find the year in which the average cinema admission price was approximately $7.40. (*Hint:* Find x when $y = 7.40$ and round to the nearest whole number.)

  c. Use the given equation to predict when the cinema admission price might be $9.00. (Use the hint for part **b.**)

44. The number of farms y in the United States from 2009 through 2012 is given by $y = -10{,}000x + 2{,}201{,}000$. In the equation, x represents the number of years after 2009. (*Source:* Based on data from the National Agricultural Statistics Service)

  a. Complete the table.

x	0	2	4
y			

  b. Find the year in which there were approximately 2,170,000 farms. (*Hint:* Find x when $y = 2{,}170{,}000$ and round to the nearest whole number.)

  c. Use the given equation to predict when the number of farms might be 2,100,000. (Use the hint for part **b.**)

Review

The following bar graph shows the top 10 tourist destinations and the number of tourists that visit each country per year. Use this graph to answer Exercises 45 through 50. See Section 7.1.

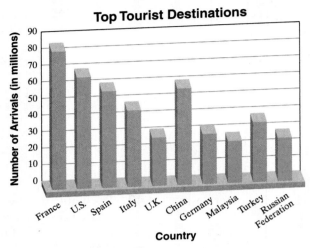

Top Tourist Destinations

Source: World Tourism Organization

45. Which country shown has the most tourist arrivals?

46. Which country shown has the least tourist arrivals?

47. Which countries shown have more than 50 million tourists per year?

48. Which countries shown have fewer than 30 million tourists per year?

49. Estimate the number of tourists per year whose destination is Germany.

50. Estimate the number of tourists per year whose destination is Malaysia.

Solve each equation for y. See Section 9.5.

51. $x + y = 5$

52. $x - y = 3$

53. $2x + 4y = 5$

54. $5x + 2y = 7$

55. $10x = -5y$

56. $4y = -8x$

Concept Extensions

Answer each exercise with true or false.

57. Point $(-1, 5)$ lies in quadrant IV.

58. Point $(3, 0)$ lies on the y-axis.

59. For the point $\left(-\dfrac{1}{2}, 1.5 \right)$, the first value, $-\dfrac{1}{2}$, is the x-coordinate and the second value, 1.5, is the y-coordinate.

60. The ordered pair $\left(2, \dfrac{2}{3} \right)$ is a solution of $2x - 3y = 6$.

For Exercises 61 through 65, fill in each blank with "0," "positive," or "negative." For Exercises 66 and 67, fill in each blank with "x" or "y."

	Point	Location
61.	(_____ , _____)	quadrant III
62.	(_____ , _____)	quadrant I
63.	(_____ , _____)	quadrant IV
64.	(_____ , _____)	quadrant II
65.	(_____ _____)	origin
66.	(number, 0)	___-axis
67.	(0, number)	___-axis

68. Give an example of an ordered pair whose location is in (or on)

    a. quadrant I   **b.** quadrant II   **c.** quadrant III

    d. quadrant IV   **e.** x-axis   **f.** y-axis

Solve. See the Concept Checks in this section.

69. Is the graph of $(3, 0)$ in the same location as the graph of $(0, 3)$? Explain why or why not.

70. Give the coordinates of a point such that if the coordinates are reversed, their location is the same.

71. In general, what points can have coordinates reversed and still have the same location?

72. In your own words, describe how to plot or graph an ordered pair of numbers.

73. Discuss any similarities in the graphs of the ordered pair solutions for Exercises **37–40**.

74. Discuss any differences in the graphs of the ordered pair solutions for Exercises **37–40**.

Write an ordered pair for each point described.

75. Point C is four units to the right of the y-axis and seven units below the x-axis.

76. Point D is three units to the left of the origin.

77. Find the perimeter of the rectangle whose vertices are the points with coordinates $(-1, 5)$, $(3, 5)$, $(3, -4)$, and $(-1, -4)$.

78. Find the area of the rectangle whose vertices are the points with coordinates $(5, 2)$, $(5, -6)$, $(0, -6)$, and $(0, 2)$.

The scatter diagram below shows the annual number of people enrolled as Gold Star Members at Costco Wholesale. The horizontal axis represents the number of years after 2008.

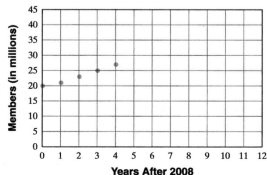

Costco's Annual Gold Star Membership

Source: Costco Wholesale Corporation

79. Estimate the annual Gold Star Membership for years 1, 2, 3, and 4.

80. Use a straightedge or ruler and this scatter diagram to predict Costco's Gold Star Membership in the year 2018.

13.2 Graphing Linear Equations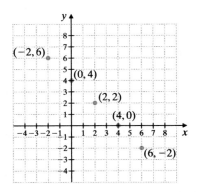

Objective

A Graph a Linear Equation by Finding and Plotting Ordered Pair Solutions.

In the previous section, we found that equations in two variables may have more than one solution. For example, both $(2, 2)$ and $(0, 4)$ are solutions of the equation $x + y = 4$. In fact, this equation has an infinite number of solutions. Other solutions include $(-2, 6)$, $(4, 0)$, and $(6, -2)$. Notice the pattern that appears in the graph of these solutions.

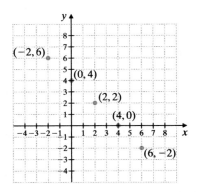

These solutions all appear to lie on the same line, as seen in the second graph. It can be shown that every ordered pair solution of the equation corresponds to a point on this line and that every point on this line corresponds to an ordered pair solution. Thus, we say that this line is the **graph of the equation** $x + y = 4$. Notice that we can show only a part of a line on a graph. The arrowheads on each end of the line below remind us that the line actually extends indefinitely in both directions.

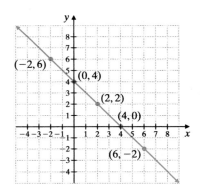

The equation $x + y = 4$ is called a *linear equation in two variables* and *the graph of every linear equation in two variables is a straight line.*

Linear Equation in Two Variables

A **linear equation in two variables** is an equation that can be written in the form

$$Ax + By = C$$

where A, B, and C are real numbers and A and B are not both 0. This form is called **standard form. The graph of a linear equation in two variables is a straight line.**

A linear equation in two variables may be written in many forms. Standard form, $Ax + By = C$, is just one of these many forms.

Following are examples of linear equations in two variables.

$$2x + y = 8 \qquad -2x = 7y \qquad y = \frac{1}{3}x + 2 \qquad y = 7$$

(Standard form)

Objective A Graphing Linear Equations

From geometry, we know that a straight line is determined by just two points. Thus, to graph a linear equation in two variables, we need to find just two of its infinitely many solutions. Once we do so, we plot the solution points and draw the line connecting the points. Usually, we find a third solution as well, as a check.

Example 1 Graph the linear equation $2x + y = 5$.

Solution: To graph this equation, we find three ordered pair solutions of $2x + y = 5$. To do this, we choose a value for one variable, x or y, and solve for the other variable. For example, if we let $x = 1$, then $2x + y = 5$ becomes

$$2x + y = 5$$
$$2(1) + y = 5 \qquad \text{Replace } x \text{ with 1.}$$
$$2 + y = 5 \qquad \text{Multiply.}$$
$$y = 3 \qquad \text{Subtract 2 from both sides.}$$

Since $y = 3$ when $x = 1$, the ordered pair $(1, 3)$ is a solution of $2x + y = 5$. Next, we let $x = 0$.

$$2x + y = 5$$
$$2(0) + y = 5 \qquad \text{Replace } x \text{ with 0.}$$
$$0 + y = 5$$
$$y = 5$$

The ordered pair $(0, 5)$ is a second solution.

The two solutions found so far allow us to draw the straight line that is the graph of all solutions of $2x + y = 5$. However, we will find a third ordered pair as a check. Let $y = -1$.

$$2x + y = 5$$
$$2x + (-1) = 5 \qquad \text{Replace } y \text{ with } -1.$$
$$2x - 1 = 5$$
$$2x = 6 \qquad \text{Add 1 to both sides.}$$
$$x = 3 \qquad \text{Divide both sides by 2.}$$

The third solution is $(3, -1)$. These three ordered pair solutions are listed in the table and plotted on the coordinate plane. The graph of $2x + y = 5$ is the line through the three points.

x	y
1	3
0	5
3	-1

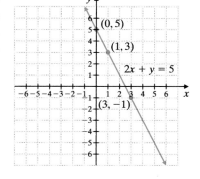

■ Work Practice 1

Practice 1

Graph the linear equation $x + 3y = 6$.

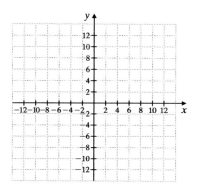

Helpful Hint All three points should fall on the same straight line. If not, check your ordered pair solutions for a mistake.

Answer

1.

Practice 2

Graph the linear equation
$-2x + 4y = 8$.

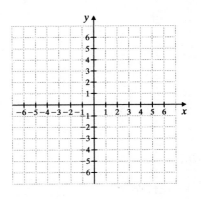

Practice 3

Graph the linear equation
$y = 2x$.

Answers

2.

3.

Example 2 Graph the linear equation $-5x + 3y = 15$.

Solution: We find three ordered pair solutions of $-5x + 3y = 15$.

Let $x = 0$.	Let $y = 0$.	Let $x = -2$.
$-5x + 3y = 15$	$-5x + 3y = 15$	$-5x + 3y = 15$
$-5 \cdot 0 + 3y = 15$	$-5x + 3 \cdot 0 = 15$	$-5 \cdot -2 + 3y = 15$
$0 + 3y = 15$	$-5x + 0 = 15$	$10 + 3y = 15$
$3y = 15$	$-5x = 15$	$3y = 5$
$y = 5$	$x = -3$	$y = \frac{5}{3}$ or $1\frac{2}{3}$

The ordered pairs are $(0, 5)$, $(-3, 0)$, and $\left(-2, 1\frac{2}{3}\right)$. The graph of $-5x + 3y = 15$ is the line through the three points.

x	y
0	5
-3	0
-2	$1\frac{2}{3}$

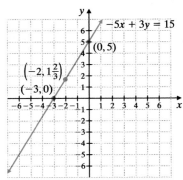

Work Practice 2

Example 3 Graph the linear equation $y = 3x$.

Solution: We find three ordered pair solutions. Since this equation is solved for y, we'll choose three x-values.

If $x = 2$, $y = 3 \cdot 2 = 6$.
If $x = 0$, $y = 3 \cdot 0 = 0$.
If $x = -1$, $y = 3 \cdot -1 = -3$.

Next, we plot the ordered pair solutions and draw a line through the plotted points. The line is the graph of $y = 3x$.

Think about the following for a moment: A line is made up of an infinite number of points. Every point on the line defined by $y = 3x$ represents an ordered pair solution of the equation, and every ordered pair solution is a point on this line.

x	y
2	6
0	0
-1	-3

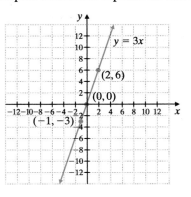

Work Practice 3

Helpful Hint

When graphing a linear equation in two variables, if it is
- solved for y, it may be easier to find ordered pair solutions by choosing x-values. If it is
- solved for x, it may be easier to find ordered pair solutions by choosing y-values.

Example 4 Graph the linear equation $y = -\frac{1}{3}x + 2$.

Solution: We find three ordered pair solutions, plot the solutions, and draw a line through the plotted solutions. To avoid fractions, we'll choose x-values that are multiples of 3 to substitute into the equation.

If $x = 6$, then $y = -\frac{1}{3} \cdot 6 + 2 = -2 + 2 = 0$.

If $x = 0$, then $y = -\frac{1}{3} \cdot 0 + 2 = 0 + 2 = 2$.

If $x = -3$, then $y = -\frac{1}{3} \cdot -3 + 2 = 1 + 2 = 3$.

x	y
6	0
0	2
-3	3

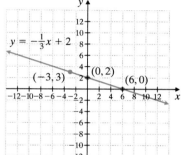

■ Work Practice 4

Let's take a moment and compare the graphs in Examples 3 and 4. The graph of $y = 3x$ tilts upward (as we follow the line from left to right) and the graph of $y = -\frac{1}{3}x + 2$ tilts downward (as we follow the line from left to right). We will learn more about the tilt, or slope, of a line in Section 13.4.

Example 5 Graph the linear equation $y = -2$.

Solution: The equation $y = -2$ can be written in standard form as $0x + y = -2$. No matter what value we replace x with, y is always -2.

x	y
0	-2
3	-2
-2	-2

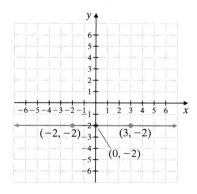

Notice that the graph of $y = -2$ is a horizontal line.

■ Work Practice 5

Linear equations are often used to model real data, as seen in the next example.

Practice 4

Graph the linear equation $y = -\frac{1}{2}x + 4$.

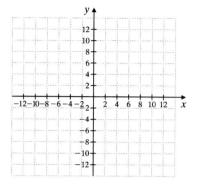

Practice 5

Graph the linear equation $x = 3$.

Answers

4.

5.

Practice 6

Use the graph in Example 6 to predict the number of registered nurses in 2022.

Helpful Hint   From Example 5, we learned that equations such as $y = -2$ are linear equations since $y = -2$ can be written as $0x + y = -2$.

Example 6   Estimating the Number of Registered Nurses

One of the occupations expected to have the most growth in the next few years is registered nurse. The number of people y (in thousands) employed as registered nurses in the United States can be estimated by the linear equation $y = 71.2x + 2734.4$, where x is the number of years after the year 2010. (*Source:* Based on data from the Bureau of Labor Statistics)

a. Graph the equation.
b. Use the graph to predict the number of registered nurses in the year 2021.

Solution:

a. To graph $y = 71.2x + 2734.4$, choose x-values and substitute into the equation.

If $x = 0$, then $y = 71.2(0) + 2734.4 = 2734.4$.
If $x = 2$, then $y = 71.2(2) + 2734.4 = 2876.8$.
If $x = 5$, then $y = 71.2(5) + 2734.4 = 3090.4$.

x	y
0	2734.4
2	2876.8
5	3090.4

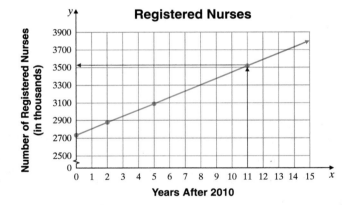

b. To use the graph to *predict* the number of registered nurses in the year 2021, we need to find the y-coordinate that corresponds to $x = 11$. (11 years after 2010 is the year 2021.) To do so, find 11 on the x-axis. Move vertically upward to the graphed line and then horizontally to the left. We approximate the number on the y-axis to be 3500. Thus, in the year 2021, we predict that there will be 3500 thousand registered nurses. (The actual value, using 11 for x, is 3517.6.)

■ Work Practice 6

Helpful Hint

Make sure you understand that models are mathematical approximations of the data for the known years. (For example, see the model in Example 6.) Any number of unknown factors can affect future years, so be cautious when using models to make predictions.

Answer
6. 3600 thousand

Calculator Explorations Graphing

In this section, we begin an optional study of graphing calculators and graphing software packages for computers. These graphers use the same point plotting technique that was introduced in this section. The advantage of this graphing technology is, of course, that graphing calculators and computers can find and plot ordered pair solutions much faster than we can. Note, however, that the features described in these boxes may not be available on all graphing calculators.

The rectangular screen where a portion of the rectangular coordinate system is displayed is called a **window**. We call it a **standard window** for graphing when both the x- and y-axes show coordinates between -10 and 10. This information is often displayed in the window menu on a graphing calculator as follows.

Xmin $= -10$
Xmax $= 10$
 Xscl $= 1$ The scale on the x-axis is one unit per tick mark.
Ymin $= -10$
Ymax $= 10$
 Yscl $= 1$ The scale on the y-axis is one unit per tick mark.

To use a graphing calculator to graph the equation $y = 2x + 3$, press the $\boxed{Y =}$ key and enter the keystrokes $\boxed{2}$ $\boxed{x}$ $\boxed{+}$ $\boxed{3}$. The top row should now read $Y_1 = 2x + 3$. Next press the $\boxed{GRAPH}$ key, and the display should look like this:

Graph the following linear equations. (Unless otherwise stated, use a standard window when graphing.)

1. $y = -3x + 7$

2. $y = -x + 5$

3. $y = 2.5x - 7.9$

4. $y = -1.3x + 5.2$

5. $y = -\dfrac{3}{10}x + \dfrac{32}{5}$

6. $y = \dfrac{2}{9}x - \dfrac{22}{3}$

Vocabulary, Readiness & Video Check

Martin-Gay Interactive Videos

Watch the section lecture video and answer the following questions.

Objective A **1.** In the lecture before ▣ Example 1, it's mentioned that we need only two points to determine a line. Why, then, are three ordered pair solutions found in Examples 1–3? ▶

2. What does a graphed line represent, as discussed at the end of ▣ Examples 1 and 3? ▶

See Video 13.2 ●

13.2 Exercise Set MyMathLab®

Objective A *For each equation, find three ordered pair solutions by completing the table. Then use the ordered pairs to graph the equation. See Examples 1 through 5.*

1. $x - y = 6$

x	y
	0
4	
	-1

2. $x - y = 4$

x	y
0	
	2
-1	

3. $y = -4x$

x	y
1	
0	
-1	

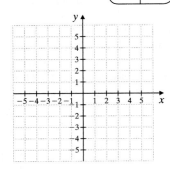

4. $y = -5x$

x	y
1	
0	
-1	

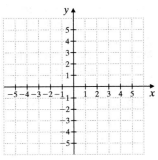

5. $y = \frac{1}{3}x$

x	y
0	
6	
-3	

6. $y = \frac{1}{2}x$

x	y
0	
-4	
2	

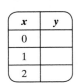

7. $y = -4x + 3$

x	y
0	
1	
2	

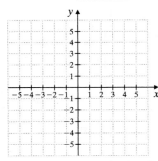

8. $y = -5x + 2$

x	y
0	
1	
2	

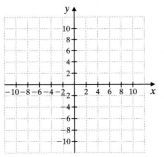

Graph each linear equation. See Examples 1 through 5.

9. $x + y = 1$

10. $x + y = 7$

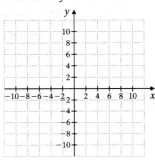

11. $x - y = -2$

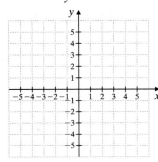

12. $-x + y = 6$

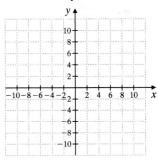

13. $x - 2y = 6$

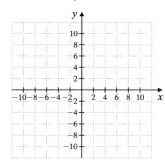

14. $-x + 5y = 5$

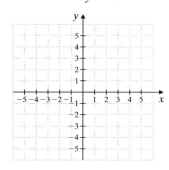

15. $y = 6x + 3$

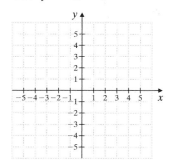

16. $y = -2x + 7$

17. $x = -4$

18. $y = 5$

19. $y = 3$

20. $x = -1$

21. $y = x$

22. $y = -x$

23. $x = -3y$

24. $x = 4y$

25. $x + 3y = 9$

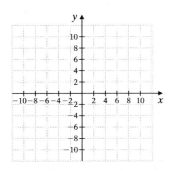

26. $2x + y = 2$

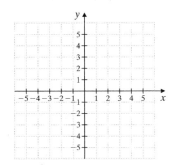

27. $y = \dfrac{1}{2}x + 2$

28. $y = \dfrac{1}{4}x + 3$

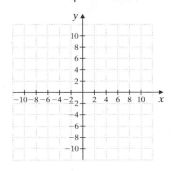

29. $3x - 2y = 12$

30. $2x - 7y = 14$

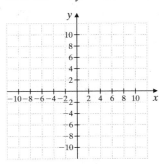

31. $y = -3.5x + 4$

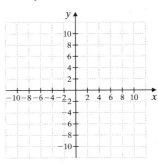

32. $y = -1.5x - 3$

Solve. See Example 6.

33. The number of students y (in thousands) taking the SAT college entrance exam each year from 2008 through 2012 can be approximated by the linear equation $y = 28x + 1552$, where x is the number of years after 2008. (*Source:* Based on data from The College Board)

a. Graph the linear equation.

b. Does the point $(7, 1748)$ lie on the line? If so, what does this ordered pair mean?

34. College is getting more expensive every year. The average cost for tuition and fees at a public two-year college y from 1991 through 2012 can be approximated by the linear equation $y = 88x + 973$, where x is the number of years after 1991. (*Source:* The College Board: Trends in College Pricing 2012)

a. Graph the linear equation.

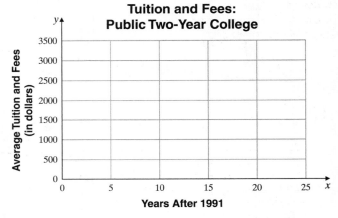

b. Does the point $(21, 2821)$ lie on the line? If so, what does this ordered pair mean?

35. The total annual revenue y (in billions of euros) for IKEA from 2001 through 2012 can be approximated by the equation $y = 1.6x + 9.1$, where x is the number of years after 2001. (*Source:* Based on data from IKEA Group)

a. Graph the linear equation.
b. Complete the ordered pair $(11, \ )$.
c. Write a sentence explaining the meaning of the ordered pair found in part **b**.

36. For the period 1970 through 2013, the annual level of sales for restaurants in the United States can be estimated by $y = 14.3x - 5.3$, where x is the number of years after 1970 and y is the sales in billions of dollars. (*Source:* Based on data from the National Restaurant Association)

a. Graph the linear equation.

b. Complete the ordered pair (43,).

c. Write a sentence explaining the meaning of the ordered pair found in part **b**.

Review

△ **37.** The coordinates of three vertices of a rectangle are $(-2, 5)$, $(4, 5)$, and $(-2, -1)$. Find the coordinates of the fourth vertex. See Section 13.1.

△ **38.** The coordinates of two vertices of a square are $(-3, -1)$ and $(2, -1)$. Find the coordinates of two pairs of possible points for the third and fourth vertices. See Section 13.1.

Complete each table. See Section 13.1.

39. $x - y = -3$

x	y
0	
	0

40. $y - x = 5$

x	y
0	
	0

41. $y = 2x$

x	y
0	
	0

42. $x = -3y$

x	y
0	
	0

Concept Extensions

Graph each pair of linear equations on the same set of axes. Discuss how the graphs are similar and how they are different.

43. $y = 5x$
$y = 5x + 4$

44. $y = 2x$
$y = 2x + 5$

45. $y = -2x$
$y = -2x - 3$

46. $y = x$
$y = x - 7$

47. Graph the nonlinear equation $y = x^2$ by completing the table shown. Plot the ordered pairs and connect them with a smooth curve.

x	y
0	
1	
−1	
2	
−2	

48. Graph the nonlinear equation $y = |x|$ by completing the table shown. Plot the ordered pairs and connect them. This curve is "V" shaped.

x	y
0	
1	
−1	
2	
−2	

△ **49.** The perimeter of the trapezoid below is 22 centimeters. Write a linear equation in two variables for the perimeter. Find y if x is 3 centimeters.

△ **50.** The perimeter of the rectangle below is 50 miles. Write a linear equation in two variables for the perimeter. Use this equation to find x when y is 20.

51. If (a, b) is an ordered pair solution of $x + y = 5$, is (b, a) also a solution? Explain why or why not.

52. If (a, b) is an ordered pair solution of $x - y = 5$, is (b, a) also a solution? Explain why or why not.

13.3   Intercepts

Objectives

A   Identify Intercepts of a Graph.

B   Graph a Linear Equation by Finding and Plotting Intercept Points.

C   Identify and Graph Vertical and Horizontal Lines.

Objective A   Identifying Intercepts

The graph of $y = 4x - 8$ is shown below. Notice that this graph crosses the y-axis at the point $(0, -8)$. This point is called the **y-intercept.** Likewise the graph crosses the x-axis at $(2, 0)$. This point is called the **x-intercept.**

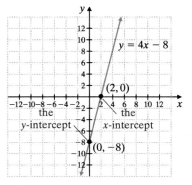

The intercepts are $(2, 0)$ and $(0, -8)$.

Helpful Hint

If a graph crosses the *x*-axis at $(2, 0)$ and the *y*-axis at $(0, -8)$, then

$$\underbrace{(2, 0)}_{\text{x-intercept}} \quad \underbrace{(0, -8)}_{\text{y-intercept}}$$

Notice that for the *x*-intercept, the *y*-value is 0 and that for the *y*-intercept, the *x*-value is 0.

Note: Sometimes in mathematics, you may see just the number -8 stated as the *y*-intercept, and 2 stated as the *x*-intercept.

Examples   Identify the *x*- and *y*-intercepts.

1.

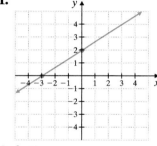

Solution:

    x-intercept: $(-3, 0)$
    y-intercept: $(0, 2)$

2.

Solution:

    x-intercepts: $(-4, 0)$, $(-1, 0)$
    y-intercept: $(0, 1)$

3.

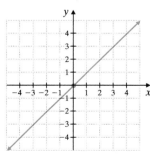

Helpful Hint

Notice that any time $(0, 0)$ is a point of a graph, then it is an *x*-intercept and a *y*-intercept. Why? It is the *only* point that lies on both axes.

(Continued on next page)

Practice 1–3

Identify the *x*- and *y*-intercepts.

1.

2.

3.

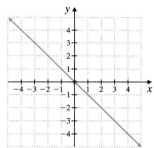

Answers

1. *x*-intercept: $(2, 0)$; *y*-intercept: $(0, -4)$

2. *x*-intercepts: $(-4, 0)$, $(2, 0)$; *y*-intercept: $(0, 2)$

3. *x*-intercept and *y*-intercept: $(0, 0)$

Practice 4

Graph $2x - y = 4$ by finding and plotting its intercepts.

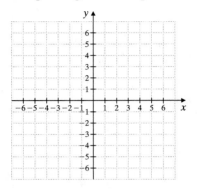

Practice 5

Graph $y = 3x$ by finding and plotting its intercepts.

Answers

4.

5.

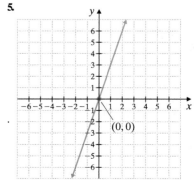

Solution:

  x-intercept: $(0, 0)$

  y-intercept: $(0, 0)$

Here, the x- and y-intercepts happen to be the same point.

◼ Work Practice 1–3

Objective B Finding and Plotting Intercepts ▶

Given an equation of a line, we can usually find intercepts easily since one coordinate is 0.

To find the x-intercept of a line from its equation, let $y = 0$, since a point on the x-axis has a y-coordinate of 0. To find the y-intercept of a line from its equation, let $x = 0$, since a point on the y-axis has an x-coordinate of 0.

Finding x- and y-Intercepts

To find the x-intercept, let $y = 0$ and solve for x.
To find the y-intercept, let $x = 0$ and solve for y.

Example 4 Graph $x - 3y = 6$ by finding and plotting its intercepts.

Solution: We let $y = 0$ to find the x-intercept and $x = 0$ to find the y-intercept.

Let $y = 0$.	Let $x = 0$.
$x - 3y = 6$	$x - 3y = 6$
$x - 3(0) = 6$	$0 - 3y = 6$
$x - 0 = 6$	$-3y = 6$
$x = 6$	$y = -2$

The x-intercept is $(6, 0)$ and the y-intercept is $(0, -2)$. We find a third ordered pair solution to check our work. If we let $y = -1$, then $x = 3$. We plot the points $(6, 0)$, $(0, -2)$, and $(3, -1)$. The graph of $x - 3y = 6$ is the line drawn through these points, as shown.

x	y
6	0
0	-2
3	-1

◼ Work Practice 4

Example 5 Graph $x = -2y$ by finding and plotting its intercepts.

Solution: We let $y = 0$ to find the x-intercept and $x = 0$ to find the y-intercept.

Let $y = 0$.	Let $x = 0$.
$x = -2y$	$x = -2y$
$x = -2(0)$	$0 = -2y$
$x = 0$	$0 = y$

Both the x-intercept and y-intercept are $(0, 0)$. In other words, when $x = 0$, then $y = 0$, which gives the ordered pair $(0, 0)$. Also, when $y = 0$, then $x = 0$, which gives the same ordered pair, $(0, 0)$. This happens when the graph passes through the origin. Since two points are needed to determine a line, we must find at least one more ordered pair that satisfies $x = -2y$. Since the equation is solved for x, we choose y-values so that there is no need to solve to find the corresponding x-value. We let $y = -1$ to find a second ordered pair solution and let $y = 1$ as a check point.

Let $y = -1$.
$$x = -2(-1)$$
$$x = 2 \qquad \text{Multiply.}$$

Let $y = 1$.
$$x = -2(1)$$
$$x = -2 \qquad \text{Multiply.}$$

The ordered pairs are $(0, 0)$, $(2, -1)$, and $(-2, 1)$. We plot these points to graph $x = -2y$.

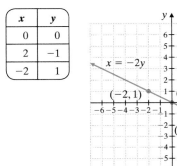

x	y
0	0
2	-1
-2	1

■ Work Practice 5

Objective C Graphing Vertical and Horizontal Lines

From Section 13.2, recall that the equation $x = 2$, for example, is a linear equation in two variables because it can be written in the form $x + 0y = 2$. The graph of this equation is a vertical line, as reviewed in the next example.

Example 6 Graph: $x = 2$

Solution: The equation $x = 2$ can be written as $x + 0y = 2$. For any y-value chosen, notice that x is 2. No other value for x satisfies $x + 0y = 2$. Any ordered pair whose x-coordinate is 2 is a solution of $x + 0y = 2$. We will use the ordered pair solutions $(2, 3)$, $(2, 0)$, and $(2, -3)$ to graph $x = 2$.

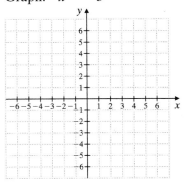

x	y
2	3
2	0
2	-3

The graph is a vertical line with x-intercept 2. Note that this graph has no y-intercept because x is never 0.

■ Work Practice 6

Practice 6

Graph: $x = -3$

Answer

6.

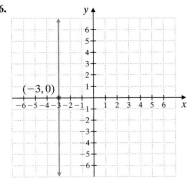

In general, we have the following.

Vertical Lines

The graph of $x = c$, where c is a real number, is a **vertical line** with x-intercept $(c, 0)$.

Practice 7

Graph: $y = 4$

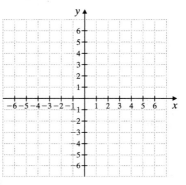

Example 7   Graph: $y = -3$

Solution: The equation $y = -3$ can be written as $0x + y = -3$. For any x-value chosen, y is -3. If we choose 4, 1, and -2 as x-values, the ordered pair solutions are $(4, -3)$, $(1, -3)$, and $(-2, -3)$. We use these ordered pairs to graph $y = -3$. The graph is a horizontal line with y-intercept -3 and no x-intercept.

x	y
4	-3
1	-3
-2	-3

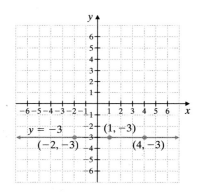

Work Practice 7

In general, we have the following.

Answer

7.

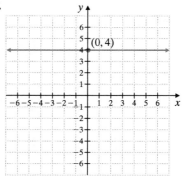

Horizontal Lines

The graph of $y = c$, where c is a real number, is a **horizontal line** with y-intercept $(0, c)$.

Calculator Explorations Graphing

You may have noticed that to use the $\boxed{Y =}$ key on a graphing calculator to graph an equation, the equation must be solved for y. For example, to graph $2x + 3y = 7$, we solve the equation for y.

$$2x + 3y = 7$$

$$3y = -2x + 7 \quad \text{Subtract } 2x \text{ from both sides.}$$

$$\frac{3y}{3} = -\frac{2x}{3} + \frac{7}{3} \quad \text{Divide both sides by 3.}$$

$$y = -\frac{2}{3}x + \frac{7}{3} \quad \text{Simplify.}$$

To graph $2x + 3y = 7$ or $y = -\frac{2}{3}x + \frac{7}{3}$, press the $\boxed{Y =}$ key and enter

$$Y_1 = -\frac{2}{3}x + \frac{7}{3}$$

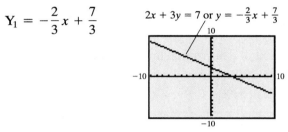

Graph each linear equation.

1. $x = 3.78y$

2. $-2.61y = x$

3. $3x + 7y = 21$

4. $-4x + 6y = 12$

5. $-2.2x + 6.8y = 15.5$

6. $5.9x - 0.8y = -10.4$

Vocabulary, Readiness & Video Check

Use the choices below to fill in each blank. Some choices may be used more than once. Exercises 1 and 2 come from Section 13.2.

x	vertical	x-intercept	linear
y	horizontal	y-intercept	standard

1. An equation that can be written in the form $Ax + By = C$ is called a(n) _____ equation in two variables.

2. The form $Ax + By = C$ is called _____ form.

3. The graph of the equation $y = -1$ is a(n) _____ line.

4. The graph of the equation $x = 5$ is a(n) _____ line.

5. A point where a graph crosses the y-axis is called a(n) _____.

6. A point where a graph crosses the x-axis is called a(n) _____.

7. Given an equation of a line, to find the x-intercept (if there is one), let _____ $= 0$ and solve for _____.

8. Given an equation of a line, to find the y-intercept (if there is one), let _____ $= 0$ and solve for _____.

Answer the following true or false.

9. All lines have an *x*-intercept *and* a *y*-intercept. _____

10. The graph of $y = 4x$ contains the point $(0, 0)$. _____

11. The graph of $x + y = 5$ has an *x*-intercept of $(5, 0)$ and a *y*-intercept of $(0, 5)$. _____

12. The graph of $y = 5x$ contains the point $(5, 1)$. _____

Martin-Gay Interactive Videos   Watch the section lecture video and answer the following questions.

See Video 13.3

Objective A **13.** At the end of ▯ Example 2, patterns are discussed. What reason is given for why *x*-intercepts have *y*-values of 0? For why *y*-intercepts have *x*-values of 0? ▶

Objective B **14.** In ▯ Example 3, the goal is to use the *x*- and *y*-intercepts to graph a line. Yet once the two intercepts are found, a third point is also found before the line is graphed. Why do you think this practice of finding a third point is continued? ▶

Objective C **15.** From ▯ Examples 5 and 6, what is the coefficient of *x* when the equation of a horizontal line is written as $Ax + By = C$? What is the coefficient of *y* when the equation of a vertical line is written as $Ax + By = C$? ▶

13.3 **Exercise Set** MyMathLab® ▶

Objective A *Identify the intercepts. See Examples 1 through 3.*

1.

2.

3.

4.

5.

6.

7.

8.

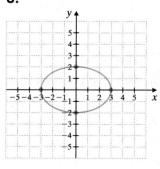

Objective **B** *Graph each linear equation by finding and plotting its intercepts. See Examples 4 and 5.*

9. $x - y = 3$

10. $x - y = -4$

11. $x = 5y$

12. $x = 2y$

13. $-x + 2y = 6$

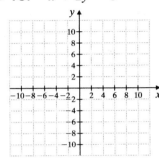

14. $x - 2y = -8$

15. $2x - 4y = 8$

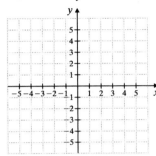

16. $2x + 3y = 6$

17. $y = 2x$

18. $y = -2x$

19. $y = 3x + 6$

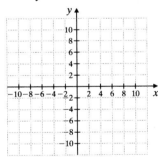

20. $y = 2x + 10$

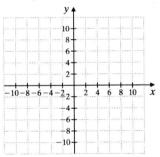

Objective **C** *Graph each linear equation. See Examples 6 and 7.*

21. $x = -1$

22. $y = 5$

23. $y = 0$

24. $x = 0$

25. $y + 7 = 0$

26. $x - 2 = 0$

27. $x + 3 = 0$

28. $y - 6 = 0$

Objectives B C Mixed Practice *Graph each linear equation. See Examples 4 through 7.*

29. $x = y$

30. $x = -y$

31. $x + 8y = 8$

32. $x + 3y = 9$

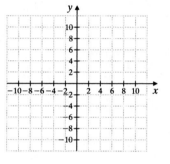

33. $5 = 6x - y$

34. $4 = x - 3y$

35. $-x + 10y = 11$

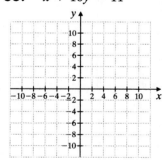

36. $-x + 9y = 10$

37. $x = -4\frac{1}{2}$

38. $x = -1\frac{3}{4}$

39. $y = 3\frac{1}{4}$

40. $y = 2\frac{1}{2}$

41. $y = -\dfrac{2}{3}x + 1$

42. $y = -\dfrac{3}{5}x + 3$

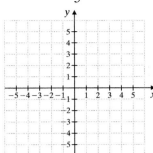

43. $4x - 6y + 2 = 0$

44. $9x - 6y + 3 = 0$

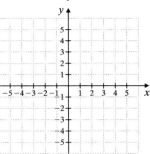

Review

Simplify. See Sections 2.2, 2.3, and 4.2.

45. $\dfrac{-6 - 3}{2 - 8}$

46. $\dfrac{4 - 5}{-1 - 0}$

47. $\dfrac{-8 - (-2)}{-3 - (-2)}$

48. $\dfrac{12 - 3}{10 - 9}$

49. $\dfrac{0 - 6}{5 - 0}$

50. $\dfrac{2 - 2}{3 - 5}$

Concept Extensions

Match each equation with its graph.

51. $y = 3$
a.

52. $y = 2x + 2$
b.

53. $x = 3$
c.

54. $y = 2x + 3$
d.

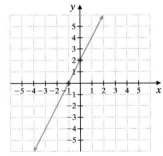

55. What is the greatest number of x- and y-intercepts that a line can have?

56. What is the smallest number of x- and y-intercepts that a line can have?

57. What is the smallest number of x- and y-intercepts that a circle can have?

58. What is the greatest number of x- and y-intercepts that a circle can have?

59. Discuss whether a vertical line ever has a y-intercept.

60. Discuss whether a horizontal line ever has an x-intercept.

The production supervisor at Alexandra's Office Products finds that it takes 3 hours to manufacture a particular office chair and 6 hours to manufacture an office desk. A total of 1200 hours is available to produce office chairs and desks of this style. The linear equation that models this situation is $3x + 6y = 1200$, where x represents the number of chairs produced and y represents the number of desks manufactured.

61. Complete the ordered pair solution $(0,\ \ )$ of this equation. Describe the manufacturing situation that corresponds to this solution.

62. Complete the ordered pair solution $(\ \ ,0)$ of this equation. Describe the manufacturing situation that corresponds to this solution.

63. If 50 desks are manufactured, find the greatest number of chairs that can be made.

64. If 50 chairs are manufactured, find the greatest number of desks that can be made.

*Two lines in the same plane that do not intersect are called **parallel lines.***

65. Use your own graph paper to draw a line parallel to the line $y = -1$ that intersects the y-axis at -4. What is the equation of this line?

66. Use your own graph paper to draw a line parallel to the line $x = 5$ that intersects the x-axis at 1. What is the equation of this line?

Solve.

67. It has been said that newspapers are disappearing, replaced by various electronic media. The average circulation of newspapers in the United States y, in millions, from 2006 to 2011 can be modeled by the equation $y = -1.7x + 52$, where x represents the number of years after 2006. (*Source:* Newspaper Association of America)

   a. Find the x-intercept of this equation (round to the nearest tenth).

   b. What does this x-intercept mean?

68. The number y of Barnes & Noble retail stores in operation for the years 2008–2012 can be modeled by the equation $y = -8.6x + 730$, where x represents the number of years after 2008. (*Source:* Based on data from Barnes & Noble, Inc.)

   a. Find the y-intercept of this equation.

   b. What does this y-intercept mean?

13.4   Slope and Rate of Change

Objectives

A Find the Slope of a Line Given Two Points of the Line.

B Find the Slope of a Line Given Its Equation.

C Find the Slopes of Horizontal and Vertical Lines.

D Compare the Slopes of Parallel and Perpendicular Lines.

E Slope as a Rate of Change.

Objective A   Finding the Slope of a Line Given Two Points

Thus far, much of this chapter has been devoted to graphing lines. You have probably noticed by now that a key feature of a line is its slant or steepness. In mathematics, the slant or steepness of a line is formally known as its **slope.** We measure the slope of a line by the ratio of vertical change (rise) to the corresponding horizontal change (run) as we move along the line.

On the line below, for example, suppose that we begin at the point $(1, 2)$ and move to the point $(4, 6)$. The vertical change is the change in y-coordinates: $6 - 2$ or 4 units. The corresponding horizontal change is the change in x-coordinates: $4 - 1 = 3$ units. The ratio of these changes is

$$\text{slope} = \frac{\text{change in } y \text{ (vertical change or rise)}}{\text{change in } x \text{ (horizontal change or run)}} = \frac{4}{3}$$

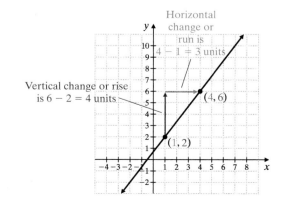

The slope of this line, then, is $\dfrac{4}{3}$. This means that for every 4 units of change in y-coordinates, there is a corresponding change of 3 units in x-coordinates.

Helpful Hint

It makes no difference what two points of a line are chosen to find its slope. The slope of a line is the same everywhere on the line.

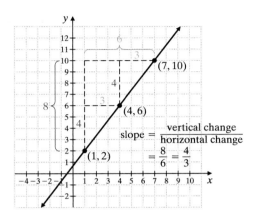

$$\text{slope} = \frac{\text{vertical change}}{\text{horizontal change}}$$
$$= \frac{8}{6} = \frac{4}{3}$$

To find the slope of a line, then, choose two points of the line. Label the two x-coordinates of the two points x_1 and x_2 (read "x sub one" and "x sub two"), and label the corresponding y-coordinates y_1 and y_2.

The vertical change or **rise** between these points is the difference in the y-coordinates: $y_2 - y_1$. The horizontal change or **run** between the points is the difference of the x-coordinates: $x_2 - x_1$. The slope of the line is the ratio of $y_2 - y_1$ to $x_2 - x_1$, and we traditionally use the letter m to denote slope: $m = \dfrac{y_2 - y_1}{x_2 - x_1}$.

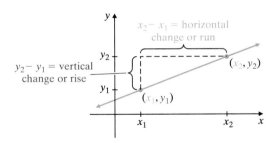

Slope of a Line

The slope m of the line containing the points (x_1, y_1) and (x_2, y_2) is given by

$$m = \frac{\text{rise}}{\text{run}} = \frac{\text{change in } y}{\text{change in } x} = \frac{y_2 - y_1}{x_2 - x_1}, \qquad \text{as long as } x_2 \neq x_1$$

Example 1 Find the slope of the line through $(-1, 5)$ and $(2, -3)$. Graph the line.

Solution: Let (x_1, y_1) be $(-1, 5)$ and (x_2, y_2) be $(2, -3)$. Then, by the definition of slope, we have the following.

(*Continued on next page*)

Practice 1

Find the slope of the line through $(-2, 3)$ and $(4, -1)$. Graph the line.

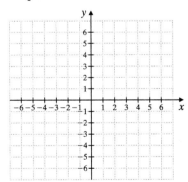

Answer

1. $m = -\dfrac{2}{3}$

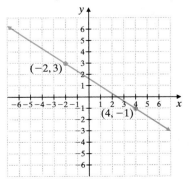

$$m = \frac{y_2 - y_1}{x_2 - x_1}$$

$$= \frac{-3 - 5}{2 - (-1)}$$

$$= \frac{-8}{3} = -\frac{8}{3}$$

The slope of the line is $-\frac{8}{3}$.

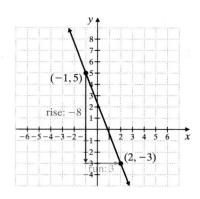

■ Work Practice 1

> **Helpful Hint**
>
> When finding slope, it makes no difference which point is identified as (x_1, y_1) and which is identified as (x_2, y_2). Just remember that whatever y-value is first in the numerator, its corresponding x-value is first in the denominator. Another way to calculate the slope in Example 1 is
>
> $$m = \frac{y_2 - y_1}{x_2 - x_1} = \frac{5 - (-3)}{-1 - 2} = \frac{8}{-3} \text{ or } -\frac{8}{3} \leftarrow \text{Same slope as found in Example 1}$$

Practice 2

Find the slope of the line through $(-2, 1)$ and $(3, 5)$. Graph the line.

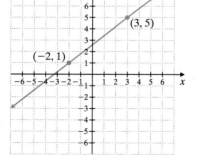

Answer

2. $m = \frac{4}{5}$

✓**Concept Check** The points $(-2, -5)$, $(0, -2)$, $(4, 4)$, and $(10, 13)$ all lie on the same line. Work with a partner and verify that the slope is the same no matter which points are used to find slope.

Example 2 Find the slope of the line through $(-1, -2)$ and $(2, 4)$. Graph the line.

Solution: Let (x_1, y_1) be $(2, 4)$ and (x_2, y_2) be $(-1, -2)$.

$$m = \frac{y_2 - y_1}{x_2 - x_1}$$

$$= \frac{-2 - 4}{-1 - 2} \quad \begin{array}{l} y\text{-value} \\ \text{corresponding } x\text{-value} \end{array}$$

$$= \frac{-6}{-3} = 2$$

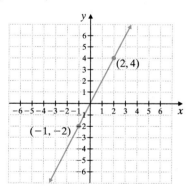

The slope is 2.

■ Work Practice 2

✓**First Concept Check Answers**

$m = \frac{3}{2}$

✓**Second Concept Check Answers**

$m = \frac{5 - 6}{3 - (-2)} = \frac{-1}{5} = -\frac{1}{5}$

✓**Concept Check** What is wrong with the following slope calculation for the points $(3, 5)$ and $(-2, 6)$?

$$m = \frac{5 - 6}{-2 - 3} = \frac{-1}{-5} = \frac{1}{5}$$

Notice that the slope of the line in Example 1 is negative and that the slope of the line in Example 2 is positive. Let your eye follow the line with negative slope from left to right and notice that the line "goes down." If you follow the line with positive slope from left to right, you will notice that the line "goes up." This is true in general.

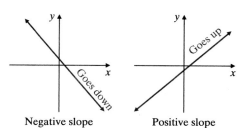

Negative slope   Positive slope

Helpful Hint To decide whether a line "goes up" or "goes down," always follow the line from left to right.

Objective B Finding the Slope of a Line Given Its Equation ▶

As we have seen, the slope of a line is defined by two points on the line. Thus, if we know the equation of a line, we can find its slope by finding two of its points. For example, let's find the slope of the line

$$y = 3x - 2$$

To find two points, we can choose two values for x and substitute to find corresponding y-values. If $x = 0$, for example, $y = 3 \cdot 0 - 2$ or $y = -2$. If $x = 1$, $y = 3 \cdot 1 - 2$ or $y = 1$. This gives the ordered pairs $(0, -2)$ and $(1, 1)$. Using the definition for slope, we have

$$m = \frac{1 - (-2)}{1 - 0} = \frac{3}{1} = 3 \quad \text{The slope is 3.}$$

Notice that the slope, 3, is the same as the coefficient of x in the equation $y = 3x - 2$. This is true in general.

> If a linear equation is solved for y, the coefficient of x is the line's slope. In other words, the slope of the line given by $y = mx + b$ is m, the coefficient of x.
>
> $$y = \underset{\underset{\text{slope}}{\uparrow}}{m}x + b$$

Example 3 Find the slope of the line $-2x + 3y = 11$.

Solution: When we solve for y, the coefficient of x is the slope.

$$-2x + 3y = 11$$
$$3y = 2x + 11 \quad \text{Add } 2x \text{ to both sides.}$$
$$y = \frac{2}{3}x + \frac{11}{3} \quad \text{Divide both sides by 3.}$$

The slope is $\frac{2}{3}$.

■ Work Practice 3

Practice 3

Find the slope of the line $5x + 4y = 10$.

Example 4 Find the slope of the line $-y = 5x - 2$.

Solution: Remember, the equation must be solved for y (not $-y$) in order for the coefficient of x to be the slope.

To solve for y, let's divide both sides of the equation by -1.

$$-y = 5x - 2$$
$$\frac{-y}{-1} = \frac{5x}{-1} - \frac{2}{-1} \quad \text{Divide both sides by } -1.$$
$$y = -5x + 2 \quad \text{Simplify.}$$

The slope is -5.

■ Work Practice 4

Practice 4

Find the slope of the line $-y = -2x + 7$.

Answers

3. $m = -\frac{5}{4}$ **4.** $m = 2$

Objective C Finding Slopes of Horizontal and Vertical Lines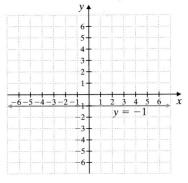

Practice 5

Find the slope of $y = 3$.

Example 5 Find the slope of the line $y = -1$.

Solution: Recall that $y = -1$ is a horizontal line with y-intercept -1. To find the slope, we find two ordered pair solutions of $y = -1$, knowing that solutions of $y = -1$ must have a y-value of -1. We will use $(2, -1)$ and $(-3, -1)$. We let (x_1, y_1) be $(2, -1)$ and (x_2, y_2) be $(-3, -1)$.

$$m = \frac{y_2 - y_1}{x_2 - x_1} = \frac{-1 - (-1)}{-3 - 2} = \frac{0}{-5} = 0$$

The slope of the line $y = -1$ is 0. Since the y-values will have a difference of 0 for every horizontal line, we can say that all **horizontal lines have a slope of 0.**

🖳 Work Practice 5

Practice 6

Find the slope of the line $x = -2$.

Example 6 Find the slope of the line $x = 5$.

Solution: Recall that the graph of $x = 5$ is a vertical line with x-intercept 5. To find the slope, we find two ordered pair solutions of $x = 5$. Ordered pair solutions of $x = 5$ must have an x-value of 5. We will use $(5, 0)$ and $(5, 4)$. We let $(x_1, y_1) = (5, 0)$ and $(x_2, y_2) = (5, 4)$.

$$m = \frac{y_2 - y_1}{x_2 - x_1} = \frac{4 - 0}{5 - 5} = \frac{4}{0}$$

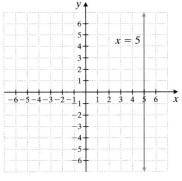

Helpful Hint   Slope of 0 and undefined slope are not the same. Vertical lines have un-defined slope, while horizontal lines have a slope of 0.

Since $\frac{4}{0}$ is undefined, we say that the slope of the vertical line $x = 5$ is undefined.

Since the x-values will have a difference of 0 for every vertical line, we can say that all **vertical lines have undefined slope.**

🖳 Work Practice 6

Answers

5. $m = 0$ **6.** undefined slope

Here is a general review of slope.

Summary of Slope

Slope m of the line through (x_1, y_1) and (x_2, y_2) is given by the equation

$$m = \frac{y_2 - y_1}{x_2 - x_1}.$$

Upward line

Positive slope: $m > 0$

Downward line

Negative slope: $m < 0$

Horizontal line $y = c$

Zero slope: $m = 0$

Vertical line $x = c$

No slope or undefined slope

Objective D Slopes of Parallel and Perpendicular Lines

Two lines in the same plane are **parallel** if they do not intersect. Slopes of lines can help us determine whether lines are parallel. Since parallel lines have the same steepness, it follows that they have the same slope.

For example, the graphs of

$$y = -2x + 4$$

and

$$y = -2x - 3$$

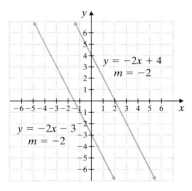

are shown. These lines have the same slope, -2. They also have different y-intercepts, so the lines are parallel. (If the y-intercepts were the same also, the lines would be the same.)

Parallel Lines

Nonvertical parallel lines have the same slope and different y-intercepts.

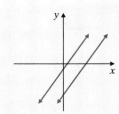

Two lines are **perpendicular** if they lie in the same plane and meet at a 90° (right) angle. How do the slopes of perpendicular lines compare? The product of the slopes of two perpendicular lines is −1.

For example, the graphs of

$$y = 4x + 1$$

and

$$y = -\frac{1}{4}x - 3$$

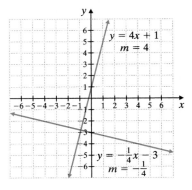

are shown. The slopes of the lines are 4 and $-\frac{1}{4}$. Their product is $4\left(-\frac{1}{4}\right) = -1$, so the lines are perpendicular.

Perpendicular Lines

If the product of the slopes of two lines is −1, then the lines are perpendicular.

   (Two nonvertical lines are perpendicular if the slope of one is the negative reciprocal of the slope of the other.)

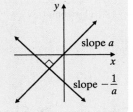

Helpful Hint

Here are examples of numbers that are negative (opposite) reciprocals.

Number	Negative Reciprocal	Their product is −1.
$\dfrac{2}{3}$	$-\dfrac{3}{2}$	$\dfrac{2}{3} \cdot -\dfrac{3}{2} = -\dfrac{6}{6} = -1$
-5 or $-\dfrac{5}{1}$	$\dfrac{1}{5}$	$-5 \cdot \dfrac{1}{5} = -\dfrac{5}{5} = -1$

Practice 7

Determine whether each pair of lines is parallel, perpendicular, or neither.

a. $x + y = 5$
  $2x + y = 5$

b. $5y = 2x - 3$
  $5x + 2y = 1$

c. $y = 2x + 1$
  $4x - 2y = 8$

Answers

7. a. neither   **b.** perpendicular
c. parallel

Here are a few important points about vertical and horizontal lines.
- Two distinct vertical lines are parallel.
- Two distinct horizontal lines are parallel.
- A horizontal line and a vertical line are always perpendicular.

△ **Example 7**   Determine whether each pair of lines is parallel, perpendicular, or neither.

a. $y = -\dfrac{1}{5}x + 1$ **b.** $x + y = 3$ **c.** $3x + y = 5$
  $2x + 10y = 3$ $-x + y = 4$ $2x + 3y = 6$

Solution:

a. The slope of the line $y = -\dfrac{1}{5}x + 1$ is $-\dfrac{1}{5}$. We find the slope of the second line by solving its equation for y.

$$2x + 10y = 3$$
$$10y = -2x + 3 \qquad \text{Subtract } 2x \text{ from both sides.}$$
$$y = \frac{-2}{10}x + \frac{3}{10} \qquad \text{Divide both sides by 10.}$$
$$y = -\frac{1}{5}x + \frac{3}{10} \qquad \text{Simplify.}$$

The slope of this line is $-\dfrac{1}{5}$ also. Since the lines have the same slope and different y-intercepts, they are parallel, as shown below on the left.

b. To find each slope, we solve each equation for y.

$$x + y = 3 \qquad\qquad -x + y = 4$$
$$y = -x + 3 \qquad\qquad y = x + 4$$

The slope is -1.   The slope is 1.

The slopes are not the same, so the lines are not parallel. Next we check the product of the slopes: $(-1)(1) = -1$. Since the product is -1, the lines are perpendicular, as shown below on the right.

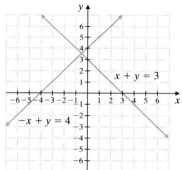

c. We solve each equation for y to find each slope. The slopes are -3 and $-\dfrac{2}{3}$. The slopes are not the same and their product is not -1. Thus, the lines are neither parallel nor perpendicular.

■ Work Practice 7

✓**Concept Check** Consider the line $-6x + 2y = 1$.
  a. Write the equations of two lines parallel to this line.
  b. Write the equations of two lines perpendicular to this line.

Objective E Slope as a Rate of Change ▶

Slope can also be interpreted as a rate of change. In other words, slope tells us how fast y is changing with respect to x. To see this, let's look at a few of the many real-world applications of slope. For example, the pitch of a roof, used by builders and architects, is its slope. The pitch of the roof on the right is $\dfrac{7}{10}\left(\dfrac{\text{rise}}{\text{run}}\right)$. This means that the roof rises vertically 7 feet for every horizontal 10 feet. The rate of change for the roof is 7 vertical feet (y) per 10 horizontal feet (x).

✓**Concept Check Answers**
Answers may vary; for example,
a. $y = 3x - 3$, $y = 3x - 1$

b. $y = -\dfrac{1}{3}x$, $y = -\dfrac{1}{3}x + 1$

The grade of a road is its slope written as a percent. A 7% grade, as shown below, means that the road rises (or falls) 7 feet for every horizontal 100 feet. $\left(\text{Recall that } 7\% = \dfrac{7}{100}.\right)$ Here, the slope of $\dfrac{7}{100}$ gives us the rate of change. The road rises (in our diagram) 7 vertical feet (y) for every 100 horizontal feet (x).

$\dfrac{7}{100} = 7\%\text{ grade}$ 7 feet

100 feet

Find the grade of the road shown.

3 feet

20 feet

Finding the Grade of a Road

At one part of the road to the summit of Pike's Peak, the road rises 15 feet for a horizontal distance of 250 feet. Find the grade of the road.

Solution: Recall that the grade of a road is its slope written as a percent.

$$\text{grade} = \frac{\text{rise}}{\text{run}} = \frac{15}{250} = 0.06 = 6\%$$

15 feet

250 feet

The grade is 6%.

Work Practice 8

Find the slope of the line and write the slope as a rate of change. This graph represents annual restaurant-industry employment y (in billions of workers) for year x. Write a sentence explaining the meaning of slope in this application.

U.S. Restaurant-Industry Employment

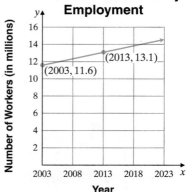

Number of Workers (in millions)

(2013, 13.1)

(2003, 11.6)

2003   2008   2013   2018   2023 x

Year

Source: National Restaurant Association

Answers

8. 15%

9. $m = 0.15$; Each year the number of workers employed in the U.S. restaurant industry increases by 0.15 million, or 150,000, workers per year.

Finding the Slope of a Line

The following graph shows the cost y (in cents) of a nationwide long-distance telephone call from Texas with a certain telephone-calling plan, where x is the length of the call in minutes. Find the slope of the line and attach the proper units for the rate of change. Then write a sentence explaining the meaning of slope in this application.

Solution: Use $(2, 34)$ and $(6, 62)$ to calculate slope.

Cost of Long-Distance Telephone Call

Cost of Call (in cents)

(6, 62)

(2, 34)

Length of Call (in minutes)

$$m = \frac{62 - 34}{6 - 2} = \frac{28}{4} = \frac{7\,\text{cents}}{1\,\text{minute}}$$

This means that the rate of change of the phone call is 7 cents per 1 minute, or the cost of the phone call is 7 cents per minute.

Work Practice 9

Calculator Explorations **Graphing**

It is possible to use a graphing calculator to sketch the graph of more than one equation on the same set of axes. This feature can be used to see parallel lines with the same slope. For example, graph the equations $y = \frac{2}{5}x$, $y = \frac{2}{5}x + 7$, and $y = \frac{2}{5}x - 4$ on the same set of axes. To do so, press the $\boxed{Y =}$ key and enter the equations on the first three lines.

$$Y_1 = \frac{2}{5}x$$

$$Y_2 = \frac{2}{5}x + 7$$

$$Y_3 = \frac{2}{5}x - 4$$

The displayed equations should look like this:

These lines are parallel, as expected, since they all have a slope of $\frac{2}{5}$. The graph of $y = \frac{2}{5}x + 7$ is the graph of $y = \frac{2}{5}x$ moved 7 units upward with a y-intercept of 7. Also, the graph of $y = \frac{2}{5}x - 4$ is the graph of $y = \frac{2}{5}x$ moved 4 units downward with a y-intercept of -4.

Graph the parallel lines on the same set of axes. Describe the similarities and differences in their graphs.

1. $y = 3.8x$, $y = 3.8x - 3$, $y = 3.8x + 9$

2. $y = -4.9x$, $y = -4.9x + 1$, $y = -4.9x + 8$

3. $y = \frac{1}{4}x$, $y = \frac{1}{4}x + 5$, $y = \frac{1}{4}x - 8$

4. $y = -\frac{3}{4}x$, $y = -\frac{3}{4}x - 5$, $y = -\frac{3}{4}x + 6$

Vocabulary, Readiness & Video Check

Use the choices below to fill in each blank. Not all choices will be used.

m	x	0	positive	undefined
b	y	slope	negative	

1. The measure of the steepness or tilt of a line is called _____.
2. If an equation is written in the form $y = mx + b$, the value of the letter _____ is the value of the slope of the graph.
3. The slope of a horizontal line is _____.
4. The slope of a vertical line is _____.
5. If the graph of a line moves upward from left to right, the line has _____ slope.
6. If the graph of a line moves downward from left to right, the line has _____ slope.
7. Given two points of a line, slope $= \dfrac{\text{change in } \underline{\hspace{2cm}}}{\text{change in } \underline{\hspace{2cm}}}$.

State whether the slope of the line is positive, negative, 0, or undefined.

8.   9.   10.   11.

Decide whether a line with the given slope slants upward or downward or is horizontal or vertical.

12. $m = \dfrac{7}{6}$ _____   13. $m = -3$ _____   14. $m = 0$ _____   15. m is undefined. _____

Martin-Gay Interactive Videos

See Video 13.4

Watch the section lecture video and answer the following questions.

Objective A 16. What important point is made during ⊞ Example 1 having to do with the order of the points in the slope formula? ▶

Objective B 17. From ⊞ Example 5, how do we write an equation in "slope-intercept form"? Once the equation is in slope-intercept form, how do we identify the slope? ▶

Objective C 18. In the lecture after ⊞ Example 8, different slopes are summarized. What is the difference between zero slope and undefined slope? What does "no slope" mean? ▶

Objective D 19. From ⊞ Example 10, what form of the equation is best to determine if two lines are parallel or perpendicular? Why? ▶

Objective E 20. Writing the slope as a rate of change in ⊞ Example 11 gave real-life meaning to the slope. What step in the general strategy for problem solving does this correspond to? ▶

13.4 Exercise Set MyMathLab® ▶

Objective A *Find the slope of the line that passes through the given points. See Examples 1 and 2.*

▶ **1.** $(-1, 5)$ and $(6, -2)$ **2.** $(-1, 16)$ and $(3, 4)$ **3.** $(1, 4)$ and $(5, 3)$ **4.** $(3, 1)$ and $(2, 6)$

▶ **5.** $(5, 1)$ and $(-2, 1)$ **6.** $(-8, 3)$ and $(-2, 3)$ ▶ **7.** $(-4, 3)$ and $(-4, 5)$ **8.** $(-2, -3)$ and $(-2, 5)$

Use the points shown on each graph to find the slope of each line. See Examples 1 and 2.

9.

▶ **10.**

11.

12.

For each graph, determine which line has the greater slope.

13.

14.

15.

16.

Objectives B C Mixed Practice *Find the slope of each line. See Examples 3 through 6.*

17. $y = 5x - 2$

18. $y = -2x + 6$

19. $y = -0.3x + 2.5$

20. $y = -7.6x - 0.1$

▶ **21.** $2x + y = 7$

22. $-5x + y = 10$

23.

24.
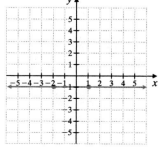

25. $2x - 3y = 10$ **26.** $3x - 5y = 1$ **27.** $x = 1$ **28.** $y = -2$

29. $x = 2y$ **30.** $x = -4y$ **31.** $y = -3$ **32.** $x = 5$

33. $-3x - 4y = 6$ **34.** $-4x - 7y = 9$ **35.** $20x - 5y = 1.2$ **36.** $24x - 3y = 5.7$

△ **Objective D** *Determine whether each pair of lines is parallel, perpendicular, or neither. See Example 7.*

37. $y = \dfrac{2}{9}x + 3$ **38.** $y = \dfrac{1}{5}x + 20$ **39.** $x - 3y = -6$ **40.** $y = 4x - 2$

$y = -\dfrac{2}{9}x$ $y = -\dfrac{1}{5}x$ $y = 3x - 9$ $4x + y = 5$

41. $6x = 5y + 1$ **42.** $-x + 2y = -2$ **43.** $6 + 4x = 3y$ **44.** $10 + 3x = 5y$

$-12x + 10y = 1$ $2x = 4y + 3$ $3x + 4y = 8$ $5x + 3y = 1$

△ *Find the slope of a line that is (a) parallel and (b) perpendicular to the line through each pair of points. See Example 7.*

45. $(-3, -3)$ and $(0, 0)$ **46.** $(6, -2)$ and $(1, 4)$ **47.** $(-8, -4)$ and $(3, 5)$ **48.** $(6, -1)$ and $(-4, -10)$

Objective E *The pitch of a roof is its slope. Find the pitch of each roof shown. See Example 8.*

49.

50.

The grade of a road is its slope written as a percent. Find the grade of each road shown. See Example 8.

51.

52.

53. One of Japan's superconducting "bullet" trains is researched and tested at the Yamanashi Maglev Test Line near Otsuki City. The steepest section of the track has a rise of 2580 meters for a horizontal distance of 6450 meters. What is the grade (slope written as a percent) of this section of track? (*Source:* Japan Railways Central Co.)

2580 meters

6450 meters

54. Professional plumbers suggest that a sewer pipe rise 0.25 inch for every horizontal foot. Find the recommended slope for a sewer pipe and write the slope as a grade, or percent. Round to the nearest percent.

0.25 inch

12 inches

55. There has been controversy over the past few years about the world's steepest street. *The Guinness Book of Records* listed Baldwin Street, in Dunedin, New Zealand, as the world's steepest street, but Canton Avenue in the Pittsburgh neighborhood of Beechview may actually be steeper. Calculate each grade to the nearest percent.

Canton Avenue	For every 30 meters of horizontal distance, the vertical change is 11 meters.	
Baldwin Street	For every 2.86 meters of horizontal distance, the vertical change is 1 meter.	

56. According to federal regulations, a wheelchair ramp should rise no more than 1 foot for a horizontal distance of 12 feet. Write the slope as a grade. Round to the nearest tenth of a percent.

Find the slope of each line and write a sentence using the slope as a rate of change. Don't forget to attach the proper units. See Example 9.

57. This graph approximates the number of U.S. households that have televisions *y* (in millions) for year *x*.

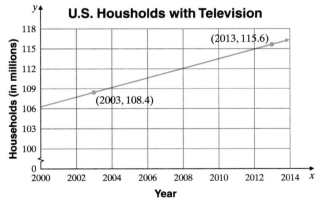

U.S. Housholds with Television

(2013, 115.6)

(2003, 108.4)

Households (in millions)

Year

Source: The Nielson Company

58. The graph approximates the amount of money *y* (in billions of dollars) spent worldwide on tourism for year *x*.

Money Spent on World Tourism

(2012, 1075)

(2000, 475)

Dollars (in billions)

Year

Source: World Tourism Organization

59. Americans are keeping their cars longer. The graph below shows the median age y (in years) of automobiles in the United States for the years shown.

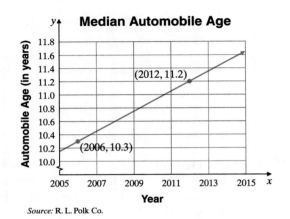

Source: R. L. Polk Co.

60. The graph below shows the total cost y (in dollars) of owning and operating a large sedan in the United States in 2013, where x is the annual number of miles driven.

Source: AAA

Review

Solve each equation for y. See Section 9.5.

61. $y - (-6) = 2(x - 4)$

62. $y - 7 = -9(x - 6)$

63. $y - 1 = -6(x - (-2))$

64. $y - (-3) = 4(x - (-5))$

Concept Extensions

Match each line with its slope.

a. $m = 0$

b. undefined slope

c. $m = 3$

d. $m = 1$

e. $m = -\dfrac{1}{2}$

f. $m = -\dfrac{3}{4}$

65.

66.

67.

68.

69.

70.
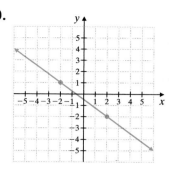

Solve. See a Concept Check in this section.

71. Verify that the points $(2, 1), (0, 0), (-2, -1)$, and $(-4, -2)$ are all on the same line by computing the slope between each pair of points. (See the first Concept Check.)

72. Given the points $(2, 3)$ and $(-5, 1)$, can the slope of the line through these points be calculated by $\dfrac{1 - 3}{2 - (-5)}$? Why or why not? (See the second Concept Check.)

73. Write the equations of three lines parallel to $10x - 5y = -7$. (See the third Concept Check.)

74. Write the equations of two lines perpendicular to $10x - 5y = -7$. (See the third Concept Check.)

The following line graph shows the average fuel economy (in miles per gallon) of passenger automobiles produced during each of the model years shown. Use this graph to answer Exercises 75 through 80.

75. What was the average fuel economy (in miles per gallon) for automobiles produced during 2008?

76. Find the decrease in average fuel economy for automobiles between the years 2010 and 2011.

77. During which of the model year(s) shown was average fuel economy the lowest?
What was the average fuel economy for that year/those years?

78. During which of the model years shown was average fuel economy the highest?
What was the average fuel economy for that year?

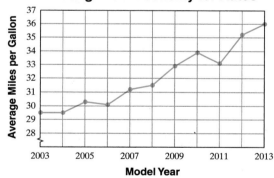

Average Fuel Economy for Autos

Source: U.S. Department of Transportation

79. Of the following line segments, which has the greatest slope: from 2007 to 2008, from 2009 to 2010, or from 2011 to 2012?

80. What line segment has a slope of 0?

81. Find x so that the pitch of the roof is $\dfrac{2}{5}$.

82. Find x so that the pitch of the roof is $\dfrac{1}{3}$.

83. There were approximately 2209 heart transplants performed in the United States in 2007. In 2012, the number of heart transplants in the United States rose to 2378. (*Source:* Organ Procurement and Transplantation Network)

   a. Write two ordered pairs of the form(year, number of heart transplants).

   b. Find the slope of the line between the two points.

   c. Write a sentence explaining the meaning of the slope as a rate of change.

84. The average price of an acre of U.S. cropland was $2670 in 2009. In 2013, the price of an acre rose to $4000. (*Source:* National Agricultural Statistics Service)

   a. Write two ordered pairs of the form(year, price of acre).

   b. Find the slope of the line through the two points.

   c. Write a sentence explaining the meaning of the slope as a rate of change.

85. Show that the quadrilateral with vertices $(1, 3)$, $(2, 1)$, $(-4, 0)$, and $(-3, -2)$ is a parallelogram.

86. Show that a triangle with vertices at the points $(1, 1)$, $(-4, 4)$, and $(-3, 0)$ is a right triangle.

Find the slope of the line through the given points.

87. $(-3.8, 1.2)$ and $(-2.2, 4.5)$

88. $(2.1, 6.7)$ and $(-8.3, 9.3)$

89. $(14.3, -10.1)$ and $(9.8, -2.9)$

90. $(2.3, 0.2)$ and $(7.9, 5.1)$

91. The graph of $y = \frac{1}{2}x$ has a slope of $\frac{1}{2}$. The graph of $y = 3x$ has a slope of 3. The graph of $y = 5x$ has a slope of 5. Graph all three equations on a single coordinate system. As the slope becomes larger, how does the steepness of the line change?

92. The graph of $y = -\frac{1}{3}x + 2$ has a slope of $-\frac{1}{3}$. The graph of $y = -2x + 2$ has a slope of -2. The graph of $y = -4x + 2$ has a slope of -4. Graph all three equations on a single coordinate system. As the absolute value of the slope becomes larger, how does the steepness of the line change?

13.5 Equations of Lines

We know that when a linear equation is solved for y, the coefficient of x is the slope of the line. For example, the slope of the line whose equation is $y = 3x + 1$ is 3. In the equation $y = 3x + 1$, what does 1 represent? To find out, let $x = 0$ and watch what happens.

$$y = 3x + 1$$
$$y = 3 \cdot 0 + 1 \quad \text{Let } x = 0.$$
$$y = 1$$

We now have the ordered pair $(0, 1)$, which means that 1 is the y-intercept.
This is true in general. To see this, let $x = 0$ and solve for y in $y = mx + b$.

$$y = m \cdot 0 + b \quad \text{Let } x = 0.$$
$$y = b$$

We obtain the ordered pair $(0, b)$, which means that point is the y-intercept.
The form $y = mx + b$ is appropriately called the *slope-intercept form* of a linear equation.

$$y = m\overset{\uparrow}{x} + \overset{\uparrow}{b}$$

slope y-intercept is $(0, b)$.

Objectives

A Use the Slope-Intercept Form to Write an Equation of a Line.

B Use the Slope-Intercept Form to Graph a Linear Equation.

C Use the Point-Slope Form to Find an Equation of a Line Given Its Slope and a Point of the Line.

D Use the Point-Slope Form to Find an Equation of a Line Given Two Points of the Line.

E Use the Point-Slope Form to Solve Problems.

Slope-Intercept Form

When a linear equation in two variables is written in **slope-intercept form,**

$$y = m\overset{\uparrow}{x} + \overset{\uparrow}{b}$$

slope $(0, b)$, y-intercept

then m is the slope of the line and $(0, b)$ is the y-intercept of the line.

Objective A Using the Slope-Intercept Form to Write an Equation

The slope-intercept form can be used to write the equation of a line when we know its slope and y-intercept.

Example 1 Find an equation of the line with y-intercept $(0, -3)$ and slope of $\frac{1}{4}$.

Solution: We are given the slope and the y-intercept. We let $m = \frac{1}{4}$ and $b = -3$ and write the equation in slope-intercept form, $y = mx + b$.

$$y = mx + b$$
$$y = \frac{1}{4}x + (-3) \quad \text{Let } m = \frac{1}{4} \text{ and } b = -3.$$
$$y = \frac{1}{4}x - 3 \quad \text{Simplify.}$$

■ Work Practice 1

Practice 1

Find an equation of the line with y-intercept $(0, -2)$ and slope of $\frac{3}{5}$.

Objective B Using the Slope-Intercept Form to Graph an Equation

We also can use the slope-intercept form of the equation of a line to graph a linear equation.

Answer

1. $y = \frac{3}{5}x - 2$

Practice 2

Use the slope-intercept form to graph the equation $y = \frac{2}{3}x - 4$.

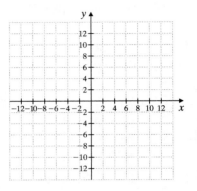

Practice 3

Use the slope-intercept form to graph $3x + y = 2$.

Answers

2.

3.

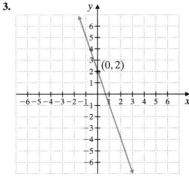

Example 2   Use the slope-intercept form to graph the equation

$$y = \frac{3}{5}x - 2.$$

Solution: Since the equation $y = \frac{3}{5}x - 2$ is written in slope-intercept form $y = mx + b$, the slope of its graph is $\frac{3}{5}$ and the y-intercept is $(0, -2)$. To graph this equation, we begin by plotting the point $(0, -2)$. From this point, we can find another point of the graph by using the slope $\frac{3}{5}$ and recalling that slope is $\frac{rise}{run}$. We start at the y-intercept and move 3 units up since the numerator of the slope is 3; then we move 5 units to the right since the denominator of the slope is 5. We stop at the point $(5, 1)$. The line through $(0, -2)$ and $(5, 1)$ is the graph of $y = \frac{3}{5}x - 2$.

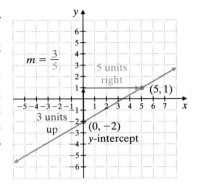

■ **Work Practice 2**

Example 3   Use the slope-intercept form to graph the equation $4x + y = 1$.

Solution: First we write the given equation in slope-intercept form.

$$4x + y = 1$$
$$y = -4x + 1$$

The graph of this equation will have slope -4 and y-intercept $(0, 1)$. To graph this line, we first plot the point $(0, 1)$. To find another point of the graph, we use the slope -4, which can be written as $\frac{-4}{1} \left(\frac{4}{-1} \text{ could also be used} \right)$. We start at the point $(0, 1)$ and move 4 units down (since the numerator of the slope is -4), and then 1 unit to the right (since the denominator of the slope is 1).

We arrive at the point $(1, -3)$. The line through $(0, 1)$ and $(1, -3)$ is the graph of $4x + y = 1$.

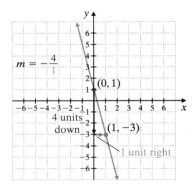

■ **Work Practice 3**

Helpful Hint

In Example 3, if we interpret the slope of -4 as $\frac{4}{-1}$, we arrive at $(-1, 5)$ for a second point. Notice that this point is also on the line.

Objective C Writing an Equation Given Its Slope and a Point ▶

Thus far, we have seen that we can write an equation of a line if we know its slope and y-intercept. We can also write an equation of a line if we know its slope and any point on the line. To see how we do this, let m represent slope and (x_1, y_1) represent a point on the line. Then if (x, y) is any other point on the line, we have that

$$\frac{y - y_1}{x - x_1} = m$$

$$y - y_1 = m(x - x_1) \quad \text{Multiply both sides by } (x - x_1).$$
$$\underset{\text{slope}}{\uparrow}$$

This is the *point-slope form* of the equation of a line.

Point-Slope Form of the Equation of a Line

The **point-slope form** of the equation of a line is $y - y_1 = m(x - x_1)$, where m is the slope of the line and (x_1, y_1) is a point on the line.

Example 4 Find an equation of the line with slope -2 that passes through $(-1, 5)$. Write the equation in slope-intercept form, $y = mx + b$, and in standard form, $Ax + By = C$.

Solution: Since the slope and a point on the line are given, we use point-slope form, $y - y_1 = m(x - x_1)$, to write the equation. Let $m = -2$ and $(-1, 5) = (x_1, y_1)$.

$$y - y_1 = m(x - x_1)$$
$$y - 5 = -2[x - (-1)] \quad \text{Let } m = -2 \text{ and } (x_1, y_1) = (-1, 5).$$
$$y - 5 = -2(x + 1) \quad \text{Simplify.}$$
$$y - 5 = -2x - 2 \quad \text{Use the distributive property.}$$

To write the equation in slope-intercept form, $y = mx + b$, we simply solve the equation for y. To do this, we add 5 to both sides.

$$y - 5 = -2x - 2$$
$$y = -2x + 3 \quad \text{Slope-intercept form}$$
$$2x + y = 3 \quad \text{Add } 2x \text{ to both sides and we have standard form.}$$

▪ Work Practice 4

Practice 4

Find an equation of the line with slope -3 that passes through $(2, -4)$. Write the equation in slope-intercept form, $y = mx + b$.

Objective D Writing an Equation Given Two Points ▶

We can also find the equation of a line when we are given any two points of the line.

Example 5 Find an equation of the line through $(2, 5)$ and $(-3, 4)$. Write the equation in the form $Ax + By = C$.

Solution: First, use the two given points to find the slope of the line.

$$m = \frac{4 - 5}{-3 - 2} = \frac{-1}{-5} = \frac{1}{5}$$

Next we use the slope $\frac{1}{5}$ and either one of the given points to write the equation in point-slope form. We use $(2, 5)$. Let $x_1 = 2$, $y_1 = 5$, and $m = \frac{1}{5}$.

$$y - y_1 = m(x - x_1) \quad \text{Use point-slope form.}$$
$$y - 5 = \frac{1}{5}(x - 2) \quad \text{Let } x_1 = 2, y_1 = 5, \text{ and } m = \frac{1}{5}.$$
$$5(y - 5) = 5 \cdot \frac{1}{5}(x - 2) \quad \text{Multiply both sides by 5 to clear fractions.}$$
$$5y - 25 = x - 2 \quad \text{Use the distributive property and simplify.}$$
$$-x + 5y - 25 = -2 \quad \text{Subtract } x \text{ from both sides.}$$
$$-x + 5y = 23 \quad \text{Add 25 to both sides.}$$

▪ Work Practice 5

Practice 5

Find an equation of the line through $(1, 3)$ and $(5, -2)$. Write the equation in the form $Ax + By = C$.

Answers
4. $y = -3x + 2$
5. $5x + 4y = 17$

Helpful Hint

When you multiply both sides of the equation from Example 5, $-x + 5y = 23$, by -1, it becomes $x - 5y = -23$.

Both $-x + 5y = 23$ and $x - 5y = -23$ are in the form $Ax + By = C$ and both are equations of the same line.

Objective E Using the Point-Slope Form to Solve Problems

Problems occurring in many fields can be modeled by linear equations in two variables. The next example is from the field of marketing and shows how consumer demand of a product depends on the price of the product.

Practice 6

The Pool Entertainment Company learned that by pricing a new pool toy at $10, local sales will reach 200 a week. Lowering the price to $9 will cause sales to rise to 250 a week.

a. Assume that the relationship between sales price and number of toys sold is linear, and write an equation describing this relationship. Write the equation in slope-intercept form. Use ordered pairs of the form (sales price, number sold).

b. Predict the weekly sales of the toy if the price is $7.50.

Example 6 The Whammo Company has learned that by pricing a newly released Frisbee at $6, sales will reach 2000 Frisbees per day. Raising the price to $8 will cause the sales to fall to 1500 Frisbees per day.

a. Assume that the relationship between sales price and number of Frisbees sold is linear, and write an equation describing this relationship. Write the equation in slope-intercept form. Use ordered pairs of the form (sales price, number sold).

b. Predict the daily sales of Frisbees if the price is $7.50.

Solution:

a. We use the given information and write two ordered pairs. Our ordered pairs are $(6, 2000)$ and $(8, 1500)$. To use the point-slope form to write an equation, we find the slope of the line that contains these points.

$$m = \frac{2000 - 1500}{6 - 8} = \frac{500}{-2} = -250$$

Next we use the slope and either one of the points to write the equation in point-slope form. We use $(6, 2000)$.

$$y - y_1 = m(x - x_1) \qquad \text{Use point-slope form.}$$
$$y - 2000 = -250(x - 6) \qquad \text{Let } x_1 = 6, y_1 = 2000, \text{ and } m = -250.$$
$$y - 2000 = -250x + 1500 \qquad \text{Use the distributive property.}$$
$$y = -250x + 3500 \qquad \text{Write in slope-intercept form.}$$

b. To predict the sales if the price is $7.50, we find y when $x = 7.50$.

$$y = -250x + 3500$$
$$y = -250(7.50) + 3500 \qquad \text{Let } x = 7.50.$$
$$y = -1875 + 3500$$
$$y = 1625$$

If the price is $7.50, sales will reach 1625 Frisbees per day.

Answers

6. a. $y = -50x + 700$ **b.** 325

▶ Work Practice 6

We also could have solved Example 6 by using ordered pairs of the form (number sold, sales price).

Here is a summary of our discussion on linear equations thus far.

Forms of Linear Equations

$Ax + By = C$	**Standard form** of a linear equation. A and B are not both 0.
$y = mx + b$	**Slope-intercept form** of a linear equation. The slope is m and the y-intercept is $(0, b)$.
$y - y_1 = m(x - x_1)$	**Point-slope form** of a linear equation. The slope is m and (x_1, y_1) is a point on the line.
$y = c$	**Horizontal line** The slope is 0 and the y-intercept is $(0, c)$.
$x = c$	**Vertical line** The slope is undefined and the x-intercept is $(c, 0)$.

Parallel and Perpendicular Lines

Nonvertical parallel lines have the same slope.
The product of the slopes of two nonvertical perpendicular lines is -1.

 ## Calculator Explorations   Graphing

A graphing calculator is a very useful tool for discovering patterns. To discover the change in the graph of a linear equation caused by a change in slope, try the following: Use a standard window and graph a linear equation in the form $y = mx + b$. Recall that the graph of such an equation will have slope m and y-intercept $(0, b)$.

First graph $y = x + 3$. To do so, press the $\boxed{Y =}$ key and enter $Y_1 = x + 3$. Notice that this graph has slope 1 and that the y-intercept is 3. Next, on the same set of axes, graph $y = 2x + 3$ and $y = 3x + 3$ by pressing $\boxed{Y =}$ and entering $Y_2 = 2x + 3$ and $Y_3 = 3x + 3$.

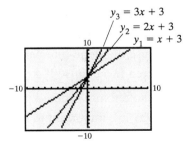

Notice the difference in the graph of each equation as the slope changes from 1 to 2 to 3. How would the graph of $y = 5x + 3$ appear? To see the change in the graph caused by a change to negative slope, try graphing $y = -x + 3$, $y = -2x + 3$, and $y = -3x + 3$ on the same set of axes.

Use a graphing calculator to graph the following equations. For each exercise, graph the first equation and use its graph to predict the appearance of the other equations. Then graph the other equations on the same set of axes and check your prediction.

1. $y = x$; $y = 6x$, $y = -6x$

2. $y = -x$; $y = -5x$, $y = -10x$

3. $y = \frac{1}{2}x + 2$; $y = \frac{3}{4}x + 2$, $y = x + 2$

4. $y = x + 1$; $y = \frac{5}{4}x + 1$, $y = \frac{5}{2}x + 1$

Vocabulary, Readiness & Video Check

Use the choices below to fill in each blank. Some choices may be used more than once and some not at all.

b	(y_1, x_1)	point-slope	vertical	standard
m	(x_1, y_1)	slope-intercept	horizontal	

1. The form $y = mx + b$ is called _____ form. When a linear equation in two variables is written in this form, _____ is the slope of its graph and (0, _____) is its y-intercept.

2. The form $y - y_1 = m(x - x_1)$ is called _____ form. When a linear equation in two variables is written in this form, _____ is the slope of its graph and _____ is a point on the graph.

For Exercises 3 through 6, identify the form that the linear equation in two variables is written in. For Exercises 7 and 8, identify the appearance of the graph of the equation.

3. $y - 7 = 4(x + 3);$ _____ form

4. $5x - 9y = 11;$ _____ form

5. $y = \dfrac{3}{4}x - \dfrac{1}{3};$ _____ form

6. $y + 2 = \dfrac{-1}{3}(x - 2)$ _____ form

7. $y = \dfrac{1}{2};$ _____ line

8. $x = -17;$ _____ line

Martin-Gay Interactive Videos

See Video 13.5

Watch the section lecture video and answer the following questions.

Objective A 9. In ◫ Example 1, what is the y-intercept? ▶

Objective B 10. We can use the slope-intercept form to graph a line. Complete these statements based on ◫ Example 2: Start by graphing the _____. From this point, find another point by applying the slope– if necessary, rewrite the slope as a(n) _____ ▶

Objective C 11. In ◫ Example 4, we use the point-slope form to find the equation of a line given the slope and a point. How do we then write this equation in standard form? ▶

Objective D 12. The lecture before ◫ Example 5 discusses how to find the equation of a line given two points. Is there any circumstance when we might want to use the slope-intercept form to find the equation of a line given two points? If so, when? ▶

Objective E 13. In ◫ Example 8, we are told to use ordered pairs of the form (time, speed). Explain why it is important to keep track of how we define our ordered pairs and/or our variables. ▶

 Exercise Set MyMathLab®

Objective A *Write an equation of the line with each given slope, m, and y-intercept, (0, b). See Example 1.*

1. $m = 5, b = 3$

2. $m = -3, b = -3$

▶ 3. $m = -4, b = -\dfrac{1}{6}$

4. $m = 2, b = \dfrac{3}{4}$

5. $m = \dfrac{2}{3}, b = 0$

6. $m = -\dfrac{4}{5}, b = 0$

7. $m = 0, b = -8$

8. $m = 0, b = -2$

9. $m = -\dfrac{1}{5}, b = \dfrac{1}{9}$

10. $m = \dfrac{1}{2}, b = -\dfrac{1}{3}$

Objective B *Use the slope-intercept form to graph each equation. See Examples 2 and 3.*

11. $y = 2x + 1$

12. $y = -4x - 1$

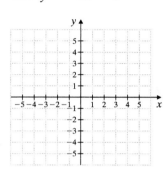

13. $y = \dfrac{2}{3}x + 5$

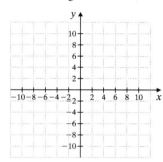

14. $y = \dfrac{1}{4}x - 3$

15. $y = -5x$

16. $y = -6x$

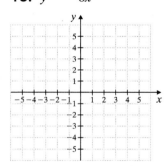

17. $4x + y = 6$

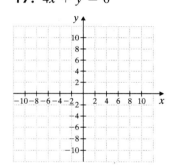

18. $-3x + y = 2$

19. $4x - 7y = -14$

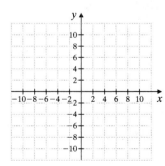

20. $3x - 4y = 4$

21. $x = \dfrac{5}{4}y$

22. $x = \dfrac{3}{2}y$

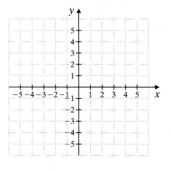

Objective C *Find an equation of each line with the given slope that passes through the given point. Write the equation in the form $Ax + By = C$. See Example 4.*

23. $m = 6;\ (2, 2)$

24. $m = 4;\ (1, 3)$

25. $m = -8;\ (-1, -5)$

26. $m = -2;\ (-11, -12)$

27. $m = \dfrac{3}{2};\quad (5, -6)$

28. $m = \dfrac{2}{3};\quad (-8, 9)$

29. $m = -\dfrac{1}{2};\quad (-3, 0)$

30. $m = -\dfrac{1}{5};\quad (4, 0)$

Objective D *Find an equation of the line passing through each pair of points. Write the equation in the form*
$Ax + By = C$. *See Example 5.*

31. $(3, 2)$ and $(5, 6)$

32. $(6, 2)$ and $(8, 8)$

33. $(-1, 3)$ and $(-2, -5)$

34. $(-4, 0)$ and $(6, -1)$

▶ **35.** $(2, 3)$ and $(-1, -1)$

36. $(7, 10)$ and $(-1, -1)$

37. $(0, 0)$ and $\left(-\dfrac{1}{8}, \dfrac{1}{13}\right)$

38. $(0, 0)$ and $\left(-\dfrac{1}{2}, \dfrac{1}{3}\right)$

Objectives A C D Mixed Practice *See Examples 1, 4, and 5. Find an equation of each line described. Write each equation in slope-intercept form when possible.*

39. With slope $-\dfrac{1}{2}$, through $\left(0, \dfrac{5}{3}\right)$

40. With slope $\dfrac{5}{7}$, through $(0, -3)$

41. Through $(10, 7)$ and $(7, 10)$

42. Through $(5, -6)$ and $(-6, 5)$

▶ **43.** With undefined slope, through $\left(-\dfrac{3}{4}, 1\right)$

44. With slope 0, through $(6.7, 12.1)$

45. Slope 1, through $(-7, 9)$

46. Slope 5, through $(6, -8)$

47. Slope -5, y-intercept $(0, 7)$

48. Slope -2, y-intercept $(0, -4)$

▶ **49.** Through $(1, 2)$, parallel to $y = 5$

50. Through $(1, -5)$, parallel to the y-axis

51. Through $(2, 3)$ and $(0, 0)$

52. Through $(4, 7)$ and $(0, 0)$

53. Through $(-2, -3)$, perpendicular to the y-axis

54. Through $(0, 12)$, perpendicular to the x-axis

55. Slope $-\dfrac{4}{7}$, through $(-1, -2)$

56. Slope $-\dfrac{3}{5}$, through $(4, 4)$

Objective E *Solve. Assume each exercise describes a linear relationship. Write the equations in slope-intercept form. See Example 6.*

57. In 2007, a total of 370 million magazines were sold in the United States. By 2012, this number was 312 million. (*Source:* MPA—The Association of Magazine Media)

    a. Write two ordered pairs of the form (years after 2007, millions of magazines sold) for this situation.

    b. Assume the relationship between years after 2007 and millions of magazines sold is linear over this period. Use the ordered pairs from part **a** to write an equation for the line relating year after 2007 to millions of magazines sold.

    c. Use the linear equation in part **b** to estimate the millions of magazines sold in 2010.

58. In 2008, crude oil field production in the United States was 1830 thousand barrels. In 2012, U.S. crude oil field production increased to 2374 thousand barrels. (*Source:* Energy Information Administration)

    a. Write two ordered pairs of the form (years after 2008, crude oil production).

    b. Assume the relationship between years after 2008 and crude oil production is linear over this period. Use the ordered pairs from part **a** to write an equation of the line relating years after 2008 to crude oil production.

    c. Use the linear equation from part **b** to estimate crude oil production in the United States in 2015, if this trend were to continue.

59. A rock is dropped from the top of a 400-foot cliff. After 1 second, the rock is traveling 32 feet per second. After 3 seconds, the rock is traveling 96 feet per second.

400 feet

  a. Assume that the relationship between time and speed is linear and write an equation describing this relationship. Use ordered pairs of the form (time, speed).

  b. Use this equation to determine the speed of the rock 4 seconds after it is dropped.

61. In 2008 there were approximately 314,000 hybrid vehicles sold in the United States. In 2012, there were approximately 434,000 such vehicles sold. (*Source:* HybridCars.com)

  a. Write an equation describing the relationship between time and the number of hybrid vehicles sold. Use ordered pairs of the form (years past 2008, number of vehicles sold).

  b. Use this equation to estimate the number of hybrid sales in 2014.

63. In 2007 there were 5545 indoor cinema sites in the United States. In 2012, there were approximately 5320 indoor cinema sites. (*Source:* National Association of Theater Owners)

  a. Write an equation describing this relationship. Use ordered pairs of the form (years past 2007, number of indoor cinema sites).

  b. Use this equation to predict the number of indoor cinema sites in 2015.

60. A Hawaiian fruit company is studying the sales of a pineapple sauce to see if this product is to be continued. At the end of its first year, profits on this product amounted to $30,000. At the end of the fourth year, profits were $66,000.

  a. Assume that the relationship between years on the market and profit is linear and write an equation describing this relationship. Use ordered pairs of the form (years on the market, profit).

  b. Use this equation to predict the profit at the end of 7 years.

62. In 2008, there were approximately 945 thousand restaurants in the United States. In 2012, there were 980 thousand restaurants. (*Source:* National Restaurant Association)

  a. Write an equation describing the relationship between time and the number of restaurants. Use ordered pairs of the form (years past 2008, number of restaurants in thousands).

  b. Use this equation to predict the number of eating establishments in 2016.

64. In 2010, the U.S. population per square mile of land area was approximately 87.4. In 2000, this person-per-square-mile population was 79.7. (*Source:* U.S. Census Bureau)

  a. Write an equation describing the relationship between year and person per square mile. Use ordered pairs of the form (years past 2000, person per square mile).

  b. Use this equation to predict the person-per-square-mile population in 2016.

65. The Pool Fun Company has learned that, by pricing a newly released Fun Noodle at $3, sales will reach 10,000 Fun Noodles per day during the summer. Raising the price to $5 will cause the sales to fall to 8000 Fun Noodles per day.

   a. Assume that the relationship between sales price and number of Fun Noodles sold is linear and write an equation describing this relationship. Use ordered pairs of the form (sales price, number sold).

   b. Predict the daily sales of Fun Noodles if the price is $3.50.

66. The value of a building bought in 1995 may be depreciated (or decreased) as time passes for income tax purposes. Seven years after the building was bought, this value was $225,000 and 12 years after it was bought, this value was $195,000.

   a. If the relationship between number of years past 1995 and the depreciated value of the building is linear, write an equation describing this relationship. Use ordered pairs of the form (years past 1995, value of building).

   b. Use this equation to estimate the depreciated value of the building in 2013.

Review

Find the value of $x^2 - 3x + 1$ for each given value of x. See Sections 1.7, 1.8, and Chapter 2.

67. 2   **68.** 5   **69.** −1   **70.** −3

Concept Extensions

Match each linear equation with its graph.

71. $y = 2x + 1$ **72.** $y = -x + 1$ **73.** $y = -3x - 2$ **74.** $y = \frac{5}{3}x - 2$

a.   **b.**   **c.**   **d.**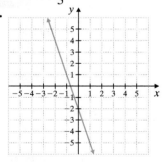

75. Write an equation in standard form of the line that contains the point $(-2, 4)$ and has the same slope as the line $y = 2x + 5$.

76. Write an equation in standard form of the line that contains the point $(3, 0)$ and has the same slope as the line $y = -3x - 1$.

△**77.** Write an equation in standard form of the line that contains the point $(-1, 2)$ and is
   a. parallel to the line $y = 3x - 1$.
   b. perpendicular to the line $y = 3x - 1$.

△**78.** Write an equation in standard form of the line that contains the point $(4, 0)$ and is
   a. parallel to the line $y = -2x + 3$.
   b. perpendicular to the line $y = -2x + 3$.

Summary on Linear Equations

Answers

Find the slope of each line.

1.

2.

3.

4.

Graph each linear equation. For Exercises 11 and 12, label the intercepts.

5. $y = -2x$

6. $x + y = 3$

7. $x = -1$

8. $y = 4$

9. _____

10. _____

11. _____

12. _____

13. _____

14. _____

15. _____

16. _____

17. _____

18. _____

19. _____

20. _____

21. _____

22. _____

23. _____

24. a. _____

b. _____

c. _____

9. $x - 2y = 6$

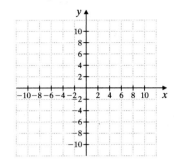

10. $y = 3x + 2$

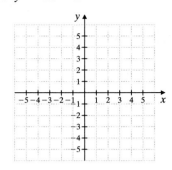

11. $y = -\dfrac{3}{4}x + 3$

12. $5x - 2y = 8$

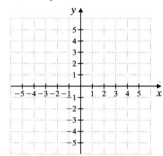

Find the slope of each line by writing the equation in slope-intercept form.

13. $y = 3x - 1$ **14.** $y = -6x + 2$ **15.** $7x + 2y = 11$ **16.** $2x - y = 0$

Find the slope of each line.

17. $x = 2$

18. $y = -4$

19. Write an equation of the line with slope $m = 2$ and y-intercept $\left(0, -\dfrac{1}{3}\right)$. Write the equation in the form $y = mx + b$.

20. Find an equation of the line with slope $m = -4$ that passes through the point $(-1, 3)$. Write the equation in the form $y = mx + b$.

21. Find an equation of the line that passes through the points $(2, 0)$ and $(-1, -3)$. Write the equation in the form $Ax + By = C$.

Determine whether each pair of lines is parallel, perpendicular, or neither.

22. $6x - y = 7$
$\quad\;\; 2x + 3y = 4$

23. $3x - 6y = 4$
$\quad\;\; y = -2x$

24. Yogurt is an ever more popular food item. In 2008, U.S. production of yogurt stood at approximately 3600 million pounds. In 2012, this number rose to 4416 million pounds of yogurt.

   a. Write two ordered pairs of the form (year, millions of pounds of yogurt produced).
   b. Find the slope of the line between these two points.
   c. Write a sentence explaining the meaning of the slope as a rate of change.

Introduction to Functions

Objective A Identifying Relations, Domains, and Ranges

In previous sections, we have discussed the relationships between two quantities. For example, the relationship between the length of the side of a square x and its area y is described by the equation $y = x^2$. Ordered pairs can be used to write down solutions of this equation. For example, $(2, 4)$ is a solution of $y = x^2$, and this notation tells us that the x-value 2 is related to the y-value 4 for this equation. In other words, when the length of the side of a square is 2 units, its area is 4 square units.

Objectives

A Identify Relations, Domains, and Ranges.

B Identify Functions.

C Use the Vertical Line Test.

D Use Function Notation.

Examples of Relationships Between Two Quantities		
Area of Square: $y = x^2$	*Equation of Line:* $y = x + 2$	***Online Advertising Revenue***
		Online Advertising Revenue
Some Ordered Pairs	*Some Ordered Pairs*	*Ordered Pairs*

x	*y*
2	4
5	25
7	49
12	144

x	*y*
−3	−1
0	2
2	4
9	11

Year	*Billions of Dollars*
2006	16.7
2007	20.3
2008	23.5
2009	26.6
2010	29.4

A set of ordered pairs is called a **relation.** The set of all x-coordinates is called the **domain** of a relation, and the set of all y-coordinates is called the **range** of a relation. Equations such as $y = x^2$ are also called relations since equations in two variables define a set of ordered pair solutions.

Example 1 Find the domain and the range of the relation
$$\{(0, 2), (3, 3), (-1, 0), (3, -2)\}.$$

Solution: The domain is the set of all x-coordinates, or $\{-1, 0, 3\}$, and the range is the set of all y-coordinates, or $\{-2, 0, 2, 3\}$.

 Work Practice 1

Practice 1

Find the domain and range of the relation $\{(-3, 5), (-3, 1), (4, 6), (7, 0)\}$.

Objective B Identifying Functions

Paired data occur often in real-life applications. Some special sets of paired data, or ordered pairs, are called *functions*.

Answer
1. domain: $\{-3, 4, 7\}$; range: $\{0, 1, 5, 6\}$

1011

> **Function**
>
> A **function** is a set of ordered pairs in which each x-coordinate has exactly one y-coordinate.

In other words, a function cannot have two ordered pairs with the same x-coordinate but different y-coordinates.

Practice 2

Are the following relations also functions?
a. $\{(2,5),(-3,7),(4,5),(0,-1)\}$
b. $\{(1,4),(6,6),(1,-3),(7,5)\}$

Example 2 Which of the following relations is also a function?

a. $\{(-1,1),(2,3),(7,3),(8,6)\}$
b. $\{(0,-2),(1,5),(0,3),(7,7)\}$

Solution:

a. Although the ordered pairs $(2,3)$ and $(7,3)$ have the same y-value, each x-value is assigned to only one y-value, so this set of ordered pairs is a function.

b. The x-value 0 is paired with two y-values, -2 and 3, so this set of ordered pairs is not a function.

▨ Work Practice 2

Relations and functions can be described by graphs of their ordered pairs.

Practice 3

Is each graph the graph of a function?

a.

b.

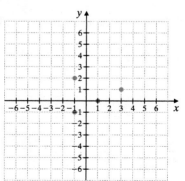

Example 3 Which graph is the graph of a function?

a.

b.

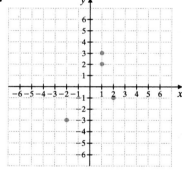

Solution:

a. This is the graph of the relation $\{(-4,-2),(-2,-1),(-1,-1),(1,2)\}$. Each x-coordinate has exactly one y-coordinate, so this is the graph of a function.

b. This is the graph of the relation $\{(-2,-3),(1,2),(1,3),(2,-1)\}$. The x-coordinate 1 is paired with two y-coordinates, 2 and 3, so this is not the graph of a function.

▨ Work Practice 3

Objective C Using the Vertical Line Test ▶

Answers

2. a. a function   **b.** not a function
3. a. a function   **b.** not a function

The graph in Example 3(b) was not the graph of a function because the x-coordinate 1 was paired with two y-coordinates, 2 and 3. Notice that when an x-coordinate is paired with more than one y-coordinate, a vertical line can be drawn that will intersect the graph at more than one point. We can use this fact to determine whether a relation is also a function. We call this the vertical line test.

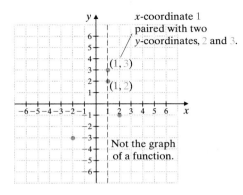

x-coordinate 1 paired with two y-coordinates, 2 and 3.

Not the graph of a function.

Vertical Line Test

If a vertical line can be drawn so that it intersects a graph more than once, the graph is not the graph of a function. (If no such vertical line can be drawn, the graph is that of a function.)

This vertical line test works for all types of graphs on the rectangular coordinate system.

Example 4   Use the vertical line test to determine whether each graph is the graph of a function.

a.   **b.**   **c.** 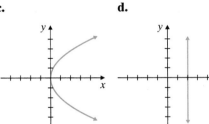   **d.**

Solution:

a. This graph is the graph of a function since no vertical line will intersect this graph more than once.

b. This graph is also the graph of a function; no vertical line will intersect it more than once.

c. This graph is not the graph of a function. Vertical lines can be drawn that intersect the graph in two points. An example of one such line is shown.

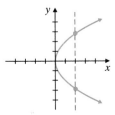

d. This graph is not the graph of a function. A vertical line can be drawn that intersects this line at every point.

■ Work Practice 4

Recall that the graph of a linear equation is a line, and a line that is not vertical will pass the vertical line test. **Thus, all linear equations are functions except those of the form $x = c$, which are vertical lines.**

Practice 5

Which of the following linear equations are functions?
a. $y = 2x$ b. $y = -3x - 1$
c. $y = 8$ d. $x = 2$

Example 5 Which of the following linear equations are functions?

a. $y = x$ b. $y = 2x + 1$ c. $y = 5$ d. $x = -1$

Solution: **a, b,** and **c** are functions because their graphs are nonvertical lines. **d** is not a function because its graph is a vertical line.

■ Work Practice 5

Examples of functions can often be found in magazines, newspapers, books, and other printed material in the form of tables or graphs such as that in Example 6.

Practice 6

Use the graph in Example 6 to answer the questions.

a. Approximate the time of sunrise on March 1.

b. Approximate the date(s) when the sun rises at 6 a.m.

Example 6 The graph shows the sunrise time for Indianapolis, Indiana, for the first of each month for one year. Use this graph to answer the questions.

a. Approximate the time of sunrise on February 1.

b. Approximate the date(s) when the sun rises at 5 a.m.

Indianapolis Sunrise

Source: Wolff World Atlas

c. Is this the graph of a function?

Solution:

a. To approximate the time of sunrise on February 1, we find the mark on the horizontal axis that corresponds to February 1. From this mark, we move vertically upward (shown in blue) until the graph is reached. From that point on the graph, we move horizontally to the left until the vertical axis is reached. The vertical axis there reads 7 a.m., as shown on the next page.

b. To approximate the date(s) when the sun rises at 5 a.m., we find 5 a.m. on the time axis and move horizontally to the right (shown in red). Notice that we will hit the graph at two points, corresponding to two dates for which the sun rises at 5 a.m. We follow both points on the graph vertically downward until the horizontal axis is reached. The sun rises at 5 a.m. at approximately the end of the month of April and the middle of the month of August.

Answers

5. **a, b,** and **c** are functions.
6. **a.** 6:30 a.m.   **b.** middle of March and middle of September

Indianapolis Sunrise

Source: Wolff World Atlas

c. The graph is the graph of a function since it passes the vertical line test. In other words, for every day of the year in Indianapolis, there is exactly one sunrise time.

■ Work Practice 6

Objective D Using Function Notation

The graph of the linear equation $y = 2x + 1$ passes the vertical line test, so we say that $y = 2x + 1$ is a function. In other words, $y = 2x + 1$ gives us a rule for writing ordered pairs where every x-coordinate is paired with at most one y-coordinate.

The variable y is a function of the variable x. For each value of x, there is only one value of y. Thus, we say the variable x is the **independent variable** because any value in the domain can be assigned to x. The variable y is the **dependent variable** because its value depends on x.

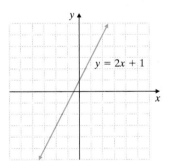

We often use letters such as f, g, and h to name functions. For example, the symbol $f(x)$ means *function of x* and is read "f of x." This notation is called **function notation.** The equation $y = 2x + 1$ can be written as $f(x) = 2x + 1$ using function notation, and these equations mean the same thing. In other words, $y = f(x)$.

The notation $f(1)$ means to replace x with 1 and find the resulting y or function value. Since

$$f(x) = 2x + 1$$

then

$$f(1) = 2(1) + 1 = 3$$

This means that, when $x = 1$, y or $f(x) = 3$, and we have the ordered pair $(1, 3)$. Now let's find $f(2), f(0),$ and $f(-1)$.

$f(x) = 2x + 1$	$f(x) = 2x + 1$	$f(x) = 2x + 1$
$f(2) = 2(2) + 1$	$f(0) = 2(0) + 1$	$f(-1) = 2(-1) + 1$
$= 4 + 1$	$= 0 + 1$	$= -2 + 1$
$= 5$	$= 1$	$= -1$

Ordered Pair:	$(2, 5)$	$(0, 1)$	$(-1, -1)$

Helpful Hint

Note that $f(x)$ is a special symbol in mathematics used to denote a function. The symbol $f(x)$ is read "f of x." It does **not** mean $f \cdot x$ (f times x).

Practice 7

Given $f(x) = x^2 + 1$, find the following and list the corresponding ordered pairs.

a. $f(1)$ **b.** $f(-3)$ **c.** $f(0)$

Example 7   Given $g(x) = x^2 - 3$, find the following and list the corresponding ordered pairs generated.

a. $g(2)$ **b.** $g(-2)$ **c.** $g(0)$

Solution:

a. $g(x) = x^2 - 3$	**b.** $g(x) = x^2 - 3$	**c.** $g(x) = x^2 - 3$
$g(2) = 2^2 - 3$	$g(-2) = (-2)^2 - 3$	$g(0) = 0^2 - 3$
$= 4 - 3$	$= 4 - 3$	$= 0 - 3$
$= 1$	$= 1$	$= -3$

Ordered Pairs:	$g(2) = 1$ gives $(2, 1)$	$g(-2) = 1$ gives $(-2, 1)$	$g(0) = -3$ gives $(0, -3)$

■ Work Practice 7

We now practice finding the domain and the range of a function. The domain of our functions will be the set of all possible real numbers that x can be replaced by. The range is the set of corresponding y-values.

Practice 8

Find the domain of each function.

a. $h(x) = 6x + 3$

b. $f(x) = \dfrac{1}{x^2}$

Example 8   Find the domain of each function.

a. $g(x) = \dfrac{1}{x}$ **b.** $f(x) = 2x + 1$

Solution:

a. Recall that we cannot divide by 0, so the domain of $g(x)$ is the set of all real numbers except 0.

b. In this function, x can be any real number. The domain of $f(x)$ is the set of all real numbers.

■ Work Practice 8

Answers

7. a. $2; (1, 2)$ **b.** $10; (-3, 10)$
c. $1; (0, 1)$
8. a. Domain: all real numbers
   b. Domain: all real numbers except 0

✓ **Concept Check Answer**
$f(2) = -7$

✓**Concept Check** Suppose that the value of f is -7 when the function is evaluated at 2. Write this situation in function notation.

Example 9 Find the domain and the range of each function graphed.

a.

b.

Solution:

a.

b.

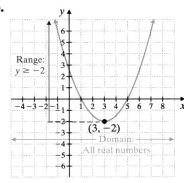

Work Practice 9

Practice 9

Find the domain and the range of each function graphed.

a.

b.

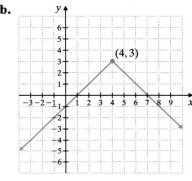

Answers

9. a. Domain: $-4 \leq x \leq 6$
Range: $-2 \leq y \leq 3$

b. Domain: all real numbers
Range: $y \leq 3$

Vocabulary, Readiness & Video Check

Use the choices below to fill in each blank. Some choices may not be used.

$x = c$	horizontal	domain	relation	$(7, 3)$	x	$\{x \mid x \leq 5\}$
$y = c$	vertical	range	function	$(3, 7)$	y	all real numbers

1. A set of ordered pairs is called a(n) _____.

2. A set of ordered pairs that assigns to each x-value exactly one y-value is called a(n) _____.

3. The set of all y-coordinates of a relation is called the _____.

4. The set of all x-coordinates of a relation is called the _____.

5. All linear equations are functions except those whose graphs are _____ lines.

6. All linear equations are functions except those whose equations are of the form _____.

7. If $f(3) = 7$, the corresponding ordered pair is _____.

8. The domain of $f(x) = x + 5$ is _____.

9. For the function $y = mx + b$, the dependent variable is _____ and the independent variable is

_____.

Martin-Gay Interactive Videos   *Watch the section lecture video and answer the following questions.*

See Video 13.6

Objective A 10. In the lecture before 🔲 Example 1, relations are discussed. Why can an equation in two variables define a relation? ▶

Objective B 11. Based on 🔲 Examples 2 and 3, can a set of ordered pairs with no repeated *x*-values, but with repeated *y*-values, be a function? For example: $\{(0, 4), (-3, 4), (2, 4)\}$. ▶

Objective C 12. After reviewing 🔲 Example 8, explain why the vertical line test works. ▶

Objective D 13. Using 🔲 Example 10, write the three function values found and their corresponding ordered pairs. One example is: $f(0) = 2$ corresponds to $(0, 2)$. ▶

13.6 Exercise Set MyMathLab®

Objective A *Find the domain and the range of each relation. See Example 1.*

1. $\{(2, 4), (0, 0), (-7, 10), (10, -7)\}$

2. $\{(3, -6), (1, 4), (-2, -2)\}$

▶ **3.** $\{(0, -2), (1, -2), (5, -2)\}$

4. $\{(5, 0), (5, -3), (5, 4), (5, 3)\}$

Objective B *Determine whether each relation is also a function. See Example 2.*

▶ **5.** $\{(1, 1), (2, 2), (-3, -3), (0, 0)\}$

6. $\{(11, 6), (-1, -2), (0, 0), (3, -2)\}$

▶ **7.** $\{(-1, 0), (-1, 6), (-1, 8)\}$

8. $\{(1, 2), (3, 2), (1, 4)\}$

Objectives B C Mixed Practice *Determine whether each graph is the graph of a function. For Exercises 9 through 12, either write down the ordered pairs or use the vertical line test. See Examples 3 and 4.*

▶ **9.**

10.

11.

12.

13.

14.

15.

16.

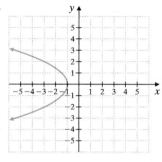

For each exercise, choose the value of x so that the relation is NOT also a function.

17. $\{(2,3), (-1,7), (x,9)\}$

    a. -1 **b.** 1 **c.** 9 **d.** 7

18. $\{(-8,0), (x,1), (5,-3)\}$

    a. 0 **b.** -3 **c.** -5 **d.** 5

Decide whether the equation describes a function. See Example 5.

19. $y - x = 7$ **20.** $2x - 3y = 9$ **21.** $y = 6$ **22.** $x = 3$

23. $x = -2$ **24.** $y = -9$ **25.** $x = y^2$ **26.** $y = x^2 - 3$

                                                     (*Hint:* For Exercises **25** and **26**, check to see whether each *x*-value pairs with exactly one *y*-value.)

The graph shows the sunset times for Seward, Alaska for the first of each month for one year. Use this graph to answer Exercises 27 through 32. See Example 6.

27. Approximate the time of sunset on June 1.

28. Approximate the time of sunset on November 1.

29. Approximate the date(s) when the sunset is at 3 p.m.

30. Approximate the date(s) when the sunset is at 9 p.m.

31. Is this graph the graph of a function? Why or why not?

32. Do you think a graph of sunset times for any location will always be a function? Why or why not?

This graph shows the U.S. hourly minimum wage for each year shown. Use this graph to answer Exercises 33 through 38.
See Example 6.

U.S. Hourly Minimum Wage

Source: U.S. Department of Labor

33. Approximate the minimum wage before October 1996.

34. Approximate the minimum wage in 2006.

35. Find the year when the minimum wage increased to over $7.00 per hour.

36. According to the graph, what hourly wage was in effect for the greatest number of years?

37. Is this graph the graph of a function? Why or why not?

38. Do you think that a similar graph of your hourly wage on January 1 of every year (whether you are working or not) would be the graph of a function? Why or why not?

This graph shows the cost of mailing a large envelope through the U.S. Postal Service by weight. Use this graph to answer Exercises 39 through 44. See Example 6.

USPS Postage for Large Envelopes

Source: United States Postal Service

39. Approximate the postage to mail a large envelope weighing more than 4 ounces but not more than 5 ounces.

40. Approximate the postage to mail a large envelope weighing more than 7 ounces but not more than 8 ounces.

41. Give the weight of a large envelope that costs $1.12 to mail.

42. If you have $3.00, what is the weight of the largest envelope you can mail for that amount of money?

43. Is this graph a function? Why or why not?

44. Do you think that a similar graph of postage to mail a first-class letter would be the graph of a function? Why or why not?

Objective D *Find $f(-2), f(0),$ and $f(3)$ for each function. See Example 7.*

45. $f(x) = 2x - 5$

46. $f(x) = 3 - 7x$

47. $f(x) = x^2 + 2$

48. $f(x) = x^2 - 4$

49. $f(x) = 3x$ **50.** $f(x) = -3x$ **51.** $f(x) = |x|$ **52.** $f(x) = |2 - x|$

Find $h(-1), h(0),$ and $h(4)$ for each function. See Example 7.

53. $h(x) = -5x$ **54.** $h(x) = -3x$ **55.** $h(x) = 2x^2 + 3$ **56.** $h(x) = 3x^2$

For each given function value, write a corresponding ordered pair.

57. $f(3) = 6$ **58.** $f(7) = -2$ **59.** $g(0) = -\dfrac{1}{2}$

60. $g(0) = -\dfrac{7}{8}$ **61.** $h(-2) = 9$ **62.** $h(-10) = 1$

Objectives A D Mixed Practice *Find the domain of each function. See Example 8.*

63. $f(x) = 3x - 7$ **64.** $g(x) = 5 - 2x$ **65.** $h(x) = \dfrac{1}{x + 5}$ **66.** $f(x) = \dfrac{1}{x - 6}$

Objectives A D Mixed Practice *Find the domain and the range of each relation graphed. See Example 9.*

67.

68.

69.

70.

71.

72.

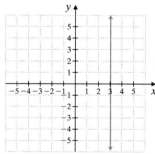

Use the graph of f below to answer Exercises 73 through 78.

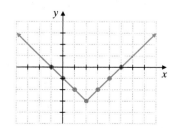

73. Complete the ordered pair solution for f. $(0, \ )$

74. Complete the ordered pair solution for f. $(3, \ )$

75. $f(0) = $ _____?

76. $f(3) = $ _____?

77. If $f(x) = 0$, find the value(s) of x.

78. If $f(x) = -1$, find the value(s) of x.

Review

Solve each inequality. See Section 9.6.

79. $2x + 5 < 7$
80. $3x - 1 \geq 11$
81. $-x + 6 \leq 9$
82. $-2x + 3 > 3$

Find the perimeter of each figure. See Sections 12.3 and 12.4.

△**83.**

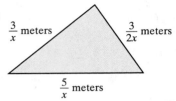

$\dfrac{3}{x}$ meters $\dfrac{3}{2x}$ meters

$\dfrac{5}{x}$ meters

△**84.**

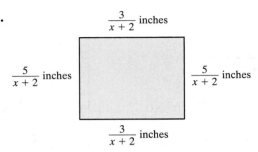

$\dfrac{3}{x + 2}$ inches

$\dfrac{5}{x + 2}$ inches $\dfrac{5}{x + 2}$ inches

$\dfrac{3}{x + 2}$ inches

Concept Extensions

Solve. See the Concept Check in this section.

85. If a function f is evaluated at -5, the value of the function is 12. Write this situation using function notation.

86. Suppose $(9, 20)$ is an ordered pair solution for the function g. Write this situation using function notation.

87. In your own words define (a) function; (b) domain; (c) range.

88. Explain the vertical line test and how it is used.

89. Since $y = x + 7$ is a function, rewrite the equation using function notation.

90. Since $y = 3$ is a function, rewrite the equation using function notation.

91. The dosage in milligrams of Ivermectin, a heart-worm preventive for a dog who weighs x pounds, is given by the function

$$f(x) = \frac{136}{25}x$$

   a. Find the proper dosage for a dog who weighs 35 pounds.
   b. Find the proper dosage for a dog who weighs 70 pounds.

92. Forensic scientists use the function

$$f(x) = 2.59x + 47.24$$

to estimate the height of a woman, in centimeters, given the length x of her femur bone in centimeters.

   a. Estimate the height of a woman whose femur measures 46 centimeters.
   b. Estimate the height of a woman whose femur measures 39 centimeters.

13.7 Graphing Linear Inequalities in Two Variables

Recall that a linear equation in two variables is an equation that can be written in the form $Ax + By = C$, where A, B, and C are real numbers and A and B are not both 0. A **linear inequality in two variables** is an inequality that can be written in one of the forms

$$Ax + By < C \qquad Ax + By \leq C$$
$$Ax + By > C \qquad Ax + By \geq C$$

where A, B, and C are real numbers and A and B are not both 0.

Objectives

A Determine Whether an Ordered Pair Is a Solution of a Linear Inequality in Two Variables.

B Graph a Linear Inequality in Two Variables.

Objective A Determining Solutions of Linear Inequalities in Two Variables

Just as for linear equations in x and y, an ordered pair is a **solution** of an inequality in x and y if replacing the variables with the coordinates of the ordered pair results in a true statement.

Example 1 Determine whether each ordered pair is a solution of the inequality $2x - y < 6$.

a. $(5, -1)$ **b.** $(2, 7)$

Solution:

a. We replace x with 5 and y with -1 and see if a true statement results.

$$2x - y < 6$$
$$2(5) - (-1) < 6 \quad \text{Replace } x \text{ with 5 and } y \text{ with } -1.$$
$$10 + 1 < 6$$
$$11 < 6 \quad \text{False}$$

The ordered pair $(5, -1)$ is not a solution since $11 < 6$ is a false statement.

b. We replace x with 2 and y with 7 and see if a true statement results.

$$2x - y < 6$$
$$2(2) - (7) < 6 \quad \text{Replace } x \text{ with 2 and } y \text{ with 7.}$$
$$4 - 7 < 6$$
$$-3 < 6 \quad \text{True}$$

The ordered pair $(2, 7)$ is a solution since $-3 < 6$ is a true statement.

 Work Practice 1

Practice 1

Determine whether each ordered pair is a solution of $x - 4y > 8$.

a. $(-3, 2)$ **b.** $(9, 0)$

Objective B Graphing Linear Inequalities in Two Variables

The linear equation $x - y = 1$ is graphed next. Recall that all points on the line correspond to ordered pairs that satisfy the equation $x - y = 1$.

Notice that the line defined by $x - y = 1$ divides the rectangular coordinate system plane into 2 sides. All points on one side of the line satisfy the inequality $x - y < 1$, and all points on the other side satisfy the inequality $x - y > 1$. The graph on the next page shows a few examples of this.

Answers

1. a. no   **b.** yes

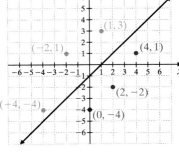

The graph of $x - y < 1$ is the region shaded blue and the graph of $x - y > 1$ is the region shaded red below.

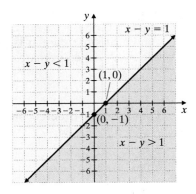

The region to the left of the line and the region to the right of the line are called **half-planes.** Every line divides the plane (similar to a sheet of paper extending indefinitely in all directions) into two half-planes; the line is called the **boundary.**

Recall that the inequality $x - y \leq 1$ means

$$x - y = 1 \quad \text{or} \quad x - y < 1$$

Thus, the graph of $x - y \leq 1$ is the half-plane $x - y < 1$ along with the boundary line $x - y = 1$.

To Graph a Linear Inequality in Two Variables

Step 1: Graph the boundary line found by replacing the inequality sign with an equal sign. If the inequality sign is $>$ or $<$, graph a dashed boundary line (indicating that the points on the line are not solutions of the inequality). If the inequality sign is $\geq$ or $\leq$, graph a solid boundary line (indicating that the points on the line are solutions of the inequality).

Step 2: Choose a point *not* on the boundary line as a test point. Substitute the coordinates of this test point into the *original* inequality.

Step 3: If a true statement is obtained in Step 2, shade the half-plane that contains the test point. If a false statement is obtained, shade the half-plane that does not contain the test point.

Example 2   Graph: $x + y < 7$

Solution:

Step 1: First we graph the boundary line by graphing the equation $x + y = 7$. We graph this boundary as a *dashed line* because the inequality sign is $<$, and thus the points on the line are not solutions of the inequality $x + y < 7$.

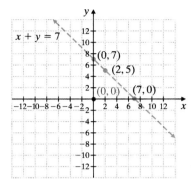

Step 2: Next we choose a test point, being careful *not* to choose a point on the boundary line. We choose $(0, 0)$, and substitute the coordinates of $(0, 0)$ into $x + y < 7$.

$x + y < 7$ Original inequality

$0 + 0 < 7$ Replace x with 0 and y with 0.

$0 < 7$ True

Step 3: Since the result is a true statement, $(0, 0)$ is a solution of $x + y < 7$, and every point in the same half-plane as $(0, 0)$ is also a solution. To indicate this, we shade the entire half-plane containing $(0, 0)$, as shown.

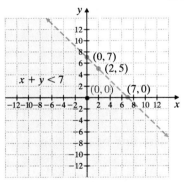

■ Work Practice 2

✓**Concept Check** Determine whether $(0, 0)$ is included in the graph of

a. $y \geq 2x + 3$

b. $x < 7$

c. $2x - 3y < 6$

Practice 2

Graph: $x - y > 3$

Answer

2.

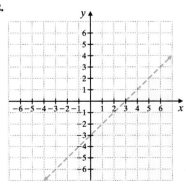

✓**Concept Check Answers**

a. no   **b.** yes   **c.** yes

Practice 3

Graph: $x - 4y \leq 4$

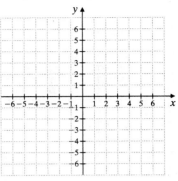

Practice 4

Graph: $y < 3x$

3.

4.

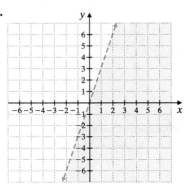

Example 3 Graph: $2x - y \geq 3$

Solution:

Step 1: We graph the boundary line by graphing $2x - y = 3$. We draw this line as a solid line because the inequality sign is $\geq$, and thus the points on the line are solutions of $2x - y \geq 3$.

Step 2: Once again, $(0, 0)$ is a convenient test point since it is not on the boundary line.

We substitute 0 for x and 0 for y into the original inequality.

$$2x - y \geq 3$$
$$2(0) - 0 \geq 3 \quad \text{Let } x = 0 \text{ and } y = 0.$$
$$0 \geq 3 \quad \text{False}$$

Step 3: Since the statement is false, no point in the half-plane containing $(0, 0)$ is a solution. Therefore, we shade the half-plane that does not contain $(0, 0)$. Every point in the shaded half-plane and every point on the boundary line is a solution of $2x - y \geq 3$.

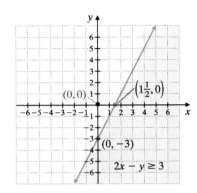

■ Work Practice 3

Helpful Hint

When graphing an inequality, make sure the test point is substituted into the **original inequality.** For Example 3, we substituted the test point $(0, 0)$ into the **original inequality** $2x - y \geq 3$, *not* $2x - y = 3$.

Example 4 Graph: $x > 2y$

Solution:

Step 1: We find the boundary line by graphing $x = 2y$. The boundary line is a dashed line since the inequality symbol is $>$.

Step 2: We cannot use $(0, 0)$ as a test point because it is a point on the boundary line. We choose instead $(0, 2)$.

$$x > 2y$$
$$0 > 2(2) \quad \text{Let } x = 0 \text{ and } y = 2.$$
$$0 > 4 \quad \text{False}$$

Step 3: Since the statement is false, we shade the half-plane that does not contain the test point $(0, 2)$, as shown.

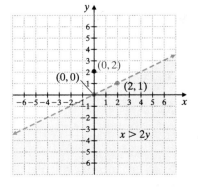

■ Work Practice 4

Example 5 Graph: $5x + 4y \le 20$

Solution: We graph the solid boundary line $5x + 4y = 20$ and choose $(0, 0)$ as the test point.

$$5x + 4y \le 20$$
$$5(0) + 4(0) \le 20 \quad \text{Let } x = 0 \text{ and } y = 0.$$
$$0 \le 20 \quad \text{True}$$

We shade the half-plane that contains $(0, 0)$, as shown.

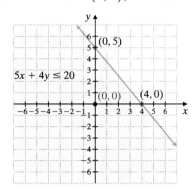

■ Work Practice 5

Example 6 Graph: $y > 3$

Solution: We graph the dashed boundary line $y = 3$ and choose $(0, 0)$ as the test point. (Recall that the graph of $y = 3$ is a horizontal line with y-intercept 3.)

$$y > 3$$
$$0 > 3 \quad \text{Let } y = 0.$$
$$0 > 3 \quad \text{False}$$

We shade the half-plane that does not contain $(0, 0)$, as shown.

■ Work Practice 6

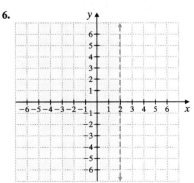

Practice 7

Graph: $y \geq \dfrac{1}{4}x + 3$

Answer

7.

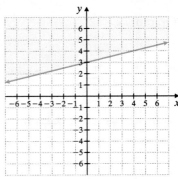

Example 7 Graph: $y \leq \dfrac{2}{3}x - 4$

Solution: Graph the solid boundary line $y = \dfrac{2}{3}x - 4$. This equation is in slope-intercept form, with slope $\dfrac{2}{3}$ and y-intercept -4.

We use this information to graph the line. Then we choose $(0, 0)$ as our test point.

$$y \leq \dfrac{2}{3}x - 4$$

$$0 \leq \dfrac{2}{3} \cdot 0 - 4$$

$$0 \leq -4 \quad \text{False}$$

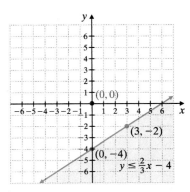

We shade the half-plane that does not contain $(0, 0)$, as shown.

■ Work Practice 7

Vocabulary, Readiness & Video Check

Use the choices below to fill in each blank. Some choices may be used more than once, and some not at all.

true	$x < 2$	$y < 2$	half-planes
false	$x \leq 2$	$y \leq 2$	linear inequality in two variables

1. The statement $5x - 6y < 7$ is an example of a _____.

2. A boundary line divides a plane into two regions called _____.

3. True or false? The graph of $5x - 6y < 7$ includes its corresponding boundary line. _____

4. True or false? When graphing a linear inequality, to determine which side of the boundary line to shade, choose a point *not* on the boundary line. _____

5. True or false? The boundary line for the inequality $5x - 6y < 7$ is the graph of $5x - 6y = 7$.

_____

6. The graph of _____ is

Martin-Gay Interactive Videos | Watch the section lecture video and answer the following questions.

Objective A **7.** From Example 1, how do we determine whether an ordered pair in x and y is a solution of an inequality in x and y? ▶

Objective B **8.** From Example 3, how do we find the equation of the boundary line? How do we determine if the points on the boundary line are solutions of the inequality? ▶

See Video 13.7

13.7 **Exercise Set** MyMathLab® ▶

Objective A *Determine whether the ordered pairs given are solutions of the linear inequality in two variables. See Example 1.*

1. $x - y > 3;\ (0, 3),\ (2, -1)$

2. $y - x < -2;\ (2, 1),\ (5, -1)$

3. $3x - 5y \le -4;\ (2, 3),\ (-1, -1)$

4. $2x + y \ge 10;\ (0, 11),\ (5, 0)$

▶ **5.** $x < -y;\ (0, 2),\ (-5, 1)$

6. $y > 3x;\ (0, 0),\ (1, 4)$

Objective B *Graph each inequality. See Examples 2 through 7.*

7. $x + y \le 1$

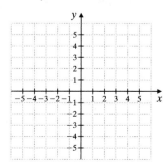

8. $x + y \ge -2$

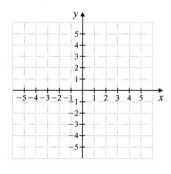

9. $2x - y > -4$

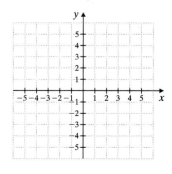

10. $x - 3y < 3$

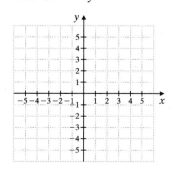

▶ **11.** $y \ge 2x$

12. $y \le 3x$

13. $x < -3y$

14. $x > -2y$

15. $y \geq x + 5$

16. $y \leq x + 1$

17. $y < 4$

18. $y > 2$

19. $x \geq -3$

20. $x \leq -1$

21. $5x + 2y \leq 10$

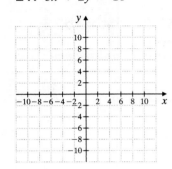

22. $4x + 3y \geq 12$

23. $x > y$

24. $x \leq -y$

25. $x - y \leq 6$

26. $x - y > 10$

27. $x \geq 0$

28. $y \leq 0$

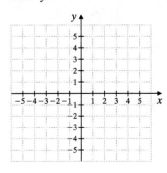

⊙ **29.** $2x + 7y > 5$

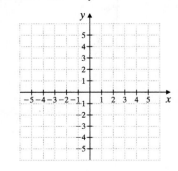

30. $3x + 5y \leq -2$

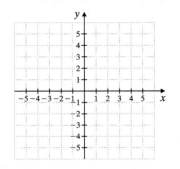

31. $y \geq \dfrac{1}{2}x - 4$

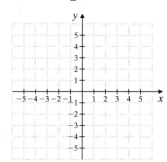

32. $y < \dfrac{2}{5}x - 3$

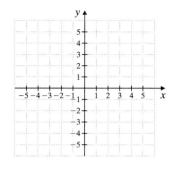

33. $y < -\dfrac{3}{4}x + 2$

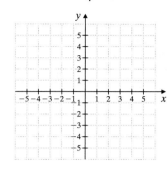

34. $y > -\dfrac{1}{3}x + 4$

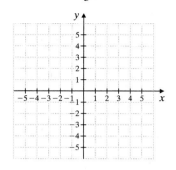

Review

Approximate the coordinates of each point of intersection. See Section 13.1.

35.

36.

37.

38.

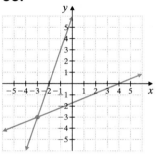

Concept Extensions

Match each inequality with its graph.

a. $x > 2$ **b.** $y < 2$ **c.** $y \leq 2x$ **d.** $y \leq -3x$

39.

40.

41.

42.

43. Explain why a point on the boundary line should not be chosen as the test point.

44. Write an inequality whose solutions are all points with coordinates whose sum is at least 13.

Determine whether $(1, 1)$ is included in each graph. See the Concept Check in this section.

45. $3x + 4y < 8$ **46.** $y > 5x$ **47.** $y \geq -\dfrac{1}{2}x$ **48.** $x > 3$

49. It's the end of the budgeting period for Dennis Fernandes and he has $500 left in his budget for car rental expenses. He plans to spend this budget on a sales trip throughout southern Texas. He will rent a car that costs $30 per day and $0.15 per mile and he can spend no more than $500.

a. Write an inequality describing this situation. Let x = number of days and let y = number of miles.

b. Graph this inequality below.

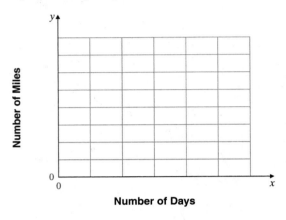

c. Why is the grid showing quadrant I only?

50. Scott Sambracci and Sara Thygeson are planning their wedding. They have calculated that they want the cost of their wedding ceremony x plus the cost of their reception y to be no more than $5000.

a. Write an inequality describing this relationship.

b. Graph this inequality below.

c. Why is the grid showing quadrant I only?

13.8 **Direct and Inverse Variation**

Objectives

A Solve Problems Involving Direct Variation.

B Solve Problems Involving Inverse Variation.

C Solve Problems Involving Other Types of Direct and Inverse Variation.

D Solve Applications of Variation.

Thus far, we have studied linear equations in two variables. Recall that such an equation can be written in the form $Ax + By = C$, where A and B are not both 0. Also recall that the graph of a linear equation in two variables is a line. In this section, we begin by looking at a particular family of linear equations—those that can be written in the form

$$y = kx$$

where k is a constant. This family of equations is called *direct variation*.

Objective A Solving Direct Variation Problems

Let's suppose that you are earning $7.25 per hour at a part-time job. The amount of money you earn depends on the number of hours you work. This is illustrated by the following table:

Hours Worked	0	1	2	3	4	
Money Earned (before deductions)	0	7.25	14.50	21.75	29.00	and so on

In general, to calculate your earnings (before deductions), multiply the constant $7.25 by the number of hours you work. If we let y represent the amount of money earned and x represent the number of hours worked, we get the direct variation equation

$$y = 7.25 \cdot x$$

earnings = $7.25 · hours worked

Notice that in this direct variation equation, as the number of hours increases, the pay increases as well.

> ### Direct Variation
>
> **y varies directly as x,** or **y is directly proportional to x,** if there is a nonzero constant k such that
>
> $$y = kx$$
>
> The number k is called the **constant of variation** or the **constant of proportionality.**

In our direct variation example, $y = 7.25x$, the constant of variation is 7.25.

Let's use the previous table to graph $y = 7.25x$. We begin our graph at the ordered pair solution $(0, 0)$. Why? We assume that the least amount of hours worked is 0. If 0 hours are worked, then the pay is $0.

As illustrated in this graph, a direct variation equation $y = kx$ is linear. Also notice that $y = 7.25x$ is a function since its graph passes the vertical line test.

Example 1 Write a direct variation equation of the form $y = kx$ that satisfies the ordered pairs in the table below.

x	2	9	1.5	−1
y	6	27	4.5	−3

Solution: We are given that there is a direct variation relationship between x and y. This means that

$$y = kx$$

By studying the given values, you may be able to mentally calculate k. If not, to find k, we simply substitute one given ordered pair into this equation and solve for k. We'll use the given pair $(2, 6)$.

$$y = kx$$
$$6 = k \cdot 2$$
$$\frac{6}{2} = \frac{k \cdot 2}{2}$$
$$3 = k \qquad \text{Solve for } k.$$

Since $k = 3$, we have the equation $y = 3x$.
To check, see that each given y is 3 times the given x.

■ Work Practice 1

Practice 1

Write a direct variation equation that satisfies:

x	4	$\frac{1}{2}$	1.5	6
y	8	1	3	12

Answer
1. $y = 2x$

Let's try another type of direct variation example.

Copyright 2015 Pearson Education, Inc.

Practice 2

Suppose that y varies directly as x. If y is 15 when x is 45, find the constant of variation and the direct variation equation. Then find y when x is 3.

Example 2   Suppose that y varies directly as x. If y is 17 when x is 34, find the constant of variation and the direct variation equation. Then find y when x is 12.

Solution: Let's use the same method as in Example 1 to find k. Since we are told that y varies directly as x, we know the relationship is of the form

$$y = kx$$

Let $y = 17$ and $x = 34$ and solve for k.

$$17 = k \cdot 34$$

$$\frac{17}{34} = \frac{k \cdot 34}{34}$$

$$\frac{1}{2} = k \qquad \text{Solve for } k.$$

Thus, the constant of variation is $\dfrac{1}{2}$ and the equation is $y = \dfrac{1}{2}x$.

To find y when $x = 12$, use $y = \dfrac{1}{2}x$ and replace x with 12.

$$y = \frac{1}{2}x$$

$$y = \frac{1}{2} \cdot 12 \qquad \text{Replace } x \text{ with 12.}$$

$$y = 6$$

Thus, when x is 12, y is 6.

▨ Work Practice 2

Let's review a few facts about linear equations of the form $y = kx$.

> ## Direct Variation: $y = kx$
>
> - There is a direct variation relationship between x and y.
> - The graph is a line.
> - The line will always go through the origin $(0, 0)$. Why?
>
>   Let $x = 0$. Then $y = k \cdot 0$ or $y = 0$.
>
> - The slope of the graph of $y = kx$ is k, the constant of variation. Why? Remember that the slope of an equation of the form $y = mx + b$ is m, the coefficient of x.
> - The equation $y = kx$ describes a function. Each x has a unique y and its graph passes the vertical line test.

Practice 3

Find the constant of variation and the direct variation equation for the line below.

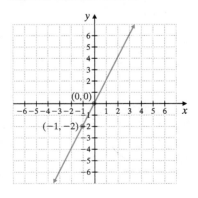

Example 3   The line is the graph of a direct variation equation. Find the constant of variation and the direct variation equation.

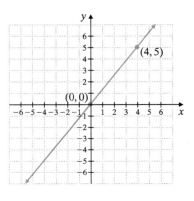

Answers

2. $k = \dfrac{1}{3}$; $y = \dfrac{1}{3}x$; $y = 1$

3. $k = 2$; $y = 2x$

Solution: Recall that k, the constant of variation, is the same as the slope of the line. Thus, to find k, we use the slope formula and find slope.

Using the given points $(0, 0)$ and $(4, 5)$, we have

$$\text{slope} = \frac{5 - 0}{4 - 0} = \frac{5}{4}$$

Thus, $k = \dfrac{5}{4}$ and the variation equation is $y = \dfrac{5}{4}x$.

■ Work Practice 3

Objective B Solving Inverse Variation Problems

In this section, we introduce another type of variation called inverse variation.

Let's suppose you need to drive a distance of 40 miles. You know that the faster you drive the distance, the sooner you arrive at your destination. Recall that there is a mathematical relationship between distance, rate, and time. It is $d = r \cdot t$. In our example, distance is a constant 40 miles, so we have $40 = r \cdot t$ or $t = \dfrac{40}{r}$.

For example, if you drive 10 mph, the time to drive the 40 miles is

$$t = \frac{40}{r} = \frac{40}{10} = 4 \text{ hours}$$

If you drive 20 mph, the time is

$$t = \frac{40}{r} = \frac{40}{20} = 2 \text{ hours}$$

Again, notice that as speed increases, time decreases. Below are some ordered pair solutions of $t = \dfrac{40}{r}$ and its graph.

Rate (mph)	r	5	10	20	40	60	80
Time (hr)	t	8	4	2	1	$\frac{2}{3}$	$\frac{1}{2}$

Notice that the graph of this variation is not a line, but it passes the vertical line test so $t = \dfrac{40}{r}$ does describe a function. This is an example of inverse variation.

Inverse Variation

y varies inversely as x, or **y is inversely proportional to x,** if there is a nonzero constant k such that

$$y = \frac{k}{x}$$

The number k is called the **constant of variation** or the **constant of proportionality.**

In our inverse variation example, $t = \dfrac{40}{r}$ or $y = \dfrac{40}{x}$, the constant of variation is 40.

We can immediately see differences and similarities in direct variation and inverse variation.

Direct Variation	$y = kx$	linear equation	both functions
Inverse Variation	$y = \frac{k}{x}$	rational equation	

Remember from Chapter 12 that $y = \dfrac{k}{x}$ is a rational equation and not a linear equation. Also notice that because x is in the denominator, x can be any value except 0. We can still derive an inverse variation equation from a table of values.

Practice 4

Write an inverse variation equation of the form $y = \dfrac{k}{x}$ that satisfies:

x	4	10	40	−2
y	5	2	$\frac{1}{2}$	−10

Example 4 Write an inverse variation equation of the form $y = \dfrac{k}{x}$ that satisfies the ordered pairs in the table below.

x	2	4	$\frac{1}{2}$
y	6	3	24

Solution: Since there is an inverse variation relationship between x and y, we know that $y = \dfrac{k}{x}$.

To find k, choose one given ordered pair and substitute the values into the equation. We'll use $(2, 6)$.

$$y = \frac{k}{x}$$

$$6 = \frac{k}{2}$$

$$2 \cdot 6 = 2 \cdot \frac{k}{2} \quad \text{Multiply both sides by 2.}$$

$$12 = k \quad \text{Solve.}$$

Since $k = 12$, we have the equation $y = \dfrac{12}{x}$.

■ Work Practice 4

Helpful Hint

Multiply both sides of the inverse variation relationship equation $y = \dfrac{k}{x}$ by x (as long as x is not 0), and we have $xy = k$. This means that if y varies inversely as x, their product is always the constant of variation k. For an example of this, check the table from Example 4:

x	2	4	$\frac{1}{2}$
y	6	3	24

$$2 \cdot 6 = 12 \qquad 4 \cdot 3 = 12 \qquad \tfrac{1}{2} \cdot 24 = 12$$

Answer

4. $y = \dfrac{20}{x}$

Example 5 Suppose that y varies inversely as x. If $y = 0.02$ when $x = 75$, find the constant of variation and the inverse variation equation. Then find y when x is 30.

Solution: Since y varies inversely as x, the constant of variation may be found by simply finding the product of the given x and y.

$$k = xy = 75(0.02) = 1.5$$

To check, we will use the inverse variation equation

$$y = \frac{k}{x}$$

Let $y = 0.02$ and $x = 75$ and solve for k.

$$0.02 = \frac{k}{75}$$

$$75(0.02) = 75 \cdot \frac{k}{75} \quad \text{Multiply both sides by 75.}$$

$$1.5 = k \quad \text{Solve for } k.$$

Thus, the constant of variation is 1.5 and the equation is $y = \frac{1.5}{x}$. To find y when $x = 30$, use $y = \frac{1.5}{x}$ and replace x with 30.

$$y = \frac{1.5}{x}$$

$$y = \frac{1.5}{30} \quad \text{Replace } x \text{ with 30.}$$

$$y = 0.05$$

Thus, when x is 30, y is 0.05.

■ **Work Practice 5**

Objective C Solving Other Types of Direct and Inverse Variation Problems ▶

It is possible for y to vary directly or inversely as powers of x.

Direct and Inverse Variation as *n*th Powers of *x*

y varies directly as a power of x if there is a nonzero constant k and a natural number n such that

$$y = kx^n$$

y varies inversely as a power of x if there is a nonzero constant k and a natural number n such that

$$y = \frac{k}{x^n}$$

Example 6 The surface area of a cube A varies directly as the square of a length of its sides. If A is 54 when s is 3, find A when $s = 4.2$.

s

(Continued on next page)

Practice 5

Suppose that y varies inversely as x. If y is 4 when x is 0.8, find the constant of variation and the inverse variation equation. Then find y when x is 20.

Practice 6

The area of a circle varies directly as the square of its radius. A circle with radius 7 inches has an area of 49π square inches. Find the area of a circle whose radius is 4 feet.

Answers

5. $k = 3.2$; $y = \dfrac{3.2}{x}$; $y = 0.16$

6. 16π sq ft

Solution: Since the surface area A varies directly as the square of side s, we have

$$A = ks^2$$

To find k, let $A = 54$ and $s = 3$.

$$A = k \cdot s^2$$
$$54 = k \cdot 3^2 \quad \text{Let } A = 54 \text{ and } s = 3.$$
$$54 = 9k \quad \quad 3^2 = 9.$$
$$6 = k \quad \quad \text{Divide by 9.}$$

The formula for surface area of a cube is then

$A = 6s^2$, where s is the length of a side.

To find the surface area when $s = 4.2$, substitute.

$$A = 6s^2$$
$$A = 6 \cdot (4.2)^2$$
$$A = 105.84$$

The surface area of a cube whose side measures 4.2 units is 105.84 sq units.

◼ Work Practice 6

Objective **D** Solving Applications of Variation

There are many real-life applications of direct and inverse variation.

Practice 7

The distance d that an object falls is directly proportional to the square of the time of the fall, t. If an object falls 144 feet in 3 seconds, find how far the object falls in 5 seconds.

Example 7   The weight of a body w varies inversely with the square of its distance from the center of Earth, d. If a person weighs 160 pounds on the surface of Earth, what is the person's weight 200 miles above the surface? (Assume that the radius of Earth is 4000 miles.)

Solution:

1. UNDERSTAND. Make sure you read and reread the problem.
2. TRANSLATE. Since we are told that weight w varies inversely with the square of its distance from the center of Earth, d, we have

$$w = \frac{k}{d^2}$$

3. SOLVE. To solve the problem, we first find k. To do so, we use the fact that the person weighs 160 pounds on Earth's surface, which is a distance of 4000 miles from the Earth's center.

$$w = \frac{k}{d^2}$$

$$160 = \frac{k}{(4000)^2}$$

$$2{,}560{,}000{,}000 = k$$

Thus, we have $w = \dfrac{2{,}560{,}000{,}000}{d^2}$.

Answer

7. 400 feet

Since we want to know the person's weight 200 miles above the Earth's surface, we let $d = 4200$ and find w.

$$w = \frac{2,560,000,000}{d^2}$$

$$w = \frac{2,560,000,000}{(4200)^2}$$ A person 200 miles above the Earth's surface is 4200 miles from the Earth's center.

$$w \approx 145$$ Simplify.

4. **INTERPRET.** *Check:* Your answer is reasonable since the farther a person is from Earth, the less the person weighs. *State:* Thus, 200 miles above the surface of the Earth, a 160-pound person weighs approximately 145 pounds.

▬ Work Practice 7

Vocabulary, Readiness & Video Check

State whether each equation represents direct or inverse variation.

1. $y = \dfrac{k}{x}$, where k is a constant. _____

2. $y = kx$, where k is a constant. _____

3. $y = 5x$ _____

4. $y = \dfrac{5}{x}$ _____

5. $y = \dfrac{7}{x^2}$ _____

6. $y = 6.5x^4$ _____

7. $y = \dfrac{11}{x}$ _____

8. $y = 18x$ _____

9. $y = 12x^2$ _____

10. $y = \dfrac{20}{x^3}$ _____

Martin-Gay Interactive Videos

See Video 13.8 ●

Watch the section lecture video and answer the following questions.

Objective A 11. Based on the lecture before ⊟ Example 1, what kind of equation is a direct variation equation? What does k represent in this equation? ⊙

Objective B 12. In ⊟ Example 4, why is it not necessary to place the given values of x and y into the inverse variation equation in order to find k? ⊙

Objective C 13. From ⊟ Examples 5–7, does a power on x change the basic direct and inverse variation formula relationships? ⊙

Objective D 14. In ⊟ Example 8, why is it reasonable to expect our answer to be a greater distance than the original distance given in the problem? ⊙

13.8 Exercise Set MyMathLab®

Objective A *Write a direct variation equation, $y = kx$, that satisfies the ordered pairs in each table. See Example 1.*

1.

x	0	6	10
y	0	3	5

2.

x	0	2	−1	3
y	0	14	−7	21

3.

x	−2	2	4	5
y	−12	12	24	30

4.

x	3	9	−2	12
y	1	3	$-\dfrac{2}{3}$	4

Write a direct variation equation, $y = kx$, that describes each graph. See Example 3.

5.

6.

7.

8.

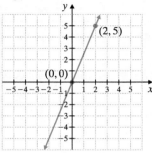

Objective B *Write an inverse variation equation, $y = \dfrac{k}{x}$, that satisfies the ordered pairs in each table. See Example 4.*

9.

x	1	−7	3.5	−2
y	7	−1	2	−3.5

10.

x	2	−11	4	−4
y	11	−2	5.5	−5.5

11.

x	10	$\dfrac{1}{2}$	$-\dfrac{1}{4}$
y	0.05	1	−2

12.

x	4	$\dfrac{1}{5}$	−8
y	0.1	2	−0.05

Objectives A B C Translating *Write an equation to describe each variation. Use k for the constant of proportionality. See Examples 1 through 6.*

13. y varies directly as x.   **14.** a varies directly as b.   **15.** h varies inversely as t.   **16.** s varies inversely as t.

17. z varies directly as x^2.   **18.** p varies inversely as x^2.   **19.** y varies inversely as z^3.   **20.** x varies directly as y^4.

21. x varies inversely as $\sqrt{y}$.   **22.** y varies directly as d^2.

Objectives A B C *Solve. See Examples 2, 5, and 6.*

23. y varies directly as x. If $y = 20$ when $x = 5$, find y when x is 10.

24. y varies directly as x. If $y = 27$ when $x = 3$, find y when x is 2.

25. y varies inversely as x. If $y = 5$ when $x = 60$, find y when x is 100.

26. y varies inversely as x. If $y = 200$ when $x = 5$, find y when x is 4.

27. z varies directly as x^2. If $z = 96$ when $x = 4$, find z when $x = 3$.

28. s varies directly as t^3. If $s = 270$ when $t = 3$, find s when $t = 1$.

29. a varies inversely as b^3. If $a = \dfrac{3}{2}$ when $b = 2$, find a when b is 3.

30. p varies inversely as q^2. If $p = \dfrac{5}{16}$ when $q = 8$, find p when $q = \dfrac{1}{2}$.

Objectives A B C D *Solve. See Examples 1 through 7.*

31. Your paycheck (before deductions) varies directly as the number of hours you work. If your paycheck is $166.50 for 18 hours, find your pay for 10 hours.

32. If your paycheck (before deductions) is $304.50 for 30 hours, find your pay for 34 hours. (See Exercise **31**.)

33. The cost of manufacturing a certain type of head-phone varies inversely as the number of headphones increases. If 5000 headphones can be manufactured for $9.00 each, find the cost per headphone to manufacture 7500 headphones.

34. The cost of manufacturing a certain composition notebook varies inversely as the number of note-books increases. If 10,000 notebooks can be manufactured for $0.50 each, find the cost per notebook to manufacture 18,000 notebooks. Round your answer to the nearest cent.

35. The distance a spring stretches varies directly with the weight attached to the spring. If a 60-pound weight stretches the spring 4 inches, find the distance that an 80-pound weight stretches the spring.

36. If a 30-pound weight stretches a spring 10 inches, find the distance a 20-pound weight stretches the spring. (See Exercise **35**.)

37. The weight of an object varies inversely as the square of its distance from the center of Earth. If a person weighs 180 pounds on Earth's surface, what is his weight 10 miles above the surface of Earth? (Assume that Earth's radius is 4000 miles and round your answer to one decimal place.)

38. For a constant distance, the rate of travel varies inversely as the time traveled. If a family travels 55 mph and arrives at a destination in 4 hours, how long will the return trip take traveling at 60 mph?

39. The distance d that an object falls is directly proportional to the square of the time of the fall, t. A person who is parachuting for the first time is told to wait 10 seconds before opening the parachute. If the person falls 64 feet in 2 seconds, find how far he falls in 10 seconds.

40. The distance needed for a car to stop, d, is directly proportional to the square of its rate of travel, r. Under certain driving conditions, a car traveling 60 mph needs 300 feet to stop. With these same driving conditions, how long does it take a car to stop if the car is traveling 30 mph when the brakes are applied?

Review

Add the equations. See Section 10.4.

41. $-3x + 4y = 7$
   $\underline{3x - 2y = 9}$

42. $x - y = -9$
   $\underline{-x - y = -14}$

43. $5x - 0.4y = 0.7$
   $\underline{-9x + 0.4y = -0.2}$

44. $1.9x - 2y = 5.7$
   $\underline{-1.9x - 0.1y = 2.3}$

Concept Extensions

45. Suppose that y varies directly as x. If x is tripled, what is the effect on y?

46. Suppose that y varies directly as x^2. If x is tripled, what is the effect on y?

47. The period of a pendulum p (the time of one complete back-and-forth swing) varies directly with the square root of its length, ℓ. If the length of the pendulum is quadrupled, what is the effect on the period, p?

48. For a constant distance, the rate of travel r varies inversely with the time traveled, t. If a car traveling 100 mph completes a test track in 6 minutes, find the rate needed to complete the same test track in 4 minutes. (*Hint:* Convert minutes to hours.)

Chapter 13 Group Activity

Finding a Linear Model

This activity may be completed by working in groups or individually.

The following table shows the actual number of international tourist arrivals to the United States for the years 2009 through 2012.

Year	International Tourist Arrivals to the United States (in millions)
2009	55
2010	60
2011	63
2012	67

Source: World Tourism Organization

1. Make a scatter diagram of the paired data in the table.

2. Use what you have learned in this chapter to write an equation of the line representing the paired data in the table. Explain how you found the equation, and what each variable represents.

3. What is the slope of your line? What does the slope mean in this context?

4. Use your linear equation to predict the number of international tourist arrivals to the United States in 2018.

5. Compare your linear equation to that found by other students or groups. Is it the same, similar, or different? How?

6. Compare your prediction from question **4** to that of other students or groups. Describe what you find.

7. Suppose that the number of international tourist arrivals to the United States for 2013 was estimated to be 65 million. If this data point is added to the chart, how does it affect your results?

Chapter 13 Vocabulary Check

Fill in each blank with one of the words listed below.

y-axis	*x*-axis	solution	linear	standard	point-slope
x-intercept	*y*-intercept	*y*	*x*	slope	relation
domain	range	direct	inverse	slope-intercept	function

1. An ordered pair is a(n) _____ of an equation in two variables if replacing the variables by the coordinates of the ordered pair results in a true statement.

2. The vertical number line in the rectangular coordinate system is called the _____.

3. A(n) _____ equation can be written in the form $Ax + By = C$.

4. A(n) _____ is a point of the graph where the graph crosses the *x*-axis.

5. The form $Ax + By = C$ is called _____ form.

6. A(n) _____ is a point of the graph where the graph crosses the *y*-axis.

7. A set of ordered pairs that assigns to each *x*-value exactly one *y*-value is called a(n) _____.

8. The equation $y = 7x - 5$ is written in _____ form.

9. The set of all *x*-coordinates of a relation is called the _____ of the relation.

10. The set of all *y*-coordinates of a relation is called the _____ of the relation.

11. A set of ordered pairs is called a(n) _____.

12. The equation $y + 1 = 7(x - 2)$ is written in _____ form.

13. To find an *x*-intercept of a graph, let _____ = 0.

14. The horizontal number line in the rectangular coordinate system is called the _____.

15. To find a *y*-intercept of a graph, let _____ = 0.

16. The _____ of a line measures the steepness or tilt of the line.

17. The equation $y = kx$ is an example of _____ variation.

18. The equation $y = \dfrac{k}{x}$ is an example of _____ variation.

Helpful Hint

Are you preparing for your test? Don't forget to take the Chapter 13 Test on page 1054. Then check your answers at the back of the text and use the Chapter Test Prep Videos to see the fully worked-out solutions to any of the exercises you want to review.

13 Chapter Highlights

Definitions and Concepts	Examples

Section 13.1   The Rectangular Coordinate System

The **rectangular coordinate system** consists of a plane and a vertical and a horizontal number line intersecting at their 0 coordinates. The vertical number line is called the **y-axis** and the horizontal number line is called the **x-axis.** The point of intersection of the axes is called the **origin.**

To **plot** or **graph** an ordered pair means to find its corresponding point on a rectangular coordinate system.

To plot or graph an ordered pair such as $(3, -2)$, start at the origin. Move 3 units to the right and from there, 2 units down.

To plot or graph $(-3, 4)$, start at the origin. Move 3 units to the left and from there, 4 units up.

An ordered pair is a **solution** of an equation in two variables if replacing the variables with the coordinates of the ordered pair results in a true statement.

(continued)

Definitions and Concepts	Examples

Section 13.1   The Rectangular Coordinate System   (*continued*)

If one coordinate of an ordered pair solution of an equation is known, the other value can be determined by substitution.	Complete the ordered pair $(0, \;)$ for the equation $x - 6y = 12$. $$x - 6y = 12$$ $$0 - 6y = 12 \quad \text{Let } x = 0.$$ $$\frac{-6y}{-6} = \frac{12}{-6} \quad \text{Divide by } -6.$$ $$y = -2$$ The ordered pair solution is $(0, -2)$.

Section 13.2   Graphing Linear Equations

A **linear equation in two variables** is an equation that can be written in the form $Ax + By = C$, where A and B are not both 0. The form $Ax + By = C$ is called **standard form.** To graph a linear equation in two variables, find three ordered pair solutions. Plot the solution points and draw the line connecting the points.	$$3x + 2y = -6 \qquad x = -5$$ $$y = 3 \qquad y = -x + 10$$ $x + y = 10$ is in standard form. Graph: $x - 2y = 5$ 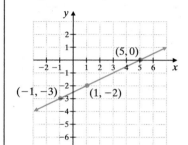 	x	y	 |---|---| | 5	0	 | 1	-2	 | -1	-3	

Section 13.3   Intercepts

An **intercept** of a graph is a point where the graph intersects an axis. If a graph intersects the x-axis at a, then $(a, 0)$ is an **x-intercept.** If a graph intersects the y-axis at b, then $(0, b)$ is a **y-intercept.**	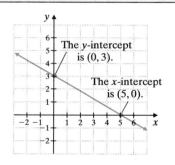 The y-intercept is $(0, 3)$. The x-intercept is $(5, 0)$.
To find the x-intercept(s), let $y = 0$ and solve for x. **To find the y-intercept(s),** let $x = 0$ and solve for y.	Find the intercepts for $2x - 5y = -10$. If $y = 0$, then $\qquad$ If $x = 0$, then $2x - 5 \cdot 0 = -10 \qquad 2 \cdot 0 - 5y = -10$ $\qquad 2x = -10 \qquad \qquad -5y = -10$ $\qquad \dfrac{2x}{2} = \dfrac{-10}{2} \qquad \qquad \dfrac{-5y}{-5} = \dfrac{-10}{-5}$ $\qquad x = -5 \qquad \qquad \qquad y = 2$

Definitions and Concepts	Examples

Section 13.3 Intercepts (*continued*)

The *x*-intercept is $(-5, 0)$. The *y*-intercept is $(0, 2)$.

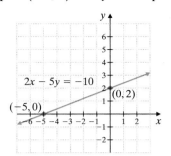

The graph of $x = c$ is a vertical line with *x*-intercept $(c, 0)$.

The graph of $y = c$ is a horizontal line with *y*-intercept $(0, c)$.

Section 13.4 Slope and Rate of Change

The **slope *m*** of the line through points (x_1, y_1) and (x_2, y_2) is given by

$$m = \frac{y_2 - y_1}{x_2 - x_1} \quad \text{as long as } x_2 \neq x_1$$

A horizontal line has slope 0.
The slope of a vertical line is undefined.
Nonvertical parallel lines have the same slope.
Two nonvertical lines are perpendicular if the slope of one is the negative reciprocal of the slope of the other.

The slope of the line through points $(-1, 6)$ and $(-5, 8)$ is

$$m = \frac{y_2 - y_1}{x_2 - x_1} = \frac{8 - 6}{-5 - (-1)} = \frac{2}{-4} = -\frac{1}{2}$$

The slope of the line $y = -5$ is 0.
The line $x = 3$ has undefined slope.

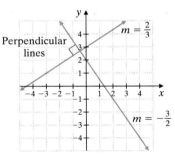

Section 13.5 Equations of Lines

Slope-Intercept Form

$$y = mx + b$$

m is the slope of the line.
$(0, b)$ is the *y*-intercept.

Find the slope and the *y*-intercept of the line $2x + 3y = 6$.
Solve for *y*:

$$2x + 3y = 6$$
$$3y = -2x + 6 \quad \text{Subtract } 2x.$$
$$y = -\frac{2}{3}x + 2 \quad \text{Divide by 3.}$$

The slope of the line is $-\dfrac{2}{3}$ and the *y*-intercept is $(0, 2)$.

(continued)

Definitions and Concepts	Examples

Section 13.5   Equations of Lines   (*continued*)

Point-Slope Form

$$y - y_1 = m(x - x_1)$$

m is the slope.
(x_1, y_1) is a point of the line.

Find an equation of the line with slope $\dfrac{3}{4}$ that contains the point $(-1, 5)$.

$$y - 5 = \frac{3}{4}[x - (-1)]$$

$4(y - 5) = 3(x + 1)$	Multiply by 4.
$4y - 20 = 3x + 3$	Distribute.
$-3x + 4y = 23$	Subtract $3x$ and add 20.

Section 13.6   Introduction to Functions

A set of ordered pairs is a **relation.** The set of all x-coordinates is called the **domain** of the relation and the set of all y-coordinates is called the **range** of the relation.

A **function** is a set of ordered pairs that assigns to each x-value exactly one y-value.

Vertical Line Test

If a vertical line can be drawn so that it intersects a graph more than once, the graph is not the graph of a function. (If no such line can be drawn, the graph is that of a function.)

The symbol $f(x)$ means **function of x.** This notation is called **function notation.**

The domain of the relation

$$\{(0, 5), (2, 5), (4, 5), (5, -2)\}$$

is $\{0, 2, 4, 5\}$. The range is $\{-2, 5\}$.

Which are graphs of functions?

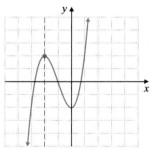

This graph is not the
graph of a function.

This graph is the graph
of a function.

If $f(x) = 3x - 7$, then

$$f(-1) = 3(-1) - 7$$
$$= -3 - 7$$
$$= -10$$

Section 13.7   Graphing Linear Inequalities in Two Variables

A **linear inequality in two variables** is an inequality that can be written in one of these forms:

$$Ax + By < C \qquad Ax + By \le C$$
$$Ax + By > C \qquad Ax + By \ge C$$

where A and B are not both 0.

$$2x - 5y < 6 \qquad\qquad x \ge -5$$
$$y > -8x \qquad\qquad y \le 2$$

Definitions and Concepts	Examples

Section 13.7   Graphing Linear Inequalities in Two Variables   (*continued*)

To Graph a Linear Inequality

1. Graph the boundary line by graphing the related equation. Draw the line solid if the inequality symbol is $\leq$ or $\geq$. Draw the line dashed if the inequality symbol is $<$ or $>$.

2. Choose a test point not on the line. Substitute its coordinates into the original inequality.

3. If the resulting inequality is true, shade the half-plane that contains the test point. If the inequality is not true, shade the half-plane that does not contain the test point.

Graph: $2x - y \leq 4$

1. Graph $2x - y = 4$. Draw a solid line because the inequality symbol is $\leq$.

2. Check the test point $(0, 0)$ in the original inequality, $2x - y \leq 4$.

   $2 \cdot 0 - 0 \leq 4$ Let $x = 0$ and $y = 0$.

   $0 \leq 4$ True

3. The inequality is true, so shade the half-plane containing $(0, 0)$, as shown.

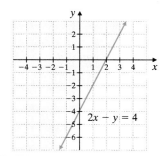

Section 13.8   Direct and Inverse Variation

y **varies directly as** *x*, or *y* is **directly proportional to** *x*, if there is a nonzero constant *k* such that

$$y = kx$$

y **varies inversely as** *x*, or *y* is **inversely proportional to** *x*, if there is a nonzero constant *k* such that

$$y = \frac{k}{x}$$

The circumference of a circle C varies directly as its radius r.

$$C = \underbrace{2\pi}_{k} r$$

Pressure P varies inversely with volume V.

$$P = \frac{k}{V}$$

Chapter 13   Review

(13.1) *Plot each point on the same rectangular coordinate system.*

1. $(-7, 0)$

2. $\left(0, 4\frac{4}{5}\right)$

3. $(-2, -5)$

4. $(1, -3)$

5. $(0.7, 0.7)$

6. $(-6, 4)$

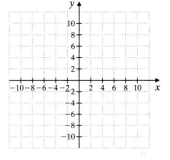

Complete each ordered pair so that it is a solution of the given equation.

7. $-2 + y = 6x;\ (7,\ \ )$

8. $y = 3x + 5;\ (\ \ , -8)$

Complete the table of values for each given equation.

9. $9 = -3x + 4y$

x	y
	0
	3
9	

10. $y = 5$

x	y
7	
-7	
0	

11. $x = 2y$

x	y
	0
	5
	-5

12. The cost in dollars of producing x compact disc holders is given by $y = 5x + 2000$.

   a. Complete the table.

x	1	100	1000
y			

   b. Find the number of compact disc holders that can be produced for $6430.

(13.2) *Graph each linear equation.*

13. $x - y = 1$

14. $x + y = 6$

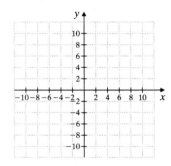

15. $x - 3y = 12$

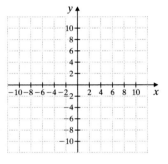

16. $5x - y = -8$

17. $x = 3y$

18. $y = -2x$

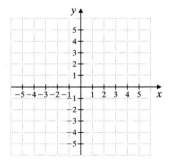

(13.3) *Identify the intercepts in each graph.*

19.

20.

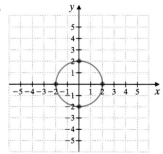

Graph each linear equation.

21. $y = -3$

22. $x = 5$

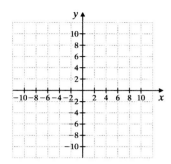

Find the intercepts of each equation.

23. $x - 3y = 12$

24. $-4x + y = 8$

(13.4) *Find the slope of each line.*

25.

26.

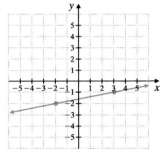

Match each line with its slope.

a.

b.

c.

d.

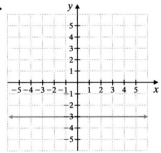

27. $m = 0$

28. $m = -1$

29. undefined slope

30. $m = 4$

Find the slope of the line that passes through each pair of points.

31. $(2, 5)$ and $(6, 8)$

32. $(4, 7)$ and $(1, 2)$

33. $(1, 3)$ and $(-2, -9)$

34. $(-4, 1)$ and $(3, -6)$

Find the slope of each line.

35. $y = 3x + 7$

36. $x - 2y = 4$

37. $y = -2$

38. $x = 0$

Determine whether each pair of lines is parallel, perpendicular, or neither.

39. $x - y = -6$
$x + y = 3$

40. $3x + y = 7$
$-3x - y = 10$

41. $y = 4x + \dfrac{1}{2}$
$4x + 2y = 1$

42. $y = 6x - \dfrac{1}{3}$
$x + 6y = 6$

Find the slope of each line and write the slope as a rate of change. Don't forget to attach the proper units.

43. The graph below approximates the total number of U.S. magazines in print for each year x.

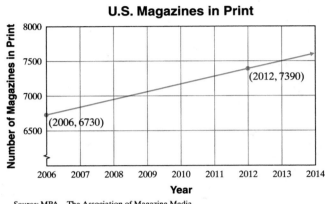

U.S. Magazines in Print

(2012, 7390)

(2006, 6730)

Source: MPA—The Association of Magazine Media

44. The graph below approximates the number of lung transplants y in the United States for year x. Round to the nearest whole.

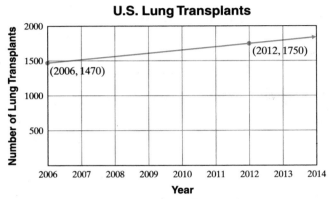

U.S. Lung Transplants

(2012, 1750)

(2006, 1470)

Source: Organ Procurement and Transplantation Network

(13.5) *Determine the slope and the y-intercept of the graph of each equation.*

45. $x - 6y = -1$

46. $3x + y = 7$

Write an equation of each line.

47. slope -5; y-intercept $\left(0, \dfrac{1}{2}\right)$

48. slope $\dfrac{2}{3}$; y-intercept $(0, 6)$

Match each equation with its graph.

49. $y = 2x + 1$

50. $y = -4x$

51. $y = 2x$

52. $y = 2x - 1$

a.

b.

c.

d.

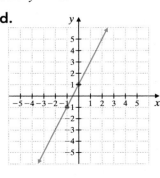

Write an equation of the line with the given slope that passes through the given point. Write the equation in the form Ax + By = C.

53. $m = 4; (2, 0)$ **54.** $m = -3; (0, -5)$ **55.** $m = \dfrac{3}{5}; (1, 4)$ **56.** $m = -\dfrac{1}{3}; (-3, 3)$

Write an equation of the line passing through each pair of points. Write the equation in the form y = mx + b.

57. $(1, 7)$ and $(2, -7)$ **58.** $(-2, 5)$ and $(-4, 6)$

(13.6) *Determine whether each relation or graph is a function.*

59. $\{(7, 1), (7, 5), (2, 6)\}$ **60.** $\{(0, -1), (5, -1), (2, 2)\}$

61.   **62.**   **63.**   **64.**

Find each indicated function value for the function $f(x) = -2x + 6$.

65. $f(0)$ **66.** $f(-2)$ **67.** $f\left(\dfrac{1}{2}\right)$ **68.** $f\left(-\dfrac{1}{2}\right)$

(13.7) *Graph each inequality.*

69. $x + 6y < 6$ **70.** $x + y > -2$ **71.** $y \geq -7$

     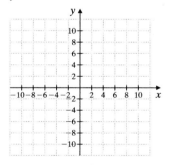

72. $y \leq -4$ **73.** $-x \leq y$ **74.** $x \geq -y$

     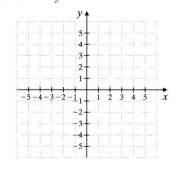

(13.8) *Solve.*

75. y varies directly as x. If $y = 40$ when $x = 4$, find y when x is 11.

76. y varies inversely as x. If $y = 4$ when $x = 6$, find y when x is 48.

77. y varies inversely as x^3. If $y = 12.5$ when $x = 2$, find y when x is 3.

78. y varies directly as x^2. If $y = 175$ when $x = 5$, find y when $x = 10$.

79. The cost of manufacturing a certain medicine varies inversely as the amount of medicine manufactured increases. If 3000 milliliters can be manufactured for $6600, find the cost to manufacture 5000 milliliters.

80. The distance a spring stretches varies directly with the weight attached to the spring. If a 150-pound weight stretches the spring 8 inches, find the distance that a 90-pound weight stretches the spring.

Mixed Review

Complete the table of values for each given equation.

81. $2x - 5y = 9$

x	y
	1
2	
	-3

82. $x = -3y$

x	y
0	
	1
6	

Find the intercepts for each equation.

83. $2x - 3y = 6$

84. $-5x + y = 10$

Graph each linear equation.

85. $x - 5y = 10$

86. $x + y = 4$

87. $y = -4x$

88. $2x + 3y = -6$

89. $x = 3$

90. $y = -2$

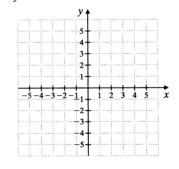

Find the slope of the line that passes through each pair of points.

91. $(3, -5)$ and $(-4, 2)$

92. $(1, 3)$ and $(-6, -8)$

Find the slope of each line.

93.

94.

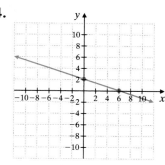

Determine the slope and y-intercept of the graph of each equation.

95. $-2x + 3y = -15$

96. $6x + y - 2 = 0$

Write an equation of the line with the given slope that passes through the given point. Write the equation in the form $Ax + By = C$.

97. $m = -5; (3, -7)$

98. $m = 3; (0, 6)$

Write an equation of the line passing through each pair of points. Write the equation in the form $Ax + By = C$.

99. $(-3, 9)$ and $(-2, 5)$

100. $(3, 1)$ and $(5, -9)$

Answers

Complete each ordered pair so that it is a solution of the given equation.

1. $12y - 7x = 5; (1, \ )$

2. $y = 17; (-4, \ )$

Find the slope of each line.

3.

4.

5. Passes through $(6, -5)$ and $(-1, 2)$

6. Passes through $(0, -8)$ and $(-1, -1)$

7. $-3x + y = 5$

8. $x = 6$

Graph.

9. $2x + y = 8$

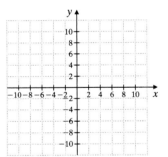

10. $-x + 4y = 5$

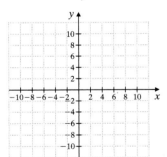

11. $x - y \geq -2$

12. $y \geq -4x$

13. $5x - 7y = 10$

14. $2x - 3y > -6$

1. _____

2. _____

3. _____

4. _____

5. _____

6. _____

7. _____

8. _____

9. _____

10. _____

11. _____

12. _____

13. _____

14. _____

15. $6x + y > -1$

16. $y = -1$

17. Determine whether the graphs of $y = 2x - 6$ and $-4x = 2y$ are parallel lines, perpendicular lines, or neither.

Find the equation of each line. Write the equation in the form $Ax + By = C$.

18. Slope $-\dfrac{1}{4}$, passes through $(2, 2)$ **19.** Passes through the origin and $(6, -7)$

20. Passes through $(2, -5)$ and $(1, 3)$ **21.** Slope $\dfrac{1}{8}$; y-intercept $(0, 12)$

Determine whether each relation is a function.

22. $\{(-1, 2), (-2, 4), (-3, 6), (-4, 8)\}$ **23.** $\{(-3, -3), (0, 5), (-3, 2), (0, 0)\}$

24. The graph shown in Exercise **3**   **25.** The graph shown in Exercise **4**

Find the indicated function values for each function.

26. $f(x) = 2x - 4$
   a. $f(-2)$
   b. $f(0.2)$
   c. $f(0)$

27. $f(x) = x^3 - x$
   a. $f(-1)$
   b. $f(0)$
   c. $f(4)$

△ **28.** The perimeter of the parallelogram below is 42 meters. Write a linear equation in two variables for the perimeter. Use this equation to find x when y is 8 meters.

15.
16.
17.
18.
19.
20.
21.
22.
23.
24.
25.
26. a.
b.
c.
27. a.
b.
c.
28.

29. The table gives the number of cable phone customers (in millions) for the years shown. (*Source:* National Cable and Telecommunications Association)

Year	Cable Phone Customers (in millions)
2008	19.6
2009	22.2
2010	23.9
2011	25.3
2012	26.7

29. a. _____

a. Write this data as a set of ordered pairs of the form (year, number of cable phone customers in millions).

b. Create a scatter diagram of the data. Be sure to label the axes properly.

b. _____

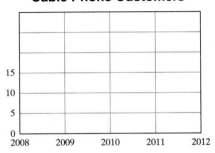

Cable Phone Customers

30. _____

30. This graph approximates the movie ticket sales y (in millions) for the year x. Find the slope of the line and write the slope as a rate of change. Don't forget to attach the proper units.

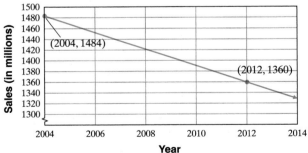

Movie Ticket Sales

(2004, 1484)

(2012, 1360)

Sales (in millions)

Year

Source: National Association of Theater Owners

31. _____

31. y varies directly as x. If $y = 10$ when $x = 15$, find y when x is 42.

32. _____

32. y varies inversely as x^2. If $y = 8$ when $x = 5$, find y when x is 15.

Answers

△**1.** The state of Colorado is in the shape of a rectangle whose length is 380 miles and whose width is 280 miles. Find its area.

2. In a pecan orchard, there are 21 trees in each row and 7 rows of trees. How many pecan trees are there?

3. Add: $1 + (-10) + (-8) + 9$

4. Add: $-2 + (-7) + 3 + (-4)$

5. Write $\dfrac{8}{3x}$ as an equivalent fraction whose denominator is $24x$.

6. Write $\dfrac{3}{2c}$ as an equivalent fraction with denominator $8c$.

7. Subtract: $14 - 8\dfrac{3}{7}$

8. Subtract: $15 - 4\dfrac{2}{5}$

9. Evaluate $-2x + 5$ for $x = 3.8$.

10. Evaluate $6x - 1$ for $x = -2.1$.

11. Write $\dfrac{22}{7}$ as a decimal. Round to the nearest hundredth.

12. Write $\dfrac{37}{19}$ as a decimal. Round to the nearest thousandth.

13. Solve $2x < -4$. Graph the solutions.

14. Solve $3x \le -9$. Graph the solution set.

Find the degree of each polynomial and tell whether the polynomial is a monomial, binomial, trinomial, or none of these.

15. a. $-2t^2 + 3t + 6$
   b. $15x - 10$
   c. $7x + 3x^3 + 2x^2 - 1$

16. a. $-7y + 2$
   b. $8x - x^2 - 1$
   c. $9y^3 - 6y + 2 + y^2$

Perform the indicated operation.

17. Add: $(-2x^2 + 5x - 1)$ and $(-2x^2 + x + 3)$

18. Add: $(9x - 5)$ and $(x^2 - 6x + 5)$

1. _____

2. _____

3. _____

4. _____

5. _____

6. _____

7. _____

8. _____

9. _____

10. _____

11. _____

12. _____

13. _____

14. _____

15. a. _____

   b. _____

   c. _____

16. a. _____

   b. _____

   c. _____

17. _____

18. _____

19. _____

20. _____

21. _____

22. _____

23. _____

24. _____

25. _____

26. _____

27. _____

28. _____

29. _____

30. _____

31. _____

32. _____

33. _____

34. _____

35. _____

36. _____

37. _____

38. _____

39. a. _____

b. _____

c. _____

40. a. _____

b. _____

c. _____

19. Multiply: $(3y + 1)^2$

20. Multiply: $(2x - 5)^2$

21. Factor: $-9a^5 + 18a^2 - 3a$

22. Factor: $2x^5 - x^3$

23. Factor: $x^2 + 4x - 12$

24. Factor: $x^2 + 4x - 21$

25. Factor: $8x^2 - 22x + 5$

26. Factor: $15x^2 + x - 2$

27. Solve: $4x^2 - 28x = -49$

28. Solve: $x^2 - 9x = -14$

29. Divide: $\dfrac{2x^2 - 11x + 5}{5x - 25} \div \dfrac{4x - 2}{10}$

30. Multiply: $\dfrac{3x^2 + 17x - 6}{5x + 5} \cdot \dfrac{2x + 2}{4x + 24}$

Write the rational expression as an equivalent rational expression with the given denominator.

31. $\dfrac{4b}{9a} = \dfrac{}{27a^2 b}$

32. $\dfrac{7x}{11y} = \dfrac{}{99x^2 y^2}$

33. Add: $1 + \dfrac{m}{m + 1}$

34. Subtract: $1 - \dfrac{m}{m + 1}$

35. Solve: $3 - \dfrac{6}{x} = x + 8$

36. Solve: $2 + \dfrac{10}{x} = x + 5$

37. Simplify: $\dfrac{\dfrac{x + 1}{y}}{\dfrac{x}{y} + 2}$

38. Simplify: $\dfrac{\dfrac{x}{2} + 2}{\dfrac{x}{2} - 2}$

Complete each ordered pair solution so that it is a solution to the equation.

39. $3x + y = 12$
  a. $(0, \ )$
  b. $(\ , 6)$
  c. $(-1, \ )$

40. $-x + 4y = -20$
  a. $(0, \ )$
  b. $(\ , 0)$
  c. $(\ , -2)$

41. Graph: $2x + y = 5$

42. Graph: $y = -2x$

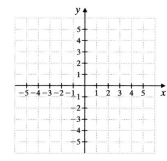

43. Find the slope of the line.
$-2x + 3y = 11$

44. Find the slope of the line.
$7x + 4y = 10$

45. Find an equation of the line with slope -2 that passes through $(-1, 5)$. Write the equation in standard form, $Ax + By = C$.

46. Find an equation of the line passing through $(2, -7)$ with slope -5. Write the equation in the form $Ax + By = C$.

47. Given $g(x) = x^2 - 3$, find the following and list the corresponding ordered pairs generated.
  a. $g(2)$
  b. $g(-2)$
  c. $g(0)$

48. Given $f(x) = 3x^2 + 2$, find the following and list the corresponding ordered pairs generated.
  a. $f(0)$
  b. $f(4)$
  c. $f(-1)$

41. _____

42. _____

43. _____

44. _____

45. _____

46. _____

47. a. _____

  b. _____

  c. _____

48. a. _____

  b. _____

  c. _____

14

Systems of Equations

In Chapter 13, we graphed equations containing two variables. As we have seen, equations like these are often needed to represent relationships between two different quantities. There are also many opportunities to compare and contrast two such equations, called a *system of equations*. This chapter presents *linear systems* and ways we solve these systems and apply them to real-life situations.

Movies are not watched just in movie theaters anymore. Consumers can purchase movies for home viewing in such varied formats as DVD, Blu-ray, and digital downloads to television, computer, or other electronic device. Technology is changing so fast that there may well be new ways of obtaining videos that are in the development stream now. The graph below represents consumer spending statistics for two different home entertainment formats, DVD and Blu-ray. In Section 14.2, Exercise 57, we will explore the relationship between consumer spending on these two home entertainment formats.

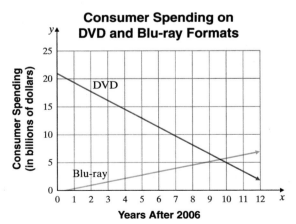

Source: Based on data from DEG: The Digital Entertainment Group

1060

A **system of linear equations** consists of two or more linear equations. In this section, we focus on solving systems of linear equations containing two equations in two variables. Examples of such linear systems are

$$\begin{cases} 3x - 3y = 0 \\ x = 2y \end{cases} \qquad \begin{cases} x - y = 0 \\ 2x + y = 10 \end{cases} \qquad \begin{cases} y = 7x - 1 \\ y = 4 \end{cases}$$

Objective A Deciding Whether an Ordered Pair Is a Solution ▶

A **solution** of a system of two equations in two variables is an ordered pair of numbers that is a solution of both equations in the system.

Example 1 Determine whether $(12, 6)$ is a solution of the system

$$\begin{cases} 2x - 3y = 6 \\ x = 2y \end{cases}$$

Solution: To determine whether $(12, 6)$ is a solution of the system, we replace x with 12 and y with 6 in both equations.

$2x - 3y = 6$ First equation	$x = 2y$ Second equation
$2(12) - 3(6) \stackrel{?}{=} 6$ Let $x = 12$ and $y = 6$.	$12 \stackrel{?}{=} 2(6)$ Let $x = 12$ and $y = 6$.
$24 - 18 \stackrel{?}{=} 6$ Simplify.	$12 = 12$ True
$6 = 6$ True	

Since $(12, 6)$ is a solution of both equations, it is a solution of the system.

■ Work Practice 1

Example 2 Determine whether $(-1, 2)$ is a solution of the system

$$\begin{cases} x + 2y = 3 \\ 4x - y = 6 \end{cases}$$

Solution: We replace x with -1 and y with 2 in both equations.

$x + 2y = 3$ First equation	$4x - y = 6$ Second equation
$-1 + 2(2) \stackrel{?}{=} 3$ Let $x = -1$ and $y = 2$.	$4(-1) - 2 \stackrel{?}{=} 6$ Let $x = -1$ and $y = 2$.
$-1 + 4 \stackrel{?}{=} 3$ Simplify.	$-4 - 2 \stackrel{?}{=} 6$ Simplify.
$3 = 3$ True	$-6 = 6$ False

$(-1, 2)$ is not a solution of the second equation, $4x - y = 6$, so it is not a solution of the system.

■ Work Practice 2

Objective B Solving Systems of Equations by Graphing ▶

Since a solution of a system of two equations in two variables is a solution common to both equations, it is also a point common to the graphs of both equations. Let's practice finding solutions of both equations in a system—that is, solutions of the system—by graphing and identifying points of intersection.

Objectives

A Decide Whether an Ordered Pair Is a Solution of a System of Linear Equations. ▶

B Solve a System of Linear Equations by Graphing. ▶

C Identify Special Systems of Linear Equations. ▶

D Without Graphing, Determine the Number of Solutions of a System. ▶

Practice 1

Determine whether $(3, 9)$ is a solution of the system

$$\begin{cases} 5x - 2y = -3 \\ y = 3x \end{cases}$$

Practice 2

Determine whether $(3, -2)$ is a solution of the system

$$\begin{cases} 2x - y = 8 \\ x + 3y = 4 \end{cases}$$

Answers
1. $(3, 9)$ is a solution of the system.
2. $(3, -2)$ is not a solution of the system.

Practice 3

Solve the system of equations by graphing.

$$\begin{cases} -3x + y = -10 \\ x - y = 6 \end{cases}$$

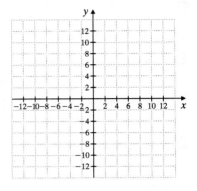

Practice 4

Solve the system of equations by graphing.

$$\begin{cases} x + 3y = -1 \\ y = 1 \end{cases}$$

Answers

3. $(2, -4)$;

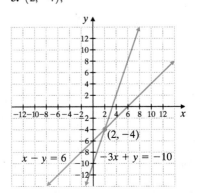

4. See page 1064.

Example 3   Solve the system of equations by graphing.

$$\begin{cases} -x + 3y = 10 \\ x + y = 2 \end{cases}$$

Solution: On a single set of axes, graph each linear equation.

$-x + 3y = 10$

x	y
0	$\frac{10}{3}$
-4	2
2	4

Helpful Hint   The point of intersection gives the solution of the system.

$x + y = 2$

x	y
0	2
2	0
1	1

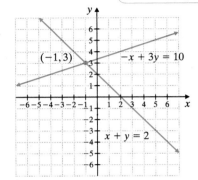

The two lines appear to intersect at the point $(-1, 3)$. To check, we replace x with -1 and y with 3 in both equations.

$-x + 3y = 10$ First equation $x + y = 2$ Second equation

$-(-1) + 3(3) \overset{?}{=} 10$ Let $x = -1$ and $y = 3$. $-1 + 3 \overset{?}{=} 2$ Let $x = -1$ and $y = 3$.

$1 + 9 \overset{?}{=} 10$ Simplify. $2 = 2$ True

$10 = 10$ True

$(-1, 3)$ checks, so it is the solution of the system.

▨ Work Practice 3

Helpful Hint

Neatly drawn graphs can help when "guessing" the solution of a system of linear equations by graphing.

Example 4   Solve the system of equations by graphing.

$$\begin{cases} 2x + 3y = -2 \\ x = 2 \end{cases}$$

Solution: We graph each linear equation on a single set of axes.

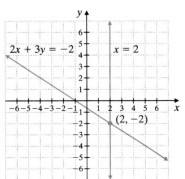

The two lines appear to intersect at the point $(2, -2)$. To determine whether $(2, -2)$ is the solution, we replace x with 2 and y with -2 in both equations.

$$2x + 3y = -2 \quad \text{First equation} \qquad\qquad x = 2 \quad \text{Second equation}$$
$$2(2) + 3(-2) \stackrel{?}{=} -2 \quad \text{Let } x = 2 \text{ and } y = -2. \qquad 2 \stackrel{?}{=} 2 \quad \text{Let } x = 2.$$
$$4 + (-6) \stackrel{?}{=} -2 \quad \text{Simplify.} \qquad\qquad 2 = 2 \quad \text{True}$$
$$-2 = -2 \quad \text{True}$$

Since a true statement results in both equations, $(2, -2)$ is the solution of the system.

▪ Work Practice 4

Objective C Identifying Special Systems of Linear Equations ▶

Not all systems of linear equations have a single solution. Some systems have no solution and some have an infinite number of solutions.

Example 5 Solve the system of equations by graphing.

$$\begin{cases} 2x + y = 7 \\ 2y = -4x \end{cases}$$

Solution: We graph the two equations in the system. The equations in slope-intercept form are $y = -2x + 7$ and $y = -2x$. Notice from the equations that the lines have the same slope, -2, and different y-intercepts. This means that the lines are parallel.

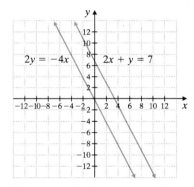

Since the lines are parallel, they do not intersect. This means that the system has *no solution*.

▪ Work Practice 5

Example 6 Solve the system of equations by graphing.

$$\begin{cases} x - y = 3 \\ -x + y = -3 \end{cases}$$

Solution: We graph each equation. The graphs of the equations are the same line. To see this, notice that if both sides of the first equation in the system are multiplied by -1, the result is the second equation.

$$x - y = 3 \qquad \text{First equation}$$
$$-1(x - y) = -1(3) \qquad \text{Multiply both sides by } -1.$$
$$-x + y = -3 \qquad \text{Simplify. This is the second equation.}$$

Any ordered pair that is a solution of one equation is a solution of the other equation and is then a solution of the system. This means that the system has an infinite number of solutions.

▪ Work Practice 6

Practice 5

Solve the system of equations by graphing.

$$\begin{cases} 3x - y = 6 \\ 6x = 2y \end{cases}$$

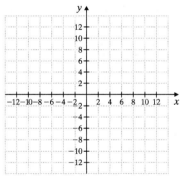

Practice 6

Solve the system of equations by graphing.

$$\begin{cases} x + y = -4 \\ -2x - 2y = 8 \end{cases}$$

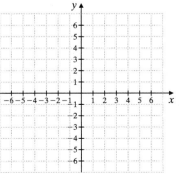

Answers
5. See page 1064. **6.** See page 1064.

Examples 5 and 6 are special cases of systems of linear equations. A system that has no solution is said to be an **inconsistent system.** If the graphs of the two equations of a system are identical, we call the equations **dependent equations.** Thus, the system in Example 5 is an inconsistent system and the equations in the system in Example 6 are dependent equations.

As we have seen, three different situations can occur when graphing the two lines associated with the equations in a linear system. These situations are shown in the figures.

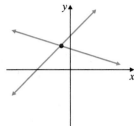

One point of intersection: one solution

Consistent system
(at least one solution)
Independent equations
(graphs of equations differ)

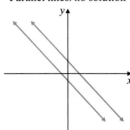

Parallel lines: no solution

Inconsistent system
(no solution)
Independent equations
(graphs of equations differ)

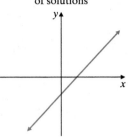

Same line: infinite number of solutions

Consistent system
(at least one solution)
Dependent equations
(graphs of equations identical)

Objective D Finding the Number of Solutions of a System Without Graphing ▶

You may have suspected by now that graphing alone is not an accurate way to solve a system of linear equations. For example, a solution of $\left(\dfrac{1}{2}, \dfrac{2}{9}\right)$ is unlikely to be read correctly from a graph. The next two sections present two accurate methods of solving these systems. In the meantime, we can decide how many solutions a system has by writing each equation in slope-intercept form.

Example 7 Without graphing, determine the number of solutions of the system.

$$\begin{cases} \dfrac{1}{2}x - y = 2 \\ x = 2y + 5 \end{cases}$$

Solution: First write each equation in slope-intercept form.

$\dfrac{1}{2}x - y = 2$ First equation

$\dfrac{1}{2}x = y + 2$ Add y to both sides.

$\dfrac{1}{2}x - 2 = y$ Subtract 2 from both sides.

$x = 2y + 5$ Second equation

$x - 5 = 2y$ Subtract 5 from both sides.

$\dfrac{x}{2} - \dfrac{5}{2} = \dfrac{2y}{2}$ Divide both sides by 2.

$\dfrac{1}{2}x - \dfrac{5}{2} = y$ Simplify.

The slope of each line is $\dfrac{1}{2}$, but they have different y-intercepts. This tells us that the lines representing these equations are parallel. Since the lines are parallel, the system has no solution and is inconsistent.

■ Work Practice 7

Practice 7

Without graphing, determine the number of solutions of the system.

$$\begin{cases} 5x + 4y = 6 \\ x - y = 3 \end{cases}$$

Answers

4. $(-4, 1)$;

5. no solution;

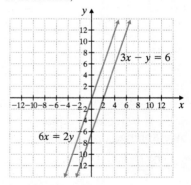

6. infinite number of solutions;

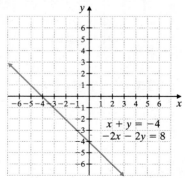

7. one solution

Example 8 Without graphing, determine the number of solutions of the system.

$$\begin{cases} 3x - y = 4 \\ x + 2y = 8 \end{cases}$$

Solution: Once again, the slope-intercept form helps determine how many solutions this system has.

$3x - y = 4$	First equation	$x + 2y = 8$	Second equation
$3x = y + 4$	Add y to both sides.	$x = -2y + 8$	Subtract 2y from both sides.
$3x - 4 = y$	Subtract 4 from both sides.	$x - 8 = -2y$	Subtract 8 from both sides.
		$\dfrac{x}{-2} - \dfrac{8}{-2} = \dfrac{-2y}{-2}$	Divide both sides by -2.
		$-\dfrac{1}{2}x + 4 = y$	Simplify.

The slope of the second line is $-\dfrac{1}{2}$, whereas the slope of the first line is 3. Since the slopes are not equal, the two lines are neither parallel nor identical and must intersect. Therefore, this system has one solution and is consistent.

■ Work Practice 8

Practice 8

Without graphing, determine the number of solutions of the system.

$$\begin{cases} -\dfrac{2}{3}x + y = 6 \\ 3y = 2x + 5 \end{cases}$$

Calculator Explorations **Graphing**

A graphing calculator may be used to approximate solutions of systems of equations. For example, to approximate the solution of the system

$$\begin{cases} y = -3.14x - 1.35 \\ y = 4.88x + 5.25, \end{cases}$$

first graph each equation on the same set of axes. Then use the Intersect feature of your calculator to approximate the point of intersection.

The approximate point of intersection is $(-0.82, 1.23)$.

Solve each system of equations. Approximate the solutions to two decimal places.

1. $\begin{cases} y = -2.68x + 1.21 \\ y = 5.22x - 1.68 \end{cases}$ **2.** $\begin{cases} y = 4.25x + 3.89 \\ y = -1.88x + 3.21 \end{cases}$

3. $\begin{cases} 4.3x - 2.9y = 5.6 \\ 8.1x + 7.6y = -14.1 \end{cases}$ **4.** $\begin{cases} -3.6x - 8.6y = 10 \\ -4.5x + 9.6y = -7.7 \end{cases}$

Answer

8. no solution

Vocabulary, Readiness & Video Check

Fill in each blank with one of the words or phrases listed below.

system of linear equations	solution	consistent
dependent	inconsistent	independent

1. In a system of linear equations in two variables, if the graphs of the equations are the same, the equations are _____ equations.

2. Two or more linear equations are called a(n) _____.

3. A system of equations that has at least one solution is called a(n) _____ system.

4. A(n) _____ of a system of two equations in two variables is an ordered pair of numbers that is a solution of both equations in the system.

5. A system of equations that has no solution is called a(n) _____ system.

6. In a system of linear equations in two variables, if the graphs of the equations are different, the equations are _____ equations.

Each rectangular coordinate system shows the graph of the equations in a system of equations. Use each graph to determine the number of solutions for each associated system. If the system has only one solution, give its coordinates.

7.

8.

9.

10.

Martin-Gay Interactive Videos

See Video 14.1

Watch the section lecture video and answer the following questions.

Objective A 11. In ⊞ Example 1, the first ordered pair is a solution of the first equation of the system. Why is this not enough to determine whether this ordered pair is a solution of the system? ▶

Objectives B 12. From ⊞ Examples 2 and 3, why is finding the solution of
C a system of equations from a graph considered "guessing" and this proposed solution checked algebraically? ▶

Objective D 13. From ⊞ Examples 5–7, explain how the slope-intercept form tells us how many solutions a system of equations has. ▶

14.1 Exercise Set MyMathLab®

Objective A *Determine whether each ordered pair is a solution of the system of linear equations. See Examples 1 and 2.*

1. $\begin{cases} x + y = 8 \\ 3x + 2y = 21 \end{cases}$
   a. $(2, 4)$
   b. $(5, 3)$

2. $\begin{cases} 2x + y = 5 \\ x + 3y = 5 \end{cases}$
   a. $(5, 0)$
   b. $(2, 1)$

3. $\begin{cases} 3x - y = 5 \\ x + 2y = 11 \end{cases}$
   a. $(3, 4)$
   b. $(0, -5)$

4. $\begin{cases} 2x - 3y = 8 \\ x - 2y = 6 \end{cases}$
   a. $(-2, -4)$
   b. $(7, 2)$

5. $\begin{cases} 2y = 4x + 6 \\ 2x - y = -3 \end{cases}$
   a. $(-3, -3)$
   b. $(0, 3)$

6. $\begin{cases} x + 5y = -4 \\ -2x = 10y + 8 \end{cases}$
   a. $(-4, 0)$
   b. $(6, -2)$

7. $\begin{cases} -2 = x - 7y \\ 6x - y = 13 \end{cases}$
   a. $(-2, 0)$
   b. $\left(\dfrac{1}{2}, \dfrac{5}{14}\right)$

8. $\begin{cases} 4x = 1 - y \\ x - 3y = -8 \end{cases}$
   a. $(0, 1)$
   b. $\left(\dfrac{1}{6}, \dfrac{1}{3}\right)$

Objectives B C *Solve each system of linear equations by graphing. See Examples 3 through 6.*

9. $\begin{cases} x + y = 4 \\ x - y = 2 \end{cases}$

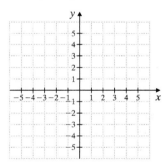

10. $\begin{cases} x + y = 3 \\ x - y = 5 \end{cases}$

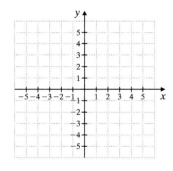

11. $\begin{cases} x + y = 6 \\ -x + y = -6 \end{cases}$

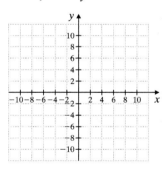

12. $\begin{cases} x + y = 1 \\ -x + y = -3 \end{cases}$

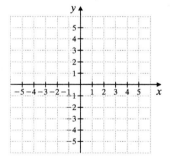

13. $\begin{cases} y = 2x \\ 3x - y = -2 \end{cases}$

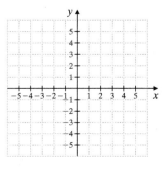

14. $\begin{cases} y = -3x \\ 2x - y = -5 \end{cases}$

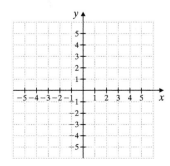

15. $\begin{cases} y = x + 1 \\ y = 2x - 1 \end{cases}$

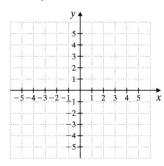

16. $\begin{cases} y = 3x - 4 \\ y = x + 2 \end{cases}$

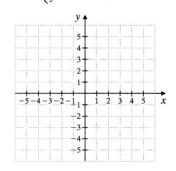

17. $\begin{cases} 2x + y = 0 \\ 3x + y = 1 \end{cases}$

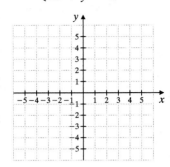

18. $\begin{cases} 2x + y = 1 \\ 3x + y = 0 \end{cases}$

19. $\begin{cases} y = -x - 1 \\ y = 2x + 5 \end{cases}$

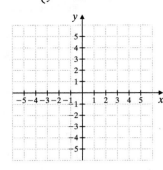

20. $\begin{cases} y = x - 1 \\ y = -3x - 5 \end{cases}$

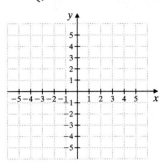

21. $\begin{cases} x + y = 5 \\ x + y = 6 \end{cases}$

22. $\begin{cases} x - y = 4 \\ x - y = 1 \end{cases}$

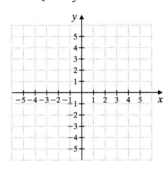

23. $\begin{cases} 2x - y = 6 \\ y = 2 \end{cases}$

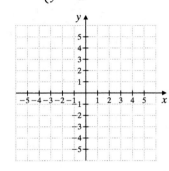

24. $\begin{cases} x + y = 5 \\ x = 4 \end{cases}$

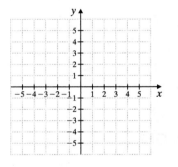

25. $\begin{cases} x - 2y = 2 \\ 3x + 2y = -2 \end{cases}$

26. $\begin{cases} x + 3y = 7 \\ 2x - 3y = -4 \end{cases}$

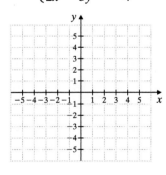

27. $\begin{cases} 2x + y = 4 \\ 6x = -3y + 6 \end{cases}$

28. $\begin{cases} y + 2x = 3 \\ 4x = 2 - 2y \end{cases}$

29. $\begin{cases} y - 3x = -2 \\ 6x - 2y = 4 \end{cases}$

30. $\begin{cases} x - 2y = -6 \\ -2x + 4y = 12 \end{cases}$

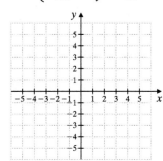

31. $\begin{cases} x = 3 \\ y = -1 \end{cases}$

32. $\begin{cases} x = -5 \\ y = 3 \end{cases}$

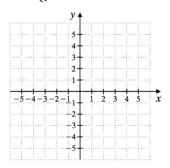

33. $\begin{cases} y = x - 2 \\ y = 2x + 3 \end{cases}$

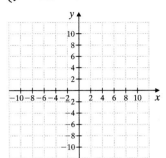

34. $\begin{cases} y = x + 5 \\ y = -2x - 4 \end{cases}$

35. $\begin{cases} 2x - 3y = -2 \\ -3x + 5y = 5 \end{cases}$

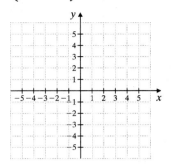

36. $\begin{cases} 4x - y = 7 \\ 2x - 3y = -9 \end{cases}$

37. $\begin{cases} 6x - y = 4 \\ \dfrac{1}{2}y = -2 + 3x \end{cases}$

38. $\begin{cases} 3x - y = 6 \\ \dfrac{1}{3}y = -2 + x \end{cases}$

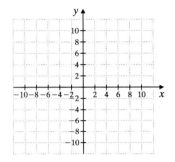

Objective D *Without graphing, decide:*

a. *Are the graphs of the equations identical lines, parallel lines, or lines intersecting at a single point?*
b. *How many solutions does the system have? See Examples 7 and 8.*

39. $\begin{cases} 4x + y = 24 \\ x + 2y = 2 \end{cases}$

40. $\begin{cases} 3x + y = 1 \\ 3x + 2y = 6 \end{cases}$

41. $\begin{cases} 2x + y = 0 \\ 2y = 6 - 4x \end{cases}$

42. $\begin{cases} 3x + y = 0 \\ 2y = -6x \end{cases}$

43. $\begin{cases} 6x - y = 4 \\ \dfrac{1}{2}y = -2 + 3x \end{cases}$

44. $\begin{cases} 3x - y = 2 \\ \dfrac{1}{3}y = -2 + 3x \end{cases}$

45. $\begin{cases} x = 5 \\ y = -2 \end{cases}$

46. $\begin{cases} y = 3 \\ x = -4 \end{cases}$

47. $\begin{cases} 3y - 2x = 3 \\ x + 2y = 9 \end{cases}$

48. $\begin{cases} 2y = x + 2 \\ y + 2x = 3 \end{cases}$

49. $\begin{cases} 6y + 4x = 6 \\ 3y - 3 = -2x \end{cases}$

50. $\begin{cases} 8y + 6x = 4 \\ 4y - 2 = 3x \end{cases}$

51. $\begin{cases} x + y = 4 \\ x + y = 3 \end{cases}$

52. $\begin{cases} 2x + y = 0 \\ y = -2x + 1 \end{cases}$

Review

Solve each equation. See Section 9.3.

53. $5(x - 3) + 3x = 1$

54. $-2x + 3(x + 6) = 17$

55. $4\left(\dfrac{y + 1}{2}\right) + 3y = 0$

56. $-y + 12\left(\dfrac{y - 1}{4}\right) = 3$

57. $8a - 2(3a - 1) = 6$

58. $3z - (4z - 2) = 9$

Concept Extensions

59. Draw a graph of two linear equations whose associated system has the solution $(-1, 4)$.

60. Draw a graph of two linear equations whose associated system has the solution $(3, -2)$.

61. Draw a graph of two linear equations whose associated system has no solution.

62. Draw a graph of two linear equations whose associated system has an infinite number of solutions.

The double line graph below shows the number of digital and analog movie screens in U.S. cinemas for the years shown. Use this graph to answer Exercises 63 and 64. (Source: Motion Picture Association of America, Inc.)

U.S. Cinema Screens

Source: Motion Picture Association of America, Inc.

63. Between what pairs of years did the number of digital cinema screens equal the number of analog cinema screens?

64. For what year(s) was the number of digital cinema screens less than the number of analog cinema screens?

The double line graph below shows the average attendance per game for the Cleveland Indians and the Pittsburgh Pirates baseball teams for the years shown. Use this for Exercises 65 and 66. (Source: Baseball Almanac)

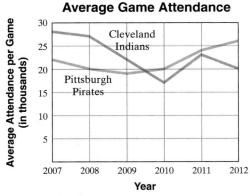

Average Game Attendance

Source: Baseball Almanac

65. In what year(s) was the average attendance per game for the Pittsburgh Pirates greater than the average attendance per game for the Cleveland Indians?

66. In what year was the average attendance per game for the Cleveland Indians closest to the average attendance per game for the Pittsburgh Pirates?

67. Construct a system of two linear equations that has $(2, 5)$ as a solution.

68. Construct a system of two linear equations that has $(0, 1)$ as a solution.

69. The ordered pair $(-2, 3)$ is a solution of the three linear equations below:

$$x + y = 1$$
$$2x - y = -7$$
$$x + 3y = 7$$

If each equation has a distinct graph, describe the graph of all three equations on the same axes.

70. Explain how to use a graph to determine the number of solutions of a system.

71. Below are tables of values for two linear equations.
   a. Find a solution of the corresponding system.
   b. Graph several ordered pairs from each table and sketch the two lines.

72. Below are tables of values for two linear equations.
   a. Find a solution of the corresponding system.
   b. Graph several ordered pairs from each table and sketch the two lines.

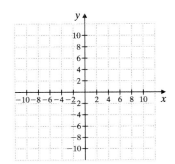

x	y
1	3
2	5
3	7
4	9
5	11

x	y
1	6
2	7
3	8
4	9
5	10

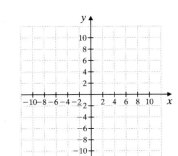

x	y
-3	5
-1	1
0	-1
1	-3
2	-5

x	y
-3	7
-1	1
0	-2
1	-5
2	-8

c. Does your graph confirm the solution from part **a**?

c. Does your graph confirm the solution from part **a**?

14.2 Solving Systems of Linear Equations by Substitution

Objective

A Use the Substitution Method to Solve a System of Linear Equations.

Objective A Using the Substitution Method

You may have suspected by now that graphing alone is not an accurate way to solve a system of linear equations. For example, a solution of $\left(\dfrac{1}{2}, \dfrac{2}{9}\right)$ is unlikely to be read correctly from a graph. In this section, we discuss a second, more accurate method for solving systems of equations. This method is called the **substitution method** and is introduced in the next example.

Practice 1

Use the substitution method to solve the system:

$$\begin{cases} 2x + 3y = 13 \\ x = y + 4 \end{cases}$$

Example 1 Solve the system:

$$\begin{cases} 2x + y = 10 & \text{First equation} \\ x = y + 2 & \text{Second equation} \end{cases}$$

Solution: The second equation in this system is $x = y + 2$. This tells us that x and $y + 2$ have the same value. This means that we may substitute $y + 2$ for x in the first equation.

$$2x + y = 10 \quad \text{First equation}$$

$$2(y + 2) + y = 10 \quad \text{Substitute } y + 2 \text{ for } x \text{ since } x = y + 2.$$

Notice that this equation now has one variable, y. Let's now solve this equation for y.

Helpful Hint Don't forget the distributive property.

$$2(y + 2) + y = 10$$
$$2y + 4 + y = 10 \quad \text{Apply the distributive property.}$$
$$3y + 4 = 10 \quad \text{Combine like terms.}$$
$$3y = 6 \quad \text{Subtract 4 from both sides.}$$
$$y = 2 \quad \text{Divide both sides by 3.}$$

Now we know that the y-value of the ordered pair solution of the system is 2. To find the corresponding x-value, we replace y with 2 in the second equation, $x = y + 2$, and solve for x.

$$x = y + 2 \quad \text{Second equation}$$
$$x = 2 + 2 \quad \text{Let } y = 2.$$
$$x = 4$$

The solution of the system is the ordered pair $(4, 2)$. Since an ordered pair solution must satisfy both linear equations in the system, we could have chosen the equation $2x + y = 10$ to find the corresponding x-value. The resulting x-value is the same.

Check: We check to see that $(4, 2)$ satisfies both equations of the original system.

First Equation

$$2x + y = 10$$
$$2(4) + 2 \stackrel{?}{=} 10$$
$$10 = 10 \quad \text{True}$$

Second Equation

$$x = y + 2$$
$$4 \stackrel{?}{=} 2 + 2 \quad \text{Let } x = 4 \text{ and } y = 2.$$
$$4 = 4 \quad \text{True}$$

Answer

1. $(5, 1)$

The solution of the system is $(4, 2)$.

A graph of the two equations shows the two lines intersecting at the point $(4, 2)$.

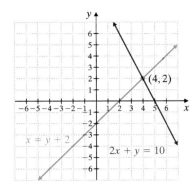

■ Work Practice 1

Example 2 Solve the system:

$$\begin{cases} 5x - y = -2 \\ y = 3x \end{cases}$$

Solution: The second equation is solved for y in terms of x. We substitute $3x$ for y in the first equation.

$$5x - y = -2 \quad \text{First equation}$$

$$5x - (3x) = -2 \quad \text{Substitute } 3x \text{ for } y.$$

Now we solve for x.

$$5x - 3x = -2$$

$$2x = -2 \quad \text{Combine like terms.}$$

$$x = -1 \quad \text{Divide both sides by 2.}$$

The x-value of the ordered pair solution is -1. To find the corresponding y-value, we replace x with -1 in the second equation, $y = 3x$.

$$y = 3x \quad \text{Second equation}$$

$$y = 3(-1) \quad \text{Let } x = -1.$$

$$y = -3$$

Check to see that the solution of the system is $(-1, -3)$.

■ Work Practice 2

To solve a system of equations by substitution, we first need an equation solved for one of its variables, as in Examples 1 and 2. If neither equation in a system is solved for x or y, this will be our first step.

Example 3 Solve the system:

$$\begin{cases} x + 2y = 7 \\ 2x + 2y = 13 \end{cases}$$

Solution: Notice that neither equation is solved for x or y. Thus, we choose one of the equations and solve for x or y. We will solve the first equation for x so that we will not introduce tedious fractions when solving. To solve the first equation for x, we subtract $2y$ from both sides.

$$x + 2y = 7 \quad \text{First equation}$$

$$x = 7 - 2y \quad \text{Subtract } 2y \text{ from both sides.}$$

(Continued on next page)

Practice 2

Use the substitution method to solve the system:

$$\begin{cases} 4x - y = 2 \\ y = 5x \end{cases}$$

Practice 3

Solve the system:

$$\begin{cases} 3x + y = 5 \\ 3x - 2y = -7 \end{cases}$$

Answers

2. $(-2, -10)$ **3.** $\left(\dfrac{1}{3}, 4\right)$

Since $x = 7 - 2y$, we now substitute $7 - 2y$ for x in the second equation and solve for y.

$$2x + 2y = 13 \qquad \text{Second equation}$$
$$2(7 - 2y) + 2y = 13 \qquad \text{Let } x = 7 - 2y.$$
$$14 - 4y + 2y = 13 \qquad \text{Apply the distributive property.}$$
$$14 - 2y = 13 \qquad \text{Simplify.}$$
$$-2y = -1 \qquad \text{Subtract 14 from both sides.}$$
$$y = \frac{1}{2} \qquad \text{Divide both sides by } -2.$$

To find x, we let $y = \dfrac{1}{2}$ in the equation $x = 7 - 2y$.

$$x = 7 - 2y$$
$$x = 7 - 2\left(\frac{1}{2}\right) \qquad \text{Let } y = \frac{1}{2}.$$
$$x = 7 - 1$$
$$x = 6$$

Check the solution in both equations of the original system. The solution is $\left(6, \dfrac{1}{2}\right)$.

■ Work Practice 3

The following steps summarize how to solve a system of equations by the substitution method.

To Solve a System of Two Linear Equations by the Substitution Method

Step 1: Solve one of the equations for one of its variables.

Step 2: Substitute the expression for the variable found in Step 1 into the other equation.

Step 3: Solve the equation from Step 2 to find the value of one variable.

Step 4: Substitute the value found in Step 3 into any equation containing both variables to find the value of the other variable.

Step 5: Check the proposed solution in the original system.

✓**Concept Check** As you solve the system

$$\begin{cases} 2x + y = -5 \\ x - y = 5 \end{cases}$$

you find that $y = -5$. Is this the solution of the system?

Practice 4

Solve the system:
$$\begin{cases} 5x - 2y = 6 \\ -3x + y = -3 \end{cases}$$

Answer

4. $(0, -3)$

✓**Concept Check Answer**

no, the solution will be an ordered pair

Example 4 Solve the system:

$$\begin{cases} 7x - 3y = -14 \\ -3x + y = 6 \end{cases}$$

Solution: Since the coefficient of y is 1 in the second equation, we will solve the second equation for y. This way, we avoid introducing tedious fractions.

$$-3x + y = 6 \qquad \text{Second equation}$$
$$y = 3x + 6$$

Next, we substitute $3x + 6$ for y in the first equation.

$$7x - 3y = -14 \quad \text{First equation}$$
$$7x - 3(3x + 6) = -14 \quad \text{Let } y = 3x + 6.$$
$$7x - 9x - 18 = -14 \quad \text{Use the distributive property.}$$
$$-2x - 18 = -14 \quad \text{Simplify.}$$
$$-2x = 4 \quad \text{Add 18 to both sides.}$$
$$x = -2 \quad \text{Divide both sides by } -2.$$

To find the corresponding y-value, we substitute -2 for x in the equation $y = 3x + 6$. Then $y = 3(-2) + 6$ or $y = 0$. The solution of the system is $(-2, 0)$. Check this solution in both equations of the system.

▨ Work Practice 4

✓**Concept Check** To avoid fractions, which of the equations below would you use to solve for x?

a. $3x - 4y = 15$ **b.** $14 - 3y = 8x$ **c.** $7y + x = 12$

Helpful Hint

When solving a system of equations by the substitution method, begin by solving an equation for one of its variables. If possible, solve for a variable that has a coefficient of 1 or -1 to avoid working with time-consuming fractions.

Example 5   Solve the system: $\begin{cases} \dfrac{1}{2}x - y = 3 \\ x = 6 + 2y \end{cases}$

Solution: The second equation is already solved for x in terms of y. Thus we substitute $6 + 2y$ for x in the first equation and solve for y.

$$\frac{1}{2}x - y = 3 \quad \text{First equation}$$
$$\frac{1}{2}(6 + 2y) - y = 3 \quad \text{Let } x = 6 + 2y.$$
$$3 + y - y = 3 \quad \text{Apply the distributive property.}$$
$$3 = 3 \quad \text{Simplify.}$$

Arriving at a true statement such as $3 = 3$ indicates that the two linear equations in the original system are equivalent. This means that their graphs are identical, as shown in the figure. There is an infinite number of solutions to the system, and any solution of one equation is also a solution of the other.

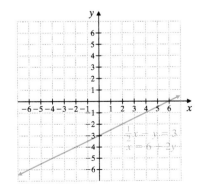

▨ Work Practice 5

Practice 5

Solve the system:
$$\begin{cases} -x + 3y = 6 \\ y = \dfrac{1}{3}x + 2 \end{cases}$$

Answer
5. infinite number of solutions

✓**Concept Check Answer**
c

Helpful Hint

Know that an infinite number of solutions does *not* mean that any ordered pair is a solution of both equations of the system.

An infinite number of solutions for Example 5 means that any of the infinite number of ordered pairs that is a solution of one equation in the system is also a solution of the other and is thus a solution of the system.

For Example 5,

$(2, 0)$ is *not* a solution of the system, but

$(6, 0)$ is a solution of the system.

Practice 6

Solve the system:

$$\begin{cases} 2x - 3y = 6 \\ -4x + 6y = 12 \end{cases}$$

Example 6 Solve the system:

$$\begin{cases} 6x + 12y = 5 \\ -4x - 8y = 0 \end{cases}$$

Solution: We choose the second equation and solve for y. (*Note:* Although you might not see this beforehand, if you solve the second equation for x, the result is $x = -2y$ and no fractions are introduced. Either way will lead to the correct solution.)

$$-4x - 8y = 0 \qquad \text{Second equation}$$
$$-8y = 4x \qquad \text{Add } 4x \text{ to both sides.}$$
$$\frac{-8y}{-8} = \frac{4x}{-8} \qquad \text{Divide both sides by } -8.$$
$$y = -\frac{1}{2}x \qquad \text{Simplify.}$$

Now we replace y with $-\frac{1}{2}x$ in the first equation.

$$6x + 12y = 5 \qquad \text{First equation}$$
$$6x + 12\left(-\frac{1}{2}x\right) = 5 \qquad \text{Let } y = -\frac{1}{2}x.$$
$$6x + (-6x) = 5 \qquad \text{Simplify.}$$
$$0 = 5 \qquad \text{Combine like terms.}$$

The false statement $0 = 5$ indicates that this system has no solution. The graph of the linear equations in the system is a pair of parallel lines, as shown in the figure.

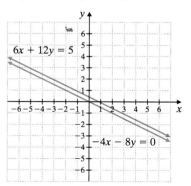

Work Practice 6

Answer

6. no solution

✓**Concept Check Answer**

a. parallel lines **b.** intersect at one point **c.** identical graphs

✓**Concept Check** Describe how the graphs of the equations in a system appear if the system has

a. no solution **b.** one solution **c.** an infinite number of solutions

Vocabulary, Readiness & Video Check

Give the solution of each system. If the system has no solution or an infinite number of solutions, say so. If the system has one solution, find it.

1. $\begin{cases} y = 4x \\ -3x + y = 1 \end{cases}$

When solving, you obtain $x = 1$.

2. $\begin{cases} 4x - y = 17 \\ -8x + 2y = 0 \end{cases}$

When solving, you obtain $0 = 34$.

3. $\begin{cases} 4x - y = 17 \\ -8x + 2y = -34 \end{cases}$

When solving, you obtain $0 = 0$.

4. $\begin{cases} 5x + 2y = 25 \\ x = y + 5 \end{cases}$

When solving, you obtain $y = 0$.

5. $\begin{cases} x + y = 0 \\ 7x - 7y = 0 \end{cases}$

When solving, you obtain $x = 0$.

6. $\begin{cases} y = -2x + 5 \\ 4x + 2y = 10 \end{cases}$

When solving, you obtain $0 = 0$.

Martin-Gay Interactive Videos   Watch the section lecture video and answer the following question.

See Video 14.2

Objective A **7.** The systems in ▦ Examples 2–4 all need one of their equations solved for a variable as a first step. What important part of the substitution method is emphasized in each example? ▶

14.2 **Exercise Set** MyMathLab® ▶

Objective A *Solve each system of equations by the substitution method. See Examples 1 and 2.*

1. $\begin{cases} x + y = 3 \\ x = 2y \end{cases}$

2. $\begin{cases} x + y = 20 \\ x = 3y \end{cases}$

▶ **3.** $\begin{cases} x + y = 6 \\ y = -3x \end{cases}$

4. $\begin{cases} x + y = 6 \\ y = -4x \end{cases}$

5. $\begin{cases} y = 3x + 1 \\ 4y - 8x = 12 \end{cases}$

6. $\begin{cases} y = 2x + 3 \\ 5y - 7x = 18 \end{cases}$

7. $\begin{cases} y = 2x + 9 \\ y = 7x + 10 \end{cases}$

8. $\begin{cases} y = 5x - 3 \\ y = 8x + 4 \end{cases}$

Solve each system of equations by the substitution method. See Examples 1 through 6.

9. $\begin{cases} 3x - 4y = 10 \\ y = x - 3 \end{cases}$

10. $\begin{cases} 4x - 3y = 10 \\ y = x - 5 \end{cases}$

11. $\begin{cases} x + 2y = 6 \\ 2x + 3y = 8 \end{cases}$

12. $\begin{cases} x + 3y = -5 \\ 2x + 2y = 6 \end{cases}$

13. $\begin{cases} 3x + 2y = 16 \\ x = 3y - 2 \end{cases}$

14. $\begin{cases} 2x + 3y = 18 \\ x = 2y - 5 \end{cases}$

15. $\begin{cases} 2x - 5y = 1 \\ 3x + y = -7 \end{cases}$

16. $\begin{cases} 3y - x = 6 \\ 4x + 12y = 0 \end{cases}$

17. $\begin{cases} 4x + 2y = 5 \\ -2x = y + 4 \end{cases}$

18. $\begin{cases} 2y = x + 2 \\ 6x - 12y = 0 \end{cases}$

19. $\begin{cases} 4x + y = 11 \\ 2x + 5y = 1 \end{cases}$

20. $\begin{cases} 3x + y = -14 \\ 4x + 3y = -22 \end{cases}$

21. $\begin{cases} x + 2y + 5 = -4 + 5y - x \\ \quad\quad 2x + x = y + 4 \end{cases}$

(*Hint:* First simplify each equation.)

22. $\begin{cases} 5x + 4y - 2 = -6 + 7y - 3x \\ \quad\quad 3x + 4x = y + 3 \end{cases}$

(*Hint:* See Exercise **21**.)

23. $\begin{cases} 6x - 3y = 5 \\ x + 2y = 0 \end{cases}$

24. $\begin{cases} 10x - 5y = -21 \\ x + 3y = 0 \end{cases}$

◉ 25. $\begin{cases} 3x - y = 1 \\ 2x - 3y = 10 \end{cases}$

26. $\begin{cases} 2x - y = -7 \\ 4x - 3y = -11 \end{cases}$

27. $\begin{cases} -x + 2y = 10 \\ -2x + 3y = 18 \end{cases}$

28. $\begin{cases} -x + 3y = 18 \\ -3x + 2y = 19 \end{cases}$

29. $\begin{cases} 5x + 10y = 20 \\ 2x + 6y = 10 \end{cases}$

30. $\begin{cases} 6x + 3y = 12 \\ 9x + 6y = 15 \end{cases}$

◉ 31. $\begin{cases} 3x + 6y = 9 \\ 4x + 8y = 16 \end{cases}$

32. $\begin{cases} 2x + 4y = 6 \\ 5x + 10y = 16 \end{cases}$

◉ 33. $\begin{cases} \frac{1}{3}x - y = 2 \\ x - 3y = 6 \end{cases}$

34. $\begin{cases} \frac{1}{4}x - 2y = 1 \\ x - 8y = 4 \end{cases}$

35. $\begin{cases} x = \frac{3}{4}y - 1 \\ 8x - 5y = -6 \end{cases}$

36. $\begin{cases} x = \frac{5}{6}y - 2 \\ 12x - 5y = -9 \end{cases}$

Review

Write equivalent equations by multiplying both sides of each given equation by the given nonzero number. See Section 3.2.

37. $3x + 2y = 6$ by -2 **38.** $-x + y = 10$ by 5 **39.** $-4x + y = 3$ by 3 **40.** $5a - 7b = -4$ by -4

Add the binomials. See Section 10.4.

41. $\begin{array}{r} 3n + 6m \\ 2n - 6m \\ \hline \end{array}$

42. $\begin{array}{r} -2x + 5y \\ 2x + 11y \\ \hline \end{array}$

43. $\begin{array}{r} -5a - 7b \\ 5a - 8b \\ \hline \end{array}$

44. $\begin{array}{r} 9q + p \\ -9q - p \\ \hline \end{array}$

Concept Extensions

Solve each system by the substitution method. First simplify each equation by combining like terms.

45. $\begin{cases} -5y + 6y = 3x + 2(x - 5) - 3x + 5 \\ 4(x + y) - x + y = -12 \end{cases}$

46. $\begin{cases} 5x + 2y - 4x - 2y = 2(2y + 6) - 7 \\ 3(2x - y) - 4x = 1 + 9 \end{cases}$

47. Explain how to identify a system with no solution when using the substitution method.

48. Occasionally, when using the substitution method, we obtain the equation $0 = 0$. Explain how this result indicates that the graphs of the equations in the system are identical.

Solve. See a Concept Check in this section.

49. As you solve the system $\begin{cases} 3x - y = -6 \\ -3x + 2y = 7 \end{cases}$, you find that $y = 1$. Is this the solution of the system?

50. As you solve the system $\begin{cases} x = 5y \\ y = 2x \end{cases}$, you find that $x = 0$ and $y = 0$. What is the solution of this system?

51. To avoid fractions, which of the equations below would you use if solving for y? Explain why.

    a. $\frac{1}{2}x - 4y = \frac{3}{4}$ **b.** $8x - 5y = 13$ **c.** $7x - y = 19$

52. Give the number of solutions for a system if the graphs of the equations in the system are

    a. lines intersecting in one point
    b. parallel lines
    c. same line

Use a graphing calculator to solve each system.

53. $\begin{cases} y = 5.1x + 14.56 \\ y = -2x - 3.9 \end{cases}$ **54.** $\begin{cases} y = 3.1x - 16.35 \\ y = -9.7x + 28.45 \end{cases}$ **55.** $\begin{cases} 3x + 2y = 14.04 \\ 5x + y = 18.5 \end{cases}$ **56.** $\begin{cases} x + y = -15.2 \\ -2x + 5y = -19.3 \end{cases}$

57. U.S. consumer spending y (in billions of dollars) on DVD-format home entertainment from 2006 to 2010 is given by $y = -1.6x + 20.9$, where x is the number of years after 2006. U.S. consumer spending y (in billions of dollars) on Blu-ray-format home entertainment from 2006 to 2010 is given by $y = 0.6x - 0.2$, where x is the number of years after 2006. (*Source:* Based on data from DEG: The Digital Entertainment Group)

    a. Use the substitution method to solve this system of equations.

$$\begin{cases} y = -1.6x + 20.9 \\ y = 0.6x - 0.2 \end{cases}$$

    Round x to the nearest tenth and y to the nearest whole.

    b. Explain the meaning of your answer to part **a**.

    c. Sketch a graph of the system of equations. Write a sentence describing the trends in the popularity of these two types of home entertainment formats.

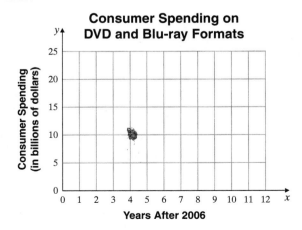

Consumer Spending on DVD and Blu-ray Formats

Consumer Spending (in billions of dollars) vs. Years After 2006

58. Promoting tourism in a state can significantly boost jobs and tax revenue for that state. For that reason, most states operate a tourism office to attract travelers and their spending. For fiscal years 2008 through 2012, Maryland's state tourism office budget y (in millions of dollars) is given by the equation $y = 0.61x + 7.62$, where x is the number of years after fiscal year 2008. For the same period, Georgia's state tourism office budget y (in millions of dollars) is given by the equation $y = -0.74x + 9.32$, where x is the number of years after fiscal year 2008. (*Source:* Based on data from the U.S. Travel Association)

    a. Use the substitution method to solve this system of equations.

$$\begin{cases} y = 0.61x + 7.62 \\ y = -0.74x + 9.32 \end{cases}$$

    Round x and y to the nearest tenth.

    b. Explain the meaning of your answer to part **a**.

    c. Sketch a graph of the system of equations. Write a sentence describing the trends in Maryland's and Georgia's state tourism office budgets between fiscal years 2008 and 2012.

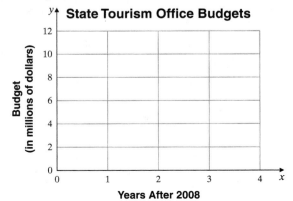

State Tourism Office Budgets

Budget (in millions of dollars) vs. Years After 2008

Solving Systems of Linear Equations by Addition

Objective

A Use the Addition Method to Solve a System of Linear Equations.

Objective A Using the Addition Method

We have seen that substitution is an accurate method for solving a system of linear equations. Another accurate method is the **addition** or **elimination method**. The addition method is based on the addition property of equality: Adding equal quantities to both sides of an equation does not change the solution of the equation. In symbols,

if $A = B$ and $C = D$, then $A + C = B + D$

To see how we use this to solve a system of equations, study Example 1.

Practice 1

Use the addition method to solve the system:
$$\begin{cases} x + y = 13 \\ x - y = 5 \end{cases}$$

Example 1 Solve the system: $\begin{cases} x + y = 7 \\ x - y = 5 \end{cases}$

Solution: Since the left side of each equation is equal to its right side, we are adding equal quantities when we add the left sides of the equations together and add the right sides of the equations together. This adding eliminates the variable y and gives us an equation in one variable, x. We can then solve for x.

$$\begin{array}{ll} x + y = 7 & \text{First equation} \\ \underline{x - y = 5} & \text{Second equation} \\ \quad 2x = 12 & \text{Add the equations to eliminate } y. \\ \quad\ \ x = 6 & \text{Divide both sides by 2.} \end{array}$$

> **Helpful Hint**
> Notice in Example 1 that our goal when solving a system of equations by the addition method is to eliminate a variable when adding the equations.

The x-value of the solution is 6. To find the corresponding y-value, we let $x = 6$ in either equation of the system. We will use the first equation.

$$\begin{array}{ll} x + y = 7 & \text{First equation} \\ 6 + y = 7 & \text{Let } x = 6. \\ \quad\ \ y = 1 & \text{Solve for } y. \end{array}$$

The solution is $(6, 1)$.

Check: Check the solution in both equations of the original system.

First Equation	**Second Equation**
$x + y = 7$	$x - y = 5$
$6 + 1 \stackrel{?}{=} 7$ Let $x = 6$ and $y = 1$.	$6 - 1 \stackrel{?}{=} 5$ Let $x = 6$ and $y = 1$.
$7 = 7$ True	$5 = 5$ True

Thus, the solution of the system is $(6, 1)$.

If we graph the two equations in the system, we have two lines that intersect at the point $(6, 1)$, as shown.

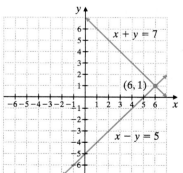

Work Practice 1

Answer
1. $(9, 4)$

Example 2 Solve the system: $\begin{cases} -2x + y = 2 \\ -x + 3y = -4 \end{cases}$

Solution: If we simply add these two equations, the result is still an equation in two variables. However, from Example 1, remember that our goal is to eliminate one of the variables so that we have an equation in the other variable. To do this, notice what happens if we multiply *both sides* of the first equation by -3. We are allowed to do this by the multiplication property of equality. Then the system

$\begin{cases} -3(-2x + y) = -3(2) \\ -x + 3y = -4 \end{cases}$ simplifies to $\begin{cases} 6x - 3y = -6 \\ -x + 3y = -4 \end{cases}$

When we add the resulting equations, the y-variable is eliminated.

$$\begin{array}{r} 6x - 3y = -6 \\ \underline{-x + 3y = -4} \\ 5x = -10 \quad \text{Add.} \\ x = -2 \quad \text{Divide both sides by 5.} \end{array}$$

To find the corresponding y-value, we let $x = -2$ in either of the original equations. We use the first equation of the original system.

$$\begin{array}{ll} -2x + y = 2 & \text{First equation} \\ -2(-2) + y = 2 & \text{Let } x = -2. \\ 4 + y = 2 & \\ y = -2 & \end{array}$$

Check the ordered pair $(-2, -2)$ in both equations of the *original* system. The solution is $(-2, -2)$.

■ Work Practice 2

Practice 2

Solve the system:
$\begin{cases} 2x - y = -6 \\ -x + 4y = 17 \end{cases}$

Helpful Hint

When finding the second value of an ordered pair solution, any equation equivalent to one of the original equations in the system may be used.

In Example 2, the decision to multiply the first equation by -3 was no accident. **To eliminate a variable** when adding two equations, **the coefficient of the variable in one equation must be the opposite of its coefficient in the other equation.**

Helpful Hint

Be sure to multiply *both sides* of an equation by the chosen number when solving by the addition method. A common mistake is to multiply only the side containing the variables.

Example 3 Solve the system: $\begin{cases} 2x - y = 7 \\ 8x - 4y = 1 \end{cases}$

Solution: When we multiply both sides of the first equation by -4, the resulting coefficient of x is -8. This is the opposite of 8, the coefficient of x in the second equation. Then the system

$\begin{cases} -4(2x - y) = -4(7) \\ 8x - 4y = 1 \end{cases}$ simplifies to

Helpful Hint Don't forget to multiply both sides by -4.

$\begin{cases} -8x + 4y = -28 \\ \underline{8x - 4y = 1} \end{cases}$

$$0 = -27 \quad \text{Add the equations.}$$

Practice 3

Solve the system:
$\begin{cases} x - 3y = -2 \\ -3x + 9y = 5 \end{cases}$

Answers
2. $(-1, 4)$ **3.** no solution

(*Continued on next page*)

When we add the equations, both variables are eliminated and we have $0 = -27$, a false statement. This means that the system has no solution. The equations, if graphed, would represent parallel lines.

■ Work Practice 3

Copyright 2015 Pearson Education, Inc.

Practice 4

Solve the system:
$$\begin{cases} 2x + 5y = 1 \\ -4x - 10y = -2 \end{cases}$$

Example 4 Solve the system: $\begin{cases} 3x - 2y = 2 \\ -9x + 6y = -6 \end{cases}$

Solution: First we multiply both sides of the first equation by 3 and then we add the resulting equations.

$$\begin{cases} 3(3x - 2y) = 3(2) \\ -9x + 6y = -6 \end{cases}$$ simplifies to $\begin{cases} 9x - 6y = 6 \\ \underline{-9x + 6y = -6} \quad \text{Add the equations.} \\ 0 = 0 \end{cases}$

Both variables are eliminated and we have $0 = 0$, a true statement. This means that the system has an infinite number of solutions. The equations, if graphed, would be the same line.

■ Work Practice 4

✓**Concept Check** Suppose you are solving the system

$$\begin{cases} 3x + 8y = -5 \\ 2x - 4y = 3 \end{cases}$$

You decide to use the addition method by multiplying both sides of the second equation by 2. In which of the following was the multiplication performed correctly? Explain.

a. $4x - 8y = 3$ **b.** $4x - 8y = 6$

In the next example, we multiply both equations by numbers so that coefficients of a variable are opposites.

Practice 5

Solve the system:
$$\begin{cases} 4x + 5y = 14 \\ 3x - 2y = -1 \end{cases}$$

Example 5 Solve the system: $\begin{cases} 3x + 4y = 13 \\ 5x - 9y = 6 \end{cases}$

Solution: We can eliminate the variable y by multiplying the first equation by 9 and the second equation by 4. Then we add the resulting equations.

$$\begin{cases} 9(3x + 4y) = 9(13) \\ 4(5x - 9y) = 4(6) \end{cases}$$ simplifies to $\begin{cases} 27x + 36y = 117 \\ \underline{20x - 36y = \ \ 24} \\ 47x = 141 \quad \text{Add the equations.} \\ x = 3 \quad \text{Solve for } x. \end{cases}$

To find the corresponding y-value, we let $x = 3$ in one of the original equations of the system. Doing so in either of these equations will give $y = 1$. Check to see that $(3, 1)$ satisfies each equation in the original system. The solution is $(3, 1)$.

■ Work Practice 5

Answers

4. infinite number of solutions

5. $(1, 2)$

✓**Concept Check Answer**

b; answers may vary

If we had decided to eliminate x instead of y in Example 5, the first equation could have been multiplied by 5 and the second by -3. Try solving the original system this way to check that the solution is $(3, 1)$.

The following steps summarize how to solve a system of linear equations by the addition method.

To Solve a System of Two Linear Equations by the Addition Method

Step 1: Rewrite each equation in standard form, $Ax + By = C$.

Step 2: If necessary, multiply one or both equations by a nonzero number so that the coefficients of the chosen variable in the system are opposites.

Step 3: Add the equations.

Step 4: Find the value of one variable by solving the resulting equation from Step 3.

Step 5: Find the value of the second variable by substituting the value found in Step 4 into either of the original equations.

Step 6: Check the proposed solution in the original system.

✓**Concept Check** Suppose you are solving the system

$$\begin{cases} -4x + 7y = 6 \\ x + 2y = 5 \end{cases}$$

by the addition method.

a. What step(s) should you take if you wish to eliminate x when adding the equations?

b. What step(s) should you take if you wish to eliminate y when adding the equations?

Example 6 Solve the system: $\begin{cases} -x - \dfrac{y}{2} = \dfrac{5}{2} \\ \dfrac{x}{6} - \dfrac{y}{2} = 0 \end{cases}$

Solution: We begin by clearing each equation of fractions. To do so, we multiply both sides of the first equation by the LCD, 2, and both sides of the second equation by the LCD, 6. Then the system

$$\begin{cases} 2\left(-x - \dfrac{y}{2}\right) = 2\left(\dfrac{5}{2}\right) \\ 6\left(\dfrac{x}{6} - \dfrac{y}{2}\right) = 6(0) \end{cases} \quad \text{simplifies to} \quad \begin{cases} -2x - y = 5 \\ x - 3y = 0 \end{cases}$$

We can now eliminate the variable x by multiplying the second equation by 2.

$$\begin{cases} -2x - y = 5 \\ 2(x - 3y) = 2(0) \end{cases} \quad \text{simplifies to} \quad \begin{cases} -2x - y = 5 \\ \underline{2x - 6y = 0} \\ \qquad -7y = 5 \quad \text{Add the equations.} \\ \qquad\quad y = -\dfrac{5}{7} \quad \text{Solve for } y. \end{cases}$$

To find x, we could replace y with $-\dfrac{5}{7}$ in one of the equations with two variables.

Instead, let's go back to the simplified system and multiply by appropriate factors to eliminate the variable y and solve for x. To do this, we multiply the first equation by -3. Then the system

$$\begin{cases} -3(-2x - y) = -3(5) \\ x - 3y = 0 \end{cases} \quad \text{simplifies to} \quad \begin{cases} 6x + 3y = -15 \\ \underline{x - 3y = \quad 0} \\ 7x \qquad = -15 \quad \text{Add the equations.} \\ \;\; x \qquad = -\dfrac{15}{7} \quad \text{Solve for } x. \end{cases}$$

Check the ordered pair $\left(-\dfrac{15}{7}, -\dfrac{5}{7}\right)$ in both equations of the original system. The solution is $\left(-\dfrac{15}{7}, -\dfrac{5}{7}\right)$.

🔳 Work Practice 6

Practice 6

Solve the system:

$$\begin{cases} -\dfrac{x}{3} + y = \dfrac{4}{3} \\ \dfrac{x}{2} - \dfrac{5}{2}y = -\dfrac{1}{2} \end{cases}$$

Answer

6. $\left(-\dfrac{17}{2}, -\dfrac{3}{2}\right)$

✓**Concept Check Answer**

a. multiply the second equation by 4

b. possible answer: multiply the first equation by -2 and the second equation by 7

Vocabulary, Readiness & Video Check

Given the system $\begin{cases} 3x - 2y = -9 \\ x + 5y = 14 \end{cases}$ *read each row (Step 1, Step 2, and Result). Then answer whether the result is true or false.*

	Step 1	Step 2	Result	True or False?
1.	Multiply 2nd equation through by -3.	Add the resulting equation to the 1st equation.	The y's are eliminated.	
2.	Multiply 2nd equation through by -3.	Add the resulting equation to the 1st equation.	The x's are eliminated.	
3.	Multiply 1st equation by 5 and 2nd equation by 2.	Add the two new equations.	The y's are eliminated.	
4.	Multiply 1st equation by 5 and 2nd equation by -2.	Add the two new equations.	The y's are eliminated.	

Martin-Gay Interactive Videos   Watch the section lecture video and answer the following question.

Objective A **5.** For the addition/elimination method, sometimes we need to multiply an equation through by a nonzero number so that the coefficients of a variable are opposites, as is shown in ⊞ Example 2. What property allows us to do this? What important reminder is made at this step? ▷

See Video 14.3

14.3 Exercise Set MyMathLab®

Objective A *Solve each system of equations by the addition method. See Example 1.*

1. $\begin{cases} 3x + y = 5 \\ 6x - y = 4 \end{cases}$ **2.** $\begin{cases} 4x + y = 13 \\ 2x - y = 5 \end{cases}$ ▷ **3.** $\begin{cases} x - 2y = 8 \\ -x + 5y = -17 \end{cases}$ **4.** $\begin{cases} x - 2y = -11 \\ -x + 5y = 23 \end{cases}$

Solve each system of equations by the addition method. If a system contains fractions or decimals, you may want to first clear each equation of the fractions or decimals. See Examples 2 through 6.

5. $\begin{cases} 3x + y = -11 \\ 6x - 2y = -2 \end{cases}$ **6.** $\begin{cases} 4x + y = -13 \\ 6x - 3y = -15 \end{cases}$ **7.** $\begin{cases} 3x + 2y = 11 \\ 5x - 2y = 29 \end{cases}$

8. $\begin{cases} 4x + 2y = 2 \\ 3x - 2y = 12 \end{cases}$ **9.** $\begin{cases} x + 5y = 18 \\ 3x + 2y = -11 \end{cases}$ **10.** $\begin{cases} x + 4y = 14 \\ 5x + 3y = 2 \end{cases}$

11. $\begin{cases} x + y = 6 \\ x - y = 6 \end{cases}$ **12.** $\begin{cases} x - y = 1 \\ -x + 2y = 0 \end{cases}$ **13.** $\begin{cases} 2x + 3y = 0 \\ 4x + 6y = 3 \end{cases}$

14. $\begin{cases} 3x + y = 4 \\ 9x + 3y = 6 \end{cases}$ **15.** $\begin{cases} -x + 5y = -1 \\ 3x - 15y = 3 \end{cases}$ **16.** $\begin{cases} 2x + y = 6 \\ 4x + 2y = 12 \end{cases}$

▷ **17.** $\begin{cases} 3x - 2y = 7 \\ 5x + 4y = 8 \end{cases}$ **18.** $\begin{cases} 6x - 5y = 25 \\ 4x + 15y = 13 \end{cases}$ **19.** $\begin{cases} 8x = -11y - 16 \\ 2x + 3y = -4 \end{cases}$

20. $\begin{cases} 10x + 3y = -12 \\ 5x = -4y - 16 \end{cases}$

21. $\begin{cases} 4x - 3y = 7 \\ 7x + 5y = 2 \end{cases}$

22. $\begin{cases} -2x + 3y = 10 \\ 3x + 4y = 2 \end{cases}$

23. $\begin{cases} 4x - 6y = 8 \\ 6x - 9y = 12 \end{cases}$

24. $\begin{cases} 9x - 3y = 12 \\ 12x - 4y = 18 \end{cases}$

25. $\begin{cases} 2x - 5y = 4 \\ 3x - 2y = 4 \end{cases}$

26. $\begin{cases} 6x - 5y = 7 \\ 4x - 6y = 7 \end{cases}$

27. $\begin{cases} \dfrac{x}{3} + \dfrac{y}{6} = 1 \\ \dfrac{x}{2} - \dfrac{y}{4} = 0 \end{cases}$

28. $\begin{cases} \dfrac{x}{2} + \dfrac{y}{8} = 3 \\ x - \dfrac{y}{4} = 0 \end{cases}$

29. $\begin{cases} \dfrac{10}{3}x + 4y = -4 \\ 5x + 6y = -6 \end{cases}$

30. $\begin{cases} \dfrac{3}{2}x + 4y = 1 \\ 9x + 24y = 5 \end{cases}$

31. $\begin{cases} x - \dfrac{y}{3} = -1 \\ -\dfrac{x}{2} + \dfrac{y}{8} = \dfrac{1}{4} \end{cases}$

32. $\begin{cases} 2x - \dfrac{3y}{4} = -3 \\ x + \dfrac{y}{9} = \dfrac{13}{3} \end{cases}$

33. $\begin{aligned} -4(x + 2) &= 3y \\ 2x - 2y &= 3 \end{aligned}$

34. $\begin{aligned} -9(x + 3) &= 8y \\ 3x - 3y &= 8 \end{aligned}$

▶ **35.** $\begin{cases} \dfrac{x}{3} - y = 2 \\ -\dfrac{x}{2} + \dfrac{3y}{2} = -3 \end{cases}$

36. $\begin{cases} \dfrac{x}{2} + \dfrac{y}{4} = 1 \\ -\dfrac{x}{4} - \dfrac{y}{8} = 1 \end{cases}$

37. $\begin{cases} \dfrac{3}{5}x - y = -\dfrac{4}{5} \\ 3x + \dfrac{y}{2} = -\dfrac{9}{5} \end{cases}$

38. $\begin{cases} 3x + \dfrac{7}{2}y = \dfrac{3}{4} \\ -\dfrac{x}{2} + \dfrac{5}{3}y = -\dfrac{5}{4} \end{cases}$

▶ **39.** $\begin{cases} 3.5x + 2.5y = 17 \\ -1.5x - 7.5y = -33 \end{cases}$

40. $\begin{cases} -2.5x - 6.5y = 47 \\ 0.5x - 4.5y = 37 \end{cases}$

41. $\begin{cases} 0.02x + 0.04y = 0.09 \\ -0.1x + 0.3y = 0.8 \end{cases}$

42. $\begin{cases} 0.04x - 0.05y = 0.105 \\ 0.2x - 0.6y = 1.05 \end{cases}$

Review

Translating *Rewrite each sentence using mathematical symbols. Do not solve the equations. See Sections 9.3 and 9.4.*

43. Twice a number, added to 6, is 3 less than the number.

44. The sum of three consecutive integers is 66.

45. Three times a number, subtracted from 20, is 2.

46. Twice the sum of 8 and a number is the difference of the number and 20.

47. The product of 4 and the sum of a number and 6 is twice the number.

48. If the quotient of twice a number and 7 is subtracted from the reciprocal of the number, the result is 2.

Concept Extensions

Solve. See a Concept Check in this section.

49. To solve this system by the addition method and eliminate the variable y,

$$\begin{cases} 4x + 2y = -7 \\ 3x - y = -12 \end{cases}$$

by what value would you multiply the second equation? What do you get when you complete the multiplication?

Given the system of linear equations $\begin{cases} 3x - y = -8 \\ 5x + 3y = 2 \end{cases}$:

50. Use the addition method and
   a. Solve the system by eliminating x.
   b. Solve the system by eliminating y.

51. Suppose you are solving the system

$$\begin{cases} 3x + 8y = -5 \\ 2x - 4y = 3 \end{cases}$$

You decide to use the addition method by multiplying both sides of the second equation by 2. In which of the following was the multiplication performed correctly? Explain.
   a. $4x - 8y = 3$
   b. $4x - 8y = 6$

52. Suppose you are solving the system

$$\begin{cases} -2x - y = 0 \\ -2x + 3y = 6 \end{cases}$$

You decide to use the addition method by multiplying both sides of the first equation by 3, then adding the resulting equation to the second equation. Which of the following is the correct sum? Explain.
   a. $-8x = 6$
   b. $-8x = 9$

53. When solving a system of equations by the addition method, how do we know when the system has no solution?

54. Explain why the addition method might be preferred over the substitution method for solving the system $\begin{cases} 2x - 3y = 5 \\ 5x + 2y = 6. \end{cases}$

55. Use the system of linear equations below to answer the questions.

$$\begin{cases} x + y = 5 \\ 3x + 3y = b \end{cases}$$

   a. Find the value of b so that the system has an infinite number of solutions.
   b. Find a value of b so that there are no solutions to the system.

56. Use the system of linear equations below to answer the questions.

$$\begin{cases} x + y = 4 \\ 2x + by = 8 \end{cases}$$

   a. Find the value of b so that the system has an infinite number of solutions.
   b. Find a value of b so that the system has a single solution.

Solve each system by the addition method.

57. $\begin{cases} 2x + 3y = 14 \\ 3x - 4y = -69.1 \end{cases}$

58. $\begin{cases} 5x - 2y = -19.8 \\ -3x + 5y = -3.7 \end{cases}$

59. As the economy and job marketplace change, demand for certain types of workers changes. The number of jobs for postal service mail carriers that is predicted for 2010 through 2020 can be approximated by $38x + 10y = 3167$. The number of jobs for market research analysts that is predicted for the same period can be approximated by $117x - 10y = -2827$. For both equations, x is the number of years since 2010, and y is the number of jobs in the thousands. (*Source*: Based on data from the U.S. Bureau of Labor Statistics)

a. Use the addition method to solve this system of equations.

$$\begin{cases} 38x + 10y = 3167 \\ 117x - 10y = -2827 \end{cases}$$

(Eliminate y first and solve for x. Round this result to the nearest whole number.)

b. Interpret your solution from part **a.**

c. Using the year in your answer to part **b**, estimate the number of mail carrier jobs and market research analyst jobs in that year.

60. In recent years, the number of newspapers printed as morning editions has been increasing and the number of newspapers printed as evening editions has been decreasing. The number y of daily morning newspapers in existence from 1995 through 2011 is approximated by the equation $153x - 10y = -6720$, where x is the number of years since 1995. The number y of daily evening newspapers in existence from 1995 through 2011 is approximated by $125x + 5y = 4350$, where x is the number of years since 1995. (*Source*: Based on data from Newspaper Association of America)

a. Use the addition method to solve this system of equations.

$$\begin{cases} 153x - 10y = -6720 \\ 125x + 5y = 4350 \end{cases}$$

(Round to the nearest whole number. Because of rounding, the y-value of your ordered pair solution may vary.)

b. Interpret your solution from part **a.**

c. Use the year in your answer to part **b** to find how many of each type of newspaper were in existence that year.

Summary on Solving Systems of Equations

Answers

Solve each system by either the addition method or the substitution method.

1. _____

2. _____

3. _____

4. _____

5. _____

6. _____

7. _____

8. _____

9. _____

10. _____

11. _____

12. _____

13. _____

14. _____

15. _____

16. _____

17. _____

18. _____

19. _____

20. _____

21. _____

22. _____

1. $\begin{cases} 2x - 3y = -11 \\ y = 4x - 3 \end{cases}$

2. $\begin{cases} 4x - 5y = 6 \\ y = 3x - 10 \end{cases}$

3. $\begin{cases} x + y = 3 \\ x - y = 7 \end{cases}$

4. $\begin{cases} x - y = 20 \\ x + y = -8 \end{cases}$

5. $\begin{cases} x + 2y = 1 \\ 3x + 4y = -1 \end{cases}$

6. $\begin{cases} x + 3y = 5 \\ 5x + 6y = -2 \end{cases}$

7. $\begin{cases} y = x + 3 \\ 3x = 2y - 6 \end{cases}$

8. $\begin{cases} y = -2x \\ 2x - 3y = -16 \end{cases}$

9. $\begin{cases} y = 2x - 3 \\ y = 5x - 18 \end{cases}$

10. $\begin{cases} y = 6x - 5 \\ y = 4x - 11 \end{cases}$

11. $\begin{cases} x + \dfrac{1}{6}y = \dfrac{1}{2} \\ 3x + 2y = 3 \end{cases}$

12. $\begin{cases} x + \dfrac{1}{3}y = \dfrac{5}{12} \\ 8x + 3y = 4 \end{cases}$

13. $\begin{cases} x - 5y = 1 \\ -2x + 10y = 3 \end{cases}$

14. $\begin{cases} -x + 2y = 3 \\ 3x - 6y = -9 \end{cases}$

15. $\begin{cases} 0.2x - 0.3y = -0.95 \\ 0.4x + 0.1y = 0.55 \end{cases}$

16. $\begin{cases} 0.08x - 0.04y = -0.11 \\ 0.02x - 0.06y = -0.09 \end{cases}$

17. $\begin{cases} x = 3y - 7 \\ 2x - 6y = -14 \end{cases}$

18. $\begin{cases} y = \dfrac{x}{2} - 3 \\ 2x - 4y = 0 \end{cases}$

19. $\begin{cases} 2x + 5y = -1 \\ 3x - 4y = 33 \end{cases}$

20. $\begin{cases} 7x - 3y = 2 \\ 6x + 5y = -21 \end{cases}$

21. Which method, substitution or addition, would you prefer to use to solve the system below? Explain your reasoning.
$$\begin{cases} 3x + 2y = -2 \\ y = -2x \end{cases}$$

22. Which method, substitution or addition, would you prefer to use to solve the system below? Explain your reasoning.
$$\begin{cases} 3x - 2y = -3 \\ 6x + 2y = 12 \end{cases}$$

14.4 Systems of Linear Equations and Problem Solving ▶

Objective A Using a System of Equations for Problem Solving ▶

Objective

A Use a System of Equations to Solve Problems.

Many of the word problems solved earlier with one-variable equations can also be solved with two equations in two variables. We use the same problem-solving steps that we have used throughout this text. The only difference is that two variables are assigned to represent the two unknown quantities and that the problem is translated into two equations.

Problem-Solving Steps

1. UNDERSTAND the problem. During this step, become comfortable with the problem. Some ways of doing this are to

   Read and reread the problem.

   Choose two variables to represent the two unknowns.

   Construct a drawing.

   Propose a solution and check. Pay careful attention to how you check your proposed solution. This will help when writing equations to model the problem.

2. TRANSLATE the problem into two equations.

3. SOLVE the system of equations.

4. INTERPRET the results: *Check* the proposed solution in the stated problem and *state* your conclusion.

Example 1 Finding Unknown Numbers

Find two numbers whose sum is 37 and whose difference is 21.

Solution:

1. UNDERSTAND. Read and reread the problem. Suppose that one number is 20. If their sum is 37, the other number is 17 because $20 + 17 = 37$. Is their difference 21? No; $20 - 17 = 3$. Our proposed solution is incorrect, but we now have a better understanding of the problem.

   Since we are looking for two numbers, we let

   x = first number and

   y = second number

2. TRANSLATE. Since we have assigned two variables to this problem, we translate our problem into two equations.

   In words: two number whose sum   is   37

   Translate: $x + y \;\; = \;\; 37$

   In words: two number whose difference   is   21

   Translate: $x - y \;\; = \;\; 21$

(Continued on next page)

Practice 1

Find two numbers whose sum is 50 and whose difference is 22.

Answer
1. 36 and 14

3. SOLVE. Now we solve the system.

$$\begin{cases} x + y = 37 \\ x - y = 21 \end{cases}$$

Notice that the coefficients of the variable y are opposites. Let's then solve by the addition method and begin by adding the equations.

$$\begin{array}{ll} x + y = 37 & \\ \underline{x - y = 21} & \text{Add the equations.} \\ 2x \phantom{{}- y} = 58 & \\ x = 29 & \text{Divide both sides by 2.} \end{array}$$

Now we let $x = 29$ in the first equation to find y.

$$\begin{array}{ll} x + y = 37 & \text{First equation} \\ 29 + y = 37 & \\ y = 8 & \text{Subtract 29 from both sides.} \end{array}$$

4. INTERPRET. The solution of the system is $(29, 8)$.

Check: Notice that the sum of 29 and 8 is $29 + 8 = 37$, the required sum. Their difference is $29 - 8 = 21$, the required difference.

State: The numbers are 29 and 8.

▣ **Work Practice 1**

Practice 2

Admission prices at a local weekend fair were $5 for children and $7 for adults. The total money collected was $3379, and 587 people attended the fair. How many children and how many adults attended the fair?

Example 2   Solving a Problem About Prices

The Cirque du Soleil show Varekai is performing locally. Matinee admission for 4 adults and 2 children is $374, while admission for 2 adults and 3 children is $285.

a. What is the price of an adult's ticket?

b. What is the price of a child's ticket?

c. Suppose that a special rate of $1000 is offered for groups of 20 persons. Should a group of 4 adults and 16 children use the group rate? Why or why not?

Solution:

1. UNDERSTAND. Read and reread the problem and guess a solution. Let's suppose that the price of an adult's ticket is $50 and the price of a child's ticket is $40. To check our proposed solution, let's see if admission for 4 adults and 2 children is $374. Admission for 4 adults is 4($50) or $200 and admission for 2 children is 2($40) or $80. This gives a total admission of $200 + $80 = $280, not the required $374. Again, though, we have accomplished the purpose of this process: We have a better understanding of the problem. To continue, we let

A = the price of an adult's ticket and

C = the price of a child's ticket

Answer

2. 365 children and 222 adults

2. TRANSLATE. We translate the problem into two equations using both variables.

In words: admission for 4 adults and admission for 2 children is $374

Translate: $4A + 2C = 374$

In words: admission for 2 adults and admission for 3 children is $285

Translate: $2A + 3C = 285$

3. SOLVE. We solve the system.

$$\begin{cases} 4A + 2C = 374 \\ 2A + 3C = 285 \end{cases}$$

Since both equations are written in standard form, we solve by the addition method. First we multiply the second equation by -2 so that when we add the equations, we eliminate the variable A. Then the system

$$\begin{cases} 4A + 2C = 374 \\ -2(2A + 3C) = -2(285) \end{cases}$$ simplifies to $$\begin{cases} 4A + 2C = 374 \\ -4A - 6C = -570 \end{cases}$$

Add the equations.

$$-4C = -196$$
$$C = 49 \text{ or } \$49, \text{ the child's ticket price}$$

To find A, we replace C with 49 in the first equation.

$4A + 2C = 374$ First equation

$4A + 2(49) = 374$ Let $C = 49$.

$4A + 98 = 374$

$4A = 276$

$A = 69$ or $69, the adult's ticket price

4. INTERPRET.

Check: Notice that 4 adults and 2 children will pay

$4(\$69) + 2(\$49) = \$276 + \$98 = \$374$, the required amount. Also, the price for 2 adults and 3 children is $2(\$69) + 3(\$49) = \$138 + \$147 = \$285$, the required amount.

State: Answer the three original questions.

a. Since $A = 69$, the price of an adult's ticket is $69.

b. Since $C = 49$, the price of a child's ticket is $49.

c. The regular admission price for 4 adults and 16 children is

$4(\$69) + 16(\$49) = \$276 + \$784$
$= \$1060$

This is $60 more than the special group rate of $1000, so they should request the group rate.

Work Practice 2

Practice 3

Two cars are 440 miles apart and traveling toward each other. They meet in 3 hours. If one car's speed is 10 miles per hour faster than the other car's speed, find the speed of each car.

Faster Car	$r \cdot t = d$		
Slower Car			

As part of an exercise program, two students, Louisa and Alfredo, start walking each morning. They live 15 miles away from each other. They decide to meet one day by walking toward one another. After 2 hours they meet. If Louisa walks one mile per hour faster than Alfredo, find both walking speeds.

Solution:

1. UNDERSTAND. Read and reread the problem. Let's propose a solution and use the formula $d = r \cdot t$ to check. Suppose that Louisa's rate is 4 miles per hour. Since Louisa's rate is 1 mile per hour faster, Alfredo's rate is 3 miles per hour. To check, see if they can walk a total of 15 miles in 2 hours. Louisa's distance is rate $\cdot$ time $= 4(2) = 8$ miles and Alfredo's distance is rate $\cdot$ time $= 3(2) = 6$ miles. Their total distance is 8 miles $+$ 6 miles $= 14$ miles, not the required 15 miles. Now that we have a better understanding of the problem, let's model it with a system of equations.

First, we let

$x =$ Alfredo's rate in miles per hour and

$y =$ Louisa's rate in miles per hour

Now we use the facts stated in the problem and the formula $d = rt$ to fill in the following chart.

	r	$\cdot\ t$	$=\ d$
Alfredo	x	2	$2x$
Louisa	y	2	$2y$

2. TRANSLATE. We translate the problem into two equations using both variables.

In words:	Alfredo's distance	$+$	Louisa's distance	$=$	15 miles
	↓	↓	↓	↓	↓
Translate:	$2x$	$+$	$2y$	$=$	15

In words:	Louisa's rate	is	1 mile per hour faster than Alfredo's
	↓	↓	↓
Translate:	y	$=$	$x + 1$

3. SOLVE. The system of equations we are solving is

$$\begin{cases} 2x + 2y = 15 \\ y = x + 1 \end{cases}$$

Answer

3. One car's speed is $68\frac{1}{3}$ mph and the other car's speed is $78\frac{1}{3}$ mph.

Let's use substitution to solve the system since the second equation is solved for y.

$$2x + 2y = 15 \qquad \text{First equation}$$
$$2x + 2(x + 1) = 15 \qquad \text{Replace } y \text{ with } x + 1.$$
$$2x + 2x + 2 = 15$$
$$4x = 13$$
$$x = \frac{13}{4} = 3\frac{1}{4} \text{ or } 3.25$$
$$y = x + 1 = 3\frac{1}{4} + 1 = 4\frac{1}{4} \text{ or } 4.25$$

4. **INTERPRET.** Alfredo's proposed rate is $3\frac{1}{4}$ miles per hour and Louisa's proposed rate is $4\frac{1}{4}$ miles per hour.

Check: Use the formula $d = rt$ and find that in 2 hours, Alfredo's distance is $(3.25)(2)$ miles or 6.5 miles. In 2 hours, Louisa's distance is $(4.25)(2)$ miles or 8.5 miles. The total distance walked is 6.5 miles + 8.5 miles or 15 miles, the given distance.

State: Alfredo walks at a rate of 3.25 miles per hour and Louisa walks at a rate of 4.25 miles per hour.

◼ Work Practice 3

Example 4 Finding Amounts of Solutions

A chemistry teaching assistant needs 10 liters of a 20% saline solution (salt water) for his 2 p.m. laboratory class. Unfortunately, the only mixtures on hand are a 5% saline solution and a 25% saline solution. How much of each solution should he mix to produce the 20% solution?

Solution:

1. **UNDERSTAND.** Read and reread the problem. Suppose that we need 4 liters of the 5% solution. Then we need $10 - 4 = 6$ liters of the 25% solution. To see if this gives us 10 liters of a 20% saline solution, let's find the amount of pure salt in each solution.

	concentration rate	$\times$	amount of solution	$=$	amount of pure salt
	$\downarrow$		$\downarrow$		$\downarrow$
5% solution:	0.05	$\times$	4 liters	$=$	0.2 liter
25% solution:	0.25	$\times$	6 liters	$=$	1.5 liters
20% solution:	0.20	$\times$	10 liters	$=$	2 liters

Since 0.2 liter + 1.5 liters = 1.7 liters, not 2 liters, our proposed solution is incorrect. But we have gained some insight into how to model and check this problem.

We let

$x =$ number of liters of 5% solution and
$y =$ number of liters of 25% solution

5% saline solution   25% saline solution   20% saline solution

(*Continued on next page*)

Now we use a table to organize the given data.

	Concentration Rate	Liters of Solution	Liters of Pure Salt
First Solution	5%	x	$0.05x$
Second Solution	25%	y	$0.25y$
Mixture Needed	20%	10	$(0.20)(10)$

2. **TRANSLATE.** We translate into two equations using both variables.

In words: liters of 5% solution + liters of 25% solution = 10 liters

$$\downarrow \qquad\qquad \downarrow \qquad\qquad \downarrow$$

Translate: $x \quad + \quad y \quad = \quad 10$

In words: salt in 5% solution + salt in 25% solution = salt in mixture

$$\downarrow \qquad\qquad \downarrow \qquad\qquad \downarrow$$

Translate: $0.05x \quad + \quad 0.25y \quad = \quad (0.20)(10)$

3. **SOLVE.** Here we solve the system

$$\begin{cases} x + y = 10 \\ 0.05x + 0.25y = 2 \end{cases}$$

To solve by the addition method, we first multiply the first equation by -25 and the second equation by 100. Then the system

$$\begin{cases} -25(x+y) = -25(10) \\ 100(0.05x + 0.25y) = 100(2) \end{cases}$$ simplifies to $\begin{cases} -25x - 25y = -250 \\ \underline{5x + 25y = 200} \\ -20x \qquad = -50 \quad \text{Add.} \\ x = 2.5 \end{cases}$

To find y, we let $x = 2.5$ in the first equation of the original system.

$$x + y = 10$$
$$2.5 + y = 10 \quad \text{Let } x = 2.5.$$
$$y = 7.5$$

4. **INTERPRET.** Thus, we propose that he needs to mix 2.5 liters of 5% saline solution with 7.5 liters of 25% saline solution.

Check: Notice that $2.5 + 7.5 = 10$, the required number of liters. Also, the sum of the liters of salt in the two solutions equals the liters of salt in the required mixture:

$$0.05(2.5) + 0.25(7.5) = 0.20(10)$$
$$0.125 + 1.875 = 2$$

State: He needs 2.5 liters of the 5% saline solution and 7.5 liters of the 25% saline solution.

▨ Work Practice 4

✓**Concept Check** Suppose you mix an amount of a 30% acid solution with an amount of a 50% acid solution. Which of the following acid strengths would be possible for the resulting acid mixture?

a. 22%   **b.** 44%   **c.** 63%

Vocabulary, Readiness & Video Check

Martin-Gay Interactive Videos   Watch the section lecture video and answer the following question.

See Video 14.4

Objective A 1. In the lecture before ▦ Example 1, the problem-solving steps for solving applications involving systems are discussed. How do these steps differ from the general problem-solving strategy steps?

14.4 Exercise Set MyMathLab®

Without actually solving each problem, choose the correct solution by deciding which choice satisfies the given conditions.

△ **1.** The length of a rectangle is 3 feet longer than the width. The perimeter is 30 feet. Find the dimensions of the rectangle.

  a. length = 8 feet; width = 5 feet
  b. length = 8 feet; width = 7 feet
  c. length = 9 feet; width = 6 feet

△ **2.** An isosceles triangle, a triangle with two sides of equal length, has a perimeter of 20 inches. Each of the equal sides is one inch longer than the third side. Find the lengths of the three sides.

  a. 6 inches, 6 inches, and 7 inches
  b. 7 inches, 7 inches, and 6 inches
  c. 6 inches, 7 inches, and 8 inches

3. Two computer disks and three notebooks cost $17. However, five computer disks and four notebooks cost $32. Find the price of each.

  a. notebook = $4; computer disk = $3
  b. notebook = $3; computer disk = $4
  c. notebook = $5; computer disk = $2

4. Two music CDs and four DVDs cost a total of $40. However, three music CDs and five DVDs cost $55. Find the price of each.

  a. CD = $12; DVD = $4
  b. CD = $15; DVD = $2
  c. CD = $10; DVD = $5

5. Kesha has a total of 100 coins, all of which are either dimes or quarters. The total value of the coins is $13.00. Find the number of each type of coin.

  a. 80 dimes; 20 quarters
  b. 20 dimes; 44 quarters
  c. 60 dimes; 40 quarters

6. Samuel has 28 gallons of saline solution available in two large containers at his pharmacy. One container holds three times as much as the other container. Find the capacity of each container.

  a. 15 gallons; 5 gallons
  b. 20 gallons; 8 gallons
  c. 21 gallons; 7 gallons

Objective A *Write a system of equations describing each situation. Do not solve the system. See Example 1.*

7. Two numbers add up to 15 and have a difference of 7.

8. The total of two numbers is 16. The first number plus 2 more than 3 times the second equals 18.

9. Keiko has a total of $6500, which she has invested in two accounts. The larger account is $800 greater than the smaller account.

10. Dominique has four times as much money in his savings account as in his checking account. The total amount is $2300.

Solve. See Examples 1 through 4.

11. Two numbers total 83 and have a difference of 17. Find the two numbers.

12. The sum of two numbers is 76 and their difference is 52. Find the two numbers.

13. A first number plus twice a second number is 8. Twice the first number plus the second totals 25. Find the numbers.

14. One number is 4 more than twice a second number. Their total is 25. Find the numbers.

15. Miguel Cabrera of the Detroit Tigers led Major League Baseball in runs batted in for the 2012 regular season. Josh Hamilton of the Texas Rangers, who came in second to Cabrera, had 11 fewer runs batted in for the 2012 regular season. Together, these two players brought home 267 runs during the 2012 regular season. How many runs batted in each did Cabrera and Hamilton account for? (*Source: Baseball Almanac*)

16. The highest scorer during the WNBA 2013 regular season was Angel McCoughtry of the Atlanta Dream. Over the season, McCoughtry scored 60 more points than the second-highest scorer, Diana Taurasi, of the Phoenix Mercury. Together, McCoughtry and Taurasi scored 1362 points during the 2013 regular season. How many points did each player score over the course of the season? (*Source:* Women's National Basketball Association)

17. Ann Marie Jones has been pricing Amtrak train fares for a group trip to New York. Three adults and four children must pay $159. Two adults and three children must pay $112. Find the price of an adult's ticket, and find the price of a child's ticket.

18. Last month, Jerry Papa purchased five DVDs and two CDs at Wall-to-Wall Sound for $65. This month he bought three DVDs and four CDs for $81. Find the price of each DVD, and find the price of each CD.

19. Johnston and Betsy Waring have a jar containing 80 coins, all of which are either quarters or nickels. The total value of the coins is $14.60. How many of each type of coin do they have?

20. Sarah and Keith Robinson purchased 40 stamps, a mixture of 44¢ and 28¢ stamps. Find the number of each type of stamp if they spent $16.80.

21. Norman and Suzanne Scarpulla own 30 shares of McDonald's Corp. stock and 68 shares of Ford Motor Co. stock. As the New York Stock Exchange opened on September 25, 2013, their stock portfolio consisting of these two stocks was worth $4107. The McDonald's stock was $80.55 more per share than the Ford stock. What was the price of each stock on that day? (*Source:* SIX Financial Information)

22. Saralee Rose has investments in Google and Facebook stock. As the NASDAQ exchange opened on September 24, 2013, Google stock was at $886.50 per share, and Facebook stock was at $50 per share. Saralee's portfolio made up of these two stocks was worth $32,964 at that time. If Saralee owns 15 more shares of Google stock than she owns of Facebook stock, how many shares of each type of stock does she own? (*Source:* SIX Financial Information)

23. Twice last month, Judy Carter rented a car from Enterprise in Fresno, California, and traveled around the Southwest on business. Enterprise rents this car for a daily fee, plus an additional charge per mile driven. Judy recalls that her first trip lasted 4 days, she drove 450 miles, and the rental cost her $240.50. On her second business trip she drove the same level of car 200 miles in 3 days, and paid $146.00 for the rental. Find the daily fee and the mileage charge.

24. Joan Gundersen rented the same car model twice from Hertz, which rents this car model for a daily fee plus an additional charge per mile driven. Joan recalls that the car rented for 5 days and driven for 300 miles cost her $178, while the same model car rented for 4 days and driven for 500 miles cost $197. Find the daily fee, and find the mileage charge.

25. Pratap Puri rowed 18 miles down the Delaware River in 2 hours, but the return trip took him $4\frac{1}{2}$ hours. Find the rate Pratap can row in still water, and find the rate of the current.

Let x = rate Pratap can row in still water and
  y = rate of the current

	$d =$	r	$\cdot$	t
Downstream		$x + y$		
Upstream		$x - y$		

26. The Jonathan Schultz family took a canoe 10 miles down the Allegheny River in $1\frac{1}{4}$ hours. After lunch it took them 4 hours to return. Find the rate of the current.

Let x = rate the family can row in still water and
  y = rate of the current

	$d =$	r	$\cdot$	t
Downstream		$x + y$		
Upstream		$x - y$		

27. Dave and Sandy Hartranft are frequent flyers with Delta Airlines. They often fly from Philadelphia to Chicago, a distance of 780 miles. On one particular trip they fly into the wind, and the flight takes 2 hours. The return trip, with the wind behind them, takes only $1\frac{1}{2}$ hours. Find the speed of the wind and find the speed of the plane in still air.

28. With a strong wind behind it, a United Airlines jet flies 2400 miles from Los Angeles to Orlando in $4\frac{3}{4}$ hours. The return trip takes 6 hours, as the plane flies into the wind. Find the speed of the plane in still air, and find the wind speed to the nearest tenth of a mile per hour.

29. Kevin Briley began a 186-mile bicycle trip to build up stamina for a triathlon competition. Unfortunately, his bicycle chain broke, so he finished the trip walking. The whole trip took 6 hours. If Kevin walks at a rate of 4 miles per hour and rides at 40 miles per hour, find the amount of time he spent on the bicycle.

30. In Canada, eastbound and westbound trains travel along the same track, with sidings to pull onto to avoid accidents. Two trains are now 150 miles apart, with the westbound train traveling twice as fast as the eastbound train. A warning must be issued to pull one train onto a siding, or else the trains will crash in $1\frac{1}{4}$ hours. Find the speed of the eastbound train and the speed of the westbound train.

31. Dorren Schmidt is a chemist with Gemco Pharmaceutical. She needs to prepare 12 ounces of a 9% hydrochloric acid solution. Find the amount of a 4% solution and the amount of a 12% solution she should mix to get this solution.

Concentration Rate	Liters of Solution	Liters of Pure Acid
0.04	x	$0.04x$
0.12	y	?
0.09	12	?

32. Elise Everly is preparing 15 liters of a 25% saline solution. Elise has two other saline solutions with strengths of 40% and 10%. Find the amount of 40% solution and the amount of 10% solution she should mix to get 15 liters of a 25% solution.

Concentration Rate	Liters of Solution	Liters of Pure Salt
0.40	x	$0.40x$
0.10	y	?
0.25	15	?

33. Wayne Osby blends coffee for a local coffee café. He needs to prepare 200 pounds of blended coffee beans selling for $3.95 per pound. He intends to do this by blending together a high-quality bean costing $4.95 per pound and a cheaper bean costing $2.65 per pound. To the nearest pound, find how much of the high-quality coffee beans and how much of the cheaper coffee beans he should blend.

34. Macadamia nuts cost an astounding $16.50 per pound, but research by an independent firm says that mixed nuts sell better if macadamias are included. The standard mix costs $9.25 per pound. Find how many pounds of macadamias and how many pounds of the standard mix should be combined to produce 40 pounds that will cost $10 per pound. Find the amounts to the nearest tenth of a pound.

35. Recall that two angles are complementary if the sum of their measures is 90°. Find the measures of two complementary angles if one angle is twice the other.

36. Recall that two angles are supplementary if the sum of their measures is 180°. Find the measures of two supplementary angles if one angle is 20° more than four times the other.

37. Find the measures of two complementary angles if one angle is 10° more than three times the other.

38. Find the measures of two supplementary angles if one angle is 18° more than twice the other.

39. Kathi and Robert Hawn had a pottery stand at the annual Skippack Craft Fair. They sold some of their pottery at the original price of $9.50 each, but later decreased the price of each by $2. If they sold all 90 pieces and took in $721, find how many they sold at the original price and how many they sold at the reduced price.

40. A charity fundraiser consisted of a spaghetti supper where a total of 387 people were fed. They charged $6.80 for adults and half price for children. If they took in $2444.60, find how many adults and how many children attended the supper.

41. The Santa Fe National Historic Trail is approximately 1200 miles between Old Franklin, Missouri, and Santa Fe, New Mexico. Suppose that a group of hikers start from each town and walk the trail toward each other. They meet after a total hiking time of 240 hours. If one group travels $\frac{1}{2}$ mile per hour slower than the other group, find the rate of each group. (*Source:* National Park Service)

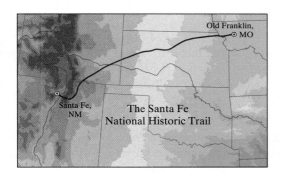

42. California 1 South is a historic highway that stretches 123 miles along the coast from Monterey to Morro Bay. Suppose that two cars start driving this highway, one from each town. They meet after 3 hours. Find the rate of each car if one car travels 1 mile per hour faster than the other car. (*Source: National Geographic*)

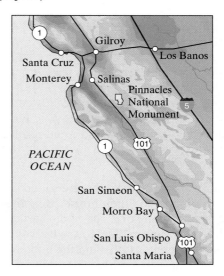

43. A 30% solution of fertilizer is to be mixed with a 60% solution of fertilizer in order to get 150 gallons of a 50% solution. How many gallons of the 30% solution and 60% solution should be mixed?

44. A 10% acid solution is to be mixed with a 50% acid solution in order to get 120 ounces of a 20% acid solution. How many ounces of the 10% solution and 50% solution should be mixed?

45. Traffic signs are regulated by the *Manual on Uniform Traffic Control Devices* (MUTCD). According to this manual, if the sign below is placed on a freeway, its perimeter must be 144 inches. Also, its length must be 12 inches longer than its width. Find the dimensions of this sign.

46. According to the MUTCD (see Exercise **45**), this sign must have a perimeter of 60 inches. Also, its length must be 6 inches longer than its width. Find the perimeter of this sign.

Review

Find the square of each expression. For example, the square of 7 is 7^2 or 49. The square of 5x is $(5x)^2$ or $25x^2$. See Section 10.1.

47. 4   **48.** 3   **49.** $6x$ **50.** $11y$ **51.** $10y^3$ **52.** $8x^5$

Concept Extensions

Solve. See the Concept Check in this section.

53. Suppose you mix an amount of candy costing $0.49 a pound with candy costing $0.65 a pound. Which of the following costs per pound could result?

     a. $0.58   **b.** $0.72   **c.** $0.29

54. Suppose you mix a 50% acid solution with pure acid (100%). Which of the following acid strengths are possible for the resulting acid mixture?

     a. 25%   **b.** 150%   **c.** 62%   **d.** 90%

△ **55.** Dale and Sharon Mahnke have decided to fence off a garden plot behind their house, using their house as the "fence" along one side of the garden. The length (which runs parallel to the house) is 3 feet less than twice the width. Find the dimensions if 33 feet of fencing is used along the three sides requiring it.

△ **56.** Judy McElroy plans to erect 152 feet of fencing to make a rectangular horse pasture. A river bank serves as one side length of the rectangle. If each width is 4 feet longer than half the length, find the dimensions.

Chapter 14 Group Activity

Break-Even Point

Sections 14.1, 14.2, 14.3, 14.4

When a business sells a new product, it generally does not start making a profit right away. There are usually many expenses associated with creating a new product. These expenses might include an advertising blitz to introduce the product to the public. These start-up expenses might also include the cost of market research and product development or any brand-new equipment needed to manufacture the product. Start-up costs like these are generally called *fixed costs* because they don't depend on the number of items manufactured. Expenses that do depend on the number of items manufactured, such as the cost of materials and shipping, are called *variable costs*. The total cost of manufacturing the new product is given by the cost equation Total cost = Fixed costs + Variable costs.

For instance, suppose a greeting card company is launching a new line of greeting cards. The company spent $7000 doing product research and development for the new line and spent $15,000 advertising the new line. The company does not need to buy any new equipment to manufacture the cards, but the paper and ink needed to make each card will cost $0.20 per card. The total cost y in dollars for manufacturing x cards is $y = 22,000 + 0.20x$.

Once a business sets a price for a new product, the company can find the product's expected *revenue*. Revenue is the amount of money the company takes in from the sales of its product. The revenue from selling a product is given by the revenue equation Revenue = Price per item × Number of items sold.

For instance, suppose that the card company plans to sell its new cards for $1.50 each. The revenue y, in dollars, that the company can expect to receive from the sales of x cards is $y = 1.50x$.

If the total cost and revenue equations are graphed on the same coordinate system, the graphs should intersect. The point of intersection is where total cost equals revenue and is called the *break-even point*. The break-even point gives the number of items x that must be manufactured and sold for the company to recover its expenses. If fewer than this number of items are produced and sold, the company loses money. If more than this number of items are produced and sold, the company makes a profit. In the case of the greeting card company, approximately 16,923 cards must be manufactured and sold for the company to break-even on this new card line. The total cost and revenue of producing and selling 16,923 cards is the same. It is approximately $25,385.

Group Activity

Suppose your group is starting a small business near your campus.

a. Choose a business and decide what campus-related product or service you will provide.

b. Research the fixed costs of starting up such a business.

c. Research the variable costs of producing such a product or providing such a service.

d. Decide how much you will charge per unit of your product or service.

e. Find a system of equations for the total cost and revenue of your product or service.

f. How many units of your product or service must be sold before your business will break even?

Chapter 14 Vocabulary Check

Fill in each blank with one of the words or phrases listed below.

system of linear equations   solution   consistent   independent

dependent   inconsistent   substitution   addition

1. In a system of linear equations in two variables, if the graphs of the equations are the same, the equations are _____ equations.

2. Two or more linear equations are called a(n) _____.

3. A system of equations that has at least one solution is called a(n) _____ system.

4. A(n) _____ of a system of two equations in two variables is an ordered pair of numbers that is a solution of both equations in the system.

5. Two algebraic methods for solving systems of equations are _____ and _____.

6. A system of equations that has no solution is called a(n) _____ system.

7. In a system of linear equations in two variables, if the graphs of the equations are different, the equations are _____ equations.

> **Helpful Hint**
> ▶ Are you preparing for your test? Don't forget to take the Chapter 14 Test on page 1108. Then check your answers at the back of the text and use the Chapter Test Prep Videos to see the fully worked-out solutions to any of the exercises you want to review.

14 Chapter Highlights

Definitions and Concepts	Examples

Section 14.1   Solving Systems of Linear Equations by Graphing

A **system of linear equations** consists of two or more linear equations.

A **solution** of a system of two equations in two variables is an ordered pair of numbers that is a solution of both equations in the system.

$$\begin{cases} 2x + y = 6 \\ x = -3y \end{cases} \quad \begin{cases} -3x + 5y = 10 \\ x - 4y = -2 \end{cases}$$

Determine whether $(-1, 3)$ is a solution of the system.

$$\begin{cases} 2x - y = -5 \\ x = 3y - 10 \end{cases}$$

Replace x with -1 and y with 3 in both equations.

$$2x - y = -5$$
$$2(-1) - 3 \stackrel{?}{=} -5$$
$$-5 = -5 \qquad \text{True}$$

$$x = 3y - 10$$
$$-1 \stackrel{?}{=} 3(3) - 10$$
$$-1 = -1 \qquad \text{True}$$

$(-1, 3)$ is a solution of the system.

Graphically, a solution of a system is a point common to the graphs of both equations.

Solve by graphing: $\begin{cases} 3x - 2y = -3 \\ x + y = 4 \end{cases}$

Definitions and Concepts	Examples

Section 14.1 Solving Systems of Linear Equations by Graphing (*continued*)

Three different situations can occur when graphing the two lines associated with the equations in a linear system.

One point of inter-
section; one solution

Same line; infinite
number of solutions

Parallel lines; no solution

Section 14.2 Solving Systems of Linear Equations by Substitution

To Solve a System of Linear Equations by the Substitution Method

Step 1: Solve one equation for a variable.

Step 2: Substitute the expression for the variable into the other equation.

Step 3: Solve the equation from Step 2 to find the value of one variable.

Step 4: Substitute the value from Step 3 in either original equation to find the value of the other variable.

Step 5: Check the solution in both original equations.

Solve by substitution.

$$\begin{cases} 3x + 2y = 1 \\ x = y - 3 \end{cases}$$

Substitute $y - 3$ for x in the first equation.

$$3x + 2y = 1$$
$$3(y - 3) + 2y = 1$$
$$3y - 9 + 2y = 1$$
$$5y = 10$$
$$y = 2 \quad \text{Divide by 5.}$$

To find x, substitute 2 for y in $x = y - 3$ so that $x = 2 - 3$ or -1. The solution $(-1, 2)$ checks.

Section 14.3 Solving Systems of Linear Equations by Addition

To Solve a System of Linear Equations by the Addition Method

Step 1: Rewrite each equation in standard form, $Ax + By = C$.

Step 2: Multiply one or both equations by a nonzero number so that the coefficients of a variable are opposites.

Step 3: Add the equations.

Step 4: Find the value of one variable by solving the resulting equation.

Step 5: Substitute the value from Step 4 into either original equation to find the value of the other variable.

Solve by addition.

$$\begin{cases} x - 2y = 8 \\ 3x + y = -4 \end{cases}$$

Multiply both sides of the first equation by -3.

$$\begin{cases} -3x + 6y = -24 \\ \underline{3x + y = -4} \end{cases}$$
$$7y = -28 \quad \text{Add.}$$
$$y = -4 \quad \text{Divide by 7.}$$

To find x, let $y = -4$ in an original equation.

$$x - 2(-4) = 8 \quad \text{First equation}$$
$$x + 8 = 8$$
$$x = 0$$

(continued)

Definitions and Concepts	Examples

Section 14.3   Solving Systems of Linear Equations by Addition   (*continued*)

Step 6:   Check the solution in both original equations.

If solving a system of linear equations by substitution or addition yields a true statement such as $-2 = -2$, then the graphs of the equations in the system are identical and the system has an infinite number of solutions.

The solution $(0, -4)$ checks.

Solve: $\begin{cases} 2x - 6y = -2 \\ x = 3y - 1 \end{cases}$

Substitute $3y - 1$ for x in the first equation.

$$2(3y - 1) - 6y = -2$$
$$6y - 2 - 6y = -2$$
$$-2 = -2 \quad \text{True}$$

The system has an infinite number of solutions.

If solving a system of linear equations yields a false statement such as $0 = 3$, the graphs of the equations in the system are parallel lines and the system has no solution.

Solve: $\begin{cases} 5x - 2y = 6 \\ -5x + 2y = -3 \end{cases}$

$$0 = 3 \quad \text{False}$$

The system has no solution.

Section 14.4   Systems of Linear Equations and Problem Solving

Problem-Solving Steps

1. UNDERSTAND. Read and reread the problem.

Two angles are supplementary if the sum of their measures is $180°$. The larger of two supplementary angles is three times the smaller, decreased by twelve. Find the measure of each angle. Let

$x =$ measure of smaller angle and

$y =$ measure of larger angle

2. TRANSLATE.

In words: the sum of supplementary angles   is $180°$

Translate: $x + y$ $=$ 180

In words: larger angle   is   3 times smaller   decreased by   12

Translate: y $=$ $3x$ $-$ 12

3. SOLVE.

Solve the system. $\begin{cases} x + y = 180 \\ y = 3x - 12 \end{cases}$

Use the substitution method and replace y with $3x - 12$ in the first equation.

$$x + y = 180$$
$$x + (3x - 12) = 180$$
$$4x = 192$$
$$x = 48$$

4. INTERPRET.

Since $y = 3x - 12$, then $y = 3 \cdot 48 - 12$ or 132.

The solution checks. The smaller angle measures $48°$ and the larger angle measures $132°$.

(14.1) *Determine whether each ordered pair is a solution of the system of linear equations.*

1. $\begin{cases} 2x - 3y = 12 \\ 3x + 4y = 1 \end{cases}$
   a. $(12, 4)$
   b. $(3, -2)$

2. $\begin{cases} 2x + 3y = 1 \\ 3y - x = 4 \end{cases}$
   a. $(2, 2)$
   b. $(-1, 1)$

3. $\begin{cases} 5x - 6y = 18 \\ 2y - x = -4 \end{cases}$
   a. $(-6, -8)$
   b. $\left(3, \dfrac{5}{2}\right)$

4. $\begin{cases} 4x + y = 0 \\ -8x - 5y = 9 \end{cases}$
   a. $\left(\dfrac{3}{4}, -3\right)$
   b. $(-2, 8)$

Solve each system of equations by graphing.

5. $\begin{cases} x + y = 5 \\ x - y = 1 \end{cases}$
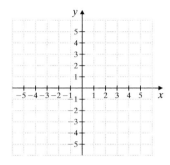

6. $\begin{cases} x + y = 3 \\ x - y = -1 \end{cases}$
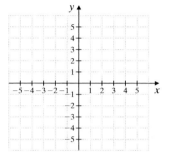

7. $\begin{cases} x = 5 \\ y = -1 \end{cases}$
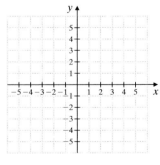

8. $\begin{cases} x = -3 \\ y = 2 \end{cases}$

9. $\begin{cases} 2x + y = 5 \\ x = -3y \end{cases}$
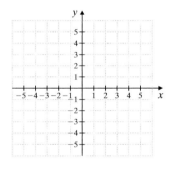

10. $\begin{cases} 3x + y = -2 \\ y = -5x \end{cases}$
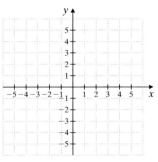

11. $\begin{cases} y = 3x \\ -6x + 2y = 6 \end{cases}$
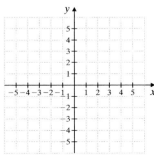

12. $\begin{cases} x - 2y = 2 \\ -2x + 4y = -4 \end{cases}$
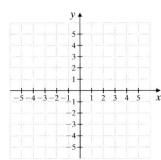

(14.2) *Solve each system of equations by the substitution method.*

13. $\begin{cases} y = 2x + 6 \\ 3x - 2y = -11 \end{cases}$

14. $\begin{cases} y = 3x - 7 \\ 2x - 3y = 7 \end{cases}$

15. $\begin{cases} x + 3y = -3 \\ 2x + y = 4 \end{cases}$

16. $\begin{cases} 3x + y = 11 \\ x + 2y = 12 \end{cases}$

17. $\begin{cases} 4y = 2x + 6 \\ x - 2y = -3 \end{cases}$

18. $\begin{cases} 9x = 6y + 3 \\ 6x - 4y = 2 \end{cases}$

19. $\begin{cases} x + y = 6 \\ y = -x - 4 \end{cases}$

20. $\begin{cases} -3x + y = 6 \\ y = 3x + 2 \end{cases}$

(14.3) *Solve each system of equations by the addition method.*

21. $\begin{cases} 2x + 3y = -6 \\ x - 3y = -12 \end{cases}$

22. $\begin{cases} 4x + y = 15 \\ -4x + 3y = -19 \end{cases}$

23. $\begin{cases} 2x - 3y = -15 \\ x + 4y = 31 \end{cases}$

24. $\begin{cases} x - 5y = -22 \\ 4x + 3y = 4 \end{cases}$

25. $\begin{cases} 2x - 6y = -1 \\ -x + 3y = \dfrac{1}{2} \end{cases}$

26. $\begin{cases} 0.6x - 0.3y = -1.5 \\ 0.04x - 0.02y = -0.1 \end{cases}$

27. $\begin{cases} \dfrac{3}{4}x + \dfrac{2}{3}y = 2 \\ x + \dfrac{y}{3} = 6 \end{cases}$

28. $\begin{cases} 10x + 2y = 0 \\ 3x + 5y = 33 \end{cases}$

(14.4) *Solve each problem by writing and solving a system of linear equations.*

29. The sum of two numbers is 16. Three times the larger number decreased by the smaller number is 72. Find the two numbers.

30. The Forrest Theater can seat a total of 360 people. They take in $15,150 when every seat is sold. If orchestra section tickets cost $45 and balcony tickets cost $35, find the number of seats in the orchestra section and the number of seats in the balcony.

31. A riverboat can go 340 miles upriver in 19 hours, but the return trip takes only 14 hours. Find the current of the river and find the speed of the riverboat in still water to the nearest tenth of a mile.

d =	r	$\cdot$	t
Upriver	$x - y$		
Downriver	$x + y$		

32. Find the amount of a 6% acid solution and the amount of a 14% acid solution Pat Mayfield should combine to prepare 50 cc (cubic centimeters) of a 12% solution.

33. A deli charges $3.80 for a breakfast of three eggs and four strips of bacon. The charge is $2.75 for two eggs and three strips of bacon. Find the cost of each egg and the cost of each strip of bacon.

34. An exercise enthusiast alternates between jogging and walking. He traveled 15 miles during the past 3 hours. He jogs at a rate of 7.5 miles per hour and walks at a rate of 4 miles per hour. Find how much time, to the nearest hundredth of an hour, he actually spent jogging and how much time he spent walking.

Mixed Review

Solve each system of equations by graphing.

35. $\begin{cases} x - 2y = 1 \\ 2x + 3y = -12 \end{cases}$

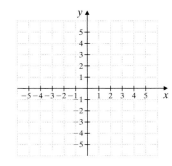

36. $\begin{cases} 3x - y = -4 \\ 6x - 2y = -8 \end{cases}$

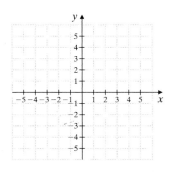

Solve each system of equations.

37. $\begin{cases} x + 4y = 11 \\ 5x - 9y = -3 \end{cases}$

38. $\begin{cases} x + 9y = 16 \\ 3x - 8y = 13 \end{cases}$

39. $\begin{cases} y = -2x \\ 4x + 7y = -15 \end{cases}$

40. $\begin{cases} 3y = 2x + 15 \\ -2x + 3y = 21 \end{cases}$

41. $\begin{cases} 3x - y = 4 \\ 4y = 12x - 16 \end{cases}$

42. $\begin{cases} x + y = 19 \\ x - y = -3 \end{cases}$

43. $\begin{cases} x - 3y = -11 \\ 4x + 5y = -10 \end{cases}$

44. $\begin{cases} -x - 15y = 44 \\ 2x + 3y = 20 \end{cases}$

45. $\begin{cases} 2x + y = 3 \\ 6x + 3y = 9 \end{cases}$

46. $\begin{cases} -3x + y = 5 \\ -3x + y = -2 \end{cases}$

Solve each problem by writing and solving a system of linear equations.

47. The sum of two numbers is 12. Three times the smaller number increased by the larger number is 20. Find the numbers.

48. The difference of two numbers is -18. Twice the smaller decreased by the larger is -23. Find the two numbers.

49. Emma Hodges has a jar containing 65 coins, all of which are either nickels or dimes. The total value of the coins is $5.30. How many of each type does she have?

50. Sarah and Owen Hebert purchased 26 stamps, a mixture of 13¢ and 22¢ stamps. Find the number of each type of stamp if they spent $4.19.

Chapter 14   Test

Step-by-step test solutions are found on the Chapter Test Prep Videos. Where available: MyMathLab® or You Tube™

Answers

Answer each question true or false.

1. A system of two linear equations in two variables can have exactly two solutions.

2. Although $(1, 4)$ is not a solution of $x + 2y = 6$, it can still be a solution of the system $\begin{cases} x + 2y = 6 \\ x + y = 5 \end{cases}$.

3. If the two equations in a system of linear equations are added and the result is $3 = 0$, the system has no solution.

4. If the two equations in a system of linear equations are added and the result is $3x = 0$, the system has no solution.

Is the ordered pair a solution of the given linear system?

5. $\begin{cases} 2x - 3y = 5 \\ 6x + y = 1 \end{cases}$; $(1, -1)$

6. $\begin{cases} 4x - 3y = 24 \\ 4x + 5y = -8 \end{cases}$; $(3, -4)$

Solve each system by graphing.

7. $\begin{cases} x - y = 2 \\ 3x - y = -2 \end{cases}$

8. $\begin{cases} y = -3x \\ 3x + y = 6 \end{cases}$

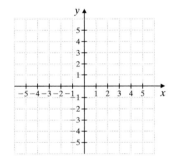

Solve each system by the substitution method.

9. $\begin{cases} 3x - 2y = -14 \\ y = x + 5 \end{cases}$

10. $\begin{cases} \dfrac{1}{2}x + 2y = -\dfrac{15}{4} \\ 4x = -y \end{cases}$

Solve each system by the addition method.

11. $\begin{cases} x + y = 28 \\ x - y = 12 \end{cases}$

12. $\begin{cases} 4x - 6y = 7 \\ -2x + 3y = 0 \end{cases}$

Solve each system using the substitution method or the addition method.

13. $\begin{cases} 3x + y = 7 \\ 4x + 3y = 1 \end{cases}$

14. $\begin{cases} 3(2x + y) = 4x + 20 \\ x - 2y = 3 \end{cases}$

1. _____

2. _____

3. _____

4. _____

5. _____

6. _____

7. _____

8. _____

9. _____

10. _____

11. _____

12. _____

13. _____

14. _____

15.
$$\begin{cases} \dfrac{x-3}{2} = \dfrac{2-y}{4} \\[2mm] \dfrac{7-2x}{3} = \dfrac{y}{2} \end{cases}$$

16.
$$\begin{cases} 8x - 4y = 12 \\ y = 2x - 3 \end{cases}$$

17.
$$\begin{cases} 0.01x - 0.06y = -0.23 \\ 0.2x + 0.4y = 0.2 \end{cases}$$

18.
$$\begin{cases} x - \dfrac{2}{3}y = 3 \\[2mm] -2x + 3y = 10 \end{cases}$$

Solve each problem by writing and using a system of linear equations.

19. Two numbers have a sum of 124 and a difference of 32. Find the numbers.

20. Find the amount of a 12% saline solution a lab assistant should add to 80 cc (cubic centimeters) of a 22% saline solution in order to have a 16% solution.

21. Although the number of farms in the United States is still decreasing, small farms are making a comeback. In 2012, Texas and Missouri were the states with the most number of farms. Texas had 139 thousand more farms than Missouri, and the total number of farms for these two states was 351 thousand. Find the number of farms for each state. (*Source:* National Agricultural Statistics Service)

22. Two hikers start at opposite ends of the St. Tammany Trails and walk toward each other. The trail is 36 miles long and they meet in 4 hours. If one hiker is twice as fast as the other, find both hiking speeds.

The graph below shows the number of music album sales that fell within the alternative or R&B music genres for the years shown. Use this graph to answer Exercises 23 and 24.

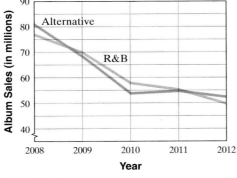

Source: Nielsen Company

23. Between what years were total album sales of R&B music equal to total album sales of alternative music?

24. List each year in which there were more album sales of alternative music than R&B music.

15. _____

16. _____

17. _____

18. _____

19. _____

20. _____

21. _____

22. _____

23. _____

24. _____

Answers

1. _____

2. _____

3. _____

4. _____

5. _____

6. _____

7. _____

8. _____

9. _____

10. _____

11. _____

12. _____

13. _____

14. _____

15. _____

16. _____

17. _____

18. _____

19. _____

20. _____

Subtract.

1. $8 - 15$

2. $4 - 7$

3. $-4 - (-5)$

4. $3 - (-2)$

5. Solve: $x = -60 + 4 + 10$

6. Solve: $4x = -2 + 3x$

7. Translate to an equation: 1.2 is 30% of what number?

8. Translate to an equation: 9 is 45% of what number?

9. What percent of 50 is 8?

10. What percent of 16 is 4?

11. Mr. Percy, the principal at Slidell High School, counted 31 freshmen absent during a particular day. If this is 4% of the total number of freshmen, how many freshmen are there at Slidell High School?

12. 2% of the apples in a shipment are rotten. If there are 29 rotten apples, how many apples are in the shipment?

Solve.

13. $-2(x - 5) + 10 = -3(x + 2) + x$

14. $4(4y + 2) = 2(1 + 6y) + 8$

15. Solve $-5x + 7 < 2(x - 3)$. Graph the solution set.

16. Solve $-7x + 4 \leq 3(4 - x)$. Graph the solution set.

Simplify each expression.

17. $\left(\dfrac{m}{n}\right)^7$

18. $(-5x^3)(-7x^4)$

19. $\left(\dfrac{2x^4}{3y^5}\right)^4$

20. $\left(\dfrac{5x^2}{4y^3}\right)^2$

21. Subtract: $(2x^3 + 8x^2 - 6x) - (2x^3 - x^2 + 1)$

22. Subtract: $(7x + 1) - (-x - 3)$

23. Divide $6x^2 + 10x - 5$ by $3x - 1$ using long division.

24. Divide $3x^2 - x - 4$ by $x - 1$ using long division.

25. Solve: $x(2x - 7) = 4$

26. Solve: $x(x - 5) = 24$

△ **27.** Find the lengths of the sides of a right triangle if the lengths can be expressed as three consecutive even integers.

28. The sum of a number and its square is 132. Find the number(s).

29. Subtract: $\dfrac{2y}{2y - 7} - \dfrac{7}{2y - 7}$

30. Add: $\dfrac{x^2 + 3}{x + 9} + \dfrac{9x - 3}{x + 9}$

31. Find the slope of the line $y = -1$.

32. Find the slope of the line $x = 2$.

33. Find an equation of the line through $(2, 5)$ and $(-3, 4)$. Write the equation in the form $Ax + By = C$.

34. Find an equation of the line through $(5, -6)$ and $(-6, 5)$. Write the equation in the form $Ax + By = C$.

35. Find the domain and the range of the relation $\{(0, 2), (3, 3), (-1, 0), (3, -2)\}$.

36. Find the domain and the range of the relation $\{(2, 3), (2, 0), (2, -2), (2, 4)\}$.

21. _____

22. _____

23. _____

24. _____

25. _____

26. _____

27. _____

28. _____

29. _____

30. _____

31. _____

32. _____

33. _____

34. _____

35. _____

36. _____

37. _____

38. _____

39. _____

40. _____

41. _____

42. _____

37. Solve the system: $\begin{cases} x + 2y = 7 \\ 2x + 2y = 13 \end{cases}$

38. Solve the system: $\begin{cases} 3y = x + 6 \\ 4x + 12y = 0 \end{cases}$

39. Solve the system: $\begin{cases} -x - \dfrac{y}{2} = \dfrac{5}{2} \\ \dfrac{x}{6} - \dfrac{y}{2} = 0 \end{cases}$

40. Solve the system: $\begin{cases} x - \dfrac{3y}{8} = -\dfrac{3}{2} \\ x + \dfrac{y}{9} = \dfrac{13}{3} \end{cases}$

41. Find two numbers whose sum is 37 and whose difference is 21.

42. The sum of two numbers is 75 and their difference is 9. Find the two numbers.

Tables

A.1　Table of Geometric Figures

Plane Figures Have Length and Width but No Thickness or Depth		
Name	Description	Figure
Polygon	Union of three or more coplanar line segments that intersect with each other only at each end point, with each end point shared by two segments.	
Triangle	Polygon with three sides (sum of measures of three angles is 180°).	
Scalene Triangle	Triangle with no sides of equal length.	
Isosceles Triangle	Triangle with two sides of equal length.	
Equilateral Triangle	Triangle with all sides of equal length.	
Right Triangle	Triangle that contains a right angle.	leg hypotenuse leg
Quadrilateral	Polygon with four sides (sum of measures of four angles is 360°).	
Trapezoid	Quadrilateral with exactly one pair of opposite sides parallel.	base leg parallel sides leg base
Isosceles Trapezoid	Trapezoid with legs of equal length.	
Parallelogram	Quadrilateral with both pairs of opposite sides parallel.	
Rhombus	Parallelogram with all sides of equal length.	
Rectangle	Parallelogram with four right angles.	

(continued)

Plane Figures Have Length and Width but No Thickness or Depth (*continued*)		
Name	**Description**	**Figure**
Square	Rectangle with all sides of equal length.	
Circle	All points in a plane the same distance from a fixed point called the **center.**	

Solid Figures Have Length, Width, and Height or Depth		
Name	**Description**	**Figure**
Rectangular Solid	A solid with six sides, all of which are rectangles.	
Cube	A rectangular solid whose six sides are squares.	
Sphere	All points the same distance from a fixed point called the **center.**	
Right Circular Cylinder	A cylinder having two circular bases that are perpendicular to its altitude.	
Right Circular Cone	A cone with a circular base that is perpendicular to its altitude.	

A.2 Table of Percents, Decimals, and Fraction Equivalents

Percent	Decimal	Fraction
1%	0.01	$\frac{1}{100}$
5%	0.05	$\frac{1}{20}$
10%	0.1	$\frac{1}{10}$
12.5% or $12\frac{1}{2}$%	0.125	$\frac{1}{8}$
$16.\overline{6}$% or $16\frac{2}{3}$%	$0.1\overline{6}$	$\frac{1}{6}$
20%	0.2	$\frac{1}{5}$
25%	0.25	$\frac{1}{4}$
30%	0.3	$\frac{3}{10}$
$33.\overline{3}$% or $33\frac{1}{3}$%	$0.\overline{3}$	$\frac{1}{3}$
37.5% or $37\frac{1}{2}$%	0.375	$\frac{3}{8}$
40%	0.4	$\frac{2}{5}$
50%	0.5	$\frac{1}{2}$
60%	0.6	$\frac{3}{5}$
62.5% or $62\frac{1}{2}$%	0.625	$\frac{5}{8}$
$66.\overline{6}$% or $66\frac{2}{3}$%	$0.\overline{6}$	$\frac{2}{3}$
70%	0.7	$\frac{7}{10}$
75%	0.75	$\frac{3}{4}$
80%	0.8	$\frac{4}{5}$
$83.\overline{3}$% or $83\frac{1}{3}$%	$0.8\overline{3}$	$\frac{5}{6}$
87.5% or $87\frac{1}{2}$%	0.875	$\frac{7}{8}$
90%	0.9	$\frac{9}{10}$
100%	1.0	1
110%	1.1	$1\frac{1}{10}$
125%	1.25	$1\frac{1}{4}$
$133.\overline{3}$% or $133\frac{1}{3}$%	$1.\overline{3}$	$1\frac{1}{3}$
150%	1.5	$1\frac{1}{2}$
$166.\overline{6}$% or $166\frac{2}{3}$%	$1.\overline{6}$	$1\frac{2}{3}$
175%	1.75	$1\frac{3}{4}$
200%	2.0	2

Common Percent Equivalences*	Shortcut Method for Finding Percent	Examples
$1\% = 0.01 \left(\text{or } \frac{1}{100}\right)$	To find 1% of a number, multiply by 0.01. To do so, move the decimal point 2 places to the left.	1% of 210 is 2.10 or 2.1. 1% of 1500 is 15. 1% of 8.6 is 0.086.
$10\% = 0.1 \left(\text{or } \frac{1}{10}\right)$	To find 10% of a number, multiply by 0.1, or move the decimal point of the number 1 place to the left.	10% of 140 is 14. 10% of 30 is 3. 10% of 17.6 is 1.76.
$25\% = \frac{1}{4}$	To find 25% of a number, find $\frac{1}{4}$ of the number, or divide the number by 4.	25% of 20 is $\frac{20}{4}$ or 5. 25% of 8 is 2. 25% of 10 is $\frac{10}{4}$ or $2\frac{1}{2}$.
$50\% = \frac{1}{2}$	To find 50% of a number, find $\frac{1}{2}$ of the number, or divide the number by 2.	50% of 64 is $\frac{64}{2}$ or 32. 50% of 1000 is 500. 50% of 9 is $\frac{9}{2}$ or $4\frac{1}{2}$.
$100\% = 1$	To find 100% of a number, multiply the number by 1. In other words, 100% of a number is the number.	100% of 98 is 98. 100% of 1407 is 1407. 100% of 18.4 is 18.4.
$200\% = 2$	To find 200% of a number, multiply the number by 2.	200% of 31 is $31 \cdot 2$ or 62. 200% of 750 is 1500. 200% of 6.5 is 13.

*See Appendix A.2.

n	n^2	$\sqrt{n}$	n	n^2	$\sqrt{n}$
1	1	1.000	51	2601	7.141
2	4	1.414	52	2704	7.211
3	9	1.732	53	2809	7.280
4	16	2.000	54	2916	7.348
5	25	2.236	55	3025	7.416
6	36	2.449	56	3136	7.483
7	49	2.646	57	3249	7.550
8	64	2.828	58	3364	7.616
9	81	3.000	59	3481	7.681
10	100	3.162	60	3600	7.746
11	121	3.317	61	3721	7.810
12	144	3.464	62	3844	7.874
13	169	3.606	63	3969	7.937
14	196	3.742	64	4096	8.000
15	225	3.873	65	4225	8.062
16	256	4.000	66	4356	8.124
17	289	4.123	67	4489	8.185
18	324	4.243	68	4624	8.246
19	361	4.359	69	4761	8.307
20	400	4.472	70	4900	8.367
21	441	4.583	71	5041	8.426
22	484	4.690	72	5184	8.485
23	529	4.796	73	5329	8.544
24	576	4.899	74	5476	8.602
25	625	5.000	75	5625	8.660
26	676	5.099	76	5776	8.718
27	729	5.196	77	5929	8.775
28	784	5.292	78	6084	8.832
29	841	5.385	79	6241	8.888
30	900	5.477	80	6400	8.944
31	961	5.568	81	6561	9.000
32	1024	5.657	82	6724	9.055
33	1089	5.745	83	6889	9.110
34	1156	5.831	84	7056	9.165
35	1225	5.916	85	7225	9.220
36	1296	6.000	86	7396	9.274
37	1369	6.083	87	7569	9.327
38	1444	6.164	88	7744	9.381
39	1521	6.245	89	7921	9.434
40	1600	6.325	90	8100	9.487
41	1681	6.403	91	8281	9.539
42	1764	6.481	92	8464	9.592
43	1849	6.557	93	8649	9.644
44	1936	6.633	94	8836	9.695
45	2025	6.708	95	9025	9.747
46	2116	6.782	96	9216	9.798
47	2209	6.856	97	9409	9.849
48	2304	6.928	98	9604	9.899
49	2401	7.000	99	9801	9.950
50	2500	7.071	100	10,000	10.000

Factoring Sums and Differences of Cubes

Although the sum of two squares usually does not factor, the sum or difference of two cubes can be factored and reveal factoring patterns. The pattern for the sum of cubes can be checked by multiplying the binomial $x + y$ and the trinomial $x^2 - xy + y^2$. The pattern for the difference of two cubes can be checked by multiplying the binomial $x - y$ by the trinomial $x^2 + xy + y^2$.

Sum or Difference of Two Cubes

$$a^3 + b^3 = (a + b)\left(a^2 - ab + b^2\right)$$
$$a^3 - b^3 = (a - b)\left(a^2 + ab + b^2\right)$$

Example 1 Factor $x^3 + 8$.

Solution:

First, write the binomial in the form $a^3 + b^3$.

$x^3 + 8 = x^3 + 2^3$ Write in the form $a^3 + b^3$.

If we replace a with x and b with 2 in the formula above, we have

$$x^3 + 2^3 = (x + 2)\left[x^2 - (x)(2) + 2^2\right]$$
$$= (x + 2)(x^2 - 2x + 4)$$

Helpful Hint

When factoring sums or differences of cubes, notice the sign patterns.

$$\underset{\text{opposite signs}}{\underset{\text{same sign}}{x^3 + y^3 = (x + y)(x^2 - xy + y^2)}} \quad \text{always positve}$$

$$\underset{\text{opposite signs}}{\underset{\text{same sign}}{x^3 - y^3 = (x - y)(x^2 + xy + y^2)}} \quad \text{always positve}$$

Example 2   Factor $y^3 - 27$.

Solution:

$$
\begin{aligned}
y^3 - 27 &= y^3 - 3^3 \qquad \text{Write in the form } a^3 - b^3. \\
&= (y - 3)\left[y^2 + (y)(3) + 3^2\right] \\
&= (y - 3)(y^2 + 3y + 9)
\end{aligned}
$$

Example 3   Factor $64x^3 + 1$.

Solution:

$$
\begin{aligned}
64x^3 + 1 &= (4x)^3 + 1^3 \\
&= (4x + 1)\left[(4x)^2 - (4x)(1) + 1^2\right] \\
&= (4x + 1)(16x^2 - 4x + 1)
\end{aligned}
$$

Example 4   Factor $54a^3 - 16b^3$.

Solution: Remember to factor out common factors first before using other factoring methods.

$$
\begin{aligned}
54a^3 - 16b^3 &= 2(27a^3 - 8b^3) \qquad && \text{Factor out the GCF 2.} \\
&= 2\left[(3a)^3 - (2b)^3\right] && \text{Difference of two cubes.} \\
&= 2(3a - 2b)\left[(3a)^2 + (3a)(2b) + (2b)^2\right] \\
&= 2(3a - 2b)(9a^2 + 6ab + 4b^2)
\end{aligned}
$$

B Exercise Set MyMathLab®

Factor the binomials completely. See Examples 1 through 4.

1. $a^3 + 27$

2. $b^3 - 8$

3. $8a^3 + 1$

4. $64x^3 - 1$

5. $5k^3 + 40$

6. $6r^3 - 162$

7. $x^3y^3 - 64$

8. $8x^3 - y^3$

9. $x^3 + 125$

10. $a^3 - 216$

11. $24x^4 - 81xy^3$

12. $375y^6 - 24y^3$

13. $27 - t^3$

14. $125 + r^3$

15. $8r^3 - 64$

16. $54r^3 + 2$

17. $t^3 - 343$

18. $s^3 + 216$

19. $s^3 - 64t^3$

20. $8t^3 + s^3$

Mixture and Uniform Motion Problem Solving

This appendix is devoted to solving problems in the categories listed. The same problem-solving steps used in previous sections are also followed in this appendix. They are listed below for review.

General Strategy for Problem Solving

1. UNDERSTAND the problem. During this step, become comfortable with the problem. Some ways of doing this are as follows:

   Read and reread the problem.

   Choose a variable to represent the unknown.

   Construct a drawing whenever possible.

   Propose a solution and check. Pay careful attention to how you check your proposed solution. This will help when writing an equation to model the problem.

2. TRANSLATE the problem into an equation.

3. SOLVE the equation.

4. INTERPRET the results: *Check* the proposed solution in the stated problem and *state* your conclusion.

Objective A Solving Mixture Problems

Mixture problems involve two or more different quantities being combined to form a new mixture. These applications range from Dow Chemical's need to form a chemical mixture of a required strength to Planter's Peanut Company's need to find the correct mixture of peanuts and cashews given taste and price constraints.

Example 1 Calculating Percent for a Lab Experiment

A chemist working on his doctoral degree at Massachusetts Institute of Technology needs 12 liters of a 50% acid solution for a lab experiment. The stockroom has only 40% and 70% solutions. How much of each solution should be mixed together to form 12 liters of a 50% solution?

Solution:

1. UNDERSTAND. First, read and reread the problem a few times. Next, guess a solution. Suppose that we need 7 liters of the 40% solution. Then we need $12 - 7 = 5$ liters of the 70% solution. To see if this is indeed the answer, find the amount of pure acid in 7 liters of the 40% solution, in 5 liters of the 70% solution, and in 12 liters of a 50% solution, the required amount and strength.

number of liters	$\times$	acid strength	$=$	amount of pure acid
7 liters	$\times$	40%	$=$	7(0.40) or 2.8 liters
5 liters	$\times$	70%	$=$	5(0.70) or 3.5 liters
12 liters	$\times$	50%	$=$	12(0.50) or 6 liters

(Continued on next page)

Practice 1

How much 20% dye solution and 50% dye solution should be mixed to obtain 6 liters of a 40% solution?

Answer

1. 2 liters of the 20% solution; 4 liters of the 50% solution

Since 2.8 liters + 3.5 liters = 6.3 liters and not 6, our guess is incorrect, but we have gained some valuable insight into how to model and check this problem.

Let

x = number of liters of 40% solution; then

$12 - x$ = number of liters of 70% solution.

2. TRANSLATE. To help us translate to an equation, the following table summarizes the information given. Recall that the amount of acid in each solution is found by multiplying the acid strength of each solution by the number of liters.

x liters $(12 - x)$ liters $(12 - x)$ liters + x liters   12 liters

40% solution   70% solution   50% solution

	No. of Liters ·	Acid Strength =	Amount of Acid
40% Solution	x	40%	$0.40x$
70% Solution	$12 - x$	70%	$0.70(12 - x)$
50% Solution Needed	12	50%	$0.50(12)$

The amount of acid in the final solution is the sum of the amounts of acid in the two beginning solutions.

In words: acid in 40% solution   +   acid in 70% solution   =   acid in 50% mixture

Translate: $0.40x$ + $0.70(12 - x)$ = $0.50(12)$

3. SOLVE.

$$0.40x + 0.70(12 - x) = 0.50(12)$$
$$0.4x + 8.4 - 0.7x = 6 \qquad \text{Apply the distributive property.}$$
$$-0.3x + 8.4 = 6 \qquad \text{Combine like terms.}$$
$$-0.3x = -2.4 \qquad \text{Subtract 8.4 from both sides.}$$
$$x = 8 \qquad \text{Divide both sides by } -0.3.$$

4. INTERPRET.

Check: To check, recall how we checked our guess.

State: If 8 liters of the 40% solution are mixed with 12 − 8 or 4 liters of the 70% solution, the result is 12 liters of a 50% solution.

▪ Work Practice 1

The next example has to do with finding an unknown number of a certain denomination of coin or bill. These problems are extremely useful in that they help you understand the difference between the number of coins or bills and the total value of the money.

For example, suppose there are seven $5 bills. The *number* of $5 bills is 7 and the *total value* of the money is $5(7) = $35.

Study the table below for more examples.

Denomination of Coin or Bill	Number of Coins or Bills	Value of Coins or Bills
20-dollar bills	17	$20(17) = $340
nickels	31	$0.05(31) = $1.55
quarters	x	$0.25(x) = $0.25x

Example 2   Finding Numbers of Denominations

Part of the proceeds from a local talent show was $2420 worth of $10 and $20 bills. If there were 37 more $20 bills than $10 bills, find the number of each denomination.

Solution:

1. UNDERSTAND the problem. To do so, read and reread the problem. If you'd like, let's guess a solution. Suppose that there are 25 $10 bills. Since there are 37 more $20 bills, we have $25 + 37 = 62$ $20 bills. The total amount of money is $10(25) + $20(62) = $1490, less than the given amount of $2420. Remember that our purpose for guessing is to help us better understand the problem.

   We are looking for the number of each denomination, so we let

   x = number of $10 bills

There are 37 more $20 bills, so

   $x + 37$ = number of $20 bills

2. TRANSLATE. To help us translate to an equation, study the table below.

Denomination	Number of Bills	Value of Bills (in dollars)
$10 bills	x	$10x$
$20 bills	$x + 37$	$20(x + 37)$

Since the total value of these bills is $2420, we have

In words: value of $10 bills plus value of $20 bills is 2420

Translate: $10x + 20(x + 37) = 2420$

3. SOLVE: $10x + 20x + 740 = 2420$ Use the distributive property.

   $30x + 740 = 2420$ Add like terms.

   $30x = 1680$ Subtract 740 from both sides.

   $\dfrac{30x}{30} = \dfrac{1680}{30}$ Divide both sides by 30.

   $x = 56$

4. INTERPRET the results.

   Check: Since x represents the number of $10 bills, we have 56 $10 bills and $56 + 37$, or 93, $20 bills. The total amount of these bills is $10(56) + $20(93) = $2420, the correct total.

   State: There are 56 $10 bills and 93 $20 bills.

Work Practice 2

Practice 2

A stack of $5 and $20 bills was counted by the treasurer of an organization. The total value of the money was $1710 and there were 47 more $5 bills than $20 bills. Find the number of each type of bill.

Answer

2. 106 $5 bills; 59 $20 bills

Objective B Solving Distance or Uniform Motion Problems ▶

This example involves the distance formula $d = r \cdot t$.

Example 3 Finding Time Given Rate and Distance

Practice 3

Sat Tranh took a short hike with his friends up Mt. Wachusett. They hiked uphill at a steady pace of 1.5 miles per hour, and downhill at a rate of 4 miles per hour. If the time to climb the mountain took an hour more than the time to hike down, how long did the entire hike take?

Example 3 Finding Time Given Rate and Distance

Marie Antonio, a bicycling enthusiast, rode her 21-speed at an average speed of 18 miles per hour on level roads and then slowed down to an average speed of 10 mph on the hilly roads of the trip. If she covered a distance of 98 miles, how long did the entire trip take if traveling the level roads took the same time as traveling the hilly roads?

Solution:

1. UNDERSTAND the problem. To do so, read and reread the problem. The formula $d = r \cdot t$ is needed. At this time, let's guess a solution. Suppose that she spent 2 hours traveling on the level roads. This means that she also spent 2 hours traveling on the hilly roads, since the times spent were the same. What is her total distance? Her distance on the level road is rate $\cdot$ time $= 18(2) = 36$ miles. Her distance on the hilly roads is rate $\cdot$ time $= 10(2) = 20$ miles. This gives a total distance of 36 miles $+$ 20 miles $= 56$ miles, not the correct distance of 98 miles. Remember that the purpose of guessing a solution is not to guess correctly (although this may happen) but to help better understand the problem and how to model it with an equation. We are looking for the length of the entire trip, so we begin by letting

    $x =$ the time spent on level roads

    Because the same amount of time was spent on hilly roads, then also

    $x =$ the time spent on hilly roads

2. TRANSLATE. To help us translate to an equation, we now summarize the information from the problem in the following table. Fill in the rates given and the variables used to represent the times, and use the formula $d = r \cdot t$ to fill in the distance column.

	Rate	$\cdot$ Time	$=$ Distance
Level	18	x	$18x$
Hilly	10	x	$10x$

    We'll draw a diagram to help visualize distance.

    Since the entire trip covered 98 miles, we have that

    In words: total distance $=$ level distance $+$ hilly distance

    Translate: 98 $=$ $18x$ $+$ $10x$

3. SOLVE.

    $$98 = 28x \quad \text{Add like terms.}$$

    $$\frac{98}{28} = \frac{28x}{28} \quad \text{Divide both sides by 28.}$$

    $$3.5 = x$$

Answer

3. 2.2 hours

4. INTERPRET the results.

Check: Recall that x represents the time spent on the level portion of the trip and also the time spent on the hilly portion. If Marie rode for 3.5 hours at 18 mph, her distance was $18(3.5) = 63$ miles. If Marie rode for 3.5 hours at 10 mph, her distance was $10(3.5) = 35$ miles. The total distance was 63 miles + 35 miles = 98 miles, the required distance.

State: The time of the entire trip was then 3.5 hours + 3.5 hours or 7 hours.

■ Work Practice 3

Example 4   Finding Train Speeds

The Kansas City Southern Railway operates in 10 states and Mexico. Suppose two trains leave Neosho, Missouri, at the same time. One travels north and the other travels south at a speed that is 15 miles per hour faster. In 2 hours, the trains are 230 miles apart. Find the speed of each train. Study the table below for more examples.

Solution:

1. UNDERSTAND the problem. Read and reread the problem. Guess a solution and check. Let's let

x = speed of train traveling north

Because the train traveling south is 15 mph faster, we have

$x + 15$ = speed of train traveling south

2. TRANSLATE. Just as for Example 3, let's summarize our information in a table. Use the formula $d = r \cdot t$ to fill in the distance column.

	r	$\cdot$ t $=$	d
North Train	x	2	$2x$
South Train	$x + 15$	2	$2(x + 15)$

Since the total distance between the trains is 230 miles, we have

In words: north train distance + south train distance = total distance

Translate: $2x$ + $2(x + 15)$ = 230

3. SOLVE.

$$2x + 2x + 30 = 230 \quad \text{Use the distributive property.}$$
$$4x + 30 = 230 \quad \text{Combine like terms.}$$
$$4x = 200 \quad \text{Subtract 30 from both sides.}$$
$$\frac{4x}{4} = \frac{200}{4} \quad \text{Divide both sides by 4.}$$
$$x = 50 \quad \text{Simplify.}$$

4. INTERPRET the results.

Check: Recall that x is the speed of the train traveling north, or 50 mph. In 2 hours, this train travels a distance of $2(50) = 100$ miles. The speed of the train traveling south is $x + 15$ or $50 + 15 = 65$ mph. In 2 hours, this train travels $2(65) = 130$ miles. The total distance between the trains is 100 miles + 130 miles = 230 miles, the required distance.

State: The northbound train's speed is 50 mph and the southbound train's speed is 65 mph.

■ Work Practice 4

Practice 4

The Kansas City Southern Railway has a station in Mexico City, Mexico. Suppose two trains leave Mexico City at the same time. One travels east and the other west at a speed that is 10 mph slower. In 1.5 hours, the trains are 171 miles apart. Find the speed of each train.

Answer

4. eastbound: 62 mph; westbound: 52 mph

Exercise Set MyMathLab®

Objective **A** *Solve. For each exercise, a table is given for you to complete and use to write an equation that models the situation. See Example 1.*

1. How much pure acid should be mixed with 2 gallons of a 40% acid solution in order to get a 70% acid solution?

	Number of Gallons ·	Acid Strength =	Amount of Acid
Pure Acid		100%	
40% Acid Solution			
70% Acid Solution Needed			

2. How many cubic centimeters (cc) of a 25% antibiotic solution should be added to 10 cubic centimeters of a 60% antibiotic solution in order to get a 30% antibiotic solution?

	Number of Cubic cm ·	Antibiotic Strength =	Amount of Antibiotic
25% Antibiotic Solution			
60% Antibiotic Solution			
30% Antibiotic Solution Needed			

3. Community Coffee Company wants to create a new flavor of Cajun coffee. How many pounds of coffee worth $7 per pound should be added to 14 pounds of coffee worth $4 per pound to get a mixture worth $5 a pound?

	Number of Pounds ·	Cost per Pound =	Value
$7 per lb Coffee			
$4 per lb Coffee			
$5 per lb Coffee Wanted			

4. Planter's Peanut Company wants to mix 20 pounds of peanuts worth $3 a pound with cashews worth $5 a pound in order to try out a mix worth $3.50 a pound. How many pounds of cashews should be added to the peanuts?

	Number of Pounds ·	Cost per Pound =	Value
$3 per lb Peanuts			
$5 per lb Cashews			
$3.50 per lb Mixture Wanted			

Complete the table. The first and sixth rows have been completed for you. See Example 2.

		Number of Coins or Bills	Value of Coins or Bills (in dollars)
	pennies	x	$0.01x$
5.	dimes	y	
6.	quarters	z	
7.	nickels	$(x + 7)$	
8.	half-dollars	$(20 - z)$	
	$5 bills	$9x$	$5(9x)$
9.	$20 bills	$4y$	
10.	$100 bills	$97z$	
11.	$50 bills	$(35 - x)$	
12.	$10 bills	$(15 - y)$	

Solve. See Examples 1 and 2.

13. Part of the proceeds from a garage sale was $280 worth of $5 and $10 bills. If there were 20 more $5 bills than $10 bills, find the number of each denomination.

	Number of Bills	Value of Bills
$5 bills		
$10 bills		
Total		

14. A bank teller is counting $20 and $50 bills. If there are six times as many $20 bills as $50 bills and the total amount of money is $3910, find the number of each denomination.

	Number of Bills	Value of Bills
$20 bills		
$50 bills		
Total		

15. How much of an alloy that is 20% copper should be mixed with 200 ounces of an alloy that is 50% copper in order to get an alloy that is 30% copper?

16. How much water should be added to 30 gallons of a solution that is 70% antifreeze in order to get a mixture that is 60% antifreeze?

17. A new self-tanning lotion for everyday use is to be sold. First, a speculative lotion mixture is made by mixing 800 ounces of everyday moisturizing lotion worth $0.30 per ounce with self-tanning lotion worth $3 per ounce. If the speculative lotion is to cost $1.20 per ounce, how many ounces of the self-tanning lotion should be in the mixture?

18. The owner of a local chocolate shop wants to develop a new trail mix. How many pounds of chocolate-covered peanuts worth $5 a pound should be mixed with 10 pounds of granola bites worth $2 a pound to get a mixture worth $3 a pound?

Objective **B** *Solve. See Example 3.*

19. Two cars leave Richmond, Virginia, at the same time after visiting the nearby Richmond International Speedway. The cars travel in opposite directions, one traveling north at 56 mph and one traveling south at 47 mph. When will the two cars be 206 miles apart?

20. Two cars leave Las Vegas, Nevada, at the same time after visiting the Las Vegas Motor Speedway. The cars travel in opposite directions, one traveling northeast at 65 mph and one traveling southwest at 41 mph. When will the two cars be 530 miles apart?

Solve. See Example 4.

21. Suppose two trains leave Corpus Christi, Texas, at the same time, traveling in opposite directions. One train travels 10 mph faster than the other. In 2.5 hours, the trains are 205 miles apart. Find the speed of each train.

22. Suppose two trains leave Cleveland, Ohio, at the same time, traveling in opposite directions. One train travels 8 mph faster than the other. In 1.5 hours, the trains are 162 miles apart. Find the speed of each train.

Solve. See Examples 3 and 4.

23. A truck and a van leave the same location at the same time and travel in opposite directions. The truck's speed is 52 mph and the van's speed is 63 mph. When will the truck and the van be 460 miles apart?

24. Two cars leave the same location at the same time and travel in opposite directions. One car's speed is 65 mph and the other car's speed is 45 mph. When will the two cars be 330 miles apart?

25. Two cars leave Pecos, Texas, at the same time and both travel east on Interstate 20. The first car's speed is 70 mph and the second car's speed is 58 mph. When will the cars be 30 miles apart?

26. Two cars leave Savannah, Georgia, at the same time and both travel north on Interstate 95. The first car's speed is 40 mph and the second car's speed is 50 mph. When will the cars be 20 miles apart?

27. A jet plane traveling at 500 mph overtakes a propeller plane traveling at 200 mph that had a 2-hour head start. How far from the starting point are the planes?

28. How long will it take a bus traveling at 60 miles per hour to overtake a car traveling at 40 mph if the car had a 1.5-hour head start?

29. A bus traveled on a level road for 3 hours at an average speed 20 miles per hour faster than it traveled on a winding road. The time spent on the winding road was 4 hours. Find the average speed on the level road if the entire trip was 305 miles.

30. The Jones family drove to Disneyland at 50 miles per hour and returned on the same route at 40 mph. Find the distance to Disneyland if the total driving time was 7.2 hours.

31. Alan and Dave Schaferkötter leave from the same point bicycling in opposite directions, Alan bicycling at 5.5 miles per hour and Dave at 6.5 mph. How long will they be able to talk on their long-range walkie-talkies if the walkie-talkies have a 35-mile range?

32. Kathleen and Cade Williams leave simultaneously from the same point hiking in opposite directions, Kathleen walking at 4 miles per hour and Cade at 5 mph. How long can they talk on their walkie-talkies if the walkie-talkies have a 20-mile radius?

33. Two hikers are 11 miles apart and walking toward each other. They meet in 2 hours. Find the rate of each hiker if one hiker walks 1.1 mph faster than the other.

34. Nedra and Latonya Dominguez are 12 miles apart hiking toward each other. How long will it take them to meet if Nedra walks at 3 mph and Latonya walks 1 mph faster?

35. Mark Martin can row upstream at 5 mph and downstream at 11 mph. If Mark starts rowing upstream until he gets tired and then rows downstream to his starting point, how far did Mark row if the entire trip took 4 hours?

36. On a 255-mile trip, Gary Alessandrini traveled at an average speed of 70 mph, got a speeding ticket, and then traveled at 60 mph for the remainder of the trip. If the entire trip took 4.5 hours and the speeding ticket stop took 30 minutes, how long did Gary speed before getting stopped?

37. A stack of $20, $50, and $100 bills was retrieved as part of an FBI investigation. There were 46 more $50 bills than $100 bills. Also, the number of $20 bills was 7 times the number of $100 bills. If the total value of the money was $9550, find the number of each type of bill.

38. A man places his pocket change in a jar every day. The jar is full and his children have counted the change. The total value is $44.86. Let x represent the number of quarters, and use the information below to find the number of each type of coin.

There are:
136 more dimes than quarters
8 times as many nickels as quarters
32 more than 16 times as many pennies as quarters

Systems of Linear Inequalities

A **solution of a system of linear inequalities** is an ordered pair that satisfies each inequality in the system. The set of all such ordered pairs is the solution set of the system. Graphing this set gives us a picture of the solution set. We can graph a system of inequalities by graphing each inequality in the system and identifying the region of overlap.

Example 1 Graph the solutions of the system: $\begin{cases} 3x \geq y \\ x + 2y \leq 8 \end{cases}$

Solution: We begin by graphing each inequality on the *same* set of axes. The graph of the solutions of the system is the region contained in the graphs of both inequalities. In other words, it is their intersection.

First let's graph $3x \geq y$. The boundary line is the graph of $3x = y$. We sketch a solid boundary line since the inequality $3x \geq y$ means $3x > y$ or $3x = y$. The test point $(1, 0)$ satisfies the inequality, so we shade the half-plane that includes $(1, 0)$.

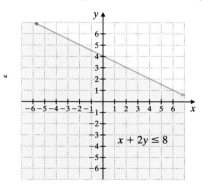

Next we sketch a solid boundary line $x + 2y = 8$ on the same set of axes. The test point $(0, 0)$ satisfies the inequality $x + 2y \leq 8$, so we shade the half-plane that includes $(0, 0)$. (For clarity, the graph of $x + 2y \leq 8$ is shown here on a separate set of axes.) An ordered pair solution of the system must satisfy both inequalities. These solutions are points that lie in both shaded regions. The solution of the system is the darkest shaded region. This solution includes parts of both boundary lines.

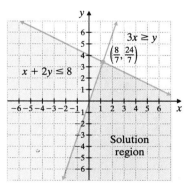

In linear programming, it is sometimes necessary to find the coordinates of the **corner point:** the point at which the two boundary lines intersect. To find the corner point for the system of Example 1, we solve the related linear system

$$\begin{cases} 3x = y \\ x + 2y = 8 \end{cases}$$

using either the substitution or the elimination method. The lines intersect at $\left(\dfrac{8}{7}, \dfrac{24}{7} \right)$, the corner point of the graph.

Graphing the Solutions of a System of Linear Inequalities

Step 1: Graph each inequality in the system on the same set of axes.

Step 2: The solutions of the system are the points common to the graphs of all the inequalities in the system.

Example 2 Graph the solutions of the system: $\begin{cases} x - y < 2 \\ x + 2y > -1 \end{cases}$

Solution: Graph both inequalities on the same set of axes. Both boundary lines are dashed lines since the inequality symbols are $<$ and $>$. The solutions of the system are the regions shown by the darkest shading. In this example, the boundary lines are not a part of the solution.

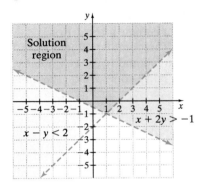

Example 3 Graph the solutions of the system: $\begin{cases} -3x + 4y < 12 \\ x \ge 2 \end{cases}$

Solution: Graph both inequalities on the same set of axes.

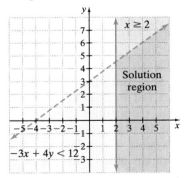

The solutions of the system are the darkest shaded regions, including a portion of the line $x = 2$.

D **Exercise Set** MyMathLab®

Graph the solutions of each system of linear inequalities. See Examples 1 through 3.

1. $\begin{cases} y \geq x + 1 \\ y \geq 3 - x \end{cases}$

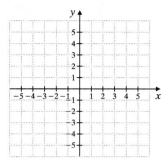

2. $\begin{cases} y \geq x - 3 \\ y \geq -1 - x \end{cases}$

3. $\begin{cases} y < 3x - 4 \\ y \leq x + 2 \end{cases}$

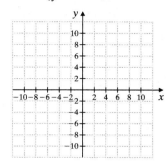

4. $\begin{cases} y \leq 2x + 1 \\ y > x + 2 \end{cases}$

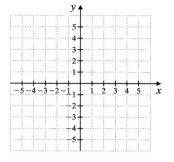

5. $\begin{cases} y < -2x - 2 \\ y > x + 4 \end{cases}$

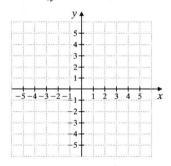

6. $\begin{cases} y \leq 2x + 4 \\ y \geq -x - 5 \end{cases}$

7. $\begin{cases} y \geq -x + 2 \\ y \leq 2x + 5 \end{cases}$

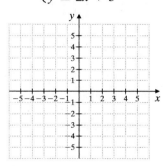

8. $\begin{cases} y \geq x - 5 \\ y \leq -3x + 3 \end{cases}$

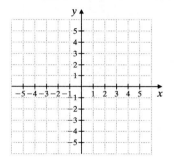

9. $\begin{cases} x \geq 3y \\ x + 3y \leq 6 \end{cases}$

10. $\begin{cases} -2x < y \\ x + 2y < 3 \end{cases}$

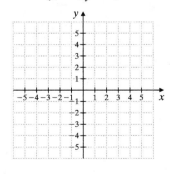

11. $\begin{cases} y + 2x \geq 0 \\ 5x - 3y \leq 12 \end{cases}$

12. $\begin{cases} y + 2x \leq 0 \\ 5x + 3y \geq -2 \end{cases}$

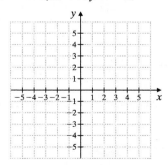

13. $\begin{cases} 3x - 4y \geq -6 \\ 2x + y \leq 7 \end{cases}$

14. $\begin{cases} 4x - y \geq -2 \\ 2x + 3y \leq -8 \end{cases}$

15. $\begin{cases} x \leq 2 \\ y \geq -3 \end{cases}$

16. $\begin{cases} x \geq -3 \\ y \geq -2 \end{cases}$

17. $\begin{cases} y \geq 1 \\ x < -3 \end{cases}$

18. $\begin{cases} y > 2 \\ x \geq -1 \end{cases}$

19. $\begin{cases} 2x + 3y < -8 \\ x \geq -4 \end{cases}$

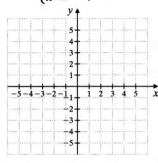

20. $\begin{cases} 3x + 2y \leq 6 \\ x < 2 \end{cases}$

21. $\begin{cases} 2x - 5y \leq 9 \\ y \leq -3 \end{cases}$

22. $\begin{cases} 2x + 5y \leq -10 \\ y \geq 1 \end{cases}$

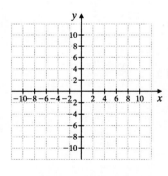

23. $\begin{cases} y \geq \dfrac{1}{2}x + 2 \\ y \leq \dfrac{1}{2}x - 3 \end{cases}$

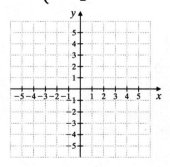

24. $\begin{cases} y \geq -\dfrac{3}{2}x + 3 \\ y < -\dfrac{3}{2}x + 6 \end{cases}$

Match each system of inequalities to the corresponding graph.

A

B

C

D

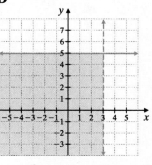

25. $\begin{cases} y < 5 \\ x > 3 \end{cases}$

26. $\begin{cases} y > 5 \\ x < 3 \end{cases}$

27. $\begin{cases} y \leq 5 \\ x < 3 \end{cases}$

28. $\begin{cases} y > 5 \\ x \geq 3 \end{cases}$

Geometric Formulas

Rectangle

Perimeter: $P = 2l + 2w$
Area: $A = lw$

Square

Perimeter: $P = 4s$
Area: $A = s^2$

Triangle

Perimeter: $P = a + b + c$
Area: $A = \frac{1}{2}bh$

Sum of Angles of Triangle

$A + B + C = 180°$

The sum of the measures of the three angles is 180.

Pythagorean Theorem (for right triangles)

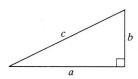

Perimeter: $P = a + b + c$
Area: $A = \frac{1}{2}ab$

One 90° (right) angle

Isosceles Triangle

Triangle has:
two equal sides and
two equal angles.

Equilateral Triangle

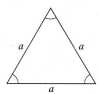

Triangle has:
three equal sides and
three equal angles.
Measure of each angle is 60°.

Trapezoid

Perimeter: $P = a + b + c + B$
Area: $A = \frac{1}{2}h(B + b)$

Parallelogram

Perimeter: $P = 2a + 2b$
Area: $A = bh$

Circle

Circumference: $C = \pi d$
$C = 2\pi r$
Area: $A = \pi r^2$

Rectangular Solid

Volume: $V = LWH$
Surface Area:
$S = 2LW + 2HL + 2HW$

Cube

Volume: $V = s^3$
Surface Area: $S = 6s^2$

Cone

Volume: $V = \frac{1}{3}\pi r^2 h$
Lateral Surface Area:
$S = \pi r\sqrt{r^2 + h^2}$

Right Circular Cylinder

Volume: $V = \pi r^2 h$
Surface Area: $S = 2\pi r^2 + 2\pi rh$

Sphere

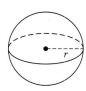

Volume: $V = \frac{4}{3}\pi r^3$
Surface Area: $S = 4\pi r^2$

Square-Based Pyramid

Volume: $V = \frac{1}{3}s^2 h$

Contents of Student Resources

Student Resources

STUDY SKILLS BUILDERS

Attitude and Study Tips

Study Skills Builder 1

Have You Decided to Complete This Course Successfully?

Ask yourself if one of your current goals is to complete this course successfully.

If it is not a goal of yours, ask yourself why. One common reason is fear of failure. Amazingly enough, fear of failure alone can be strong enough to keep many of us from doing our best in any endeavor.

Another common reason is that you simply haven't taken the time to think about or write down your goals for this course. To help accomplish this, answer the questions below.

Exercises

1. Write down your goal(s) for this course.

2. Now list steps you will take to make sure your goal(s) in Exercise **1** are accomplished.

3. Rate your commitment to this course with a number between 1 and 5. Use the diagram below to help.

High Commitment		Average Commitment		Not Committed at All
5	4	3	2	1

4. If you have rated your personal commitment level (from the exercise above) as a 1, 2, or 3, list the reasons why this is so. Then determine whether it is possible to increase your commitment level to a 4 or 5.

Good luck, and don't forget that a positive attitude will make a big difference.

Study Skills Builder 2

Tips for Studying for an Exam

To prepare for an exam, try the following study techniques:

- Start the study process days before your exam.
- Make sure that you are up to date on your assignments.
- If there is a topic that you are unsure of, use one of the many resources that are available to you. For example,

  See your instructor.
  View a lecture video on the topic.
  Visit a learning resource center on campus.
  Read the textbook material and examples on the topic.

- Reread your notes and carefully review the Chapter Highlights at the end of any chapter.
- Work the review exercises at the end of the chapter.
- Find a quiet place to take the Chapter Test found at the end of the chapter. Do not use any resources when taking this sample test. This way, you will have a clear indication of how prepared you are for your exam. Check your answers and use the Chapter Test Prep Videos to make sure that you correct any missed exercises.

Good luck, and keep a positive attitude.

Exercises

Let's see how you did on your last exam.

1. How many days before your last exam did you start studying for that exam?

2. Were you up to date on your assignments at that time or did you need to catch up on assignments?

3. List the most helpful text supplement (if you used one).

4. List the most helpful campus supplement (if you used one).

5. List your process for preparing for a mathematics test.

6. Was this process helpful? In other words, were you satisfied with your performance on your exam?

7. If not, what changes can you make in your process that will make it more helpful to you?

Study Skills Builder 3

What to Do the Day of an Exam

Your first exam may be soon. On the day of an exam, don't forget to try the following:

- Allow yourself plenty of time to arrive.
- Read the directions on the test carefully.
- Read each problem carefully as you take your test. Make sure that you answer the question asked.
- Watch your time and pace yourself so that you may attempt each problem on your test.
- Check your work and answers.
- ***Do not turn your test in early.*** If you have extra time, spend it double-checking your work.

Good luck!

Exercises

Answer the following questions based on your most recent mathematics exam, whenever that was.

1. How soon before class did you arrive?

2. Did you read the directions on the test carefully?

3. Did you make sure you answered the question asked for each problem on the exam?

4. Were you able to attempt each problem on your exam?

5. If your answer to Exercise **4** is no, list reasons why.

6. Did you have extra time on your exam?

7. If your answer to Exercise **6** is yes, describe how you spent that extra time.

Study Skills Builder 4

Are You Satisfied with Your Performance on a Particular Quiz or Exam?

If not, don't forget to analyze your quiz or exam and look for common errors. Were most of your errors a result of:

- *Carelessness?* Did you turn in your quiz or exam before the allotted time expired? If so, resolve to use any extra time to check your work.

- *Running out of time?* Answer the questions you are sure of first. Then attempt the questions you are unsure of, and delay checking your work until all questions have been answered.

- *Not understanding a concept?* If so, review that concept and correct your work so that you make sure you understand it before the next quiz or the final exam.

- *Test conditions?* When studying for a quiz or exam, make sure you place yourself in conditions similar to test conditions. For example, before your next quiz or exam, take a sample test without the aid of your notes or text.

(For a sample test, see your instructor or use the Chapter Test at the end of each chapter.)

Exercises

1. Have you corrected all your previous quizzes and exams?

2. List any errors you have found common to two or more of your graded papers.

3. Is one of your common errors not understanding a concept? If so, are you making sure you understand all the concepts for the next quiz or exam?

4. Is one of your common errors making careless mistakes? If so, are you now taking all the time allotted to check over your work so that you can minimize the number of careless mistakes?

5. Are you satisfied with your grades thus far on quizzes and tests?

6. If your answer to Exercise **5** is no, are there any more suggestions you can make to your instructor or yourself to help? If so, list them here and share them with your instructor.

Study Skills Builder 5

How Are You Doing?

If you haven't done so yet, take a few moments and think about how you are doing in this course. Are you working toward your goal of successfully completing this course? Is your performance on homework, quizzes, and tests satisfactory? If not, you might want to see your instructor to see if he/she has any suggestions on how you can improve your performance. Reread Section 1.1 for ideas on places to get help with your mathematics course.

Exercises

Answer the following.

1. List any textbook supplements you are using to help you through this course.

2. List any campus resources you are using to help you through this course.

3. Write a short paragraph describing how you are doing in your mathematics course.

4. If improvement is needed, list ways that you can work toward improving your situation as described in Exercise **3**.

Study Skills Builder 6

Are You Preparing for Your Final Exam?

To prepare for your final exam, try the following study techniques:

- Review the material that you will be responsible for on your exam. This includes material from your textbook, your notebook, and any handouts from your instructor.

- Review any formulas that you may need to memorize.

- Check to see if your instructor or mathematics department will be conducting a final exam review.

- Check with your instructor to see whether final exams from previous semesters/quarters are available to students for review.

- Use your previously taken exams as a practice final exam. To do so, rewrite the test questions in mixed order on blank sheets of paper. This will help you prepare for exam conditions.

- If you are unsure of a few concepts, see your instructor or visit a learning lab for assistance. Also, view the video segment of any troublesome sections.

- If you need further exercises to work, try the Cumulative Reviews at the end of the chapters.

Once again, good luck! I hope you are enjoying this textbook and your mathematics course.

Organizing Your Work

Study Skills Builder 7

Learning New Terms

Many of the terms used in this text may be new to you. It will be helpful to make a list of new mathematical terms and symbols as you encounter them and to review them frequently. Placing these new terms (including page references) on 3 × 5 index cards might help you later when you're preparing for a quiz.

Exercises

1. Name one way you might place a word and its definition on a 3 × 5 card.

2. How do new terms stand out in this text so that they can be found?

Study Skills Builder 8

Are You Organized?

Have you ever had trouble finding a completed assignment? When it's time to study for a test, are your notes neat and organized? Have you ever had trouble reading your own mathematics handwriting? (Be honest—I have.)

When any of these things happen, it's time to get organized. Here are a few suggestions:

- Write your notes and complete your homework assignments in a notebook with pockets (spiral or ring binder).
- Take class notes in this notebook, and then follow the notes with your completed homework assignment.
- When you receive graded papers or handouts, place them in the notebook pocket so that you will not lose them.
- Mark (possibly with an exclamation point) any note(s) that seem extra important to you.
- Mark (possibly with a question mark) any notes or homework that you are having trouble with.
- See your instructor or a math tutor for help with the concepts or exercises that you are having trouble understanding.

- If you are having trouble reading your own handwriting, *slow down* and write your mathematics work clearly!

Exercises

1. Have you been completing your assignments on time?

2. Have you been correcting any exercises you may be having difficulty with?

3. If you are having trouble understanding a mathematical concept or correcting any homework exercises, have you visited your instructor, a tutor, or your campus math lab?

4. Are you taking lecture notes in your mathematics course? (By the way, these notes should include worked-out examples solved by your instructor.)

5. Is your mathematics course material (handouts, graded papers, lecture notes) organized?

6. If your answer to Exercise **5** is no, take a moment and review your course material. List at least two ways that you might better organize it.

Study Skills Builder 9

Organizing a Notebook

It's never too late to get organized. If you need ideas about organizing a notebook for your mathematics course, try some of these:

- Use a spiral or ring binder notebook with pockets and use it for mathematics only.
- Start each page by writing the book's section number you are working on at the top.
- When your instructor is lecturing, take notes. *Always* include any examples your instructor works for you.
- Place your worked-out homework exercises in your notebook immediately after the lecture notes from that section. This way, a section's worth of material is together.
- Homework exercises: Attempt and check all assigned homework.
- Place graded quizzes in the pockets of your notebook or a special section of your binder.

Exercises

Check your notebook organization by answering the following questions.

1. Do you have a spiral or ring binder notebook for your mathematics course only?

2. Have you ever had to flip through several sheets of notes and work in your mathematics notebook to determine what section's work you are in?

3. Are you now writing the textbook's section number at the top of each notebook page?

4. Have you ever lost or had trouble finding a graded quiz or test?

5. Are you now placing all your graded work in a dedicated place in your notebook?

6. Are you attempting all of your homework and placing all of your work in your notebook?

7. Are you checking and correcting your homework in your notebook? If not, why not?

8. Are you writing in your notebook the examples your instructor works for you in class?

Study Skills Builder 10

How Are Your Homework Assignments Going?

It is very important in mathematics to keep up with homework. Why? Many concepts build on each other. Often your understanding of a day's concepts depends on an understanding of the previous day's material.

Remember that completing your homework assignment involves a lot more than attempting a few of the problems assigned.

To complete a homework assignment, remember these four things:

- Attempt all of it.
- Check it.
- Correct it.
- If needed, ask questions about it.

Exercises

Take a moment and review your completed homework assignments. Answer the questions below based on this review.

1. Approximate the fraction of your homework you have attempted.

2. Approximate the fraction of your homework you have checked (if possible).

3. If you are able to check your homework, have you corrected it when errors have been found?

4. When working homework, if you do not understand a concept, what do you do?

Student Resources

MyMathLab and MathXL

Study Skills Builder 11

Tips for Turning in Your Homework on Time

It is very important to keep up with your mathematics homework assignments. Why? Many concepts in mathematics build upon each other.

Remember these four tips to help ensure your work is completed on time:

- Know the assignments and due dates set by your instructor.
- Do not wait until the last minute to submit your homework.
- Set a goal to submit your homework 6–8 hours before the scheduled due date in case you have unexpected technology trouble.
- Schedule enough time to complete each assignment.

Following the tips above will also help you avoid potentially losing points for late or missed assignments.

Exercises

Take a moment to consider your work on your homework assignments to date and answer the following questions:

1. What percentage of your assignments have you turned in on time?

2. Why might it be a good idea to submit your homework 6–8 hours before the scheduled deadline?

3. If you have missed submitting any homework by the due date, list some of the reasons why this occurred.

4. What steps do you plan to take in the future to ensure your homework is submitted on time?

Study Skills Builder 12

Tips for Doing Your Homework Online

Practice is one of the main keys to success in any mathematics course. Did you know that MyMathLab/MathXL provides you with **immediate feedback** for each exercise? If you are incorrect, you are given hints to work the exercise correctly. You have **unlimited practice opportunities** and can rework any exercises you have trouble with until you master them, and submit homework assignments unlimited times before the deadline.

Remember these success tips when doing your homework online:

- Attempt all assigned exercises.
- Write down (neatly) your step-by-step work for each exercise before entering your answer.
- Use the immediate feedback provided by the program to help you check and correct your work for each exercise.
- Rework any exercises you have trouble with until you master them.
- Work through your homework assignment as many times as necessary until you are satisfied.

Exercises

Take a moment to think about your homework assignments to date and answer the following:

1. Have you attempted all assigned exercises?

2. Of the exercises attempted, have you also written out your work before entering your answer—so that you can check it?

3. Are you familiar with how to enter answers using the MathXL player so that you avoid answer-entry-type errors?

4. List some ways the immediate feedback and practice supports have helped you with your homework. If you have not used these supports, how do you plan to use them with the success tips above on your next assignment?

Study Skills Builder 13

Organizing Your Work

Have you ever used any readily available paper (such as the back of a flyer, another course assignment, Post-its, etc.) to work out your homework exercises before entering the answer in MathXL? To save time, have you ever entered answers directly into MathXL without working the exercises on paper? When it's time to study, have you ever been unable to find your completed work or read and follow your own mathematics handwriting?

When any of these things happen, it's time to get organized. Here are some suggestions:

- Write your step-by-step work for each homework exercise (neatly) on lined, loose-leaf paper and keep this in a 3-ring binder.
- Refer to your step-by-step work when you receive feedback that your answer is incorrect in MathXL. Double-check using the steps and hints provided by the program and correct your work accordingly.
- Keep your written homework with your class notes for that section.

- Identify any exercises you are having trouble with and ask questions about them.
- Keep all graded quizzes and tests in this binder as well to study later.

If you follow the suggestions above, you and your instructor or tutor will be able to follow your steps and correct any mistakes. You will also have a written copy of your work to refer to later to ask questions and study for tests.

Exercises

1. Why is it important that you write out your step-by-step work for homework exercises and keep a hard copy of all work submitted online?

2. If you have gotten an incorrect answer, are you able to follow your steps and find your error?

3. If you were asked today to review your previous homework assignments and first test, could you find them? If not, list some ways you might better organize your work.

Study Skills Builder 14

Getting Help with Your Homework Assignments

There are many resources available to you through MathXL to help you work through any homework exercises you may have trouble with. It is important that you know what these resources are and know when and how to use them.

Let's review the features found in the homework exercises:

- **Help Me Solve This**—provides step-by-step help for the exercise you are working. You must work an additional exercise of the same type (without this help) before you can get credit for having worked it correctly.
- **View an Example**—allows you to view a correctly worked exercise similar to the one you are having trouble with. You can then go back to your original exercise and work it on your own.
- **E-Book**—allows you to read examples from your text and find similar exercises.

- **Video**—your text author, Elayn Martin-Gay, works an exercise similar to the one you need help with. **Not all exercises have an accompanying video clip.
- **Ask My Instructor**—allows you to e-mail your instructor for help with an exercise.

Exercises

1. How does the "Help Me Solve This" feature work?

2. If the "View an Example" feature is used, is it necessary to work an additional problem before continuing the assignment?

3. When might be a good time to use the "Video" feature? Do all exercises have an accompanying video clip?

4. Which of the features above have you used? List those you found the most helpful to you.

5. If you haven't used the features discussed, list those you plan to try on your next homework assignment.

Study Skills Builder 15

Tips for Preparing for an Exam

Did you know that you can rework your previous homework assignments in MyMathLab and MathXL? This is a great way to prepare for tests. To do this, open a previous homework assignment and click "similar exercise." This will generate new exercises similar to the homework you have submitted. You can then rework the exercises and assignments until you feel confident that you understand them.

To prepare for an exam, follow these tips:

- Review your written work for your previous homework assignments along with your class notes.
- Identify any exercises or topics that you have questions on or have difficulty understanding.
- Rework your previous assignments in MyMathLab and MathXL until you fully understand them and can do them without help.

- Get help for any topics you feel unsure of or for which you have questions.

Exercises

1. Are your current homework assignments up to date and is your written work for them organized in a binder or notebook? If the answer is no, it's time to get organized. For tips on this, see Study Skills Builder 13—Organizing Your Work.

2. How many days in advance of an exam do you usually start studying?

3. List some ways you think that working previous homework assignments can help you prepare for your test.

4. List two or three resources you can use to get help for any topics you are unsure of or have questions on.

Good luck!

Study Skills Builder 16

How Well Do You Know the Resources Available to You in MyMathLab?

There are many helpful resources available to you in MyMathLab. Let's take a moment to locate and explore a few of them now. Go into your MyMathLab course, and visit the Multimedia Library, Tools for Success, and E-Book.

Let's see what you found.

Exercises

1. List the resources available to you in the Multimedia Library.

2. List the resources available to you in the Tools for Success folder.

3. Where did you find the English/Spanish Audio Glossary?

4. Can you view videos from the E-Book?

5. Did you find any resources you did not know about? If so, which ones?

6. Which resources have you used most often or find most helpful?

Additional Help Inside and Outside Your Textbook

Study Skills Builder 17

How Well Do You Know Your Textbook?

The questions below will help determine whether you are familiar with your textbook. For additional information, see Section 1.1 in this text.

1. What does the ◐ icon mean?

2. What does the ◥ icon mean?

3. What does the △ icon mean?

4. Where can you find a review for each chapter? What answers to this review can be found in the back of your text?

5. Each chapter contains an overview of the chapter along with examples. What is this feature called?

6. Each chapter contains a review of vocabulary. What is this feature called?

7. There are practice exercises that are contained in this text. What are they and how can they be used?

8. This text contains a student section in the back entitled Student Resources. List the contents of this section and how they might be helpful.

9. What exercise answers are available in this text? Where are they located?

Study Skills Builder 18

Are You Familiar with Your Textbook Supplements? Below is a review of some of the student supplements available for additional study. Check to see if you are using the ones most helpful to you.

- Chapter Test Prep Videos. These videos provide video clip solutions to the Chapter Test exercises in this text. You will find them extremely useful when studying for tests or exams.
- Interactive DVD Lecture Series. These are keyed to each section of the text. The material is presented by me, Elayn Martin-Gay, and I have placed a ▶ by the exercises in the text that I have worked on the video.
- The *Student Solutions Manual*. This contains worked-out solutions to odd-numbered exercises as well as every exercise in the Integrated Reviews, Chapter Reviews, Chapter Tests, and Cumulative Reviews.
- Pearson Tutor Center. Mathematics questions may be phoned, faxed, or e-mailed to this center.
- MyMathLab is a text-specific online course. MathXL is an online homework, tutorial, and assessment system.

Take a moment and determine whether these are available to you.

As usual, your instructor is your best source of information.

Exercises

Let's see how you are doing with textbook supplements.

1. Name one way the Lecture Videos can be helpful to you.
2. Name one way the Chapter Test Prep Videos can help you prepare for a chapter test.
3. List any textbook supplements that you have found useful.
4. Have you located and visited a learning resource lab located on your campus?
5. List the textbook supplements that are currently housed in your campus' learning resource lab.

Study Skills Builder 19

Are You Getting All the Mathematics Help That You Need?
Remember that, in addition to your instructor, there are many places to get help with your mathematics course. For example:

- This text has an accompanying video lesson for every section, and the CD in this text contains worked-out solutions to every Chapter Test exercise.
- The back of the book contains answers to odd-numbered exercises.
- A *Student Solutions Manual* is available that contains worked-out solutions to odd-numbered exercises as well as solutions to every exercise in the Integrated Reviews, Chapter Reviews, Chapter Tests, and Cumulative Reviews.
- Don't forget to check with your instructor for other local resources available to you, such as a tutor center.

Exercises

1. List items you find helpful in the text and all student supplements to this text.
2. List all the campus help that is available to you for this course.
3. List any help (besides the textbook) from Exercises **1** and **2** above that you are using.
4. List any help (besides the textbook) that you feel you should try.
5. Write a goal for yourself that includes trying everything you listed in Exercise **4** during the next week.

Bigger Picture—
Study Guide Outline

OUTLINE: PART 1

Operations on Sets of Numbers and Solving Equations

I. Operations on Sets of Numbers

  A. Whole Numbers

    1. Add or Subtract: (Sec. 1.3)

$$\begin{array}{r} 14 \\ +\,39 \\ \hline 53 \end{array} \qquad \begin{array}{r} 300 \\ -\,27 \\ \hline 273 \end{array}$$

    2. Multiply or Divide: (Sec. 1.5, 1.6)

$$\begin{array}{r} 238 \\ \times\,47 \\ \hline 1666 \\ 9520 \\ \hline 11{,}186 \end{array} \qquad \begin{array}{r} 127\ \text{R}\,2 \\ 7\overline{)891} \\ -7 \\ \hline 19 \\ -14 \\ \hline 51 \\ -49 \\ \hline 2 \end{array}$$

    3. Exponent: (Sec. 1.7)   4 factors of 3

$$3^4 = \overbrace{3 \cdot 3 \cdot 3 \cdot 3} = 81$$

    4. Order of Operations: (Sec. 1.7)

$$\begin{aligned} 24 \div 3 \cdot 2 - (2 + 8) &= 24 \div 3 \cdot 2 - (10) && \text{Simplify within parentheses.} \\ &= 8 \cdot 2 - 10 && \text{Multiply or divide from left to right.} \\ &= 16 - 10 && \text{Multiply or divide from left to right.} \\ &= 6 && \text{Add or subtract from left to right.} \end{aligned}$$

    5. Square Root: (Sec. 7.3)

      $\sqrt{25} = 5$ because $5 \cdot 5 = 25$ and 5 is a positive number.

  B. Integers

    1. Add: (Sec. 2.2) $-5 + (-2) = -7$ Adding like signs: Add absolute values. Attach the common sign.

                      $-5 + 2 = -3$ Adding unlike signs: Subtract absolute values. Attach the sign of the number with the larger absolute value.

    2. Subtract: Add the first number to the opposite of the second number. (Sec. 2.3)

         $7 - 10 = 7 + (-10) = -3$

    3. Multiply or Divide: Multiply or divide as usual. If the signs of the two numbers are the same, the answer is positive. If the signs of the two numbers are different, the answer is negative. (Sec. 2.4)

         $-5 \cdot 5 = -25, \quad \dfrac{-32}{-8} = 4$

C. Fractions

1. **Simplify:** Factor the numerator and denominator. Then divide out factors of 1 by dividing out common factors in the numerator and denominator. (Sec. 4.2)

    Simplify: $\dfrac{20}{28} = \dfrac{4 \cdot 5}{4 \cdot 7} = \dfrac{5}{7}$

2. **Multiply:** Numerator times numerator over denominator times denominator. (Sec. 4.3)

    $\dfrac{5}{9} \cdot \dfrac{2}{7} = \dfrac{10}{63}$

3. **Divide:** First fraction times the reciprocal of the second fraction. (Sec. 4.3)

    $\dfrac{2}{11} \div \dfrac{3}{4} = \dfrac{2}{11} \cdot \dfrac{4}{3} = \dfrac{8}{33}$

4. **Add or Subtract:** Must have same denominators. If not, find the LCD, and write each fraction as an equivalent fraction with the LCD as denominator. (Sec. 4.4, Sec. 4.5)

    $\dfrac{2}{5} + \dfrac{1}{15} = \dfrac{2}{5} \cdot \dfrac{3}{3} + \dfrac{1}{15} = \dfrac{6}{15} + \dfrac{1}{15} = \dfrac{7}{15}$

D. Decimals

1. **Add or Subtract:** Line up decimal points. (Sec. 5.2)

    $$\begin{array}{r} 1.27 \\ + \ 0.6 \\ \hline 1.87 \end{array}$$

2. **Multiply:** (Sec. 5.3)

    $$\begin{array}{r} 2.56 \\ \times \ 3.2 \\ \hline 512 \\ 7680 \\ \hline 8.192 \end{array}$$

    2.56   2 decimal places
    × 3.2   1 decimal place
    512   2 + 1 = 3
    8.192   3 decimal places

3. **Divide:** (Sec. 5.4)

    $8)\overline{5.6}$ gives 0.7 $0.6)\overline{0.7\,86}$ gives 1.36

II. Solving Equations

A. Equations in General: Simplify both sides of the equation by removing parentheses and adding any like terms. Then use the addition property to write variable terms on one side and constants (or numbers) on the other side. Then use the multiplication property to solve for the variable by dividing both sides of the equation by the coefficient of the variable. (Sec. 3.3)

Solve: $2(x - 5) = 80$

$\begin{aligned} 2x - 10 &= 80 & &\text{Use the distributive property.} \\ 2x - 10 + 10 &= 80 + 10 & &\text{Add 10 to both sides.} \\ 2x &= 90 & &\text{Simplify.} \\ \dfrac{2x}{2} &= \dfrac{90}{2} & &\text{Divide both sides by 2.} \\ x &= 45 & &\text{Simplify.} \end{aligned}$

B. Proportions: Set cross products equal to each other. Then solve. (Sec. 6.1)

$\dfrac{14}{3} = \dfrac{2}{n}$ or $14 \cdot n = 3 \cdot 2$ or $14 \cdot n = 6$ or $n = \dfrac{6}{14} = \dfrac{3}{7}$

C. Percent Problems

1. **Solved by Equations:** Remember that "of" means multiplication and "is" means equals. (Sec. 6.3)

   "12% of some number is 6" translates to

   $$12\% \cdot n = 6 \text{ or } 0.12 \cdot n = 6 \text{ or } n = \frac{6}{0.12} \text{ or } n = 50$$

2. **Solved by Proportions:** Remember that percent, p, is identified by % or "percent"; base, b, usually appears after "of"; and amount, a, is the part compared to the whole. (Sec. 6.4)

   "12% of some number is 6" translates to

   $$\frac{6}{b} = \frac{12}{100} \text{ or } 6 \cdot 100 = b \cdot 12 \text{ or } \frac{600}{12} = b \text{ or } 50 = b$$

OUTLINE: PART 2

Simplifying Expressions and Solving Equations

I. Simplifying Expressions

A. Exponents (Sec. 10.1, 10.2)

$$x^7 \cdot x^5 = x^{12}; \; \left(x^7\right)^5 = x^{35}; \; \frac{x^7}{x^5} = x^2; \; x^0 = 1; \; 8^{-2} = \frac{1}{8^2} = \frac{1}{64}$$

B. Polynomials

1. **Add:** Combine like terms. (Sec. 10.4)

$$\left(3y^2 + 6y + 7\right) + \left(9y^2 - 11y - 15\right) = 3y^2 + 6y + 7 + 9y^2 - 11y - 15$$
$$= 12y^2 - 5y - 8$$

2. **Subtract:** Change the sign of the terms of the polynomial being subtracted, then add. (Sec. 10.4)

$$\left(3y^2 + 6y + 7\right) - \left(9y^2 - 11y - 15\right) = 3y^2 + 6y + 7 - 9y^2 + 11y + 15$$
$$= -6y^2 + 17y + 22$$

3. **Multiply:** Multiply each term of one polynomial by each term of the other polynomial. (Sec. 10.5)

$$(x + 5)\left(2x^2 - 3x + 4\right) = x\left(2x^2 - 3x + 4\right) + 5\left(2x^2 - 3x + 4\right)$$
$$= 2x^3 - 3x^2 + 4x + 10x^2 - 15x + 20$$
$$= 2x^3 + 7x^2 - 11x + 20$$

4. **Divide:** (Sec. 10.7)

   a. To divide by a monomial, divide each term of the polynomial by the monomial.

   $$\frac{8x^2 + 2x - 6}{2x} = \frac{8x^2}{2x} + \frac{2x}{2x} - \frac{6}{2x} = 4x + 1 - \frac{3}{x}$$

b. To divide by a polynomial other than a monomial, use long division.

$$2x + 5 \overline{)\ 2x^2 - 7x + 10} \quad\quad x - 6 + \frac{40}{2x + 5}$$

$$\frac{2x^2 + 5x}{-12x + 10}$$
$$\frac{-12x - 30}{40}$$

C. Factoring Polynomials

See the Chapter 11 Integrated Review for steps.

$$3x^4 - 78x^2 + 75 = 3\left(x^4 - 26x^2 + 25\right)$$
$$= 3\left(x^2 - 25\right)\left(x^2 - 1\right)$$
$$= 3(x + 5)(x - 5)(x + 1)(x - 1)$$

Factor out GCF— always first step.

Factor trinomial.

Factor further— each a difference of squares.

D. Rational Expressions

1. **Simplify:** Factor the numerator and denominator. Then divide out factors of 1 by dividing out common factors in the numerator and denominator. (Sec. 12.1)

$$\frac{x^2 - 9}{7x^2 - 21x} = \frac{(x + 3)(x - 3)}{7x(x - 3)} = \frac{x + 3}{7x}$$

2. **Multiply:** Multiply numerators, then multiply denominators. (Sec. 12.2)

$$\frac{5z}{2z^2 - 9z - 18} \cdot \frac{22z + 33}{10z} = \frac{5 \cdot z}{(2z + 3)(z - 6)} \cdot \frac{11(2z + 3)}{2 \cdot 5 \cdot z} = \frac{11}{2(z - 6)}$$

3. **Divide:** First fraction times the reciprocal of the second fraction. (Sec. 12.2)

$$\frac{14}{x + 5} \div \frac{x + 1}{2} = \frac{14}{x + 5} \cdot \frac{2}{x + 1} = \frac{28}{(x + 5)(x + 1)}$$

4. **Add or Subtract:** Must have same denominator. If not, find the LCD and write each fraction as an equivalent fraction with the LCD as denominator. (Sec. 12.3, 12.4)

$$\frac{9}{10} - \frac{x + 1}{x + 5} = \frac{9(x + 5)}{10(x + 5)} - \frac{10(x + 1)}{10(x + 5)}$$
$$= \frac{9x + 45 - 10x - 10}{10(x + 5)} = \frac{-x + 35}{10(x + 5)}$$

E. Radicals

1. **Simplify Square Roots:** If possible, factor the radicand so that one factor is a perfect square. Then use the product rule and simplify. (Sec. 15.2)

$$\sqrt{75} = \sqrt{25 \cdot 3} = \sqrt{25} \cdot \sqrt{3} = 5\sqrt{3}$$

2. **Add or Subtract:** Only like radicals (same index and radicand) can be added or subtracted. (Sec. 15.3)

$$8\sqrt{10} - \sqrt{40} + \sqrt{5} = 8\sqrt{10} - 2\sqrt{10} + \sqrt{5} = 6\sqrt{10} + \sqrt{5}$$

3. **Multiply or Divide:** (Sec. 15.4) $\sqrt{a} \cdot \sqrt{b} = \sqrt{ab}; \dfrac{\sqrt{a}}{\sqrt{b}} = \sqrt{\dfrac{a}{b}}.$

$$\sqrt{11} \cdot \sqrt{3} = \sqrt{33}; \frac{\sqrt{140}}{\sqrt{7}} = \sqrt{\frac{140}{7}} = \sqrt{20} = \sqrt{4 \cdot 5} = 2\sqrt{5}$$

4. **Rationalizing the Denominator:** (Sec. 15.4)

    a. If denominator is one term,

$$\frac{5}{\sqrt{11}} = \frac{5 \cdot \sqrt{11}}{\sqrt{11} \cdot \sqrt{11}} = \frac{5\sqrt{11}}{11}$$

    b. If denominator is two terms, multiply by 1 in the form of $\dfrac{\text{conjugate of denominator}}{\text{conjugate of denominator}}$.

$$\frac{13}{3 + \sqrt{2}} = \frac{13}{3 + \sqrt{2}} \cdot \frac{3 - \sqrt{2}}{3 - \sqrt{2}} = \frac{13(3 - \sqrt{2})}{9 - 2} = \frac{13(3 - \sqrt{2})}{7}$$

II. Solving Equations and Inequalities

A. Linear Equations: Power on variable is 1 and there are no variables in denominator. (Sec. 9.3)

$7(x - 3) = 4x + 6$	Linear equation (If fractions, multiply by LCD.)
$7x - 21 = 4x + 6$	Use the distributive property.
$3x - 21 = 6$	Subtract $4x$ from both sides.
$3x = 27$	Add 21 to both sides.
$x = 9$	Divide both sides by 3.

B. Linear Inequalities: Same as linear equation except if you multiply or divide by a negative number, then reverse direction of inequality. (Sec. 9.6)

$-4x + 11 \leq -1$	Linear inequality
$-4x \leq -12$	Subtract 11 from both sides.
$\dfrac{-4x}{-4} \geq \dfrac{-12}{-4}$	Divide both sides by -4 and reverse the direction of the inequality symbol.
$x \geq 3$	Simplify.

C. Quadratic and Higher Degree Equations: Solve: First write the equation in standard form (one side is 0).

    1. If the polynomial on one side factors, solve by factoring. (Sec. 11.6)

    2. If the polynomial does not factor, solve by the quadratic formula. (Sec. 16.3)

By Factoring:	**By Quadratic Formula:**
$x^2 + x = 6$	$x^2 + x = 5$
$x^2 + x - 6 = 0$	$x^2 + x - 5 = 0$
$(x - 2)(x + 3) = 0$	$a = 1, b = 1, c = -5$
$x - 2 = 0 \text{ or } x + 3 = 0$	$x = \dfrac{-1 \pm \sqrt{1^2 - 4(1)(-5)}}{2 \cdot 1}$
$x = 2 \text{ or } \quad x = -3$	$= \dfrac{-1 \pm \sqrt{21}}{2}$

D. Equations with Rational Expressions: Make sure the proposed solution does not make a denominator 0. (Sec. 12.5)

$$\frac{3}{x} - \frac{1}{x - 1} = \frac{4}{x - 1} \qquad \text{Equation with rational expressions}$$

$$x(x - 1) \cdot \frac{3}{x} - x(x - 1) \cdot \frac{1}{x - 1} = x(x - 1) \cdot \frac{4}{x - 1} \qquad \text{Multiply through by } x(x - 1).$$

$$3(x - 1) - x \cdot 1 = x \cdot 4 \quad \text{Simplify.}$$

$$3x - 3 - x = 4x \quad \text{Use the distributive property.}$$

$$-3 = 2x \quad \text{Simplify and move variable terms to right side.}$$

$$-\frac{3}{2} = x \quad \text{Divide both sides by 2.}$$

E. Equations with Radicals: To solve, isolate a radical, then square both sides. You may have to repeat this. Check possible solution(s) in the original equation. (Sec. 15.5)

$$\sqrt{x + 49} + 7 = x$$

$$\sqrt{x + 49} = x - 7 \quad \text{Subtract 7 from both sides.}$$

$$x + 49 = x^2 - 14x + 49 \quad \text{Square both sides.}$$

$$0 = x^2 - 15x \quad \text{Set terms equal to 0.}$$

$$0 = x(x - 15) \quad \text{Factor.}$$

$$\cancel{x = 0} \text{ or } x = 15 \quad \text{Set each factor equal to 0 and solve.}$$

Practice Final Exam

Chapters 1–8

1. _____

2. _____

3. _____

4. _____

5. _____

6. _____

7. _____

8. _____

9. _____

10. _____

11. _____

12. _____

13. _____

14. _____

15. _____

16. _____

17. _____

18. _____

19. _____

20. _____

21. _____

22. _____

23. _____

24. _____

25. _____

26. _____

Simplify by performing the indicated operations.

1. $2^3 \cdot 5^2$

2. $16 + 9 \div 3 \cdot 4 - 7$

3. $18 - 24$

4. $5 \cdot (-20)$

5. $\sqrt{49}$

6. $(-5)^3 - 24 \div (-3)$

7. $0 \div 49$

8. $62 \div 0$

9. $-\dfrac{8}{15y} - \dfrac{2}{15y}$

10. $\dfrac{11}{12} - \dfrac{3}{8} + \dfrac{5}{24}$

11. $\dfrac{3a}{8} \cdot \dfrac{16}{6a^3}$

12. $-\dfrac{16}{3} \div -\dfrac{3}{12}$

13. $\dfrac{19}{-2\frac{3}{11}}$

14. $\dfrac{0.23 + 1.63}{-0.3}$

15. 10.2×4.01

16. Write 0.6% as a decimal.

17. Write 6.1 as a percent.

18. Write $\dfrac{3}{8}$ as a percent.

19. Write 0.345 as a fraction.

20. Write $-\dfrac{13}{26}$ as a decimal.

21. Round 34.8923 to the nearest tenth.

Evaluate each expression for the given replacement value(s).

22. $5(x^3 - 2)$ for $x = 2$

23. $10 - y^2$ for $y = -3$

24. $x \div y$ for $x = \dfrac{1}{2}$ and $y = 3\dfrac{7}{8}$

25. Simplify: $-(3z + 2) - 5z - 18$

△ **26.** Write an expression that represents the perimeter of the equilateral triangle (a triangle with three sides of equal length). Then simplify the expression.

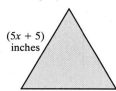

(5x + 5) inches

Solve each equation.

27. $\dfrac{n}{-7} = 4$

28. $-4x + 7 = 15$

29. $-4(x - 11) - 34 = 10 - 12$

30. $\dfrac{x}{5} + x = -\dfrac{24}{5}$

31. $2(x + 5.7) = 6x - 3.4$

32. $\dfrac{5}{y + 1} = \dfrac{4}{y + 2}$

△ **33.** Find the perimeter and area.

20 yards

| Rectangle | 10 yards |

34. Find the average of $-12, -13, 0,$ and 9.

Solve.

35. The difference of three times a number and five times the same number is 4. Find the number.

36. During a 258-mile trip, a car used $10\dfrac{3}{4}$ gallons of gas. How many miles would we expect the car to travel on 1 gallon of gas?

37. In a 10-kilometer race, there are 112 more men entered than women. Find the number of female runners if the total number of runners in the race is 600.

38. In a sample of 85 fluorescent bulbs, 3 were found to be defective. At this rate, how many defective bulbs should be found in 510 bulbs?

39. A \$120 framed picture is on sale for 15% off. Find the discount and the sale price.

40. Approximate to the nearest hundredth of a centimeter the length of the missing side of a right triangle with legs of 4 centimeters each.

41. Find the complement of a 78° angle.

42. Given that $m \parallel n$, find the measures of $x, y,$ and z.

27. _____

28. _____

29. _____

30. _____

31. _____

32. _____

33. _____

34. _____

35. _____

36. _____

37. _____

38. _____

39. _____

40. _____

41. _____

42. _____

43. _____

44. _____

45. _____

46. _____

47. _____

48. _____

49. _____

50. _____

51. _____

52. _____

53. _____

54. _____

55. _____

56. _____

57. _____

58. _____

59. _____

60. _____

61. _____

△ **43.** Find the perimeter and area.

6 in.
11 in.
7 in.
23 in.

△ **44.** Find the circumference and area. Give the exact values and then approximations using $\pi \approx 3.14$.

9 in.

Convert.

45. $2\frac{1}{2}$ gallons to quarts

46. 2.4 kilograms to grams

Chapters 9–16

Evaluate.

47. -3^4

48. 4^{-3}

Perform the indicated operations and simplify if possible.

49. $7 + 2(5y - 3)$

50.
$$5x^3 + x^2 + 5x - 2$$
$$-\left(8x^3 - 4x^2 + x - 7\right)$$

51. $(4x - 2)^2$

52. $(3x + 7)\left(x^2 + 5x + 2\right)$

Factor.

53. $6t^2 - t - 5$

54. $180 - 5x^2$

55. $3a^2 + 3ab - 7a - 7b$

56. $3x^3 - 21x^2 + 30x$

Simplify. Write answers with positive exponents only.

57. $\left(\dfrac{4x^2y^3}{x^3y^{-4}}\right)^2$

58. $\dfrac{5 - \dfrac{1}{y^2}}{\dfrac{1}{y} + \dfrac{2}{y^2}}$

Perform the indicated operations and simplify if possible.

59. $\dfrac{x^2 - 9}{x^2 - 3x} \div \dfrac{x^2 + 4x + 1}{2x + 10}$

60. $\dfrac{5a}{a^2 - a - 6} - \dfrac{2}{a - 3}$

61. $(x^2 + 7x + 10) \div (x + 5)$
(Long division)

Solve each equation or inequality.

62. $4(n - 5) = -(4 - 2n)$

63. $(3x - 5)(x + 2) = -6$

64. $-5(x - 1) + 6 \leq -3(x + 4) + 1$

65. $2x^2 - 6x + 1 = 0$

66. $\dfrac{4}{y} - \dfrac{5}{3} = -\dfrac{1}{5}$

67. $\dfrac{a}{a - 3} = \dfrac{3}{a - 3} - \dfrac{3}{2}$

68. $\sqrt{2x - 2} = x - 5$

Graph the following.

69. $5x - 7y = 10$

70. $y = -1$

71. $y \geq -4x$

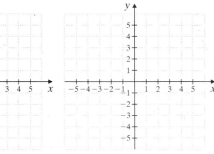

Find the slope of each line.

72. through $(6, -5)$ and $(-1, 2)$

73. $-3x + y = 5$

Write equations of the following lines. Write each equation in standard form.

74. through $(2, -5)$ and $(1, 3)$

75. slope $\dfrac{1}{8}$; y-intercept $(0, 12)$

Solve each system of equations.

76. $\begin{cases} 3x - 2y = -14 \\ \quad\quad y = x + 5 \end{cases}$

77. $\begin{cases} 4x - 6y = 7 \\ -2x + 3y = 0 \end{cases}$

Answer the questions about functions.

78. If $f(x) = x^3 - x$, find

   a. $f(-1)$

   b. $f(0)$

   c. $f(4)$

79. Decide whether the following is a function:

$$\{(-3, -3), (0, 5), (-3, 2), (0, 0)\}$$

Simplify.

80. $\sqrt{54}$

81. $\sqrt{24x^8}$

62. _____

63. _____

64. _____

65. _____

66. _____

67. _____

68. _____

69. _____

70. _____

71. _____

72. _____

73. _____

74. _____

75. _____

76. _____

77. _____

   a.

   b.

78. c. _____

79. _____

80. _____

81. _____

82. _____

83. _____

84. _____

85. _____

86. _____

87. _____

88. _____

89. _____

90. _____

91. _____

Perform the indicated operations and simplify if possible.

82. $\sqrt{18} - \sqrt{75} + 7\sqrt{3} - \sqrt{8}$ **83.** $\dfrac{\sqrt{40x^4}}{\sqrt{2x}}$

84. $\sqrt{2}\left(\sqrt{6} - \sqrt{5}\right)$

Rationalize each denominator.

85. $\dfrac{8}{\sqrt{5y}}$ **86.** $\dfrac{8}{\sqrt{6} + 2}$

Graph the quadratic equation. Label the vertex and the intercepts with their coordinates.

87. $y = x^2 - 7x + 10$

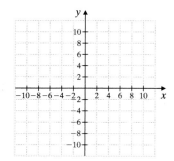

Solve each application.

88. A number plus five times its reciprocal is equal to six. Find the number.

89. A number increased by two-thirds of the number is 35. Find the number.

90. California has more public libraries than any other state. It has 387 more public libraries than Ohio. If the total number of public libraries for these states is 1827, find the number of public libraries in California and the number in Ohio. (*Source:* Institute of Museum and Library Services)

91. A pleasure boat traveling down the Red River takes the same time to go 14 miles upstream as it takes to go 16 miles downstream. If the current of the river is 2 miles per hour, find the speed of the boat in still water.

Subject Index